Lineberger Memorial

Library

STATIUS

II

LCL 207

STATIUS

THEBAID, BOOKS 1–7

EDITED AND TRANSLATED BY

D. R. SHACKLETON BAILEY

HARVARD UNIVERSITY PRESS

CAMBRIDGE, MASSACHUSETTS
LONDON, ENGLAND
2003

5/0 M-W ³/04 21.50

Library of Congress Catalog Card Number 2003051117
CIP data available from the Library of Congress

ISBN 0-674-01208-9

CONTENTS

THEBAID

ACHILLEID

INTRODUCTION

Apart from a marginal mention by his younger contemporary Juvenal, what is known of the poet's life and personality comes from his *Silvae*. His name, Publius Papinius Statius, is given in his manuscripts. The surname (*cognomen*) Statius was by origin an Italian personal name, and so like other such borne by slaves, who after getting their freedom would take it as a surname and pass it on to their descendants. The poet of course was no slave, neither was his father, whose name is nowhere actually attested. Statius' father was a native of Velia on the southwest coast of Italy, but moved to Neapolis (Naples), a Greek colony, which remained a centre of Hellenic culture after acquiring Roman citizenship. Here his son was born, probably about 50 AD. Papinius senior was a savant and a poet, winning prizes for his compositions at the regularly recurring festivals both in Naples (the Augustalia) and in Greece (Pythian, Isthmian, and Nemean Games). He was probably a Knight, but may have lost his qualification because of a financial reverse, after which he made a career as a teacher of literature, especially Greek, and Roman antiquities. According to his son, pupils flocked in from far and wide, and Romans of high rank were schooled to fit them for their futures, particularly as members of the great priestly colleges. While planning a poem on the eruption of Vesuvius in 79 he died[1] and was buried on a small property he (or his son) owned near Alba Longa, a few miles from the capital.

Following in his father's footsteps the young Statius won prizes at the Augustalia and later at the Alban festival instituted by the Emperor Domitian (ruled 81–96), where he producd a poem on the founder's German and Dacian campaigns. Probably after his father's death he moved to Rome and competed unsuccessfully at the great Capitoline festival, possibly in 90—the disappointment of his life. That may have had something to do with his subsequent decision to return to Naples, where he will have died in about 96. He married Claudia, widow of a well-known singer and mother of a musically gifted daughter. He himself was childless, but in his closing years he made up for it with a favourite slave boy whom he freed and whose early death he laments in his last extant poem (*Silvae* 5.5). But contrary to what has sometimes been assumed from v. 73 of the same, there was no adoption (vv. 10–11).

Thebaid

Statius' *magnum opus*, an epic in twelve Books on the mythological theme of the Seven against Thebes, in which he had been preceded by the fifth–fourth century Antimachus of Colophon, was published after twelve years of work (*Thebaid* 12.811) and torturous revision (*Silvae* 4.7.26), probably in 92. Meanwhile the *Silvae* with prob-

---

[1] Not, however, necessarily soon after it but at any rate before March 90; see the discussion in Coleman's edition of *Silvae* Book IV, pp. xviii–iv.

able composition dates 89–96 appeared in three instalments; see Introduction to the same in volume I of this edition of Statius. In 95 he began a new epic, ambitiously planned to cover the life and death of Achilles, but broke it off in its second Book, leaving the hero on his way to Troy.

Virgil was Statius' unapproachable idol: 'Rival not divine Aeneis, but follow from afar and ever venerate her footsteps,' so he takes leave of his *Thebaid* (12.310–19). At the same time he had high hopes for the latter's immortality, claiming that the Emperor already deigns to notice it and that the youth of Italy is learning it by heart—presumably at school. Extracts, therefore, had already become available, taken down perhaps in shorthand or handed out at periodic recitations before audiences that included senators (*Silvae* 5.2.161). Writing about a quarter of a century later, Juvenal tells us that these exhibitions were eagerly looked forward to and enthusiastically received, but financially unrewarding—the poet went hungry. However, with a property at Alba and the support of the Emperor and wealthy patrons, Statius was assuredly no pauper.

The *Thebaid* is set firmly in epic tradition, complete with sky-dwellers and infernals, heroes and elders, tyrants and prophets, Games and catalogues, and a generous supply of lions to populate relentless similes. The war at Thebes occupies the latter half; it is held in frame by the successive dooms of the champions. Their diversity mitigates the monotony of slaughter, along with forceful or pathetic figures and narratives. In the earlier Books the poet has a freer range, creating loosely connected tableaux, episodes within episodes: Coroebus and the monster, Hypsipyle's story. Imagination is not lacking: Polynices' journey and arrival at Argos, Tydeus' embassy and ambush

3

once read are not forgotten. Lacking is the dynamic, psyche fused with theme, that gave wings to Dido's death and, yes, to Pompey's funeral. *Si vis me flere, dolendum est.* Statius sees his pageant from outside.

There is style: 'dense and elaborate' (Coleman), replete with conceit and hyperbole, stretching language to the point of obscurity, favouring spacious periods intricately articulated; a feast for amateurs of the ornate, but for some a challenge readily declined. It is constant throughout in *Silvae* and *Thebaid*; as to the *Achilleid*, an implicit palinode, more later.

There is metrical technique. No question about Statius' mastery there, second only to if not rivalling Virgil's, earning an incidental accolade from Housman ('this superb versifier'), who 'read the *Thebaid* not more than three times, nor ever with intent care and interest' (*Cl. Papers* 1197).

In the Middle Ages the author of the *Thebaid* was a prime favourite, Dante's sweet poet, highlighted by the encounter in *Purgatorio*. For Julius Caesar Scaliger in the cinquecento, as D. W. T. Vessey has reminded us, Statius was, aside from Virgil ('we should add Homer,' and I for one should add Lucan), 'both of Latin and Greek Epic writers easily the chief'—not after all so lavish a tribute as it sounds. In the shadow of nineteenth-century Romanticism and its aftermath Statius' reputation went into a long eclipse, but the last three decades of the twentieth saw a marked revival of interest and appreciation, however parochial, for both parts of his oeuvre.

Well over a hundred extant manuscripts of the *Thebaid* testify to its vogue in medieval and renaissance culture.

One of them, Parisinus 8031 (P), called Puteanus after a sixteenth-century owner, is of the ninth or tenth century, probably a product of Corbie Abbey. Like Juvenal's Montepessulanus, it has no peer. The rest, leaving aside those later than the twelfth century as negligible, are collectively known as ω. Hill's edition, for example, uses seventeen, plus two fragmenta, and lists another three, plus five fragmenta, as 'rarius citata.' P and ω derive from a common archetype of uncertain date and provenance. But it is no longer permissible to say, with J. H. Mozley, that the latter hang very much together; closer research has blurred the edges, as with Martial's three families. P readings abound throughout in individual members or minority combinations of members, and certain of them can be classed as intermediate.[2] But this being a matter of virtually no practical importance, my critical notes, necessarily skeletal, do not cite ω manuscripts individually but use ψ to indicate minority readings within the group (whether shared with P or not) when these seem worth notice. Add that ς has its usual function as denoting early readings of conjectural status, whether or not they happen to occur in a late manuscript. Where my text prints a correction, my notes regularly give the manuscript reading followed by the name of the corrector in parenthesis, except that many early ones are passed over as obvious and generally accepted.

Of interest is the occurrence of variants (e.g. 1.32 *pierio* P: *laurigero* ω; 3.527 *celi* P: *nili* ω) which cannot be due to graphical error. Whatever their origin, the theory of a second edition made by the poet himself can be ruled out sim-

---

[2] See R. Lesueur's Budé edition, I, lxiii.

ply because he cannot be thought responsible for some of them.[3]

By common consent the general superiority of P entitles it to preference over ω except where ω prevails by merit; a principle that every editor must apply as his judgment, or want of it, dictates.

Scholia (Σ) attributed to one Lactantius Placidus, thought to have lived between the fourth and sixth century, were edited by R. Jahnke in 1898. As commentary they are of little help, but their readings have evidential value.

Statius' works were first edited in Rome in 1419. D. E. Hill's list of the *Thebaid*'s nine most illustrious editors ('clarissimi cuiusque editoris'), with brief descriptive comments,[4] begins with J. F. Gronovius (1653). The lists of critical articles and monographs include other great names: Bentley, N. Heinsius, Markland, Madvig, Housman. More recently L. Håkanson's *Thebaid* (1973), following his *Silvae*, stands out.

Lately, however, Statian scholarship has taken a different road, and again I am deeply indebted to Kathleen Coleman for her expert survey of this activity, relating to the epics, in this volume.

There is no modern commentary on the *Thebaid*, though a number of Books have been edited separately (see Coleman's survey).

Translations, verse and prose, exist in several lan-

---

[3] On the similar situation in Martial see p. vii of my Teubner edition: 'trium recensionum lectiones varias ad poetam non redire ex ipsarum natura certo certius est.'

[4] See also Lesueur, I, lxxiv–lxxvi.

guages. Mine is mostly independent of these, though I have kept an eye on Mozley's Loeb translation (1928) and occasionally consulted Lesueur's and a verse rendering by A. D. Melville (Oxford 1992). Statius' style makes the proper balance between fidelity and readability particularly hard for his interpreters to capture, provoking diversities of understanding and nuance to be distinguished from mere blunders. As in the *Silvae*, my notes, supplemented by the index of names, provide a minimum of requisite information plus revelatory or argumentative matter as occasion arises.

Achilleid

The *Thebaid* disposed of, Statius launched a second epic on the life and death of Achilles. According to its opening it was to contain the hero's career from his youthful adventure in Scyros on. One Book and part of a second survives, leaving him *en route* for the Trojan War.

The obvious assumption is that death or ill-health leading to death made him abandon the project. After the publication of *Silvae* Book IV in 95[5] nothing is heard of him, apart from the posthumous publication of Book V. As for the *Achilleid*, *Silvae* 4.7.21–24 mentions a stoppage, flatteringly ascribed to the absence of the friend to whom the piece is addressed (probably written in 94 between spring and early autumn); yet in 5.2.161–64, probably written in the summer of 95, he is looking forward to public recitations of his ongoing composition.

But suppose he had been able to stay at work long

[5] On this date see Coleman's edition, p. xii.

enough to complete the project. The Scyros episode is a light-hearted story with details supplied, as far as we know, by the poet's own imagination.[6] It makes pleasant reading and the tone is a world apart from the sombre and sanguinary tale of the Seven. But after Achilles' arrival at the war—what? A rehash of the *Iliad*? An unpromising prospect surely. Did Statius find himself in a cul-de-sac?

Furthermore: if the style of the surviving *Achilleid* is the man, here is a new Statius. All that is meant by 'mannerism' has almost disappeared. The new look is Ovidian, short of Ovid's levity. The revolution[7] must have been deliberate, not imposed by the theme. Mannerism, pervasive in the *Silvae* as in the *Thebaid*, need not change with genre. We may suppose that after his disappointment at the Capitoline festival, which evidently rankled (*Silvae* 3.5.28–33; 5.3.231–33), he simply decided that it was time for a change. But I have failed to think of a good literary parallel.

Not all manuscripts of the *Thebaid* contain the *Achilleid*, but a good many (including P) do, so that the textual situation is essentially the same. The workmanlike edition with commentary by O. A. W. Dilke (Cambridge, 1954) remains unique.

---

[6] The trumpet blast which brought Achilles out of disguise (1.874ff.) diverges from the usual account; see J. G. Frazer, *Apollodorus* (Loeb edition), II, 74, n.1. Apollodorus and Hyginus have it from a common source if not from Statius himself.

[7] Mostly unremarked in secondary literature. Mozley is an honourable exception: 'the poet's style is simpler and less artificial than in the *Thebaid*.'

RECENT SCHOLARSHIP ON THE *THEBAID* AND *ACHILLEID*: AN OVERVIEW*

KATHLEEN M. COLEMAN

Given the renaissance of interest in post-Virgilian epic in the latter decades of the twentieth century, this essay is perforce drastically selective. It does not include items on Statius' background and formation, since these topics are covered in the essay on the *Silvae* that is the companion to this one (Coleman 2003). Nor does it venture to assess scholarship on the vast influence of the *Thebaid* in the Middle Ages, powerfully epitomized for readers of Dante by his meeting with Statius and Virgil in Purgatory. The enormous range of modern studies on the *Thebaid* has been summarized as far as the middle of the nineteen-nineties (Dominik 1996a); the focus in what follows is on English-language scholarship, although it would be unfair to omit reference to a pioneering work of the "Statius renaissance" in German (Schetter 1960). For the *Achilleid*, however, adequate coverage demands that scholarship in other languages be given prominence. Although treated

---

* In preparing this survey I have sought advice from Bruce Gibson, Peter Heslin, and Charles McNelis, to all of whom I am properly grateful.

selectively here, a multilingual volume of essays celebrating Statius' nineteen-hundredth anniversary provides a representative cross-section of trends in contemporary criticism on his entire *oeuvre* (Delarue *et al.* 1996).

Thebaid

The first half of the twentieth century failed to find much to appreciate in the *Thebaid*. Because Statius explicitly envisages his epic following in the footsteps of the *Aeneid*, his self-acknowledged debt to Virgil at times earned him labels along the lines of "derivative," "slavish imitator," and "lacking in originality."[1] These views have been variously and resoundingly refuted in the late twentieth-century rehabilitation of Statius' reputation as a consummate epic artist, although the concept of "defensive imitation" still betrays the tenacity of the old view (Williams 1986). But the problem is not only aesthetic; it is also ideological. Even while earning admiration for his literary qualities, Statius has been tarred with the brush of Domitianic despotism, a repressive regime that the *Thebaid* has been assumed to vindicate (Vessey 1973). Towards the end of the century, however, a revisionist interpretation promoted the poem as a commentary upon the evils of civil war, and hence an explicit challenge to the legitimacy of the Flavian

---

[1] A random example expresses the insult with Gallic elegance: "Les épopées de Stace sont des oeuvres artificielles, sans originalité dans l'invention et surtout sans sincérité," J. Humbert, *Histoire illustrée de la Littérature Latine. Précis méthodique* (Paris and Toulouse, 1932), 298.

10

regime (Ahl 1986) and to the brutal means that Vespasian employed to restore order after the "year of the four emperors" in AD 69 (Dominik 1989). Indeed, the latter view has been developed into a somewhat inflexible thesis equating power in the *Thebaid* with relentless cruelty, and concluding that Statius' audience (like the inhabitants of the free world in the twentieth century) would necessarily recoil from the horror of this picture (Dominik 1994b).

The view that sees Statius as a heroic voice for the opposition has been adduced to explain certain characteristics of the narrative. The contemporary political and intellectual climate has been held to account for such features as the prominence of suicide in both Statius' *Thebaid* and Silius' *Punica*, suicide and assassination being held to be the only options for escaping from a tyranny (McGuire 1989). Despite the risks of anachronism, a more extensive study by the same author interprets all three instances of Flavian epic (*Punica*, *Thebaid*, and Valerius Flaccus' *Argonautica*) as protest literature (McGuire 1997). An influential general study of the post-Virgilian epic tradition, however, shows that epic is a genre that shares one of the primary concerns of any imperial system, namely a preoccupation with finding a balance amid "the instabilities of power" (Hardie 1993). All the successors to Virgil, Hardie argues, confront this problem in some way, as they also confront the struggle between good and evil, and the issue of succession, both political and literary. Not that Statius necessarily finds an equilibrium: on the contrary, the *Thebaid* can be said to display a marked imbalance, war and violence far outweighing forgiveness and peace. It has recently been suggested that this imbalance need not,

11

however, be read as a critique of the Domitianic regime, but rather as a reflection of Statius' view of mankind as a whole (Franchet d'Espèrey 1999).

In the *Thebaid* Greek myth can be seen as a vehicle for a particularly Roman preoccupation with the relationship between politics and the family (Hardie 1993). On this analysis, the relationship that is at the heart of the Roman power structure lies at the heart of the *Thebaid* also; in this respect Statius demonstrates a self-conscious debt to his predecessors, especially Lucan. Succession is thwarted as one hero after another is snatched away by death. Still, Hardie's study concedes that a model for smooth succession seems to be offered in the choice of Theodamas to take over the role of seer from Amphiaraus after his tragic and premature death; the smooth transfer of office is posited as a model for cooperation and for continuity of authority. If, however, Flavian epic seems to reflect the male-dominated structure of contemporary Roman society, a recent feminist study of the role of women in the entire genre of Roman epic has highlighted a contrasting dimension (Keith 2000). Keith argues that Statius and his contemporaries employ the theme of civil war to reflect conflict between the sexes, and to explore the function of female impulses (personified, most obviously, in the Furies) in precipitating conflict.

Contemporary relevance, however, is not restricted to the sphere of politics and moral codes. The funeral games for Archemorus (previously called Opheltes) in *Thebaid* 6 have long been recognized as heir to the games for Patroclus in *Iliad* 23 and to their Roman counterpart, the games in honor of Anchises in *Aeneid* 5. But a recent study points to unique aspects of Statius' treatment of this mo-

12

tif (Thuillier 1996). Thuillier argues that some details in Statius' presentation reflect conventions in the contemporary Roman circus, stadium, and boxing ring, and suggests that they may derive from Statius' familiarity with the gymnastic competitions that formed part of the *certamina* in which he is known to have competed as a literary contestant. This practical approach is at one end of the critical spectrum; at the other lies the contention that all poems are ultimately about the craft of writing poetry. This latter theory has been variously applied to the *Thebaid*. In one study, the ambiguous relationship between Hypsipyle and her father Thoas has been interpreted as a reflection of ambiguity in Statius' relationship with Virgil (Nugent 1996). In another, madness—in both its creative and its destructive aspects—is seen as a metaphor for epic composition, a metaphor already employed by Virgil and subsequently developed by Statius (Hershkowitz 1998).

The bursts of irrationality that periodically threaten to engulf the characters have their structural counterpart in the abruptly episodic nature of the narrative. Scholars have begun to appreciate this structural feature as a deliberate device whereby the progress of the plot is repeatedly delayed. This strategy has a venerable epic pedigree stretching back to the *Odyssey* (though paradoxically the *Odyssey* is the only major epic whose influence is overtly absent from the *Thebaid*, which has no "Odyssean" half) (Hardie 1993 and 1997). Hence the perpetual postponement of the critical duel between the rival brothers is no longer to be seen as a structural flaw caused by Statius' desire to exploit every epic device at the expense of narrative cohesion. Rather, his self-conscious references to delays in the story are interpreted as drawing attention to the chaos and confusion of the whole Theban tragedy (Feeney 1991). The care with which Statius positions and structures scenes within the epic has also begun to be appreciated. A case study of Polynices' first and last fight (the first with Tydeus, over the palace doorstep, and the last with Eteocles, over the kingdom) reveals a complex system of structural parallels and inversions that turns the instance of a trivial quarrel into a commentary on a drama of mortal combat; arching from Book 1 to Book 11, these conflicts frame the entire narrative (excluding the "coda" of Book 12) (Bonds 1985).

Indeed, far from comprising a meandering and formless discourse,[2] the episodic structure of the *Thebaid* is now recognized as a very tightly controlled design, even if consensus has not yet been reached on its precise configuration. Parallels and correspondences have been usefully set out in diagrammatic form in a study that emphasizes Statius' Ovidian legacy of a *carmen perpetuum*, "continuous song" (Vessey 1973). On one recent interpretation, the overall structure of the poem comprises three major phases, in which dialogue, narrative, and description are juxtaposed in parallel and contrasting sequences to emphasize key themes and create contrasts in atmosphere and tone (Dominik 1996b). Another view posits simultaneous progression on two separate planes: the divine, in six major sequences, and the human, in four sequences of three books each (Delarue 2000). These approaches, and

[2] Cf. W. C. Summers, *The Silver Age of Latin Literature from Tiberius to Hadrian* (London, 1920), 51 (on the *Thebaid*): "Nothing could be much worse than the composition: the first six books drag terribly. . ."

others like them, are helpful in drawing attention to major axes in the structure of the poem, though ultimately its dynamic movement resists mathematical symmetry.

In the analysis of the epic's structure, special attention has been paid to Statius' debt to Virgil. A study of Book 1 has demonstrated that the first three hundred lines establish the *Thebaid*'s Virgilian pedigree in a series of remarkable structural similarities and transpositions; the rest of the book then fans out to embrace a wide range of episodic models, not only from the entire *Aeneid* but also from a wide generic spectrum of antecedents in Latin poetry (Hill 1989). The middle of the epic also attests Statius' debt to Virgil, and the creative use that he makes of it. A new analysis shows that Book 7 articulates a fresh martial beginning after the hesitations of the first hexad, which is not "Odyssean," as in the *Aeneid*, but rather "Callimachean" in its overriding preoccupation with stories of origins and beginnings; characteristically, Statius combines his debt to Virgil with a sophisticated new departure in epic design (McNelis, forthcoming).

Alongside focus on the structure of the poem, intertextuality as a mode of criticism has demonstrated that Statius' adaptation of motifs in his predecessors creates a commentary of great vigor and subtlety upon the themes and situations of epic. A case study of Parthenopaeus as a "simultaneous reading" of several warrior youths in the *Aeneid* shows that Statius combines a multiplicity of correspondences and contrasts to create a portrayal that is profoundly enriched by recognition of the myriad Virgilian strands in its woof and warp (Hardie 1989). Virgil, however, is not the only poet whose influence informs the narrative fabric of the *Thebaid*; the characters in this poem

15

have been shown to respond in detail to Ovid's Theban narrative in Books 3 and 4 of the *Metamorphoses* (Keith 2002). And Statius' reading included even his immediate contemporaries, as has been demonstrated with reference to his reception of Homeric motifs via the intermediary of his coeval Valerius Flaccus (Smolenaars 1991). Immediate contemporaries (and the critical approaches of inter-textual analysis) have unfortunately been excluded from a compendious study that traces Statius' models for specific thematic elements such as Tisiphone's hiss or the reflection of the sun on the shield of Mars (Taisne 1994).

Since all the ingredients of the epic "recipe" are present in the *Thebaid*, we are in danger of taking them for granted. Starting from Edward Gibbon's famous complaint two hundred years earlier to the effect that an epic catalogue is merely an irritating interruption, a contribution to Statius' nineteen-hundredth anniversary volume offers a stimulating deconstruction of the catalogues of the *Thebaid* (Georgacopoulou 1996). This study shows that each of the numerous catalogues in the poem is a repository of memory that is either integral to the narrative or else summarizes a theme that will not be addressed *in extenso* elsewhere. The detached authorial voice usually narrates the catalogues pertaining to the Argives; a more subjective perspective is contributed to the Theban material in those instances where the narrator is one of the characters from Thebes itself. This variety is further compounded by instances where a catalogue is delivered in not one voice but two. Georgacopoulou concludes that the catalogues do indeed suspend the action, while simultaneously functioning as a repeated motif that unifies the narrative.

16

The traditional role assigned to the gods in epic had been destabilized by Lucan's radical renunciation of divine agency in human affairs. But Statius found fertile new ways of reintegrating them and revitalizing their role. It has been observed that his human characters interact more effectively with the powers of the Underworld than with the celestial gods above, and only they (and not the gods) are capable of moving between all three realms (Feeney 1991). The role of Jupiter in particular has provoked conflicting interpretations. Feeney's influential reading builds upon an earlier study of Jupiter's role across Flavian epic (Schubert 1984). Feeney argues that in the *Thebaid* Jupiter is consistently reduced in status and his efficacy usurped, either by personifications representing elemental forces in human nature or by the heroes themselves, most notably Theseus; Jupiter becomes almost a caricature of his own traditional qualities. This tendency towards allegory Feeney interprets as a definitive step towards the intellectual context of the Middle Ages, although we have been reminded that the allegorizing interpretation should not be exaggerated at the expense of the individuality of the gods (Hutchinson 1993).

Statius' response to the problem of divine responsibility for human tragedy has been clarified in a recent study showing that the balance between the authority of Jupiter and the power of fate is not a neat subdivision (Davis 1994). Jupiter treats fate as an instrument to justify his own actions; yet events both at Thebes and at Argos are presented just as much in terms of generic heredity, a heredity that the characters are aware of and upon which they base their assessment of one another. Hence, Davis concludes, the *Thebaid* is inevitably topical, and cannot be abstracted

17

from contemporary society and politics, in that "the forces which govern the world of the *Thebaid* govern the world at large." This interpretation is different from the views glossed at the beginning of this article that posit the *Thebaid* as a text of protest or subversion; a Domitian prone to suspect dissidents of treason was also a well-educated emperor who paid close attention to the administration of the Empire. An epic poem investigating the role of power and authority in shaping the human condition is not necessarily incompatible with the outlook and preoccupations of such a person. A caution against overdetermined readings that equate a tyrannical Jupiter with the Domitian of popular perception has been expressed in the context of the hazards inherent in speaking out against tyranny (Hill 1996).

The *Thebaid* has been said to "challenge" the entire epic tradition. The martial theme, offset by the comradely relationship between Polynices and Tydeus (subsequent to their fracas over the doorstep), infuses epic with something of the tenor of Euripidean tragedy. Indeed, in handling the gods Statius has been said to dress up tragedy in an epic costume, alternating between the two poles of *furor* and *pathos* (Criado 2000). In exploring the savage irrationality of war through the different viewpoints of the individual characters, Statius deepens his readers' understanding of the grim subtext to the *Aeneid* (Henderson 1993). A character such as the Lemnian queen Hypsipyle recalls not only Dido but also, in certain aspects, Aeneas; while her manner and appearance encourage a parallel with Dido, her reactions to events are often quite different, so that the immediate comparison sets up expectations that are then undermined by Hypsipyle's behavior (Gruzelier 1994).

The speeches of the *Thebaid* have been classified typologically, and analyzed as a means of advancing the plot, delineating character, and developing the major themes of the epic (Dominik 1994a). A nuanced study has been devoted to the number and interaction of the speech partners, the immediate circumstances in which the speeches are delivered, the gestures that accompany them (sometimes objectively described by the narrator, sometimes remarked on by the interlocutors themselves), and the interruptions that fracture the discourse in telling ways (e.g. parentheses, or aposiopesis, i.e. an abrupt halt in mid-sentence) (Frings 1991). These features are shown to contribute great variety to the characterization and plot development of the *Thebaid*. Frings observes that neither the characters nor the stages of the plot are necessarily described by the narrator; rather, character is revealed through the speech and actions of individuals, and the plot is developed through action that is reported by one or other of the participants.

In the vanguard of the movement to rehabilitate the *Thebaid*, the poem was read as an "elaborate and sustained allegory of the emotions" (Vessey 1973). Since then, the violence—emotional as well as physical—that saturates the poem has prompted detailed studies of the ancient view of negative passions and irrational behavior. A study of the motif of hatred between brothers, *odia fraterna*, compares Statius' treatment with Seneca's in *Thyestes* (Frings 1992). Frings argues that Statius surpasses the deployment of this motif by Seneca in extending it beyond the human plane

19

to the divine, so that the enmity between Eteocles and Polynices reflects the hatred between Jupiter and Pluto. In Frings' view, however, the terrible inevitability that this divine paradigm imposes upon human behavior is redeemed, if slightly, by man's simultaneous capacity for positive relationships, as represented by the friendship between Polynices and Tydeus. Madness, too, has been explored as an epic motif (Hershkowitz 1998). In the *Thebaid* madness is shown by Hershkowitz to be associated with sexual deviance, and to be fundamental to Statius' characterization of all the children of the royal house of Thebes, including the virgins Antigone and Ismene. Meanwhile, man's precarious position, poised between god and beast (or: Heaven and Hell), is a theme of post-Virgilian epic that is strikingly exemplified in the lapse of the heroic Tydeus into cannibalistic impotence (Feeney 1991, Hardie 1993).

The *Thebaid* has been called a "Stoic" epic, because the doom-laden narrative unfolds in a fated series of events, *fatorum series* (Vessey 1973). But it has been demonstrated that, insofar as distinctively Stoic elements can be distinguished from the general tenor of Roman thought, Stoicism in Flavian epic is largely the literary inheritance of the *Aeneid*, though displaying also the influence of Seneca and Lucan (Billerbeck 1986). On this analysis, Statius shows fewer Stoic elements than Valerius Flaccus, and Silius Italicus far more than either of these two. More recently, the fundamental Stoicism of the *Thebaid* has been challenged in a study that examines whether the concept of hatred, central to the epic, conforms to the psychological aspects of Stoic doctrine (Fantham 1997). Fantham argues that in the *Thebaid*, where the gods display hatred even before the humans do, hatred of human by human is presented as a fundamental evil that dominates the narrative and can only be overcome by piety and clemency. Like the other negative passions that give rise to it, hatred is shown to have no place in the proper pursuit of retribution, and it is only to persons free from the tyranny of the passions that Statius entrusts punishment and the dispensing of justice.

The close of the epic demonstrates that this is a story that cannot really end: male violence and, especially, female mourning are without limit. Just as the death of Turnus at the end of the *Aeneid* brings anything but closure to the moral issues at the heart of the poem, so the hatred between the warring brothers in the *Thebaid* bequeaths a continuing legacy after their deaths (Hardie 1993). The debate about the end of the poem essentially revolves around the status of Book 12 in its entirety: is it integral to the poem's structure, or an anticlimactic coda? What is the significance of the absence of the gods from the last thousand lines of the poem? One recent verdict supporting the cohesion of the whole suggests that it privileges individual acts of heroism, such as Theseus' in Book 12, over the entire machinery of divine revenge for the crimes committed against *pietas* by the royal house of Thebes (Kytzler 1996).

The narrative proper, however, ends at the point where Theseus strips Creon of his armor and denounces his wickedness (*Theb.* 12.781). A close examination of the remaining thirty-eight lines of the poem shows that they comprise three "supplements," which are interpreted as offering alternative forms of closure in response to the unfinished state of the *Aeneid* (Braund 1996). But the very end of

21

the poem is unprecedented in the formal epic tradition, though memorably anticipated in Ovid's "anti-epic," the *Metamorphoses*: in the last ten lines of the *Thebaid*, in emphatically modest phrasing, the poet expresses a hope for literary immortality. Why does Statius choose this ending? A cogent answer suggests that it sets upon the epic a neat and orderly seal in contrast to the limitless chaos of the narrative, and that, paying tribute to Virgil, it affords the irony of an entirely non-Virgilian (and indeed non-Homeric) authorial epilogue (Hardie 1997). Yet the end of the *Thebaid* continues to stimulate a variety of observations: the heroic deeds of battle giving way to female lament, Statius' personified epic behaves in a distinctly feminine way (Dietrich 1999); the authorial "afterword" matches the scenes of aftermath that are well established in Roman battle narratives and exemplified four times in the *Thebaid*, most notably in Book 12 itself (Pagán 2000); the question that Statius poses about the immortality of the *Thebaid* is so phrased as to gloss the entire spectrum of his predecessors in the epic genre, from Ennius to Lucan (Dominik 2003). In terms of supplying a provocative ending, the *Thebaid* has indeed proved to be a worthy successor to the *Aeneid*.

One more issue demands attention: no matter how sophisticated a poet's thought or how artful his handling of the tradition that he has inherited, the impact and individuality of a poem ultimately depend upon the micro-details of the poet's use of language. This aspect of a poem is hard to demonstrate economically; and fluctuations in taste can obscure it altogether. The luxurious style of the *Thebaid* clashed with the stark preferences of the late twentieth century; blame was laid at the door of "mannerism," a mode of expression that transgresses classical norms of restraint and exploits volleys of rhetorical effects (Vessey 1973 and 1992). A recent appreciation of Latin literature between the reigns of Nero and Hadrian, however, has illuminated the brilliance and audacity of Statius' style (Hutchinson 1993). Comprising a series of chronological case studies under different stylistic headings, Hutchinson's analysis repeatedly illustrates Statius' mastery of an immense range of tone, from dramatic grandeur to profound simplicity. It shows how, far from fragmenting the cohesion of the narrative, the contemporary taste for epigrammatic conceit and dazzling paradox is deployed with consummate discrimination and subtlety to sustain Statius' vast sweep of narrative. Discursiveness balances cohesion in a tightly controlled design that orchestrates a finely calibrated network of Virgilian allusions and responses.

Already in late antiquity Statius' epics, like the epics of Homer and Virgil, attracted commentators. A commentary ascribed to a certain Lactantius Placidus is to be dated no later than the sixth or the late fifth century, and perhaps earlier. Its comments ("scholia") testify to the issues of diction, structure, narrative, and characterization that late antiquity considered interesting, and its citations have enabled scholars to correct some of the erroneous readings in the text of the *Thebaid* transmitted in the medieval manuscript tradition (Sweeney 1969 and 1997). The nineteen-eighties saw the publication of the most reliable text of the *Thebaid* in the modern era, with generous space devoted to variants (Hill 1983). Modern commentaries on a lesser or greater scale, all but two (alas) predating Hill's text, are available for seven complete books: 1 (Caviglia 1973),

2 (Mulder 1954), 3 (Snijder 1968), 7 (Smolenaars 1994), 9 (Dewar 1991), 10 (Williams 1972), and 11 (Venini 1970). A single commentary has also been devoted to the climactic episode in Book 12 in which, in defiance of Creon's ban, Argia and Antigone find Polynices' corpse and cremate it on what turns out to be Eteocles' pyre (Hoffmann 1999). Given that sound commentaries are of enduring value, it is also worth mentioning two editions from the nineteen-thirties, accompanied by a translation into Dutch and a commentary in Latin; these deal respectively with Book 1 (Heuvel 1932) and the episode of Opheltes' funeral at the beginning of Book 6 (Fortgens 1934). The extant fragment of the *Achilleid*, on the other hand, has had no commentary devoted to it since the nineteen-fifties (Jannaccone 1950, Dilke 1954), other than the useful annotations to the text and facing French translation in the Budé series (Méheust 1971).

Achilleid

Any epic poem invites comparison with its predecessors in the "epic tradition," most especially a fragment such as the *Achilleid* which, being incomplete, offers only limited scope for self-contained analysis of structure, characterization, diction, and all the other features exhibited by a literary work in its entirety. What remains of the *Achilleid* offers a vivid contrast with the *Thebaid*, yet little critical attention has been devoted to a sustained comparison between the two. The *Achilleid*, manifestly playful and irreverent in its surviving portion, has been called "Ovidian" in contrast to the "Virgilian" *Thebaid* (Fantham 1979, Hinds 1997), and its focus on a single protagonist (albeit in competition with some powerful supporting roles) has earned it the label "Odyssean," in comparison to an "Iliadic" *Thebaid* (Delarue 2000). Whereas Statius' style in the *Thebaid* has seemed dense and ornate to the point of satiety, the *Achilleid* has been credited with a *faux-naif* appearance of simplicity that belies the subtlety of Statius' juxtapositions and the innovative nature of his diction (Vessey 1986).

Yet the relative lack of interest in setting the *Achilleid* beside the *Thebaid* is understandable, since the subject of Achilles demands comparison, first and foremost, with Homer. Here an immediate hierarchy suggests itself to account for the characteristics of Statius' treatment: the evolution from "oral" to "literary" epic (or "primary" to "secondary"). Such a rigid distinction, however, may impose a straitjacket on the text; reading as performance is an aspect of Roman culture that is often overlooked. Just as the plot and structure of the *Iliad* create an eminently readable poem ("readable," that is, in the accepted modern sense), so the virtuoso rhetorical features and sophisticated structural symmetry of the *Achilleid* (two bulky Scyros episodes bracketing a slender interlude at Aulis) are arguably best appreciated when the work is heard being read aloud (Johnson 1994).

The question has been raised: would the finished poem have qualified as an epic at all? Both implicitly and explicitly, the *Achilleid* declares its literary allegiance to the refined canons of the Hellenistic poets and to the sophisticated wit of Ovid. Literary influence is not inhibited by generic boundaries. The prominence of the theme of love combines the influence of Ovid's "anti-epic," the *Metamorphoses*, with elegiac elements from his irreverent love

25

poetry. Drama, too, has left its imprint: Seneca's treatment of Andromache's attempt to hide her son Astyanax from harm in the *Troades* finds echoes in Statius' handling of the parallel situation in the *Achilleid* (Fantham 1979). On one reading, the private and domestic values of the poem make "epic" an ambiguous designation for a work so firmly affiliated to the epic tradition in its choice of eponymous hero, and yet so distant from it in its elegiac treatment of the characters and the plot (Rosati 1994). Still, Statius' programmatic statements at the beginning belie the tenor of the surviving portion, encouraging the belief that the completed work would have commandeered an arsenal of varied generic elements in a serious bid for inclusion in the epic canon (Aricò 1986 and 1996).

But the very novelty of Statius' approach poses a challenge to the "epic tradition" as an intellectual construct. Hence the multiplicity of generic influences at work here has been interpreted as evidence of Statius' attempt to revitalize and enlarge the epic tradition. The complexity of his responses to earlier poets outside the epic canon is part of a process of dynamic engagement that alters the balance within that very canon. His intertextual allusions are therefore seen to confer epic status on Catullus 64, the "epyllion" on the marriage of Peleus and Thetis (clearly of signal importance for an epic about their son), and to affirm the epic affiliations of the *Metamorphoses* of Ovid (Hinds 1997). Simply put, the *Achilleid* seems to be taking Latin epic in a new direction (Hinds 1998). It is self-evident that only the most sophisticated alternative model has any hope of challenging the supremacy of the Homeric-Virgilian epic "code." Thus the prologue to the *Achilleid* has been read as a programmatic statement of Statius' intention to write an epic that is an allegory of the difficulty of completing the task that he has set himself (Barchiesi 1996).

Did Statius in fact start as he meant to go on? Or would the exuberant beginning of the *Achilleid* have simmered down into a narrative more like the *Thebaid*? A teaser of one and a quarter books provokes speculation about the rest, although we are not even sure how many more Statius was planning. To fill the remaining books with the standard epic fare of heroic exploits and bloody battles would have involved a dramatic shift of tone and focus. Perhaps Statius intended, rather, to build the rest of his epic around the subsequent erotic adventures of his hero, whose string of conquests encompassed heroines as diverse as Agamemnon's doomed daughter at Aulis and the Amazon queen, Penthesilea; the *Heroides,* Ovid's collection of fictitious letters from heroines to their fickle lovers, could have provided suitable impetus (Koster 1979).

The striking delineation of feminine emotions in the surviving fragment has already been foreshadowed in the female characters of the *Thebaid*, most memorably Hypsipyle. The prominence of Thetis in the surviving portion of the poem displays Statius' sophisticated manipulation of maternal psychology to drive the plot (Mendelsohn 1990). By the end of Book 1 her worst fears have been realized, and her son's bid for independence has precipitated him towards the doom that she knows is waiting for him at Troy. But by entrusting her child to the avuncular centaur Chiron Thetis effectively upstages herself, since Chiron is to supplant her in her son's affections. Once again, Statius demonstrates acute psychological insight: the relationship between foster-father and son, of which Chiron and Achil-

27

les are the archetype, is one that is replicated in several examples in the *Silvae*, including the relationship between Statius and his own foster-child in *Silvae* 5.5 (Fantham 1999).

The "subversive" reading that was in vogue in criticism of the *Silvae* in the nineteen-seventies and nineteen-eighties, and that we have seen applied to the *Thebaid*, has been tried on the *Achilleid* as well. It has been argued that in the portrayal of Achilles Statius chose to emphasize aspects that would evoke flaws in the character, appearance, and achievements of the emperor; it has even been suggested that such effrontery may have cost Statius his life, which would account for the fragmentary nature of the poem (Benker 1987). At the other extreme, a "propagandist" reading interprets Achilles' capitulation to the lure of battle as an endorsement of Domitian's military campaigns on the Danube (Aricò 1986). On a third and more reasonable interpretation, however, contemporary relevance in the *Achilleid* may rather be found in the portrayal of domestic scenes and civilized values, reflecting the world of the *Silvae*, in which Statius endorses his patrons' leisured and graceful lifestyle (Konstan 1997).

Despite its fragmentary nature, the *Achilleid* held great appeal for subsequent generations. Similarities have been noted between the education of Achilles as portrayed in the *Achilleid* and in the poetry and rhetoric of late antiquity. While the Greek rhetoricians of the Roman Empire from the late first century onwards may have shared with the *Achilleid* a common source, the Latin poets from Ausonius to Corippus seem to have been influenced directly by Statius (Pavlovskis 1965). If the *Iliad* generated a paradigm of Achilles as a great warrior dominated by towering anger, the *Achilleid* and its roughly contemporary poem, the *Ilias Latina*, are responsible for the more sentimental picture of Achilles as a warrior whose immense physical prowess is matched by a comparable capacity to conquer women's hearts. It is this romanticized portrait that captured the imagination of the Middle Ages (King 1987). The poem's medieval popularity is attested by a vast plethora of manuscripts, manifold witness to the regularizing impulse that divided the extant 1,128 lines into self-contained episodes of 200–300 lines each, in an attempt to approximate the scope of a proper epic by transforming the fragment into five numbered books (Clogan 1968). Indeed, our modern attempt to confront and embrace the fragmentary nature of the *Achilleid* may be the one facet of our reaction that differentiates us from our medieval ancestors; for the first time since the Middle Ages, this beguiling virtuoso piece is at last captivating a new audience.

BIBLIOGRAPHY

Ahl 1986: Ahl, F. "Statius' 'Thebaid': a reconsideration," *Aufstieg und Niedergang der römischen Welt* II 32.5 (1986), 2803–2912

Aricò 1986: Aricò, G. "L' 'Achilleide' di Stazio: tradizione letteraria e invenzione narrativa," *Aufstieg und Niedergang der römischen Welt* II 32.5 (1986), 2925–2964

Aricò 1996: Aricò, G. "Rileggendo l'*Achilleide*," in: F. Delarue, S. Georgacopoulou, P. Laurens, A.-M. Taisne (eds), *Epicedion: Hommage à P. Papinius Statius = La Licorne* 38 (Poitiers, 1996), 185–199

Barchiesi 1996: Barchiesi, A. "La guerra di Troia non avrà luogo: il proemio dell'*Achilleide* di Stazio," in: L. Munzi (ed.), *Forme della parodia, parodia delle forme nel mondo greco e latino. Atti del convegno Napoli, 9 maggio 1995* (Naples, 1998) = *Annali dell'Istituto universitario orientale di Napoli. Sezione filologico-letteraria* 18 (1996), 45–62

Benker 1987: Benker, M. *Achill und Domitian: Herrscherkritik in der 'Achilleis' des Statius* (Erlangen, 1987)

Billerbeck 1986: Billerbeck, M. "Aspects of Stoicism in Flavian epic," *Papers of the Liverpool Latin Seminar* 5 (1986), 341–356

Bonds 1985: Bonds, W. S. "Two combats in the *Thebaid*," *Transactions of the American Philological Association* 115 (1985), 225–235

Braund 1996: Braund, S. M. "Ending epic: Statius, Theseus and a merciful release," *Proceedings of the Cambridge Philological Society* n.s. 42 (1996), 1–23

Caviglia 1973: Caviglia, F. *La Tebaide: libro I. Introduzione, testo, traduzione e note* (Rome, 1973)

Clogan 1968: Clogan, P. M. *The Medieval* Achilleid *of Statius. Edited with introduction, variant readings, and glosses* (Leiden, 1968)

Coleman 2003: Coleman, K. M. "Recent scholarship on the *Silvae* and their context: an overview," in: D. R. Shackleton Bailey (ed. and trans.), *Statius: Silvae* (Cambridge, MA, and London, 2003), 11–21

Criado 2000: Criado, C. *La teologia de la 'Tebaida' Estaciana: el anti-virgilianismo de un clasicista* (Hildesheim and New York, 2000)

Davis 1994: Davis, P. J. "The fabric of history in Statius' *Thebaid*," in: C. Deroux (ed.), *Studies in Latin Literature and Roman History* vol. 7 (Brussels, 1994), 464–483

Delarue *et al.* 1996: F. Delarue, S. Georgacopoulou, P. Laurens, A.-M. Taisne (eds), *Epicedion: Hommage à P. Papinius Statius = La Licorne* 38 (Poitiers, 1996)

Delarue 2000: Delarue, F. *Stace, poète épique. Originalité et cohérence* (Louvain and Paris, 2000)

Dewar 1991: Dewar, M. *Statius, Thebaid IX: edited with an English translation and commentary* (Oxford, 1991)

Dietrich 1999: Dietrich, J. S. "Thebaid's feminine ending," *Ramus* 28 (1999), 40–53

Dilke 1954: Dilke, O. A. W. *Statius, Achilleid: edited with introduction, apparatus criticus and notes* (Cambridge, 1954; repr. New York, 1979)

Dominik 1989: Dominik, W. J. "Monarchal power and imperial politics in Statius' *Thebaid*," *Ramus* 18 (1989) = A. J. Boyle (ed.), *The Imperial Muse. Flavian Epicists to Claudian* (Bendigo, 1990), 74–97

Dominik 1994a: Dominik, W. J. *Speech and Rhetoric in Statius'* Thebaid (Hildesheim, 1994)

Dominik 1994b: Dominik, W. J. *The Mythic Voice of Statius: Power and Politics in the* Thebaid (Leiden, 1994)

Dominik 1996a: Dominik, W. J. "Statius' *Thebaid* in the twentieth century," in: R. Faber and B. Seidensticker (eds), *Worte, Bilder, Töne. Studien zur Antike und Antikerezeption Bernhard Kytzler zu ehren* (Würzburg, 1996), 129–141

Dominik 1996b: Dominik, W. J. "A short narrative reading of Statius' *Thebaid*," in: F. Delarue, S. Georgacopoulou, P. Laurens, A.-M. Taisne (eds), *Epicedion: Hommage à P. Papinius Statius = La Licorne* 38 (Poitiers, 1996), 55–69

Dominik 2003: Dominik, W. J. "Following in whose foot-

31

steps? The epilogue to Statius' *Thebaid*," in A. F. Basson and W. J. Dominik (eds), *Literature, Art, History: Studies on Classical Antiquity and Tradition in Honour of W. J. Henderson* (Frankfurt, 2003), 91–109

Fantham 1979: Fantham, E. "Statius' Achilles and his Trojan model," *Classical Quarterly* n.s. 29 (1979), 457–462

Fantham 1997: Fantham, E. "'Envy and fear the begetter of hate': Statius' *Thebaid* and the genesis of hatred," in: S. M. Braund and C. Gill (eds), *The Passions in Roman Thought and Literature* (Cambridge, 1997), 185–212

Fantham 1999: Fantham, E. "*Chironis exemplum*: on teachers and surrogate fathers in *Achilleid* and *Silvae*," *Hermathena* 167 (1999), 59–70

Feeney 1991: Feeney, D. C. *The Gods in Epic* (Oxford, 1991)

Fortgens 1934: Fortgens, H. W. *P. Papinii Statii de Opheltis funere carmen epicum, Thebaidos liber VI 1–295, versione Batava commentarioque exegetico instructum* (Zutphen, 1934)

Franchet d'Espèrey 1999: Franchet d'Espèrey, S. *Conflit, violence et non-violence dans la Thébaïde de Stace* (Paris, 1999)

Frings 1991: Frings, I. *Gespräch und Handlung in der Thebais des Statius* (Stuttgart, 1991)

Frings 1992: Frings, I. *Odia fraterna als manieristisches Motiv: Betrachtungen zu Senecas Thyest und Statius' Thebais* (Mainz and Stuttgart, 1992)

Georgacopoulou 1996: Georgacopoulou, S. "Ranger/déranger: catalogues et listes de personnages dans la *Thébaïde*," in: F. Delarue, S. Georgacopoulou, P. Laurens, A.-M. Taisne (eds), *Epicedion: Hommage à P.*

Papinius Statius = La Licorne 38 (Poitiers, 1996), 93–129

Gruzelier 1994: Gruzelier, C. "The influence of Virgil's Dido on Statius' portrayal of Hypsipyle," *Prudentia* 26 (1994), 153–165

Hardie 1989: Hardie, P. "Flavian epicists on Virgil's epic technique," *Ramus* 18 (1989) = A. J. Boyle (ed.), *The Imperial Muse. Flavian Epicist to Claudian* (Bendigo, 1990), 3–20

Hardie 1993: Hardie, P. *The Epic Successors of Virgil: A Study in the Dynamics of a Tradition* (Cambridge, 1993)

Hardie 1997: Hardie, P. "Closure in Latin epic," in: D. H. Roberts, F. M. Dunn, D. P. Fowler (eds), *Classical Closure. Reading the End in Greek and Latin Literature* (Princeton, 1997), 139–162

Henderson 1993: Henderson, J. "Form remade: Statius' *Thebaid*," in: A. J. Boyle (ed.), *Roman Epic* (London and New York, 1993), 162–191

Hershkowitz 1998: Hershkowitz, D. *The Madness of Epic. Reading Insanity from Homer to Statius* (Oxford, 1998)

Heuvel 1932: Heuvel, H. *Publii Papinii Statii Thebaidos liber primus, versione Batava commentarioque exegetico instructus* (Zutphen, 1932)

Hill 1983: Hill, D. E. (ed.), *P. Papinii Statii Thebaidos libri XII* (Leiden, 1983)

Hill 1989: Hill, D. E. "Statius' *Thebaid*: a glimmer of light in a sea of darkness," *Ramus* 18 (1989) = A. J. Boyle (ed.), *The Imperial Muse. Flavian Epicists to Claudian* (Bendigo, 1990), 98–118

Hill 1996: Hill, D. E. "*Thebaid* I revisited," in: F. Delarue, S. Georgacopoulou, P. Laurens, A.-M. Taisne (eds),

Epicedion: Hommage à P. Papinius Statius = La Licorne 38 (Poitiers, 1996), 35–54

Hinds 1997: Hinds, S. "Do-it-yourself literary tradition: Statius, Martial and others," *Materiali e discussioni per l'analisi dei testi classici* 39 (1997), 187–207

Hinds 1998: Hinds, S. *Allusion and Intertext. Dynamics of Appropriation in Roman Poetry* (Cambridge, 1998)

Hoffmann 1999: Hoffmann, M. *Statius, Thebais 12, 312–463: Einleitung, Übersetzung, Kommentar* (Göttingen, 1999)

Hutchinson 1993: Hutchinson, G. O. *Latin Literature from Seneca to Juvenal. A Critical Study* (Oxford, 1993)

Jannaccone 1950: Jannaccone, S. *P. Papinio Stazio: L'Achilleide. Testo critico e commento* (Florence, 1950)

Johnson 1994: Johnson, W. R. "Information and form: Homer, Achilles, and Statius," in: S. Oberhelman, V. Kelly, R. J. Golsan (eds), *Epic and Epoch. Essays on the Interpretation and History of a Genre* (Lubbock, Texas, 1994), 25–39

Keith 2000: Keith, A. M. *Engendering Rome* (Cambridge, 2000)

Keith 2002: Keith, A. "Ovidian personae in Statius's *Thebaid,*" in: G. Tissol and S. Wheeler (eds), *Reception of Ovid in Antiquity = Arethusa* 35 (2002), 381–402

King 1987: King, K. C. *Achilles: Paradigms of the War Hero from Homer to the Middle Ages* (Berkeley, 1987)

Konstan 1997: Konstan, D. "Afterword," in: D. R. Slavitt (trans.), *Broken Columns. Two Roman Epic Fragments*: The Achilleid *of Publius Papinius Statius and* The Rape of Proserpine *of Claudius Claudianus* (Philadelphia, 1997), 79–96

Koster 1979: Koster, S. "Liebe und Krieg in der 'Achilleis'

des Statius," *Würzburger Jahrbücher für die Altertums-wissenschaft* n.F. 5 (1979), 189–208

Kytzler 1996: Kytzler, B. "*Pandere Thebas*. Welches Thema hat die *Thebais*?" in: F. Delarue, S. Georga-copoulou, P. Laurens, A.-M. Taisne (eds), *Epicedion: Hommage à P. Papinius Statius = La Licorne* 38 (Poitiers, 1996), 25–34

McGuire 1989: McGuire, D. T., Jr. "Textual strategies and political suicide in Flavian epic," *Ramus* 18 (1989) = A. J. Boyle (ed.), *The Imperial Muse. Flavian Epicists to Claudian* (Bendigo, 1990), 21–45

McGuire 1997: McGuire, D. T. *Acts of Silence: Civil War, Tyranny, and Suicide in the Flavian Epics* (Hildesheim and New York, 1997)

McNelis 2004: McNelis, C. "Middle-march: Statius' *Thebaid* 7 and the beginning of battle narrative," in: S. Kyriakidis and F. De Martino (eds), *Middles in Latin Poetry* (Bari, forthcoming)

Méheust 1971: Méheust, J. *Stace: Achilléide. Texte établi et traduit* (Paris, 1971)

Mendelsohn 1990: Mendelsohn, D. "Empty nest, abandoned cave: maternal anxiety in *Achilleid* 1," *Classical Antiquity* 9 (1990), 295–308

Mulder 1954: Mulder, H. M. *Publii Papinii Statii Thebaidos liber secundus commentario exegetico aestheticoque instructus* (Groningen, 1954)

Nugent 1996: Nugent, S. G. "Statius' Hypsipyle: following in the footsteps of the *Aeneid*," *Scholia* 5 (1996), 46–71

Pagán 2000: Pagán, V. E. "The mourning after: Statius *Thebaid* 12," *American Journal of Philology* 121 (2000), 423–452

Pavlovskis 1965: Pavlovskis, Z. "The education of Achilles,

as treated in the literature of Late Antiquity," *La parola del passato* 20 (1965), 281–297

Rosati 1994: Rosati, G. *Stazio: Achilleide. Introduzione, traduzione e note* (Milan, 1994), 5–61 = "L'*Achilleide* di Stazio, un'epica dell'ambiguità," *Maia* 44 (1992), 233–266

Schetter 1960: Schetter, W. *Untersuchungen zur epischen Kunst des Statius* (Wiesbaden, 1960)

Schubert 1984: Schubert, W. *Jupiter in den Epen der Flavierzeit* (Frankfurt, Berne, New York, 1984)

Smolenaars 1991: Smolenaars, J. J. L. "Quellen und Rezeption. Die Verarbeitung homerischer Motive bei Valerius Flaccus und Statius," in: M. Korn and H. J. Tschiedel (eds), *Ratis omnia vincet. Untersuchungen zu den Argonautica des Valerius Flaccus* (Hildesheim, 1991), 57–71

Smolenaars 1994: Smolenaars, J. J. L. *Statius Thebaid VII: A commentary* (Leiden, 1994)

Snijder 1968: Snijder, H. *P. Papinius Statius: Thebaid. A commentary on book III with text and introduction* (Amsterdam, 1968)

Sweeney 1969: Sweeney, R. D. *Prolegomena to an Edition of the Scholia to Statius* (Leiden, 1969)

Sweeney 1997: Sweeney, R. D. *Lactantii Placidi in Statii Thebaida commentum* Vol. 1 (Stuttgart and Leipzig, 1997)

Taisne 1994: Taisne, A.-M. *L'esthétique de Stace. La peinture des correspondances* (Paris, 1994)

Thuillier 1996: Thuillier, J.-P. "Stace, *Thébaïde* 6: les jeux funèbres et les réalités sportives," *Nikephoros* 9 (1996), 151–167

Venini 1970: Venini, P. *P. Papini Stati Thebaidos liber*

undecimus. Introduzione, testo critico, commento e traduzione (Florence, 1970)

Vessey 1973: Vessey, D. W. T. *Statius and the Thebaid* (Cambridge, 1973)

Vessey 1986: Vessey, D. W. T. "*Pierius menti calor incidit*: Statius' epic style," *Aufstieg und Niedergang der römischen Welt* II 32.5 (1986), 2965–3019

Vessey 1992: Vessey, D. W. T. "Introduction," in: A. D. Melville (trans.), *Statius: Thebaid* (Oxford, 1992), ix-xliii

Williams 1972: Williams, R. D. *P. Papini Stati Thebaidos liber decimus. Edited with a commentary* (Leiden, 1972)

Williams 1986: Williams, G. "Statius and Vergil: defensive imitation," in: J. D. Bernard (ed.), *Vergil at 2000: Commemorative Essays on the Poet and His Influence* (New York, 1986), 207–224

ABBREVIATIONS

Housman	A. E. Housman, *Classical Papers* (Cambridge 1972)
OLD	Oxford Latin Dictionary
RE	Pauly–Wissowa: *Realencyclopädie der classischen Altertumswissenschaft*
SB	D. R. Shackleton Bailey (this edition)
SB[1]	Museum Helveticum 40 (1983) 51–60
SB[2]	Harvard Studies in Classical Philology 100 (2000) 463–76
TLL	*Thesaurus Linguae Latinae*

Conventional abbreviations for classical authors and works are used in the critical notes.

THEBAID

LIBER I

Fraternas acies alternaque regna profanis
decertata odiis sontesque evolvere Thebas
Pierius menti calor incidit. unde iubetis
ire, deae? gentisne canam primordia dirae,
5 Sidonios raptus et inexorabile pactum
legis Agenoreae scrutantemque aequora Cadmum?
longa retro series, trepidum si Martis operti
agricolam infandis condentem proelia sulcis
expediam penitusque sequar, quo carmine muris
10 iusserit Amphion Tyriis accedere montes,
unde graves irae cognata in moenia Baccho,
quod saevae Iunonis opus, cui sumpserit arcus
infelix Athamas, cur non expaverit ingens
Ionium socio casura Palaemone mater.
15 atque adeo iam nunc gemitus et prospera Cadmi
praeteriisse sinam: limes mihi carminis esto
Oedipodae confusa domus, quando Itala nondum

10 tyrios PωΣ (*Gronovius*)

---

1 Agenor, king of Tyre, ordered his son Cadmus to go in search
of his daughter Europa, who had been carried off overseas by
Jupiter in the form of a bull, and not to return without her. Eventually Cadmus found himself at the site of Thebes.

40

BOOK 1

Pierian fire falls upon my soul: to unfold fraternal warfare, and alternate reigns fought for in unnatural hate, and
guilty Thebes. Where do you command me to begin, goddesses? Shall I sing the origins of the dire folk, the rape
Sidonian, the inexorable compact of Agenor's ordinance,
and Cadmus searching the seas?[1] Far back goes the tale,
were I to recount the affrighted husbandman of covered
soldiery hiding battle in unholy furrows[2] and pursue to
the uttermost what followed: with what music Amphion
bade mountains draw nigh the Tyrian walls, what caused
Bacchus' fierce wrath against a kindred city,[3] what savage
Juno wrought,[4] at whom hapless Athamas took up his bow,
wherefore Palaemon's mother did not fear the vast Ionian
when she made to plunge in company with her son.[5] No;
already shall I let the sorrows and happy days of Cadmus
be bygones. Let the limit of my lay be the troubled house
of Oedipus. For not yet do I dare breathe forth Italian

[2] Dragon's teeth, sown by Cadmus in the Theban Field of
Mars, came up as warriors, who fought each other until only five
survived.   [3] Thebes, whose king Pentheus had resisted him
(theme of Euripides' *Bacchae*). But his wrath was against the king,
not the city. Bacchus was the son of Jupiter and Cadmus' daughter
Semele.   [4] See Semele in Index.
  [5] See Ino in Index.

41

signa nec Arctoos ausim spirare triumphos
bisque iugo Rhenum, bis adactum legibus Histrum
20 et coniurato deiectos vertice Dacos
aut defensa prius vix pubescentibus annis
bella Iovis. tuque, o Latiae decus addite famae
quem nova maturi subeuntem exorsa parentis
aeternum sibi Roma cupit, licet artior omnes
25 limes agat stellas et te plaga lucida caeli,
Pleiadum Boreaeque et hiulci fulminis expers,
sollicitet, licet ignipedum frenator equorum
ipse tuis alte radiantem crinibus arcum
imprimat aut magni cedat tibi Iuppiter aequa
30 parte poli, maneas hominum contentus habenis,
undarum terraeque potens, et sidera dones.
tempus erit, cum Pierio tua fortior oestro
facta canam: nunc tendo chelyn; satis arma referre
Aonia et geminis sceptrum exitiale tyrannis
35 nec furiis post fata modum flammasque rebelles
seditione rogi tumulisque carentia regum
funera et egestas alternis mortibus urbes,
caerula cum rubuit Lernaeo sanguine Dirce
et Thetis arentes assuetum stringere ripas
40 horruit ingenti venientem Ismenon acervo.
quem prius heroum, Clio, dabis? immodicum irae
Tydea? laurigeri subitos an vatis hiatus?
urguet et hostilem propellens caedibus amnem

---

22 tuque ω: teque P *ante corr.*   23 mature *Lachmann*
28 late *Schrader*

---

6 After Domitian's campaigns against the German Chatti and
the Dacians, which can be left to historians, we come to the fight-

standards and northern triumphs—Rhine twice subju-
gated, Hister twice brought under obedience, Dacians
hurled down from their leagued mountain, or, earlier yet,
Jove's warfare warded off in years scarce past childhood.[6]
And you, glory added to Latium's fame, whom, as you take
on your aged father's enterprises anew,[7] Rome wishes hers
for eternity: though a narrower path move all the planets
and a radiant tract of heaven invite you, free of Pleiades
and Boreas and forked lightning; though the curber of the
fire-footed horses[8] himself set his high-shining halo on
your locks or Jupiter yield you an equal portion of the
broad sky, may you remain content with the governance of
mankind, potent over sea and land, and waive the stars. A
time will come when stronger in Pierian frenzy I shall sing
your deeds. For now I but tune my lyre; enough to recount
Aonian arms, sceptre fatal to tyrants twain, fury outlasting
death and flames renewing battle in the strife of the pyre,[9]
kings' bodies lacking burial, and cities emptied by mutual
slaughter, when Dirce's blue water blushed with Lernaean
blood and Thetis was aghast at Ismenos, as wont to skirt
dry banks he came on in a mighty heap. Clio, which of
the heroes do you offer first? Tydeus, untrammelled in
his wrath? Or the laurelled seer's sudden chasm? Stormy
Hippomedon too is upon me, pushing the river his enemy

ing on the Capitol in 69 A.D. (the year of the four emperors) between supporters of Vitellius and Vespasian; cf. *Silvae* 1.1.79.
Domitian was on the spot, though his role was in fact insignificant.

[7] The brief reign of Domitian's elder brother Titus (79–81) is
ignored.   [8] The Sun.

[9] As described in Book 12, the brothers' funeral fire split in
two.

turbidus Hippomedon, plorandaque bella protervi
45 Arcados atque alio Capaneus horrore canendus.
    Impia iam merita scrutatus lumina dextra
merserat aeterna damnatum nocte pudorem
Oedipodes longaque animam sub morte trahebat.
illum indulgentem tenebris imaeque recessu
50 sedis inaspectos caelo radiisque penates
servantem tamen assiduis circumvolat alis
saeva dies animi, scelerumque in pectore Dirae.
tunc vacuos orbes, crudum ac miserabile vitae
supplicium, ostentat caelo manibusque cruentis
55 pulsat inane solum saevaque ita voce precatur:
    'Di, sontes animas angustaque Tartara poenis
qui regitis, tuque umbrifero Styx livida fundo,
quam video, multumque mihi consueta vocari
annue, Tisiphone, perversaque vota secunda:
60 si bene quid merui, si me de matre cadentem
fovisti gremio et traiectum vulnere plantas
firmasti, si stagna peti Cirrhaea bicorni
interfusa iugo, possem cum degere falso
contentus Polybo, trifidaeque in Phocidos arto

48 trahebat Σ *ad* 11.582: tene- Pω

---

10 Night and death hover over the doomed (*Aeneid* 6.866, Horace, *Satires* 2.1.58). In Oedipus' case the hovering thing is the night of his own conscience, the only daylight he now knows. His story is the subject of Sophocles' *Oedipus Rex*.

11 Has he emerged from his underground den? I rather think not, though Tisiphone can hear him, if not see him, from the underworld (line 89). *Inane solum* is not Tartarus (as the scholiast explains) but the floor he stands on, hollow because the under-

with corpses. And I must mourn the fight of the overbold Arcadian, and sing Capaneus in consternation never felt before.

Oedipus had already probed his impious eyes with guilty hand and sunk deep his shame condemned to ever-lasting night; he dragged out his life in a long-drawn death. He devotes himself to darkness, and in the lowest recess of his abode he keeps his home on which the rays of heaven never look; and yet the fierce daylight of his soul flits around him with unflagging wings and the Avengers of his crimes are in his heart.[10] Then does he show the sky his vacant orbs,[11] the raw, pitiable punishment of survival, and strike the hollow earth with bleeding hands, and utter this wrathful prayer:

'Gods that rule guilty souls and Tartarus too small for punishments; and Styx, livid in your shadowed depth, you that I see;[12] and Tisiphone, on whom I so often call: give me your nod and favour my warped desire. If I have done aught of service, if you cherished me in your lap when I dropped from my mother and strengthened me when they pierced my feet; if I sought Girrha's pool poured out be-tween two mountain peaks[13] and in quest of father (though I might have lived content with the impostor Polybus) entwined the aged king[14] in that narrow place of triply sun-

world is below. 'Show the sky' does not put him in the open, since to the blind the ceiling and the sky come to the same thing. He just lifts up his head.

[12] He 'sees' only darkness and Styx is dark.

[13] Of Parnassus. Oedipus had gone to Delphi to consult the oracle about his parentage. The pool is the spring of Castalia.

[14] Laius, his real father, though neither knew it.

65 longaevum implicui regem secuique trementis
ora senis, dum quaero patrem, si Sphingos iniquae
callidus ambages te praemonstrante resolvi,
si dulces furias et lamentabile matris
conubium gavisus ini noctemque nefandam
70 saepe tuli natosque tibi, scis ipsa, paravi,
mox avidus poenae digitis cedentibus ultro
incubui miseraque oculos in matre reliqui:
exaudi, si digna precor quaeque ipsa furenti
subiceres. orbum visu regnisque carentem
75 non regere aut dictis maerentem flectere adorti,
quos genui quocumque toro; quin ecce superbi
—pro dolor!—et nostro iamdudum funere reges
insultant tenebris gemitusque odere paternos.
hisne etiam funestus ego? et videt ista deorum
80 ignavus genitor? tu saltem debita vindex
huc ades et totos in poenam ordire nepotes.
indue quod madidum tabo diadema cruentis
unguibus abripui, votisque instincta paternis
i media in fratres, generis consortia ferro
85 dissiliant. da, Tartarei regina barathri,
quod cupiam vidisse nefas. nec tarda sequetur
mens iuvenum: modo digna veni, mea pignora nosces.'
      Talia dicenti crudelis diva severos
advertit vultus. inamoenum forte sedebat
90 Cocyton iuxta, resolutaque vertice crines
lambere sulphureas permiserat anguibus undas.
ilicet igne Iovis lapsisque citatior astris

71 cedentibus P (v. *Håkanson*): caed- ω

dered Phocis and cut off the trembling old man's head; if under your tutelage I had cunning to solve the riddle of the cruel Sphinx; if I joyfully entered sweet madness and my mother's lamentable wedlock, enduring many a night of evil and making children for *you*, as well you know; if thereafter, avid for punishment, I pressed down upon yielding fingers[15] and left my eyes upon my hapless mother:[16] hear oh hear, if my prayer be worthy and such as you yourself might whisper to my frenzy. Those I begot (no matter in what bed) did not try to guide me, bereft of sight and sceptre, or sway my grieving with words. Nay behold (ah agony!), in their pride, kings this while by my calamity, they even mock my darkness, impatient of their father's groans. Even to *them* am I unclean? And does the sire of the gods see it and do naught? Do you at least, my rightful champion, come hither and range all my progeny for punishment. Put on your head this gore-soaked diadem that I tore off with my bloody nails. Spurred by a father's prayers, go against the brothers, go between them, let steel make partnership of blood fly asunder. Queen of Tartarus' pit, grant the wickedness I would fain see. Nor will the young men's spirit be slow to follow. Come you but worthy, you shall know them my true sons.'

The cruel goddess turned her stern countenance upon him as he spoke. As it chanced, she was sitting by unlovely Cocytos and had loosed the hair from her head and let the serpents lick the sulphurous waters. At once she leapt up from the gloomy bank, swifter than Jove's fire or falling

[15] A characteristic inversion.
[16] Her corpse. As in Sophocles, Jocasta's suicide here precedes the blinding, whereas in 11.637ff. it is the other way round.

tristibus exsiluit ripis: discedit inane
vulgus et occursus dominae pavet. illa per umbras
95 et caligantes animarum examine campos
Taenariae limen petit irremeabile portae.
sensit adesse Dies, piceo Nox obvia nimbo
lucentes turbavit equos; procul arduus Atlans
horruit et dubia caelum cervice remisit.
100 arripit extemplo Maleae de valle resurgens
notum iter ad Thebas; neque enim velocior ullas
itque reditque vias cognatave Tartara mavult.
centum illi stantes umbrabant ora cerastae,
turba minor diri capitis; sedet intus abactis
105 ferrea lux oculis, qualis per nubila Phoebes
Atracia rubet arte labor; suffusa veneno
tenditur ac sanie gliscit cutis; igneus atro
ore vapor, quo longa sitis morbique famesque
et populis mors una venit; riget horrida tergo
110 palla, et caerulei redeunt in pectora nodi:
Atropos hos atque ipsa novat Proserpina cultus.
tum geminas quatit ira manus: haec igne rogali
fulgurat, haec vivo manus aëra verberat hydro.
    Ut stetit, abrupta qua plurimus arce Cithaeron
115 occurrit caelo, fera sibila crine virenti
congeminat, signum terris, unde omnis Achaei
ora maris late Pelopeaque regna resultant.
audiit et medius caeli Parnasos et asper
Eurotas, dubiamque iugo fragor impulit Oeten

---

17 Taenarus and Malea, the two southern extremities of the
Peloponnese, are some forty miles apart. By poetic licence, in
which he is apt to indulge, Statius choses to conflate them; cf.

stars. The phantom crowd disperses, fearing their mistress' encounter. Through shades and fields dark with the swarm of ghosts she makes for the threshold of Taenarus' gate, past which none may return. Day felt her at hand, Night met him with a pitchy cloud and scared his bright horses. Afar steep Atlas shuddered and let go the sky from his unsteady neck. Straightway rising from Malea's valley,[17] she hastens along the familiar road to Thebes. No route does she travel faster to and fro, nor likes kindred Tartarus better. One hundred asps erect shaded her face, lesser population of her fearful head.[18] In her sunken eyes sits a steely glow, as when Atracian art makes labouring Phoebe blush through clouds.[19] Suffused with venom, her skin stretches and swells with matter. In her black mouth is a fiery vapour, whereby comes long drought and distempers and famine and a common death upon the nations. At her back lies stiffly a horrid mantle and blue-black knots return upon her breast. Atropos and Proserpine herself refurbish her attire. Then wrath shakes both her hands: the one glares with funeral fire, the other lashes the air with a living snake.

She halted where Cithaeron's highest peak meets the sky and with green tresses utters hiss after fierce hiss, a sign to earth; the whole coast of the Achaean sea and the realms of Pelops echo wide. Half way to heaven Parnassus heard and rough[20] Eurotas; the sound pushed

2.33f. *Valle* may refer to low ground east of Malea. From the map in *RE* Taenarus does not look as if it has any valleys to speak of.

[18] Most of the snakes were at the *back* of her head.

[19] I.e. as when Thessalian witches make a lunar eclipse.

[20] Connoting Spartan discipline.

120 in latus, et geminis vix fluctibus obstitit Isthmos.
ipsa suum genetrix curvo delphine vagantem
abripuit frenis gremioque Palaemona pressit.
     Atque ea Cadmeo praeceps ubi culmine primum
constitit assuetaque infecit nube penates,
125 protinus attoniti fratrum sub pectore motus,
gentilisque animos subiit furor aegraque laetis
invidia atque parens odii metus, inde regendi
saevus amor, ruptaeque vices iurisque secundi
ambitus impatiens, et summo dulcius unum
130 stare loco, sociisque comes discordia regnis.
sic ubi delectos per torva armenta iuvencos
agricola imposito sociare affectat aratro,
illi indignantes, quis nondum vomere multo
ardua nodosos cervix descendit in armos,
135 in diversa trahunt atque aequis vincula laxant
viribus et vario confundunt limite sulcos:
haud secus indomitos praeceps discordia fratres
asperat. alterni placuit sub legibus anni
exsilio mutare ducem. sic iure maligno
140 Fortunam transire iubent, ut sceptra tenentem
foedere praecipiti semper novus angeret heres.
haec inter fratres pietas erat, haec mora pugnae
sola nec in regem perduratura secundum.
et nondum crasso laquearia fulva metallo,
145 montibus aut alte Grais effulta nitebant
atria, congestos satis explicitura clientes;
non impacatis regum advigilantia somnis
pila, nec alterna †ferri statione gementes†
excubiae, nec cura mero committere gemmas

137 anceps *Hall*   148 ferrum . . . gerentes *SB*[1]

Oeta's unsteady[21] range sideways and Isthmos scarce with-
stood twin waves. Palaemon's mother[22] herself snatched
him from the reins as he roamed on his curving dolphin
and pressed him to her bosom.

When first she stayed her headlong course at the Cadmean citadel and tainted the dwelling with her wonted
mist, shock stirred the brothers' hearts. The family madness invaded their minds, envy sick at another's good fortune and fear, parent of hate, then fierce love of rule,
breach of give and take, ambition intolerant of second
place, hankering to stand at the top alone, strife, the companion of shared sovereignty. So when a farmer essays
to yoke two bullocks chosen from the fierce herd at one
plough, they rebel; not yet has many a ploughshare bowed
their lofty necks into their brawny shoulders. They pull opposite ways and with equal strength loosen their bonds,
perplexing the furrows with motley track. Not otherwise
does headlong strife enrage the tameless brethren. It was
agreed that each change rule for banishment as the alternate year decreed. Thus by an ungenerous law they bid
Fortune change sides, so that the holder of the sceptre be
ever tormented by a new heir as the compact hurries by.
This was brotherly love between the two, this the sole stay
of conflict, one that would not endure till the second king!
And not yet did panelled ceilings shine fulvous with thick
metal or lofty halls propped upon Greek marble, with
space to spread assembled clients. There were no spears
watching over the restless slumbers of monarchs nor steel-
bearing (?) sentinels in alternating station, nor were they at

21 Proleptic: shaken by the noise.
22 Ino/Leucothea.

150 atque aurum violare cibis: sed nuda potestas
    armavit fratres, pugna est de paupere regno.
    dumque uter angustae squalentia iugera Dirces
    verteret aut Tyrii solio non altus ovaret
    exsulis ambigitur, periit ius fasque bonumque
155 et vitae mortisque pudor. quo tenditis iras,
    a, miseri? quid si peteretur crimine tanto
    limes uterque poli, quem Sol emissus Eoo
    cardine, quem porta vergens prospectat Hibera,
    quasque procul terras obliquo sidere tangit
160 avius aut Borea gelidas madidive tepentes
    igne Noti? quid si Phrygiae Tyriaeque sub unum
    convectentur opes? loca dira arcesque nefandae
    suffecere odio, furiisque immanibus emptum
    Oedipodae sedisse loco.
                              Iam sorte iacebat
165 dilatus Polynicis honos. quis tunc tibi, saeve,
    quis fuit ille dies, vacua cum solus in aula
    respiceres ius omne tuum cunctosque minores,
    et nusquam par stare caput! iam murmura serpunt
    plebis Echioniae, tacitumque a principe vulgus
170 dissidet, et, qui mos populis, venturus amatur.
    atque aliquis, cui mens humili laesisse veneno
    summa nec impositos umquam cervice volenti
    ferre duces, 'hancne Ogygiis,' ait, 'aspera rebus
    Fata tulere vicem, totiens mutare timendos
175 alternoque iugo dubitantia subdere colla?
    partiti versant populorum fata manuque
    Fortunam fecere levem. semperne vicissim

158 portu . . . hibero Pω (ς, *Gruter*)
161 quid ω: non PΣ   164 carebat PωΣ (SB[1])

pains to trust jewels to wine and pollute gold with victuals: naked power armed the brethren, their fight is for a pauper crown. While they disputed who should plough cramped Dirce's barren acres or lord it on the Tyrian exile's lowly throne, law human and divine, morality and decency in life and death, went by the board. Alas you wretches, to what end do you stretch your wrath?[23] What if by such crime you sought both of heaven's boundaries, that to which the Sun looks when he is sent forth from the eastern hinge and that to which he gazes as he sinks from his Iberian gate, and those lands he touches from afar with slanting ray, lands the North Wind chills or the moist South warms with his heat? What if the riches of Phrygia and Tyre be brought together in one? A place of terror, a citadel accursed, sufficed your hate, monstrous madness did it cost to sit where Oedipus had sat.

Already Polynices' royalty lay low, deferred by the lot. What a day that was for you, cruel monarch, when alone in empty palace you saw authority all yours, every man your inferior, nowhere a head standing as high! Already grumbling creeps among the Echionian commons and the crowd is at silent odds with the prince. As is the way of a populace, the man of the future is the favourite. Thus one of them, whose bent it was to harm the highest with lowly venom nor ever to bear with a willing neck the rulers placed over him: 'Have the harsh Fates dealt this portion to Thebes, so often to change them we must fear and bow doubting necks beneath an alternating yoke? Dividing with each other they direct the destiny of peoples and by force have made Fortune fickle. Am I always to be given as

[23] I.e. what you are fighting for is of little value.

exsulibus servire dabor? tibi, summe deorum
terrarumque sator, sociis hanc addere mentem
180 sedit? an inde vetus Thebis extenditur omen,
ex quo Sidonii nequiquam blanda iuvenci
pondera Carpathio iussus sale quaerere Cadmus
exsul Hyanteos invenit regna per agros,
fraternasque acies fetae telluris hiatu
185 augurium seros demisit ad usque nepotes?
cernis ut erectum torva sub fronte minetur
saevior assurgens dempto consorte potestas.
quas gerit ore minas, quanto premit omnia fastu!
hicne umquam privatus erit? tamen ille precanti
190 mitis et affatu bonus et patientior aequi.
quid mirum? non solus erat. nos vilis in omnes
prompta manus casus, domino cuicumque parati,
qualiter hinc gelidus Boreas, hinc nubifer Eurus
vela trahunt, nutat mediae fortuna carinae.
195 heu dubio suspensa metu tolerandaque nullis
aspera sors populis! hic imperat, ille minatur.'
    At Iovis imperiis rapidi super atria caeli
lectus concilio divum convenerat ordo
interiore polo. spatiis hinc omnia iuxta,
200 primaeque occiduaeque domus et fusa sub omni
terra atque unda die. mediis sese arduus infert
ipse deis, placido quatiens tamen omnia vultu,
stellantique locat solio; nec protinus ausi
caelicolae, veniam donec pater ipse sedendi
205 tranquilla iubet esse manu. mox turba vagorum

185 dimisit Pω (ς, *Hall*)
200 effusa Pω (*Markland*)

54

a slave to exiles taking turns? Did you resolve, supreme
creator of heaven and earth, to make the partners[24] so will?
Or does the ancient omen for Thebes extend from the time
when Cadmus, ordered to search the Carpathian Sea in
vain for the Sidonian bull's seductive freight, found in exile
a kingdom in Hyantean fields and sent down fraternal warfare from the opening of pregnant earth as an augury to his
remote posterity? See you how power, rising crueller with
none to share it, threatens us straight of stance and stern of
brow? What menace in his countenance, how his pride
abases all things! Will *he* ever be a private citizen? Ah, but
the other was gentle to the suppliant, kind of speech and
more tolerant of justice. No wonder; he was not alone. As
for us, we are a cheap company, ready to hand for any
venture, for any master to use. Even as chill Boreas pulls
canvass one way and cloudy Eurus another and the vessel's
fate wavers between (alas harsh lot, hanging in doubtful
suspense, too hard for any folk to bear!); the one commands, the other threatens.'

Now at Jove's decree the chosen hierarchy of the gods
had assembled in council in the hall of the whirling firmament, at the sky's centre. From this point all is at close distance, the halls of rising and setting, land and sea spread
out under every heaven. He himself proceeds towering
through the midst of the deities, making all things quake
though his countenance be serene, and places himself on
his starry throne. Nor dare heaven's denizens follow suit
straightway, but wait until the Father himself with tranquil
gesture orders licence to be seated. Presently a crowd of

[24] Eteocles and Polynices (SB[2]), not 'your kith and kin' or
'your allies (the Thebans).'

semideum et summis cognati Nubibus Amnes
et compressa metu servantes murmura Venti
aurea tecta replent. mixta convexa deorum
maiestate tremunt, radiant maiore sereno
210   culmina et arcano florentes lumine postes.
postquam iussa quies siluitque exterritus orbis,
incipit ex alto (grave et immutabile sanctis
pondus adest verbis, et vocem Fata sequuntur):
   'Terrarum delicta nec exsaturabile Diris
215   ingenium mortale queror. quonam usque nocentum
exigar in poenas? taedet saevire corusco
fulmine, iam pridem Cyclopum operosa fatiscunt
bracchia et Aeoliis desunt incudibus ignes.
atque adeo tuleram falso rectore solutos
220   Solis equos, caelumque rotis errantibus uri,
et Phaëthontea mundum squalere favilla.
nil actum, neque tu valida quod cuspide late
ire per illicitum pelago, germane, dedisti.
nunc geminas punire domos, quis sanguinis auctor
225   ipse ego, descendo. Perseos alter in Argos
scinditur, Aonias fluit hic ab origine Thebas.
mens cunctis imposta manet: quis funera Cadmi
nesciat et totiens excitam a sedibus imis
Eumenidum bellasse aciem, mala gaudia matrum
230   erroresque feros nemorum et reticenda deorum

---

25 They forged Jupiter's thunderbolts inside Mt Aetna. Similarly Vulcan, working in the Aeolian Islands off the northeast coast
of Sicily.

26 The genealogies may be left to commentators: 'The an-
cients did not agree on mythological stemmatics, and Statius is
often quite vague' (Vessey).

wandering demigods and Rivers kin to the lofty Clouds and Winds keeping their roars under fear's restraint fill the golden edifice. The dome trembles with the mingled majesty of the deities, the towers shine in a larger blue, and the portals bloom with a mystic light. Silence was ordered and mute in terror fell the world. From on high he begins. His holy words have weight heavy and immutable and the Fates follow his voice:

'Earth's sins and the mind of man that no demons of vengeance can satiate I do protest. How much longer shall I be driven to punish the guilty? Weary am I of raging with flashing bolt, the busy arms of the Cyclopes[25] have long been faint and the Aeolian anvils out of fire. And indeed I suffered the loosing of the Sun's horses under a false driver, the burning of the sky as the wheels ran wild, the world caked with Phaëthon's ashes. It availed not; nor yet that you, my brother, with your strong spear let the sea go at large through territory not its own. Now I descend to punish two houses, my own blood. One stream branches to Persean Argos, the other flows from its fount to Aonian Thebes.[26] The character stamped on all of them abides. Who would not know of Cadmus' calamities, how often the host of Furies, summoned from their infernal dwellings, made war, the evil joys of mothers[27] and their wild wanderings in the forests, the gods' reproaches[28] best unspoken.

[27] Bacchanals.

[28] Sometimes understood as 'crimes against the gods,' which makes doubtful Latin and indifferent sense (with *reticenda*). Jupiter may be supposed to be thinking of his own affair with Semele and the slayings of the Niobids and Pentheus.

crimina? vix lucis spatio, vix noctis abactae
enumerare queam mores gentemque profanam.
scandere quin etiam thalamos hic impius heres
patris et immeritae gremium incestare parentis
235 appetiit, proprios (monstrum!) revolutus in ortus.
ille tamen superis aeterna piacula solvit
proiecitque diem, nec iam amplius aethere nostro
vescitur; at nati (facinus sine more!) cadentes
calcavere oculos. iam iam rata vota tulisti,
240 dire senex. meruere tuae, meruere tenebrae
ultorem sperare Iovem. nova sontibus arma
iniciam regnis, totumque a stirpe revellam
exitiale genus. belli mihi semina sunto
Adrastus socer et superis adiuncta sinistris
245 conubia. hanc etiam poenis incessere gentem
decretum; neque enim arcano de pectore fallax
Tantalus et saevae periit iniuria mensae.'
       Sic pater omnipotens. ast illi saucia dictis
flammato versans inopinum corde dolorem
250 talia Iuno refert: 'mene, o iustissime divum,
me bello certare iubes? scis, semper ut arces
Cyclopum magnique Phoronei incluta fama
sceptra viris opibusque iuvem, licet improbus illic
custodem Phariae somno letoque iuvencae
255 exstinguas, saeptis et turribus aureus intres.
mentitis ignosco toris: illam odimus urbem
quam vultu confessus adis, ubi conscia magni
signa tori tonitrus agis et mea fulmina torques.

---

[29] 'Expelled' by artificial light; see SB[2]. He means 'in the space
of a day and a wakeful night.'   [30] Adrastus' ancestor Tantalus served up his son Pelops for the gods to eat.

58

Scarce in the space of daylight and of night expelled[29] could I enumerate the unholy ways of that race. Why, this impious heir essayed to climb into his father's bed and to defile the womb of his innocent mother, returning (oh monstrous!) to his own origin. He, however, has paid an everlasting penalty to the High Ones, casting the daylight away, and no longer does he feed upon our air; but his sons (outrageous deed!) trampled his eyes as they fell. Now, now your prayers are answered, dire ancient. Your darkness has deserved, ay truly, to hope for Jove as its avenger. I shall bring new warfare on the guilty reigns and tear the whole deadly stock out from the root. Let Adrastus' gift of his daughter in a marriage unblessed of heaven be my seed of battle. This line also I have resolved to assail and punish, for false Tantalus and the outrage of the cruel banquet[30] have not vanished from my secret heart.'

So spoke the Father Almighty. But wounded by his words and with sudden pain in her burning heart thus Juno makes answer: 'Most just of the gods, is it I whom you bid go to war, I? You know how always with men and wealth I aid the towers of the Cyclopes and great Phoroneus' sceptre famed in story, even though you in that land scruple not to destroy the warder[31] of the Pharian heifer by sleep and death and to enter the guarded turret[32] in golden guise. I forgive the couchings you deny. But I hate that city where you go and do not hide your face, where you make thunder, the signal and accomplice of our mighty union, and hurl

[31] Hundred-eyed Argus, set by Juno to watch Io. Mercury killed him on Jupiter's orders as he slept.

[32] Of Danaë.

facta luant Thebae: cur hostes eligis Argos?
260 quin age, si tanti est thalami discordia sancti,
et Samon et veteres armis exscinde Mycenas,
verte solo Sparten. cur usquam sanguine festo
coniugis ara tuae, cumulo cur turis Eoi
laeta calet? melius votis Mareotica fumat
265 Coptos et aerisoni lugentia flumina Nili.
quod si prisca luunt auctorum crimina gentes
subvenitque tuis sera haec sententia curis,
percensere aevi senium, ⟨a⟩ quo tempore tandem
terrarum furias abolere et saecula retro
270 emendare sat est? iamdudum ab sedibus illis
incipe, fluctivaga qua praeterlabitur unda
Sicanios longe relegens Alpheos amores:
Arcades hic tua (nec pudor est) delubra nefastis
imposuere locis, illic Mavortius axis
275 Oenomai Geticoque pecus stabulare sub Haemo
dignius, abruptis etiamnum inhumata procorum
reliquiis trunca ora rigent; tamen hic tibi templi
gratus honos; placet Ida nocens mentitaque manes
Creta tuos. me Tantaleis consistere terris
280 quae tandem invidia est? belli deflecte tumultus
et generis miseresce tui. sunt impia late
regna tibi, melius generos passura nocentes.'

260 tanta Pω (*Gronovius*)
268 *add. Madvig*
279 terris ψ: tectis Pω

33 Alluding to Semele.
34 Alluding to the *sistrum* (metal rattle) used by Isis worship-

BOOK 1

my bolts.³³ Let Thebes expiate her deeds; but why choose Argos as her foe? Nay then, if the discord of our sacred bedchamber is a price worth paying, raze Samos with battle and ancient Mycenae, level Sparte with the ground. Why does your spouse's rejoicing altar warm anywhere with festal blood and pile of eastern incense? Better that Mareotic Coptos smoke with vows and the mourning streams of brazen-clanging Nile.³⁴ But if the peoples expiate the ancient crimes of their first ancestors and this late resolve has entered your anxious thoughts, to pass time's old age in review, how far back, I ask, does it suffice to cancel earth's mad doings and purge the ages in reverse? Begin straightway with those dwellings³⁵ where the wave-wandering waters of Alpheus glide, distantly retracing his Sicanian love. Here the men of Arcady set your shrine (nor do you blush) in abominable ground; there was the chariot of Oenomaus, gift of Mars, and horses worthier to be stabled under Getic Haemus.³⁶ There even now stark and unburied are the mangled heads of the suitors, torn from their remains.³⁷ And yet the grace of a temple there pleases you; guilty Ida³⁸ and Crete that tells falsely of your death is to your liking. Why grudge *me* a home in the land of Tantalus? Turn aside war's turmoils and pity your own blood. You have wicked realms spread wide that will better suffer guilty husbands for their daughters.'

pers in the annual mourning for Osiris. Juno means 'let Isis (identified with Io) be worshipped rather than me.'

³⁵ Olympia, centre of Jupiter worship.   ³⁶ Like the man-eating horses of Thracian Diomedes.   ³⁷ Lit. 'maimed of their remains (i.e. bodies).'   ³⁸ In Crete, where Jupiter was supposed to be buried (Cretans were proverbially liars).

61

Finierat precibus miscens convicia Iuno.
at non ille gravis dictis, quamquam aspera †motu,†
285 reddidit haec: 'equidem haud rebar te mente secunda
laturam, quodcumque tuos, licet aequus, in Argos
consulerem, neque me, detur si copia, fallit
multa super Thebis Bacchum ausuramque Dionen
dicere, sed nostri reverentia ponderis obstat.
290 horrendos etenim latices, Stygia aequora fratris,
obtestor, mansurum et non revocabile verbum,
nil fore quod dictis flectar. quare impiger alis
portantes praecede Notos, Cyllenia proles,
aëra per liquidum regnisque illapsus opacis
295 dic patruo: superas senior se attollat ad auras
Laius, exstinctum nati quem vulnere nondum
ulterior Lethes accepit ripa profundi
lege Erebi; ferat hic diro mea iussa nepoti:
germanum exsilio fretum Argolicisque tumentem
300 hospitiis, quod sponte cupit, procul impius aula
arceat, alternum regni infitiatus honorem.
hinc causae irarum, certo reliqua ordine ducam.'
    Paret Atlantiades dictis genitoris et inde
summa pedum propere plantaribus illigat alis
305 obnubitque comas et temperat astra galero.
tum dextrae virgam inseruit, qua pellere dulces
aut suadere iterum somnos, qua nigra subire
Tartara et exsangues animare assueverat umbras.
desiluit, tenuique exceptus inhorruit aura.

---

284 motu *ω*: -us P *ante corr., Gruter: anne captu?*

---

39 Pluto's, whose Styx (by which the gods took their oaths) corresponds to the sea in the upper world.

Juno ended, reproach blent with supplication. But the words of his reply were not hard, though harsh to apprehend (?): 'Indeed I did not think you would take kindly to any intent of mine against your Argos, just though I be, neither am I unaware that given opportunity Bacchus and Dione would venture lengthy pleas on behalf of Thebes; but reverence for my authority forbids. And verily I call the dread waters, my brother's Stygian sea,[39] to witness, pronouncement fixed and irrevocable: no words shall ever change my purpose. Therefore, my son of Cyllene, stir your wings, speed faster than the winds that bear you, glide through the clear air to the realms of darkness and thus address your uncle: Let old Laius ascend to the upper atmosphere; slain by his son's sword, Lethe's bank has not yet received him, according to deep Erebus' law.[40] Let him bear my commands to his fell grandson, whose brother counts on exile and waxes proud with Argive hospitality. Him let the ruler keep far from the palace (as is his own desire), flouting kinship and repudiating the royal dignity alternate. Hence cause of ire; the rest I shall guide in sure process.'

Atlas' grandson[41] obeys his sire's words and hastily thereupon binds the winged sandals on to his ankles and with his wide hat covers his locks and tempers the stars. Then he thrusts the wand in his right hand; with this he was wont to banish sweet slumber or recall it, with this to enter black Tartarus and give life to bloodless phantoms. Down he leapt and shivered as the thin air received him. No

[40] Under which unburied dead wandered for a hundred years outside the boundary of the underworld (Lethe).

[41] Mercury's mother Maia was Atlas' daughter.

310 nec mora, sublimes raptim per inane volatus
carpit et ingenti designat nubila gyro.
    Interea patriis olim vagus exsul ab oris
Oedipodionides furto deserta pererrat
Aoniae. iam iamque animis male debita regna
315 concipit, et longum signis cunctantibus annum
stare gemit. tenet una dies noctesque recursans
cura virum, si quando humilem decedere regno
germanum et semet Thebis opibusque potitum
cerneret; hac aevum cupiat pro luce pacisci.
320 nunc queritur ceu tarda fugae dispendia, sed mox
attollit flatus ducis et sedisse superbum
deiecto iam fratre putat: spes anxia mentem
extrahit et longo consumit gaudia voto.
tunc sedet Inachias urbes Danaëiaque arva
325 et caligantes abrupto sole Mycenas
ferre iter impavidum, seu praevia ducit Erinys,
seu fors illa viae, sive hac immota vocabat
Atropos. Ogygiis ululata furoribus antra
deserit et pingues Baccheo sanguine colles.
330 inde plagam, qua molle sedens in plana Cithaeron
porrigitur lassumque inclinat ad aequora montem,
praeterit. hinc arte scopuloso in limite pendens
infames Scirone petras Scyllaeaque rura
purpureo regnata seni ditemque Corinthon
335 linquit et in mediis audit duo litora campis.

[321] superbus Pω (ς)   [334] mitem Pω (*Schrader*)

---

[42] The anticipated joy of returning to Thebes as king.
[43] When Atreus served up the sons of his brother Thyestes to their father and the Sun reversed course.

pause; he takes swift and lofty flight through the void and traces a vast arc across the clouds.

Meanwhile, long now a wandering exile from his native land, the son of Oedipus stealthily strays over lonely reaches of Aonia. Already his mind envisages the royalty overdue and groans at the long year's halt and the loitering of the constellations. One thought obsesses him day and night, ever recurring: would he one day see his brother humbly leave the throne and himself in possession of Thebes and power? For that day he would willingly barter a lifetime. One moment he complains of the dragging stretch of exile, but anon he hoists princely pride and fancies he sits haughty, his brother already cast down. Torturing hope drags out his soul and in prolonged desire exhausts his joy.[42] Then he decides to take his way boldly to the cities of Inachus and Danaë's fields and Mycenae darkened with sun cut short.[43] Does a guiding Fury lead him on, or is it the chance of the road, or was inexorable Atropos summoning him that way? He leaves the glades where Ogygian madness howls and hills fat with Bacchic gore.[44] Thence he passes the tract where Cithaeron stretches out, gently sinking into the flat, and inclines his weary steep to the sea. From here the rocky path is high and narrow. He leaves Sciron's ill-famed cliffs and Scylla's fields where the purple ancient[45] ruled and wealthy Corinth; and in mid land hears two shores.

[44] Where Bacchanals tore their victims to pieces.
[45] Nisus, king of Megara, whose life-preserving lock of hair was cut off by his daughter Scylla (distinct from the marine monster).

Iamque per emeriti surgens confinia Phoebi
Titanis late mundo subvecta silenti
rorifera gelidum tenuaverat aëra biga;
iam pecudes volucresque tacent, iam Somnus avaris
340   irrepsit curis pronusque ex aethere nutat,
grata laboratae referens oblivia vitae.
sed nec puniceo rediturum nubila caelo
promisere iubar, nec rarescentibus umbris
longa repercusso nituere crepuscula Phoebo:
345   densior a terris et nulli pervia flammae
subtexit nox atra polos. iam claustra rigentis
Aeoliae percussa sonant, venturaque rauco
ore minatur hiems, venti transuersa frementes
confligunt axemque emoto cardine vellunt,
350   dum caelum sibi quisque rapit; sed plurimus Auster
inglomerat noctem, tenebrosa volumina torquens,
defunditque imbres sicco quos asper hiatu
praesolidat Boreas; nec non abrupta tremescunt
fulgura, et attritus subita face rumpitur aether.
355   iam Nemea, iam Taenariis contermina lucis
Arcadiae capita alta madent; ruit agmine magno
Inachus et gelidas surgens Erasinus in undas.
pulverulenta prius calcandaque flumina nullae
aggeribus tenuere morae, stagnoque refusa est
360   funditus et veteri spumavit Lerna veneno.
frangitur omne nemus, rapiunt antiqua procellae
bracchia silvarum, nullisque aspecta per aevum
solibus umbrosi patuere aestiva Lycaei.
    Ille tamen, modo saxa iugis fugientia ruptis

343 crebrescentibus *Imhof*
357 in undas P *ante corr.*: ad arctos ω

And now Phoebus' work is done; Titanis rises nearby, through the wide spaces, borne up in the silent sky, thinning the cool atmosphere with her dewy car. Now beasts and birds are still, now Sleep steals upon greedy cares, hanging down from the air, bringing back sweet forgetfulness of toilsome living. But no clouds in a red sky promised daylight's return, nor in lessening [46] shadows did a long twilight gleam with reflected sun. Black night that no ray can pierce comes ever denser from earth, veiling the heavens. Now the dungeons of icy Aeolia sound with buffets and a coming storm hoarsely threatens. The winds roar across each other and colliding pluck at the arch of heaven, dislocating the hinges, as each snatches the sky for himself. But Auster most of all concentrates the night, hurling convoluted murk and pouring down rain that harsh Boreas with his dry mouth makes solid before it falls. Quivering lightnings burst out, the chafed air is broken by sudden flashes. Now Nemea is drenched and the high Arcadian summits adjoining the forests of Taenarus. [47] Inachus [48] rushes in torrent, and Erasinus rising into icy waves. No restraint of dykes held back the rivers, that had been dusty tracks. Lerna's swamp surged from its depths, foaming with ancient venom. Every forest is shattered; gusts snatch aged branches, the summer stations of shady Lycaeus, seen by no suns in history, are laid open.

Now he wondered at rocks fleeing from ruptured

---

[46] The conjecture *crebrescentibus* ('as the shadows thicken') is tempting.   [47] Geographical license again. Cape Taenarus is not adjacent to Arcadia (cf. 2.50).

[48] Statius seems to have thought that the river Inachus had its source in Nemea; cf. 575 with Håkanson's note.

365 miratus, modo nubigenas e montibus amnes
 aure pavens passimque insano turbine raptas
 pastorum pecorumque domos, non segnius amens
 incertusque viae per nigra silentia vastum
 haurit iter; pulsat metus undique et undique frater.
370 ac velut hiberno deprensus navita ponto,
 cui neque Temo piger neque amico sidere monstrat
 Luna vias, medio caeli pelagique tumultu
 stat rationis inops, iam iamque aut saxa malignis
 exspectat summersa vadis aut vertice acuto
375 spumantes scopulos erectae incurrere prorae:
 talis opaca legens nemorum Cadmeius heros
 accelerat, vasto metuenda umbone ferarum
 excutiens stabula, et prono virgulta refringit
 pectore (dat stimulos animo vis maesta timoris)
380 donec ab Inachiis victa caligine tectis
 emicuit lucem devexa in moenia fundens
 Larisaeus apex. illo spe concitus omni
 evolat, hinc celsae Iunonia templa Prosymnae
 laevus habens, hinc Herculeo signata vapore
385 Lernaei stagna atra vadi, tandemque reclusis
 infertur portis. actutum regia cernit
 vestibula; hic artus imbri ventoque rigentes
 proicit ignotaeque acclinis postibus aulae
 invitat tenues ad dura cubilia somnos.
390 Rex ibi tranquille, medio de limite vitae
 in senium vergens, populos Adrastus habebat,
 dives avis et utroque Iovem de sanguine ducens.
 hic sexus melioris inops sed prole virebat

   379 *dist. Håkanson*
   390 tranquille ψΣ, *O. Mueller*: -llae Pω: -llos *Hall*

68

heights, now his ears feared cloud-born rivers coursing
from the mountains and the dwellings of shepherds and
flocks swept everywhere away in the mad whirl. Distraught
and doubtful of his way, no less swiftly did he devour his
desolate route through the black silences. Terror strikes
from every side, terror and his brother. As a mariner
caught in a winter sea, to whom neither lazy Wain nor
Moon with friendly radiance shows directions, stands
clueless in mid commotion of land and sea, expecting every moment rocks sunk in treacherous shallows, or foaming cliffs with spiky tops to run upon the rearing prow:
so the Cadmean hero traversing the dark forest quickens
pace, shaking out the perilous lairs of wild beasts with
his huge shield, and with thrusting breast bursts open
the thickets (grim force of fear spurs him on), until the
darkness was overborne by the dwellings of Inachus and
Larisa's pinnacle flashes out, beaming light upon the shelv-
ing town. Thither he darts, urged on by all his hope, to the
left of Juno's temple of lofty Prosymna on one hand, with
the black pools of Lerna's marsh, marked by the heat of
Hercules,[49] on the other. At last the gates are open and in
he comes. At once he sees the royal forecourt; here he
flings down limbs stiffened by wind and rain and leaning
against the doors of the unknown palace invites light slumbers to his hard couch.

There king Adrastus governed his people in tranquillity, verging from life's midway into old age. Rich was he in
ancestry, back to Jove on either side. The better sex he
lacked, but flourished in female offspring, supported by

[49] The fire with which he cauterized the Hydra's severed
necks.

feminea, gemino natarum pignore fultus.
395   cui Phoebus generos (monstrum exitiabile dictu!
mox adaperta fides) fato ducente canebat
saetigerumque suem et fulvum adventare leonem.
id volvens non ipse pater, non docte futuri
Amphiaraë vides, etenim vetat auctor Apollo.
400   tantum in corde sedens aegrescit cura parenti.
      Ecce autem antiquam fato Calydona relinquens
Olenius Tydeus (fraterni sanguinis illum
conscius horror agit) eadem sub nocte sopora
lustra terit, similesque Notos dequestus et imbres,
405   infusam tergo glaciem et liquentia nimbis
ora comasque gerens subit uno tegmine, cuius
fusus humo gelida partem prior hospes habebat.
hic vero ambobus rabiem Fortuna cruentam
attulit: haud passi sociis defendere noctem
410   culminibus; paulum alternis in verba minasque
cunctantur, mox ut iactis sermonibus irae
intumuere satis, tum vero erectus uterque
exsertare umeros nudamque lacessere pugnam.
celsior ille gradu procera in membra simulque
415   integer annorum; sed non et viribus infra
Tydea fert animus, totosque infusa per artus
maior in exiguo regnabat corpore virtus.
iam crebros ictus ora et cava tempora circum
obnixi ingeminant, telorum aut grandinis instar
420   Rhipaeae, flexoque genu vacua ilia tundunt.
non aliter quam Pisaeo sua lustra Tonanti
cum redeunt crudisque virum sudoribus ardet
pulvis; at hinc teneros caveae dissensus ephebos

twin pledge of daughters. To him Phoebus prophesied (a
deadly prodigy to tell, but the truth of it was soon revealed)
that husbands for them were on their way by fate's leading:
a bristly pig and a tawny lion. That pondering, neither the
father himself nor Amphiaraus skilled in futurity sees light,
for Apollo the source forbids. Only in the parental heart
anxiety sits and festers.

But see! Fate makes Olenian Tydeus leave ancient
Calydon, driven by guilty terror of a brother's blood,[50] and
in the slumbrous night tread the selfsame wild. Like wind
and rain aggrieve him and with ice lying on his back and
face and hair astream with tempest showers he comes
to that single shelter whereof the earlier stranger held
part, stretched on the cold ground. Here Fortune brought
bloody rage to both. They brooked not to ward off the
night under a shared roof. For a brief while they delay, exchanging verbal threats; presently, when their wrath had
swelled enough with hurling of speech, each rose and
bared his shoulders and challenged to naked combat. The
one walked taller, long of limb and in prime of years; but no
lesser strength backs Tydeus' bold spirit, and valour in-
stilled through every member reigned all the greater in his
small frame.[51] Now strenuously they shower blows thick
and fast on face and hollow temples, like darts or Rhipaean
hail, or on bended knee pound unprotected loins. Even as
when his lustral terms return to the Pisaean Thunderer[52]
and the dust warms with the crude sweat of men—but yonder the discord of the crowd spurs on the tender youths

[50] The killing was accidental.
[51] Homeric (*Iliad* 5.801)—a mythical James Cagney.
[52] At the beginning of an Olympiad (four-year cycle).

71

concitat, exclusaeque exspectant praemia matres:
425 sic alacres odio nullaque cupidine laudis
accensi incurrunt, scrutatur et intima vultus
unca manus penitusque oculis cedentibus intrat.
forsan et accinctos lateri (sic ira ferebat)
nudassent enses, meliusque hostilibus armis
430 lugendus fratri, iuvenis Thebane, iaceres,
ni rex insolitum clamorem et pectore ab alto
stridentes gemitus noctis miratus in umbris,
movisset gressus, magnis cui sobria curis
pendebat somno iam deteriore senectus.
435 isque ubi progrediens numerosa luce per alta
atria dimotis aduerso limine claustris
terribilem dictu faciem, lacera ora putresque
sanguineo videt imbre genas: 'quae causa furoris,
externi iuvenes (neque enim meus audeat istas
440 civis in usque manus), quisnam implacabilis ardor
exturbare odiis tranquilla silentia noctis?
usque adeone angusta dies, et triste parumper
pacem animo somnumque pati? sed prodite tandem
unde orti, quo fertis iter, quae iurgia? nam vos
445 haud humiles tanta ira docet, generisque superbi
magna per effusum clarescunt signa cruorem.'
    Vix ea, cum mixto clamore obliqua tuentes
incipiunt una: 'rex o mitissime Achivum,
quid verbis opus? ipse undantes sanguine vultus
450 aspicis.' haec passim turbatis vocis amarae
confudere sonis; inde orsus in ordine Tydeus
continuat: 'maesti cupiens solacia casus
monstriferae Calydonis opes Acheloiaque arva
deserui; vestris haec me ecce in finibus ingens
455 nox operit. tecto caelum prohibere quis iste

and their excluded mothers wait for the prizes: so, lively with hate nor inspired by any desire of glory, they rush in. The clawing hand searches the inmost places of the visage and enters deep into the yielding eyes. And mayhap they would have unsheathed the swords that girt their sides (so anger urged) and the young Theban would have fallen by an enemy's weapon for his brother to mourn (and better so), save that the king, whose old age, sober and care-ridden, hovered in asleep no longer sound, wondered at this unwonted hubbub in the dark of night and the groans shrilling from the depth of their breasts and thither took his way. Passing through the lofty halls in the light of many a torch and unbarring the doors, he sees a sight dreadful to tell on the threshold before him—torn faces and cheeks clotted with gory shower. 'Why this madness, young strangers?—for no countryman of mine would dare violence such as this. What this implacable urge to disrupt night's tranquil silence with your brawls? Is the day so short, does it so irk you to suffer peace of mind and sleep for a little while? But come, reveal: where are you from, whither your way, what your quarrel? For such wrath argues you of no mean degree and great signs of proud race show plain in your blood-letting.'

Scarce had he spoken when they begin together with mingled shouting and looks askance. 'Most clement king of the Achaeans, what need of words? You see for yourself faces astream with blood': such words do they confound at large in jumbled accents of angry utterance. Then Tydeus takes up an ordered tale: 'Craving solace for sad chance, I left the wealth of monster-bearing Calydon and Achelous' fields. Here, see, night of night cloaks me in your bounds. Who is this fellow that forbade me to shelter from the

73

arcuit? an quoniam prior haec ad limina forte
molitus gressus? pariter stabulare bimembres
Centauros unaque ferunt Cyclopas in Aetna
compositos. sunt et rabidis iura insita monstris
460   fasque suum: nobis sociare cubilia terrae–
sed quid ego? aut hodie spoliis gavisus abibis,
quisquis es, his, aut me, si non effetus oborto
sanguis hebet luctu, magni de stirpe creatum
Oeneos et Marti non degenerare paterno
465   accipies.' 'nec nos animi nec stirpis egentes—'
ille refert contra, sed mens sibi conscia fati
cunctatur proferre patrem. tunc mitis Adrastus:
'immo agite, et positis, quas nox inopinaque suasit
aut virtus aut ira, minis succedite tecto.
470   iam pariter coeant animorum in pignora dextrae.
non haec incassum divisque absentibus acta;
forsan et has venturus amor praemiserit iras,
ut meminisse iuvet.' nec vana voce locutus
fata senex, siquidem hanc perhibent post vulnera iunctis
475   esse fidem, quanta partitum extrema protervo
Thesea Pirithoo, vel inanem mentis Oresten
opposito rabidam Pylade vitasse Megaeram.
tunc quoque mulcentem dictis corda aspera regem
iam faciles (ventis ut decertata residunt
480   aequora, laxatisque diu tamen aura superstes
immoritur velis) passi, subiere penates.
       Hic primum lustrare oculis cultusque virorum
telaque magna vacat: tergo videt huius inanem
impexis utrimque iubis horrere leonem,
485   illius in speciem quem per Teumesia tempe

474 post ω: per P

weather? Or was it because he happened to turn his steps
to this threshold before me? They say that biformed Centaurs lodge together and Cyclopes in Aetna lie down with
one another. Savage monsters have their inbred rules,
their law. For us to share beds of earth—but why go on?
Today you shall either leave rejoicing in these spoils, whoever you are, or, unless my strength be outworn or dulled
by my grief, you shall find me of great Oeneus' stock, no
degenerate from my father's Mars.'[53] The other rejoins:
'Neither do I lack courage or race'—but his heart, conscious of fate, hesitates to announce his father. Then kindly
Adrastus: 'Nay come, put aside the threats that night and
sudden valour or sudden wrath inspired, and pass under
my roof. Let your right hands now join and pledge your
hearts. This that has passed is not in vain, nor were the
gods elsewhere. It may even be that your anger is harbinger of amity to come, to be pleasant in memory.' Nor was
the old man's prophesy idle. For 'tis said that after these
wounds they were bonded in such loyalty as made Theseus
share the worst with reckless Pirithous, or Pylades face
Megaera's fury to shield a maddened Orestes. Even then
they suffered the king as he soothed their ruffled hearts
with his words, and passed into the palace, pliable now, as a
sea for which the winds have fought falls to rest; and a long,
lingering breeze yet dies upon the drooping canvass.

Here first he has time to survey the heroes' garb and
mighty weapons. On the back of one he sees on either
side[54] a lion's pelt, stiff with uncombed mane, like to him
that in Teumesos' valley Amphitryon's son in youthful

[53] The genealogy varies.
[54] Hanging from both shoulders.

Amphitryoniades fractum iuvenalibus annis
ante Cleonaei vestitus proelia monstri.
terribiles contra saetis ac dente recurvo
Tydea per latos umeros ambire laborant
490 exuviae, Calydonis honos. stupet omine tanto
defixus senior, divina oracula Phoebi
agnoscens monitusque datos vocalibus antris.
obtutu gelida ora premit, laetusque per artus
horror iit; sensit manifesto numine ductos
495 affore, quos nexis ambagibus augur Apollo
portendi generos, vultu fallente ferarum,
ediderat. tunc sic tendens ad sidera palmas:
'Nox, quae terrarum caelique amplexa labores
ignea multivago transmittis sidera lapsu,
500 indulgens reparare animum dum proximus aegris
infundat Titan agiles animantibus ortus,
tu mihi perplexis quaesitam erroribus ultro
advehis alma fidem veterisque exordia fati
detegis: assistas operi tuaque omina firmes.
505 semper honoratam dimensis orbibus anni
te domus ista colet; nigri tibi, diva, litabunt
electa cervice greges, lustraliaque exta
lacte novo perfusus edet Vulcanius ignis.
salve prisca fides tripodum obscurique recessus.
510 deprendi, Fortuna, deos.' sic fatus, et ambos
innectens manibus tecta interioris ad aulae
progreditur. canis etiamnum altaribus ignes

511 ulterioris Pω (*Schrader*)

---

55 The killing of the Nemean lion was Hercules' first Labour.

years broke and clothed himself therewith before his bout with the monster of Cleonae.[55] Set against that, the glorious spoils of Calydon strive to surround Tydeus' broad shoulders, terrible with bristles and backward-curving tusk. Stunned motionless by so great an omen, the old king recognizes Phoebus' oracle divine, warning issued from the vocal cavern. Fixed his eyes, mute his frozen lips, and a shudder of joy ran through his frame. He saw that here would be[56] the sons-in-law led by manifest deity whose portended advent in the delusive semblance of wild beasts augur Apollo had announced in riddling wise. Then stretching his palms to the stars, 'Night,' he cried, 'that embracing the toils of heaven and earth do send the fiery stars across in their wide-ranging course, granting sick creatures to recruit their spirit until the morrow's sun prompt them rise to action, graciously you offer me the proof I have long sought in perplexity and error, unveiling the rudiments of ancient destiny: stand to the work and make firm your omens. Ever shall this house do you honour and worship as the years measure out their circles. Black herds with chosen neck shall be your sacrifice, goddess, and Vulcan's flame, drenched with fresh milk, shall consume the lustral entrails. Hail ancient truth of tripods, dark recesses![57] Fortune, I have caught the gods.' So he spoke, and taking both by the hand, proceeds to the chambers of the inner palace. On the grey altars heat still kept

[56] The future infinitive *affore* has been variously explained. I take it as corresponding to an indicative *aderunt*, 'will be (are like to be) here.'

[57] The cave where the Delphic priestess (the Pythia) delivered her oracles.

sopitum cinerem et tepidi libamina sacri
servabant; adolere focos epulasque recentes
515 instaurare iubet. dictis parere ministri
certatim accelerant; vario strepit icta tumultu
regia: pars ostro tenues auroque sonantes
emunire toros alteque inferre tapetas,
pars teretes levare manu ac disponere mensas.
520 ast alii tenebras et opacam vincere noctem
aggressi tendunt auratis vincula lychnis.
his labor inserto torrere exsanguia ferro
viscera caesarum pecudum, his cumulare canistris
perdomitam saxo Cererem. laetatur Adrastus
525 obsequio fervere domum, iamque ipse superbis
fulgebat stratis solioque effultus eburno.
parte alia iuvenes siccati vulnera lymphis
discumbunt, simul ora notis foedata tuentur
inque vicem ignoscunt. tunc rex longaevus Acasten
530 (natarum haec altrix eadem et fidissima custos
lecta sacrum iustae Veneri occultare pudorem)
imperat acciri tacitaque immurmurat aure.
    Nec mora praeceptis, cum protinus utraque virgo
arcano egressae thalamo: mirabile visu,
535 Pallados armisonae pharetrataeque ora Dianae
aequa ferunt, terrore minus. nova deinde pudori
visa virum facies: pariter pallorque ruborque
purpureas hausere genas, oculique verentes
ad sanctum rediere patrem. postquam ordine mensae
540 victa fames, signis perfectam auroque nitentem
Iasides pateram famulos ex more poposcit,
qua Danaus libare deis seniorque Phoroneus

532 tactaque *Eden*

sleeping ash and offerings of sacrifice yet warm. He gives order to rouse the fires and renew the recent feast. The servants hasten in rivalry to obey his word. The royal abode hums with various bustle. Some furnish the couches with fine-spun purples and rustling gold, piling high the cushions, some polish the round tables and set them in place. Yet others essay to overcome dark night's shades, stretching chains with gilded lamps. To these falls the task of roasting bloodless flesh of slaughtered beasts on spits, to those the heaping of baskets with grain crushed by the millstone. Adrastus is happy in the busy obedience of the house, and now himself shone propped up on proud draperies and ivory throne. Elsewhere the young men recline, their wounds dry with ablution, and gaze at their bruised and battered faces and forgive each other. Then the long-lived king bids summon Acaste, his daughters' nurse and faithful guardian, chosen to hide modesty sacred to lawful love. He murmurs in her silent ear.[58]

Prompt was she to his command and straightway the two girls left their secret bower. A wonder to behold, they bear faces matching armed Pallas' and quiver-bearing Diana's, all but the terror. Then they saw men's visages, new to their bashful eyes. Pallor and blush together consumed their radiant cheeks, and their eyes in shame returned to their reverend sire. When appetite was vanquished by the course of the banquet, Iasus' scion, as was his custom, asked the attendants to bring the bowl wrought with reliefs and shining with gold wherefrom Danaus and old Phoroneus used to pour libations to the gods. Its chased

[58] Eden (*Cl. Quart*. 1998, p. 321) proposes *tactaque* 'touching her ear,' by way of admonition to keep his words in mind.

assueti. tenet haec operum caelata figuras:
aureus anguicomam praesecto Gorgona collo
545 ales habet, iam iamque vagas (ita visus) in auras
exsilit; illa graves oculos languentiaque ora
paene movet vivoque etiam pallescit in auro.
hinc Phrygius fulvis venator tollitur alis,
Gargara desidunt surgenti et Troia recedit;
550 stant maesti comites frustraque sonantia lassant
ora canes umbramque petunt et nubila latrant.
hanc undante mero fundens vocat ordine cunctos
caelicolas, Phoebum ante alios, Phoebum omnis ad aras
laude ciet comitum famulumque evincta pudica
555 fronde manus, cui festa dies largoque refecti
ture vaporatis lucent altaribus ignes.

'Forsitan, o ivuenes, quae sint ea sacra quibusque
praecipuum causis Phoebi obtestemur honorem,'
rex ait, 'exquirant animi. non inscia suasit
560 religio, magnis exercita cladibus olim
plebs Argiva litat; animos advertite, pandam.
postquam caerulei sinuosa volumina monstri,
terrigenam Pythona, deus, septem orbibus atris
amplexum Delphos squamisque annosa terentem
565 robora, Castaliis dum fontibus ore trisulco
fusus hiat nigro sitiens alimenta veneno,
perculit, absumptis numerosa in vulnera telis,
Cirrhaeique dedit centum per iugera campi

553 aras ω: aram P

---

59 Perseus, 'golden' with reference to Danaë's golden shower
(Håkanson).

surface held worked figures: the golden flyer[59] carries the snake-tressed Gorgon's severed head, and even now, so seems it, leaps into the wandering airs; almost she moves her heavy eyes and drooping countenance and pales even in the living gold. Here the Phrygian hunter[60] is raised aloft on tawny wings, Gargara sinks as he mounts and Troy recedes; his comrades stand dismayed. In vain the hounds weary their sounding mouths, attacking the shadow and barking at the clouds. With this he pours the streaming wine and invokes all the sky-dwellers in turn, Phoebus before all. The band of his companions and servants, garlanded with chaste foliage,[61] all praise Phoebus and summon him to the altar. For him the festal day, for him glow the fires revived by lavish incense on the smoking hearth.

'Perchance, young sirs,' says the king, 'you are curious to know the meaning of these rites and for what reason we declare chief honour to Phoebus. Not void of knowledge has religion so persuaded. Tried of old with sore afflictions do the Argive people make sacrifice. Pay heed, I shall unfold. The god had struck down earthborn Python, dark monster of the winding coils, embracing Delphi with his seven black circlets and grinding ancient oaks with his scales, even as he sprawled by the Castalian spring and opened his triple-cleft mouth in thirst of nourishment for his black venom. Many the wounds on which the god spent his darts, till finally he left the creature outspread over a hundred acres of Cirrha's plain. Then, seeking to expiate the recent slaying, he came to the modest dwelling of our

[60] Ganymede.
[61] Laurel, chaste because Daphne was changed into a laurel while fleeing from Apollo.

vix tandem explicitum, nova deinde piacula caedis
570   perquirens nostri tecta haud opulenta Crotopi
attigit. huic primis et pubem ineuntibus annis
mira decore pios servabat nata penates
intemerata toris. felix, si Delia numquam
furta nec occultum Phoebo sociasset amorem!
575   namque ut passa deum Nemeaei ad fluminis undam,
bis quinos plena cum fronte resumeret orbes
Cynthia, sidereum Latonae feta nepotem
edidit; ac poenae metuens (neque enim ille coactis
donasset thalamis veniam pater) avia rura
580   eligit ac natum saepta inter ovilia furtim
montivago pecoris custodi mandat alendum.
non tibi digna, puer, generis cunabula tanti
gramineos dedit herba toros et vimine querno
texta domus; clausa arbutei sub cortice libri
585   membra tepent, suadetque leves cava fistula somnos,
et pecori commune solum. sed Fata nec illum
concessere larem; viridi nam caespite terrae
proiectum temere et patulo caelum ore trahentem
dira canum rabies morsu depasta cruento
590   disicit. hic vero attonitas ut nuntius aures
matris adit, pulsi ex animo genitorque pudorque
et metus; ipsa ultro saevis plangoribus amens
tecta replet, vacuumque ferens velamine pectus
occurrit confessa patri; nec motus et atro
595   imperat (infandum!) cupientem occumbere leto.
sero memor thalami maestae solacia morti,
Phoebe, paras monstrum infandis Acheronte sub imo

572 pio Pω (*Bentley*)
592 saevis ω: maestis P

Crotopus.[62] He had a daughter in his virtuous home, in early years scarce past childhood, of marvellous beauty, a virgin inviolate. Happy had she been if she had never shared Delian dalliance and Phoebus' secret love. For by the water of Nemea's stream[63] she suffered the god, and when Cynthia resumed her full countenance for the tenth time, gave birth to a child, Latona's starlike grandson. Fearing chastisement (for no mercy would that father have shown in forgiveness of forced union), she chooses a pathless tract and amid the sheepfolds secretly consigns her son to a hillfaring keeper of the flock for him to rear. The grass gave the boy his bed, cradle unworthy of his high birth, and his house was woven of oaken withies. His limbs were snug in a wrapping of arbutus bark, a hollow pipe lulls him to light slumbers, he shares the ground with the sheep. But not even such a home did the Fates permit. For as he lay stretched carelessly on the green sod, wide-mouthed to drink the sky, the fell rage of dogs, feeding with bloody bite, tears him asunder. But when the news of it reached his mother's shocked ears, driven from her mind were father, shame, and fear. Unprompted she fills the house with wild laments, distraught, and with breast uncovered comes to her father and confesses all. He pities her not, but gives order (oh unspeakable!) that she meet the black death she desires. Too late Phoebus remembers their union. To solace her sad end he gets him a monster conceived in the

---

[62] Crotopus was king of Argos and Adrastus' ancestor. But here he seems to be a man of the people (Eitrem *RE* XI.1419.26). In 2.221 he is confused with the monster-killer Coroebus, a confusion not peculiar to Statius (ibid. 2027f.). A tangled skein.

[63] Inachus; see on 357.

conceptum Eumenidum thalamis, cui virginis ora
pectoraque; aeternum stridens a vertice surgit
600 et ferrugineam frontem discriminat anguis.
haec tum dira lues nocturno squalida passu
illabi thalamis, animasque a stirpe recentes
abripere altricum gremiis morsuque cruento
devesci et multum patrio pinguescere luctu.
605 haud tulit armorum praestans animique Coroebus
seque ultro lectis iuvenum, qui robore primi
famam posthabita faciles extendere vita,
obtulit. illa novos ibat populata penates
portarum in bivio; lateri duo corpora parvum
610 dependent, et iam unca manus vitalibus haeret
ferratique ungues tenero sub corde tepescunt:
obvius huic, latus omne virum stipante corona,
fit iuvenis, ferrumque ingens sub pectore duro
condidit, atque imas animae mucrone corusco
615 scrutatus latebras tandem sua monstra profundo
reddit habere Iovi. iuvat ire et visere iuxta
livente in morte oculos uterique nefandam
proluviem et crasso squalentia pectora tabo,
qua nostrae cecidere animae. stupet Inacha pubes
620 magnaque post lacrimas etiamnum gaudia pallent.
hi trabibus duris (solacia vana dolori)
proterere exanimos artus asprosque molares
deculcare genis; nequit iram explere potestas.
illam et nocturno circum stridore volantes
625 impastae fugistis aves, rabidamque canum vim
oraque sicca ferunt trepidorum inhiasse luporum.
saevior in miseros fatis ultricis ademptae
Delius insurgit, summaque biverticis umbra

Furies' gruesome chambers at Acheron's bottom. It had the face and bosom of a girl; from its head rises a serpent ever hissing, parting the livid brow. This dreadful pest, moving by night, slides squalid into bedrooms and tears lives newly born from their mothers' breasts, to devour them with bloody bite and feed fat on the land's mourning. That was too much for Coroebus, outstanding in arms and courage; he offered himself to a chosen few young men, the toughest, right ready to hold life below enduring fame. *She* was wending her way between double gates[64] after laying waste a new household. At her side hang the bodies of two little ones and already her clawed hand is in their vitals and the iron nails grow warm beneath a tender heart. The young man confronts her surrounded by the warrior band and buries his great blade in her flinty breast; searching her spirit's inmost hiding places with the flashing point, at length he returns his monster to nether Jove to keep. 'Twas pleasure to come and see from close at hand the eyes dark in death, the abominable efflux of the womb, and the breasts filthy with thick gore where our lives were lost. The men of Inachus were stunned; after tears great joy, but pallor still. Some crush the lifeless limbs with hard stakes, vain solace for sorrow, and stamp sharp rocks upon her visage. The power is theirs, but cannot satisfy their wrath. Birds fled from her unfed, flying around with midnight screech; and ravening dogs, 'tis said, and the jaws of frightened wolves gaped dry. Deprived of his avengeress, the Delian rose all the fiercer for her fate against the hapless folk.

---

[64] From *Aeneid* 9.238 *in bivio portae quae proxima ponti*, also of doubtful meaning. Possibly 'in the two-way road outside the gate.' The plural *portae* is often used of a double gate.

Parnasi residens arcu crudelis iniquo
630 pestifera arma iacit, camposque et celsa Cyclopum
tecta superiecto nebularum intendit amictu.
labuntur dulces animae, Mors fila Sororum
ense metit captamque tenens fert manibus urbem.
quaerenti quae causa duci, quis ab aethere laevus
635 ignis et in totum regnaret Sirius annum,
idem auctor Paean rursus iubet ire cruento
inferias monstro iuvenes, qui caede potiti.
fortunate animi longumque in saecula digne
promeriture diem! non tu pia degener arma
640 occulis aut certae trepidas occurrere morti.
comminus ora ferens Cirrhaei in limine templi
constitit et sacras ita vocibus asperat iras:
    "Non missus, Thymbraee, tuos supplexve penates
advenio: mea me pietas et conscia virtus
645 has egere vias. ego sum qui caede subegi,
Phoebe, tuum mortale nefas, quem nubibus atris
et squalente die, nigra quem tabe sinistri
quaeris, inique, poli. quod si monstra effera magnis
cara adeo superis, iacturaque vilior orbi
650 mors hominum, et saevo tanta inclementia caelo est,
quid meruere Argi? me, me, divum optime, solum
obiecisse caput Fatis praestabat. an illud
lene magis cordi quod desolata domorum
tecta vides, ignique datis cultoribus omnis
655 lucet ager? sed quid fando tua tela manusque

631 incendit Pω (*Madvig*)
634 quis Pω: quid *Gronovius*

86

Seated in the topmost shade of twin-peaked Parnassus, the cruel god discharges pest-bearing shafts from his hostile bow, covering the fields and the lofty towers of the Cyclopes[65] with a blanket of fog. Sweet lives fail, Death with his sword severs the Sisters' threads and gripping the captured town bears it to the shades. Their lord asks the reason: what the sinister fire from heaven,[66] why Sirius reigned all the year round? Paean is still the mover; this time he commands that the young men who compassed the slaughter be sacrificed to the bloody monster. Happy in your bravery, you that worthily shall earn long life down the ages! You do not basely hide your patriot deed of arms or fear to meet certain death. He[67] stood at the threshold of Cirrha's shrine, facing square, and with these words sharpens the sacred ire:

"Thymbraean, I come to your dwelling not sent or in supplication. My love of country and conscious valour made me journey hither. Phoebus, I am he who laid low in death your mortal evil, he whom you, cruel god, seek with black clouds and murky daylight, with dark corruption of the baleful heavens. But if savage monsters are so dear to great gods and the world can more easily sacrifice the lives of men, if the cruel heavens are so merciless, what has Argos deserved? Better that I, I only, best of deities, should have offered my head to the Fates. Or does that gentle way[68] please you rather, to see homes desolate and all the land alight with husbandmen given to fire? But why delay

[65] Supposed to have been active as builders in the area.

[66] The answer to the first question is Sirius the Dog star. In the second *quid* (why) has to be understood from *quis*.

[67] Coroebus.   [68] Irony. On 652–57 see SB[2].

demoror? exspectant matres, supremaque fiunt
vota. mihi satis est. merui ne parcere velles.
proinde move pharetras arcusque intende sonoros
insignemque animam leto demitte; sed illum,
660   pallidus Inachiis qui desuper imminet Argis,
dum morior, dispelle globum."
                         Sors aequa merentes
respicit. ardentem tenuit reverentia caedis
Letoiden, tristemque viro summissus honorem
largitur vitae; nostro mala nubila caelo
665   diffugiunt, at tu stupefacti a limine Phoebi
exoneratus abis. inde haec stata sacra quotannis
sollemnes recolunt epulae, Phoebeaque placat
templa novatus honos.
                 Has forte invisitis aras
vos quae progenies? quamquam Calydonius Oeneus
670   et Porthaoniae, dudum si certus ad aures
clamor iit, tibi iura domus. tu pande quis Argos
advenias, quando haec variis sermonibus hora est.'
    Deiecit maestos extemplo Ismenius heros
in terram vultus, taciteque ad Tydea laevum
675   obliquare oculos; tum longa silentia movit:
'non super hos divum tibi sum quaerendus honores,
unde genus, quae terra mihi, quis defluat ordo
sanguinis antiqui: piget inter sacra fateri.
sed si praecipitant miserum cognoscere curae,
680   Cadmus origo patrum, tellus Mavortia Thebe,
est genetrix Iocasta mihi.' tum motus Adrastus:

---

657 *dist. SB*[2]   666 exoratus Pω (*Hall*)
670 si dudum Pω (*edd. ante O. Mueller*)
674 laesum Pω (*Koestlin*)

with my words your darts, your violence? The mothers wait, they offer their last prayers.[69] For me it is enough. I have deserved no grace from you. So stir your quiver and stretch your twanging bow, send a noble soul down to death. But while I am dying, dispel the mass that hangs dim over Inachian Argos."

Just measure heeds the deserving. Scruple to slay seized Leto's hot son, and yielding he bestows upon the hero the sad benison of life. The evil mists dissipate from our sky and he departs from marvelling Phoebus' threshold, cleared of blame. Thence comes it that every year this solemn feast celebrates the rites appointed and worship renewed appeases Phoebus' shrine.

You two that visit this altar by chance, what is your stock?—though for you there is Calydonian Oeneus and membership of Porthaon's house, if sure was the shout that came to my ears just now. But *you*, unfold. Who are you that come to Argos? For now is the time for various converse.'

Forthwith the Ismenian hero cast sad eyes down to earth and silently looked askance at Tydeus on his left. Then he broke a lengthy silence: 'Not at this divine worship should you ask whence my breed, what my country, what line of ancient blood flows down. It irks me to confess it amid the ritual. But if you are agog to know an unfortunate, from Cadmus stems my ancestry, my land is Martian Thebes, Jocasta is my mother.' Adrastus was moved. 'Why

69 For the pestilence to end.

89

'hospitiis' (agnovit enim) 'quid nota recondis?
scimus,' ait, 'nec sic aversum Fama Mycenis
volvit iter. regnum et furias oculosque pudentes
685   novit et Arctois si quis de solibus horret
quique bibit Gangen aut nigrum occasibus intrat
Oceanum et si quos incerto litore Syrtes
destituunt. ne perge queri casusque priorum
annumerare tibi: nostro quoque sanguine multum
690   erravit pietas, nec culpa nepotibus obstat.
tu modo dissimilis rebus mereare secundis
excusare tuos. sed iam temone supino
languet Hyperboreae glacialis portitor Ursae.
fundite vina focis, servatoremque parentum
695   Letoiden votis iterumque iterumque canamus.
    Phoebe parens, seu te Lyciae Pataraea nivosis
exercent dumeta iugis, seu rore pudico
Castaliae flavos amor est tibi mergere crines,
seu Troiam Thymbraeus habes, ubi fama volentem
700   ingratis Phrygios umeris subiisse molares,
seu iuvat Aegaeum feriens Latonius umbra
Cynthus et assiduam pelago non quaerere Delon:
tela tibi longeque feros lentandus in hostes
arcus et aetherii dono cessere parentis

692 etiam Pω: et iam ψ (*edd.*)
704 parentes PωΣ (*Barth*)

---

70 Sometimes used as equivalent to Argos, sometimes distinct.
71 Almost a repetition of Lucan 5.23 *Hyperboreae pluastrum glaciale sub Ursae.* From Homer (*Iliad* 18.487) on, the Bears are called Wagons and in Germanicus 25f Bears and Wagons are ex-

hide from your hosts,' he said (for he recognized him),
'what they well know? Yes, we know, nor does Fame journey so far from Mycenae.[70] Whoso shivers from Arctic sunshine or drinks Ganges or enters Ocean dark with sunsets
or finds himself stranded on Syrtes' wavering shores—all
know of the reign and the madness and the shame-struck
eyes. Complain not still nor reckon to yourself the misfor-
tunes of your forbears. In my line too respect of kin went
oft awry, but the guilt does no hurt to later generations.
Only may you be different and deserve with Fortune's
favour to excuse your family. But now the icy carrier of
the Hyperborean Bear[71] grows faint, his pole is backward
bent. Pour wine upon the hearth and let us again and yet
again sing prayers to Leto's son, our parents' saviour.

Father Phoebus, whether Patara's thickets task you in
Lycia's snowy hills, or your pleasure be to dip your yellow
hair in Castalia's chaste waters, or as Thymbra's patron you
frequent Troy, where story has it that you willingly bore
blocks of Phrygian stone on your unrequited shoulders,[72]
or whether you favour Latona's Cynthus, whose shadow
strikes the Aegean, with no need to seek for Delos now
steady in the deep:[73] yours by gift of your heavenly parent
are darts and the bow you bend against fierce foes and

plicitly synonymous. But also our King Charles' Wain or Plough is
regarded as part of the Greater Bear, or, more often, of the neighbouring constellation of Boötes or Arctophylax (Bearward): so
Lucan 2.722 *plaustra Boötae* and often. Probably thinking of
Boötes, Statius substitutes *portitor* for Lucan's *plaustrum*.

[72] Building Troy along with Neptune. According to some accounts its king Laomedon bilked them of their due.

[73] Delos, previously mobile, was stabilized at Apollo's birth.

705 aeternum florere genas; tu doctus iniquas
    Parcarum praenosse manus fatumque quod ultra est
    et summo placitura Iovi, quis letifer annus,
    bella quibus populis, quae mutent sceptra cometae;
    tu Phryga summittis citharae, tu matris honori
710 terrigenam Tityon Stygiis extendis harenis;
    te viridis Python Thebanaque mater ovantem
    horruit in pharetris, ultrix tibi torva Megaera
    ieiunum Phlegyan subter cava saxa iacentem
    aeterno premit accubitu dapibusque profanis
715 instimulat, sed mixta famem fastidia vincunt:
    adsis o memor hospitii, Iunoniaque arva
    dexter ames, seu te roseum Titana vocari
    gentis Achaemeniae ritu, seu praestat Osirim
    frugiferum, seu Persei sub rupibus antri
720 indignata sequi torquentem cornua Mithram.'

cheeks eternally abloom; you have skill to know the cruel spinning of the Parcae and the fate that lies beyond and highest Jove's future decrees—what peoples a year of pestilence betide, what peoples wars, what sceptres comets change: you subject the Phrygian[74] to your lyre and for your mother's honour spread earthborn Tityos over Stygian sands, green Python and the Theban mother[75] shuddered to see you triumphing with your quiver, for you avenging, grim Megaera presses starving Phlegyas with everlasting table fellowship as he lies under hollow cliffs, urging him with unholy viands, but mingled nausea overcomes his hunger: oh come, mindful of our hospitality, and bestow your love and favour upon Juno's fields, whether 'tis best to call you rosy Titan in the fashion of the Achaemenian race, or Osiris the grain-bringer, or Mithras twisting the horns wroth to follow in the rocks of Perses' cavern.'[76]

[74] Marsyas; see Celaenae in Index.

[75] Niobe.

[76] 'The reference is to the sun worship of the Persians: Mithras is frequently represented dragging a bull to be sacrificed. "Persean," from Perses, son of Perseus and Andromeda, founder of the Persian nation, cf. Herodotus 7.61' (Mozley). Osiris too appears here as a sun god by conflation with Re-Horus.

LIBER II

Interea gelidis Maia satus aliger umbris
iussa gerens magni remeat Iovis; undique pigrae
ire vetant nubes et torpidus implicat aër,
nec Zephyri rapuere gradum, sed foeda silentis
5   aura poli. Styx inde novem circumflua campis,
hinc obiecta vias torrentum incendia claudunt.
pone senex trepida succedit Laius umbra
vulnere tardus adhuc; capulo nam largius illi
transabiit animam cognatis ictibus ensis
10   impius et primas Furiarum pertulit iras;
it tamen et medica firmat vestigia virga.
tum steriles luci possessaque manibus arva
et ferrugineum nemus astupet, ipsaque Tellus
miratur patuisse retro, nec livida tabes
15   invidiae functis quamquam et iam lumine cassis
defuit. unus ibi ante alios, cui laeva voluntas
semper et ad superos (hinc et gravis exitus aevi)
insultare malis rebusque aegrescere laetis,
'vade,' ait, 'o felix, quoscumque vocaris in usus,
20   seu Iovis imperio, seu maior adegit Erinys

3 turbidus Pω (*Baehrens*): turpi- *cod. saec. xi*
9 animam P: costas ω

94

BOOK 2

Meanwhile Maia's winged son returns from the chill shades bearing great Jove's command. From every side sluggish clouds forbid his passage and torpid air envelops him; no Zephyrs speeded his course, but the foul breath of the silent hemisphere. On one side Styx flowing round nine tracts, on the other blazing torrents block and bound his path. After comes old Laius' trembling shade, still slow from his wound. For the impious blade transfixed his life beyond the hilt with kindred thrust and rammed home the Furies' first wrath.[1] Yet on he goes, steadying his steps with the healing wand.[2] Then the barren groves and ghost-haunted fields and forest of sombre hue stand amazed, and Earth herself marvels to have opened rearwards; nor did even the dead and lightless lack the livid corruption of envy. One in particular, whose warped will it ever was even in the upper world (hence his life ended ill) to insult misfortune and wax sour at prosperity, 'Go,' he cries, 'happy one, for whatever uses you are summoned—whether Jove's command or a greater Fury has forced you to face

---

[1] Thus inaugurating the series of horrors centring on Oedipus.
[2] Mercury's. How Laius did this is not made clear, but the wand had magic properties; cf. 30 and 70.

ire diem contra, seu te furiata sacerdos
Thessalis arcano iubet emigrare sepulcro,
heu dulces visure polos solemque relictum
et virides terras et puros fontibus amnes,
25   tristior has iterum tamen intrature tenebras.'
    Illos et caeco recubans in limine sensit
Cerberus atque omnes capitum surrexit hiatus;
saevus et intranti populo, iam nigra tumebat
colla minax, iam sparsa solo turbaverat ossa,
30   ni deus horrentem Lethaeo vimine mulcens
ferrea tergemino domuisset lumina somno.
    Est locus (Inachiae dixerunt Taenara gentes)
qua formidatum Maleae spumantis in auras
it caput et nullos admittit culmine visus.
35   stat sublimis apex ventosque imbresque serenus
despicit et tantum fessis insiditur astris.
[illic exhausti posuere cubilia venti,
fulminibusque iter est; medium cava nubila montis
insumpsere latus, summos nec praepetis alae
40   plausus adit colles, nec rauca tonitrua pulsant.]
ast ubi prona dies, longos super aequora fines
exigit atque ingens medio natat umbra profundo.
interiore sinu scandentia litora curvat
Taenaros, expositos non audax frangere fluctus.
45   illic Aegaeo Neptunus gurgite fessos
in portum deducit equos; prior haurit harenas
ungula, postremi solvuntur in aequora pisces.
hoc, ut fama, loco pallentes devius umbras

26 ut Pω (*Watt*)
37–40 *om.* Pω, *add. in marg. man. rec.* Pψ
43–44 frangentia . . . scandere Pω (*Koestlin*)

the daylight or a Thessalian priestess[3] in frenzy bids you
leave your secret tomb, you shall see the sweet sky, alas,
and the sun you left behind and the green earth and the
pure founts of rivers; yet the sadder shall you enter this
gloom a second time.'

Cerberus too, lying on the dark threshold, saw them
and reared all his gaping heads. Fierce as he was even to
the entering multitude, his black neck was already swelling
in menace, already he had jumbled the bones scattered on
the ground, but that the god soothed him as he bristled
with Lethe's wand and tamed his steely eyes in triple slumber.

There is a place (the peoples of Inachus called it Taenarus) where the dread promontory of foaming Malea
rises into the air;[4] its peak admits no gaze. Lofty stands the
summit and serene, looking down on winds and rain; only
the weary stars make it their seat. [There the exhausted
winds have placed their sleeping quarters and there is
a path for lightnings. Hollow clouds take the mountain's
midway flanks; the highest slopes no flap of flying wing approaches nor hoarse thunders strike.] But when the sun
moves downwards, a huge shadow draws long lines over
the waters and swims in the midst of the deep. Inside an inner bay Taenarus curves climbing shores, not daring to
break the open billows. There Neptune brings into harbour his horses weary from the Aegean flood; their fore-
hooves paw the sands, their fishy rears dissolve into the water. At this spot, 'tis said, a winding path drives pale ghosts

[3] I.e. a witch. They were credited with the power to raise the
dead.
[4] See on 1.100.

97

trames agit nigrique Iovis vacua atria ditat
50 mortibus. Arcadii perhibent si vera coloni,
     stridor ibi et gemitus poenarum, atroque tumultu
     fervet ager; saepe Eumenidum vocesque manusque
     in medium sonuere diem, Letique triformis
     ianitor agricolas campis auditus abegit.
55   Hac et tunc fusca volucer deus obsitus umbra
     exsilit ad superos, infernaque nubila vultu
     discutit et vivis afflatibus ora serenat.
     inde per Arcturum mediaeque silentia Lunae
     arva super populosque meat. Sopor obvius illi
60 Noctis agebat equos, trepidusque assurgit honori
     numinis et recto decedit limite caeli.
     inferior volat umbra deo, praereptaque noscit
     sidera principiumque sui; iamque ardua Cirrhae
     pollutamque suo despectat Phocida busto.
65 ventum erat ad Thebas; gemuit prope limina nati
     Laius et notos cunctatus inire penates.
     ut vero et celsis suamet iuga nixa columnis
     vidit et infectos etiamnum sanguine currus,
     paene retro turbatus abit: nec summa Tonantis
70 iussa sed Arcadiae retinent spiramina virgae.
         Et tunc forte dies noto signata Tonantis
     fulmine, praerepti cum te, tener Euhie, partus
     transmisere patri. Tyriis ea causa colonis
     insomnem ludo certatim educere noctem
75 suaserat; effusi passim per tecta, per agros,

67 et celsis Pψ: exc- ω
69–70 nec . . . nec Pω (*SB*[1]: sed . . . sed *Dubner*)
72 praerupti Pω (*Heinsius*)

and enriches the vast halls of black Jupiter[5] with deaths. If the husbandmen of Arcady[6] speak true, there is screaming here and groaning of punishments, the land is astir with dark tumult. Often have the voices and hands of the Furies sounded into the broad of day, and the triformed janitor of Death[7] been heard by rustics driving them from the fields.

Then too by this way the swift god enveloped in dusky shadow leapt into the upper world and shook the subterranean mists from his countenance, clearing his face with draughts of living air. Thence by Arcturus[8] and the silence of full moon he passes over fields and peoples. Sleep met him driving Night's horses and rises hastily to honour the deity, turning aside from heaven's straight pathway. The shade flies below the god, recognizing the ravished stars and his own beginning. And now he looks down on Cirrha's heights and Phocis polluted by his own burial. They had arrived at Thebes. Laius groaned at his son's threshold and scrupled to enter the familiar dwelling. But when he saw his yoke resting on the lofty pillars and the chariot still bloodstained, he almost turned tail in confusion; nor do the high commands of the Thunderer hold him back, but the breathings[9] of the Arcadian wand.

It chanced to be the day marked by the Thunderer's famed bolt when your forestalled delivery, tender Euhius, handed you over to your father. That gave the Tyrian settlers their reason to draw out a sleepless night in sportive rivalry. Stretched everywhere, indoors or in the fields,

5 Pluto.

6 I.e. Laconia, again by poetic license; cf. 1.355f.

7 Cerberus.   8 Travelling north.   9 Apparently a magic power emanating from the wand; cf. on 11.

THEBAID

serta inter vacuosque mero crateras anhelum
proflabant sub luce deum; tunc plurima buxus
aeraque taurinos sonitu vincentia pulsus;
ipse etiam gaudens nemorosa per avia sanas
80 impulerat matres Baccho meliore Cithaeron:
qualia per Rhodopen rabido convivia coetu
Bistones aut mediae ponunt convallibus Ossae;
illis semianimum pecus excussaeque leonum
ore dapes et lacte novo domuisse cruorem
85 luxus; at Ogygii si quando afflavit Iacchi
saevus odor, tunc saxa manu, tunc pocula pulchrum
spargere et immerito sociorum sanguine fuso
instaurare diem festasque reponere mensas.
    Nox ea cum tacita volucer Cyllenius aura
90 regis Echionii stratis allapsus, ubi ingens
fuderat Assyriis exstructa tapetibus alto
membra toro. pro gnara nihil mortalia fati
corda sui! capit ille dapes, habet ille soporem.
tunc senior quae iussus agit; neu falsa videri
95 noctis imago queat, longaevi vatis opacos
Tiresiae vultus vocemque et vellera nota
induitur. mansere comae propexaque mento
canities pallorque suus, sed falsa cucurrit
infula per crines, glaucaeque innexus olivae
100 vittarum provenit honos; dehinc tangere ramo
pectora et has visus Fatorum expromere voces:
'non somni tibi tempus, iners qui nocte sub alta,

84 cruorem ω: furo- P

10 Drums.
11 Not raving, like those that murdered Pentheus.

100

amid garlands and empty wine bowls they were exhaling the panting god as day approached. Then sounded many a boxwood pipe and cymbals louder than the beating of bullhide.[10] Cithaeron himself had merrily driven sane[11] mothers through the wooded wilds under a kinder Bacchus. Such feasts do Bistones in wild assembly lay out on Rhodope or amid Ossa's vales; for them a sheep half living, food shaken from lions' jaws, and blood diluted with new milk is luxury; but if ever the fierce odour of Ogygian Iacchus breathes upon them, then they love to scatter stones and winecups, and after spilling guiltless blood of comrades to begin the day afresh and reset the festal boards.

Such the night when from the silent air the swift Cyllenian glided to the Echionian monarch's bed, where he had spread his huge frame on a high mattress, his limbs piled on Assyrian[12] draperies. Ah mortal hearts all unknowing of their destinies! He banquets, he sleeps—even he! Then the ancient does as he was bidden; and lest he could seem a false vision of the night, he takes upon himself the shadowed[13] features and voice and familiar woollen circlets of long-lived Tiresias. His hair remained, as did the white beard combed down from the chin and his own pallor; but a false headband ran through his locks and the grace of fillets entwined with grey olive emerged to view. Then he seemed to touch the king's breast with a branch and utter these words of destiny: 'No slumber time is this

[12] Perhaps simply meaning eastern, but Sardanapalus, the archetypal voluptuary, was king of Assyria.

[13] Tiresias was blind.

germani secure, iaces; ingentia dudum
acta vocant rerumque graves, ignave, paratus.
105 tu, veluti magnum si iam tollentibus Austris
Ionium nigra iaceat sub nube magister
immemor armorum versantisque aequora clavi,
cunctaris. iamque ille novis (scit Fama) superbit
conubiis viresque parat, quis regna capessat,
110 quis neget, inque tua senium sibi destinat aula.
dant animos socer augurio fatalis Adrastus
dotalesque Argi, nec non in foedera vitae
pollutus placuit fraterno sanguine Tydeus.
hinc tumor, et longus fratri promitteris exsul.
115 ipse deum genitor tibi me miseratus ab alto
mittit: habe Thebas, caecumque cupidine regni
ausurumque eadem germanum expelle, nec ultra
fraternos inhiantem obitus sine fidere coeptis
fraudibus aut Cadmo dominas inferre Mycenas.'
120   Dixit, et abscedens (etenim iam pallida turbant
sidera lucis equi) ramos ac vellera fronti
deripuit, confessus avum, dirique nepotis
incubuit stratis; iugulum mox caede patentem
nudat et undanti perfundit vulnere somnum.
125 illi rupta quies; attollit membra toroque
eripitur plenus monstris, vanumque cruorem
excutiens simul horret avum fratremque requirit.
qualis ubi audito venantum murmure tigris

126 eripitur P: erigitur ω

---

14 When called upon to step down in his turn.
15 *Erigitur* is quite acceptable, but *eripitur* has better author-

for you who lie sluggish in the depths of night, heedless of your brother. Mighty deeds summon you the while, lie-abed, and weighty preparations. You dally, like a skipper lying prone beneath a dark cloud when the winds are already raising the great Ionian, unmindful of his tackle and sea-churning rudder. Even now *he* (Rumour knows) plumes himself on a new wedlock, gathers strength to seize the monarchy and to deny it,[14] and promises himself an old age in your palace. Adrastus, fated by prophecy to be father of his bride, and Argos, her dowry, embolden him, and Tydeus, stained by a brother's blood, is his chosen partner in a lifetime bond. Hence swollen pride; and you are promised to your brother in long-lasting banishment. Pitying from on high, the sire of the gods himself sends me to you. Keep Thebes, drive out your kin, blind with lust for monarchy, as he would you, nor suffer him to trust in the mischief he has started, coveting his brother's death, or to foist Mycenae's rule on Cadmus.'

He spoke and departing (for already the steeds of light are putting the paling stars to rout) tore the branches and fillets from his head, revealing himself—the grandfather. Then bending over his fell grandson's couch, he bares the gaping wound of his throat and drenches the sleeper with a stream of gore. The king's slumber was broken. He raises his body and wrenches[15] from the bed, full of horrors. As he shakes off the phantom blood, he shudders at his grandfather and in the same motion seeks his brother. As when a tigress hears the noise of the hunters, she bristles into her

ity and a livelier sense. Hill's objection that the verb is not found reflexively is hardly formidable, especially as *rapere* is so used (*rapitur, se rapere*).

103

horruit in maculas somnosque excussit inertes,
130 bella cupit laxatque genas et temperat ungues,
mox ruit in turmas natisque alimenta cruentis
spirantem fert ore virum: sic excitus ira
ductor in absentem consumit proelia fratrem.
      Et iam Mygdoniis elata cubilibus alto
135 depulerat caelo gelidas Aurora tenebras,
rorantes excussa comas multumque sequenti
sole rubens; illi roseus per nubila seras
advertit flammas alienumque aethera tardo
Lucifer exit equo, donec pater igneus orbem
140 impleat atque ipsi radios vetet esse sorori,
cum senior Talaionides nec longa morati
Dircaeusque gradum pariterque Acheloius heros
corripuere toris. illos post verbera fessos
exceptamque hiemem cornu perfuderat omni
145 Somnus; at Inachio tenuis sub pectore regi
tracta quies, dum mente deos inceptaque versat
hospitia, et quae sint generis ascita repertis
fata movet. postquam mediis in sedibus aulae
congressi inque vicem dextras iunxere locumque,
150 quo serere arcanas aptum atque evolvere curas,
insidunt, prior his dubios compellat Adrastus:
      'Egregii iuvenum, quos non sine numine regnis
invexit Nox dextra meis, quibus ipse per imbres
fulminibus mixtos intempestumque Tonantem
155 has meus usque domos vestigia fecit Apollo,
non equidem obscurum vobis plebique Pelasgae
esse rear, quantis conubia nostra procorum

135 impulerat Pω (*Lachmann, qui etiam* disp-)
153 dextra P: atra ω

stripes[16] and shakes off the sloth of sleep; athirst for battle she loosens her jaws and flexes her claws, then rushes upon the troop and carries in her mouth a breathing man, food for her bloody young; so in fury does the chieftain fight it out against his absent brother.

And now Aurora had risen from her Mygdonian couch and thrust the cold shadows from heaven's height, shaking the dew from her tresses and blushing deep with the pursuing sun. From her through clouds rosy Lucifer turns his waning fires as with slow steed he leaves the sky no longer his until the fiery father fills full his orb and forbids even his sister's rays. Then did Talaus' time-worn son and with no long delay the Dircaean hero together with him of Achelous hasten from their beds. On those two, wearied after buffets and beating storm, had Sleep poured out all his horn; but in the breast of the Inachian monarch slumber was drawn thin as he revolves the gods' intent and the new-formed ties of hospitality and asks himself what destinies the finding of these sons-in-law has made his own. They meet in the central apartments of the palace and join hands in turn, then sit them down where secret concerns might be broached and unfolded fitly. As the two hesitated, Adrastus first addressed them:

'Young men and goodly, whom not without a higher will has favouring Night brought to my realm, whose steps my Apollo himself has guided to this my dwelling through rains and lightning and freak of weather, I cannot think it unknown to you and the Pelasgian folk how eagerly a crowd of suitors seek marriage into my house; for I have

---

[16] On *maculae* of a tiger's stripes see SB[2].

turba petant studiis; geminae mihi namque, nepotum
laeta fides, aequo pubescunt sidere natae.
160 quantus honos, quantusque pudor (ne credite patri)
et super hesternas licuit cognoscere mensas.
has tumidi solio et late dominantibus armis
optavere viri (longum enumerare Pheraeos
Oebaliosque duces) et Achaea per oppida matres,
165 spem generis, nec plura tuus despexerat Oeneus
foedera Pisaeisque socer metuendus habenis.
sed mihi nec Sparta genitos nec ab Elide missos
iungere fas generos: vobis hic sanguis et aulae
cura meae longo promittitur ordine fati.
170 di bene, quod tales stirpemque animosque venitis
ut responsa iuvent: hic durae tempore noctis
partus honos, haec illa venit post verbera merces.'
    Audierant, fixosque oculos per mutua paulum
ora tenent, visique inter sese ordine fandi
175 cedere. sed cunctis Tydeus audentior actis
incipit: 'o quam te parcum in praeconia famae
mens agitat matura tuae, quantumque ferentem
Fortunam virtute domas! cui cedat Adrastus
imperiis? quis te solio Sicyonis avitae
180 excitum infrenos componere legibus Argos
nesciat? atque utinam his manibus permittere gentes,
Iuppiter aeque, velis, quas Doricus alligat intus

163 phereos Σ: phaer- P: phar(a)eos ω
182 intus P: undis ω

---

17 Thessalian and Spartan. On *Pharaeos*, supposedly from
Pharae, an obscure place in Achaea(?), see Håkanson. That there

two daughters growing into womanhood under an equal star, happy pledge of grandchildren. Their grace and modesty (credit not their father) you could e'en judge at yesterday's feast. Men proud in throne and far-dominating arms ('twere long to tell over the Pheraean and Oebalian[17] chieftains), and mothers throughout the towns of Achaea have desired them, hope of posterity; nor did your Oeneus despise more matches[18] or that other father[19] feared for his Pisaean bridle. But for me it is not lawful to choose husbands among Sparta's children or comers from Elis: to you is promised in destiny's long sequence my blood and the care of my palace. Thanks be to the gods, such you come in birth and spirit that the oracles are welcome. This is the prize you have won in the space of a harsh night, this the reward that follows those fisticuffs.'

They heard and for a while held their eyes fixed on each other's faces, each seeming to yield first speech. But Tydeus, in every action the bolder, begins: 'Ah, how grudgingly does your ripe wisdom prompt you to proclaim your renown! How by virtue do you tame favouring Fortune! To whom should Adrastus yield in lordship? Who but knows that summoned from the throne of your ancestral Sicyon you bring law and order to unruly Argos?[20] And would that kind Jupiter might consign to these your hands the peoples that Dorian Isthmus binds within and those others that its

were places of that name in Laconia and Messene does not make this unlikely option less unattractive.

[18] For his daughter Deianira, who married Hercules.

[19] Oenomaus, whose daughter Hippodamia married Pelops.

[20] According to *Iliad* 2.572 Adrastus originally reigned in Sicyon, and so Statius, as also in 4.49.

Isthmos et alterno quas margine summovet ultra.
non fugeret diras lux intercisa Mycenas,
185 saeva nec Eleae gemerent certamina valles,
Eumenidesque aliis aliae sub regibus, et quae
tu potior, Thebane, queri. nos vero volentes
expositique animis.' sic alter fatus, et alter
subicit: 'anne aliquis soceros accedere tales
190 abnuat? exsulibus quamquam patriaque fugatis
nondum laeta Venus, tamen omnis corde resedit
tristitia, affixique animo cessere dolores.
nec minus haec laeti trahimus solacia, quam si
praecipiti convulsa Noto prospectet amicam
195 puppis humum. iuvat ingressos felicia regni
omina quod superest fati vitaeque laborum
fortuna transire tua.' nec plura morati
consurgunt dictis, impensius aggerat omne
promissum Inachius pater, auxilioque futurum
200 et patriis spondet reduces inducere regnis.
    Ergo alacres Argi, fuso rumore per urbem
advenisse duci generos primisque hymenaeis
egregiam Argian nec formae laude secundam
Deipylen tumida iam virginitate iugari,
205 gaudia mente parant. socias it Fama per urbes
finitimisque agitatur agris procul usque Lycaeos
Partheniosque super saltus Ephyraeaque rura,
nec minus Ogygias eadem dea turbida Thebas

183 infra PωΣ (*Alton*)   *post* 185 *lac. ind.* Dubner
188 interfatus Pω (*Hall*)

---

21 See Atreus in Index.
22 Again referring to Oenomaus.

further boundary removes on the far side. The interrupted light would not have fled dire Mycenae[21] nor the valleys of Elis bewailed cruel contests[22] nor had there been[23] different Furies under different kings nor all that you, Theban, can better deplore. But as to us, we are willing and our hearts lie open.' So spoke the one,[24] and the other adds: 'Would any man not join such a father-in-law? Not yet is Venus our joy, exiled as we are and banished from our native lands. None the less, the sorrow in our hearts has all settled back and the pains there anchored have withdrawn. No less happily do we take this solace than if a ship wrenched by a rushing gale were to see friendly land ahead. Glad are we to enter on fair omens of royalty and pass what is left of destiny and life's labours under your fortune.' No further tarrying in speech, they rise. The Inachian father heaps every promise higher and pledges to be their helper and to bring them back to their native kingdoms.

So the report spreads through the city that bridegrooms have come for the king's daughters and that admired Argia and Deipyle, her peer in beauty, virgins already ripe, are to be joined in first nuptials. Cheerfully Argos makes ready to rejoice. Rumour goes through allied cities, and is busy far in the neighbouring countryside, even to the glades of Lycaeus and Parthenius and beyond, and Ephyre's fields; nor less does the same troubler goddess leap upon Ogygian Thebes. With all her wings she

[23] Understanding *fuissent*. But the ellipse is very harsh and a line may be missing after 185.

[24] The manuscripts have *interfatus*, 'spoke between' or 'interrupted,' against the context.

insilit: haec totis perfundit moenia pennis
210   Labdaciumque ducem praemissae consona nocti
territat; hospitia et thalamos et foedera regni
permixtumque genus (quae tanta licentia monstro,
quis furor?) et iam bella canit.
                Diffuderat Argos
exspectata dies: laeto regalia coetu
215   atria complentur, species est cernere avorum
comminus et vivis certantia vultibus aera.
tantum ausae perferre manus! pater ipse bicornis
in laevum prona nixus sedet Inachus urna;
hunc tegit Iasiusque senex placidusque Phoroneus
220   et bellator Abas indignatusque Tonantem
Acrisius nudoque ferens caput ense Coroebus
torvaque iam Danai facinus meditantis imago;
exin mille duces. foribus cum immissa superbis
unda fremit vulgi, procerum manus omnis et alto
225   quis propior de rege gradus stant ordine primi.
interior sacris calet et sonat aula tumultu
femineo; casta matrem cinxere corona
Argolides, pars virginibus circum undique fusae
foedera conciliant nova solanturque timorem.
230   ibant insignes vultuque habituque verendo
candida purpureum fusae super ora pudorem
deiectaeque genas; tacite subit ille supremus
virginitatis amor, primaeque modestia culpae
confundit vultus; tunc ora rigantur honestis
235   imbribus, et teneros lacrimae iuvere parentes.
non secus ac supero pariter si cardine lapsae

213 est iam (*Lachmann*)

110

overspreads the city and affrights the Labdacian ruler with echoes of the night just passed: she chants of guests and weddings, pacts of royalty and mingling of families, and now (such licence has the monster, such her madness!) of war.

The awaited day had spread Argos abroad. The royal halls fill up with a happy throng; they can see from close at hand semblances of ancestors and bronze vying with living faces. So much have hands dared execute! Father Inachus himself, two-horned, sits leaning leftward on his sloping urn. Old Iasius[25] flanks him and gentle Phoroneus and warrior Abas and Acrisius in wrath against the Thunderer and Coroebus[26] bearing a head upon his naked sword and the grim likeness of Danaus, his crime already in his heart. A thousand leaders follow. The wave of commoners clamours, admitted by the proud doors, while all the band of notables and they whose rank more nearly approaches the king's majesty stand first in order. The inner palace is warm with fire of sacrifice and loud with women's tumult. A chaste band of Argive dames surrounds the mother, others circle the girls, commending their new ties and comforting their fears. Conspicuous they moved, majestic in visage and garb, blushing modesty on their fair faces, eyes downcast. Last love of virginity creeps silently upon them and bashfulness of first fault troubles their countenances. Then seemly rains bedew their faces and their tears rejoice their tender parents. It was as though Pallas and Phoebus'

[25] Alternative form of Iasus (not adjectival).

[26] The monster-killer, here confused with Crotopus; see on 1.570.

Pallas et asperior Phoebi soror, utraque telis,
utraque torva genis flavoque in vertice nodo,
illa suas Cyntho comites agat, haec Aracyntho;
240 tunc, si fas oculis, non umquam longa tuendo
expedias, cui maior honos, cui gratior, aut plus
de Iove; mutatosque velint transumere cultus,
et Pallas deceat pharetras et Delia cristas.
    Certant laetitia superosque in vota fatigant
245 Inachidae, quae cuique domus sacrique facultas.
hi fibris animaque litant, hi caespite nudo,
nec minus auditi, si mens accepta, merentur
ture deos, fractisque obtendunt limina silvis.
ecce metu subito (Lachesis sic dura iubebat)
250 impulsae mentes, excussaque gaudia patri,
et turbata dies. innuptam limite adibant
Pallada, Monychiis cui non Argiva per urbes
posthabita est Larisa iugis; hic more parentum
Iasides, thalamis ubi casta adolesceret aetas,
255 virgineas libare comas primosque solebant
excusare toros. celsam subeuntibus arcem
in gradibus summi delapsus culmine templi,
Arcados Euhippi spolium, cadit aereus orbis,
praemissasque faces, festum nubentibus ignem,
260 obruit, eque adytis simul exaudita remotis

251 limine Pω (*Baehrens*)

---

27 Sterner than Phoebus. The comparison with Adrastus'
daughters does not begin felicitously, but Pallas and Diana were
both daughters of Jupiter, both beautiful.

28 Taken as 'at her threshold' (Mozley), *limine* is hard to con-
strue and belied by 256f. The women are not at the threshold of
the temple but advancing up the road that leads to it when the

112

sterner sister,[27] both grim of weapons and of eye, blond braid upon their heads, were to glide together from the sky above leading their companions, the one from Cynthus, the other from Aracynthus; then could you never by long gazing (were your eyes permitted) determine which had the grander grace, which the more charming, which had more of Jupiter. And should they wish to change dress with each other, Pallas would beseem the quiver and Delia the helmet crest.

The sons of Inachus vie in joy and weary the gods with vows, each according to his home and means of worship. Some offer sacrifice with entrails and lives, others on the bare sod, deserve of the gods with incense (heard no less are they, if their hearts gain acceptance), and strew their thresholds with woodland fragments. But see, a sudden terror (so harsh Lachesis ordained) shocked their souls; the father's joy was shaken from him and the day marred. They were approaching virgin Pallas by the road,[28] she who values Argive Larisa among cities no less than Monychian heights. Here, when their chaste years grow ripe for wedlock, by ancestral usage Iasus' daughters were wont to dedicate their maiden locks and make excuse for their first marriage bed. As they breasted the lofty citadel, a brazen shield, spoil of Arcadian Euhippus, fell from the temple's topmost summit onto the steps, overwhelming the torches at the head of the procession, the brides' festal fire; along with that, while they still dared not step firmly forward, they were terrified by the sound of a mighty trum-

shield falls on the steps as they approach. In a phrase like *limite adibant* an epithet would usually be needed. Not so here, where *limite* stands on its own feet, fixing the women's whereabouts.

nondum ausos firmare gradum tuba terruit ingens.
in regem conversi omnes formidine prima,
mox audisse negant; cunctos tamen omina rerum
dira movent, variisque metum sermonibus augent.
265 nec mirum: nam tu infaustos donante marito
ornatus, Argia, geris dirumque monile
Harmoniae. longa est series, sed nota, malorum.
persequar, unde novis tam saeva potentia donis.
　　Lemnius hoc, ut prisca fides, Mavortia longum
270 furta dolens, capto postquam nil obstat amori
poena nec ultrices castigavere catenae,
Harmoniae dotale decus sub luce iugali
struxerat. hoc, docti quamquam maiora, laborant
Cyclopes, notique operum Telchines amica
275 certatim iuvere manu; sed plurimus ipsi
sudor. ibi arcano florentes igne zmaragdos
cingit et infaustas percussum adamanta figuras
Gorgoneosque orbes Siculaque incude relictos
fulminis extremi cineres viridumque draconum
280 lucentes a fronte iubas; hic flebile germen
Hesperidum et dirum Phrixei velleris aurum;
tum varias pestes raptumque interplicat atro
Tisiphones de crine ducem, et quae pessima ceston

269 haec Pω (*Schrader*)
278–79 relectos . . . hesterni *Heinsius*

---

29 Vulcan, who loved the island, which had sheltered him
when Jupiter threw him out of Olympus. The Homeric story
(*Odyssey* 8.266ff.) tells how he entrapped his wife Venus and her
lover Mars with a bed which he had fitted with chains.

114

pet from the depths of the shrine. At the first alarm all turn
to the king, then deny their ears. But the dire omens of
things to come move them all and they swell the fear with
various talk. And no wonder. For Argia wears the unlucky
ornament that her husband gave, the dire necklace of Harmonia. Long is the sequence of woes but well known.
Whence the new gift came by so cruel a power I shall tell.

The Lemnian,[29] so goes the old belief, who had long
resented Mars' stolen pleasures, when punishment failed
to hinder detected love and avenging chains to castigate,
had wrought this for Harmonia, dotal adornment for her
wedding day. The Cyclopes worked on it, though skilled in
larger labours, and the Telchines, craftsmen renowned,
lent friendly hands in emulation. But he himself sweated
most of all. Around it he sets a circle of emeralds flower-
ing with hidden fire, adamant stamped with ill-omened
shapes, Gorgon eyes, ashes of a thunderbolt end left on
Sicilian anvil, crests shining from the heads of green serpents; here is tearful fruit of the Hesperides[30] and the dire
gold of Phrixus' fleece. Then he entwines various harms, a
chieftain torn from Tisiphone's black hair and the most
noxious of the powers that attest the Girdle.[31] These he

[30] According to the account followed by Statius, their golden
apples were carried off by Hercules, who killed a guardian
snake. Bewailing the loss, the Nymphs were changed into trees
(Apollonius Rhodius 4.1396ff.). The partially parallel legend of
the Heliades, sisters of Phaëthon changed into poplars, is not
relevant.

[31] Cestos, the girdle of Venus, provocative of sexual desire; cf.
Iliad 14.214.

vis probat; haec circum spumis lunaribus unguit
285 callidus atque hilari perfundit cuncta veneno.
non hoc Pasithea blandarum prima sororum,
non Decor Idaliusque puer, sed Luctus et Irae
et Dolor et tota pressit Discordia dextra.
prima fides operi, Cadmum comitata iacentem
290 Harmonia versis in sibila dira querelis
Illyricos longo sulcavit pectore campos.
improba mox Semele vix dona nocentia collo
induit, et fallax intravit limina Iuno.
teque etiam, infelix, perhibent, Iocasta, decorum
295 possedisse nefas; vultus hac laude colebas,
heu quibus, heu, placitura toris! post longior ordo.
tunc donis Argia nitet vilesque sororis
ornatus sacro praeculta supervenit auro.
viderat hoc coniunx perituri vatis, et aras
300 ante omnes epulasque trucem secreta coquebat
invidiam, saevis detur si quando potiri
cultibus, heu nihil auguriis adiuta propinquis.
quos optat gemitus, quantas cupit impia clades!
digna quidem: sed quid miseri decepta mariti
305 arma, quid insontes nati meruere furores?
　　Postquam regales epulas et gaudia vulgi
bisseni clausere dies, Ismenius heros
respicere ad Thebas iamque et sua quaerere regna.

---

32 Cf. Valerius Flaccus 6.447, Apuleius, *Metamorphoses* 1.3.
Witches were supposed to get spume from the moon when they
drew her down to earth, thereby making their poisons deadlier.
　　33 Cupid.　　34 In disguise, of course, to persuade Semele
to make the fatal request of her lover Jupiter that he appear to her
in his full splendour.

cunningly smears about with lunar spume[32] and over the whole spreads gay poison. Not Pasithea, chief of the charming sisters, nor Beauty, nor the Idalian boy[33] shaped it, but Mourning and Anger and Grief and Strife with all the power of her hand. The work first proved itself when Harmonia's plaints turned to dire hisses and in company with prostrate Cadmus she furrowed Illyria's plains with her trailing breast. Then Semele overbold scarce set the baneful gift upon her neck when false Juno crossed the threshold.[34] They say that you too, hapless Jocasta, possessed the beauteous curse. With this glory you decked your countenance[35] to please—ah, what a marriage bed! Thereafter a long series.[36] Now Argia shines with the gift, outdoing her sister's paltry gauds with superior splendour of accursed gold. The wife of the doomed prophet saw it and at all the altars and banquets secretly nursed a fierce envy; if only she might some day possess herself of the cruel bauble! Alas, the auguries so close at hand availed her nothing. Ah, the laments she prays for, impious woman, the disasters she desires! She merits them; but the cheated arms of her hapless husband, the guiltless madness of her son—what did *they* deserve?

Twice six days ended the royal feasting and the people's celebration. Now the Ismenian hero turns his eyes to Thebes and seeks his own kingdom as well. For to his mind

---

[35] But this is a necklace. Licence or inadvertence?

[36] Beginning with Eriphyle, who in exchange for the necklace persuaded her husband Amphiaraus to take part in the war. Their son Alcmaeon later killed her in revenge and was driven mad by the Furies.

quippe animum subit illa dies qua, sorte benigna
310 fratris, Echionia steterat privatus in aula,
respiciens descisse deos trepidoque tumultu
dilapsos comites, nudum latus omne fugamque
Fortunae. namque una soror producere tristes
exsulis ausa vias; etiam hanc in limine primo
315 liquerat et magna lacrimas incluserat ira.
tunc quos excedens hilares, quis cultus iniqui
praecipuus ducis, et profugo quos ipse notarat
ingemuisse sibi per noctem ac luce sub omni
digerit; exedere animum dolor iraque demens
320 et, qua non gravior mortalibus addita curis,
spes, ubi longa venit. talem sub pectore nubem
consilii volvens Dircen Cadmique negatas
apparat ire domos. veluti dux taurus amata
valle carens, pulsum solito quem gramine victor
325 iussit ab erepta longe mugire iuvenca,
cum profugo placuere tori cervixque recepto
sanguine magna redit fractaeque in pectora quercus,
bella cupit pastusque et capta armenta reposcit
iam pede, iam cornu melior; pavet ipse reversum
330 victor, et attoniti vix agnovere magistri:
non alias tacita iuvenis Teumesius iras
mente acuit. sed fida vias arcanaque coniunx
senserat; utque toris primo complexa iacebat
aurorae pallore virum, 'quos, callide, motus
335 quamve fugam moliris?' ait. 'nil transit amantes.
sentio, pervigiles acuunt suspiria questus,
numquam in pace sopor. quotiens haec ora natare
fletibus et magnas latrantia pectora curas

338 latrantia PΣ: iacta- ω

comes that day when by his brother's favouring lot he stood
in the Echionian palace a private man; the gods, he saw,
had left him, his companions scattered in panic confusion,
none stood at his side, Fortune had fled. Only his sister[37]
dared bear the exile company on his sad way. Even her he
had left on the threshold, stifling his tears in mighty rage.
Every night and day he makes the count; whom had he
himself marked rejoicing as he left, who paid particular
court to the unrighteous ruler,[38] and who had a tear for
the fugitive? Grief and mad wrath devoured his soul, and
hope, heaviest of mortal cares when long deferred. Re-
volving such a cloud of counsel in his breast, he makes
ready to go to Dirce and the forbidden home of Cadmus.
Like a leader bull banished from his beloved valley, whom
a victor has driven from his familiar meadow and condemned to low afar from his stolen heifer; but when the
fugitive's sinews are to his liking and his great neck back
again full-blooded and oaks shatter against his breast, he
craves battle and reclaims pasture and captured herd,
stronger now than ever in hoof and horn—the victor himself fears him returned and the wondering herdsmen
scarce recognize: not otherwise does the young Teumesian
hone his wrath in the silence of his heart. But his faithful
wife sensed his secret urge to be away. Lying on their bed
at the first pale of dawn, her arms around him: 'Trickster,'
she said, 'what moves, what flight are you plotting? Nothing escapes a lover. I feel it, sighs sharpen your sleepless
plaints, never do you slumber in peace. How often when I
touch you do I catch your face awash with tears and your

[37] Antigone.   [38] *Quis (= quibus) cultus praecipuus (fuis-*
set) instead of *quis (= quibus) cultum praecipuum (fuisse).*

119

admota deprendo manu! nil foedere rupto
340 conubiisve super moveor viduaque iuventa,
etsi crudus amor necdum post flammea toti
intepuere tori: tua me, properabo fateri,
angit, amate, salus. tune incomitatus, inermis
regna petes? poterisque tuis decedere Thebis,
345 si neget? atque illum sollers deprendere semper
Fama duces tumidum narrat raptoque superbum
difficilemque tibi: necdum consumpserat annum.
me quoque nunc vates, nunc exta minantia divos
aut avium lapsus aut turbida noctis imago
350 terret et (a, memini!) numquam mihi falsa per umbras
Iuno venit. quo tendis iter? ni conscius ardor
ducit et ad Thebas melior socer.'

                              Hic breve tandem
risit Echionius iuvenis tenerumque dolorem
coniugis amplexu solatus et oscula maestis
355 tempestiva genis posuit lacrimasque repressit:
'solve metus animo: dabitur, mihi crede, merentum
consiliis tranquilla dies. te fortior annis
nondum cura decet. sciat haec Saturnius olim
fata parens, oculosque polo demittere si quos
360 Iustitia et rectum terris defendere curat:
fors aderit lux illa tibi, qua moenia cernes
coniugis et geminas ibis regina per urbes.'

      Sic ait, et caro raptim se limine profert.
Tydea iam socium coeptis, iam pectore fido

---

[39] The expression is Homeric (*Odyssey* 20.13); cf. 411 *ignea corda fremunt*.

breast barking[39] grievous cares! A broken bond, my marriage, a widowed youth move me not, though my love is fresh and our bed has not all cooled after the bridal: 'tis your safety, beloved—I hasten to confess it—that tortures me. Shall you seek your kingdom uncompanioned, unarmed? And will you be able to leave your Thebes should he refuse? And Rumour, ever skilful to find rulers out, reports him puffed up and arrogant with his plunder and obdurate toward you; and he had not yet used up his year! Prophets too alarm me now and entrails making threat of gods or gliding birds or troubled vision of the night and Juno comes to me in the dark, she who never (ah, I remember!) played me false.[40] Whither your journey? Unless a secret passion draws you and a better father-in-law in Thebes.'

Here at length the young Echionian briefly laughed and comforted his wife's tender grief with an embrace, planting timely kisses on her sad eyes and checking her tears: 'Loose fears from your heart; a day of peace, believe me, will be granted to the counsels of the deserving. Care stronger than your years does not yet become you. Let the Saturnian father one day know these destinies, and Justice, if she choose to send down a glance from heaven and defend right on earth: mayhap the time will come for you to see your husband's walls and walk a queen through two cities.'

So he speaks and hastens forth from the beloved threshold. Sadly he addresses Tydeus, now partner in his

[40] Or the exclamation could be taken with *venit*. The motif recurs in 5.621f. *numquam impune per umbras / attonitae mihi visa Venus.*

365   aequantem curas (tantus post iurgia mentes
      vinxit amor) socerumque affatur tristis Adrastum.
      fit mora consilio, cum multa moventibus una
      iam potior cunctis sedit sententia, fratris
      praetemptare fidem tutosque in regna precando
370   explorare aditus. audax ea munera Tydeus
      sponte subit; nec non et te, fortissime gentis
      Aetolum, multum lacrimis conata morari
      Deipyle, sed iussa patris tutique regressus
      legato iustaeque preces vicere sororis.
375   Iamque emensus iter silvis ac litore durum,
      qua Lernaea palus, ambustaque sontibus alte
      intepet Hydra vadis, et qua vix carmine raro
      longa sonat Nemea nondum pastoribus ausis,
      qua latus Eoos Ephyres quod vergit ad Euros
380   Sisyphiique sedent portus irataque terrae
      curva Palaemonio secluditur unda Lechaeo.
      hinc praetervectus Nisum et te, mitis Eleusin,
      laevus abit, iamque arva gradu Teumesia et arces
      intrat Agenoreas. ibi durum Eteoclea cernit
385   sublimem solio saeptumque horrentibus armis.
      iura ferus populo trans legem ac tempora regni
      iam fratris de parte dabat; sedet omne paratus
      in facinus queriturque fidem tam sero reposci.
      Constitit in mediis (ramus manifestat olivae
390   legatum) causasque viae nomenque rogatus
      edidit; utque rudis fandi pronusque calori
      semper erat, iustis miscens tamen aspera coepit:

369 Pω pertemptare Pω (ς)

enterprise and loyally matching his cares (so strong a love has bound them after their quarrel), and Adrastus, his wife's father. Counsel long delays, as considering many courses all finally settle on one as best: to test first his brother's good faith, exploring by plea safe access to sovereignty. Bold Tydeus volunteers for the task. You also, bravest of Aetolians, did Deipyle try hard with tears to hold back; but her father's commands and an envoy's assurance of safe return and her sister's just pleas prevailed.

And now he covers the rough path through forest and shore, where lies Lerna's swamp and the scorched Hydra is warm deep down in the guilty waters; and where the length of Nemea the shepherds are still fearful and their song rarely heard;[41] where Ephyre's side slopes toward eastern winds and the harbour of Sisyphus sits and the curving wave, angry at the land, is kept apart by Palaemon's Lechaeum. From there he passed by Nisus and to the left of gentle Eleusin, and now walks the Teumesian fields and enters the towers of Agenor. There he sees harsh Eteocles aloft on his throne, fenced with bristling lances. Beyond the lawful period of his reign, the fierce ruler already governs the people out of his brother's portion. He sits ready for any crime and grumbles that his promise is claimed so late.

Tydeus stood in their midst; the olive branch manifests the ambassador. Asked his name and the reason for his journey, he announced them. Unpracticed in speaking and ever quick-tempered as he was, his words were mingled,

[41] The Hydra of Lerna and the shepherds of Nemea keep traces of their past. The former is still warm from Hercules' burning of her heads (cf. 1.384), the latter still fear the lion he slew.

'si tibi plana fides et dicti cura maneret
foederis, ad fratrem completo iustius anno
395   legatos hinc ire fuit teque ordine certo
fortunam exuere et laetum descendere regno,
ut vagus ille diu passusque haud digna per urbes
ignotas pactae tandem succederet aulae.
sed quia dulcis amor regni blandumque potestas,
400   posceris. astriferum iam velox circulus orbem
torsit et amissae redierunt montibus umbrae
ex quo frater inops ignota per oppida tristes
exsul agit casus; et te iam tempus aperto
sub Iove ferre dies terrenaque frigora membris
405   ducere et externos summissum ambire penates.
pone modum laetis; satis ostro dives et auro
conspicuus tenuem germani pauperis annum
risisti; moneo regnorum gaudia temet
dedoceas patiensque fugae mereare reverti.'
410   Dixerat. ast illi tacito sub pectore dudum
ignea corda fremunt, iacto velut aspera saxo
comminus erigitur serpens, cui subter inanes
longa sitis latebras totumque agitata per artus
convocat in fauces et squamea colla venenum:
415   'cognita si dubiis fratris mihi iurgia signis
ante forent nec clara odiorum arcana paterent,
sufficeret vel sola fides. quam torvus et illum
mente gerens, ceu saepta novus iam moenia laxet
fossor et hostiles inimicent classica turmas,
420   praefuris! in medios si comminus orsa tulisses
Bistonas aut refugo pallentes sole Gelonos,

---

417 quam Pω: qua ⟲   torvus (-vos Housman) et ω: servo
sed P

just but harsh, as he began: 'If clear good faith and care for uttered pledge abode with you, 'twas fairer that envoys go hence to your brother now that the year is out and that you put off your dignity as in order determined and cheerfully descend from royalty, so that after long wandering through strange cities and sufferings unmeet he should at last succeed to the covenanted palace. But since love of royalty is sweet and power seduces, it is required of you. Already the swift axis has turned the starry globe and the lost shades have come back to the mountains since your brother has been living his sad adventures in towns unknown, a pauper exile. Now it is time for you too to bear days under the open sky and draw earth's chills through your limbs and humbly court foreign hearths. Set a limit to good times. Rich in purple and conspicuous in gold, you have mocked the lean year of your penniless brother long enough. I counsel you: unlearn the joys of royalty and by patience of exile deserve to return.'

He spoke. But the other's fiery heart growls the while in his silent breast. So an angry snake rears up close at the cast of a stone; long his thirst down in his hollow den; stirred through his body, it calls all his venom into his jaws and scaly neck: 'Were the signs uncertain that gave me foreknowledge of my brother's quarrel nor plain to view his secret hate, sufficient in itself would be the proof. How grimly furious in advance are you, his mental image, as though stranger sappers were already loosening our fenced walls and trumpets calling enemy squadrons to the assault! If you had brought your message face to face into the midst of the Bistones or the Geloni that the fleeing sun

parcior eloquio et medii reverentior aequi
inciperes. neque te furibundae crimine mentis
arguerim: mandata refers. nunc omnia quando
425 plena minis, nec sceptra fide nec pace sequestra
poscitis, et propior capulo manus, haec mea regi
Argolico, nondum aequa tuis, vice dicta reporta:
quae sors iusta mihi, quae non indebitus annis
sceptra dicavit honos, teneo longumque tenebo:
430 te penes Inachiae dotalis regia dono
coniugis, et Danaae (quid enim maioribus actis
invideam?) cumulentur opes. felicibus Argos
auspiciis Lernamque regas: nos horrida Dirces
pascua et Euboicis artatas fluctibus oras,
435 non indignati miserum dixisse parentem
Oedipoden: tibi larga (Pelops et Tantalus auctor)
nobilitas, propiorque fluat de sanguine iuncto
Iuppiter. anne feret luxu consueta paterno
hunc regina larem? nostrae cui iure sorores
440 anxia pensa trahant, longo quam sordida luctu
mater et ex imis auditus forte tenebris
offendat sacer ille senex. iam pectora vulgi
assuevere iugo: pudet heu plebisque patrumque:
ne totiens incerta ferant mutentque gementes
445 imperia et dubio pigeat parere tyranno.
non parcit populis regnum breve; respice quantus
horror, ut attoniti nostro in discrimine cives.
hosne ego, quis certa est sub te duce poena, relinquam?
iratus, germane, venis. fac velle: nec ipsi,

447 horror et *Koestlin*

makes pale, your opening would have been more sparing of eloquence and more heedful of impartial justice. Yet I would not accuse you of crazed wits; you deliver your commission. Now since all is full of threats and you demand the sceptre without good faith or peace to mediate and the hand is at the hilt, take these my words back in turn to the Argive king, words still not matching yours. The sceptre that a just lot and a grace due to my years have made mine I hold and long shall. To you belongs dotal kingship by gift of your Inachian bride. Let Danaë's riches pile high—for why should I be jealous of a greater career? Rule Argos and Lerna with happy auspices, while I keep Dirce's rough pastures and the shores narrowed by Euboea's waves, not disdaining to call poor Oedipus my father. Yours be generous nobility—Pelops and Tantalus your ancestors—with Jupiter flowing closer from allied blood.[42] Will the queen accustomed to her father's luxury endure a home like this?—where our sisters would in duty spin anxious threads for her, where our mother, unkempt in long mourning, and that accursed ancient, heard perhaps from lowest darkness, would offend her? By now the people's hearts have grown used to the yoke. Alas, I take shame for commons and elders both. Must they so often bear uncertainty and change rulers groaning and grudge obedience to a doubtful lord? A brief reign spares not the folk. See the dread, the dismay of the citizens in our contest. Shall I abandon these whom certain punishment awaits under your sway? Brother, you come in anger. Suppose me willing: the elders themselves, if I know their

[42] Polynices, himself descended from Jupiter, had married another less remote descendant; cf. 1.224–26.

450 si modo notus amor meritique est gratia, patres
reddere regna sinent.'
                    Non ultra passus, et orsa
iniecit mediis sermonibus obvia: 'reddes,'
ingeminat, 'reddes; non si te ferreus agger
ambiat aut triplices alio tibi carmine muros
455 Amphion auditus agat, nil tela nec ignes
obstiterint, quin ausa luas nostrisque sub armis
captivo moribundus humum diademate pulses.
tu merito; ast horum miseret, quos sanguine viles
coniugibus natisque infanda ad proelia raptos
460 proicis excidio, bone rex. o quanta, Cithaeron,
funera sanguineusque vadis, Ismene, rotabis!
haec pietas, haec magna fides! nec crimina gentis
mira equidem duco: sic primus sanguinis auctor
incestique patrum thalami; sed fallit origo:
465 Oedipodis tu solus eras. haec praemia morum
ac sceleris, violente, feres. nos poscimus annum.
sed moror.'
                    Haec audax etiamnum in limine retro
vociferans, iam tunc impulsa per agmina praeceps,
evolat. Oeneae vindex sic ille Dianae
470 erectus saetis et aduncae fulmine malae,
cum premeret Pelopea phalanx, saxa obvia volvens

465 oedipodes Pω (*Jortin*)

---

43 A verb ('you shall see') has to be supplied from what follows—zeugma, a figure much employed by Statius.
44 A foolish flourish. If Polynices was not Oedipus' son, whose
was he and what right did he have to the throne?

affection and if there be gratitude for desert, will not allow me to return the throne.'

Tydeus bore it no further, but even as the words continued flung in his counterspeech: 'You shall return it' and again 'Return it you shall. Though an iron rampart surround you or Amphion with another song be heard and make you triple walls, neither steel nor fire shall protect you from the price of your deeds as you die beneath our arms, striking the ground with captive diadem. So you deserve; but these I pity whose blood is cheap, whom you fling forth to their destruction, snatched from their wives and children into accursed battle, good king. What carnage, Cithaeron,[43] and you, Ismenos, shall you roll in your bloody waters! This is brotherly love, this mighty faith! Nor do I wonder at the crimes of your race. Thus was the first author of your blood, thus the impure wedlock of your fathers. But the source deceives: you alone came of Oedipus.[44] This, man of violence, is the reward you shall reap of your ways and your crime. We demand our year— but I tarry.'

This still on the threshold he boldly shouts behind him and in the shouting dashes out headlong through the reeling ranks. So Oenean Diana's avenger,[45] proud with his spines and the thunderbolt of his curving jaw,[46] as the Pelopean band presses him hard, rolling rocks in his path

[45] The Calydonian boar sent by Diana to punish Oeneus for neglecting her worship. 'Oeneus' Diana' has to convey 'Diana whom Oeneus offended' or the like, but is that really possible? *Evolat Oenides. vindex*? In the simile the boar seems to be on the offensive, despite *premeret* in 471.

[46] Or *erectus* = 'erect,' i.e. bristling with spines and tusks.

fractaque perfossis arbusta Acheloia ripis,
iam Telamona solo, iam stratum Ixiona linquens
te, Meleagre, subit: ibi demum cuspide lata
475 haesit et obnixo ferrum laxavit in armo.
talis adhuc trepidum linquit Calydonius heros
concilium infrendens, ipsi ceu regna negentur,
festinatque vias ramumque precantis olivae
abicit. attonitae tectorum e limine summo
480 aspectant matres, saevoque infanda precantur
Oenidae tacitoque simul sub pectore regi.
    Nec piger ingenio scelerum fraudisque nefandae
rector eget. iuvenum fidos, lectissima bello
corpora, nunc pretio, nunc ille hortantibus ardens
485 sollicitat dictis, nocturnaque proelia saevus
instruit, et (sanctum populis per saecula nomen)
legatum insidiis tacitoque invadere ferro
(quid regnis non vile?) cupit. quas quaereret artes
si fratrem, Fortuna, dares? o caeca nocentum
490 consilia! o semper timidum scelus! exit in unum
plebs ferro iurata caput: ceu castra subire
apparet aut celsum crebri arietis ictibus urbis
inclinare latus, densi sic agmine facto
quinquaginta altis funduntur in ordine portis.
495 macte animi, tantis dignus qui crederis armis!
    Fert via per dumos propior, qua calle latenti
praecelerant densaeque legunt compendia silvae.
lecta dolis sedes: gemini procul urbe malignis
faucibus urguentur colles, quos umbra superne
500 montis et incurvis claudunt iuga frondea silvis

474 ibi ω: tibi P   475 lassavit *Madvig*
479 limine P: culm- ω

and broken trees from Achelous' perforated banks, now leaves Telamon stretched on the ground, now Ixion, and turns on Meleager. Here at last he stops at thrust of spear and loosens the steel in his struggling shoulder. Like to him the Calydonian hero leaves the still fearful council grinding his teeth, as though himself were denied the throne. He hastens on his way, throwing aside the branch of suppliant olive. From the thresholds' edge of their dwellings the matrons watch amazed and heap curses on the fierce son of Oeneus, and in their secret hearts on the king to boot.

Nor is the ruler idle. He lacks not wit for crimes and heinous treachery. He urges trusty young men, bodies chosen for battle, now with gold, now with ardent persuasion, and viciously sets up a fight by night, eager to violate by ambush and stealthy steel an ambassador, name sacred to peoples throughout the centuries—but what does royalty not hold cheap? What arts would he devise if Fortune gave him his brother? Blind counsels of the wicked! Crime cowardly ever! A populace goes forth sworn in arms against a single life. 'Twas as if they were about to attack a camp or topple a city's high flank with frequent blows of battering ram. So in close array fifty pour out in order from the lofty gates. Honour to your valour, you that are deemed worthy of such an armament!

A short cut leads through thickets. By a hidden track they hasten ahead through the dense forest, saving distance. A spot for guile is chosen. Far from the city a grudging pass constrains two hills; enclosing it is the shade of the heights above, leafy ridges with curving woods. Nature set

---

THEBAID

(insidias Natura loco caecamque latendi
struxit opem), mediasque arte secat aspera rupes
semita, quam subter campi devexaque latis
arva iacent spatiis. contra importuna crepido,
505 Oedipodioniae domus alitis; hic fera quondam
pallentes erecta genas suffusaque tabo
lumina, concretis infando sanguine plumis
reliquias amplexa virum semesaque nudis
pectoribus stetit ossa premens visuque trementi
510 collustrat campos, si quis concurrere dictis
hospes inexplicitis aut comminus ire viator
audeat et dirae commercia iungere linguae;
nec mora, quin acuens exsertos protinus ungues
liventesque manus strictosque in vulnera dentes
515 terribili applausu circum hospita surgeret ora;
et latuere doli, donec de rupe cruenta
(heu simili deprensa viro!) cessantibus alis
tristis inexpletam scopulis affligeret alvum.
monstrat silva nefas: horrent vicina iuvenci
520 gramina, damnatis avidum pecus abstinet herbis.
non Dryadum placet umbra choris non commoda sacris
Faunorum, diraeque etiam fugere volucres
prodigiale nemus. tacitis huc gressibus acti
deveniunt peritura cohors, hostemque superbum
525 annixi iaculis et humi posita arma tenentes
exspectant, densaque nemus statione coronant.
    Coeperat umenti Phoebum subtexere palla
Nox et caeruleam terris infuderat umbram.

509 trementi ω: fr- P
514 fractosque Pω (*Housman*)   vulnera P: -re ω

132

up ambush for the place,[47] dark aid to hiding. A rough, narrow path divides the rocks midway; below lies a plain, a broad stretch of sloping fields. Opposite is a grim ledge, the home of Oedipus' fowl.[48] Here once the savage creature stood, lifting up her pallid cheeks and eyes suffused with putrefaction, her feathers clotted with hideous gore, covering human remains, pressing half-eaten bones with her naked breast, and with wavering stare surveyed the plain, watching for a stranger who might dare to meet her in riddling words, a traveller to approach and have commerce with her evil tongue.[49] And speedily sharpening her protended nails, with livid hands and teeth bared to wound, with frightful flapping she would rise around the stranger's face. Her wiles stayed hidden until a man like (alas!) to herself[50] caught her; and from her bloody cliff, cowed with flagging wings, she dashed her insatiate belly upon the rocks. The forest shows the horror; cattle dread the nearby meadows, the greedy flock shuns the sentenced grass. The shade pleases not the choirs of Dryads nor lends itself to the rites of Fauns, even foul birds flee the monstrous grove. Hither with muted steps comes the doomed band. Leaning on their spears and with their shields upon the ground they await the haughty foe, circling the wood with close guard.

Night had begun to screen Phoebus with her dewy mantle and had cast her dark shadow athwart the earth.

[47] Another inversion, after *faucibus urguentur colles* instead of *collibus urguentur fauces* in 499.

[48] The Sphinx.

[49] Wayfarers were confronted with her riddle.

[50] Also cunning and also a monster.

ille propinquabat silvis et ab aggere celso
530 scuta virum galeasque videt rutilare comantes,
qua laxant rami nemus adversaque sub umbra
flammeus aeratis lunae tremor errat in armis.
obstipuit visis, ibat tamen, horrida tantum
spicula et inclusum capulo tenus admovet ensem,
535 ac prior 'unde, viri, quidve occultatis in armis?'
non humili terrore rogat. nec reddita contra
vox, fidamque negant suspecta silentia pacem.
ecce autem vasto Cthonii contorta lacerto,
quo duce freta cohors, fuscas intervolat auras
540 hasta; sed audenti deus et Fortuna recessit.
per tamen Olenii tegimen suis atraque saetis
terga super laevos umeros vicina cruori
effugit et viduo iugulum ferit irrita ligno.
tunc horrere comae sanguisque in corda gelari.
545 huc ferus atque illuc animum pallentiaque ira
ora ferens (nec tanta putat sibi bella parari):
'ferte gradum contra campoque erumpite aperto!
quis timor audendi, quae tanta ignavia? solus,
solus in arma voco.' neque in his mora; quos ubi plures
550 quam ratus innumeris videt excursare latebris,
hos deire iugis, illos e vallibus imis
crescere, nec paucos campo, totumque sub armis
collucere iter, ut clausas indagine profert
in medium vox prima feras, quae sola medendi
555 turbata ratione via est, petit ardua dirae
Sphingos et abscisis infringens cautibus uncas
exsuperat iuga dura manus, scopuloque potitus,

530 galeas ω: cristas P   543 terit *Hall*
551 deire PΣ: prodire ω   557 dira Pω (*Håkanson*)

134

Drawing near the woods, from a tall mound he sees the red gleam of soldiers' shields and crested helmets where the branches leave an opening in the grove and in the fronting shade tremulous moonlight strays flickering upon brazen armour. Astounded by what he saw, he yet kept on, only drawing closer his bristling darts and the hilt of his sheathed sword. Then in no ignoble alarm he questions first: 'Whence come you, men, in arms and what do you hide?' No voice responds and the suspect silence prompts distrust of peace. But see! A spear hurled by the huge arm of Cthonius, trusted leader of the band, flies through the darkling air; but the god and Fortune shunned the venture. Yet through the covering of Olenian boar and the black bristly hide above his left shoulder and close to the blood it takes its flight and with widowed wood[51] strikes frustrate on the throat. His hair stood on end and the blood froze to his heart. Fiercely he points mind and visage pale with anger this way and that, nor thinks so many mean war against him: 'Come face me! Out, out into the open! What fear to dare, what arrant cowardice is this? Alone I challenge you to arms, alone.' Nor do they tarry. He sees them in numbers greater than he had thought rushing out from countless hiding places, some descending from the ridges, others multiplying from the depth of the valley, from the plain not a few, all the road gleaming with weaponry, as when a first shout brings net-encircled beasts into the open. Distraught, he has but one resource; he seeks the steep place of the fell Sphinx. Tearing his clutching hands on the sheer crag, he scales the harsh height and gains a

[51] Having lost its metal head in the boarskin.

unde procul tergo metus et via prona nocendi,
saxum ingens, quod vix plena cervice gementes
560   vertere humo et muris valeant inferre iuvenci,
rupibus avellit; dein toto sanguine nixus
sustinet, immanem quaerens librare ruinam,
qualis in adversos Lapithas erexit inanem
magnanimus cratera Pholus. stupet obvia leto
565   turba superstantem atque emissi turbine montis
obruitur; simul ora virum, simul arma manusque
fractaque commixto sederunt pectora ferro.
quattuor hic adeo disiecti mole sub una
congemuere; fuga tremefactum protinus agmen
570   excutitur coeptis. neque enim temnenda iacebant
funera: fulmineus Dorylas, quem regibus ardens
aequabat virtus, Martisque e semine Theron
terrigenas confisus avos, nec vertere cuiquam
frena secundus Halys (sed tunc pedes occubat arvis)
575   Pentheumque trahens nondum te Phaedimus aequo,
Bacche, genus. quorum ut subitis exterrita fatis
agmina turbatam vidit laxare catervam,
quae duo sola manu gestans acclinia monti
fixerat, intorquet iacula et fugientibus addit.
580   mox in plana libens, nudo ne pectore tela
inciderent, saltu praeceps defertur et orbem,
quem procul oppresso vidit Therone volutum,
corripuit, tergoque et vertice tegmina nota
saeptus et hostili propugnans pectora parma
585   constitit. inde iterum densi glomerantur in unum
Ogygidae firmantque gradum; trahit ocius ensem

---

560 murisque (du- P) valent Pω (*Hall: alii alia*)
561 avellit ω: ev- P   568 disiecta P: deiecti ω (ς, *Barth*)

cliff where danger from the rear is remote and the way to hurt runs downward. From the rocks he plucks a huge boulder, which groaning steers with full strength of neck could scarce tear from the ground and bring within walls;[52] then striving with all his might, he raises and seeks to balance the monstrous bulk, like great-hearted Pholus hoisting an empty mixing bowl against his Lapith adversaries. Stupified, the crowd in death's path sees him standing above. He hurls the mountain and its rush overwhelms them. Their faces are squashed and their weapons and hands and shattered breasts, mingled with steel. Four groaned together here, scattered under a single mass. Straightway the terrified troop are shaken from their attempt. For they who lay fallen were of no small note: Dorylas the thunderbolt, whose ardent valour matched him with kings; Theron of Mars' seed, confident in his earthborn ancestors; Halys, rider second to none, but now a footsoldier, he lies dead upon the ground; Phaedimus of Pentheus' line—Bacchus has not yet forgiven. Appalled by their sudden fate the ranks break in confusion. As Tydeus sees it, he hurls two javelins (these only he had carried and planted them leaning against the mountain) in the wake of his fleeing foes. Then of his own will he leaps down to the level and lest weapons fall on his unprotected breast snatches up the shield that he had seen roll away when Theron was crushed. His back and head guarded by their familiar coverings, defending his breast with the enemy buckler, he took his stand. Once again the sons of Ogygus gather in one dense body and stand fast. Tydeus swiftly

[52] To be used for building or as a projectile in a siege?

Bistonium Tydeus, Mavortia munera magni
Oeneos, et partes pariter divisus in omnes
hos obit atque illos ferroque micantia tela
590 decutit; impeditant numero seque ipsa vicissim
arma premunt, nec vis conatibus ulla, sed ipsae
in socios errare manus et corpora turba
involvi prolapsa sua; manet ille ruentes
angustus telis et inexpugnabilis obstat.
595 non aliter Getica, si fas est credere, Phlegra
armatum immensus Briareus stetit aethera contra,
hinc Phoebi pharetras, hinc torvae Pallados angues,
inde Pelethroniam praefixa cuspide pinum
Martis, at hinc lasso mutata Pyracmoni temnens
600 fulmina, cum toto nequiquam obsessus Olympo
tot queritur cessare manus: non segnior ardet
huc illuc clipeum obiectans, seque ipse recedens
circumit; interdum trepidis occurrit et instat
spicula devellens, clipeo quae plurima toto
605 fixa tremunt armantque virum; saepe aspera passus
vulnera, sed nullum vitae in secreta receptum
nec mortem sperare valet. rotat ipse furentem
Deilochum, comitemque illi iubet ire sub umbras
Phegea sublata minitantem bella securi
610 Dircaeumque Gyan et Echionium Lycophonten.
iam trepidi sese quaerunt numerantque, nec idem
caedis amor, tantamque dolent rarescere turbam.
  Ecce Chromis Tyrii demissus origine Cadmi

593 involvit Pω (ς, *Heinsius*)   595 geticae . . . phlegrae
Pω (*Schrader*)   599 pyragmone Pω (*Hill, duce O. Mueller*)
  610 lycophontem Pω (*Housman*)
  612 tantamque ω: plenam P *ante corr.*

draws his Bistonian sword, the Martian gift of great Oeneus, and divided all ways alike faces this group and that, shaking off the steel-flashing shafts. They clog each other[53] with their number, their shields press one another, their efforts lack force, their blows go wild against their own comrades, their bodies lurch entangled in their own multitude; whereas *he* awaits the attackers, presenting a slim target to the spears, impregnable. Not otherwise in Getic Phlegra, if we may believe it, did vast Briareus stand against heaven in arms, despising Phoebus' quiver on one side and the snakes of frowning Pallas on another, there Mars' steel-tipped Pelethronian pine, here thunderbolt after thunderbolt till Pyracmon grows weary; assailed in vain by all Olympus, he complains that so many hands[54] are idle. No less lively is Tydeus' ardour. This way and that he thrusts his shield, retires circling himself, anon accosts the trembling foe and bears upon them, plucking away the many missiles that stick a-quiver all over his shield, arming him. Often he suffers sharp wounds, but none penetrates life's secret places, none can hope to kill. Himself whirls furious Deilochus[55] and bids Phegeus, as he threatens battle with uplifted axe, go join him in the shades, and Dircaean Gyas and Echionian Lycophontes. Now fearfully they seek themselves and count; their appetite for slaughter has abated and ruefully they note the thinning of so large a crew.

But here comes Chromis, descended from Tyrian

[53] *Se* has to be understood with *impeditant* from the following *seque*.   [54] He had a hundred.

[55] Sends him head over heels?

(hunc utero quondam Dryope Phoenissa gravato
615 rapta repente choris onerisque oblita ferebat,
dumque trahit prensis taurum tibi cornibus, Euhan,
procidit impulsus nimiis conatibus infans)
tunc audax iaculis et capti pelle leonis
pinea nodosae quassabat robora clavae
620 increpitans: 'unusne, viri, tot caedibus unus
ibit ovans Argos? vix credet Fama reverso.
heu socii, nullaene manus, nulla arma valebunt?
haec regi promissa, Cydon, haec, Lampe, dabamus?'
dum clamat, subit ore cavo Teumesia cornus,
625 nec prohibent fauces; atque illi voce repleta
intercepta natat prorupto in sanguine lingua.
stabat adhuc, donec transmissa morte per artus
labitur immorsaque cadens obmutuit hasta.
    Vos quoque, Thespiadae, cur infitiatus honora
630 arcuerim fama? fratris moribunda levabat
membra solo Periphas (nil indole clarius illa
nec pietate fuit), laeva marcentia colla
sustentans dextraque latus; singultibus artum
exhaurit thoraca dolor, nec vincla coercent
635 undantem fletu galeam, cum multa gementi
pone gravis curvas perfringit lancea costas
exit et in fratrem cognataque pectora telo
conserit. ille oculos etiamnum in luce natantes
sistit et aspecta germani morte resolvit.
640 at cui vita recens et adhuc in vulnere vires
'hos tibi complexus, haec dent,' ait, 'oscula nati.'

619 nodosam . . . clavam P: -sa . . . -va ω (*Jortin*)
637 ferro Σ *ad 3.152*
638 etiamnum ω: et adhuc P (*e 640*): extrema *Markland*

Cadmus. Him once Phoenician Dryope bore in her laden womb, as suddenly snatched by the dancers she forgot her burden, and as she dragged a bull by the horn for your sake, Euhan, the child was pushed by her frantic efforts and fell forth. Then bold with spears and the hide of a captured lion, he was brandishing a knotty pinewood club, thus upbraiding them: 'Shall one man, warriors, one man go to Argos triumphing in so many slain? Fame will scarce believe him when he returns. Alack, comrades, shall no hands, no weapons avail? Were these the promises we made the king, Cydon? These, Lampus?' As he shouts, a Teumesian[56] javelin enters his open mouth, nor does his throat bar it. His voice is choked and the severed tongue swims in a gush of blood. Even yet he stood, until death coursed through his limbs and he collapsed. Silent he dropped, biting the spear.

You too, sons of Thespius, why should I deny and keep you from honourable fame? Periphas was raising his brother's dying body from the ground (none more than he renowned for natural gifts or love of kin), propping with his left hand the drooping neck and with his right the side. Grief exhausts the corselet scarce large enough for his sobs and the straps do not contain the helmet awash with tears. But as he groans and groans, a heavy lance from behind shatters his rib cage and issues forth into his brother, knitting the kindred breasts with the weapon. The other fixes his eyes still swimming in the light, and seeing his brother's death relaxes them. But his spirit was hardly gone and strength was still in the wound: 'May your sons give you[57] such embrace, such kisses,' he said. So they fell prostrate,

[56] I.e. Theban, from Tydeus' shield.   [57] Tydeus.

procubuere pares fatis, miserabile votum
mortis, et alterna clauserunt lumina dextra.
    Protinus idem ultro iaculo parmaque Menoeten
645 proterrebat agens trepidis vestigia retro
passibus urguentem, donec defecit iniqua
lapsus humo, pariterque manus distractus in ambas
orat et a iugulo nitentem sustinet hastam:
'parce per has stellis interlabentibus umbras,
650 per superos noctemque tuam; sine tristia Thebis
nuntius acta feram vulgique per ora paventis
contempto te rege canam: sic irrita nobis
tela cadant, nullique tuum penetrabile ferro
pectus, et optanti victor reveharis amico.'
655 dixerat. ille nihil vultum mutatus 'inanes
perdis,' ait, 'lacrimas; et tu, ni fallor, iniquo
pollicitus mea colla duci. nunc arma diemque
proice; quid timidae sequeris compendia vitae?
bella manent.' simul haec et crassum sanguine telum
660 iam redit. ille super dictis infensus amaris
prosequitur victos: 'non haec trieterica vobis
nox patrio de more venit; non orgia Cadmi
cernitis aut avidas Bacchum scelerare parentes.
nebridas et fragiles thyrsos portare putastis
665 imbellem ad sonitum maribusque incognita veris
foeda Celaenaea committere proelia buxo?
hic aliae caedes, alius furor: ite sub umbras,
o timidi paucique!' haec intonat; ast tamen illi
membra negant, lassusque ferit praecordia sanguis.
670 iam sublata manus cassos defertur in ictus,
tardatique gradus, clipeum nec sustinet umbo

---

58 To die together.   59 Lascivious dances.

alike in their doom, their sad prayer of death[58] answered, and closed their eyes with each other's hands.

Forthwith the warrior drove a terrified Menoetes before him with spear and shield as he hurried backward his panic steps till he tripped on the rough ground and collapsed. Both hands spread wide in entreaty, he stays the thrusting weapon from his throat: 'Have mercy I pray by these shades and the stars that glide among them, by the High Ones and this your night. Suffer me to bear sad tidings to Thebes, to sing your praises before the trembling folk in scorn of the king. So may our weapons fall idle nor any steel avail to pierce your breast, so may you return victorious to the prayer of your friend.' Unchanged of countenance, Tydeus made answer: 'You waste vain tears. You too, if I mistake not, promised my head to your unjust chief. Now cast forth arms and the light of day. Why seek to husband a dastard life? War is to come.' With the words the weapon returns thick with blood. Angrily he pursues his beaten foes with bitter speech: 'This night is not your triennial returning by ancestral custom; you look not at Cadmus' orgies or mothers greedy to stain Bacchus with crime. Did you think you were carrying fawnskins and frail wands to unwarlike music, joining shameful battle[59] that real men know not of to the sound of Celaenae's pipe?[60] Here are different slayings, different frenzy. To the shades with you, cowardly handful!' Thus he thunders, but his limbs refuse their office and the blood throbbing in his breast is weary. Now his raised hand is borne down in frustrate blows, his steps are slow, its boss[61] no longer holds up

[60] As played by Marsyas. Pipes were used in the rites of Cybele and of Bacchus.   [61] I.e. the hand behind it.

nutantem spoliis; gelidus cadit imber anhelo
pectore, tum crines ardentiaque ora cruentis
roribus et taetra morientum aspergine manant:
675   ut leo, qui campis longe custode fugato
Massylas depastus oves, ubi sanguine multo
luxuriata fames cervixque et tabe gravatae
consedere iubae, mediis in caedibus astat
aeger, hians, victusque cibis; nec iam amplius irae
680   crudescunt: tantum vacuis ferit aëra malis
molliaque eiecta delambit vellera lingua.
    Ille etiam Thebas spoliis et sanguine plenus
isset et attonitis sese populoque ducique
ostentasset ovans, ni tu, Tritonia virgo,
685   flagrantem multaque operis caligine plenum
consilio dignata virum: 'sate gente superbi
Oeneos, absentes cui dudum vincere Thebas
annuimus, iam pone modum nimiumque secundis
parce deis: huic una fides optanda labori.
Fortuna satis usus abi.'
690   Restabat acerbis
funeribus socioque gregi non sponte superstes
Haemonides (ille haec praeviderat, omina doctus
aëris et nulla deceptus ab alite) Maeon,
nec veritus prohibere ducem, sed Fata monentem
695   privavere fide. vita miserandus inerti
damnatur; trepido Tydeus immitia mandat:
'quisquis es Aonidum, quem crastina munere nostro
manibus exemptum mediis Aurora videbit,
haec iubeo perferre duci: cinge aggere portas,
700   tela nova, fragiles aevo circum inspice muros,

672 mutatum Pω (*Lachmann*)

the shield that nods with weight of spoils, a chill rain falls from his panting breast, his hair and burning face flow with bloody dew and the foul splashings of the dying. Even as a lion who has chased the shepherd far from the fields and gorged on Massylian sheep, when his hunger has revelled in blood galore and his neck and mane have sunk heavy with filth, stands sick amid the slaughter, gaping and o'erdone with food, nor any more does his fury swell; he only strikes air with empty jaws and licks soft wool with protruded tongue.

Replete with spoils and blood, Tydeus would have gone to Thebes and shown himself in triumph to people and ruler if you, Tritonian maid, had not deigned to counsel him, aflame as he was and quite dazed from his work: 'Offspring of proud Oeneus' race, to whom I have just granted victory over absent Thebes, make now an end and spare the too favouring gods. Ask only that this exploit be believed. You have used Fortune enough. Go.'

There was left an unwilling surviver from the sad carnage of his comrades, Maeon son of Haemon. He had foreseen it all, for skilled in the omens of the air no bird deceived him; Neither did he fear to forbid the ruler, but the Fates robbed his warnings of credence. Poor wretch, he is doomed to an unprofitable life. To him afraid Tydeus gives a pitiless charge: 'Whosoever you are of Aonia's sons whom tomorrow's dawn shall see saved from the midst of death by my grace, I command you to bring your lord this message: set a rampart round your gates, refurbish your weapons, look to the circuit of your walls grown frail with

---

700 circumspice ω: -um inspice P

praecipue stipare viros densasque memento
multiplicare acies. fumantem hunc aspice late
ense meo campum: tales in bella venimus.'
    Haec ait, et meritae pulchrum tibi, Pallas, honorem
705 sanguinea de strage parat, praedamque iacentem
comportat gaudens ingentiaque acta recenset.
quercus erat tenerae iam longum oblita iuventae
aggere camporum medio, quam plurimus ambit
frondibus incurvis et crudo robore cortex.
710 huic leves galeas perfossaque vulnere crebro
inserit arma ferens, huic truncos ictibus enses
subligat et tractas membris spirantibus hastas.
corpora tunc atque arma simul cumulata superstans
incipit (oranti nox et iuga longa resultant):
715 'diva ferox, magni decus ingeniumque parentis,
bellipotens, cui torva genis horrore decoro
cassis, et asperso crudescit sanguine Gorgon,
nec magis ardentes Mavors hastataque pugnae
impulerit Bellona tubas, huic annue sacro,
720 seu Pandionio nostras invisere caedes
monte venis, sive Aonia devertis Itone
laeta choris, seu tu Libyco Tritone repexas
lota comas, quo te biiugo temone frementem
intemeratarum volucer rapit axis equarum:
725 nunc tibi fracta virum spolia informesque dicamus
exuvias. at si patriis Porthaonis arvis
inferar et reduci pateat mihi Martia Pleuron,
aurea tunc mediis urbis tibi templa dicabo
collibus, Ionias qua despectare procellas

---

712 tractas P: fr- ω   720 caedes ω: voces P: noctes
Postgate   723 qua Pω (*SB*)

time, above all take care to group your men tightly and multiply dense ranks. Behold this tract smoking far and wide with my sword. Such are we that come to war.'

So he speaks and prepares to do fair homage to Pallas his benefactor from the bleeding wreckage. Joyfully he collects the booty from the ground and reviews his great deeds. There was an oak, long forgetful of its tender youth, on a mound in the middle of the plain, encased in wealth of bark, with curving branches and crude timber. To this he brings and fixes shaven helmets and shields gashed with many a wound, binding swords broken off in blows and spears drawn from breathing limbs. Then standing over the bodies and piled weaponry he begins—night and the long ridges echo his speech: 'Fierce goddess, glory and wit of your great father, mighty in war, on whose cheeks sits the grim helm in fearful beauty, as the blood-bespattered Gorgon glowers (nor would Mars and Bellona spear-armed for battle rouse more fiery trumpet blasts), favour this rite—whether you come from Pandion's mount to witness my carnage or turn aside from Aonian Itone,[62] dance-lover, or comb back your hair washed in Libyan Triton, whither bear you as you clamour the swift wheels of your inviolate mares in your pair-drawn chariot: now do I dedicate to you broken spoils of warriors, shapeless trophies. But if my way leads me to my native Porthaonian land and Martian Pleuron open her gates to my return, then shall I dedicate to you a golden temple amid the city's heights, where it may please you to look down on Ionian tempests, where wild

[62] There were several places of that name. This one will have been near Coronea, where there was a cult of Athene Itonia.

730   dulce sit, et flavo tollens ubi vertice pontum
      turbidus obiectas Achelous Echinadas exit.
      hic ego maiorum pugnas vultusque tremendos
      magnanimum effingam regum, figamque superbis
      arma tholis, quaeque ipse meo quaesita revexi
735   sanguine, quaeque dabis captis, Tritonia, Thebis.
      centum ibi virgineis votae Calydonides aris
      Actaeas tibi rite faces et ab arbore casta
      nectent purpureas niveo discrimine vittas,
      pervigilemque focis ignem longaeva sacerdos
740   nutriet, arcanum numquam inspectura pudorem.
      tu bellis, tu pace feres de more frequentes
      primitias operum, non indignante Diana.'
      dixerat, et dulces iter instaurabat ad Argos.

740 inspectura ωΣ: spret- P

BOOK 2

Achelous raises the sea with his yellow head and leaves the Echinades in his path. Here I shall fashion battles of ancestors and dread faces of great-hearted kings, shall nail arms to proud domes, arms that I have brought back won by my blood[63] and arms that you, Tritonia, shall bestow when Thebes is taken. There a hundred Calydonian maidens vowed to your virgin altars shall duly twine Actaean torches from your chaste tree[64] and purple fillets striped with snow-white.[65] And an aged priestess shall feed an unsleeping fire, who shall never scrutinize the secret thing[66] of reverence. In war and in peace you shall receive many a customary first fruit, nor shall Diana take umbrage.'[67] He spoke and took again his road to sweet Argos.

[63] In the fight just ended. The spoils would be transferred from the oak to Aetolia.

[64] The olive.

[65] I doubtfully translate as a harsh hyperbaton: *faces ab arbore casta et . . . vittas nectent.*

[66] The Palladium (image of the goddess). According to Lucan 1.597f. *only* the priestess could see it.

[67] She had been excluded from such tributes, hence the Calydonian boar.

LIBER III

   At non Aoniae moderator perfidus aulae
nocte sub ancipiti, quamvis umentibus astris
longus ad auroram superet labor, otia somni
accipit; invigilant animo scelerisque parati
5   supplicium exercent curae; tum plurima versat,
pessimus in dubiis augur, timor. 'ei mihi,' clamat,
'unde morae?' (nam prona ratus facilemque tot armis
Tydea, nec numero virtutem animumque rependit)
'num regio diversa viae? num missus ab Argis
10 subsidio globus? an sceleris data fama per urbes
finitimas? paucosne, pater Gradive, manuve
legimus indecores? at enim fortissimus illic
et Chromis et Dorylas et nostris turribus aequi
Thespiadae; totos raperent mihi funditus Argos.
15 nec tamen ille meis, reor, impenetrabilis armis
aere gerens solidoque aptos adamante lacertos
venerat; heu segnes, quorum labor haeret in uno,
si conserta manus.' vario sic turbidus aestu
angitur ac sese culpat super omnia, qui non
20 orantem in mediis legatum coetibus ense
perculerit foedasque palam satiaverit iras.

1 aulae ω: orae P
16 datos Pω (*SB*: satos *Heinsius* (*cf.* 7.43)

BOOK 3

But the perfidious governor of the Aonian palace takes not sleep's repose in the dubious[1] night, even though the dewy stars have long to labour before the dawn. Cares keep vigil in his mind and wreak punishment for plotted crime, and fear (in times of doubt the worst of prophets) revolves many things. 'Woe is me!' he cries. 'Why the delay?' For he had thought it an easy run: Tydeus would be no hard work for so large a force; he did not weigh courage and spirit against number. 'Did they go by different roads? Was a band sent from Argos to help him? Did rumour of the crime spread through neighbouring cities?[2] Were they that I chose too few, father Gradivus, or inglorious fighters? But bravest Chromis and Dorylas are there and the scions of Thespius, equal to our towers; they could raze all Argos to the ground at my behest. And yet methinks him not impenetrable to my arms; he did not come with limbs made up of bronze and solid adamant. Oh cowards, struggling helpless against one man—if combat was joined!' Thus he agonizes, in a tumult of shifting passion, blaming himself above all for that he had not cut down the envoy as he spoke in mid assembly and sated his foul fury in the

[1] Of doubtful issue.
[2] Who might interfere.

iam pudet incepti, iam paenitet. ac velut ille
fluctibus Ioniis Calabrae datus arbiter alno
(nec rudis undarum, portus sed linquere amicos
25 purior Olenii frustra gradus impulit astri),
cum fragor hiberni subitus Iovis, omnia mundi
claustra tonant multusque polos inclinat Orion,
ipse quidem malit terras pugnatque reverti,
fert ingens a puppe Notus, tunc arte relicta
30 ingemit et caecas sequitur iam nescius undas:
talis Agenoreus ductor caeloque morantem
Luciferum et seros maerentibus increpat ortus.
    Ecce sub occiduas versae iam Noctis habenas
astrorumque obitus, ubi primum maxima Tethys
35 impulit Eoo cunctantem Hyperiona ponto,
ima flagellatis, signum lugubre malorum,
ponderibus trepidavit humus, motusque Cithaeron
antiquas dedit ire nives; tunc visa levari
culmina septenaeque iugo concurrere portae.
40 et prope sunt causae: gelido remeabat Eoo
iratus Fatis et tristis morte negata
Haemonides; necdum ora patent, dubiusque notari
signa dabat magnae longe manifesta ruinae
planctuque et gemitu; lacrimas nam protinus omnes
45 fuderat. haud aliter saltu devertitur orbus
pastor ab agrestum nocturna strage luporum,
cuius erile pecus silvis inopinus abegit

47 adegit *Ellis*

---

3 See Index.   4 Lowers the sky in tempest.
5 Oblivious of his surroundings; cf Martial 3.67.1 *cessatis,
pueri, nihilque nostis* as explained in my Loeb edition.

open. Now he is ashamed of the enterprise, now wishes it undone. Like to a skipper given charge of a Calabrian craft on Ionian waters (no stranger he to the waves, but a clear rising of the Olenian star[3] deceived him into quitting the friendly harbour), when comes a sudden crash in the wintry sky and all the confines of the firmament thunder and Orion lustily bends the poles;[4] he himself would fain be ashore and struggles to go back, but a mighty gale astern bears him on; then abandoning his skill, he groans and follows the blind waves, no longer knowing aught.[5] Such the Agenorean leader, upbraiding Lucifer's dallying in the sky and dawn that rises too slow for men in trouble.

Lo! as Night had already turned and her car was setting and the stars were sinking, what time great Tethys first urged forth Hyperion as he tarried in the eastern sea, the ground quaked in its depth as the masses within were scourged[6] (sad sign of trouble) and Cithaeron moved, granting departure to his ancient snows. The rooftops were seen to rise and the seven gates to meet the mountain ridge.[7] The cause is close at hand: Haemon's son was returning in the chill of dawn, angry at the Fates and sorrowful at death denied. His face is not yet plain, but dim as he was to view, he gave from afar manifest signs of great calamity by beating his breast and groaning; as for tears, he had shed them all straightway. So leaves the pasture a herdsman bereft of his charge by wild wolves slaughtering by night; a sudden downpour and the gusty horns of the

---

[6] By subterranean storms? Cf. Seneca, *Natural Questions* 6.7.6.

[7] An extravagance. The earthquake signalized the bad news.

imber et hibernae ventosa cacumina lunae.
luce patent caedes; domino perferre recentes
50 ipse timet casus, haustaque informis harena
questibus implet agros, stabulique silentia magni
odit et amissos longo ciet ordine tauros.
    Illum congestae portarum ad limina matres
ut solum videre (nefas!), nulla agmina circum
55 magnanimosque duces, nil ausae quaerere tollunt
clamorem, qualis bello supremus apertis
urbibus, aut pelago iam descendente carina.
ut primum invisi cupido data copia regis:
'hanc tibi de tanto donat ferus agmine Tydeus
60 infelicem animam, sive haec sententia divum,
seu Fortuna fuit, seu, quod pudet ira fateri,
vis invicta viri. vix credo et nuntius: omnes
procubuere, omnes. noctis vaga lumina testor
et socium manes et te, mala protinus ales
65 qua redeo, non hanc lacrimis meruisse nec astu
crudelem veniam atque inhonorae munera lucis;
sed mihi iussa deum placitoque ignara moveri
Atropos atque olim non haec data ianua leti
eripuere necem. iamque ut mihi prodiga vitae
70 pectora et extremam nihil horrescentia mortem
aspicias: bellum infandum ominibusque negatam
movisti, funeste, aciem, dum pellere leges
et consanguineo gliscis regnare superbus
exsule; te series orbarum excisa domorum
75 planctibus assiduis, te diro horrore volantes
quinquaginta animae circum noctesque diesque

73 gliscis ωΣ: gestis P

winter moon had driven his master's cattle away into the woods and in the morning the carnage lies plain to view; he fears to tell his lord in person what has happened; ugly with dust upscraped, he fills the fields with his laments, hating the silence of the great stall, and summons in long series the lost bulls.

When the mothers massed at the threshold of the gate saw him alone (horror!) with no surrounding troop of high-hearted chieftains, they dared not ask a question but raised a cry like the last yell when warring cities are opened up or at sea when a ship goes down. As soon as he was granted the audience he craved of the hated king: 'From so large a company fierce Tydeus spares you this unhappy life, whether this was heaven's decree or Fortune or, what anger is ashamed to confess, the man's invincible might: I that report it scarce believe. All are fallen, all. Night's wandering lights I call to witness and my comrades' ghosts and the evil omen[8] coming straight on my return: not by tears or cunning did I win this cruel favour, the gift of inglorious life. But the gods' command and Atropos who knows not how to move from her decree and destruction by this door long ago refused me,[9] snatched death away. And now, so you may see my heart spendthrift of life, no whit afraid of final doom: murderer, 'tis an unholy war you have launched, battle by omens disapproved, as you itch to banish law and reign in pride with your kinsman in exile. A line of orphaned, extirpated homes shall haunt you with continual lament—fifty spirits flying around you with dire

---

[8] The earthquake. [9] He was destined not to die in battle; cf. 9.254f., Lucan 7.676f. (of Pompey) *fatisque negatum / parte absente mori*. 'Atropos' = 'not turning.'

assilient; neque enim ipse moror.' iam moverat iras
rex ferus, et tristes ignescunt sanguine vultus.
inde ultro Phlegyas et non cunctator iniqui
80   Labdacus (hos regni ferrum penes) ire manuque
proturbare parant. sed iam nudaverat ensem
magnanimus vates, et nunc trucis ora tyranni,
nunc ferrum aspectans: 'numquam tibi sanguinis huius
ius erit aut magno feries imperdita Tydeo
85   pectora; vado equidem exsultans ereptaque fata
insequor et comites feror exspectatus ad umbras.
te superis fratrique—' et iam media orsa loquentis
absciderat plenum capulo latus; ille dolori
pugnat et ingentem nisu duplicatus in ictum
90   corruit, extremisque animae singultibus errans
alternus nunc ore venit, nunc vulnere sanguis.
excussae procerum mentes, turbataque mussant
concilia; ast illum coniunx fidique parentes
servantem vultus et torvum in morte peracta,
95   non longum reducem laetati, in tecta ferebant.
sed ducis infandi rabidae non hactenus irae
stare queunt; vetat igne rapi, pacemque sepulcri
impius ignaris nequiquam manibus arcet.
      Tu tamen egregius fati mentisque nec umquam
100   (sic dignum est) passure situm, qui comminus ausus
vadere contemptum reges, quaque ampla veniret
libertas, sancire viam: quo carmine dignam,
quo satis ore tuis famam virtutibus addam,
augur amate deis? non te caelestia frustra
105   edocuit lauruque sua dignatus Apollo est,

                    *   *   *   *   *

et nemorum Dodona parens Cirrhaeaque virgo

terror by night and day; for I myself tarry not.' The fierce
king had already raised his wrath, his scowling face fires up
with blood. Phlegyas and Labdacus, no loiterer he at mischief, custodians of the realm's weaponry, make ready to
go unbidden and thrust him forth by force. But the great-
hearted seer had already bared his sword and gazing now
at the fierce tyrant's visage, now at the steel: 'Never shall
you hold this blood in your power or strike a breast that
great Tydeus left unscathed. I go rejoicing and press upon
the doom that was snatched away and am borne to the
comrade shades that await my coming. You to the gods and
your brother'—and now his side plugged to the hilt cut
short his speech midway. He fights the pain and doubles up
thrusting against the mighty blow; he falls and with the last
sobbing breaths the blood goes this way and that, coming
now from the mouth, now from the wound. The lords are
shocked, councillors mutter in consternation. Him his wife
and loyal parents, not for long happy in his return, were
bearing to his home, his countenance unmoved and grim
in death accomplished. But the wild wrath of the infamous
ruler cannot halt there; he forbids funeral fire and impi-
ously but idly denies the peace of the tomb to the unwit-
ting ghost.

But you, splendid of fate and soul nor ever to suffer
oblivion (so 'tis meet), who dared go flout monarchs face to
face and hallow a path for ample freedom—what song,
what utterance of mine shall suffice to add due lustre to
your merit, augur beloved of the gods? Not for nothing
did Apollo teach you heavenly wisdom and judge you deserving of his laurel * * * and Dodona, mother of groves,
and the Cirrhean maiden in Apollo's silence shall be

157

gaudebit tacito populos suspendere Phoebo.
nunc quoque Tartareo multum divisus Averno
Elysias, i, carpe plagas, ubi manibus axis
110 invius Ogygiis nec sontis iniqua tyranni
iussa valent; durant habitus et membra cruentis
inviolata feris, nudoque sub axe iacentem
et nemus et tristis volucrum reverentia servat.
At nuptae exanimes puerique aegrique parentes
115 moenibus effusi per plana, per avia, passim
quisque suas avidi ad lacrimas, miserabile, currunt,
certamen, quos densa gradu comitantur euntes
milia solandi studio; pars visere flagrant
unius acta viri et tantos in nocte labores:
120 fervet iter gemitu et plangoribus arva reclamant.
ut vero infames scopulos silvamque nefandam
perventum, ceu nulla prius lamenta nec atri
manassent imbres, sic ore miserrimus uno
exoritur fragor, aspectuque accensa cruento
125 turba furit: stat sanguineo discissus amictu
Luctus atrox caesoque invitat pectore matres.
scrutantur galeas frigentum inventaque monstrant
corpora, prociduae super externosque suosque.
hae pressant in tabe comas, hae lumina signant
130 vulneraque alta rigant lacrimis, pars spicula dextra
nequiquam parcente trahunt, pars molliter aptant
bracchia trunca loco et cervicibus ora reponunt.

107 audebit Pω (*Markland*)
130 rigant P: replent ω

glad[10] to hold the peoples in suspense. Now too go, take your way through Elysian tracts far removed from Tartarean Avernus, where the sky is barred to Ogygian shades and the guilty tyrant's orders have no power. Your garb and limbs endure untouched by bloody beasts, and the forest and the sad reverence of the birds[11] keep you safe as you lie beneath the naked sky.

Swooning wives and children and sick parents pour from the city through the plain, the wilderness, everywhere, each running eager to find their own sorrow, a pitiful contest. As they go, thousands go thronging with them, fain to console. Some are afire to visit the deeds of one man, the night's mighty toils. The way is loud with lament, the fields echo with beating of breasts. But when they came to the ill-famed rocks and the accursed wood, it was as though no prior wailing, no bitter tears[12] had flowed—a clamour most pitiful rises in a single voice; inflamed by the bloody sight, the multitude maddens. There stands Mourning, terrible, his raiment torn and bleeding, and striking his bosom invites the mothers. They scrutinize the helmets of the cold ones and point to the bodies they have found, falling prostrate upon strangers and their own. Some press their hair in the gore, some seal eyes and wash deep wounds with tears, some draw out darts with hands that vainly spare, some gently fit severed arms in place and restore heads to necks.

[10] Because the prophetic seizure might be the death of her. Housman cites Lucan 5.114–20; cf. 614.

[11] *Nemus* has been variously explained, most naturally of the forest animals, despite *feris* preceding. The birds mourn Maeon as an augur.   [12] Lit. 'black rains.'

At vaga per dumos vacuique in pulvere campi
magna parens iuvenum, gemini nunc funeris, Ide
135 squalentem sublata comam liventiaque ora
ungue premens (nec iam infelix miserandaque, verum
terror inest lacrimis), per et arma et corpora passim
canitiem impexam dira tellure volutans
quaerit inops natos omnique in corpore plangit.
140 Thessalis haud aliter bello gavisa recenti,
cui gentile nefas hominem revocare canendo,
multifida attollens antiqua lumina cedro
nocte subit campos versatque in sanguine functum
vulgus et explorat manes, cui plurima busto
145 imperet ad superos: animarum maesta queruntur
concilia, et nigri pater indignatur Averni.
    Illi in secessu pariter sub rupe iacebant
felices, quos una dies, manus abstulit una,
pervia vulneribus media trabe pectora nexi.
150 ut vidit lacrimisque oculi patuere profusis:
'hosne ego complexus genetrix, haec oscula, nati,
vestra tuor? sic vos extremo in fine ligavit
ingenium crudele necis? quae vulnera tractem,
quae prius ora premam? vosne illa potentia matris,
155 vos uteri fortuna mei, qua tangere divos
rebar et Ogygias titulis anteire parentes?
at quanto melius dextraque in sorte iugatae
quis steriles thalami nulloque ululata dolore
respexit Lucina domum! mihi quippe malorum
160 causa labor; sed nec bellorum in luce patenti
conspicui fatis aeternaque gentibus ausi

141 revocare ω: renovare Pψ

But Ide, great mother of sons, now of twin corpses, wanders through the thickets and the dust of the open plain, with hair standing up in squalor and pressing her bruised face with her nails—no more unhappy and pitiable, there is terror in her tears. Through weapons and bodies everywhere she helplessly seeks her boys and wails at every corpse, rolling her grey tresses on the direful earth. Not otherwise does a woman of Thessaly, whose nation's crime it is to bring the dead back to life by spells, visit the fields by night rejoicing in a recent battle, and holding high her splintered torch of ancient cedarwood turn the lifeless throng over in their blood and explore the dead— to which carcass[13] should she give most orders in the upper world? The sorrowful conclaves of the souls complain and dark Avernus' father is wroth.

They were lying together beneath a rock apart, fortunate in that one day, one hand took them off, bound by a shaft that linked their wound-pierced breasts. When she saw, her eyes opening wide for the stream of tears, 'Children,' she said, 'such your embrace, such your kisses do I see—your mother? Did death's cruel device so knit you in your ending? What wounds am I to stroke, which face press first? Are *you* the power a mother wields, the fortune of my womb, whereby I thought to touch the gods and surpass Ogygian parents in my glory? How much better joined, happy in their lot, are those whose chambers are barren, whose houses Lucina never regarded, summoned by labour's howl! For to me travail was cause of sorrow. But not in the open light of battle, conspicuous in your fate and daring deeds to live in the memory of nations, did you seek

[13] I.e. spirit, recalled to its body from the underworld.

quaesistis miserae vulnus memorabile matri,
sed mortem obscuram numerandaque funera passi,
heu quantus furto cruor et sine laude iacetis!
165 quin ego non dextras miseris complexibus ausim
dividere et tanti consortia rumpere leti:
ite diu fratres indiscretique supremis
ignibus et caros urna confundite manes.'
    Nec minus interea digesta strage suorum
170 hic Cthonium coniunx, hic mater Penthea clamat
Astyoche, puerique rudes, tua, Phaedime, proles,
amissum didicere patrem, Marpessaque pactum
Phyllea, sanguineumque lavant Acamanta sorores.
tunc ferro retegunt silvas collisque propinqui
175 annosum truncant apicem, qui conscius actis
noctis et inspexit gemitus; ibi grandior aevo
ante rogos, dum quisque suo nequit igne revelli,
concilium infaustum dictis mulcebat Aletes:
    'Saepe quidem infelix varioque exercita ludo
180 Fatorum gens nostra fuit, Sidonius ex quo
hospes in Aonios iecit sata ferrea sulcos,
unde novi fetus et formidata colonis
arva suis. sed nec veteris cum regia Cadmi
fulmineum in cinerem monitis Iunonis iniquae
185 consedit, neque funerea cum laude potitus
infelix Athamas trepido de monte veniret,
semianimem heu laeto referens clamore Learchum,
hic gemitus Thebis, nec tempore clarius illo
Phoenissae sonuere domus, cum lassa furorem
190 vicit et ad comitum lacrimas expavit Agave.
una dies similis fato specieque malorum

---

163 numeranda ω: -rosa P   173 Phylea *coni. Klotz*

a wound for a grieving mother to tell of; you suffered a fameless end, a death for numbering,[14] lying, alas, in so much blood stealthily, with none to praise. Nay, I dare not separate your hands locked in pitiful embrace and break the union of such a passing. Go, long be brothers, unsevered in the final pyre, and mingle your fond ashes in the urn.'

No less meanwhile, as they sort out their loved ones' carnage, does his wife lament Cthonius, and Pentheus his mother Astyoche. Your offspring, Phaedimus, boys unfledged, learned of their father's loss. Marpessa washes Phylleus, her betrothed, his sisters bleeding Acamas. Then they strip the woods with steel and mutilate the ancient summit of the neighbouring hill, that knew the night's work and watched the groaning. There before the pyres, as each one refuses to be torn from a particular fire, old Aletes soothed the ill-starred assembly with his words:

'Often to be sure has our race fared ill, tried by diverse sport of the Fates, ever since the stranger from Sidon flung his iron seed into Aonian furrows, whence came strange births and fields feared of their farmers. But no such lamentation was at Thebes when the palace of ancient Cadmus sank into thunderbolt ash at the bidding of cruel Juno, nor yet when hapless Athamas achieved funereal glory as he came down from the quivering mountain bearing—with joyous shout, alas!—a half-living Learchus. Neither did Phoenician homes echo more loudly when weary Agave overcame her madness and took fright at her companions' tears. *One* day was like to this in doom and equal in aspect

[14] Just one of many, a statistic as it were.

aequa fuit, qua magniloquos luit impia flatus
Tantalis, innumeris cum circumfusa ruinis
corpora tot raperet terra, tot quaereret ignes.
195   talis erat vulgi status, et sic urbe relicta
primaevique senesque et longo examine matres
inuidiam planxere deis miseroque tumultu
bina per ingentes stipabant funera portas.
meque ipsum memini (necdum apta laboribus aetas)
200   flesse tamen gemituque meos aequasse parentes.
illa tamen superi. nec quod tibi, Delia, castos
prolapsum fontes specula temerare profana
heu dominum insani nihil agnovere Molossi,
deflerim magis, aut verso quod sanguine fluxit
205   in subitos regina lacus: sic dura Sororum
pensa dabant visumque Iovi. nunc regis iniqui
ob noxam immeritos patriae tot culmina cives
exuimus, nec adhuc calcati foederis Argos
fama subit, et iam bellorum extrema dolemus.
210   quantus equis quantusque viris in pulvere crasso
sudor! io quanti crudele rubebitis amnes!
viderit haec bello viridis manus: ast ego doner
dum licet igne meo terraque insternar avita!'
haec senior, multumque nefas Eteoclis acervat
215   crudelem infandumque vocans poenasque daturum.
unde ea libertas? iuxta illi finis et aetas
tota retro, seraeque decus velit addere morti.
        Haec sator astrorum iamdudum e vertice mundi

---

199 laboribus P: dolor-ω   203 nihil P: non ω

---

15 *Planxere = fecere plangendo.*

of calamity, the day Tantalus' daughter expiated her prideful vaunts and encompassed by ruin past count snatched all those bodies from the earth, sought all those fires. Such was the people's state, so did young and old and mothers in lengthy swarm leave the city and wail reproach[15] to the gods in piteous tumult as they thronged twin burials at the great gates.[16] I remember how I myself, though my years were not yet apt for toils, wept none the less and matched my parents with my groans. But those things were the doing of the High Ones. Nor would I more lament, Delia, that mad Molossian hounds knew not their master when he went so far as to profane your chaste waters with his sacrilegious spying or that a queen flowed into a sudden lake, her blood transformed;[17] the harsh spinning of the Sisters so gave, so willed it Jove. Now by the guilt of a wicked king we have shed so many innocent countrymen, crowns of the fatherland. The report of the trampled pact has not yet reached Argos and already we grieve for war's worst. What sweat in muddy dust for horses and for men! Ah, how high shall rivers be cruelly reddened! That is the business of youth green to war. As for me, let me be given my fire while I may and covered with my ancestral earth!' Thus the elder, piling Eteocles' villainy high, calling him cruel and abominable and sure to pay. Whence such freedom? His end was near, his life all behind him; he would fain bring honour to death delayed.

The sire of the stars had watched the while from the

---

[16] The bodies of the Niobids were carried out of the city for burial, two from each of the seven gates (so here, but in other accounts the number of victims varies).

[17] References to Actaeon and Dirce.

prospectans primoque imbutas sanguine gentes
220 Gradivum acciri propere iubet. ille furentes
Bistonas et Geticas populatus caedibus urbes
turbidus aetherias currus urguebat ad arces,
fulmine cristatum galeae iubar armaque in auro
tristia, terrificis monstrorum animata figuris,
225 incutiens: tonat axe polus clipeique cruenta
lux rubet, et solem longe ferit aemulus orbis.
hunc ubi Sarmaticos etiamnum efflare labores
Iuppiter et tota perfusum pectora belli
tempestate videt: 'talis mihi, nate, per Argos,
230 talis abi, sic ense madens, hac nubilus ira.
exturbent resides frenos et cuncta perosi
te cupiant, tibi praecipites animasque manusque
devoveant; rape cunctantes et foedera turba,
cui dedimus; tibi fas ipsos incendere bello
235 caelicolas pacemque meam. iam semina pugnae
ipse dedi: remeat portans immania Tydeus
ausa, ducis scelus et, turpis primordia belli,
insidias fraudesque, suis quas ultus in armis.
adde fidem. vos, o superi, meus ordine sanguis,
240 ne pugnare odiis, neu me temptare precando
certetis; sic Fata mihi nigraeque Sororum
iuravere colus: manet haec ab origine mundi
fixa dies bello, populique in proelia nati.
quod ni me veterum poenas sancire malorum
245 gentibus et diros sinitis punire nepotes,
arcem hanc aeternam mentisque sacraria nostrae
testor et Elysios, etiam mihi numina, fontes:

234 cui P: quae ω

world's summit, watched the peoples stained in first bloodshed; and he bids Gradivus be summoned in haste. He had
ravaged the raging Bistones and the Getic towns with carnage. Wildly he was urging his chariot to the heavenly citadel, brandishing the splendour of his bolt-crested helm
and shield sombre in gold, alive with monsters' fearsome
forms. The sky thunders with his wheels and his buckler's
light blushes blood red, its orb striking the sun in distant
challenge. When Jupiter sees him still breathing out
Sarmatian toils, his breast steeped in all the tempest of
war: 'My son, in such sort and no other, I pray you, get you
forth through Argos. Let your sword drip so, your wrath so
lour. Let them drive out sluggish restraints and, hating all
things, crave you, dedicate lives and hands to you headlong. Sweep them on if they falter. Confound treaties. To
you we have given it, to you 'tis lawful to set the very hosts
of heaven aflame with war, and my peace withal. I myself
have already sown the seeds of battle. Tydeus returns,
bearing tidings of a monstrous attempt, the ruler's crime
and the beginnings of a dishonourable war, ambush and
treachery avenged with his own weapons. Make him believed. As for you, High Ones, my blood descendants, vie
not in hate and strife nor attempt me with rival entreaty.
Thus the Fates, the dark distaffs of the Sisters, have sworn
to me. This day stands fixed for war from the world's origin,
these peoples were born to battle. But if you do not permit
me to exact retribution from the nations for old misdeeds
and to punish evil posterity, I swear by this eternal citadel,
the shrine of my mind, and the Elysian waters that I too

ipse manu Thebas correptaque moenia fundo
excutiam versasque solo super Inacha tecta
250   effundam turres aut stagna in caerula verram
imbre superiecto, licet ipsa in turbine rerum
Iuno suos colles templumque amplexa laboret.'

Dixit, et attoniti iussis; mortalia credas
pectora, sic cuncti vocemque animosque tenebant:
255   non secus ac longa ventorum pace solutum
aequor et imbelli recubant ubi litora somno,
silvarumque comas et abacto flamine nubes
mulcet iners aestas; tunc stagna lacusque sonori
detumuere, tacent exusti solibus amnes.

260   Gaudet ovans iussis et adhuc temone calenti
fervidus in laevum torsit Gradivus habenas.
iamque iter extremum caelique abrupta tenebat,
cum Venus ante ipsos nulla formidine gressum
figit equos; cessere retro iam iamque rigentes
265   suppliciter posuere iubas. tunc pectora summo
acclinata iugo vultumque obliqua madentem
incipit (interea dominae vestigia iuxta
spumantem proni mandunt adamanta iugales):
'bella etiam in Thebas, socer o pulcherrime, bella
270   ipse paras ferroque tuos abolere nepotes?
nec genus Harmoniae nec te conubia caelo
festa nec hae quicquam lacrimae, furibunde, morantur?

269 pulcherrime ω: -ma P

18 The Styx ('Elysian' = 'in the underworld'), by which the gods
swore their oaths, balances the citadel (of heaven), sanctuary of
Jupiter's mind and will.
19 Lit. 'fathers-in-law.' Mars' and (Venus') daughter had mar-

reverence:[18] with my own hands I shall seize Thebes and her walls, raze her from her foundations, tear up her towers and discharge them over Inachian dwellings or pour rain down upon them and sweep them into the blue deep—though Juno herself suffer in the universal turmoil, embracing her hills and temple.'

He spoke and they were amazed at his ordinance. You might have thought them mortal hearts, so did they all hold voice and mind in check. 'Twas as when the sea lies becalmed, winds keep a long peace, and shores stretch in strifeless slumber, while idle summer soothes forest leaves and clouds, breezes dismissed; the meres and loud lakes have subsided, the sun-scorched rivers make no sound.

Gradivus triumphed in his orders and still aglow in his hot chariot turned the reins leftward. Now he was at journey's end, heaven's downward plunge, when Venus takes fearless stand full in the horses' front. They fell back, lowering their stiff manes little by little in supplication. Then, leaning her bosom against the top of the yoke, with tearful face turned to one side, she begins—meanwhile the horses bend their heads and champ the foaming adamant at their mistress' feet: 'War against Thebes, O paragon of parents,[19] do you yourself plan war and destruction of your own grandchildren by the sword? Harmonia's race, marriage festival in heaven, and these tears—do they not for a

ried Cadmus, who as sower of the dragon's teeth is regarded as progenitor of the Thebans. In strictness 'Harmonia's race' (271) should not include the Thebans as a whole, nor were they Mars' descendants (*nepotes*), unless because by some accounts the dragon was his child. But again this may be merely lax terminology. Cf. 10.893 *Harmoniae populos*.

criminis haec merces? hoc fama pudorque relictus,
hoc mihi Lemniacae de te meruere catenae?
275 perge libens; at non eadem Vulcania nobis
obsequia, et laesi servit tamen ira mariti.
illum ego perpetuis mihi desudare caminis
si iubeam vigilesque operi transmittere noctes,
gaudeat ornatusque novos ipsique laboret
280 arma tibi; tu—sed scopulos et aëna precando
flectere corda paro; solum hoc tamen anxia, solum
obtestor, quid me Tyrio sociare marito
progeniem caram infaustisque dabas hymenaeis,
dum fore praeclaros armis et vivida rebus
285 pectora vipereo Tyrios de sanguine iactas
demissumque Iovis serie genus? a! mea quanto
Sithonia mallem nupsisset virgo sub Arcto
trans Borean Thracasque tuos! indigna parumne
pertulimus, divae Veneris quod filia longum
290 reptat et Illyricas deiectat virus in herbas?
nunc gentem immeritam—' lacrimas non pertulit ultra
Bellipotens; hastam laeva transumit et alto
(haud mora) desiluit curru clipeoque receptam
laedit in amplexu dictisque ita mulcet amicis:
295   'O mihi bellorum requies et sacra voluptas
unaque pax animo; soli cui tanta potestas
divorumque hominumque, meis occurrere telis
impune et media quamvis in caede frementes
hos assistere equos, hunc ensem avellere dextrae:
300 nec mihi Sidonii genialia foedera Cadmi
nec tua cara fides (ne falsa incessere gaude!)
exciderunt: prius in patrui deus infera mergar

moment hold you, madman? Is this the reward of guilt? Is this what my fame and honour abandoned and Lemnos' chains have deserved of you? Go your way rejoicing. Ah, but not so does Vulcan obey me. My wronged husband's wrath serves me still. Were I to tell him to sweat for me with ceaseless furnace, pass sleepless nights at work, he would be glad and toil at new gear, even weapons for you. You—but I make to move rocks and a heart of bronze with my pleading. Yet this only in anguish I adjure you, only this: why did you have me join my dear child to a Tyrian husband in ill-starred nuptials, boasting that Tyrians of viper blood, race descended of Jupiter's line,[20] shall be renowned in arms, hearts lively for action? Oh, how I wish my girl had rather married beneath the Sithonian Bear, beyond Boreas and your Thracians! Was it not shame enough for me to bear that goddess Venus' daughter crawls at length and spits venom on Illyrian grass? Now the innocent folk—.' The Lord of War could bear her tears no longer. Changing his spear to his left hand, he leapt incontinent from his lofty chariot and took her to his shield, hurting her in his embrace. With fond words thus he soothes her:

'My respite from the wars, my sacred pleasure, my soul's only peace! Only you of gods and men have power so great, to meet my weapons unscathed, to stand at these horses' heads though they neigh in the midst of slaughter, to pluck this sword from my hand. I have not forgotten the nuptial bond with Sidonian Cadmus, nor your dear loyalty—take not pleasure in false reproach. Sooner let me, god that I am, be plunged into my uncle's nether pools and

[20] Through Cadmus.

stagna et pallentes agar exarmatus ad umbras.
sed nunc Fatorum monitus mentemque supremi
305 iussus obire patris (neque enim Vulcania tali
imperio manus apta legi), quo pectore contra
ire Iovem dictasque parem contemnere leges,
cui modo (pro vires!) terras caelumque fretumque
attremere oranti tantosque ex ordine vidi
310 delituisse deos? sed ne mihi corde supremos
concipe, cara, metus: quando haec mutare potestas
nulla datur, cum iam Tyriis sub moenibus ambae
bellabunt gentes, adero et socia arma iuvabo.
tunc me sanguineo late defervere campo
315 res super Argolicas haud sic deiecta videbis;
hoc mihi ius, nec Fata vetant.'

                                    Sic orsus aperto
flagrantes immisit equos. non ocius alti
in terras cadit ira Iovis, si quando nivalem
Othryn et Arctoae gelidum caput institit Ossae
320 armavitque in nube manum: volat ignea moles
saeva dei mandata ferens, caelumque trisulca
territat omne coma iamdudum aut ditibus agris
signa dare aut ponto miseros involvere nautas.
    Iamque remensus iter fesso Danaëia Tydeus
325 arva gradu viridisque legit devexa Prosymnae
terribilis visu: stant fulti pulvere crines,
squalidus ex umeris cadit alta in vulnera sudor,
insomnesque oculos rubor excitat, oraque retro
sorbet anhela sitis; mens altum spirat honorem
330 conscia factorum. sic nota in pascua taurus
bellator redit, adverso cui colla suoque

    329 sorbet ω: solvit P

driven disarmed to the pallid shades. But now, enjoined to carry out the Fates' admonishments and the will of the Father supreme (for Vulcan's hand is no fit choice for such a mission), how minded should I make to go against Jove and flout his uttered law? Just now I saw earth and sky and sea tremble before him as he spoke (what might!), saw great gods skulk in procession. But, dear one, I pray you, form no final fears in your heart. Since no power is given to change these things, when both nations shall do battle beneath the Tyrian walls, I shall be there and aid our allied arms. All over that bloody field you shall see me then boil down[21] upon the fortunes of Argos, not deject as you are now. That is my right and the Fates forbid it not.'

So saying he drove his flaming horses into the open. Not more swiftly does the wrath of lofty Jupiter fall to earth, should he take stand on snowy Othrys or the chill peak of Arctic Ossa and arm his hand in the cloud. Flies the fiery mass, bearing the god's cruel commission, affrighting the while all heaven with triple tail, to give a sign to wealthy fields or plunge hapless mariners into the deep.[22]

And now Tydeus has retraced his journey and with weary steps passes through the Danaan fields and the slopes of verdant Prosymna, fearsome he to behold. His hair stands up propped by dust, soiled sweat pours from his shoulders into his deep wounds, redness inflames his sleepless eyes, panting thirst sucks back his breath, but his spirit, conscious of his deeds, breathes high honour. So does the fighting bull return to his familiar pasture; his neck and shoulders swim with blood, his enemy's and

---

[21] The metaphor seems to be of a pot boiling over.
[22] The infinitives are best taken as final after *volat*.

173

sanguine proscissisque natant palearibus armi;
tunc quoque lassa tumet virtus multumque superbit
aequore despecto; vacua iacet hostis harena
335   turpe gemens crudosque vetat sentire dolores.
talis erat; medias etiam non destitit urbes,
quidquid et Asopon veteresque interiacet Argos,
inflammare odiis, multumque et ubique retexens:
legatum sese Graia de gente petendis
340   isse super regnis profugi Polynicis, at inde
vim, noctem, scelus, arma, dolos; ea foedera passum
regis Echionii, fratri sua iura negari.
prona fides populis; deus omnia credere suadet
Armipotens, geminatque acceptos Fama pavores.
345   Utque introgressus portas (et forte verendus
concilio pater ipse duces cogebat Adrastus),
improvisus adest, iam illinc a postibus aulae
vociferans: 'arma, arma, viri, tuque optime Lernae
ductor, magnanimum si quis tibi sanguis avorum,
350   arma para! nusquam pietas, non gentibus aequum
fas aut cura Iovis; melius legatus adissem
Sauromatas rabidos servatoremque cruentum
Bebrycii nemoris. nec iussa incuso pigetve
officii: iuvat isse, iuvat, Thebasque nocentes
355   explorasse manu. bello me, credite, bello,
ceu turrem validam aut artam compagibus urbem,
delecti insidiis instructique omnibus armis
nocte doloque viri nudum ignarumque locorum
nequiquam clausere; iacent in sanguine mixti
360   ante urbem vacuam. nunc, o nunc tempus in hostes,
dum trepidi exsanguesque metu, dum funera portant,

334 pectore Pω (*SB¹*)   335 dolores ω: labo- P

174

his own, his dewlaps are torn and his shoulders swim; even then his weary valour swells and he walks proudly, despising the ground; his foe lies on the open sand, shamefully groaning, nor lets him feel his raw pain. Such was Tydeus. Nor did he cease to inflame the cities on his way, whatever lies between Asopos and ancient Argos, retelling the tale everywhere over and over; how he had gone as envoy from a people of Greece to seek exiled Polynices' kingdom, but then came violence, night, crime, weapons, treachery. Such the Echionian monarch's pledge as he had suffered it. The brother was denied his rights. The people are quick to believe. The god, the Lord of Arms, persuades them to credit everything. Rumour doubles admitted fears.

Entering the gates, he is suddenly there—by chance venerable father Adrastus was convoking the leaders in council—shouting even from the palace door: 'Arms, arms, warriors! And you, most worthy lord of Lerna, if blood of high-hearted ancestors be in your veins, arms prepare! Gone is love of kin, the peoples know not justice or moral law or heed of Jupiter. I had better have gone envoy to wild Sarmatians or the bloody keeper of the Bebrycian forest. Not that I blame the orders or regret my office. I am glad I went, yes glad, and probed guilty Thebes with my own hand. With war, believe it, war, did men invest me, like a strong tower or a close-framed city. They were picked for ambush and equipped with every kind of weapon, they beset me with night and guile, defenceless and ignorant of the country. It was in vain. They lie mingled in their blood before an empty town. Now, oh now is the time to attack while the enemy are in panic, pale

---

³⁴⁵ verendus P: -dos ω   ³⁵² avidos Pω (*Wakefield*)

nunc, socer, haec dum non manus excidit; ipse ego fessus
quinquaginta illis heroum immanibus umbris
vulneraque ista ferens putri insiccata cruore
protinus ire peto!'

365   Trepidi de sedibus astant
Inachidae, cunctisque prior Cadmeius heros
accurrit vultum deiectus et 'o ego divis
invisus vitaeque nocens haec vulnera cerno
integer? hosne mihi reditus, germane, parabas?

370 in me haec tela dabas? pro vitae foeda cupido!
infelix, facinus fratri tam grande negavi.
et nunc vestra quidem maneant in pace quieta
moenia, nec vobis tanti sim causa tumultus
hospes adhuc. scio (nec me adeo res dextra levavit)

375 quam durum natis, thalamo quam triste revelli,
quam patria; non me ullius domus anxia culpet
respectentve truces obliquo lumine matres.
ibo libens certusque mori, licet optima coniunx
auditusque iterum revocet socer; hunc ego Thebis,

380 hunc, germane, tibi iugulum et tibi, maxime Tydeu,
debeo.'
     Sic variis praetemptat pectora dictis
obliquatque preces. commotae questibus irae
et mixtus lacrimis caluit dolor. omnibus ultro
non iuvenum modo, sed gelidis et inertibus aevo

---

362 *ita* P: dum capulo nondum manus ω
370 dabas ω: mei P   372 quieta P: serena ω
381 pert- Pω (ς)

---

23 How would he know? Statius seems to forget that Polynices
had no wife or child in Thebes.

with fright, while they are carrying in their dead; now, my father, while this hand is not forgotten. I myself, weary from those huge shades of fifty heroes and bearing these wounds with the blood dried and foul, I ask to go and go now."

The sons of Inachus start from their seats towards him in agitation and before them all the Cadmean hero runs up with countenance downcast: 'Oh hated of the gods and guilty in my life that I am, do I see these wounds myself unscathed? Was this the return you purposed for me, my brother? Were you aiming these weapons at me? Oh hideous lust of living! Wretch that I am, I denied my brother so great a crime. And now, friends, let your walls at least rest in peace and quiet, nor let me be the cause for you of such commotion. I am still but a guest. I know (nor has good fortune raised me up so far) how hard it is and sad to be torn from children and wife and fatherland.[23] Let no man's home blame me for its distress, no angry mothers eye me askance. I shall go willingly to certain death, though my best of wives and her father, whom I heard before,[24] call me back a second time. I owe this throat to Thebes, to you, brother, and to you, great Tydeus!'

Thus with various speech he tests their hearts and slants entreaty. His plaints stir anger and indignation grows warm, mingled with tears. One thought comes unbidden to all hearts, not young men's only but to the chill

[24] When he stopped the fight at the palace door; see SB[1]. The scholiast's explanation that Adrastus had previously forbidden Polynices to go to Thebes assumes something not in the poem (2.364–71).

385 pectoribus mens una subit, viduare penates,
finitimas adhibere manus, iamque ire. sed altus
consiliis pater imperiique haud flectere molem
inscius: 'ista quidem superis curaeque medenda
linquite, quaeso, meae: nec te germanus inulto
390 sceptra geret, neque nos avidi promittere bellum.
at nunc egregium tantoque in sanguine ovantem
excipite Oeniden, animosaque pectora laxet
sera quies: nobis dolor haud rationis egebit.'
   Turbati extemplo comites et pallida coniunx
395 Tydea circum omnes fessum bellique viaeque
stipantur. laetus mediis in sedibus aulae
constitit, ingentique exceptus terga columna,
vulnera dum lymphis Epidaurius eluit Idmon
(nunc velox ferro, nunc ille tepentibus herbis
400 mitior), ipse alta seductus mente renarrat
principia irarum, quaeque orsus uterque vicissim,
quis locus insidiis, tacito quae tempora bello,
qui contra quantique duces, ubi maximus illi
sudor, et indicio servatum Maeona tristi
405 exponit. cui fida manus proceresque socerque
astupet oranti, Tyriusque incenditur exsul.
   Solverat Hesperii devexo margine ponti
flagrantes Sol pronus equos rutilamque lavabat
Oceani sub fonte comam; cui turba profundi
410 Nereos et rapidis accurrunt passibus Horae,
frenaque et auratae textum sublime coronae
deripiunt, laxant calidis umentia loris
pectora; pars meritos vertunt ad molle iugales
gramen et erecto currum temone supinant.

399 tepentibus P: poten- ω

178

and sluggish with age: to leave their homes bereft, summon neighbouring force, and on the instant march. But father Adrastus, deep of counsel and no novice in manipulating the weight of command: 'Leave all this, I pray you, to the High Ones and my care for remedy. Neither shall your brother wield the sceptre and you fail of satisfaction nor yet are we eager to let war loose. But now all welcome Oeneus' noble son triumphing in so great a bloodshed. Let rest at last relax his courageous spirit. For my part indignation shall not go short of reason.'

Straightway his troubled comrades and pale bride all throng around Tydeus weary with battle and travel. Happily he took stand in the midst of the hall, leaning his back against a huge pillar while Epidaurian Idmon bathes his wounds—Idmon, now swift with the knife, now gentle with warm herbs. Himself, withdrawn into his mind's depths he recounts once more the beginnings of anger, what each said in his turn, the place chosen for ambush, the time for silent war, the opposing leaders, who and how great, where his work was heaviest; and he tells how Maeon was spared to take sad news. The faithful band, the nobles, and his wife's father are amazed at his speech and the Tyrian exile kindles.

The sinking Sun had loosed his fiery steeds at the sloping edge of the western sea and was bathing his ruddy hair in Ocean's fount. To him run deep Nereus' throng and the swift-stepping Hours. They strip away the reins and the lofty texture of his golden crown and relieve his sweating breast from the hot straps. Some turn the faithful horses to soft pasture and set the chariot on its back, pole in the air.

415 Nox subiit curasque hominum motusque ferarum
     composuit nigroque polos involvit amictu,
     illa quidem cunctis, sed non tibi mitis, Adraste,
     Labdacioque duci: nam Tydea largus habebat
     perfusum magna virtutis imagine somnus.
420   Et iam noctivagas inter deus armifer umbras
     desuper Arcadiae fines Nemeaeaque rura
     Taenariumque cacumen Apollineasque Therapnas
     armorum tonitru ferit et trepidantia corda
     implet amore sui. comunt Furor Iraque cristas,
425 frena ministrat equis Pavor armiger. at vigil omni
     Fama sono vanos rerum succincta tumultus
     antevolat currum flatuque impulsa gementum
     alipedum trepidas denso cum murmure plumas
     excutit: urguet enim stimulis auriga cruentis
430 facta, infecta loqui, curruque infestus ab alto
     terga comasque deae Scythica pater increpat hasta.
     qualis ubi Aeolio dimissos carcere Ventos
     dux prae se Neptunus agit magnoque volentes
     incitat Aegaeo; tristis comitatus eunti
435 circum lora fremunt Nimbique Hiemesque profundae
     Nubilaque et vulso terrarum sordida fundo
     Tempestas: dubiae motis radicibus obstant
     Cyclades, ipsa tua Mycono Gyaroque revelli,
     Dele, times magnique fidem testaris alumni.
440   Septima iam nitidum terris Aurora deisque
     purpureo vehit ore diem, Perseius heros
     cum primum arcana senior sese extulit aula,

433 volentes P: volan- ω
434 incitat P: inicit ω

180

Night came on, laying to rest the cares of men and the movements of beasts, and wrapped the heavens in her cloak of darkness, gentle to all beside but not to you, Adrastus, or to the Labdacian chief. As for Tydeus, bounteous sleep held him steeped in valour's great semblance.[25]

And now among night-wandering shades the weapon-bearing god strikes from aloft with thunder of arms Arcadia's boundaries and Nemea's fields and the peak of Taenarus and Apollo's Therapne, and fills fluttering hearts with desire for himself. Madness and Wrath arrange his plume, Panic, his squire,[26] gives reins to his horses. But Rumour, alert to every sound and girt with false news of tumult, flies before his car; sped forward by the breath of the groaning coursers, she shakes out her ruffled feathers with a deep whirring; for the driver urges her with bloody goads to speak both true and false, and the father[27] from his lofty chariot angrily chides the back and hair of the goddess with his Scythian lance. Even as Neptune their leader drives the Winds before him discharged from their Aeolian prison and urges them nothing loath over the great Aegean; a gloomy company roars about his reins as he goes, Squalls and deep Storms and Clouds and murky Hurricane that tears earth's foundation; tottering on their shaken roots the Cyclades oppose, Delos herself fears to be torn from her Myconos and Gyaros and calls on her great foster son for succour.

Now the blushing countenance of a seventh dawn brings shining day to earth and gods, when the old Persean hero first comes forth from his private apartments. Dis-

---

[25] Dreaming of his brave deeds.
[26] Bellona has this function in 7.73.   [27] Mars.

181

multa super bello generisque tumentibus amens
incertusque animi, daret armis iura novosque
445 gentibus incuteret stimulos, an frena teneret
irarum et motos capulis astringeret enses.
hinc pacis tranquilla movent, atque inde pudori
foeda quies, flectique nova dulcedine pugnae
difficiles populi; dubio sententia tandem
450 sera placet, vatum mentes ac provida veri
sacra movere deum. sollers, tibi cura futuri,
Amphiaraë, datur, iuxtaque Amythaone cretus
iam senior (sed mente viret Phoeboque) Melampus
associat passus: dubium cui pronus Apollo
455 oraque Cirrhaea satiarit largius unda.
principio fibris pecudumque in sanguine divos
explorant; iam tum pavidis maculosa bidentum
corda negant diraque nefas minitantia vena.
ire tamen vacuoque sedet petere omina caelo.
460   Mons erat audaci seductus in aethera dorso
(nomine Lernaei memorant Aphesanta coloni)
gentibus Argolicis olim sacer; inde ferebant
nubila suspenso celerem temerasse volatu
Persea, cum raptos pueri perterrita mater
465 prospexit de rupe gradus ac paene secuta est.
hoc gemini vates sanctam canentis olivae
fronde comam et niveis ornati tempora vittis
evadunt pariter, madidos ubi lucidus agros
ortus et algentes laxavit sole pruinas.
470 ac prior Oeclides solitum prece numen amicat:

454 pronus P: dexter ω

traught he was, much perplexed in mind concerning war
and his high-flying sons-in-law, whether to let arms have
their way and put new spurs to the peoples or hold anger's
reins and fasten the moved swords in their scabbards. The
tranquil boons of peace sway him on the one hand, on the
other the shame of inglorious quiet and peoples hard to
turn from newfound delight in battle. As he wavers, at
length a late resolve commends itself, to move the minds of
prophets and the truth-prescient rites of deities. To you,
wise Amphiaraus, is given the care of the future, and beside you Melampus son of Amythaon joins his steps, now
riper in years but young in mind and Phoebus' gift. 'Tis
doubtful to which of them Apollo leans and whose mouth
he has more lavishly sated with water of Cirrha. To start,
they explore the gods with entrails and in the blood of
cattle; even then they take alarm as the spotted hearts of
sheep threatening evil with ill-boding vein say them nay.
None the less they resolve to go and seek omens in the
open sky.

A mountain there was whose bold ridge drew away into
the ether (the husbandmen of Lerna call it by the name of
Aphesas), long time sacred to the Argive folk. They used
to say that from it swift Perseus violated the clouds as he
hovered in flight,[28] while his terrified mother saw from
the crag her boy's rapt steps and almost followed. Hither
the two seers, their holy hair adorned with leafage of grey
olive and their temples with snowy fillets, together ascend
when bright sunrise has melted the frigid frost on the wet
fields. And first the son of Oecleus bespeaks with prayer

---

[28] Perseus was given winged sandals for his fight with Medusa.
The name Aphesas is connected with ἀφίημι, 'let go,' with noun
ἄφεσις.

'Iuppiter omnipotens (nam te pernicibus alis
addere consilium volucresque implere futuri
ominaque et causas caelo deferre latentes
accipimus), non Cirrha deum promiserit antro
475 certius, aut frondes lucis quas fama Molossis
Chaonias sonuisse tibi, licet aridus Hammon
invideat Lyciaeque parent contendere sortes
Niliacumque pecus patrioque aequalis honori
Branchus et undosae quem rusticus accola Pisae
480 Pana Lycaonia nocturnum exaudit in umbra:
ditior ille animi, cui tu, Dictaee, secundas
impuleris manifestus aves. mirum unde, sed olim
hic honor alitibus, superae seu conditor aulae
sic dedit effusum chaos in nova semina texens,
485 seu quia mutatae nostraque ab origine versis
corporibus subiere notos, sed purior axis
amotumque nefas et rarum insistere terris
vera docent: tibi, summe sator terraeque deumque,
scire licet: nos Argolicae primordia pugnae
490 venturumque sinas caelo praenosse laborem.
si datur et duris sedet haec sententia Parcis
solvere Echionias Lernaea cuspide portas,
signa feras laevusque tones; tunc omnis in astris
consonet arcana volucris bona murmura lingua.
495 si prohibes, hic necte moras dextrisque profundum
alitibus praetexe diem.' sic fatus et alto
membra locat scopulo; tunc plura ignotaque iungit
numina et immensi fruitur caligine mundi.

479 qui PωΣ (*O. Mueller*)
482 olim ω: olīs P: olimst *O. Mueller*
486 seu Pω (*SB²*)

the favour of the wonted deity: 'Almighty Jupiter (for we are taught that you give wisdom to fleet wings, filling birds with the future, and bring down from heaven omens and hidden causes), not Cirrha could send forth the god from her cavern more surely or those Chaonian leaves that are famed to make sounds at your behest in Molossian groves: though parched Hammon envy and the Lycian oracle[29] make to compete and the beast of the Nile[30] and Branchus, who matches his father's repute, and Pan,[31] whom the rustic dweller in wave-swept Pisa hears by night in Lycaonian shade, richer in spirit is he to whom you, Dictaean, manifest yourself by starting favourable birds. Marvellous the cause, but from long ago birds have this honour: whether the founder of the heavenly palace so disposed when he wove sprawling chaos into new seeds, or whether they went upon the winds changed with bodies transformed from what once were ours, but the purer sky with evil removed and rare landing upon earth teaches them truth— for you, supreme begetter of earth and gods, 'tis lawful to know. Permit us to learn beforehand by the sky the beginnings of the Argive strife and the toil to come. If 'tis granted and the harsh Parcae so resolve that we loosen the Echionian gates with Lerna's spear, bring a sign, thunder on the left; then let every flying creature among the stars utter good sounds in unison with secret tongue. If you forbid, here weave delay and with birds on the right screen the abyss of day.' So he spoke, and disposed his limbs on a high rock. Then he adds deities, more and unknown, and enjoys the darkness of the vast universe.

---

[29] Of Apollo, at Patara.   [30] Apis, the bull god, at Memphis.   [31] With an oracle at Lycosura in Arcadia.

Postquam rite diu partiti sidera cunctas
500 perlegere animis oculisque sequacibus auras,
tunc Amythaonius longo post tempore vates:
'nonne sub excelso spirantis limite caeli,
Amphiaraë, vides, cursus ut nulla serenos
ales agat liquidoque polum complexa meatu
505 pendeat aut fugiens placabile clanxerit omen?
non comes obscurus tripodum, non fulminis ardens
vector adest, flavaeque sonans avis unca Minervae
non venit auguriis melior; quin vultur et altis
desuper accipitres exsultavere rapinis.
510 monstra volant: dirae strident in nube volucres,
nocturnaeque gemunt striges et feralia bubo
damna canens. quae prima deum portenta sequamur?
hisne dari, Thymbraee, polum? simul ora recurvo
ungue secant rabidae planctumque imitantibus alis
515 exagitant Zephyros et plumea pectora caedunt.'
    Ille sub haec: 'equidem varii, pater, omina Phoebi
saepe tuli: iam tum, prima cum pube virentem
semideos inter pinus me Thessala reges
duceret, his casus terraeque marisque canentem
520 obstipuere duces, nec me ventura locuto
saepius in dubiis auditus Iasoni Mopsus.
sed similes non ante metus aut astra notavi
prodigiosa magis; quamquam maiora parantur.
huc adverte animum: clara regione profundi

---

499 cunctas ψ: -ta P: -tis ω   505 clanxerit P*corr.*, *Klotz*:
pl- P *ante corr.*, ωΣ   508 qui Pω (ς)

510 stridunt Pω (ς)

519 hic Pω (*SB*): *cf. Val. Fl. 1.234* sic sociis Mopsoque canit. De
pleonasmo his/duces vide Housman 1200 sq.

After they had duly apportioned the stars and long scrutinized all the air with their minds and close-following
eyes, then at last spoke Amythaon's prophet son: 'See you
not, Amphiaraus, how beneath the lofty boundary of the
breathing sky no winged creature plies a tranquil course or
hangs circling the heavens in liquid flight or screams a
kindly omen as it flees? No dark companion of the tripods,
no fiery bearer of the thunderbolt is at hand, no hooked
and hooting fowl of blond Minerva comes with favouring
augury.[32] Nay, vultures and hawks exult from above in their
lofty plunder. Monsters are flying, direful birds shriek in
the clouds, screech owls of night and the horned one wail,
chanting death and disaster. Which portents of the gods
should we follow first? Lord of Thymbra, can the heavens
be given over to these? All together in fury they cut each
other's faces with curving talons and with flappings like
mourners' blows they harry the Zephyrs and strike their
feathery breasts.'

The other answered: 'Often, my father, have I endured
changeful Phoebus' omens. Even then, when in the green
of first youth the Thessalian pine[33] bore me among royal
demigods, the chiefs were amazed to hear me sing the
chances of land and sea, and Jason in doubt listened to me
no less often than to Mopsus as I told of things to come.
But never before have I observed terrors like these or
heavens more prodigious. Yet greater things are in store.
Look hither: in the bright region of the deep ether count-

[32] The three birds are raven, eagle, and owl.
[33] The Argo.

---

521 iasone PωΣ (*Barth*)   522 monstra *O. Mueller*

525 aetheros innumeri statuerunt agmina cycni,
sive hos Strymonia Boreas eiecit ab Arcto,
seu fecunda refert placidi clementia Nili.
fixerunt cursus: has rere in imagine Thebas.
nam sese immoti gyro atque in pace silentes
530 ceu muris valloque tenent. sed fortior ecce
adventat per inane cohors; septem ordine fulvo
armigeras summi Iovis exsultante caterva
intuor: Inachii sint hi tibi, concipe, reges.
invasere globum nivei gregis uncaque pandunt
535 caedibus ora novis et strictis unguibus instant.
cernis inexperto rorantes sanguine ventos,
et plumis stillare diem? quae saeva repente
victores agitat leto Iovis ira sinistri?
hic excelsa petens subita face solus inarsit
540 summisitque animos, illum vestigia adortum
maiorum volucrum tenerae deponitis alae,
hic hosti implicitus pariter ruit, hunc fuga retro
volvit agens sociae linquentem fata catervae,
hic nimbo glomeratus obit, hic praepete viva
545 pascitur immoriens; spargit cava nubila sanguis.
quid furtim illacrimas? illum, venerande Melampu,
qui cadit, agnosco.' trepidos sic mole futuri
cunctaque iam rerum certa sub imagine passos
terror habet vates; piget irrupisse volantum

---

34 The birds foreshadow the fate of six out of the seven:
Capaneus, Parthenopaeus, Polynices, Adrastus, Hippomedon,
Tydeus. Finally Amphiaraus sees his own fate.

35 I.e. 'no need to keep your knowledge from me, I already
know.'

less swans have marshalled their columns, whether Boreas expelled them from the Strymonian Bear or the fertile gentleness of placid Nile recalls them. They have halted their flight. These consider as symbolizing Thebes; for in peace and silence they hold themselves motionless in a ring, as though behind walls and rampart. But look, a braver band approaches through the void. I see seven arms-bearers of highest Jupiter, an exultant troop in tawny line. Imagine them to be the Inachian kings. They have invaded the circle of the snowy flock; opening their hooked beaks for fresh slaughter and with talons drawn they bear down. Do you see how the winds drizzle with blood as ne'er before, how the day drips with feathers? What fierce wrath of baleful Jove suddenly drives the victors to death? One, seeking the heights, has all at once taken fire from the sun's torch and abated his pride; another his young wings let down as he attempts the tracks of bigger birds; this one plunges entangled with his foe; him flight rolls backward as he leaves his allied squadron to their fate; another perishes caught up in a storm-wrack; another dying feeds upon a living bird;[34] blood bespatters the hollow clouds. Why do you weep aside?[35] Reverend Melampus,[36] he yonder that falls, I know him.' Terror seizes the seers, thus frightened by the weight of the future, as they suffer all that will betide under a sure semblance. They wish they had not broken in upon the assemblies of the birds and intruded

---

[36] The vocative *Melampu* from (unattested) *Melampūs* (Μελάμπους, Blackfoot) is to be noticed as supporting Οἰδίπου in Sophocles, *Oedipus at Colonus* 461 and elsewhere against Οἰδίπους, sometimes substituted by conjecture. But note Argipūs ('Fleetfoot') in 9.266.

550 concilia et caelo mentem insertasse vetanti,
auditique odere deos.
                    Unde iste per orbem
primus venturi miseris animantibus aeger
crevit amor? divumne feras hoc munus, an ipsi,
gens avida et parto non umquam stare quieti,
555 eruimus quae prima dies, ubi terminus aevi,
quid bonus ille deum genitor, quid ferrea Clotho
cogitet? hinc fibrae et volucrum per nubila sermo
astrorumque vices numerataque semita lunae
Thessalicumque nefas. at non prior aureus ille
560 sanguis avum scopulisque satae vel robore gentes
artibus his usae; silvas amor unus humumque
edomuisse manu; quid crastina volveret aetas
scire nefas homini. nos, pravum et flebile vulgus,
scrutati penitus superos: hinc pallor et irae,
565 hinc scelus insidiaeque et nulla modestia voti.
     Ergo manu vittas damnataque vertice serta
deripit abiectaque inhonorus fronde sacerdos
inviso de monte redit; iam bella tubaeque
comminus, absentesque fremunt sub pectore Thebae.
570 ille nec aspectum vulgi, nec fida tyranni
colloquia aut coetus procerum perferre, sed atra
sede tegi, et superum clausus negat acta fateri
(te pudor et curae retinent per rura, Melampu):
bissenos premit ora dies populumque ducesque

---

561 mentibus (*SB²*)   564 scrutati ω: -ari P

---

37 Using a horoscope. But the date of birth would normally be
known. Perhaps this is a loose way of saying 'an entire life.' Or it
could relate to a child conceived but not yet born (SB²).

their purpose on heaven that forbade them. They hate the gods that heard their prayer.

Whence first for hapless mortals grew worldwide this sick craving for what is to come? Shall we call it a gift of the gods or do we ourselves, a greedy race never content to rest with what we have, dig out which day is the first[37] and where life ends, what that kindly begetter of the gods and what iron Clotho have in view? Hence entrails and the talk of birds in the clouds and the comings and goings of the stars and the counted path of the moon and the abomination of Thessaly. But that earlier golden race of our ancestors and the peoples born of rocks and timber[38] used not these skills.[39] Their one desire was to tame forest and earth with their hands; what the morrow's years might bring 'twas sin for man to know. We, a perverted and pathetic multitude, peer deep into the High Ones; hence pallor and anger, hence crime and treachery and prayer beyond all moderation.

So the priest tears down the fillets renounced and the garlands from his head, casts aside his branches and returns sans emblems of honour from the hated mountain. Now war's trumpets are at hand and absent Thebes clamours in his breast. He endures not the sight of the multitude nor confidential talk with the ruler nor gatherings of the notables, but hiding cloistered in his dark abode refuses to divulge the doings of the High Ones. (Melampus shame and anxiety hold back in the countryside.) For twice six days he keeps his mouth closed, racking people and

[38] As the Arcadians were supposed to have been.
[39] See SB[2].

575 extrahit incertis. et iam suprema Tonantis
iussa fremunt agrosque viris annosaque vastant
oppida; bellipotens prae se deus agmina passim
mille rapit; liquere domos dilectaque laeti
conubia et primo plorantes limine natos:
580 tantus in attonitos cecidit deus. arma paternis
postibus et fixos superum ad penetralia currus
vellere amor; tunc fessa putri robigine pila
haerentesque situ gladios in saeva recurant
vulnera et attrito cogunt iuvenescere saxo.
585 hi teretes galeas magnorumque aerea suta
thoracum et tunicas Chalybum squalore crepantes
pectoribus temptare, alii Gortynia lentant
cornua; iam falces avidis et aratra caminis
rastraque et incurvi saevum rubuere ligones.
590 caedere nec validas sanctis e stirpibus hastas,
nec pudor emerito clipeum vestisse iuvenco.
irrupere Argos maestique ad limina regis
bella animis, bella ore fremunt; it clamor ad auras,
quantus Tyrrheni gemitus salis, aut ubi temptat
595 Enceladus mutare latus; super igneus antris
mons tonat: exundant apices, fluctusque Pelorus
contrahit, et sperat tellus abrupta reverti.
　　　　Atque hic ingenti Capaneus Mavortis amore
excitus et longam pridem indignantia pacem
600 corda tumens (huic ampla quidem de sanguine prisco
nobilitas; sed enim ipse manu praegressus avorum
facta, diu tuto superum contemptor et aequi
impatiens largusque animae, modo suaserit ira),

586 chalybum *edd.* (*Hill*)

leaders with uncertainty. And now the Thunderer's supreme commands clamour and empty fields and ancient towns of their menfolk. Everywhere the God of War sweeps a thousand columns before him. Joyfully they left their homes and loved wives and children weeping at the threshold: so powerfully did the god fall upon them in their amazement. Eagerly they pluck weapons from family doorposts and chariots fixed to the shrines of the High Ones. Then they refurbish pikes weary with rotting rust and swords sticking neglected in their scabbards to deal cruel wounds, and make them young again with rub of stone. Some try on rounded helmets and at their breasts the bronze mail of great jerkins and tunics creaking with disused iron. Others draw bows of Gortyn. Now sickles and ploughshares and harrows and curving hoes cruelly redden in greedy furnaces. They scruple not to hew strong shafts from sacred stocks and to cover a shield from an ox past service. Into Argos they burst and at the sad king's doors they cry war with their hearts and war with their mouths. The shouting goes aloft, loud as the groaning of Tyrrhenian waters or as when Enceladus tries to change his side; above, the fiery mountain thunders in its caverns, the peaks gush forth, Pelorus contracts his waves, and the severed earth hopes to return.[40]

Capaneus was spurred by mighty love of Mars, his swelling breast had long protested lengthy peace. Ample nobility was his from ancient blood, but he himself had outstripped the doughty deeds of his forbears. Long had he despised the High Ones with impunity, impatient of justice and prodigal of life if anger urged. Like a denizen

[40] With Sicily reunited with the mainland.

unus ut e silvis Pholoës habitator opacae
605 inter et Aetnaeos aequus consurgere fratres,
ante fores, ubi turba ducum vulgique frementis,
Amphiaraë, tuas 'quae tanta ignavia,' clamat,
'Inachidae uosque o socio de sanguine Achivi?
unius (heu pudeat!) plebeia ad limina civis
610 tot ferro accinctae gentes animisque paratae
pendemus? non si ipse cavo sub vertice Cirrhae
(quisquis is est, timidis Famaeque ita visus) Apollo
mugiat insano penitus seclusus in antro,
exspectare queam dum pallida virgo tremendas
615 nuntiet ambages. virtus mihi numen et ensis
quem teneo. iamque hic timida cum fraude sacerdos
exeat, aut hodie, volucrum quae tanta potestas,
experiar.'
Laetum fremit assensuque furentem
implet Achaea manus. tandem prorumpere adactus
620 Oeclides: 'alio curarum agitante tumultu
non equidem effreno iuvenis clamore profani
dictorumque metu, licet hic insana minetur,
elicior tenebris; alio mihi debita fato
summa dies, vetitumque dari mortalibus armis.
625 sed me vester amor nimiusque arcana profari
Phoebus agit; vobis ventura atque omne quod ultra est
pandere maestus eo; nam te, vesane, moneri
ante nefas, unique tacet tibi noster Apollo.
quo, miseri, Fatis superisque obstantibus arma,
630 quo rapitis? quae vos Furiarum verbera caecos
exagitant? adeone animarum taedet? et Argos

628 tacet P: silet ω

194

of darkling Pholoë from out the forest or one that might rise equal among Aetna's brethren,[41] he stands before Amphiaraus' doors, where leaders and clamouring multitude had congregated, crying: 'What poltroonery is this, sons of Inachus and you Achaeans of allied blood? So many peoples, sword-girt and ready-hearted, do we hang in doubt at the plebeian[42] threshold of a single citizen? Oh for shame! Were Apollo himself, whoever he is (cowards and Rumour so think of him), to bellow under Cirrha's hollow peak, deep withdrawn in his frenzied cavern, I could not wait for the pale maiden[43] to announce her fearsome riddles. Valour is my deity, and the sword in my hand. Now let this priest come forth with his craven cheat, or this day I shall test the vaunted power of birds.'

The Achaean band yells joyfully and fills out his madness with their assent. Forced at length to burst forth, thus the son of Oecles: 'Tumult of other cares harasses me. Not for a young blasphemer's unbridled clamour or for fear of his words, frantic though his threats, am I drawn from darkness. My last day is owed me by a different fate; it may not be granted to mortal arms. But my love for you and too potent Phoebus drive me to speak secrets out. Sadly I am going to lay bare to you things to come and whatever lies beyond. As for *you*, madman, warning you would be sin, to you alone our lord Apollo is silent. Wretches, whither, oh whither do you rush your arms when the Fates and the High Ones oppose? What Furies' lash drives you in your blindness? Are you so weary of your lives? Do you hate

---

[41] A Centaur or a Cyclops.   [42] As distinct from the royal palace.   [43] The Pythia (Delphic priestess), pale because prophetic frenzy was apt to kill (cf. 106f.).

exosi? nil dulce domi? nulla omina curae?
quid me Persei secreta ad culmina montis
ire gradu trepido superumque irrumpere coetus
635 egistis? potui pariter nescire quis armis
casus, ubi atra dies, quae fati exordia cunctis,
quae mihi. consulti testor penetralia mundi
et volucrum affatus et te, Thymbraee, vocanti
non alias tam saeve mihi, quae signa futuri
640 pertulerim: vidi ingentis portenta ruinae,
vidi hominum divumque metus hilaremque Megaeram
et Lachesin putri vacuantem saecula penso.
proicite arma manu: deus ecce furentibus obstat,
ecce deus! miseri, quid pulchrum sanguine victo
645 Aoniam et diri saturare novalia Cadmi?
sed quid vana cano, quid fixos arceo casus?
ibimus.' hic presso gemuit semel ore sacerdos.
        Illum iterum Capaneus: 'tuus o furor auguret uni
ista tibi, ut serves vacuos inglorius annos
650 et tua non umquam Tyrrhenus tempora circum
clangor eat. quid vota virum meliora moraris?
scilicet ut vanis avibus natoque domoque
et thalamis potiare iacens, sileamus inulti
Tydeos egregii perfossum pectus et arma
655 foederis abrupti? quod si bella effera Graios
ferre vetas, i Sidonios legatus ad hostes:
haec pacem tibi serta dabunt. tua prorsus inani
verba polo causas abstrusaque momina rerum
eliciunt! miseret superum, si carmina curae
660 humanaeque preces. quid inertia pectora terres?

636 ubi P: et ω
658 nomina P: sem- ωΣ (*Baehrens*: nem- *Courtney*)

Argos? Is nothing sweet at home? Care you for no omens? Why did you force me to go with trembling step to the secret top of Perseus' mountain and break in upon the gatherings of the High Ones? I might have stayed ignorant along with you; what the outcome of the fight, where the black day, what fate begins for all, and what for me. I call the secret places of the universe I questioned, and the speech of birds, and you, Lord of Thymbra, never before so harsh to my appeal, to witness what signs of futurity I endured. I saw portents of mighty downfall, I saw terrors of men and gods, and Megaera laughing and Lachesis voiding the generations with her rotting thread. Throw away your weapons. See, the god opposes your frenzy, see, the god! Wretches, where is the glory in drenching Aonia and dire Cadmus' meadows with your vanquished blood? But why do I prophesy in vain? Why ward off fortunes fixed? We shall go.' Here the priest groaned and closed his mouth once for all.

Him again Capaneus: 'Let your ravings make these auguries just to yourself, that you keep empty, inglorious years and Tyrrhenian clangour never echo around your temples. Why do you delay the better hopes of the brave? Forsooth, so that you may have your silly birds and your son and house and marriage chamber as you lie abed, are we to leave most noble Tydeus unavenged, naught saying of his pierced breast and the pact broken in arms? But if you forbid the Greeks to wage wild war, go you as envoy to our Sidonian foes. These chaplets will afford you peace. For a certainty your words draw causes and hidden impulses of things from the open sky! 'Tis pity of the High Ones if they take heed of spells and human prayers. Why

primus in orbe deos fecit timor! et tibi tuto
nunc eat iste furor; sed prima ad classica cum iam
hostilem Ismenon galeis Dircenque bibemus,
ne mihi tunc, moneo, lituos atque arma volenti
665 obvius ire pares venisque aut alite visa
bellorum proferre diem: procul haec tibi mollis
infula terrificique aberit dementia Phoebi:
illic augur ego et mecum quicumque parati
insanire manu.'
               Rursus fragor intonat ingens
670 hortantum et vasto subter volat astra tumultu;
ut rapidus torrens, animos cui verna ministrant
flamina et exuti concreto frigore montes,
cum vagus in campos frustra prohibentibus exit
obicibus, resonant permixto turbine tecta,
675 arva, armenta, viri, donec stetit improbus alto
colle minor magnoque invenit in aggere ripas.
haec alterna ducum nox interfusa diremit.

   At gemitus Argia viri non amplius aequo
corde ferens sociumque animo miserata dolorem,
680 sicut erat, laceris pridem turpata capillis,
et fletu signata genas, ad celsa verendi
ibat tecta patris parvumque sub ubere caro
Thessandrum portabat avo iam nocte suprema
ante novos ortus, ubi sola superstite Plaustro
685 Arctos ad Oceanum fugientibus invidet astris,
utque fores iniit magnoque affusa parenti est:
'cur tua cum lacrimis maesto sine coniuge supplex

665 ventisque PωΣ (*Heinsius*)
680 turpata P: turbata ω

frighten you untutored hearts? Fear first made gods in the world. And for now let this your raving go unpunished. But when we drink hostile Ismenos and Dirce with our helmets to the sound of first trumpets, I warn you, do not then seek to balk me as I crave clarions and arms and to put off the day of battle at sight of entrails or bird. No help for you then in this soft fillet and the folly of bogy Phoebus. There I am the augur and all who are ready to play the fighting madman with me.'

Again thunders out the great roar of the backers and flies in vast tumult to the stars. 'Twas like a swift torrent, encouraged by spring breezes and mountains stripped of their frozen chill, when it comes wandering out into the plain over obstructions that vainly stay its course: dwellings, fields, cattle, men resound in the mingled swirl, until the ungovernable flow halts bested before a high hill or finds banks in some great rampart. Night interposing parted this altercation of chieftains.

But Argia no longer bore her husband's misery calmly, pitying the distress she shared. Just as she was, her beauty long marred by tearing of her hair and with marks of weeping on her face, she went to her venerable father's lofty dwelling, carrying little Thessander[44] at her breast to his loved grandsire. Night was ending before a new dawn, when only Arctos with surviving wagon envied the stars as they fled to Ocean. When she entered the door and cast herself down before her great parent: 'Why I seek your threshold at night in tearful supplication without my sor-

[44] Elsewhere Thersander (-dros), surely the proper form (cf. θάρσος, Thersites). The variant here will derive from Thessandrus in *Aeneid* 2.261, though probably a different person.

limina nocte petam, cessem licet ipsa profari,
scis genitor. sed iura deum genialia testor
690 teque, pater, non ille iubet sed pervigil angor.
ex quo primus Hymen movitque infausta sinistram
Iuno facem, semper lacrimis gemituque propinquo
exturbata quies. non si mihi tigridis horror
aequoreasque super rigeant praecordia cautes,
695 ferre queam; tu solus opem, tu summa medendi
iura tenes; da bella, pater, generique iacentis
aspice res humiles, atque hanc, pater, aspice prolem
exsulis; huic olim generis pudor. o ubi prima
hospitia et iunctae testato numine dextrae?
700 hic certe est quem Fata dabant, quem dixit Apollo.
non egomet tacitos Veneris furata calores
culpatamve facem: tua iussa verenda tuosque
dilexi monitus. nunc qua feritate dolentis
despiciam questus! nescis, pater optime, nescis
705 quantus amor castae misero nupsisse marito.
et nunc maesta quidem grave et illaetabile munus,
ut timeam doleamque, rogo; sed cum oscula rumpet
maesta dies, cum rauca dabunt abeuntibus armis
signa tubae saevoque genas fulgebitis auro,
710 ei mihi, care parens, iterum fortasse rogabo!'
    Illius umenti carpens pater oscula vultu:
'non equidem has umquam culparim, nata, querelas;
pone metus, laudanda rogas nec digna negari.
sed mihi multa dei (nec tu sperare quod urgues
715 desine), multa metus regnique volubile pondus
subiciunt animo. veniet qui debitus istis,

694 aequoreaeque Pω (*Barth*)
699 testato ω: funesto P: manifesto *Baehrens*

rowing spouse you know, father, even if I were slow to tell. But I call the divine laws of wedlock to witness and you, sire, 'tis not he that commands me but sleepless suffering. Ever since Hymen and inauspicious Juno first raised the ill-omened torch, my rest has always been troubled by weeping and groaning at my side. Not if I were a bristling tigress or my heart harder than the cliffs of the sea could I bear it. Only you can aid, yours is the high authority to heal. Give war, father; regard the lowly fortunes of your fallen son-in-law and this child of an exile. One day he will be ashamed of his birth. Ah, where is that first welcome, hands joined with gods to witness? He of a surety is the man the Fates gave, of whom Apollo told. I stole no secret fires of love, no guilty torch; 'twas your revered commands, your admonitions I cared for. What cruelty now for me to despise the sorrower's complaint! Good father, you know not, you know not the love of a chaste bride wedded to an unhappy husband. In sadness now I ask a heavy, joyless boon—to fear and grieve. But when the sorrowful day shall break our kisses and the trumpets give their harsh signals to the departing host and your faces shall gleam with cruel gold, then, alas, perhaps, dear father, I shall ask a second time.'[45]

The father answered, taking kisses from her tearful face: 'Never, daughter, should I blame these plaints. Lay fears aside; what you ask is praiseworthy nor meet to be denied. But the gods (nay, cease not to hope for what you urge) and my qualms, and the ever shifting burden of ruling give me many a thought. The right mode in this matter

[45] To cancel the expedition.

nata, modus neque te incassum flevisse quereris.
tu solare virum, neu sint dispendia iustae
dura morae: magnos cunctamur, nata, paratus.
720 proficitur bello.' dicentem talia nascens
lux monet ingentesque iubent assurgere curae.

721 monet ψ: movet Pω

will come, my child, neither shall you complain that you wept for naught. Comfort your husband; and take not hard the tarryings of a just delay. Great preparations, my child, are in our delaying. 'Tis gain for the war.' As he so speaks, the nascent light advises him and cares of great moment bid him rise.

LIBER IV

Tertius horrentem Zephyris laxaverat annum
Phoebus et angusto cogebat limite vernum
longius ire diem, cum fracta impulsaque Fatis
consilia et tandem miseris data copia belli.

5   prima manu rutilam de vertice Larisaeo
ostendit Bellona facem dextraque trabalem
hastam intorsit agens, liquido quae stridula caelo
fugit et Aoniae celso stetit aggere Dirces.
mox et castra subit ferroque auroque coruscis

10 mixta viris turmale fremit; dat euntibus enses,
plaudit equos, vocat ad portas; hortamina fortes
praeveniunt, timidisque etiam brevis addita virtus.
      Dicta dies aderat. cadit ingens rite Tonanti
Gradivoque pecus, nullisque secundus in extis

15 pallet et armatis simulat sperare sacerdos.
iamque suos circum pueri nuptaeque patresque
funduntur mixti summisque a postibus obstant.

---

2 angusto . . . vernum P: -tum . . . -no ω Σ: -tam . . . -no ψ
4 miseris Pψ: -ri ω

---

1 Two years had passed since Polynices left Thebes and a year
since Tydeus' embassy.   2 *Secundus* of the diviner echoes
Aeneid 11.739. My suggestion in SB[2] is cancelled.

BOOK 4

Thrice[1] had Phoebus relaxed harsh winter with his Zephyrs and was constraining the vernal day to take longer than its narrow bound when wise counsels were shattered by the urging Fates and licence given to the wretches at last for war. First from Larisa's peak Bellona showed her red torch and with her right hand sent her massive spear whirling; it sped whistling through the clear sky and landed on the lofty rampart of Aonian Dirce. Next she enters the camp and mingling with the warriors that flash with steel and gold she yells loud as a squadron, gives swords to the departing, claps horses, summons to the gates. The brave do not wait to be exhorted, even cowards gain brief access of courage.

The appointed day arrives. A huge number of beasts fall in ritual sacrifice to the Thunderer and Gradivus, and the priest, finding no good in the entrails,[2] feigns hope to the men in arms. And now children and wives and fathers pour mingling around their own and block their way from the outermost doorways.[3] Weeping is

---

[3] *Summis* = *extremis*, the last ditch, as it were. The departing warrior forces his way out of his house against the family's efforts to hold him back. For the preposition cf. 564 *oppositis Semelen a ventre lacertis.*

nec modus est lacrimis: rorant clipeique iubaeque
triste salutantum, et cunctis dependet ab armis
20 suspiranda domus; galeis iuvat oscula clausis
inserere amplexuque truces deducere conos.
illi, quis ferrum modo, quis mors ipsa placebat,
dant gemitus fractaeque labant singultibus irae.
sic ubi forte viris longum super aequor ituris,
25 cum iam ad vela Noti et scisso redit ancora fundo,
haeret amica manus: certant innectere collo
bracchia, manantesque oculos hinc oscula turbant,
hinc magni caligo maris, tandemque relicti
stant in rupe tamen; fugientia carbasa visu
30 dulce sequi, patriosque dolent crebrescere ventos.
[stant tamen et nota puppim de rupe salutant.]
    Nunc mihi, Fama prior mundique arcana Vetustas,
cui meminisse ducum vitasque extendere curae,
pande viros, tuque, o nemoris regina sonori,
35 Calliope, quas ille manus, quae moverit arma
Gradivus, quantas populis solaverit urbes,
sublata molire lyra: neque enim altior ulli
mens hausto de fonte venit.
                                        Rex tristis et aeger
pondere curarum propiorque abeuntibus annis
40 inter adhortantes vix sponte incedit Adrastus,
contentus ferro cingi latus; arma manipli
pone ferunt. volucres portis auriga sub ipsis
comit equos, et iam inde iugo luctatur Arion.
huic armat Larisa viros, huic celsa Prosymna,
45 aptior armentis Midea pecorosaque Phlius,
quaeque pavet longa spumantem valle Charadron

29–30 *absunt in* ψ   31 *abest in* P, *damnavit Barth*

unrestrained. Shields and crests are bedewed as they bid
sorrowful farewells and from every suit of arms hangs a
family to be sighed for. They are fain to push kisses through
closed vizors and draw down fierce helmet tops with their
embrace. Those who but now called for the sword, for
death itself, utter groans; broken, their anger collapses in
sobs. So when men are haply about to go far overseas,
when the wind is at the sails and the anchor returns from
the ploughed bottom, a fond company clings; they vie to
twine their arms about a neck, kisses and the great sea's fog
blur their flowing eyes; at last abandoned, they will yet
stand on a cliff; 'tis sweet to follow the fleeing canvass with
their gaze and they grieve that their country's winds blow
stronger.

Now, old-time Fame and secret Antiquity of the world,
whose care it is to remember leaders and extend their lives,
set me forth the men. And you, queen of the tuneful grove,
Calliope, raise your lyre and tell what bands, what arms
Gradivus set moving, how many cities he left deserted of
their peoples. For to none comes deeper understanding
from the fount you drain.

King Adrastus, sad and sick with weight of cares and
nearer to departing years, walks scarce of his own accord
amid words of good cheer, content with the steel that girds
his side; soldiers bear his shield behind him. His driver
grooms the swift horses right at the gate and Arion is
already fighting the yoke. For him Larisa arms her menfolk and lofty Prosymna and Midea more fit for herds and
sheep-wealthy Phlius and Neris fearing Charadros as he

Neris, et ingenti turritae mole Cleonae
et Lacedaemonium Thyrea lectura cruorem.
iunguntur memores transmissi ab origine regis,
50 qui Drepani scopulos et oliviferae Sicyonis
culta serunt, quos pigra vado Langia tacenti
lambit et anfractu riparum incurvus Elisson.
saevus honos fluvio: Stygias lustrare severis
Eumenidas perhibetur aquis; huc mergere suetas
55 ora et anhelantes poto Phlegethonte cerastas,
seu Thracum vertere domos, seu tecta Mycenes
impia Cadmeumve larem; fugit ipse natantes
amnis, et innumeris livescunt stagna venenis.
it comes Inoas Ephyre solata querelas
60 Cenchreaeque manus, vatum qua conscius amnis
Gorgoneo percussus equo, quaque obiacet alto
Isthmos et a terris maria inclinata repellit.
haec manus Adrastum numero ter mille secuti
exsultant; pars gaesa manu, pars robora flammis
65 indurata diu (non unus namque maniplis
mos neque sanguis) habent, teretes pars vertere fundas

48 thyla electura P: thyre lec- ω (*Weber*)
49 regis ψ, *Gronovius*: reges Pω
51 langia ω: strangilla P
52 elisson P: -os ω   54 sueta P: -tae ω (*Baehrens*)
66 habet Pψ: inest ω (*O. Mueller*)

---

4 Adrastus; cf. 2.179.
5 Later on located in the Nemea region. The feminine (cf. 724, though masculine in 837) supports this reading against P's unknown Strangilla, since feminine rivers are a great rarity. Properly the name will have belonged to the Nymph of the spring.

foams down his long valley and Cleonae of the massy tower and Thyrea fated one day to harvest Spartan blood. With them go the men who sow the rocks of Drepanum and the fields of olive-bearing Sicyon, mindful of the king whom they originally sent elsewhere,[4] they whom lazy Langia[5] laves with silent flow and Elisson[6] curving through his sinuous banks. A grim honour has that river; with his stern waters he is reputed to wash the Stygian Eumenides. They are wont, 'tis said, to sink their faces therein and the horned snakes that pant from draughts of Phlegethon, whether they have wrecked Thracian dwellings[7] or Mycenae's impious roofs or the house of Cadmus. The river himself flees them as they swim and his pools darken with countless poisons. Along too goes Ephyre, who comforted Ino's plaints,[8] and the bands of Cenchreae, where the stream cognizant of poets was struck out by the Gorgon's horse[9] and where Isthmos lies athwart the deep and repels the sloping seas from land. This band, three thousand strong, follows Adrastus exulting. Some carry pikes, some stakes long hardened in the fire (for each troop has its own fashion, its own blood), some are wont to whirl

6 'Winding.' Hardly to be identified with the scholiast as Ilyssus in Attica (cf. 8.766; 12.631). Where Statius found the connection with the Furies is unknown.

7 Home of Tereus.

8 For Palaemon; see on 9.401–03.

9 'The spring struck out by the hoof of Pegasus was usually placed on Helicon (Hippocrene), but was sometimes identified with Pirene, the fountain at Corinth, cf. *Silvae* 2.7.2' (Mozley). Pegasus, the winged horse, sprang from the head of the Gorgon Medusa, slain by Perseus.

assueti vacuamque diem praecingere gyro.
ipse annis sceptrisque subit venerabilis aeque:
ut possessa diu taurus meat arduus inter
70 pascua iam laxa cervice et inanibus armis,
dux tamen: haud illum bello attemptare iuvencis
sunt animi; nam trunca vident de vulnere multo
cornua et ingentes plagarum in pectore nodos.
    Proxima longaevo profert Dircaeus Adrasto
75 signa gener, cui bella favent, cui commodat iras
cuncta cohors: huic et patria de sede volentes
advenere viri, seu quos movet exsul et haesit
tristibus aucta fides, seu quis mutare potentes
praecipuum, multi, melior quos causa querenti
80 conciliat; dederat nec non socer ipse regendas
Aegion Arenenque, et quas Theseia Troezen
addit opes, ne rara movens inglorius iret
agmina, neu raptos patriae sentiret honores.
idem habitus, eadem arma viro quae debitus hospes
85 hiberna sub nocte tulit: Teumesius implet
terga leo et gemino lucent hastilia ferro,
aspera vulnifico subter latus ense riget Sphinx.
iam regnum matrisque sinus fidasque sorores
spe votisque tenet, tamen et de turre suprema
90 attonitam totoque exstantem corpore longe
respicit Argian; haec mentem oculosque reducit
coniugis et dulces avertit pectore Thebas.

---

vacuoque Pω (*Garrod*)   extantem ω: insta- P

---

[10] Editors keep *vacuo*, which must then be regarded as trans-ferred.

[11] One of the towns known under these names was on the north coast of the Peloponnese, the other in Messene. There is no

210

rounded slings and gird the empty[10] sky with a circle. He himself joins them, venerable alike in years and sceptre, like a bull moving tall among the pastures he has long possessed; his neck is slack now and his shoulders empty, but still he is the leader; the steers have no stomach to attempt him in battle, for they see his horns broken from many a blow and the massive nodules of breast wounds.

Next to aged Adrastus his Dircaean son-in-law displays his standards, he in whose support they fight, to whom the whole army lends its wrath. To him come also volunteers from his native land. Some the exile moves and their loyalty has held, strengthened by misfortune, some chiefly want a change of ruler, many are won to his complaint by his better cause. Moreover, his father-in-law himself had given him Aegion and Arene[11] to rule and the power that Theseus' Troezen[12] brings, lest he march inglorious leading a scanty force and be conscious of his country's ravished honours. His dress and arms were those he wore as a destined guest that winter's night. A Teumesian lion fills his back and the points of two javelins gleam. At his side a threatening Sphinx sits rigid on his wound-dealing sword. Already in hope and prayer he possesses his realm and his mother's bosom and his faithful sisters, yet looks far back to Argia as she stands out with all her body from a turret-edge distraught. She calls back her husband's mind and eyes and turns sweet Thebes from his heart.

evidence for places so named in Argolis. The scholiast calls them cities of Arcadia. How Adrastus came to dispose of their contingents is not clear, but his reason might be to give his son-in-law a show of independence.

[12] Birthplace of Theseus, where his maternal grandfather Pittheus was king.

Ecce inter medios patriae ciet agmina gentis
fulmineus Tydeus, iam laetus et integer artus,
95   ut primae strepuere tubae: ceu lubricus alta
anguis humo verni blanda ad spiramina solis
erigitur liber senio et squalentibus annis
exutus laetisque minax interviret herbis:
a miser, agrestum si quis per gramina hianti
100   obvius et primo fraudaverit ora veneno.
huic quoque praesentes Aetolis urbibus affert
belli fama viros: sensit scopulosa Pylene
fletaque cognatis avibus Meleagria Pleuron
et praeceps Calydon et quae Iove provocat Iden
105   Olenos Ioniis et fluctibus hospita portu
Chalcis et Herculea turpatus gymnade vultus
amnis; adhuc imis vix truncam attollere frontem
ausus aquis glaucoque caput summersus in antro
maeret, anhelantes aegrescunt pulvere ripae.
110   omnibus aeratae propugnant pectora crates,
pilaque saeva manu; patrius stat casside Mavors.
undique magnanimum pubes delecta coronant
Oeniden, hilarem bello noctisque decorum
vulneribus; non ille minis Polynicis et ira
115   inferior, dubiumque adeo cui bella gerantur.
     Maior at inde novis it Doricus ordo sub armis:

---

[100] fraudaverit P: sicca- ωΣ   [101] praesentes P: -stantes ω
[113] notisque Pω (ς, *Jortin*)

---

[13] Meleager's sisters wept for him until Diana turned them
into birds called Meleagrides (guinea fowl).

See, bolt-like Tydeus in the midst rouses the hosts of his countrymen, happy now and sound of body, as the first trumpets bray; like a slippery snake rising at the coaxing breath of vernal sunshine from deep earth, free of mould and stripped of musty years—a green threat among the lush grasses; woe to the rustic who comes in his way as he gapes in the herbage to rob his fangs of their first venom. For Tydeus too rumour of war brings warriors to aid from Aetolia's cities. Rocky Pylene heard and Meleager's Pleuron bewept by sister birds[13] and steep Calydon and Olenos, who challenges Ida with her Jupiter,[14] and Chalcis[15] that with her haven hosts the Ionian waves, and the river whose face was marred by wrestling Heracles;[16] even now he scarce dares to lift his mutilated brow from the watery depths and glooms with head sunk in his green cavern, while his banks pant and sicken with dust. The breasts of all are protected by wicker shields covered with bronze, they carry fierce pikes and their country's[17] Mars stands on their helmets. On all sides a chosen band surrounds the great-hearted son of Oeneus, cheerful for the fray and decorated with the night's scars. Equal he in threat and wrath to Polynices; 'tis doubtful for whom the war is waged.

But mightier after these comes the Doric rank, newly

[14] Apparently conflated with Olenos in Achaea, where the goat Amalthea was said to have fostered Jupiter.

[15] In Aetolia. *Chalcide* should probably be retained after all in *Silv.* 5.3.155.

[16] Achelous, who lost a horn wrestling with Hercules.

[17] Father of the eponymous Aetolus. Oeneus and Tydeus are both credited with his paternity.

qui ripas, Lyrcee, tuas, tua litora multo
vomere suspendunt, fluviorum ductor Achivum,
Inache (Persea neque enim violentior exit
120 amnis humo, cum Taurum aut Pliadas hausit aquosas
spumeus et genero tumuit Iove); quos celer ambit
Asterion Dryopumque trahens Erasinus aristas;
et qui rura domant Epidauria (dexter Iaccho
collis at Hennaeae Cereri negat); avia Dyme
125 mittit opem densasque Pylos Neleia turmas
(nondum nota Pylos iuvenisque aetate secunda
Nestor, et ire tamen peritura in castra negavit).
hos agitat pulchraeque docet virtutis amorem
arduus Hippomedon; capiti tremit aerea cassis
130 ter niveum scandente iuba, latus omne sub armis
ferrea suta terunt, umeros ac pectora late
flammeus orbis habet, perfectaque vivit in auro
nox Danai: sontes Furiarum lampade nigra
quinquaginta ardent thalami; pater ipse cruentis
135 in foribus laudatque nefas atque inspicit enses.
illum Palladia sonipes Nemeaeus ab arce
devehit arma pavens umbraque immane volanti
implet agros longoque attollit pulvere campum.
non aliter silvas umeris et utroque refringens
140 pectore montano duplex Hylaeus ab antro

---

18 The constellation of the Bull, which included the group of
stars called Hyades, supposed to bring rain.

19 Jupiter had seduced Inachus' daughter Io. His name can
signify rain, as Bacchus wine or Ceres bread.

20 They produce wine but no corn.

21 Another geographical oddity. From Argolis and the neighbouring Epidaurus the spotlight shifts to Dyme and Pylos, respec-

armed; they that lift your bank, Lyrceus, with many a ploughshare and your shores, Inachus, leader of Achaean streams (for no rougher river comes out of Persean soil when he has drunk of Taurus[18] or the watery Pleiades and foams and swells with Jupiter, his son-in-law[19]); they that swift Asterion encircles and Erasinus with Dryopian harvests in tow, and they that till the Epidaurian fields (kind to Iacchus is the hill, but Ceres of Henna is refused);[20] distant Dyme sends aid and Neleian Pylos[21] her dense squadrons—not yet is Pylos famous, Nestor is still young in his second period,[22] but he refused to join a doomed army. These tall Hippomedon moves and teaches them the love of beauteous valour. On his head sways a brazen helm with triply-climbing snowy plume,[23] iron mail chafes all his flanks beneath his shield, a fiery circle amply covers shoulders and breasts and the night of Danaus lives chased upon the gold; fifty guilty marriage chambers blaze with the darkling torch of the Furies and the father himself in the bloodstained doorway lauds the crime and scrutinizes the swords. A Nemean steed carries him down from Pallas' citadel,[24] fearing his arms, and fills the fields with a monstrous flying shadow, raising the plain with a long trail of dust. Not otherwise does double Hylaeus hurtle from his mountain cave, breaking the woods with his shoulders and

tively on the northwest and southwest coasts of the Peloponnese. The former was a well-known town, the latter famous (cf. on 224). Hippomedon was an Argive.

[22] Nestor lived for three *saecla* (generations, but sometimes understood as centuries).   [23] The text has been queried. Exactly what it means is doubtful; cf. Dodds on Euripides, *Bacchae* 123 (Hill).   [24] In Argos.

praecipitat: pavet Ossa vias, pecudesque feraeque
procubuere metu; non ipsis fratribus horror
afuit, ingenti donec Peneia saltu
stagna subit magnumque obiectus detinet amnem.
145   Quis numerum ferri gentesque et robora dictu
aequarit mortale sonans? suus excit in arma
antiquam Tiryntha deus; non fortibus illa
infecunda viris famave immanis alumni
degenerat, sed lapsa situ fortuna, neque addunt
150 robur opes; rarus vacuis habitator in arvis
monstrat Cyclopum ductas sudoribus arces.
dat tamen haec iuvenum ter centum pectora, vulgus
innumerum bello, quibus haud ammenta nec enses
triste micant: flavae capiti tergoque leonum
155 exuviae, gentilis honos; et pineus armat
stipes, inexhaustis artantur tela pharetris.
Herculeum paeana canunt vastataque monstris
omnia; frondosa longum deus audit ab Oeta.
dat Nemea comites, et quas in proelia vires
160 sacra Cleonaei cogunt vineta Molorchi.
gloria nota casae, foribus simulata salignis
hospitis arma dei, parvoque ostenditur arvo
robur ubi et laxos qua reclinaverit arcus
ilice, qua cubiti sedeant vestigia terra.
165   At pedes et toto despectans vertice bellum
quattuor indomitis Capaneus erepta iuvencis
terga superque rigens iniectu molis aënae
versat onus; squalet triplici ramosa corona
Hydra recens obitu: pars anguibus aspera vivis
170 argento caelata micat, pars arte reperta

twofold breast; Ossa dreads his path, cattle and wild beasts fall down in terror; even his brothers are not without fear, until with a mighty leap he reaches Peneus' pools and dams the great river with his bulk.

Who of mortal voice could match in words the quantity of steel, the peoples, and the might? Ancient Tiryns is roused to arms by her god.[25] Not barren is she of brave men nor degenerate from the fame of her huge son, but her fortune has sunk in decay and wealth adds not its power. A rare dweller in the empty fields points to the towers raised by Cyclopes'[26] sweat. Yet she gives three hundred warrior hearts, for war a countless multitude. No javelin straps have they or swords flashing bale. On head and back they carry yellow lionskins, their national ornament, and pine staves arm them, arrows cram their inexhaustible quivers. They sing the paean of Hercules and a world cleared of monsters; far away from leafy Oeta the god hears. Nemea gives comrades, as do the hallowed vineyards of Cleonaean Molorchus the strength they gather for battle. Famous is the glory of the cottage, the guest god's arms are portrayed on its willow doors and in the little field is shown the holm oak on which he leaned his club and loosened bow, the ground where sit the marks of his elbow.

Capaneus goes on foot looking down upon the war by a whole head. He bears four hides stripped from unbroken steers and piled thereon the stiff weight of a brazen mass. The foul Hydra lies newly slain branching with triple crown. Part flashes rough with live snakes, chased in silver;

[25] Hercules.
[26] Cf. 1.252.

conditur et fulvo moriens nigrescit in auro;
circum amnis torpens et ferro caerula Lerna.
at laterum tractus spatiosaque pectora servat
nexilis innumero Chalybum subtemine thorax,
175 horrendum, non matris, opus; galeaeque corusca
prominet arce Gigans; atque uni missilis illi
cuspide praefixa stat frondibus orba cupressus.
huic parere dati quos fertilis Amphigenia
planaque Messene montosaque nutrit Ithome,
180 quos Thryon et summis ingestum montibus Aepy,
quos Helos et Pteleon, Getico quos flebile vati
Dorion; hic fretus doctas anteire canendo
Aonidas mutos Thamyris damnatus in annos
ore simul citharaque (quis obvia numina temnat?)
185 conticuit praeceps, qui non certamina Phoebi
nosset et illustres Satyro pendente Celaenas.
    Iamque et fatidici mens expugnata fatiscit
auguris; ille quidem casus et dira videbat
signa, sed ipsa manu cunctanti iniecerat arma
190 Atropos obrueratque deum, nec coniugis absunt
insidiae, vetitoque domus iam fulgurat auro.
hoc aurum vati Fata exitiale monebant
Argolico; scit et ipsa (nefas!), sed perfida coniunx
dona viro mutare velit, spoliisque potentis
195 imminet Argiae raptoque excellere cultu.
illa libens (nam regum animos et pondera belli
hac nutare videt, pariter si providus heros

193 ipse Pω (ς, *Sandstroem*)
197 ni *vel* nisi ψ

part is hidden with a skill newly discovered[27] and dying darkens in tawny gold. Around is the sluggish river and Lerna dark blue in steel. But his spacious flanks and broad breast are guarded by a corselet woven of countless iron threads, a thing of fear, no mother's work. From the helmet's coruscating peak rises a Giant. A cypress stands bereft of foliage with point attached, none but he can throw it. To his obedience are given they that fertile Amphigenia nurtures and flat Messene and mountainous Ithome, likewise Thryon and Aepy piled on its hilltop and Helos and Pteleon and Dorion weeping for the Getic bard. Here Thamyris, who trusted to surpass the skilled daughters of Aonia in song, was condemned to silent years. His voice and lyre fell suddenly mute, for who should scorn deities to their face? He knew not of Phoebus' contest and Celaenae famed for the hanging Satyr.[28]

And now the fate-speaking augur's resolve wilts perforce. To be sure he sees the event, the dire signs, but Atropos herself had put arms into his doubting hand and overwhelmed the god.[29] Nor is his wife's treachery lacking, and already his house flares with forbidden gold. This gold the Fates warned would bring destruction to the Argive seer. Herself she knows it (ah, crime!), but the faithless spouse would fain barter her husband for a gift and covets the spoils of powerful Argia, wishful to shine in stolen finery. Cheerfully Argia (for she sees that if the prescient hero take the field with the rest, the minds of kings and the

[27] By Hercules when he cauterized the Hydra's heads (Housman, 1203).

[28] Marsyas, hung up to be flayed.

[29] Apollo, i.e. the gift of prophecy.

militet) ipsa sacros gremio Polynicis amati
deposuit nexus haud maesta atque insuper addit:
200 'non haec apta mihi nitidis ornatibus,' inquit,
'tempora, nec miserae placeant insignia formae
te sine: sat dubium coetu solante timorem
fallere et incultos aris adverrere crines.
scilicet (infandum!), cum tu claudare minanti
205 casside ferratusque sones, ego divitis aurum
Harmoniae dotale geram? dabit aptius isto
Fors decus, Argolicasque habitu praestabo maritas,
cum regis coniunx, cum te mihi sospite templa
votivis implenda choris; nunc induat illa
210 quae petit et bellante potest gaudere marito.'
sic Eriphylaeos aurum fatale penates
irrupit scelerumque ingentia semina movit,
et grave Tisiphone risit gavisa futuris.
    Taenariis hic celsus equis, quam dispare coetu
215 Cyllarus ignaro generarat Castore prolem,
quassat humum; vatem cultu Parnasia monstrant
vellera: frondenti crinitur cassis oliva
albaque puniceas interplicat infula cristas.
arma simul pressasque iugo moderatur habenas.
220 hinc atque inde morae iaculis, et ferrea curru
silva tremit; procul ipse gravi metuendus in hasta
eminet et clipeo victum Pythona coruscat.

199 deposuit nexus ω: exuerat cultus P
203 advertere ω: avert- P (*Eutyches, GLK 5.482.7*)
204 infandum P: heu superi ω
206 aptior isto (ista ω) . . . deus Pω (*Zander*)
219 pressas Pψ: prensas ω

scales of war sway this way) herself put the accursed chain in the bosom of her beloved Polynices nothing loath, and adds to boot: 'These times suit not bright ornaments for me, nor should I take pleasure in decking unhappy beauty without you. Enough to cheat my doubt and fear with consoling company and sweep my undressed hair at the altars. Should I—abominable thought!—wear rich Harmonia's golden dower while you are cased in threatening helm and clank in steel? Fortune shall give me more timely[30] ornament than this and my habit shall outshine Argos' brides when I am a king's consort and with you preserved to me the temples must be filled with votive choirs. For now let her put it on who seeks it and can be merry with her husband at the wars.' So the fatal gold invaded Eriphyle's dwelling and set moving mighty seeds of crime. Tisiphone smiled grimly, rejoicing in the future.

Aloft above Taenarian horses, offspring begot by Cyllarus in an unequal union unbeknown to Castor, he shakes the ground. Parnassian wool adorns him, marking the prophet. His helmet is wreathed with leafy olive and a white fillet twines in the scarlet plume. He handles at once his arms and the reins pressed down upon the yoke. On either side are slots[31] for darts and an iron forest quivers in the car. Himself towers far seen with his weighty spear and flashes vanquished Python upon his shield. Apollo's

[30] Lit. 'more appropriate.'
[31] Lit. 'delays.' The meaning is not certain.

huius Apollineae currum comitantur Amyclae,
quos Pylos et dubiis Malea vitata carinis
225 plaudentique habiles Caryae resonare Dianae,
quos Pharis volucrumque parens Cythereia Messe,
Taygetique phalanx et oloriferi Eurotae
dura manus. deus ipse viros in pulvere crudo
Arcas alit nudaeque modos virtutis et iras
230 ingenerat; vigor inde animis et mortis honorae
dulce sacrum. gaudent natorum fata parentes
hortanturque mori; deflent namque omnis ephebum
turba, coronato contenta est funere mater.
frena tenent duplexque inserto missile nodo,
235 exserti ingentes umeros, chlamys horrida pendet,
et cono Ledaeus apex. non hi tibi solum,
Amphiaraë, merent: auget resupina maniplos
Elis, depressae populus subit incola Pisae,
qui te flave natant terris Alphee Sicanis,
240 advena tam longo non umquam infecte profundo.
curribus innumeris late putria arva lacessunt
et bellis armenta domant: ea gloria genti
infando de more et fractis durat ab usque
axibus Oenomai; strident spumantia morsu
245 vincula et effossas niveus rigat imber harenas.
      Tu quoque Parrhasias ignara matre catervas

224 Helos *Kohlman* (*vide quae annotavi*)
232 iamque Pω (*Damsté*)

---

32 Pylos has already occurred in 125, where it does not seem to belong. Here too it is out of place. The conjecture *Helos* (in Laconia, distinct from Messenian Helos in 181) is supported by

Amyclae follows his chariot, and Pylos,[32] and Malea shunned by timorous keels, and Caryae skilled to make music to Diana's applause[33] and Pharis and Cytherean Messe, parent of birds, likewise the phalanx of Taygetus and the tough band of swanny Eurotas. The Arcadian god[34] himself nurtures the warriors in the raw dust, implanting the fashions and furies of naked valour. Hence vigour to their spirit and the sweet rite of an honourable death. Parents rejoice at their children's fate and urge them to die; for all the multitude weep for a youth, while his mother is content with his wreathed corpse. Reins they hold and two javelins knotted together; their massive shoulders are bare, a rough cloak hangs down and Leda's crest[35] is on their helmets. Not they alone, Amphiaraus, serve under you. Sloping Elis swells your troops and the folk of low-lying Pisa come forward who swim in yellow Alpheos— arrival in Sicanian lands, never tainted by the long seaway. With chariots beyond count they churn their crumbling fields far and wide and tame horses for war. That glory has endured for the breed from Oenomaus' abominable custom and his broken axles. The foaming bits rattle with the bites and a snowy shower bedews the hollowed earth.

You also, Parthenopaeus, unknown to your mother

a mention after Amyclae in the Homeric catalogue (*Iliad* 2.584) and by the context here. On the other hand the Pylians are in Amphiaraus' following in 8.365. Adding to the embarrassment is the absence of a verb (like *nutrit* in 179) to govern *quos*, leading Lachmann to suggest that a line has fallen out after 225.

[33] Diana had a temple there with annual dances in her honour.

[34] Mercury, patron of gymnastics.

[35] Of swan's feathers.

(a rudis armorum, tantum nova gloria suadet!),
Parthenopaee, rapis; saltus tunc forte remotos
torva parens (neque enim haec iuveni foret ire potestas)
250 pacabat cornu gelidique aversa Lycaei.
pulchrior haud ulli triste ad discrimen ituro
vultus et egregiae tanta indulgentia formae;
nec desunt animi, veniat modo fortior aetas.
quas non ille duces nemorum fluviisque dicata
255 numina, quas magno non abstulit igne Napaeas?
ipsam, Maenalia puerum cum vidit in umbra,
Dianam, tenero signantem gramina passu,
ignovisse ferunt comiti, Dictaeaque tela
ipsam et Amyclaeas umeris aptasse pharetras.
260 prosilit audaci Martis percussus amore,
arma, tubas audire calens et pulvere belli
flaventem sordere comam captoque referri
hostis equo: taedet nemorum, titulumque nocentem
sanguinis humani pudor est nescire sagittas.
265 igneus ante omnes auro micat, igneus ostro,
undantemque sinum nodis irrugat Hiberis,
imbelli parma pictus Calydonia matris
proelia; trux laeva sonat arcus, et aspera plumis
terga Cydonea gorytos harundine pulsat
270 electro pallens et iaspide clarus Eoa.
cornipedem trepidos suetum praevertere cervos,
velatum geminae deiectu lyncis et arma
mirantem gravioris heri, sublimis agebat,
dulce rubens viridique genas spectabilis aevo.

247 annorum Pω (ς)   255 abstulit P: impu- ω

36 His mother Atalanta.

sweep onward Parrhasian squadrons—a novice in arms,
alas; so potent the love of untasted glory. Your stern parent,
as it fell out, was pacifying distant glades with her bow on
the far side of chill Lycaeus—but for that the youth could
not have gone. No fairer face would go forth to grim peril,
no peerless form so much favoured. Nor does he want for
courage, only let come robuster years. What woodland
princesses and spirits to rivers dedicate did he not sweep
away with burning passion, what Nymphs of the dell?
Diana herself, they say, when she saw the lad tracing
his tender steps on the grass in Maenalus' shade, forgave
her companion,[36] and herself fitted Dictaean shafts and
Amyclaean quiver to his shoulders. Forth he dashes, smitten by Mars' audacious ardour, burning to hear arms and
trumpets and soil his yellow hair with the dust of battle and
return on a foeman's captured horse. He is weary of the
woods and ashamed that his arrows know not the guilty
glory of human blood. Flaming with gold he flashes foremost, flaming with purple, creasing the folds of his robe
with Iberian[37] knots. On his fledgling shield are painted his
mother's Calydonian combats.[38] At his left side rattles his
bold bow, his back is rough with feathers[39] and struck by
Cydonian shafts in a quiver pale with electrum and bright
with eastern jasper. Aloft he rode a charger[40] wont to out-
speed the panicked deer, covered with two lynx hides, now
marvelling at the arms of a weightier master. His comely
flush and the freshness of youth upon his cheeks drew all

[37] Of metal mined in Spain. Whether this refers to a cuirass or
a belt is doubtful.　　[38] The boar hunt.

[39] Little pieces of metal making a corselet; cf. 11.543.

[40] Lit. 'horn-foot,' as often.

225

275 Arcades huic veteres, astris lunaque priores,
   agmina fida datis, nemorum quos stirpe rigenti
   fama satos, cum prima pedum vestigia tellus
   admirata tulit; nondum arva domusque nec urbes,
   conubiisve modus; quercus laurique ferebant
280 cruda puerperia, ac populos umbrosa creavit
   fraxinus, et feta viridis puer excidit orno.
   hi lucis stupuisse vices noctisque feruntur
   nubila et occiduum longe Titana secuti
   desperasse diem. rarescunt alta colonis
285 Maenala, Parthenium fugitur nemus, agmina bello
   Rhipeque et Stratie ventosaque donat Enispe.
   non Tegea, non ipsa deo vacat alite felix
   Cyllene templumque Aleae nemorale Minervae
   et rapidus Clitor et qui tibi, Pythie, Ladon
290 paene socer candensque iugis Lampia nivosis
   et Pheneos nigro Styga mittere credita Diti.
   venit et Idaeis ululatibus aemulus Azan
   Parrhasiique duces, et quae risistis, Amores,
   grata pharetrato Nonacria rura Tonanti,
295 dives et Orchomenos pecorum et Cynosura ferarum.
   Aepytios idem ardor agros Psophidaque celsam
   vastat et Herculeo vulgatos robore montes,
   monstriferumque Erymanthon et aerisonum Stymphalon.
   Arcades hi, gens una viris, sed dissona cultu
300 scinditur: hi Paphias myrtos a stirpe recurvant
   et pastorali meditantur proelia trunco,
   his arcus, his tela sudes, hic casside crines

302 hic casside ω: his cassida P

eyes. To him the Arcadians, an old race earlier than stars and moon, give loyal troops. They were born, as legend tells, from the stiff forest trees when the astonished earth first felt the print of feet. Not yet were there fields and houses or cities or marriage rules. Oaks and laurels bore stout offspring, the shady ash created peoples, a vigorous boy dropped from the pregnant rowan. 'Tis said the changes of the light and the darkness of night astounded them and that following the setting Titan from afar they despaired of day. Lofty Maenalus is thinned of husbandmen, the Parthenian forest is deserted, Rhipe and Stratie and windy Enispe give troops for the war. Tegea stands not idle, nor Cyllene herself, happy in her winged god, nor Aleae, forest shrine of Minerva, and swift Clitor and Ladon,[41] almost father of the Pythian's bride, and Lampia, white on her snowy ridges, and Pheneos, believed to send Styx to dusky Dis. Azan came, rivalling the howls of Ida,[42] and the Parrhasian chiefs and the Nonacrian countryside pleasant to the quiver-bearing Thunderer[43] (the Loves laughed), and Orchomenos rich in cattle and Cynosura in wild beasts. The same impulse denudes Aepytus' fields and lofty Psophis and mountains famed for Hercules' club—monster-bearing Erymanthus and bronze-sounding Stymphalos.[44] Arcadians are these, one race of men but divided in their habit. Some bend Paphian myrtles back from the root and practise battles with shepherds' staves, some are armed with bows, some with stakes. One covers his hair

---

[41] River, father of Daphne.   [42] I.e. of Cybele's votaries.

[43] Where he seduced Callisto disguised as Diana.

[44] Hercules frightened the monster-birds there with a bronze rattle.

integit, Arcadii morem tenet ille galeri,
ille Lycaoniae rictu caput asperat ursae.
305　hos belli coetus iurataque pectora Marti
militе vicinae nullo iuvere Mycenae;
funereae tunc namque dapes mediique recursus
Solis, et hic alii miscebant proelia fratres.
　　Iamque Atalantaeas implerat nuntius aures
310　ire ducem bello totamque impellere natum
Arcadiam: tremuere gradus, elapsaque iuxta
tela; fugit silvas pernicior alite vento
saxa per et plenis obstantia flumina ripis,
qualis erat, correpta sinus et vertice flavum
315　crinem sparsa Noto; raptis velut aspera natis
praedatoris equi sequitur vestigia tigris.
ut stetit adversisque impegit pectora frenis
(ille ad humum pallens): 'unde haec furibunda cupido,
nate, tibi, teneroque unde improba pectore virtus?
320　tu bellis aptare viros, tu pondera ferre
Martis et ensiferas inter potes ire catervas?
quamquam ubinam vires? nuper te pallida vidi,
dum premis obnixo venabula comminus apro,
poplite succiduo resupinum ac paene ruentem;
325　et ni curvato torsissem spicula cornu,
nunc ubi bella tibi? nil te mea tela iuvabunt
nec teretes arcus maculis nec discolor atris
hic, cui fidis, equus; magnis conatibus instas,
vix Dryadum thalamis Erymanthiadumque furori

308–43 *manu recentiore suppl. in* P
322 utinam ω (*SB*)　　quires *Postgate*

---

45 Callisto, daughter of Lycaon, was turned into a bear.

with a helmet, another holds to the old-style Arcadian hat,
yet another makes his head rugged with the gaping jaws of
a Lycaonian bear.[45] These warlike gatherings, these hearts
sworn to Mars were not helped by neighbouring Mycenae
with any soldiers. For then was the deadly banquet and
the sun's midday retreat, there too other brothers joined
battle.[46]

Now the news had filled Atalanta's ears, that her son
was going a captain to war and moving all Arcadia. Her
steps tottered, her weapon fell by her side. Swifter than
winged wind she flees the forest over rocks and rivers
that blocked her way with brimming banks, just as she
was, her robe girt up, the yellow hair on her head scattering in the breeze, as an angry tigress bereft of her cubs
follows the tracks of the robber horse. Anon she halts
and thrusts her bosom against his bridle (he pale and
downcast):[47] 'Whence this mad desire, my son? Whence
this unconscionable valour in your youthful breast? Can
you train men for war? Can you bear the burdens of Mars
and move among sword-bearing squadrons? But where
the strength? Only lately I turned pale to see you pressing
your hunting spear against a thrusting boar in close combat, forced back upon bent knee and near collapse; and if I
had not shot an arrow from my curving bow, where would
your war be now? My shafts will not avail you nor the
smooth bow nor this piebald horse with the black spots, in
whom you trust. You embark on a great enterprise, a boy
scarce ripe for the chambers of Dryads and the passion of

---

[46] See Atreus in Index. Mycenae was in Argolis, well to the east
of Arcadia.   [47] Readers are left to assume that Atalanta
found her son in the 'Greek' camp.

330 Nympharum mature puer. sunt omina vera:
     mirabar cur templa mihi tremuisse Dianae
     nuper et inferior vultu dea visa, sacrisque
     exuviae cecidere tholis; hoc segnior arcus
     difficilesque manus et nullo in vulnere certae.
335 exspecta dum maior honos, dum firmius aevum,
     dum roseis venit umbra genis vultusque recedunt
     ore mei; tunc bella tibi ferrumque, quod ardes,
     ipsa dabo et nullo matris revocabere fletu.
     nunc refer arma domum! vos autem hunc ire sinetis,
340 Arcades, o saxis nimirum et robore nati?'
     plura cupit; fusi circum natusque ducesque
     solantur minuuntque metus, et iam horrida clangunt
     signa tubae. nequit illa pio dimittere natum
     complexu multumque duci commendat Adrasto.
345   At parte ex alia Cadmi Mavortia plebes,
     maesta ducis furiis nec molli territa fama,
     quando his vulgatum descendere viribus Argos,
     tardius illa quidem regis causaeque pudore,
     verum bella movet. nulli destringere ferrum
350 impetus aut umeros clipeo clausisse paterno
     dulce nec alipedum iuga comere, qualia belli
     gaudia; deiecti trepidas sine mente, sine ira
     promisere manus; hic aegra in sorte parentem
     unanimum, hic dulces primaevae coniugis annos
355 ingemit et gremio miseros accrescere natos.
     bellator nulli caluit deus; ipsa vetusto
     moenia lapsa situ magnaeque Amphionis arces

Erymanthian Nymphs. Omens tell true. I marvelled why of late Diana's temple seemed to me to tremble and the goddess herself had a look of the underworld[48] and why spoils fell from her sacred dome. 'Twas this that slackened my bow and made my hands clumsy, unsure in every stroke. Wait till your dignity be greater, your age stouter, till shadow comes to your rosy cheeks and my face leaves yours. Then myself shall give you war and the steel you burn for and no mother's tears shall call you back. For now bring your arms back home. And you Arcadians, surely born of rocks and timber, shall you let him go?' She would say more, but around her in a throng her son and the leaders comfort her and allay her fears. And now the harsh trumpet-signals bray. She cannot let her son leave her fond embrace and much she commends him to king Adrastus.

In another quarter the Martian people of Cadmus, dismayed by the king's madness and alarmed by grievous report—it was bruited abroad that Argos was about to come down in this strength—slowly to be sure for shame of the ruler and the cause but all the same, make ready for war. None was impatient to draw the sword nor were they happy to cover their shoulders with paternal shield or to groom paired horses—war's joys. Downcast, they put forward nervous hands, without commitment, without anger. One grieves for a loving parent in sad case, another for a young wife's beguiling years and the poor offspring growing in her womb. For none did the warrior god wax warm. Even the walls have crumbled with ancient neglect. Amphion's great towers lay bare flanks worn and decayed.

---

[48] I.e. of Hecate, her underworld self, as suggested by Håkanson. Lit. 'lower in countenance.'

iam fessum senio nudant latus, et fide sacra
aequatos caelo surdum atque ignobile muros
360 firmat opus. tamen et Boeotis urbibus ultrix
aspirat ferri rabies, nec regis iniqui
subsidio quantum socia pro gente moventur.
ille velut pecoris lupus expugnator opimi,
pectora tabenti sanie gravis hirtaque saetis
365 ora cruentata deformis hiantia lana,
decedit stabulis huc illuc turbida versans
lumina, si duri comperta clade sequantur
pastores, magnique fugit non inscius ausi.
      Accumulat crebros turbatrix Fama pavores:
370 hic iam dispersos errare Asopide ripa
Lernaeos equites, hic te, bacchate Cithaeron,
ille rapi Teumeson ait noctisque per umbras
nuntiat excubiis vigiles arsisse Plataeas.
nam Tyrios sudare lares et sanguine Dircen
375 irriguam fetusque novos iterumque locutam
Sphinga petris, cui non et scire licentia passim
et vidisse fuit? novus his super anxia turbat
corda metus: sparsis subito correpta canistris
silvestris regina chori decurrit in aequum
380 vertice ab Ogygio trifidamque huc tristis et illuc
lumine sanguineo pinum disiectat et ardens
erectam attonitis implet clamoribus urbem:
'omnipotens Nysaee pater, cui gentis avitae
pridem lapsus amor, tu nunc horrente sub Arcto
385 bellica ferrato rapidus quatis Ismara thyrso
pampineumque iubes nemus irreptare Lycurgo,

---

49 'Someone had seen from a distance the watchfire burning in
Plataeae, a Boeotian town properly on the alert, and came along

BOOK 4

Mute ignoble toil strengthens the ramparts that the sacred lyre once levelled with heaven. And yet avenging lust for battle breathes also on the cities of Boeotia; they are moved not so much to aid the unjust monarch as on behalf of an allied folk. *He* is like a wolf that has stormed a fat sheepfold; his chest is heavy with rotting gore, the gaping bristly mouth ugly with bloodstained wool; leaving the pens, he turns uneasy glances this way and that to see whether the hardy shepherds have discovered the disaster and follow; conscious of great audacity, he flees.

Bustling Rumour piles scare on scare. One says that Lernaean horsemen are already scattered abroad on the bank of Asopos. Another tells of Cithaeron, haunt of Bacchanals, captured, of Teumesos another, and reports Plataeae, with her sentries watchful through the dark night, afire.[49] For who, wherever he might be, had not licence to know and be eyewitness to Tyrian household gods sweating, Dirce running blood, strange births, and the Sphinx speaking again among her rocks? Above all this, new terror troubles their anxious hearts: the queen of the woodland choir[50] is suddenly caught up; scattering the baskets, she runs down from the Ogygian summit into the plain and grimly with bloodshot eyes waves her triple pine to and fro, in her passion filling the startled city with frenzied cries: 'Nysaean father almighty, you have long since shed your love for your ancestral people. Now under the shivering Bear you run with iron-tipped wand shaking warlike Ismara and command the vine-clad forest to creep

with a report that the Argives had captured the place and set it on fire' (SB[1]).

[50] Leader of the Bacchanals.

233

aut tumidum Gangen aut claustra novissima Rubrae
Tethyos Eoasque domos flagrante triumpho
perfuris, aut Hermi de fontibus aureus exis:
390   at tua progenies, positis gentilibus armis
quae tibi festa litant, bellum lacrimasque metumque
cognatumque nefas, iniusti munera regni,
pendimus. aeternis potius me, Bacche, pruinis
trans et Amazoniis ululatum Caucason armis
395   siste ferens, quam monstra ducum stirpemque profanam
eloquar. en urgues (alium tibi, Bacche, furorem
iuravi): similes video concurrere tauros;
idem ambobus honos unusque ab origine sanguis;
ardua collatis obnixi cornua miscent
400   frontibus alternaque truces moriuntur in ira.
tu peior, tu cede, nocens qui solus avita
gramina communemque petis defendere montem.
a miseri morum! bellastis sanguine tanto
et saltum dux alter habet.' sic fata gelatis
405   vultibus et Baccho iam demigrante quievit.
    At trepidus monstro et variis terroribus impar
longaevi rex vatis opem tenebrasque sagaces
Tiresiae, qui mos incerta paventibus, aeger
consulit. ille deos non larga caede iuvencum,
410   non alacri penna aut verum salientibus extis,
nec tripode implicito numerisque sequentibus astra,
turea nec supra volitante altaria fumo
tam penitus, durae quam Mortis limite manes
elicitos, patuisse refert; Lethaeaque sacra

---

410 salientibus P *ante corr.*: spiran -ω

---

51 Red Sea = Persian Gulf.

over Lycurgus; or you rage in blazing triumph by swollen
Ganges or the furthest limits of Red Tethys[51] and the lands
of morning, or emerge all golden from Hermus' springs.[52]
But we your children, laying aside the weapons of our
nation[53] that do you festal worship, suffer war and tears
and terror and kindred crime, gifts of a wrongful reign.
Carry me, Bacchus, and set me among the everlasting
frosts beyond Caucasos where Amazonian armies howl,
rather than that I should tell of monstrous acts of rulers
and a brood unhallowed. Lo, you drive me. Not this the
madness I swore to you, Bacchus. I see a pair of bulls clash;
both handsome, with one blood of origin. They lock lofty
horns butting head to head and fiercely die in mutual
wrath. You are the worse; give way, you sinner, you that
seek to defend alone hereditary pasture and common hill.
Woe on your ways! So much bloodshed in your warring and
another chief holds the meadow!' So she spoke, and as
Bacchus withdrew, her face froze to rest.

Alarmed by the portent and unequal to the various
terrors, sick at heart the king asks counsel and help of the
aged seer, the wise blindness of Tiresias, as was the wont of
those fearing the unknown. He says the gods do not so
thoroughly reveal themselves by lavish slaughter of steers
or swift pinnion or entrails leaping to show truth or by
riddling tripod or numbers that track the stars, nor yet by
smoke flowing over incense-bearing altars, as do spirits
summoned from the boundary of cruel death.[54] He makes

[52] Hermus was a gold-bearing river.
[53] The Bacchic wands (thyrsi).
[54] The long sentence seems to have plunged off the rails.
Manes elicitos should rather be *manibus elicitis*.

235

415 et mersum Ismeni subter confinia ponto
miscentis parat ante ducem, circumque bidentum
visceribus laceris et odori sulphuris aura
graminibusque novis et longo murmure purgat.
      Silva capax aevi validaque incurva senecta,
420 aeternum intonsae frondis, stat pervia nullis
solibus; haud illam brumae minuere, Notusve
ius habet aut Getica Boreas impactus ab Ursa.
subter operta quies, vacuusque silentia servat
horror et exclusae pallet male lucis imago.
425 nec caret umbra deo: nemori Latonia cultrix
additur; hanc piceae cedrique et robore in omni
effictam sanctis occultat silva tenebris.
huius inaspectae luco stridere sagittae
nocturnique canum gemitus, ubi limina patrui
430 effugit inque novae melior redit ora Dianae;
aut ubi fessa iugis, dulcesque altissima somnos
lux monet, hic late iaculis circum undique fixis
effusam pharetra cervicem excepta quiescit.
extra immane patent, tellus Mavortia, campi,
435 fetus ager Cadmo. durus qui vomere primo
post consanguineas acies sulcosque nocentes
ausus humum versare et mollia sanguine prata

432 monet ψ: movet ω (431–33 *om.* P)
437 mollia P: putria ω

---

55 By way of preliminary purification. *Miscentis = miscentis
se* has very few parallels, none classical, and may be fairly held
against the author.
56 Diana.

ready rites of Lethe and the ruler immersed below the
confines of Ismenos as the river mingles with the sea,[55] and
purifies all around with mangled entrails of sheep and
breath of odorous sulphur and fresh herbs and lengthy in-
cantations.

There stands a wood enduring time, bent by robust old
age, with boughs forever unshorn, that no suns can penetrate. Winters diminished it not, nor does the South Wind
have power over it nor the North hurled down from the
Getic Bear. Beneath is hidden quiet; an empty terror keeps
the silence and a semblance of the light shut out makes an
eerie pallor. Nor does the shade lack its deity; Latonia[56]
frequents it, appendage to the grove. Her image carved in
pine and cedar and every timber is hidden in the forest's
sacred gloom. Her arrows whistle unseen in the wood and
the howling of her dogs is heard by night, when she escapes her uncle's threshold and returns to the countenance
of a new and better Diana;[57] or when she is weary from the
mountains and the sun at his zenith counsels sweet slumber, she here plants her darts all around her and with head
hung back on her receptive quiver takes her repose. Outside is a vast stretch of plain, the land of Mars, the field that
fructified for Cadmus. Hard was he that after the kindred
fray and the guilty furrows first dared till the soil with
ploughshare and dug up the blood-softened[58] meadows!

[57] When she left the underworld for the upper world, Hecate
changed her form, becoming the huntress Diana (Artemis) again;
cf. Lucan 6.736–38.

[58] *Putria* may be right; cf. 444 and 1.437, 3.364. In 454 the
ground is dry.

eruit! ingentes infelix terra tumultus
lucis adhuc medio solaque in nocte per umbras
440 exspirat, nigri cum vana in proelia surgunt
terrigenae; fugit incepto tremibundus ab arvo
agricola insanique domum rediere iuvenci.
    Hic senior vates (Stygiis accommoda quippe
terra sacris, vivoque placent sola pinguia tabo)
445 velleris obscuri pecudes armentaque sisti
atra monet, quaecumque gregum pulcherrima cervix
ducitur. ingemuit Dirce maestusque Cithaeron,
et nova clamosae stupuere silentia valles.
tum fera caeruleis intexit cornua sertis
450 ipse manu tractans, notaeque in limite silvae
principio largos novies tellure cavata
inclinat Bacchi latices et munera verni
lactis et Actaeos imbres suadumque cruorem
manibus; aggeritur quantum bibit arida tellus.
455 trunca dehinc nemora advolvunt, maestusque sacerdos
tres Hecatae totidemque satis Acheronte nefasto
virginibus iubet esse focos; tibi, rector Averni,
quamquam infossus humo superat tamen agger in auras
pineus; hunc iuxta cumulo minor ara profundae
460 erigitur Cereri; frontes atque omne cupressus
intexit plorata latus. iamque ardua ferro
signati capita et frugum libamine puro

444 vivo P: multo ω

---

59 Håkanson takes *adhuc* with *medio*: 'the sense is that the
plain is haunted even in the middle of the day'—forgetting that
the southern noon, like midnight, is preeminently a time for un-
canny powers to be abroad; see Gow on Theocritus 1.15.

238

Even yet at midday[59] or in the shades of lonely night the unlucky soil breathes out mighty tumult when the black sons of earth rise up to phantom combat. The farmer flees trembling from the field he has begun and the steers go back home in frenzy.

Here the aged seer (for well suited is the ground for Stygian rites, the soil fat with living[60] gore is to his liking) gives order that sheep dark of fleece and black herds be stationed, all the finest necks that halter leads. Dirce and sad Cithaeron groaned and the echoing valleys marvelled at the sudden silence. Then with his own hands he twined the fierce horns with garlands dark of hue and at the edge of the familiar wood he first tips lavish draughts of Bacchus into the earth hollowed in nine places and gifts of vernal milk and Attic rain[61] and blood persuasive to spirits. As much as the dry earth will drink is poured. Then they roll up tree trunks and the gloomy priest orders three hearths made for Hecate and as many for the virgin daughters of accursed Acheron.[62] For you, ruler of Avernus, rises into the air a piny mound, though dug into the soil. Next to that is reared an altar of lesser pile to Ceres of the depth.[63] In front and on every side lamented cypress twines. And now the cattle collapse into the strokes, their tall heads marked

---

[60] Cf. 5.162 *in sanguine vivo*. With *tabo*, decayed blood, *vivo* seems abusive, but one is reluctant to accept the commonplace *multo*.   [61] Honey from Mt Hymettus.   [62] The Furies, whose father is Erebus in 11.136 and apparently Pluto in 11.69.

[63] Similarly 5.156 *inferna Ceres*, an odd way of referring to Ceres' daughter (Proserpina), who is often called *Iuno inferna* or the like. Normally in such expressions the name is transferred to a counterpart of the real owner, not just a connection.

in vulnus cecidere greges; tunc innuba Manto
exceptum pateris praelibat sanguen, et omnes
465 ter circum acta pyras sancti de more parentis
semineces fibras et adhuc spirantia reddit
viscera, nec rapidas cunctatur frondibus atris
subiectare faces. atque ipse sonantia flammis
virgulta et tristes crepuisse ut sensit acervos
470 Tiresias (illi nam plurimus ardor anhelat
ante genas impletque cavos vapor igneus orbes)
exclamat (tremuere rogi et vox terruit ignem):
        'Tartareae sedes et formidabile regnum
Mortis inexpletae, tuque, o saevissime fratrum,
475 cui servire dati manes aeternaque sontum
supplicia atque imi famulatur regia mundi,
solvite pulsanti loca muta et inane severae
Persephones vulgusque cava sub nocte repostum
elicite, et plena redeat Styga portitor alno.
480 ferte simul gressus, nec simplex manibus esto
in lucem remeare modus; tu separe coetu
Elysios, Persei, pios, virgaque potenti
nubilus Arcas agat; contra per crimina functis,
qui plures Erebo pluresque e sanguine Cadmi,
485 angue ter excusso et flagranti praevia taxo,
Tisiphone, dux pande diem, nec lucis egentes
Cerberus occursu capitum detorqueat umbras.'
        Dixerat, et pariter senior Phoebeaque virgo
erexere animos; illi formidine nulla,
490 quippe in corde deus; solum timor obruit ingens

<hr>

472 terruit P: impulit ωΣ   490 timor P: tremor ω

<hr>

64 Pluto (Dis, Hades), brother of Jupiter and Neptune.

with steel and pure scattering of meal. Then maiden
Manto makes first libation of blood received in bowls and
moving thrice around all the pyres after the fashion of her
venerable parent offers half-dead fibres and entrails still
alive, nor delays to put consuming torches to the black
leafage. When Tiresias himself perceived the branches
crackling in the flames and the sad piles roaring (for fierce
heat pants before his face and fiery vapour fills his hollow
orbs), he exclaims (the pyres shuddered, his voice terrified
the flame):

'Dwellings of Tartarus, and dread realm of insatiable
Death, and you, cruelest of the brothers,[64] to whom are
given the ghosts to serve you and the eternal punishments
of the guilty, you whom the palace of the lowest world
obeys, open to my knocking the silent places and the void
of stern Persephone. Draw out the multitude laid by in
hollow night and let the ferryman retrace Styx with a full
boat. All step out together; but let the ghosts have more
ways than one of returning to the light. Daughter of
Perses, separate the pious dwellers in Elysium from the
concourse and let the misty Arcadian bring them with
his potent rod; whereas for those who died in crime, in
Erebus a majority and mostly of Cadmus' blood,[65] do you,
Tisiphone, lead the way: open up the day, shaking out your
snakes three times and marching before them with blazing
yew; nor let Cerberus block with his heads and turn aside
the shades that crave the light.'

He spoke. The old man and Phoebus' maiden were all
attention. They had no fear, for the god was in their
breasts. Only the son of Oedipus is overwhelmed by a

[65] An extravagant hyperbole.

Oedipodioniden, vatisque horrenda canentis
nunc umeros nunc ille manus et vellera prensat
anxius inceptisque velit desistere sacris.
qualis Gaetulae stabulantem ad confraga silvae
495 venator longo motum clamore leonem
exspectat firmans animum et sudantia nisu
tela premens; gelat ora pavor gressusque tremescunt,
quis veniat quantusque, sed horrida signa frementis
accipit et caeca metitur murmura cura.
500   Atque hic Tiresias nondum adventantibus umbris:
'testor,' ait, 'divae, quibus hunc saturavimus ignem
laevaque convulsae dedimus carchesia terrae,
iam nequeo tolerare moram. cassusne sacerdos
audior? an, rabido iubeat si Thessala cantu,
505 ibitis? et, Scythicis quotiens medicata venenis
Colchis aget, trepido pallebunt Tartara motu?
nostri cura minor? si non attollere bustis
corpora nec plenas antiquis ossibus urnas
egerere et mixtos caelique Erebique sub unum
510 funestare deos libet aut exsanguia ferro
ora sequi atque aegras functorum carpere fibras,
ne tenues annos nubemque hanc frontis opacae
spernite, ne, moneo: et nobis saevire facultas.
scimus enim [et] quidquid dici noscique timetis
515 et turbare Hecaten (ni te, Thymbraee, vererer)
et triplicis mundi summum, quem scire nefastum.
illum—sed taceo: prohibet tranquilla senectus.
iamque ego vos—' avide subicit Phoebeia Manto:

505 medicata P: armata ω
514 scimus enim ω: novimus P   et *secl. SB*

242

mighty dread. In his agitation he grasps now the shoulders, now the hands, now the fillets of the seer as he intones his fearsome chant and would fain abandon the rites commenced. Even as a hunter waits for a lion that long shouting rouses from his den in the rough of a Gaetulian forest, steeling his courage and gripping his weapon that sweats with the effort; fear freezes his face and his steps tremble as he wonders what creature approaches, how big—but he hears the roaring, dread sign, and measures the sound in blind trepidation.

Then Tiresias, since the ghosts were not yet approaching: 'I call you to witness, goddesses, for whom we have drenched this fire and with left hand given our cups to the torn earth, I can brook no further delay. Am I, the priest, heard for nothing? If a Thessalian witch's rabid chant were to command you, will you come? Or when a Colchian drugged with Scythian poisons drives, shall Tartarus turn pale and start in fright? And do you care less for me? If I have no mind to raise bodies from tombs or empty urns filled with ancient bones or profane the gods of Erebus and heaven commingled or pursue bloodless faces with the knife and pluck the sick entrails of the dead, do not, I warn you, do not contemn my thinning years and the cloud upon my darkened brow. I too have means to be cruel. For I know whatever you fear spoken or known. I can harry Hecate, did I not respect you, Lord of Thymbra, him[66] too, highest of the triple world, whom to know is blasphemy. Him—but I hold my peace: tranquil eld forbids. And now I—.' Eagerly Phoebus' Manto puts in her word: 'You are

[66] Cf. Lucan 6.744ff. According to the scholiast he is the Demiurge, or creator, of Plato's *Timaeus*.

243

'audiris, genitor, vulgusque exsangue propinquat.
520   panditur Elysium chaos, et telluris opertae
dissilit umbra capax, silvaeque et nigra patescunt
flumina: liventes Acheron eiectat harenas,
fumidus atra vadis Phlegethon incendia volvit,
et Styx discretis interflua manibus obstat.
525   ipsum pallentem solio circumque ministras
funestorum operum Eumenidas Stygiaeque severos
Iunonis thalamos et torva cubilia cerno.
in speculis Mors atra sedet dominoque silentes
annumerat populos; maior superimminet ordo.
530   arbiter hos dura versat Gortynius urna
vera minis poscens adigitque expromere vitas
usque retro et tandem poenarum lucra fateri.
quid tibi monstra Erebi, Scyllas et inane furentes
Centauros solidoque intorta adamante Gigantum
535   vincula et angustam centeni Aegaeonis umbram?'
    'Immo,' ait, 'o nostrae regimen viresque senectae,
ne vulgata mihi. quis enim remeabile saxum
fallentesque lacus Tityonque alimenta volucrum
et caligantem longis Ixiona gyris
540   nesciat? ipse etiam, melior cum sanguis, opertas
inspexi sedes, Hecate ducente, priusquam
obruit ora deus totamque in pectora lucem
detulit. Argolicas magis huc appelle precando
Thebanasque animas; alias avertere gressus
545   lacte quater sparsas maestoque excedere luco,
nata, iube; tum qui vultus habitusque, quis ardor
sanguinis affusi, gens utra superbior adsit,
dic agedum nostramque mone per singula noctem.'

527 torva P: maesta ω   531 nimis Pω (*Heinsius*)

heard, father; the bloodless multitude approaches. The Elysian void is revealed, the capacious darkness of hidden earth bursts asunder, woods and black rivers come to view: Acheron ejects livid sands, smoking Phlegethon rolls dark fires in his waters and interflowing Styx bars separated ghosts. Himself I see, pale upon his throne and around him the Furies, servants of his deadly works, and the stern bower and grim couch of Stygian Juno.[67] Black Death sits on the lookout and counts the silent peoples for her master; a greater series wait their turn. The Gortynion judge[68] shakes them in his harsh urn, demanding truth with threats, forces them to set forth their lives back to their beginning and confess at last the punishments they evaded. Why tell you of the monsters of Erebus, the Scyllas and idly raging Centaurs, the Giants' chains twisted in solid adamant, and the cramped shade of hundredfold Aegaeon?'

'Nay,' said he, 'guide and strength of my old age, tell me not what all men know. For who but would have heard of the ever-returning rock and the cheating pool and Tityos, food of birds, and Ixion, dizzy on his long circlings? I myself, when my blood ran faster, beheld the hidden dwellings with Hecate as my guide, before the god o'erwhelmed my face and bore all light down into my breast. Rather bring Argive and Theban souls hither with your prayers and bid all others, my daughter, sprinkled four times with milk, turn their steps away and depart the dismal grove. Then tell me, come, their countenances and mien, their appetite for the spilt blood, which of the two peoples makes the prouder show; advise my darkness point by point.'

[67] Proserpina.   [68] Minos (Gortynian = Cretan).

245

Iussa facit carmenque serit, quo dissipat umbras,
550 quo reciet sparsas; qualis, si crimina demas,
Colchis et Aeaeo simulatrix litore Circe.
tunc his sacrificum dictis affata parentem:
'primus sanguineo summittit inertia Cadmus
ora lacu, iuxtaque virum Cythereia proles
555 insequitur, geminusque bibit de vertice serpens.
terrigenae comites illos, gens Martia, cingunt,
quis aevi mensura dies; manus omnis in armis,
omnis et in capulo; prohibent obstantque ruuntque
spirantum rabie, nec tristi incumbere fossae
560 cura, sed alternum sitis exhaurire cruorem.
proxima natarum manus est fletique nepotes.
hic orbam Autonoën, et anhelam cernimus Ino
respectantem arcus et ad ubera dulce prementem
pignus, et oppositis Semelen a ventre lacertis.
565 Penthea iam fractis genetrix Cadmeia thyrsis
iamque remissa deo pectusque adaperta cruentum
insequitur planctu; fugit ille per avia Lethes
et Stygios super usque lacus, ubi mitior illum
flet pater et lacerum componit corpus Echion.
570 tristem nosco Lycum dextramque in terga reflexum
Aeoliden, umero iactantem funus onusto.
necdum ille aut habitus aut versae crimina formae

---

557 his Pω (*Nauke ex* Σ)   559 fosso P: sulco ω (ς)
560 sitis exhaurire P: cuperent hau- ωΣ
566 adaperta Pω (ς, *Gronovius*)

---

69 Lit. 'semblance-making.' Circe changed men into beasts.
70 Cadmus and Haemonia.

She does as commanded and sows a spell wherewith she disperses the shades and when scattered calls them back; like to the Colchian, but for the crimes, and deceiving[69] Circe on the shore of Aea. Then in these words she addressed her priestly parent: 'First Cadmus lowers his feeble mouth into the bloody pool and Cytherea's daughter follows next her husband. The two serpents[70] drink from the head top. Their earthborn companions, the Martian race, surround them, whose lifespan was a day, every hand on weapon, every hand on hilt. They block and bar and rush with the fury of living beings, nor care to bend to the gloomy trench but thirst to drain each other's blood. Next comes a band of daughters and lamented grandchildren. Here we see bereaved Autonoë and panting Ino as she looks back at the bow[71] and presses her sweet child to her breast, and Semele with arms outstretched to protect her belly. His Cadmean mother follows Pentheus with lamentation, her wand now broken, now released of the god, her breasts open[72] and bleeding. He flees through Lethe's wilderness even beyond the Stygian lake, where his kindlier[73] father Echion weeps him and composes his torn body. Sad Lycus I recognize and the son of Aeolus,[74] his right hand bent behind his back, tossing a corpse[75] on his laden shoulder. Nor does Aristaeus' son[76] change his

[71] Her husband Athamas was in pursuit.

[72] *Adoperta* (covered) has been defended as referring to Agave's return to sanity, but sane or not, mourners do not cover their breasts when beating them.

[73] Kindlier than his mother.

[74] Athamas.   [75] Learchus, his son.   [76] Actaeon.

247

mutat Aristaeo genitus: frons aspera cornu,
tela manu, reicitque canes in vulnus hiantes.
575　ecce autem magna subit invidiosa caterva
Tantalis et tumido percenset funera luctu,
nil deiecta malis; iuvat effugisse deorum
numina et insanae plus iam permittere linguae.'
　　Talia dum patri canit intemerata sacerdos,
580　illius elatis tremefacta assurgere vittis
canities tenuisque impelli sanguine vultus.
nec iam firmanti baculo nec virgine fida
nititur, erectusque solo, 'desiste canendo,
nata,' ait, 'externae satis est mihi lucis, inertes
585　discedunt nebulae, et vultum niger exuit aër.
umbrisne an supero demissus Apolline complet
spiritus? en video quaecumque audita. sed ecce
maerent Argolici deiecto lumine manes!
torvus Abas Proetusque nocens mitisque Phoroneus
590　truncatusque Pelops et saevo pulvere sordens
Oenomaus largis umectant imbribus ora.
auguror hinc Thebis belli meliora. quid autem

574 *anne* ungue manus?
586 dimissus P: me m- ω (*Dowden*)

77 The spirits appear as artists depicted them in the enactment
of their earthly tragedies, though *necdum* indicates that these
forms are only temporary. Actaeon, changed into a stag, defends
himself from the hounds who are about to tear him apart. Sometimes in art he is portrayed in human form, wearing a deerskin and
with antlers on his head, and so here if *tela manu* is sound. But this
item is irrelevant, and the reader, without a picture in front of him,
expects something descriptive of a stag, as *ungue manus*, 'hands

aspect yet or the reproach of his altered form. His brow is rough with horns, a weapon in his hand,[77] and he repels the hounds agape to tear him. And see! Tantalus' daughter comes, to be envied for her long train, and counts over her bodies[78] in arrogant mourning, no wise downcast by her woes; she rejoices to have escaped the power of the gods and to give more licence now to her crazy tongue.'[79]

As the inviolate priestess thus tells her tale to her father, his white hair stands up in trembling, his fillets rise, blood urges his haggard visage. No longer does he lean on his steadying staff or the faithful maiden, but standing erect from the ground: 'Cease your tale, my daughter,' says he. 'I have light enough from without, the dull mists disperse, and the dark air strips away my face.[80] Inspiration fills me, whether sent from the shades or from Apollo above. Behold, I see all that I heard. But look, the Argive ghosts are sorrowful with eyes downcast. Grim Abas, guilty[81] Proteus, mild Phoroneus, maimed[82] Pelops, and Oenomaus[83] soiled with cruel dust bedew their faces with floods of tears. Hence I augur the better of the war for

(rough) with hooves'; cf. Ovid, *Metamorphoses* 3.196 *cum pedibusque manus, cum longis bracchia mutat / cruribus*.

[78] The slaughtered Niobids.

[79] The punishment could not be repeated.

[80] Another inversion.

[81] Because of his treatment of Bellerophon (*Iliad* 6.156ff.).

[82] His father Tantalus butchered him and served him up to the gods for dinner. They put him together again, but a missing shoulder had to be replaced with ivory.

[83] Argive sympathizers as ancestors of Adrastus and the royal family of Mycenae, which is sometimes equated with Argos, as in 2.119. *Pelopeus* sometimes = Argive.

hi grege condenso (quantum arma et vulnera monstrant,
pugnaces animae) nobis in sanguine multo
595 oraque pectoraque et falso clamore levatas
intendunt sine pace manus? rex, fallor? an hi sunt
quinquaginta illi? cernis Cthoniumque Chrominque
Phegeaque et nostra praesignem Maeona lauro.
ne saevite, duces, nihil hic mortalibus ausum,
600 credite, consiliis: hos ferrea neverat annos
Atropos. existis casus: bella horrida nobis,
atque iterum Tydeus.' dicit, vittaque ligatis
frondibus instantes abigit monstratque cruorem.
    Stabat inops comitum Cocyti in litore maesto
605 Laius, immiti quem iam deus ales Averno
reddiderat, dirumque tuens obliqua nepotem
(noscit enim vultu) non ille aut sanguinis haustus,
cetera ceu plebes, aliumve accedit ad imbrem,
immortale odium spirans. sed prolicit ultro
610 Aonius vates: 'Tyriae dux inclute Thebes,
cuius ab interitu non ulla Amphionis arces
vidit amica dies, o iam satis ulte cruentum
exitium, et multum placata minoribus umbra,
quos, miserande, fugis? iacet ille in funere longo,
615 quem fremis, et iunctae sentit confinia mortis,
obsitus exhaustos paedore et sanguine vultus
eiectusque die: sors leto durior omni,
crede mihi! quaenam immeritum vitare nepotem
causa tibi? confer vultum et satiare litanti
620 sanguine venturasque vices et funera belli
pande, vel infensus vel res miserate tuorum.

---

[84] As a prophet.
[85] Explained by the scholiast as referring to the calamities of

BOOK 4

Thebes. But what of this crowding flock? Fighting souls, as their weapons and wounds show, why do they display their faces and breasts bathed in blood and stretch their hands toward us raised with false clamour, truceless? King, am I in error or are these those fifty? Do you see Cthonius and Chromis and Phegeus and Maeon marked out by our laurel?[84] Be not angry, captains, no venture here of mortal devising, believe it. Iron Atropos had spun these years. You have left life's chances behind you. For us war's horrors, and Tydeus once again.' He speaks and as they press drives them off with boughs by fillet bound and beckons to the blood.

On Cocytus' sad shore stood Laius all by himself—the winged god had already returned him to pitiless Avernus—peering sideways at his fell grandson, whose face he recognized. Breathing deathless hate, he does not approach like the rest of the crowd to drink the blood or other pourings, but the Aonian seer drew him forth: 'Ruler renowned of Tyrian Thebes, since whose death no day has looked kindly on Amphion's citadel, now enough avenged of your bloody taking-off, shade well appeased by your posterity,[85] whom, piteous one, do you flee? He whom you curse[86] lies in a long burial and feels death linked in close neighbourhood, his exhausted visage sunk in filth and blood, cast out from the light of day. His lot is harder than any death, believe me. What cause have you to shun your innocent grandson? Come face to face and take your fill of sacrificial blood and set forth happenings to be and war's calamities, whether in anger or pity for your family's fortunes. Then shall I grant

Oedipus and his sons, though the worst for the latter was still to come. [86] Oedipus.

tunc ego et optata vetitam transmittere Lethen
puppe dabo placidumque pia tellure reponam
et Stygiis mandabo deis.'
                                    Mulcetur honoris
625 muneribus tingitque genas, dein talia reddit:
'cur tibi versanti manes, aequaeve sacerdos,
lectus ego augurio tantisque potissimus umbris
qui ventura loquar? satis est meminisse priorum.
nostrane praeclari (pudeat) consulta nepotes
630 poscitis? illum, illum sacris adhibete nefastis,
qui laeto fodit ense patrem, qui semet in ortus
vertit et indignae regerit sua pignora matri.
et nunc ille deos Furiarumque atra fatigat
concilia et nostros rogat haec in proelia manes.
635 quod si adeo placui deflenda in tempora vates,
dicam equidem, quo me Lachesis, quo torva Megaera
usque sinunt: bellum, innumero venit undique bellum
agmine, Lernaeosque trahit fatalis alumnos
Gradivus stimulis; hos terrae monstra deumque
640 tela manent, pulchrique obitus et ab igne supremo
sontes lege morae. certa est victoria Thebis,
ne trepida, nec regna ferox germanus habebit
sed Furiae; geminumque nefas miserosque per enses
(ei mihi!) crudelis vincit pater.' haec ubi fatus
645 labitur et flexa dubios ambage relinquit.
        Interea gelidam Nemeen et conscia laudis
Herculeae dumeta vaga legione tenebant
Inachidae; iam Sidonias avertere praedas,

---

[87] With the blood.

you to cross forbidden Lethe in the longed-for boat and place you at peace in pious earth and consign you to the gods of Styx.'

Soothed by the flattering gifts, he moistens his cheeks[87] and thus returns: 'Priest, my coeval, why as you reviewed the shades choose me for augury, me in all the multitude of ghosts to tell the future? It is enough to remember the past. My splendid grandsons, ask you counsel of me? For shame! Bring *him* to your evil rites, him who stabs his father with joyous sword, who turns himself to his beginnings and thrusts back her child on his undeserving mother. And now he wearies the gods and the dark councils of the Furies and asks my ghost for help towards these battles. But if I am so welcome as a prophet for tearful times, speak I will, so far as Lachesis and grim Magaera permit. War is coming, war from every quarter in countless host, and by fate's decree Gradivus draws on Lerna's children with his goads. Portents of earth await them and weapons of the gods and beauteous death and guilty ordinance delaying the final fire.[88] Victory for Thebes is certain. Fear not. Neither shall your fierce brother have the realm; the Furies shall have it. Through twin impiety and unhappy swords, alas, your cruel father prevails.' So saying, he sinks and leaves them perplexed at his tortuous riddle.

Meanwhile the sons of Inachus in errant host held chill[89] Nemea and the thickets that knew Hercules' glory. Already they burn with impatience to carry off Sidonian

---

[88] Foreshadowing the deaths of Amphiaraus, Capaneus, and Parthenopaeus (*pulchri obitus*; see SB[1]), and Creon's denial of burial.   [89] Because shady.

sternere, ferre domos ardent instantque. quis iras
650 flexerit, unde morae, medius quis euntibus error,
Phoebe, doce: nos rara manent exordia famae.
    Marcidus edomito bellum referebat ab Haemo
Liber; ibi armiferos geminae iam sidera brumae
orgia ferre Getas canumque virescere dorso
655 Othryn et Icaria Rhodopen assueverat umbra,
et iam pampineos materna ad moenia currus
promovet; effrenae dextra laevaque sequuntur
lynces, et uda mero lambunt retinacula tigres.
post exsultantes spolia armentalia portant
660 seminecesque lupos scissasque Mimallones ursas.
nec comitatus iners: sunt illic Ira Furorque
et Metus et Virtus et numquam sobrius Ardor
succiduique gradus et castra simillima regi.
isque ubi pulverea Nemeen effervere nube
665 conspicit et solem radiis ignescere ferri,
necdum compositas belli in certamina Thebas,
concussus visis, quamquam ore et pectore marcet,
aeraque tympanaque et biforem reticere tumultum
imperat, attonitas qui circum plurimus aures,
670 atque ita: 'me globus iste meamque exscindere gentem
apparat; ex longo recalet furor; hoc mihi saevum
Argos et indomitae bellum ciet ira novercae.
usque adeone parum cineri data mater iniquo
natalesque rogi quaeque ipse micantia sensi
675 fulgura? reliquias etiam fusaeque sepulcrum
paelicis et residem ferro petit improba Theben.
nectam fraude moras; illum, illum tendite campum,

661 manent ω: mon- P   665 solis . . . ferrum ⌐, *Madvig*
670 globus iste P: manus ista ω   676 improba ω: impia P

plunder, to raze and ravage homes. Tell, Phoebus, who turned their wrath aside, whence came delay, what wandering stayed their march. We have only scattered beginnings of the story.

Languorous Liber was bringing back his warfare from conquered Haemus. There through the stars of two winters he had trained the martial Getae to carry his emblems and hoary Othrys' ridge and Rhodope to grow green with Icarian foliage.[90] And now he brings his vine-clad car to his mother's city. Wild lynxes follow left and right and tigers lick the wine-wet reins. In the rear triumphing Mimallones carry spoils of the herd and half-dead wolves and cloven bears. No lazy retinue is his: Wrath and Madness are there, and Fear and Valour and Ardour never sober and staggering steps and a camp like to its king. When he sees Nemea astir with a dusty cloud and the sun take fire with the steel's rays[91] while Thebes is not yet prepared for clash of battle, he is aghast at the sight. Though faint in speech and heart, he commands the cymbals and drums and double pipes that blare about his deafened ears to be mute, and thus he speaks: 'This host plans to destroy me and my race. From far back their rage heats afresh. Savage Argos and the wrath of my implacable stepmother excite this war against me. My mother given to cruel ashes, the pyre I was born in, the lightnings I myself saw flash—are not these enough? The ruthless goddess attacks with steel even the relics, the tomb of the cremated concubine and an inactive Thebes. By guile I shall weave delay. On to

90 Vines.
91 An audacious inversion even for Statius.

255

tendite, io comites.' Hyrcanae ad signa iugales
intumuere iubas, dicto prius astitit Argis.
680   Tempus erat medii cum solem in culmina mundi
tollit anhela dies, ubi tardus hiantibus arvis
stat vapor atque omnes admittunt aethera luci.
undarum vocat ille deas mediusque silentum
incipit: 'agrestes, fluviorum numina, Nymphae,
685 et nostri pars magna gregis, perferte laborem
quem damus. Argolicos paulum mihi fontibus amnes
stagnaque et errantes obducite pulvere rivos.
praecipuam Nemeen, qua nostra in moenia bellis
nunc iter, ex alto fugiat liquor; adiuvat ipse
690 Phoebus adhuc summo, cesset ni vestra uoluntas,
limite; vim coeptis indulgent astra, meaeque
aestifer Erigones spumat canis. ite volentes,
ite in operta soli; post vos ego gurgite pleno
eliciam, et quae dona meis amplissima sacris
695 vester habebit honos, nocturnaque furta licentum
cornipedum et cupidas Faunorum arcebo rapinas.'
    Dixerat; ast illis tenvior percurrere visus
ora situs, viridisque comis exaruit umor.
protinus Inachios haurit sitis ignea campos:
700 diffugere undae, squalent fontesque lacusque,
et cava ferventi durescunt flumina limo.
aegra solo macies, tenerique in origine culmi
inclinata seges, deceptum margine ripae

---

679 arvis Pω (*Watt*)   697 tenvior ω: -uis P
698 exhorruit Pω (ⲥ)   702–03 *habent* ψ: *om.* Pω

---

92 Surely more appropriate to Cybele's lions than Bacchus'
tigers?

yonder plain, on comrades, on!' The Hyrcanian yoke fellows fluffed out their manes[92] at the signal, and before the words were out he stood at Argos.[93]

It was the hour when panting day raises the sun to heaven's midmost summit, when sluggish heat stands in the gaping fields and every grove admits the ether. He calls the goddesses of the waves and in the midst of their silent company begins: 'Nymphs of the wild, river deities, no small part of my following, faithfully perform the task I set. Pray choke with dust for a while the Argive streams at their springs and the meres and the wandering brooks. In Nemea especially, where war now takes its way against my city, let liquid flee from the depth. Phoebus himself aids, still at the height of his road, only let your good will not flag. The stars grant power to my endeavour and the heat-bearing dog of my Erigone foams. Go with a will, go into the covert places of the earth. Later I shall draw you out in full channel and your honour shall have the finest gifts at my worship, and I shall ward off the nighttime tricks of the licentious Hornfeet[94] and the lustful ravishings of the Fauns.'

He spoke. A thin mould seemed to spread over their faces and the green moisture dried out from their hair. Straightway fiery thirst drains the Inachian fields. The waters disperse, the springs and lakes are encrusted, the riverbeds harden with hot mud. The soil is sick with drought and the grain bends at the base of the tender stalk.

[93] *Argis*, replacing the vague *arvis*, gives Bacchus a venue to which he summons the Naiads of the region. 688 implies that he was not at Nemea, where the Argive army had halted.

[94] Satyrs.

257

stat pecus, atque amnes quaerunt armenta natatos.
705   sic ubi se magnis refluus suppressit in antris
Nilus et Eoae liquentia pabula brumae
ore premit, fumant desertae gurgite valles
et patris undosi sonitus exspectat hiulca
Aegyptos, donec Phariis alimenta rogatus
710   donet agris magnumque inducat messibus annum.
     Aret Lerna nocens, aret Lyrceus et ingens
Inachus advolvensque natantia saxa Charadros
et numquam in ripis audax Erasinus et aequus
fluctibus Asterion, ille alta per avia notus
715   audiri et longe pastorum rumpere somnos.
[sic Hyperionios cum lux effrena per orbem
rapta ruit Phaëthontis equos, magnumque laborem
discordes gemuere poli, dum pontus et arva
stellarumque ruunt crines, non amnibus undae,
720   non lucis mansere comae, sed multus ubique
ignis, ubique faces et longa fluminis instar
indiget Aegaeon deceptus imagine ripae.]
una tamen tacitas, sed iussu numinis, undas,
haec quoque, secreta nutrit Langia sub umbra.
725   nondum illi raptus dederat lacrimabile nomen
Archemorus, nec fama deae; tamen avia servat
(720)   et nemus et fluvium; manet ingens gloria Nympham,
cum tristem Hypsipylen ducibus sudatus Achaeis
ludus et atra sacrum recolet trieteris Ophelten.
730   Ergo nec ardentes clipeos vectare nec artos
thoracum nexus (tantum sitis horrida torret)
(725)   sufficiunt; non ora modo angustisque perusti

716–22 *habet cod. Lipsiensis saec. XI, qui 722 ante 716: om.* Pω,
nisi quod 717 post 723 habet P   731 torret P: torquet ω

The flock stands disappointed at the bank's edge, the herds seek in vain for the rivers they once swam. So when ebbing Nile hides himself in his great caverns and holds in his mouth the liquid nurture of an eastern winter,[95] the valleys smoke forsaken by the flood and gaping Egypt awaits the sounds of her watery father,[96] until at their prayers he grants sustenance to the Pharian fields and brings on a great harvest year.

Dry is guilty Lerna, dry Lyrceus and mighty Inachus and Charadros rolling rocks in his flood and bold Erasious that never keeps his banks and Asterion equalling sea waves, a familiar sound in the pathless heights, breaking the shepherds' slumbers from afar. Langia alone—but she too by the god's command—feeds silent waters under secret shade. Not yet had reft Archemorus[97] given the goddess a mournful renown, no fame is hers. Yet in seclusion she keeps wood and stream. Great glory awaits the Nymph when every other year the games[98] at which Achaea's leaders sweat and the festival of death shall renew the memory of sad Hypsipyle and sacred Opheltes.

Therefore no longer do they have strength to carry hot shields or the tight fabric of corselets; so harsh thirst parches them. Not only are their mouths and constricted

[95] Ethiopian snows.
[96] Nile.
[97] 'Beginner of doom'; cf. 5.739 and Apollodorus 3.6.4, where the name is said to have been given to the dead Opheltes at Amphiaraus' prompting.
[98] Nemean.

THEBAID

faucibus, interior sed vis quatit: aspera pulsu
corda, gelant venae et siccis cruor aeger adhaeret
735 visceribus; tunc sole putris, tunc pulvere tellus
exhalat calidam nubem. non spumeus imber
(730) manat equum: siccis illidunt ora lupatis,
ora catenatas procul exsertantia linguas;
nec legem dominosve pati, sed perfurit arvis
740 flammatum pecus. huc illuc impellit Adrastus
exploratores, si stagna Licymnia restent,
(735) si quis Amymones superet liquor: omnia caecis
ignibus hausta sedent, nec spes umentis Olympi,
ceu flavam Libyen desertaque pulveris Afri
745 collustrent nullaque umbratam nube Syenen.
     Tandem inter silvas (sic Euhius ipse pararat)
(740) errantes subitam pulchro in maerore tuentur
Hypsipylen; illi dependet et ad ubera Opheltes
non suus, Inachii proles infausta Lycurgi.
750 quamvis et neglecta comam nec dives amictu,
regales tamen ore notae, nec mersus acerbis
(745) exstat honos. tunc haec adeo stupefactus Adrastus:
'diva potens nemorum (nam te vultusque pudorque
mortali de stirpe negant), quae laeta sub isto
755 igne poli non quaeris aquas, succurre propinquis
gentibus; arquitenens seu te Latonia casto
(750) de grege transmisit thalamis, seu lapsus ab astris
non humilis fecundat amor (neque enim ipse deorum
arbiter Argolidum thalamis novus), aspice maesta

748–50 illi quamvis et . . . dependet Pω (SB²)

---

99 I.e. reduced to sand by the heat of the sun, if the text is
sound.

throats burnt up, an inner force convulses them. Their
hearts beat roughly, their veins congeal, tainted blood
clings to their dry vitals. Then the earth, friable with sun
and dust(?),[99] breathes out hot vapour. No foamy rain flows
from the horses. Their mouths champ on dry bits, mouths
that thrust bridled tongues far out. They suffer not their
masters' rule; inflamed, the animals rage over the land.
Adrastus sends scouts this way and that; are the Licymnian
meres[100] still there, does any of Amymone's water survive?
All stagnate, drained by hidden fires, nor is there hope of
a watery sky. They might as well scour yellow Libya and
the sandy deserts of Africa and Syene that no cloud ever
shades.

At last as they wander in the forest (so Euhius himself
had planned it) suddenly they see Hypsipyle, fair in her
sadness. Opheltes, not hers but the ill-starred child of
Inachian Lycurgus, hangs at her breast, her hair is dishevelled, her clothing poor; yet on her face are marks of royalty, her dignity shows, not sunk in her misfortune. Then
Adrastus in amazement thus addresses her: 'Goddess,
Lady of the woods (for your countenance and modesty say
you are of no mortal stock), happy in that under this blazing sky you seek not for water, help neighbour peoples.
Whether the bow-bearing daughter of Leto sent you from
her chaste company to a nuptial chamber or a love of no
mean order descended from the stars to make you fruitful
(for the lord of the gods himself is no stranger to Argive
bedchambers), look upon our unhappy columns. Our pur-

[100] Licymnius was the eponymous hero of Licymna, the citadel of Tiryns. The lakes or swamps will have been in the vicinity.

760 agmina. nos ferro meritas exscindere Thebas
mens tulit, imbelli sed nunc sitis aspera fato
(755) summittitque animos et inertia robora carpit.
da fessis in rebus opem, seu turbidus amnis,
seu tibi foeda palus; nihil hac in sorte pudendum,
765 nil humile est; tu nunc Ventis pluvioque rogaris
pro Iove, tu refugas vires et pectora bellis
(760) exanimata reple: sic hoc tibi sidere dextro
crescat onus. tantum reduces det flectere gressus
Iuppiter, o quanta belli donabere praeda!
770 Dircaeos tibi, diva, greges numerumque rependam
sanguinis et magna lucus signabitur ara.'
(765) dixit, et orantis media inter anhelitus ardens
verba rapit, cursuque animae labat arida lingua;
idem omnes pallorque viros flatusque soluti
oris habet.
775   Reddit demisso Lemnia vultu:
'diva quidem vobis, etsi caelestis origo est,
(770) unde ego? mortales utinam haud transgressa fuissem
luctibus! altricem mandati cernitis orbam
pignoris; at nostris an quis sinus, uberaque ulla,
780 scit deus; et nobis regnum tamen et pater ingens.
sed quid ego haec, fessosque optatis demoror undis?
(775) mecum age nunc, si forte vado Langia perennes
servat aquas; solet et rabidi sub limite Cancri
semper, et Icarii quamvis iuba fulguret astri,
785 ire tamen.' simul haerentem, ne tarda Pelasgis
dux foret, a! miserum vicino caespite alumnum
(780) (sic Parcae volvere) locat ponique negantis

771 sanguinis et P: plebis et hic ωΣ
783 rabidi Pψ: rapidi ω   787 ponitque negantem Pω (ς)

pose was to raze guilty Thebes with the sword, but now harsh thirst humbles our courage in a fate unwarlike, eats away our idle strength. Aid us in our sorry case, whether you have a muddy river or a foul swamp. In our plight nothing is shameful, nothing is mean. To you we now appeal in lieu of Winds and rainy Jupiter. Do you replenish our fleeing powers and hearts listless for war. So may this burden grow for you under a favouring star. Only let Jupiter grant us to retrace our steps, what spoils of war will our gift make yours! I shall repay you, goddess, with Dircaean flocks and quantity of blood, and here a great altar shall mark the grove.' He spoke and a hot panting grabs his words in mid utterance, his dry tongue falters with the passage of his breath. All his men are seized with a like pallor, their mouths blow helplessly.

The Lemnian answers, her face downcast: 'How should I be a goddess for you, even though my origin be of heaven? Would that I had not transcended mortality by my sorrows! You see the bereaved foster mother of a child entrusted to my care. But heaven knows whether mine have bosom and breast—and yet I had a kingdom and a mighty father. But why do I talk and keep the weary from the waves they crave? Come with me now, let us see whether Langia keeps her perennial waters in their channel. Always she is wont to run, under the path of the raging Crab and though the hackle of the Icarian star[101] be blazing.' The poor babe clings to her; and lest she be too slow a guide to the Pelasgi, alas, she places him on the ground nearby (so the Parcae ordained), and when he will not be put aside,

---

[101] Sirius.

floribus aggestis et amico murmure dulces
solatur lacrimas: qualis Berecyntia mater,
790   dum parvum circa iubet exsultare Tonantem
Curetas trepidos; illi certantia plaudunt
(785) orgia, sed magnis resonat vagitibus Ide.
    At puer in gremio vernae telluris et alto
gramine nunc faciles sternit procursibus herbas
795   in vultum nitens, caram modo lactis egeno
nutricem clangore ciens iterumque renidens
(790) et teneris meditans verba illuctantia labris
miratur nemorum strepitus aut obvia carpit
aut patulo trahit ore diem nemorique malorum
800   inscius et vitae multum securus inerrat.
sic tener Odrysia Mavors nive, sic puer ales
(795) vertice Maenalio, talis per litora reptans
improbus Ortygiae latus inclinabat Apollo.
    Illi per dumos et opaca virentibus umbris
805   deuia, pars cingunt, pars arta plebe sequuntur
praecelerantque ducem. medium subit illa per agmen
(800) non humili festina modo; iamque amne propinquo
rauca sonat vallis, saxosumque impulit aures
murmur: ibi exsultans conclamat ab agmine primus,
810   sicut erat levibus tollens vexilla maniplis,
Argus, 'aquae!' longusque uirum super ora cucurrit
(805) clamor, 'aquae!' sic Ambracii per litora ponti
nauticus in remis iuvenum monstrante magistro
fit sonus inque vicem contra percussa reclamat

---

796 *anne* ciet?

---

102 *Ciet* for *ciens* would much improve the structure, the rare
but well attested lengthening of the vowel before the caesura ac-

consoles his sweet tears with bunches of flowers and loving murmurs: like the Berecyntian Mother as she bids the trembling Curetes dance around the tiny Thunderer; they strike their mystic drums in competition, but Ide resounds with his mighty wails.

But the boy in the bosom of the vernal earth, the lush herbage, now buts and levels the pliant grasses with his forward plunges, now calls[102] for his dear nurse, crying loud for milk; and again he smiles and essays words that struggle with his tender lips. He wonders at the forest noises or plucks at what comes his way or with open mouth draws in the day. So he wanders in the wood unknowing of harm, quite careless of his life. Such was tender Mars in the Odrysian snow, such the winged boy[103] on Maenalus' summit, such mischievous Apollo as he crawled along the shore and tilted Ortygia's side.

They make their way through the bushes, the devious places dim with green shades. Some surround the guide, others follow in a mass or push ahead. She goes onward in the middle of the troop, hastening with dignity. Now they are near the stream; the noisy valley sounds and stony plashing strikes their ears. Argus was first in the line. Just as he was, lifting up a standard for the nimble[104] platoons, he raises a joyous shout of 'Water!' And over the warriors' mouths ran the long clamour: 'Water.' So along the shores of the Ambracian sea sounds the cry of the sailors at the oars as the helmsman points (and loud the land returns the

counting for the corruption.

[103] Mercury is represented with wings on his hat and feet.

[104] Apparently proleptic; they would run when he shouted.

815 terra, salutatus cum Leucada pandit Apollo.
  incubuere vadis passim discrimine nullo
(810) turba simul primique, nequit secernere mixtos
  aequa sitis, frenata suis in curribus intrant
  armenta, et pleni dominis armisque feruntur
820 quadripedes; hos turbo rapax, hos lubrica fallunt
  saxa, nec implicitos fluvio reverentia reges
(815) proterere aut mersisse vado clamantis amici
  ora. fremunt undae, longusque a fontibus amnis
  diripitur; modo lene virens et gurgite puro
825 perspicuus, nunc sordet aquis egestus ab imis
  alveus; inde tori riparum et proruta turbant
(820) gramina; iam crassus caenoque et pulvere torrens,
  quamquam expleta sitis, bibitur tamen. agmina bello
  decertare putes iustumque in gurgite Martem
830 perfurere aut captam tolli victoribus urbem.
   Atque aliquis regum medio circumfluus amni:
(825) 'silvarum, Nemea, longe regina virentum,
  lecta Iovis sedes, quantum? non Herculis actis
  dura magis, rabidi cum colla comantia monstri
835 angeret et tumidos animam angustaret in artus!
  hac saevisse tenus populorum in coepta tuorum
(830) sufficiat; tuque o cunctis insuete domari
  solibus, aeternae largitor corniger undae,
  laetus eas, quacumque domo gelida ora resolvis
840 immortale tumens; neque enim tibi cana repostas

  827 *sic* Σ: torrens ω: sordens P
  833 quamtum *vel* quantum ω: quam tu P (*vide SB*[2])

echo), saluting Apollo[105] when he brings Leucas into view. Everywhere common soldiers and officers plunge indiscriminate into the stream, equal thirst cannot separate the mingled throng. Bridled horses enter in their chariots, chargers full of riders and arms are swept along. Some the whirling current, some the slippery rocks play false. They do not scruple to trample kings caught in the flood or drown the face of a yelling friend. The waves crash and from its source the long river is torn asunder. Once it was a gentle green, transparent in its liquid flow; now its channel is soiled, churned up from the depths, the ridges of the banks and uprooted herbage tumbles it. Now rushing thick with mud and dust, they drink it none the less, though their thirst is slaked. 'Twas as though armies were fighting a pitched battle raging in the flood or victors sacking a taken town.

Thus spoke one of the kings standing in the middle surrounded by the stream: 'Nemea, queen supreme of green glades, chosen seat of Jupiter, where does it end? Even to the deeds of Hercules you were no crueler when he choked the hairy neck of the rabid monster[106] and squeezed his breath into his swollen limbs. Let it suffice you to have fought your people's enterprise thus far. And you,[107] unused to yield to any sun, horned bestower of everlasting water, may you happily flow, whatever the home wherein you let loose your cool mouth in immortal surge. For hoary winter does not return you hidden snows,

[105] See Leucas in Index.

[106] The drought was worse than the Nemean lion, both incidents in a larger frame. *Actis* corresponds to *coepta* in 836.

[107] Here male, with horns like any other river.

bruma nives raptasque alio de fonte refundit
(835) arcus aquas gravidive indulgent nubila Cauri,
sed tuus et nulli ruis expugnabilis astro.
te nec Apollineus Ladon nec Xanthus uterque
845 Spercheosque minax Centaureusque Lycormas
praestiterint; tu pace mihi, tu nube sub ipsa
(840) armorum festasque super celebrabere mensas
(a Iove primus honos), bellis modo laetus ovantes
accipias fessisque libens iterum hospita pandas
850 flumina defensasque velis agnoscere turmas.'

nor does the rainbow pour you back waters seized from some other spring or the clouds of gravid Caurus favour you; you are your own and no star can defeat your course. Apollo's Ladon shall not surpass you, nor either Xanthus, nor threatening Spercheus, nor the Centaur's[108] Lycormas. You I shall celebrate in peace, you beneath the very cloud of arms, over festal banquets, honoured next to Jove; only welcome us gladly in our triumph, open again your stream to our weariness in ready hospitality, and graciously recognize the army you have protected.'

[108] Nessus, mortally wounded by Hercules as he carried Deianira across the river Evenus, earlier called Lycormas.

LIBER V

Pulsa sitis fluvio, populataque gurgitis alveum
agmina linquebant ripas amnemque minorem;
acrior et campum sonipes rapit et pedes arva
implet ovans. rediere viris animique minaeque
5   votaque, sanguineis mixtum ceu fontibus ignem
hausissent belli magnasque in proelia mentes.
dispositi in turmas rursus legemque severi
ordinis, ut cuique ante locus ductorque, monentur
instaurare vias. tellus iam pulvere primo
10 crescit, et armorum transmittunt fulgura silvae.
qualia trans pontum Phariis defensa serenis
rauca Paraetonio decedunt agmina Nilo,
cum fera ponit hiems: illae clangore fugaci,
umbra fretis arvisque, volant, sonat avius aether.
15 iam Borean imbresque pati, iam nare solutis
amnibus et nudo iuvat aestivare sub Haemo.
    Hic rursus simili procerum vallante corona
dux Talaionides, antiqua ut forte sub orno
stabat et admoti nixus Polynicis in hastam:
20 'attamen, o quaecumque es,' ait, 'cui gloria tanta,
venimus, innumeras Fato debere cohortes,

1 alvum ω: altum P (ς)   13 ponit ω Σ: cogit P
21 innumerae Pω (*SB1*)   fatum Pω (ς, *Garrod*)

270

BOOK 5

Thirst quenched by the river, the army was leaving its ravaged bed and banks—a smaller stream. Brisker now the
courser devours the plain and the foot soldier exultant
throngs the fields. Spirit and threat and hope return to the
warriors, as though they had consumed war-fire mingled in
bloody waters and hearts high for battle. Marshalled again
into their formations and the stern rule of rank, each with
his former place and captain, they are ordered to resume
their march. Now earth rises in the first dust and the woods
transmit the flash of arms. Even as the noisy swarms sheltered overseas by Pharian calm leave Paraetonian Nile
when wild winter subsides; they fly with fleeing clamour, a
shadow over sea and land, the pathless ether resounds;
now they are fain to suffer North Wind and rains, swim in
melted rivers, and pass summer under naked[1] Haemus.

Then once more speaks the leader, Talaus' son, circled
by a band of noble peers, as he stands beneath an ancient
ash, leaning on the spear of Polynices at his side: 'And yet
come tell us, whosoever you be to whom we have brought
such glory, the glory of owing countless cohorts to fate,[2] an

[1] Free of snow.
[2] I.e. of saving the soldiers' lives.

quem non ipse deum sator aspernetur honorem,
dic age, quando tuis alacres absistimus undis,
quae domus aut tellus, animam quibus hauseris astris,
25 dic quis et ille pater. neque enim tibi numina longe,
transierit Fortuna licet, maiorque per ora
sanguis, et afflicto spirat reverentia vultu.'
      Ingemit, et paulum fletu cunctata modesto
Lemnias orsa refert: 'immania vulnera, rector,
30 integrare iubes, Furias et Lemnon et artis
arma inserta toris debellatosque pudendo
ense mares; redit ecce nefas et frigida cordi
Eumenis. o miserae, quibus hic furor additus! o nox!
o pater! illa ego nam, pudeat ne forte benignae
35 hospitis, illa, duces, raptum quae sola parentem
occului. quid longa malis exordia necto?
et vos arma vocant magnique in corde paratus.
hoc memorasse sat est: claro generata Thoante
servitium Hypsipyle vestri fero capta Lycurgi.'
40   Advertere animos, maiorque et honora videri
parque operi tanto; cunctis tunc noscere casus
ortus amor, pater ante alios hortatur Adrastus:
'immo age, dum primi longe edimus agmina vulgi
(nec facilis Nemea latas evolvere vires,
45 quippe obtenta comis et ineluctabilis umbra),
pande nefas laudesque tuas gemitusque tuorum,
unde hos advenias regno deiecta labores.'
      Dulce loqui miseris veteresque reducere questus.
incipit: 'Aegaeo premitur circumflua Nereo

43 longe damus Pω (SB)

honour which the begetter of the gods himself would not despise, come tell us, as we briskly leave your waters, what is your home and country, under what stars you draw your breath. And say, who is that father? For the gods are not far from you, though Fortune has deserted, high blood is in your aspect, awe breathes in your afflicted face.'

The Lemnian sighs, stays awhile in modest tears, then makes reply: 'Ruler, you bid me freshen monstrous wounds—Furies and Lemnos and weapons brought into narrow beds and men fought down with swords of shame. Ah, to my heart the crime returns, the cold Fury. Alas for them on whom was brought this madness! Ah night! Ah father! For I am she, captains, lest perchance you be ashamed of your kindly hostess, she who alone snatched her parent away and hid him. Why do I weave a long preamble to a tale of woe? And arms summon you and the great enterprise you have at heart. This much it is enough to tell: I am Hypsipyle, child of famous Thoas; a captive, I bear the thraldom of your Lycurgus.'

They paid heed. Greater she seemed, deserving of respect, equal to such a work. Then in all arose a wish to learn the story. First of them all father Adrastus urges her: 'Nay come, while we bring out our leading columns in long array (not ready is Nemea to roll out a broad power, screened as she is by foliage and enmeshed in forest shade), set forth the crime and your merit and the laments of your people, from whence you came to your troubles here, cast out from your realm.'

The unhappy love to talk and bring back old sorrows. She begins: 'Aegean Nereus surrounds the isle of Lemnos,

50 Lemnos, ubi ignifera fessus respirat ab Aetna
    Mulciber. ingenti tellurem proximus umbra
    vestit Athos nemorumque obscurat imagine pontum.
    Thraces arant contra, Thracum fatalia nobis
    litora, et inde nefas. florebat dives alumnis
55 terra, nec illa Samo fama Delove sonanti
    peior et innumeris quas spumifer assilit Aegon.
    dis visum turbare domos, nec pectora culpa
    nostra vacant: nullos Veneri sacravimus ignes,
    nulla deae sedes; movet et caelestia quondam
60 corda dolor lentoque irrepunt agmine Poenae.
    illa Paphon veterem centumque altaria linquens,
    nec vultu nec crine prior, solvisse iugalem
    ceston et Idalias procul ablegasse volucres
    fertur. erant certe media quae noctis in umbra
65 divam alios ignes maioraque tela gerentem
    Tartareas inter thalamis volitasse Sorores
    vulgarent, utque implicitis arcana domorum
    anguibus et saeva formidine nupta replesset
    limina nec fidi populum miserata mariti.
70 protinus a Lemno teneri fugistis Amores:
    mutus Hymen versaeque faces et frigida iusti
    cura tori. nullae redeunt in gaudia noctes,
    nullus in amplexu sopor est, Odia aspera ubique
    et Furor et medio recubat Discordia lecto.
75 cura viris tumidos adversa Thracas in ora
    eruere et saevam bellando frangere gentem.
    cumque domus contra stantesque in litore nati,
    dulcius Edonias hiemes Arctonque prementem

78 prementem P: fr- ω

274

where Mulicber[3] draws breath weary from fire-burning
Aetna. Athos close by clothes the land with his huge
shadow and darkens the sea with the image of his forests.
Thracians plough opposite, the shores of the Thracians
were our doom, thence came the crime. The land was
wealthy, flourishing in her children, no less in fame than
Samos or sounding Delos or the countless isles on which
Aegon dashes his foam. It pleased the gods to set our
homes in turmoil, nor were our hearts free of blame; we
consecrated no fires to Venus, the goddess had no dwelling
among us. Hurt sometimes moves even heavenly hearts
and the powers of vengeance creep slowly in. She leaves
ancient Paphos and her hundred altars, changed in countenance and hair; they say she loosened her girdle of love
and banished afar her Idalian birds. Of a certainty there
were some women who put it about how in the mid darkness of night the goddess had flitted through bedchambers
bearing other fires and larger weapons in company with
the Tartarean Sisters, and how she had filled secret places
in our homes with twined snakes and our nuptial thresholds with fierce terror, pitying not her husband's people, faithful though he be. Forthwith, tender Loves, you
fled from Lemnos. Hymen fell silent, his torches reversed;
chilled was the care of the lawful couch. No nights return
for joys, none sleeps in an embrace, everywhere is harsh
Hate and Madness, Strife lies in the middle of the bed. The
men are set to root out the vaunting Thracians on the facing coast and to break the savage race by war. Their homes
front them and their children standing on the shore, but
they would rather take Edonian winters and the Bear upon

3 Vulcan.

excipere, aut tandem tacita post proelia nocte
80   fractorum subitas torrentum audire ruinas.
illae autem tristes (nam me tunc libera curis
virginitas annique tegunt) sub nocte dieque
assiduis aegrae in lacrimis solantia miscent
colloquia, aut saevam spectant trans aequora Thracen.
85   Sol operum medius summo librabat Olympo
lucentes, ceu staret, equos; quater axe sereno
intonuit, quater antra dei fumantis anhelos
exseruere apices, ventisque absentibus Aegon
motus et ingenti percussit litora ponto:
90   cum subito horrendas aevi matura Polyxo
tollitur in furias thalamisque insueta relictis
evolat. insano veluti Teumesia Thyias
rapta deo, cum sacra vocant Idaeaque suadet
buxus et a summis auditus montibus Euhan:
95   sic, erecta genas aciemque offusa trementi
sanguine, desertam rabidis clamoribus urbem
exagitat clausasque domos et limina pulsans
concilium vocat; infelix comitatus eunti
haerebant nati. atque illae non segnius omnes
100 erumpunt tectis, summasque ad Pallados arces
impetus: huc propere stipamur et ordine nullo
congestae; stricto mox ense silentia iussit
hortatrix scelerum et medio sic ausa profari:
       "Rem summam instinctu superum meritique doloris,
105 o viduae (firmate animos et pellite sexum!)
Lemniades, sancire paro; si taedet inanes
aeternum servare domos turpemque iuventae

95 effusa Pω (ς, *Barth*)   96 rabidis ω: rapi- Pψ
103 orsa *Bentley*

their heads or after battle at last in the silent night hear the sudden crash of broken torrents. Their sad wives (as for me, maidenhood free of cares and my years were my protection then) by night and day languish in constant tears, they mingle consoling converse or gaze across the sea at cruel Thrace.

Halfway through his task, the sun was poising his bright horses on Olympus' summit as though standing still. Four times it thundered in a clear sky, four times the cavern of the smoking god[4] put forth panting crests, Aegon was stirred though winds were absent and struck the shores with a mighty surge, when of a sudden old Polyxo rises into a fearsome frenzy, leaves her chamber against her habit, and darts forth. Like a Teumesian Thyiad seized by the frantic god, when the rites call and Ida's boxwood urges and Euhan is heard from the mountain tops, so, with eyelids upstanding and pupils suffused with quivering blood she rouses the deserted city with her crazy clamours; beating on closed houses and thresholds, she calls an assembly. Her children clung to her as she went, ill-starred companions. All the women promptly burst forth from their dwellings and rush to the citadel of Pallas on the height. Thither we crowd in haste, piled together in confusion. Then drawing a sword, the promptress of crime commanded silence and so from our midst dared to speak:

"Widows of Lemnos, I come at the urging of the High Ones and just indignation to approve a great matter. Steel your courage and drive out your sex. If you are weary of

4 Vulcan.

277

flore situm et longis steriles in luctibus annos,
inveni, promitto, viam (nec numina desunt)
110   qua renovanda Venus: modo par insumite robur
luctibus. atque adeo primum hoc mihi noscere detur:
tertia canet hiems: cui conubialia vincla
aut thalami secretus honos? cui coniuge pectus
intepuit? cuius vidit Lucina labores,
115   dicite, vel iustos cuius pulsantia menses
vota tument? qua pace feras volucresque iugari
mos datus. heu segnes! potuitne ultricia Graius
virginibus dare tela pater laetusque dolorum
sanguine securos iuvenum perfundere somnos:
120   at nos vulgus iners? quod si propioribus actis
est opus, ecce animos doceat Rhodopeia coniunx,
ulta manu thalamos pariterque epulata marito.
nec vos immunis scelerum securave cogo.
plena mihi domus atque ingens, en cernite, sudor.
125   quattuor hos una, decus et solacia patris,
in gremio, licet amplexu lacrimisque morentur,
transadigam ferro saniemque et vulnera fratrum
miscebo patremque super spirantibus addam.
ecqua tot in caedes animum promittit?"

                                               Agebat
130   pluribus; adverso nituerunt vela profundo:
Lemnia classis erat. rapuit gavisa Polyxo
fortunam atque iterat: "superisne vocantibus ultro
desumus? ecce rates! deus hos, deus ultor in iras
apportat coeptisque favet. nec imago quietis

    127 sanguenque *Håkanson*
    128 super ωΣ: simul P *ante corr.*

keeping empty house forever, and the flower of your youth
in shameful blight and barren years passed in long lament,
I have found, I promise it, a way (and the gods are not
wanting) for love's renewal.[5] Only take strength to match
your griefs. And let me know this first: the third winter
is white: who had bonds of wedlock or secret grace of
the bedchamber? Whose bosom warmed with her mate?
Whose pains did Lucina see, tell me, or whose prayers
swell, kicking the appointed months? Custom grants that
wild beasts and birds be joined under that covenant. Cowards! Could a Grecian father[6] give weapons of vengeance
to virgins and drench young men with blood in unsuspect-
ing sleep, joying in the treachery? Are we a bunch of do-
littles? But if we need a deed nearer home, see, let the wife
of Rhodope[7] teach us spirit, who avenged her marriage
with her hands and feasted along with her spouse. Nor
am I that urge you without part in crimes and carefree.
My house is full and greatly, see for yourselves, have I
laboured. These four together, their father's pride and
comfort, in my lap, though they stay me with hugs and
tears, shall I run through with steel, mingling the brothers'
gore and wounds, and on them add the father while they
still breathe. Does any one of you promise a stomach for so
many slaughters?"

She was urging more, but in the sea before them shone
sails; it was the Lemnian fleet. Delighted, Polyxo seized
her luck and once again: "The High Ones call us of themselves. Do we fail them? See, the ships! A god, an avenging
god, brings them to our wrath and favours the enterprise.

---

[5] As later revealed (137f.), Venus had promised to provide a
new stud.   [6] Danaus.   [7] Tereus' wife Procne.

135 vana meae: nudo astabat Venus ense videri
    clara mihi somnosque super. 'quid perditis aevum?'
    inquit, 'age aversis thalamos purgate maritis.
    ipsa faces alias melioraque foedera iungam.'
    dixit, et hoc ferrum stratis, hoc, credite, ferrum
140 imposuit. quin, o miserae, dum tempus agi rem,
    consulite; en validis spumant eversa lacertis
    aequora. Bistonides veniunt fortasse maritae."
    hinc stimuli ingentes, magnusque advolvitur astris
    clamor. Amazonio Scythiam fervere tumultu
145 lunatumque putes agmen descendere, ubi arma
    indulget pater et saevi movet ostia Belli.
    nec varius fremor aut studia in contraria rapti
    dissensus, ut plebe solet: furor omnibus idem,
    idem animus solare domos iuvenumque senumque
150 praecipitare colos plenisque affrangere parvos
    uberibus ferroque omnes exire per annos.
    tunc viridi luco (late iuga celsa Minervae
    propter opacat humum niger ipse, sed insuper ingens
    mons premit et gemina pereunt caligine soles),
155 hic sanxere fidem. tu Martia testis Enyo
    atque inferna Ceres, Stygiaeque Acheronte recluso
    ante preces venere deae; sed fallit ubique
    mixta Venus, Venus arma tenet, Venus admovet iras.
    nec de more cruor: natum Charopeia coniunx
160 obtulit. accingunt sese et mirantia ferro

    135 nuda (nudo ω) stabat Pω (*Garrod*)
    140 agi Σ: agit Pω
    152 viridi luco lucus P: -dis late lucus ω (*SB*)

    ───────────────────────────────

    8 Than a dream.   9 Mars.

Nor idle was the vision of my sleep: Venus stood beside me with naked sword, plain to see, plainer than slumber:[8] 'Why are you wasting your lives?' she says, 'Come, purge your chambers of estranged husbands. Myself will give you other torches and better unions.' She spoke, and placed this sword, this sword, believe it, on the coverlet. Nay, unhappy friends, while the time for action serves, take counsel. Look, the seas foam, churned by strong arms. Perchance Bistonian brides are coming." Hence mighty goads; and a great shout rolled starward. 'Twas as though Scythia was afire with Amazonian tumult and the crescent-shielded host descending when their father[9] allows them arms and opens the gates of cruel War. The uproar is not various, with discordant voices caught up into conflicting factions, as is the way of a populace. The same madness is for all, the same will to make homes desolate, cut short life's threads for old and young, break little ones[10] at the full breast, and carry the sword through every generation. Then in a green grove that broadly shades the ground close to Minerva's high hill, dark itself, but upon it the great mountain presses down and the suns perish in a double murk—here they pledged their faith. Martian Enyo was witness and Ceres of the underworld,[11] the Stygian goddesses came before they were invoked, Acheron was opened; but Venus was everywhere, mingling though unseen, Venus holds the weapons, Venus brings the wrath. Nor was the blood as of wont:[12] Charops' wife offered her son. They gird themselves for action and break his wonder-

10 What little ones? Cf. 114.
11 Proserpina; cf. 4.459f.
12 It was human.

pectora congestis avidae simul undique dextris
perfringunt, ac dulce nefas in sanguine vivo
coniurant, matremque recens circumvolat umbra.
    Talia cernenti mihi quantus in ossibus horror,
165 quisve per ora color! qualis cum cerva cruentis
circumuenta lupis, nullum cui pectore molli
robur et in volucri tenuis fiducia cursu,
praecipitat suspensa fugam, iam iamque teneri
credit et elusos audit concurrere morsus.
170   Illi aderant, primis iamque offendere carinae
litoribus, certant saltu contingere terram
praecipites. miseri, quos non aut horrida virtus
Marte sub Odrysio, aut medii inclementia ponti
hauserit! alta etiam superum delubra vaporant
175 promissasque trahunt pecudes: niger omnibus aris
ignis, et in nullis spirat deus integer extis.
tardius umenti noctem deiecit Olympo
Iuppiter et versum miti, reor, aethera cura
sustinuit, dum Fata vetant, nec longius umquam
180 cessavere novae perfecto sole tenebrae.
sera tamen mundo venerunt astra, sed illis
et Paros et nemorosa Thasos crebraeque relucent
Cyclades; una gravi penitus latet obruta caelo
Lemnos, in hanc tristes nebulae et plaga caeca superne
185 texitur, una vagis Lemnos non agnita nautis.
iam domibus fusi et nemorum per opaca sacrorum
ditibus indulgent epulis vacuantque profundo
aurum immane mero, dum quae per Strymona pugnae,

161 congestis ψ: -tisque Pω
179 vetant ω: -at P

ing breast with steel, hands stretching greedily from every side at once. In the living blood they swear the delicious crime and the new ghost flits around the mother.

As I saw such things, what shuddering was in my bones, what colour on my face! Like a deer surrounded by bloody wolves, whose soft heart knows no strength, whose meagre trust is in her speed; in terror she flees headlong and each moment thinks herself caught, hearing the snap of the bites she has eluded.

They were come. And now the keels have met the strand's verge and vying in their haste they leap ashore. Wretches, whom neither their grim valour in Odrysian warfare nor the separating sea's inclemency has taken off! And they fill lofty shrines of the High Ones with smoke of incense and drag the promised victims. At all the altars the flame is black, in no entrails breathes[13] the god unflawed. Slower than of wont Jupiter cast night down from dewy Olympus and with gentle care, methinks, held back the turning sky, even as the Fates forbid; nor did new darkness ever tarry longer after the sun's work was done. Yet however late, the stars came to the heavens; but Paros and wooded Thasos and the crowd of Cyclades shine back at them, while Lemnos alone hides deep, enveloped by a heavy sky. Gloomy fogs are woven against her and an overhanging tract of darkness. Lemnos alone is unrecognized by wandering sailors. Now stretched out in their homes and in the shade of sacred groves they indulge in sumptuous banquets and empty great golden goblets of their depth of wine, as they tell at their leisure of fights along the

[13] Probably from *Aeneid* 4.64 *spirantia consulit exta*, where Servius interprets 'palpitating, as though still alive.'

quis Rhodope gelidove labor sudatus in Haemo
190 enumerare vacat. nec non, manus impia, nuptae
serta inter festasque dapes quo maxima cultu
quaeque iacent. dederat mites Cytherea suprema
nocte viros longoque brevem post tempore pacem
nequiquam et miseros perituro afflaverat igni.
195 conticuere chori, dapibus ludoque licenti
fit modus et primae decrescunt murmura noctis,
cum consanguinei mixtus caligine Leti
rore madens Stygio morituram amplectitur urbem
Somnus et implacido fundit gravia otia cornu
200 secernitque viros. vigilant nuptaeque nurusque
in scelus, atque hilares acuunt fera tela Sorores.
invasere nefas, cuncto sua regnat Erinys
pectore. non aliter Scythicos armenta per agros
Hyrcanae clausere leae, quas exigit ortu
205 prima fames, avidique implorant ubera nati.
    Quos tibi iam dubito scelerum de mille figuris
expediam casus. Helymum temeraria Gorge
evinctum ramis altaque in mole tapetum
efflantem somno crescentia vina superstans
210 vulnera disiecta rimatur veste, sed illum
infelix sopor admota sub morte refugit.
turbidus incertumque oculis vigilantibus hostem
occupat amplexu, nec segnius illa tenentis
pone adigit costas donec sua pectora ferro
215 tangeret. is demum sceleri modus; ora supinat
blandus adhuc oculisque tremens et murmure Gorgen
quaerit et indigno non solvit bracchia collo.
non ego nunc vulgi quamquam crudelia pandam

206 nam Pω (SB)

Strymon, of sweat and toil on Rhodope or icy Haemus.
Amid the garlands and festal fare lie their wives, impious
band, each decked in her finest. On their last night
Cytherea had made their husbands gentle, vainly granting
a brief truce after so long, and touched the unhappy men
with a breath of short-lived passion. The dances fall silent,
a term is set to the feasting and wanton sport, the sounds
of early night die down. Mingled with the darkness of
his kinsman Death and dripping with Stygian dew, Sleep
enfolds the doomed city, pouring heavy ease from his
unforgiving horn, and separates the men. Wives and sons'
wives are awake for crime and the Sisters cheerfully
sharpen their savage weaponry. They fell to their wicked
work; in every heart reigns its Fury. Not otherwise do
Hyrcanian lionesses encircle herds in Scythian fields; early
hunger drives them forth at dawn and their greedy cubs
implore their udders.

Which of crime's thousand shapes I should now relate
to you I know not. Audacious Gorge stands over Helymus
as wreathed in branches on a great pile of cushions he
breathes out his wine that gathers strength in his sleep; she
probes in his disordered garments for a place to strike, but
his unlucky slumber deserts him at death's approach. Confused with eyes doubtfully awake, he seizes the enemy in
an embrace, but she promptly drives from behind into his
ribs as he holds her until she touches her own breast with
the steel. That finished the crime. He lets his head fall back
and still affectionate with quivering eyes and murmur he
seeks Gorge nor loosens his arms from her unworthy neck.
I shall not now set forth the deaths of the crowd, cruel

285

funera, sed propria luctus de stirpe recordor:
220 quod te, flave Cydon, quod te per colla refusis
intactum, Crenaee, comis quibus ubera mecum
obliquumque a patre genus, fortemque, timebam
quem desponsa, Gyan vidi lapsare cruentae
vulnere Myrmidones, quodque inter serta torosque
225 barbara ludentem fodiebat Epopea mater.
flet super aequaevum soror exarmata Lycaste
Cydimon, heu similes perituro in corpore vultus
aspiciens floremque genae et quas finxerat auro
ipsa comas, cum saeva parens iam coniuge fuso
230 astitit impellitque minis atque inserit ensem.
ut fera, quae rabiem placido desueta magistro
tardius arma movet stimulisque et verbere crebro
in mores negat ire suos, sic illa iacenti
incidit undantemque sinu collapsa cruorem
235 excipit et laceros premit in nova vulnera crines.
    Ut vero Alcimeden etiamnum in murmure truncos
ferre patris vultus et egentem sanguinis ensem
conspexi, riguere comae atque in viscera saevus
horror iit: meus ille Thoas, mea dira videri
240 dextra mihi! extemplo thalamis turbata paternis
inferor. ille quidem dudum (quis magna tuenti
somnus?) agit versans secum, etsi lata recessit
urbe domus, quinam strepitus, quae murmura noctis,
cur fremibunda quies. trepido scelus ordine pando,
245 quis dolor, unde animi: "vis nulla arcere furentes;
hac sequere, o miserande; premunt aderuntque moranti,

---

14 As a virgin.
15 The old man had not much to give.

though they were, but I recall bereavements in my own family. I saw you fall, blond Cydon, and you, Crenaeus, with your untouched locks flowing down your neck; you were my foster brothers, my father's sons on the side. You too, strong Gyas, my betrothed whom I feared,[14] I saw fall by the stroke of bloody Myrmidone, and how his barbarous mother stabbed Epopeus as he played among the chaplets and couches. Lycaste weeps disarmed over her brother of equal age, Cydimus, watching the face alas so like her own upon his doomed body, and the bloom on his cheek and the locks she had herself twined with gold, when their savage mother, who had already slain her husband, takes stand beside her, urging her with threats and putting the sword in her hands. Like a wild beast that under a gentle master has lost the habit of fury and is slow to show fight, refusing to resume its old ways despite goads and many a lash, so she falls upon him as he lies and collapsing receives his streaming blood in her bosom and presses her torn hair into the fresh wounds.

But when I saw Alcimede carrying her father's severed but still murmuring head and a sword in need of blood,[15] my hair stood stiff and a cruel shudder pierced my vitals. To me he seemed my Thoas and the fell hand seemed mine. Forthwith I hie me distraught to my father's chamber. He was long awake to be sure (what sleep for him that has great charge?), asking himself (though our house lay far back from the city) what the noises, what the sounds in the night, why clamourous the quiet. To him as he trembled I reveal the crime in sequence, what the grief, whence the bold spirit: "They are mad, no force can keep them off. Follow this way, unfortunate. They press, they will be on you if you tarry, and mayhap you will fall with

et mecum fortasse cades." his motus et artus
erexit stratis. ferimur per devia vastae
urbis et ingentem nocturnae caedis acervum
250   passim, ut quosque sacris crudelis vespera lucis
straverat, occulta speculamur nube latentes.
hic impressa toris ora exstantesque reclusis
pectoribus capulos magnarum et fragmina trunca
hastarum et ferro laceras per corpora vestes,
255   crateras pronos epulasque in caede natantes
cernere erat, iugulisque modo torrentis apertis
sanguine commixto redeuntem in pocula Bacchum.
hic iuvenum manus et nullis violabilis armis
turba senes, positique patrum super ora gementum
260   semineces pueri trepidas in limine vitae
singultant animas. gelida non saevius Ossa
luxuriant Lapitharum epulae, si quando profundo
Nubigenae caluere mero: vix primus ab ira
pallor, et impulsis surgunt ad proelia mensis.
265   Tunc primum sese trepidis sub nocte Thyoneus
detexit, nato portans extrema Thoanti
subsidia, et multa subitus cum luce refulsit.
agnovi: non ille quidem turgentia sertis
tempora nec flava crinem distinxerat uva:
270   nubilus indignumque oculis liquentibus imbrem
alloquitur: "dum Fata dabant tibi, nate, potentem
Lemnon et externis etiam servare timendam
gentibus, haud umquam iusto mea cura labori
destitit: absciderunt tristes crudelia Parcae
275   stamina, nec dictis, supplex quae plurima fudi
ante Iovem frustra, lacrimisque avertere luctus

---

[16] Centaurs.

me." Thus alarmed, he roused himself from the couch. We take our way through byways of the deserted city, hiding in secret darkness, descrying everywhere a huge pile of the night's massacre, as the cruel evening had laid them low in the sacred groves. Here could be seen faces pressed down on couches, sword hilts standing out from opened breasts, broken fragments of large spears and knife-torn clothes among the bodies, mixing bowls overturned, victuals swimming in gore, and Bacchus mixed with blood returning in torrents from severed throats into the wine cups. Here is a company of young men, here a gathering whom no weapons should violate, the old; and half-dead boys, placed on the faces of their moaning parents, sob out their trembling spirits on the threshold of life. In no crueler fashion do the feasts of the Lapithae on chill Ossa run riot when the cloud-born ones[16] have grown warm with deep draughts of wine; scarce comes anger's first pallor and they upset the tables and rise to battle.[17]

Then for the first time Thyoneus revealed himself to us in our trepidation, bringing last-minute aid to his son Thoas, and shone out in a sudden blaze of light. I knew him, though he had not bound his swelling temples with garlands nor his hair with yellow grapes. Cloudy, his eyes shedding an unseemly rain, he addresses us: "My son, while I was permitted by the Fates to keep Lemnos for you powerful and feared even by foreign peoples, my care never ceased from this lawful toil. The gloomy Parcae have severed their cruel threads, nor has it fallen to me to avert these woes by words, of which I have poured many in vain,

---

[17] As though the famous banquet fight between Centaurs and Lapiths was recurrent.

contigit; infandum natae concessit honorem.
accelerate fugam, tuque, o mea digna propago,
hac rege, virgo, patrem, gemini qua bracchia muri
280 litus eunt: illa, qua rere silentia, porta
stat funesta Venus ferroque accincta furentes
adiuuat (unde manus, unde haec Mavortia divae
pectora?). tu lato patrem committe profundo:
succedam curis." ita fatus in aëra rursus
285 solvitur et nostrum, visus arcentibus umbris,
mitis iter longae claravit limite flammae.
qua data signa sequor; dein curvo robore clausum
dis pelagi Ventisque et Cycladas Aegaeoni
amplexo commendo patrem, nec fletibus umquam
290 sit modus alternis, ni iam dimittat Eoo
Lucifer astra polo. tunc demum litore rauco
multa metu reputans et vix confisa Lyaeo
dividor, ipsa gradu nitente, sed anxia retro
pectora; nec requies quin et surgentia caelo
295 flamina et e cunctis prospectem collibus undas.
    Exoritur pudibunda dies, caelumque retexens
aversum Lemno iubar et declinia Titan
opposita iuga nube refert. patuere furores
nocturni, lucisque novae formidine cunctis
300 (quamquam inter similes) subitus pudor; impia terrae
infodiunt scelera aut festinis ignibus urunt.
    Iam manus Eumenidum captasque refugerat arces

---

280 rere P(?), ς: rara ω   290 fit Pω (*Gronovius*)
300 habitus PωΣ (*Bentley*)

---

18 Venus, given leave to punish the Lemnians.
19 The Aegean Sea personified.

suppliant before Jove, and tears. To his daughter[18] he has given a heinous privilege. Hasten your flight both, and do you, maiden, my worthy offspring, guide your father by the way where the arms of the double wall go down to the sea. At that gate where you think all is silence stands baleful Venus and girt with sword encourages the mad-women (whence the goddess' violence, whence this Martian heart?). Entrust your father to the broad deep. I shall take over your cares." So speaking, he dissolves again into air and as the shadows block our vision the kindly god lights up our track with a long strip of flame. I follow the guidance given. Then to the gods of the sea and the Winds and Aegaeon[19] embracing the Cyclades I entrust my father hidden in curved timber. Our mutual tears would have no term, were not Lucifer now dismissing the stars from eastern heaven. Then indeed on the sounding shore, with many a fear in mind and scarce trusting Lyaeus, I separate. With urgent step I go, but my troubled heart looks back; nor do I rest from viewing from every hill the breezes rising in the sky and the waves.

Dawn comes up ashamed and Titan revealing[20] the heavens turns his rays from Lemnos, bringing back his chariot aslant behind a cloud. The madness of the night showed plain, and in fear of the new light sudden shame was upon them all, though all were in like case. They bury their impious crimes in earth or burn them in hasty fires.

Now the band of the Furies and Venus full-sated had

[20] *Retexens*, properly 'unraveling,' is here used in the sense of *retegens* (which would not have scanned). Håkanson explains the anomaly as due to a probably subconscious reminiscence of *Aeneid* 4.119 *radiisque retexerit* (from *retego*) *orbem*.

exsaturata Venus; licuit sentire quid ausae,
et turbare comas et lumina tingere fletu.
305 insula dives agris opibusque armisque virisque,
nota situ et Getico nuper ditata triumpho,
non maris incursu, non hoste, nec aethere laevo
perdidit una omnes orbata excisaque mundo
indigenas: non arva viri, non aequora vertunt,
310 conticuere domus, cruor altus et oblita crasso
cuncta rubent tabo, magnaeque in moenibus urbis
nos tantum et saevi spirant per culmina manes.
ipsa quoque arcanis tecti in penetralibus alto
molior igne pyram, sceptrum super armaque patris
315 inicio et notas regum velamina vestes,
ac prope maesta rogum confusis crinibus asto
ense cruentato, fraudemque et inania busta
plango metu, si forte premam, cassumque parenti
omen et hac dubios leti precor ire timores.
320 his mihi pro meritis, ut falsi criminis astu
parta fides, regna et solio considere patris
(supplicium!) datur. anne illis obsessa negarem?
accessi, saepe ante deos testata fidemque
immeritasque manus; subeo (pro dira potestas!)
325 exsangue imperium et maestam sine culmine Lemnon.
   Iam magis atque magis vigiles dolor angere sensus,
et gemitus clari, et paulatim invisa Polyxo,
iam meminisse nefas, iam ponere manibus aras
concessum et multum cineres iurare sepultos.
330 sic ubi ductorem trepidae stabulique maritum,

308 fundo ς   315 velamina P: gesta- ω
316 ignibus Pω (ς, *Lachmann*)
318 ne ς   premant Pω (*SB*)

fled the captured city. The women could realize what they
had dared and disorder their hair and bathe their eyes with
weeping. The island, prosperous in land and wealth, in
arms and men, known of its site[21] and lately enriched by a
Getic triumph, at one blow, not by invasion of the sea or
enemy or hostile atmosphere, lost all its people, orphaned
and cut out from the world. Men no longer turn the fields
or the waters. Silent the houses, deep the blood, all things
stained red with clotted gore. Only we are left in the buildings of the great city and on the rooftops fierce spirits
breathe. I too in the secret recesses of our dwelling build a
high-flaming pyre and cast thereon my father's sceptre and
arms and his well known garments, the dress of kings. In
sadness with disordered hair and bloody sword I stand
near and fearfully lament the cheat, the empty mound,
hoping to cover up;[22] and I pray that the omen bring no
harm to my parent and that doubting fears of his death be
so discharged.[23] For these merits, when the trick of a false
crime won credence, it was given me to reign and sit upon
my father's throne—punishment! So beset, was I to refuse
them? I agreed, but only after calling often on the gods and
the truth and my innocence. I take on (ah dire authority!) a
bloodless power, a Lemnos sad and headless.

Now more and more grief torments their wakeful
senses, lamentations are loud, and little by little they come
to hate Polyxo. Now it is permitted to remember the atrocity, now to build altars to the spirits and often swear by the
buried dust. So when trembling heifers see thunderstruck

---

[21] Everyone knew where it was.   [22] *Premant* makes no
sense. This idiom expresses something expected or hoped for.
[23] That the false funeral substitute for a real one; see SB[1].

quem penes et saltus et aduncae gloria gentis,
Massylo frangi stupuere sub hoste iuvencae,
it truncum sine honore pecus, regemque peremptum
ipse ager, ipsi amnes et muta arbusta queruntur.
335   Ecce autem aerata dispellens aequora prora
Pelias intacti late subit hospita ponti
pinus; agunt Minyae, geminus fragor ardua canet
per latera: abruptam credas radicibus ire
Ortygiam aut fractum pelago decurrere montem.
340 ast ubi suspensis siluerunt aequora tonsis,
mitior et senibus cycnis et pectine Phoebi
vox media de puppe venit, maria ipsa carinae
accedunt. post nosse datum est: Oeagrius illic
acclinis malo mediis intersonat Orpheus
345 remigiis tantosque iubet nescire labores.
illis in Scythicum Borean iter oraque Ponti
Cyaneis artata moris. nos, Thracia visu
bella ratae, vario tecta incursare tumultu,
densarum pecudum aut fugientum more volucrum.
350 heu ubi nunc Furiae? portus amplexaque litus
moenia, qua longe pelago despectus aperto,
scandimus et celsas turres; huc saxa sudesque
armaque maesta virum atque infectos caedibus enses

---

331 adultae Pω (*SB²*)   334 armenta Pω (*SB²*)
346 primi PΣ: -mum ω (*Markland*)
347 maris P: vadis ωΣ (*SB²*)   350 furiae *edd.* (*Hill*)

---

24 Lit. 'hooked.' Cattle are hooked because their horns are
hooked, as are eagles because of their beaks and talons; cf. 12.212
uncis alitibus, Ovid, *Fasti* 6.196 *praepes adunca Iovis*. Statius may
well have been thinking of Homer's ἕλικες (SB²). As for *adultae*,

the leader and husband of the stall, to whom belong the pastures and glory of the horned[24] folk, broken under a Massylian foe;[25] the herd goes maimed, its pride departed; the very land, the very rivers, and the mute trees[26] bemoan the slain king.

But see! Dividing the waters with her brazen prow comes the pine of Pelion, guest at large of the virgin[27] sea. The Minyae drive her, a double splashing whitens at her tall bows, you might think Ortygia was on the move reft from her roots or that a broken mountain was running over the main. But when the oars were held in the air and the sea fell silent, a voice gentler than aged swans and Phoebus' quill comes from the vessel's midst and the very waters draw near the ship. Later we came to learn: there Oeagrian Orpheus leaning against the mast makes music amid the rowers and bids them forget their heavy toils. Their voyage was to Scythian Boreas and the shores of Pontus narrowed by Cyanean blocks.[28] At sight of them we took them for Thracian warfare and ran to our homes in a mingled flurry like thronging cattle or fleeing birds. Alas, where now the Furies? We climb the harbour and the walls around the shore, which give a long view down over the open sea, and lofty towers. Hither in trembling haste they haul rocks and stakes and their husbands' mourning ar-

did not the steers and heifers and calves take pride in their chief bull?   [25] A lion.

[26] *Armenta*, 'herds' makes an anticlimax; see SB[2].

[27] Argo was recognized as the first ship to sail, but poets are not thereby inhibited from talking of earlier navigations, as Statius does at large in this Book and Valerius Flaccus in 2.108.

[28] See SB[2].

subvectant trepidae; quin et squalentia texta
355 thoracum et vultu galeas intrare soluto
non pudet; audaces rubuit mirata catervas
Pallas, et averso risit Gradivus in Haemo.
tunc primum ex animis praeceps amentia cessit,
nec ratis illa salo, sed divum sera per aequor
360 iustitia et poenae scelerum adventare videntur.
iamque aberant terris quantum Gortynia currunt
spicula, caeruleo gravidam cum Iuppiter imbri
ipsa super nubem ratis armamenta Pelasgae
sistit agens; inde horror aquis, et raptus ab omni
365 sole dies miscet tenebras, quis protinus unda
concolor; obnixi lacerant cava nubila venti
diripiuntque fretum, nigris redit umida tellus
verticibus, totumque Notis certantibus aequor
pendet et arquato iam iam prope sidera dorso
370 frangitur; incertae nec iam prior impetus alno,
sed labat exstantem rostris modo gurgite in imo,
nunc caelo Tritona ferens. nec robora prosunt
semideum heroum, puppemque insana flagellat
arbor et instabili procumbens pondere curvas
375 raptat aquas, remique cadunt in pectus inanes.
nos quoque per rupes murorumque aggere ab omni,
dum labor ille viris fretaque indignantur et Austros,
desuper invalidis fluitantia tela lacertis
(quid non ausa manus?) Telamona et Pelea contra
380 spargimus, et nostro petitur Tirynthius arcu.
illi (quippe simul bello pelagoque laborant),
pars clipeis munire ratem, pars aequora fundo

361 terris Pψ: terrae ω, *fort. recte*
376 per turres *Damsté*

296

mour and slaughter-tainted swords. They are not ashamed even to don scaly coats of mail and put helmets on their nerveless faces. Pallas blushed in amazement at the bold bands and Gradivus in distant Haemus laughed. Then for the first time headlong frenzy left their minds. Not that ship, they thought, but the gods' tardy justice, the punishment of crime, was approaching over the salt sea. And now they were away from land the length of a Gortynian arrow's flight when Jupiter sends a cloud pregnant with dark rain and sets it just over the rigging of the Pelasgian ship. The waters roughen and the day, snatched from all its sunshine, mingles darkness matched in a trice by the colour of the waves. Thrusting winds lash hollow clouds and tear the deep apart, wet earth comes back to view in the black whirlpools. As the winds battle, the whole sea hangs poised; now its arching back nears the stars and it breaks. The ship falters, her onward drive slackens and she falls, carrying the Triton projecting from her prow now at the bottom of the flood, now in the heavens. Nor avails the strength of the demigod heroes; the crazy mast thrashes the stern and with its unstable weight leans forward to snatch up the billowing waves. The oars fall back empty on the rowers' chests. While the warriors are in these straits and protest sea and winds, we too along the cliffs and from every high point on the walls scatter from above with our feeble arms our wobbling missiles against Telamon and Peleus (what did our violence not dare?) and our bows aim at the Tirynthian. As for them, hard pressed by war and water both, some protect the ship with their shields, others

egerere; ast alii pugnant, sed inertia motu
corpora, suspensaeque carent conamine vires.
385 instamus iactu telorum, et ferrea nimbis
certat hiems, ustaeque sudes fractique molares
spiculaque et multa crinitum missile flamma
nunc pelago, nunc puppe cadunt; dat operta fragorem
pinus et abiunctis regemunt tabulata cavernis.
390 talis Hyperborea virides nive verberat agros
Iuppiter; obruitur campis genus omne ferarum,
deprensaeque cadunt volucres, et messis amaro
strata gelu, fragor inde iugis, inde amnibus irae.
ut vero elisit nubes Iove tortus ab alto
395 ignis et ingentes patuere in fulmine nautae,
deriguere animi, manibusque horrore remissis
arma aliena cadunt, rediit in pectora sexus.
cernimus Aeacidas murisque immane minantem
Ancaeum et longa pellentem cuspide rupes
400 Iphiton; at toto manifestus in agmine supra est
Amphitryoniades puppemque alternus utrimque
ingravat et medias ardet descendere in undas.
at levis et miserae nondum mihi notus Iason
transtra per et remos impressaque terga virorum
405 nunc magnum Oeniden, nunc ille hortatibus Idan
et Talaum et cana rorantem aspergine ponti
Tyndariden iterans gelidique in nube parentis
vela laborantem Calain subnectere malo
voce manuque rogat; quatiunt impulsibus illi
410 nunc freta, nunc muros, sed nec spumantia cedunt

386 ustae ψ: vastae Pω, *Prisc. GLK 2.161.21*
389 ab iunctis ψΣ   400 attonito Pω (*Menke*)
408 laboranti *Bentley*

bale the sea from the hold, others fight; but their bodies
are clumsy from the motion, their suspended might lacks
energy. We urge the harder with discharge of bolts, the
iron storm vies with the downpour, burnt stakes and broken millstones and darts and missiles with tresses of abun-
dant flame fall now in the sea, now in the ship, the covered
pine resounds and the planks in the hollows down under[29]
groan in response. So does Jupiter lash green fields with
Hyperborean snow; every kind of wild beast on the plain
is buried, the birds are caught and fall, the harvest is flattened with noxious ice, there is roaring in the mountains
and wrath in the rivers. But when fire flung from Jove aloft
smashed the clouds and the huge mariners showed plain in
the flash, hearts froze, hands relaxed in a shudder, alien
weapons fell, their sex returned to their hearts. We see
the sons of Aeacus and Ancaeus direly threatening our
walls and Iphitus pushing off the cliffs with his long spear.
But Amphitryon's son towers conspicuous in all the band,
weighing down the ship now on one side, now on the other,
and burns to plunge into the waves. But Jason, known to
me, alas, not yet, passes nimbly over benches and oars,
footing the backs of the heroes, urging and urging again
with voice and hand now Oeneus' great son, now Idas and
Talaus and a son of Tyndareus[30] as he drips with the sea's
white spray and Calais as he struggles in his father's[31] icy
fog to bind the sails to the mast. With their strokes they
shake now the sea, now the walls; but the foaming waters

[29] The meaning of *abiunctis* is uncertain.
[30] Whether Castor or Pollux.
[31] His father was the North Wind (Boreas, Aquilo).

aequora, et incussae redeunt a turribus hastae.
ipse graves fluctus clavumque audire negantem
lassat agens Tiphys palletque et plurima mutat
imperia ac laevas dextrasque obtorquet in undas
415 proram navifragis avidam concurrere saxis,
donec ab extremae cuneo ratis Aesone natus
Palladios oleae, Mopsi gestamina, ramos
extulit et, socium turba prohibente, poposcit
foedera; praecipites vocem involvere procellae.
420 tunc modus armorum, pariterque exhausta quierant
flamina, confusoque dies respexit Olympo.
quinquaginta illi, trabibus de more revinctis,
eminus abrupto quatiunt nova litora saltu,
magnorum decora alta patrum, iam fronte sereni
425 noscendique habitu, postquam tumor iraque cessit
vultibus. arcana sic fama erumpere porta
caelicolas, si quando domos litusque rubentum
Aethiopum et mensas amor est iterare minores;
dant fluvii montesque locum, tum terra superbit
430 gressibus et paulum respirat caelifer Atlans.
    Hic et ab asserto nuper Marathone superbum
Thesea et Ismarios, Aquilonia pignora, fratres,
utraque quis rutila stridebant tempora penna,
cernimus, hic Phoebo non indignante priorem
435 Admetum et durae similem nihil Orphea Thracae,
tunc prolem Calydone satam generumque profundi

425 timor Pω (*Bentley*)
428 intrare Pω (*Schrader* (Σ *contulit Garrod*))

---

32 Or, reading *timor,* 'fear and rage.'

yield not and the spears return from the turrets they hit.
Tiphys himself wearies the massive billows and the helm
that will not hear him, grows pale, and with many a change
of orders turns the prow, so greedy to collide with wrecker
rocks, to waters left and right; until from the vessel's uttermost angle Aeson's son hoisted branches of Palladian olive,
Mopsus' wear, and asked for a truce, though his comrade
crew forbade. The rushing tempest swallowed his voice.
Then came a stay of arms and with it the wearied gales had
subsided and from the turmoil of Olympus day looked
again. The fifty heroes, their bark duly moored, leap from
the sheer height and shake the unknown shore, tall pride
of great parents, now calm of brow and of looks to be recognized once swelling rage[32] had left their faces. So the
sky-dwellers are said to burst forth from their secret gate
should it be their wish to visit again the houses and shore
and humbler banquets of the red Ethiopians;[33] rivers and
mountains give them passage, Earth is proud to feel their
tread, and sky-bearer Atlas takes a brief respite.

Here we see Theseus proud of Marathon lately freed,[34]
and the Ismarian brothers, children of Aquilo, both with
red feathers whirring at their temples, here Admetus,
whom Phoebus thought it no shame to call his better, and
Orpheus, so unlike hard Thrace, and the offspring born of
Calydon,[35] and the son-in-law of the deep's Nereus.[36] The

---

[33] In Homer (*Iliad* 1.423) the gods visit the Ethiopians and
feast with them. 'Red' indicates the eastern Ethiopians, dwelling
by the 'Red Sea' (Persian Gulf).

[34] By the slaying of the wild bull.

[35] Meleager.

[36] Peleus.

Nereos. ambiguo visus errore lacessunt
Oebalidae gemini; chlamys huic, chlamys ardet et illi,
ambo hastile gerunt, umeros exsertus uterque,
440 nudus uterque genas, simili coma fulgurat astro.
audet iter magnique sequens vestigia mutat
Herculis et tarda quamvis se mole ferentem
vix cursu tener aequat Hylas Lernaeaque tollens
arma sub ingenti gaudet sudare pharetra.

445 Ergo iterum Venus, et tacitis corda aspera flammis
Lemniadum pertemptat Amor. tunc regia Iuno
arma habitusque virum pulchraeque insignia gentis
mentibus insinuat, certatimque ordine cunctae
hospitibus patuere fores; tunc primus in aris
450 ignis, et infandis venere oblivia curis;
tunc epulae felixque sopor noctesque quietae,
nec superum sine mente, reor, placuere fatentes.
forsitan et nostrae fatum excusabile culpae
noscere cura, duces. cineres Furiasque meorum
455 testor ut externas non sponte aut crimine taedas
attigerim (scit cura deum), etsi blandus Iason
virginibus dare vincla novis: sua iura cruentum
Phasin habent, alios, Colchi, generatis amores.

Iamque exuta gelu tepuerunt sidera longis
460 solibus, et velox in terga revolvitur annus.
iam nova progenies partusque in vota soluti,
et non speratis clamatur Lemnos alumnis.
nec non ipsa tamen, thalami monimenta coacti,
enitor geminos, duroque sub hospite mater

---

37 Castor and Pollux, whose 'earthly father' Tyndareus was
Oebalus' son.
38 Cf. 4.602 *atque iterum Tydeus*.

twin scions of Oebalus[37] challenge the eye with ambiguous error; one wears a glowing cloak, the other the same, both wield a spear, each is bare-shouldered and smooth-faced, each on his hair has a shining star. Young Hylas dares the voyage, following and adapting great Hercules' stride, whom running he scarce matches, slowly though the other moves his bulk; and lifting the arms of Lerna he rejoiced to sweat beneath the huge quiver.

So 'tis Venus again[38] and Love tests the fierce hearts of Lemnos' women with silent fires. Then royal Juno puts into their minds the arms and bearing of the heroes, the signs of noble lineage. One after another all doors vie to welcome the strangers. Then fire is on the altars for the first time and the cares that might not be spoken are forgotten. Then come feasts and happy sleep and nights of rest; confessing, they pleased, not, I think, without the will of the High Ones. Mayhap, captains, you would care to know my own transgression; Fate may be its excuse. I swear by the ashes and Furies of my kin, it was not by my will or guilt that I kindled stranger torches[39] (the gods care and know), though Jason had charm to capture young maidens. Bloody Phasis has its own laws; other are the loves you Colchians engender.[40]

And now the stars, shedding their chill, grow warm with the long sunshine and the rapid year turns back. Now comes new progeny and births to answer prayer. Lemnos is loud with unhoped-for children. I too with the rest bring forth twins, memorials of a forced bed though they be, and made a mother by my ungentle guest I revive their grand-

[39] I.e. married a stranger.
[40] In imagination Hypsipyle addresses Medea.

465   nomen avi renovo; nec quae fortuna relictis
nosse datur: iam plena quater quinquennia surgunt
si modo Fata sinunt aluitque rogata Lycaste.
    Detumuere animi maris, et clementior Auster
vela vocat: ratis ipsa moram portusque quietos
470   odit et adversi tendit retinacula saxi.
inde fugam Minyae, sociosque appellat Iason
efferus, o utinam iam tunc mea litora rectis
praetervectus aquis, cui non sua pignora cordi,
non promissa fides; certe stat fama remotis
475   gentibus: aequorei redierunt vellera Phrixi.
    Ut stata lux pelago venturumque aethera sensit
Tiphys et occidui rubuere cubilia Phoebi,
heu iterum gemitus, iterumque novissima nox est.
vix reserata dies, et iam rate celsus Iason
480   ire iubet, primoque feritur verbere pontus.
illos e scopulis et summo vertice montis
spumea porrecti dirimentes terga profundi
prosequimur visu, donec lassavit euntes
lux oculos longumque polo contexere visa est
485   aequor et extremi pressit freta margine caeli.
    Fama subit portus vectum trans alta Thoanta
fraterna regnare Chio, mihi crimina nulla
et vacuos arsisse rogos. fremit impia plebes

466 pergunt Pω (*Watt*: deg- *Damsté*)
476 ut Pω Σ: *anne* iam?
480 ferit dux v- pontum (*SB*)

---

41 One of them was called Thoas.   42 Lit. 'for the sea.'
43 As when the Lemnian men were about to leave for Thrace.
44 See critical note. *Ferit dux* can only be defended as an ex-

sire's name.[41] What fortune befell them after I left I may not know. Full four times five years are they growing up, if only the Fates allow and Lycaste raised them as I asked.

The violence of the sea settled down and a milder South Wind calls the sails. The ship herself is weary of tarrying in the tranquil haven and strains her cable against the opposing rock. The Minyae long to go and Jason calls on his comrades—the brute; would that he had sailed straight past my shores in the first place, uncaring for his children and pledged word! To be sure his fame stands among distant nations, the fleece of sailor Phrixus has returned.

The day for sailing[42] is appointed. Tiphys discerned the morrow's weather and setting Phoebus' bedchamber grew red. Once again laments, once again it is the final night.[43] Scarce has day broken, and now Jason, standing high on the ship, gives the word to go; the sea is struck by the first lash.[44] From cliffs and mountaintop we follow them with our gaze as they part the foamy surface of the spreading deep, until the light wearied our travelling eyes, seeming to weave the long sea and the sky into one, and pressed down the waters with heaven's farthest edge.

Rumour comes to the harbour, telling that Thoas has crossed the deep and reigns in his brother's[45] Chios, that I am innocent, that the burning pyre was empty. The impi-

---

traordinary lapse on the poet's part. As captain Jason would not be at the oars and at the oars he could not be standing high on the ship. And the rowers would strike the sea together. Add that *dux* after *Iason* is the merest surplusage. The trouble may have started with *feritur* written *ferit'*.

45 His name was Oenopion, also son of Bacchus and Ariadne. He ruled Chios; sometimes regarded as founder of the city.

sontibus accensae stimulis facinusque reposcunt.
490 quin etiam occultae vulgo increbrescere voces:
"solane fida suis, nos autem in funera laetae?
non deus haec fatumque? quid imperat urbe nefanda?"
talibus exanimis dictis (et triste propinquat
supplicium, nec regna iuvant) vaga litora furtim
495 incomitata sequor funestaque moenia linquo,
qua fuga nota patris. sed non iterum obvius Euhan,
nam me praedonum manus huc appulsa tacentem
abripit et vestras famulam transmittit in oras.'
  Talia Lernaeis iterat dum regibus exsul
500 Lemnias et longa solatur damna querela
immemor absentis (sic di suasistis) alumni,
ille graves oculos languentiaque ora comanti
mergit humo fessusque diu puerilibus actis
labitur in somnos, prensa manus haeret in herba.
505   Interea campis, nemoris sacer horror Achaei,
terrigena exoritur serpens tractuque soluto
immanem sese vehit ac post terga relinquit.
livida fax oculis, tumidi stat in ore veneni
spuma virens, ter lingua vibrat, terna agmina adunci
510 dentis, et auratae crudelis gloria frontis
prominet. Inachio sanctum dixere Tonanti
agricolae, cui cura loci et silvestribus aris
pauper honos; nunc ille dei circumdare templa

497 latentem *Baehrens*   506 exoritur P: erigitur ω
510 frontis ω: -ti P

---

[46] The purport (widely misunderstood) is: 'Oh, so she is the one and only innocent and we murderesses! Wasn't it fate? And if

ous vulgar make a clamour, fired by the stings of guilt, and demand their crime. Nay, hidden voices begin to thicken in the multitude: "Was she alone loyal to her own and we happy to slay? Was it not all a god and fate? Why does she rule in the wicked city?"[46] Terrified at such words (a cruel punishment approaches and my royalty is no help) alone I follow the winding shore in secret and leave the accursed city by the known path of my father's flight. But Euhan did not meet me a second time. A band of pirates landing at the spot snatched me away (I made no sound[47]) and took me to your country as a slave.'

So the Lemnian exile told her tale anew to the Lernaean kings, solacing her losses with lengthy plaint, oblivious (so the gods would have it) of her absent charge. *He* sinks his heavy eyes and drooping head on the lush ground and wearied with length of childish doings glides into sleep. His hand stays clutching the grass.

Meanwhile an earthborn serpent arises in the meadow, holy horror of the Achaean wood, dragging his huge form in a loose slide and leaving it behind him. A livid fire is in his eyes, a green foam of swelling venom in his mouth. Threefold his tongue flickers, triple are the rows of his curving fangs, and the cruel splendour on his gilded brow stands forth. The husbandmen called him sacred to the Inachian Thunderer, who had care of the place and poor men's offerings on woodland altars. Now gliding in a wavy circle he surrounds the god's shrine, now he scrapes the

we are such bad lots, what is she doing as our queen?' Hypsipyle's innocence would prove that fate was not to blame.

[47] She preferred to go with the pirates than be found by the Lemnians.

orbe vago labens, miserae nunc robora silvae
515   atterit et vastas tenuat complexibus ornos;
saepe super fluvios geminae iacet aggere ripae
continuus, squamisque incisus adaestuat amnis.
sed nunc, Ogygii iussis quando omnis anhelat
terra dei tepidaeque latent in pulvere Nymphae,
520   saevior anfractu laterum sinuosa retorquens
terga solo siccique nocens furit igne veneni.
stagna per arentesque lacus fontesque repressos
volvitur et vacuis fluviorum in vallibus errat,
incertusque sui liquidum nunc aëra lambit
525   ore supinato, nunc arva gementia radens
pronus adhaeret humo, si quid viridantia sudent
gramina; percussae calidis afflatibus herbae,
qua tulit ora, cadunt, moriturque ad sibila campus:
quantus ab Arctois discriminat aethera Plaustris
530   Anguis et usque Notos alienumque exit in orbem;
quantus et ille sacri spiris intorta movebat
cornua Parnasi, donec tibi, Delie, fixus
vexit harundineam centeno vulnere silvam.

    Quis tibi, parve, deus tam magni pondera fati
535   sorte dedit? tune hoc vix prima ad limina vitae
hoste iaces? an ut inde sacer per saecula Grais
gentibus et tanto dignus morerere sepulcro?
occidis extremae destrictus verbere caudae
ignaro serpente, puer; fugit ilicet artus
540   somnus, et in solam patuerunt lumina mortem.
cum tamen attonito moriens vagitus in auras
excidit et ruptis immutuit ore querelis,

519 trepidae Pω (ς, *Koestlin*)
524 incensusque siti *Schrader*

timber of the hapless forest and thins down huge ash trees
with his embraces. Often he lies stretched over both rising
banks of a river in one line, and the stream froths at the cut
of his scales. But now, when all the land is panting by order
of the Ogygian god, and the Nymphs lurk warm[48] in the
sand, he waxes angry, twisting his sinuous back with the
curve of his flanks upon the ground, raging balefully with
the fire of his dry venom. Through the arid meres and lakes
and stopped springs he rolls, wandering in the empty river
valleys, and uncertain of himself[49] now licks the liquid air
with mouth back-turned, now scrapes the groaning fields
clinging bent forward to the soil, hoping for moisture in
the green herbage. The grasses fall where he brings his
face, smitten by his hot breath, the plain dies at his hiss:
large as the Serpent that divides the heavens on from
the Arctic Wains and passes out to the South Winds and
an alien hemisphere; or as he that moved the horns of
sacred Parnassus as he twined them with his coils until you
pierced him, Delian, and he bore an arrow forest with a
hundred wounds.

What god's allotting, little one, gave you the burden of
so great a fate? By *this* enemy do you lie low scarcely at
life's first threshold? Or was it to make you die sacred
through the ages henceforth to the peoples of Greece,
worthy of so grand a tomb? Grazed by the lash of the tail
tip, you perish, child, and the snake knows not of it. Sleep
fled your limbs straightway and your eyes opened only to
death. But when from your shocked lips[50] a dying wail
passed out upon the air and the plaint hushed broken like

[48] See Håkanson.   [49] Cf. Seneca, *Hercules Furens* 184.
[50] Taking *attonito* with *ore*.

qualia non totas peragunt insomnia voces,
audiit Hypsipyle, facilemque negantia cursum
545 exanimis genua aegra rapit; iam certa malorum
mentis ab augurio sparsoque per omnia visu
lustrat humum quaerens et nota vocabula parvo
nequiquam ingeminans: nusquam ille, et prata recentes
amisere notas. viridi piger accubat hostis
550 collectus gyro spatiosaque iugera complet
sic etiam, obliqua cervicem expostus in alvo.
horruit infelix visu longoque profundum
incendit clamore nemus; nec territus ille,
sed iacet. Argolicas ululatus flebilis aures
555 impulit; extemplo monitu ducis advolat ardens
Arcas eques causamque refert. tunc squamea demum
torvus ad armorum radios fremitumque virorum
colla movet: rapit ingenti conamine saxum,
quo discretus ager, vacuasque impellit in auras
560 arduus Hippomedon, quo turbine bellica quondam
librati saliunt portarum in claustra molares.
cassa ducis virtus: iam mollia colla refusus
in tergum serpens venientem exhauserat ictum.
dat sonitum tellus, nemorumque per avia densi
565 dissultant nexus. 'at non mea vulnera,' clamat
et trabe fraxinea Capaneus subit obvius, 'umquam
effugies, seu tu pavidi ferus incola luci,
sive deis, utinamque deis, concessa voluptas,
non, si consertum super haec mihi membra Giganta
570 subveheres.' volat hasta tremens et hiantia monstri
ora subit linguaeque secat fera vincla trisulcae,

555 impulit ω: -it et P: implet et *coni. Hill*
563 evaserat ⊊

the unfinished utterances of a dream, Hypsipyle heard. In deathly fear she hurries faint knees that will not run easily. Now certain of disaster by her mind's augury and scattering her gaze in all directions, she ranges the ground in search, vainly crying over and over words familiar to the babe. Nowhere is he, and the meadow has lost the recent tracks. The sluggish enemy lies gathered in a green round, filling broad acres even so, his neck exposed aslant on his belly. The wretched woman shuddered at the sight and with scream upon scream stirred the forest to its depth; the snake is not alarmed but merely lies. The lamentable shrieks struck upon the Argives' ears; forthwith at the leader's command the Arcadian knight[51] flies eagerly to the spot and brings back the cause. Then finally at the flash of arms and the shouting of men the grim snake moves his scaly neck. Tall Hippomedon with a mighty effort seizes a rock, a boundary mark, and hurls it into the empty air with a whirl as when poised millstones leap against barred gates in war. Vain the chieftain's prowess; already the serpent had turned back his supple neck, voiding the coming blow. The earth resounds and in the pathless forest close bondings spring asunder. 'But *my* wounds,' cries Capaneus, coming up to confront him with ashen spear, 'you shall never escape, whether you be the savage denizen of an affrighted grove or a pleasure granted to the gods (and to the gods let it be![52]), no, not if you brought a Giant against me joined above this body.'[53] The spear flies quivering and enters the monster's gaping jaws, severing the cruel fasten-

---

[51] Parthenopaeus.　　　　[52] 'Statius loses no opportunity of emphasizing Capaneus' hostility to the gods' (Mozley).

[53] The Giants had snakes for legs.

perque iubas stantes capitisque insigne corusci
emicat, et nigri sanie perfusa cerebri
figitur alta solo. longus vix tota peregit
575 membra dolor, rapido celer ille volumine telum
circumit avulsumque ferens in opaca refugit
templa dei; hic magno tellurem pondere mensus
implorantem animam dominis assibilat aris.
illum et cognatae stagna indignantia Lernae,
580 floribus et vernis assuetae spargere Nymphae,
et Nemees reptatus ager, lucosque per omnes
silvicolae fracta gemuistis harundine Fauni.
ipse etiam e summa iam tela poposcerat aethra
Iuppiter et dudum nimbique hiemesque coibant,
585 ni minor ira deo gravioraque tela mereri
servatus Capaneus; moti tamen aura cucurrit
fulminis et summas libavit vertice cristas.
    Iamque pererratis infelix Lemnia campis,
liber ut angue locus, modico super aggere longe
590 pallida sanguineis infectas roribus herbas
prospicit. huc magno cursum rapit effera luctu
agnoscitque nefas, terraeque illisa nocenti
fulminis in morem non verba in funere primo,
non lacrimas habet: ingeminat misera oscula tantum
595 incumbens animaeque fugam per membra tepentem
quaerit hians. non ora loco, non pectora restant,
rapta cutis, tenvia ossa patent nexusque madentes

574 alta *ω*: hasta P: acta ⊊, *Heinsius*
593 funeris . . . fulmine *Gossage*

---

54 Or perhaps 'not so great' (as it would be when he actually
did destroy Capaneus). Not 'the god restrained his wrath.'

ings of his triple tongue, and through the standing crest
and the ornament of his darting head it flashes out and
sticks deep into the soil, soaked in the discharge of his
black brain. Scarce has the pain made its long way through
all his body, with a rapid jerk he coils around the weapon
and tears it up, then flees with it into the god's dark shrine;
there measuring the earth with his great bulk he hisses his
beseeching life-breath at his master's altar. Him the indignant swamp of kindred Lerna lamented and the Nymphs
that used to strew him with spring flowers, and the fields of
Nemea where he crept, and the woodland Fauns with
broken reeds in every grove. Jupiter himself had already
called for his weapons from highest heaven, and storm
clouds and tempests were gathering—but that the god's
wrath is not great enough[54] and Capaneus is spared to deserve a heavier missile. Yet the coursing wind of the stirred
thunderbolt tasted the tip of the crest upon his head.[55]

And now the hapless Lemnian wanders through the
fields, now that the place is rid of the serpent, and at the
top of a small distant knoll she pales to see grass stained
with bloody dews. Hither she tears, wild with her heavy
grief, and recognizes the tragedy. Dashed to the guilty
earth like a thunderbolt, she found no words or tears in the
first onset of disaster. In her misery she only bends over the
body raining kisses and with open mouth seeks the flight of
the warm spirit.[56] The face no longer remains in place nor
the breast, the skin is torn away, the thin bones show and

[55] Jupiter could change the course of a thunderbolt after its
release; cf. 7.201.

[56] Tries to catch the last breath.

313

sanguinis imbre novi, totumque in vulnere corpus.
ac velut aligerae sedem fetusque parentis
600 cum piger umbrosa populatus in ilice serpens,
illa redit querulaeque domus mirata quietem
stat superimpendens advectosque horrida maesto
excutit ore cibos, cum solus in arbore paret
sanguis et errantes per capta cubilia plumae.
605   Ut laceros artus gremio miseranda recepit
intexitque comis, tandem laxata dolori
vox invenit iter, gemitusque in verba soluti:
'o mihi desertae natorum dulcis imago,
Archemore, o rerum et patriae solamen ademptae
610 servitiique decus, qui te, mea gaudia, sontes
exstinxere dei, modo quem digressa reliqui
lascivum et prono vexantem gramina cursu?
heu ubi siderei vultus? ubi verba ligatis
imperfecta sonis risusque et murmura soli
615 intellecta mihi? quotiens tibi Lemnon et Argo
sueta loqui et longa somnum suadere querela!
sic equidem luctus solabar et ubera parvo
iam materna dabam, cui nunc venit irritus orbae
lactis et infelix in vulnera liquitur imber.
620 nosco deos: o dira mei praesagia somni
nocturnique metus, et numquam impune per umbras
attonitae mihi visa Venus! quos arguo divos?
ipsa ego te (quid enim timeam moritura fateri?)
exposui Fatis. quae mentem insania traxit?
625 tantane me tantae tenuere oblivia curae?

---

602 stat super ω: iam stupet P   603 paret P: cara ω
606 dolore Pω (*Heinsius*)   615 argos Pω (*Gronovius*)
620 dira ψ: dura Pω

the joints drenched in a rain of fresh blood, the whole body
is in the wound. So when a sluggish snake has ravaged the
dwelling and young of a winged parent in a shady ilex tree,
she returns and wondering at the silence of the twittering
home she stands hanging over it; aghast she tosses from
her mouth the food she brought, while in the tree is seen
only blood and feathers straying about the captured nest.

She took the torn limbs to her bosom, poor soul, and
twined them in her hair. At last her voice was loosed to
find a passage for her sorrow and her moans dissolved
into words: 'Sweet semblance of the children who have
forsaken me, Archemorus,[57] solace of my lost estate and
country, pride of my servitude, what guilty gods took your
life, my joy, whom but now in parting I left at play, crushing
the grasses as you hastened in your forward crawl? Ah,
where is your starry face? Where your words unfinished in
constricted sounds, and laughs and gurgles that only I
could understand? How often would I talk to you of Lemnos and the Argo and lull you to sleep with my long tale of
woe! So I would console my sorrow and give the little one a
mother's breasts. Now in my bereavement the milky flow
comes to me in vain, dropping hapless into your wounds.
I recognize the gods. Ah dire presages of my slumber,
terrors of the night, and Venus, who never in the darkness
appeared to my startled eyes save to my cost! What gods do
I accuse? 'Twas I myself—I am to die, so why fear to confess?—who exposed you to the Fates. What madness drew
my mind? Could such forgetfulness of such a charge take

[57] Either the name is premature or Hypsipyle had heard of the
prophecy given to Lycurgus (647).

dum patrios casus famaeque exorsa retracto
ambitiosa meae (pietas haec magna fidesque!),
exsolvi tibi, Lemne, nefas. ubi letifer anguis?
ferte, duces, meriti si qua est mihi gratia duri,
630   si quis honos dictis; aut vos exstinguite ferro,
ne tristes dominos orbamque inimica revisam
Eurydicen, quamquam haud illi mea cura dolendo
cesserit. hocne ferens onus illaetabile matris
transfundam gremio? quae me prius ima sub umbras
635   mergat humus?' simul haec terraque et sanguine vultum
sordida magnorum circa vestigia regum
vertitur et tacite maerentibus imputat undas.
   Et iam sacrifici subitus per tecta Lycurgi
nuntius implerat lacrimis ipsumque domumque,
640   ipsum adventantem Persei vertice sancto
montis, ubi averso dederat prosecta Tonanti,
et caput iratis rediens quassabat ab extis.
hic sese Argolicis immunem servat ab armis,
haud animi vacuus, sed templa araeque tenebant.
645   necdum etiam responsa deum monitusque vetusti
exciderant voxque ex adytis accepta profundis:
'prima, Lycurge, dabis Dircaeo funera bello.'
id cavet, et maestus vicini pulvere Martis
angitur ad lituos periturisque invidet armis.
650   Ecce (fides superum!) laceras comitata Thoantis
aduehit exsequias, contra subit obvia mater,
femineos coetus plangentiaque agmina ducens.

---

58 *Vertitut* ('turns' from one to another) and *imputat* are commonly misunderstood; cf. Apuleius, *Metamorphoses* 6.2 *pedes eius advoluta et uberi fletu rogans dei vestigia.*

hold of me? As in my vanity I rehearsed the story of my
country and the tale of my renown (such sense of duty,
such fidelity!), I paid you, Lemnos, the crime I owed.
Where is the deadly snake? Bring me, chieftains, if you
have any gratitude for my grievous service, any favour for
my words; or slay me yourselves with the sword so that I
may not see my sad masters again and bereaved Eurydice,
a thing of hate—though my love and grief yield not to hers.
Shall I bear this melancholy burden to pour into his
mother's lap? What earth should first sink me in profound-
est dark?' Therewith, her face foul with soil and blood, she
grovels around the feet of the great kings, and as they
grieve, silently claims credit for the waters.[58]

And now a sudden report that ran through the dwelling
of Lycurgus as he was at sacrifice filled himself and his
house with tears—himself as he approached from the top
of Perseus' mountain[59] where he had offered portions[60] to
the unfriendly Thunderer, shaking his head as he returned
from the angry entrails. Here he was keeping himself, taking no part in the Argive war; not that he lacked courage,
but temple and altars held him back. Nor yet had the gods'
oracle and warnings of old dropped from his mind, the
word received from the depth of the shrine: 'Lycurgus, you
shall give first death[61] to the Dircaean war.' Of that he is
aware; the dust of Mars close by saddens him, he winces at
the trumpets, and wishes the doomed army ill.

See! The gods do not deceive. Thoas' daughter comes,
bringing with her the mangled remains. To meet her the
mother advances leading a gathering of women, a mourn-

---

[59] Cf. 3.460.   [60] *Prosecta*, lit. 'severed portions.'
[61] Hence 'Archemorus.'

at non magnanimo pietas ignava Lycurgo:
fortior illa malis, lacrimasque insana resorbet
655 ira patris; longo rapit arva morantia passu
vociferans: 'illa autem ubinam, cui parva cruoris
laetave damna mei? vivitne? impellite raptam,
ferte citi comites; faxo omnis fabula Lemni
et pater et tumidae generis mendacia sacri
660 exciderint.' ibat letumque inferre parabat
ense furens rapto; venienti Oeneius heros
impiger obiecta proturbat pectora parma,
ac simul infrendens: 'siste hunc, vesane, furorem,
quisquis es!' et pariter Capaneus acerque reducto
665 affuit Hippomedon rectoque Erymanthius ense,
ac iuvenem multo praestringunt lumine; at inde
agrestum pro rege manus. quos inter Adrastus
mitius et sociae veritus commercia vittae
Amphiaraus ait: 'ne, quaeso! absistite ferro,
670 unus avum sanguis, neve indulgete furori,
tuque prior.' sed non sedato pectore Tydeus
subicit: 'anne ducem servatricemque cohortis
Inachiae ingratis coram tot milibus audes
mactare in tumulos (quanti pro funeris ultor!),
675 cui regnum genitorque Thoas et lucidus Euhan
stirpis avus? timidone parum, quod gentibus actis
undique in arma tuis inter rapida agmina pacem
solus habes? habeasque, et te victoria Graium
inveniat tumulis etiamnum haec fata gementem.'
680 Dixerat, et tandem cunctante modestior ira

654 ille Pω (*SB*²)

ing host. But great-hearted Lycurgus' love for his son is up and doing. It takes strength from calamity; a father's furious anger sucks back his tears, and with long strides he despatches the fields that stay him, shouting 'And where is she to whom spilt blood of mine is a trifle or a pleasure? Does she live? Take her, thrust her, comrades, bring her quickly. I shall make her forget all her rigmarole of Lemnos, and her father, and the lie of race divine that she is so proud of.' Snatching up a sword and advancing, he was about to deal death in his rage, when the hero son of Oeneus went into action, pushing back the other's chest with blocking shield and gnashing his teeth: 'Stop this madness, lunatic, whoever you are.' Capaneus likewise was on the spot and fierce Hippomedon and the Erymanthian (sword drawn back the one, levelled the other), dazzling the young man with many a flash. From the other side a band of peasants rally to their king. Between them Adrastus in gentler style and Amphiaraus respecting the commerce of a fillet like his own: 'Not so, I pray. Put away the steel. Our ancestry is one. Indulge not rage. And be you first.' But Tydeus is not pacified. 'Our guide,' he cries, 'saviour of the Inachian host, do you dare slaughter her for a grave before so many thousands of the thankless[62]—in vengeance for what a mighty death! She that was a queen, whom Thoas begot, whose grandsire was Euhan the shining? Coward, is it not enough that when your countrymen from every quarter have flocked to arms, you only amid the hurrying columns are at peace? Keep it, and let the victory of the Greeks find you still at the graveside bewailing this fatality.'

He spoke. The other's anger pauses now and more mea-

---

[62] They would be thankless if they let it happen.

ille refert: 'equidem non vos ad moenia, Thebas
rebar et hostiles huc advenisse catervas.
pergite in excidium, socii si tanta voluptas
sanguinis, imbuite arma domi, atque haec irrita dudum
685   templa Iovis (quid enim haud licitum?) ferat impius ignis,
si vilem, tanti premerent cum pectora luctus,
in famulam ius esse ratus dominoque ducique.
sed videt haec, videt ille deum regnator, et ausis,
sera quidem, manet ira tamen.' sic fatus, et arces
690   respicit.
          Atque illic alio certamine belli
tecta fremunt; volucres equitum praeverterat alas
Fama recens, geminos alis amplexa tumultus:
illi ad fata rapi atque illi iam occumbere leto,
sic meritam, Hypsipylen iterant creduntque nec irae
695   fit mora, iamque faces et tela penatibus instant;
vertere regna fremunt raptumque auferre Lycurgum
cum Iove cumque aris; resonant ululatibus aedes
femineis, versusque dolor dat terga timori.
      Alipedum curru sed enim sublimis Adrastus
700   secum ante ora virum fremibunda Thoantida portans
it medius turmis et 'parcite, parcite!' clamat.
'nil actum saeve, meritus nec tale Lycurgus
excidium, gratique inventrix fluminis ecce.'

---

681 thebes Pω (*Håkanson ex cod.*)   699 alipedi *Jortin*

---

63 The mountain and Jupiter's temple from which he had just
come down.   64 In the city. But *illic* after *arces* is misleading
and has caused confusion.

65 One being Lycurgus' confrontation with the 'Greek' leaders

BOOK 5

sured is his reply: 'For my part I did not think it was you
outside the walls but that Thebes and her hostile troops
had come hither. March in to destroy us if allied blood is
so much your pleasure, flesh your weapons at home and
let impious fire consume this Jove's already unavailing
temple—for what is not permitted?—seeing that as master
and ruler I thought I had the right to deal with a worthless
slave when such sorrow weighed upon my heart. But he
sees it, he, the ruler of the gods, and his anger at your
deeds, though late, abides.' So he spoke and looked to the
heights.[63]

There[64] the dwellings are loud with another clash of
arms. Recent Rumour had gone ahead of the swift squadrons, embracing twin tumults[65] with her wings. Some say
and say again that Hypsipyle, their benefactress, is being
dragged to her doom, others that she is already suffering
death. They believe and their anger tarries not. Now
torches and weapons threaten the palace, they shout to
overthrow the monarchy, to seize Lycurgus and carry him
off along with Jupiter[66] and his altars. The dwelling resounds with women's screams and grief turns about,
fleeing before terror.

But Adrastus, aloft in his chariot of coursers, carrying
Thoas' daughter alongside before the clamorous faces of
the men, passes through their midst and cries: 'Enough,
enough! No cruelty has been done, Lycurgus has not deserved such deadly usage. And she who found the grateful

outside the city, the other (imminent) in the city itself. The horsemen (*alas*) are the 'Greeks.' So I tentatively interpret, but the
wording is unclear and *alas . . . alis* has been suspected with
reason.   [66] His statue.

321

sic ubi diversis maria evertere procellis
705 hinc Boreas Eurusque, illinc niger imbribus Auster,
pulsa dies regnantque hiemes, venit aequoris alti
rex sublimis equis, geminusque ad spumea Triton
frena natans late pelago dat signa cadenti,
et iam plana Thetis, montesque et litora crescunt.
710   Quis superum tanto solatus funera voto
pensavit lacrimas inopinaque gaudia maestae
rettulit Hypsipylae? tu, gentis conditor, Euhan,
qui geminos iuvenes Lemni de litore vectos
intuleras Nemeae mirandaque fata parabas.
715 causa viae genetrix, nec inhospita tecta Lycurgi
praebuerant aditus; et protinus ille tyranno
nuntius exstinctae miserando vulnere prolis.
ergo adsunt comites (pro Fors et caeca futuri
mens hominum!) regique favent; sed Lemnos ad aures
720 ut primum dictusque Thoas, per tela manusque
irruerant, matremque avidis complexibus ambo
diripiunt flentes alternaque pectora mutant.
illa velut rupes immoto saxea visu
haeret et expertis non audet credere divis.
725 ut vero et vultus et signa Argoa relictis
ensibus atque umeris amborum intextus Iason,
cesserunt luctus, turbataque munere tanto
corruit, atque alio maduerunt lumina fletu.
addita signa polo, laetoque ululante tumultu
730 tergaque et aera dei motas crepuere per auras.

stream—behold!' So when Boreas and Eurus on one side,
Auster with his black rains on the other have upheaved the
sea with their diverse blasts, the day is banished and storms
rule; then comes the king of the deep aloft on his horses,
twofold Triton swimming alongside the foamy bridles
gives signal far and wide to the falling waters. And now
Thetis is flat, mountains and shores increase.

Which of the High Ones solaced her calamity, balancing her tears with an answer to her great prayer, and
brought back unlooked-for joy to sad Hypsipyle? You it
was, Euhan, founder of the family, who had brought the
two youths[67] from Lemnos' shore to Nemea, preparing a
wondrous destiny. Their mother was the reason for their
journey and the hospitable dwelling of Lycurgus had given
them entry, when the report reached the king of his offspring piteously killed. So they are there as his companions
and (oh chance and men's minds blind to the future!) support the king. But as soon as Lemnos and Thoas' name
come to their ears, they rush through weapons and hands
and, both weeping, tear their mother apart with greedy
embraces, taking her to their bosoms in turn. She stays
fixed like a stony rock, her eyes unmoving, not daring to
trust the gods she has experienced. But when she sees
their faces and the signs of Argo on the swords Jason had
left behind and Jason's name inwoven on their shoulders,
her sorrows left her, and overcome by so great a boon she
collapsed, her eyes bedewed with other tears. Signs too
were manifest in heaven, cries of tumultuous joy and the
drums and cymbals of the god crashed through the resonant air.

[67] Thoas and Euneus, sons of Jason and Hypsipyle.

Tunc pius Oeclides, ut prima silentia vulgi
mollior ira dedit, placidasque accessus ad aures:
'audite, o ductor Nemeae lectique potentes
Inachidae, quae certus agi manifestat Apollo.
735   iste quidem Argolicis haud olim indebitus armis
luctus adest, recto descendunt limite Parcae:
et sitis interitu fluviorum et letifer anguis
et puer, heu nostri signatus nomine fati,
Archemorus, cuncta haec superum demissa suprema
740   mente fluunt. differte animos festinaque tela
ponite; mansuris donandus honoribus infans.
et meruit; det pulchra suis libamina Virtus
manibus, atque utinam plures innectere pergas,
Phoebe, moras, semperque novis bellare vetemur
745   casibus, et semper Thebe funesta recedat.
at vos magnorum transgressi fata parentum
felices, longum quibus hinc per saecula nomen,
dum Lernaea palus et dum pater Inachus ibit,
dum Nemea tremulas campis iaculabitur umbras,
750   ne fletu violate sacrum, ne plangite divos:
nam deus iste, deus, Pyliae nec fata senectae
maluerit, Phrygiis aut degere longius annis.'
finierat, caeloque cavam nox induit umbram.

732 accessus ψ: -ssit Pω
742 sui *Poynton*   virtus *edd.* (*Hill*)

Then spoke the pious son of Oecles as soon as the softening anger of the multitude gave silence and tranquil
ears allowed approach: 'Hear, ruler of Nemea and sons of
Inachus, chosen chiefs, what sure Apollo manifests for us
to do. This sorrow is owed to Argive arms from time long
past, the Parcae come down in a straight line. The thirst
from the perishing of the streams, the death-bearing
snake, and the boy marked, alas, by our destiny's name,
Archemorus, all these flow down from the supreme will of
the High Ones. Hold your anger, lay by your hasty weapons. The child must be accorded lasting honours. And he
has deserved them. Let Valour make fair libation to the
dead that is her own[68] and, Phoebus, may you go on to
weave more delays and we be barred from war by ever new
chances and may deadly Thebes ever further recede.[69] But
you,[70] fortunate ones, who have passed beyond the destiny
of great parents, whom long fame awaits through the ages
while Lerna's swamp and father Inachus shall flow, while
Nemea shall cast her quivering shadows over the fields,
violate not the rite with weeping, bewail not the gods. For
a god he is, a god, nor would he rather be fated to a Pylian
eld or to live longer than Phrygian years.'[71] He ended, and
night wrapped hollow darkness round the sky.

[68] Valour (Virtus) stands for the army, which was indirectly responsible for the child's death (SB[2]). Or *sui* ('libation of herself')
may be right: athletic prowess will herald military performance.

[69] Amphiaraus (not Adrastus, as Lesueur), seems to be thinking aloud.

[70] Lycurgus and Eurydice. 'Great parents' are not *their* parents, but illustrious parents in general.

[71] I.e. live longer than Nestor or Priam.

LIBER VI

Nuntia multivago Danaas perlabitur urbes
Fama gradu, sancire novo sollemnia busto
Inachidas ludumque super, quo Martia bellis
praesudare paret seseque accendere virtus.
5 Graium ex more decus: primus Pisaea per arva
hunc pius Alcides Pelopi †certavit† honorem
pulvereumque fera crinem detersit oliva;
proxima vipereo celebratur libera nexu
Phocis, Apollineae bellum puerile pharetrae;
10 mox circum tristes servata Palaemonis aras
nigra superstitio, quotiens animosa resumit
Leucothea gemitus et amica ad litora festa
tempestate venit: planctu conclamat uterque
Isthmos, Echioniae responsant flebile Thebae.
15 et nunc eximii regum, quibus Argos alumnis

6 *anne* coeptavit?   8 celebratur P: -avit ω

---

1 The Olympian games, founded in legend by Hercules, were
the first of the four great Greek athletic festivals. Pelops' tomb was
at Olympia and honour was paid to it (Pindar, *Olympians* 1.93 and
10.24), but that the games were founded in his honour seems to be
Statius' extrapolation. *Certavit*, for which the translation substitutes *coeptavit*, has been implausibly explained as referring to an

BOOK 6

Rumour travels at large gliding through the Danaan cities
with report that the sons of Inachus are founding rites for a
new tomb and games to boot, in which martial valour will
sweat in preparation for war and set itself alight, a festival
according to Greek custom. Pious Alcides first began this
honour for Pelops in Pisa's fields[1] and brushed his dusty
hair with wild olive.[2] Next was Phocis celebrated free of
the serpent's bond, the boyhood battle of Apollo's quiver.[3]
After that came a black cult observed at Palaemon's
gloomy altars as often as brave Leucothea renews her lamentations and returns to the friendly shore at festival time;
Isthmos on either side is loud with mourning and
Echionian Thebes makes tearful response.[4] And now the
flower of kings, Argos' children linking her with heaven,

otherwise unattested tradition ascribing the foundation to Pelops.
Honorem has also been taken as an internal accusative: 'vied for
glory in the games' (Melville). It would be a very harsh one.

[2] Victors at Olympia were given crowns of wild olive. Statius
makes Hercules take part in the games he founded.

[3] The Pythian games at Delphi commemorated Apollo's slaying of the serpent Python.

[4] The Isthmian games at Corinth commemorated the death of
the child Melicertes / Palaemon, whom his Theban mother Ino
plunged into the sea along with herself.

conexum caelo, quorumque ingentia tellus
Aonis et Tyriae suspirant nomina matres,
concurrunt nudasque movent in proelia vires.
ceu primum ausurae trans alta ignota biremes,
20 seu Tyrrhenam hiemem seu stagna Aegaea lacessant,
tranquillo prius arma lacu clavumque levesque
explorant remos atque ipsa pericula discunt;
at cum experta cohors, tunc pontum irrumpere fretae
longius ereptasque oculis non quaerere terras.
25   Clara laboriferos caelo Tithonia currus
extulerat vigilesque deae pallentis habenas
et Nox et cornu fugiebat Somnus inani;
iam plangore viae, gemitu iam regia mugit
flebilis, acceptos longe nemora avia frangunt
30 multiplicantque sonos. sedet ipse exutus honoro
vittarum nexu genitor squalentiaque ora
sparsus et incultam ferali pulvere barbam.
asperior contra planctusque egressa viriles
exemplo famulas premit hortaturque volentes
35 orba parens, lacerasque super procumbere nati
reliquias ardet totiensque avulsa refertur.
arcet et ipse pater. mox ut maerentia dignis
vultibus Inachii penetrarunt limina reges,
ceu nova tunc clades et primo saucius infans
40 vulnere letalisve irrumperet atria serpens,
sic alium ex alio quamquam lassata fragorem
pectora congeminant, integratoque resultant
accensae clamore fores: sensere Pelasgi
invidiam et lacrimis excusant crimen obortis.
45   Ipse, datum quotiens intercisoque tumultu

---

35 procumbere ω: prorumpere P

whose mighty names Aonia's land and Tyrian mothers utter sighing, meet and stir their naked strength to combat.[5] Even as ships about to venture for the first time across unknown seas, whether they challenge Tyrrhene storm or spreading Aegean, first test rigging and helm and light oars on a calm lake and learn actual perils; but when their crews are trained, then confidently they break far into the main nor does their gaze seek the lost land.

Bright Tithonia had raised her toil-bearing chariot in the sky, Night and Sleep with empty horn were fleeing from the pale goddess' wakeful reins. Now the streets are loud with wailing, now the tearful palace with moans; the pathless forests afar take and break and multiply the sounds. The father himself sits stripped of his honourable fillet, his unkempt head and untended beard scattered with funeral dust. Fronting him the bereaved mother, more violent than he and lamenting more than man, urges her handmaidens by her example, exhorting them though willing, and yearns to plunge upon her child's torn remains, returning as often as she is hauled away. Even the father holds her back. Then, when the Inachian kings entered the mourning threshold with mien to match, as though the tragedy were new and the infant suffering his first wound and the deadly serpent breaking into the hall, their breasts though weary redouble loud blows one after another and the doors reecho kindled with fresh clamour. The Pelasgi feel the reproach and excuse the charge with flow of tears.

Adrastus himself, whenever he has the chance and the

[5] Origin of the Nemean games.

conticuit stupefacta domus, solatur Adrastus
alloquiis genitorem ultro, nunc fata recensens
resque hominum duras et inexorabile pensum,
nunc aliam prolem mansuraque numine dextro
50 pignora. nondum orsis modus, et lamenta redibant.
ille quoque affatus non mollius audit amicos
quam trucis Ionii rabies clamantia ponto
vota virum aut tenues curant vaga fulmina nimbos.
    Tristibus interea ramis teneraque cupresso
55 damnatus flammae torus et puerile feretrum
texitur: ima virent agresti stramina cultu;
proxima gramineis operosior area sertis,
et picturatus morituris floribus agger;
tertius assurgens Arabum strue tollitur ordo
60 Eoas complexus opes incanaque glebis
tura et ab antiquo durantia cinnama Belo.
summa crepant auro, Tyrioque attollitur ostro
molle supercilium, teretes hoc undique gemmae
irradiant, medio Linus intertextus acantho
65 letiferique canes: opus admirabile semper
oderat atque oculos flectebat ab omine mater.
arma etiam et veterum exuvias circumdat avorum
gloria mixta malis afflictaeque ambitus aulae,
ceu grande exsequiis onus atque immensa ferantur
70 membra rogo, sed cassa tamen sterilisque dolentes
fama iuvat, parvique augescunt funere manes.
inde ingens lacrimis honor et miseranda voluptas,
muneraque in cineres annis graviora feruntur;
namque illi et pharetras brevioraque tela dicarat

70 rogo Pψ: t(h)oro ω

noise is suspended and the house lapses into stunned silence, unprompted consoles the father with words of comfort. Now he rehearses destinies and the cruelty of man's condition and the inexorable thread, now speaks of other offspring and children who would remain with heaven's blessing. His speech unfinished, the laments return. Lycurgus too is no more mollified by well-meant words than the rage of the fierce Ionian heeds the clamour of men's prayers upon the deep or wandering lightnings thin showers.

Meanwhile a couch doomed to flame, a childish bier, is woven from sad branches of tender cypress. The lowest part is strewn with rustic greenery, next is a space more elaborate with herbal wreaths and a mound decked with flowers soon to die. The third tier rears high with an Arabian heap, comprising eastern wealth and white lumps of incense and cinnamon lasting from ancient Belus. The top rattles with gold, a soft overhang of Tyrian purple rises high, flashing at all points with polished jewels; in the middle among acanthus is woven Linus and the deadly hounds. The mother always hated this splendid work and averted her eyes from the omen. Glory mingling with distress and pride of the afflicted palace places arms too and trappings of ancient forbears around the bier, as though a great load was being borne to burial, a vast body for the pyre; vain and barren fame yet pleases the grieving and the tiny dead grows bigger by his funeral. Thence comes great honour to the tears[6] and a piteous pleasure. Gifts are borne for burning more weighty than his years; for his father in premature vow had reserved quivers for him and minia-

[6] As shed for a great loss.

75 festinus voti pater insontesque sagittas;
iam tunc et nota stabuli de gente probatos
in nomen pascebat equos cinctusque sonantes
armaque maiores expectatura lacertos.
[†spes avidi quas non in nomen credula vestes†
80 urguebat studio cultusque insignia regni
purpureos sceptrumque minus, cuncta ignibus atris
damnat atrox suaque ipse parens gestamina ferri,
si damnis rabidum queat exsaturare dolorem.]
    Parte alia gnari monitis exercitus instat
85 auguris aëriam truncis nemorumque ruina,
montis opus, cumulare pyram, quae crimina caesi
anguis et infausti cremet atra piacula belli.
[his labor accisam Nemeen umbrosaque tempe
praecipitare solo lucosque ostendere Phoebo.]
90 sternitur extemplo veteres incaedua ferro
silva comas, largae qua non opulentior umbrae
Argolicos inter saltusque educta Lycaeos
extulerat super astra caput: stat sacra senectae
numine, nec solos hominum transgressa veterno
95 fertur avos, Nymphas etiam mutasse superstes
Faunorumque greges. aderat miserabile luco
excidium: fugere ferae, nidosque tepentes
absiliunt (metus urguet) aves; cadit ardua fagus
Chaoniumque nemus brumaeque illaesa cupressus,
100 procumbunt piceae, flammis alimenta supremis,
ornique iliceaeque trabes metuendaque suco
taxus et infandos belli potura cruores
fraxinus atque situ non expugnabile robur.
hinc audax abies et odoro vulnere pinus
105 scinditur, acclinant intonsa cacumina terrae
alnus amica fretis nec inhospita vitibus ulmus.

ture darts and guiltless arrows, and even then was rearing[7]
in his name proven horses of his stable's well-known breed,
and clattering belts and shields expecting bigger arms.

Elsewhere at the bidding of the schooled augur the
army presses to pile up an airy pyre, like a mountain, with
tree trunks and forest wreckage, to burn up the sin of the
snake's slaying and dark offerings, of expiation[8] for their ill-
omened war. Straightway a wood whose ancient foliage
never knew the axe is felled, than which none richer in lavish shade was raised in the glades of Argolis and Lycaeus to
lift its head above the stars. It stood sacred in the majesty
of age, said not only to surpass men's ancestors in antiquity
but to have seen generations of Nymphs and Fauns come
and go. Piteous destruction was at hand for that grove. The
beasts fled, the birds flitted from their warm nests—fear
drives. Falls the towering beech, the Chaonian forest and
the cypress that winter cannot harm, spruces fall, aliment
for funeral flames, and mountain ashes, and trunks of ilex,
and yew of dangerous sap, and ash that will drink blood
shed in accursed war, and age-proof robur.[9] Then the daring fir[10] and the pine with aromatic wound is split, and the
alder, friend to seas, and the vine-welcoming elm lean un-

---

[7] Lit. 'feeding.' With the belts and shields a different verb
(as *parabat*) is understood.   [8] In atonement for the death of
the sacred snake (cf. 5.511–13). But something wider may be
adumbrated, as though the war were a crime in itself.

[9] A species of oak apparently distinct from the 'Chaonian
forest.'   [10] Used in shipbuilding.

79–83 *et* 88–89 *absunt in* P, *damnant edd. plerique*
86 onus Pω (ς, *Weber*)

THEBAID

dat gemitum tellus: non sic eversa feruntur
Ismara cum fracto Boreas caput extulit antro,
non grassante Noto citius nocturna peregit
110 flamma nemus. linquunt flentes dilecta locorum,
otia cana, Pales Silvanusque arbiter umbrae
semideumque pecus, migrantibus aggemit illis
silva, nec amplexae dimittunt robora Nymphae.
ut cum possessas avidis victoribus arces
115 dux raptare dedit, vix signa audita, nec urbem
invenias; ducunt sternuntque abiguntque feruntque
immodici, minor ille fragor quo bella gerebant.
    Iamque pari cumulo geminas, hanc tristibus umbris
ast illam superis, aequus labor auxerat aras,
120 cum signum luctus cornu grave mugit adunco
tibia, cui teneros suetum producere manes
lege Phrygum maesta. Pelopem monstrasse ferebant
exsequiale sacrum carmenque minoribus umbris
utile, quo geminis Niobe consumpta pharetris
125 squalida bissenas Sipylon deduxerat urnas.
    Portant inferias arsuraque fercula primi
Graiorum, titulisque pios testantur honores
gentis quisque suae; longo post tempore surgit
colla super iuvenum (numero dux legerat omni)
130 ipse fero clamore torus. cinxere Lycurgum
Lernaei proceres, genetricem mollior ambit
turba; nec Hypsipyle raro subit agmine: vallant
Inachidae memores, sustentant livida nati

11 The comma which I have placed after *locorum* discloses the
syntax, with *otia cana* in apposition to *dilecta locorum* = *dilecta
loca* (SB[2]).

334

shorn tops on the ground. The earth groans. Not so is
Ismara overturned and carried off when Boreas lifts his
head from his fractured cavern nor does nocturnal fire
more swiftly destroy a forest under the South Wind's assault. Pales and Silvanus, lord of shade, and the demigod
herd leave the places they love, haunts of ancient peace,[11]
and as they depart the wood groans in sympathy, while the
Nymphs loose not the oaks from their embrace. As when a
commander gives a captured town over to greedy victors to
plunder, scarce is the signal heard and the city is gone; unrestrained they drag and flatten, drive off, carry off; with
less noise they made war.

And now equal toil had raised twin altars of like mass,
one to the gloomy shades, the other to the High Ones,
when the pipe with curving horn booms low in sign of
mourning, the pipe that by Phrygia's sad ordinance was
wont to lead out youthful dead. They used to say that
Pelops showed this funeral rite and chant to serve children's ghosts; with it in mourning garb Niobe consumed by
twin quivers brought her twelve urns to Sipylos.[12]

The Grecian leaders bring their funeral gifts and offerings for burning, each with labels testifying in piety to his
family honours. After a long interval there rises on the
necks of young men (the leader had chosen them from all
the host) amid wild shouting the bier itself. The Lernaean
chiefs surround Lycurgus, a gentler company encircles the
queen, Hypsipyle too comes well-attended. The children
of Inachus remember and guard her, her sons hold up her

[12] Statius' source is unknown. Pelops and Niobe were the children of Tantalus, king of Sipylos in Lydia. Phrygian music was pas-
sionate and exciting, used in the worship of Cybele.

bracchia et inventae concedunt plangere matri.
135 Illic infaustos ut primum egressa penates
Eurydice, nudo vocem de pectore rumpit
planctuque et longis praefata ululatibus infit:
'non hoc Argolidum coetu circumdata matrum
speravi te, nate, sequi, nec talia demens
140 fingebam votis annorum elementa tuorum,
nil saevum reputans: etenim his in finibus aevi
unde ego bella tibi Thebasque ignara timerem?
cui superum nostro committere sanguine pugnas
dulce? quis hoc armis vovit scelus? at tua nondum,
145 Cadme, domus, nullus Tyrio grege plangitur infans.
primitias egomet lacrimarum et caedis acerbae,
ante tubas ferrumque, tuli, dum deside cura
credo sinus fidos altricis et ubera mando.
quidni ego? narrabat servatum fraude parentem
150 insontesque manus. en quam ferale putemus
abiurasse sacrum et Lemni gentilibus unam
immunem furiis! haec illa (et creditis) ausa,
haec pietate potens solis abiecit in arvis,
non regem dominumque, alienos impia partus,
155 hoc tantum, silvaeque infamis tramite liquit,
quem non anguis atrox (quid enim hac opus, ei mihi, leti
mole fuit?), tantum caeli violentior aura

152 ausae Pω (*SB; cf.* Σ): *alii aliter*

---

13 The Decii 'devoted' themselves for Roman victories. Eurydice envisages her son as having been 'devoted' for the success of
the 'Greek' arms.
14 Lit. 'the breasts,' i.e. the suckling of the child. Or perhaps,

bruised arms and allow their newfound mother to lament.

No sooner had Eurydice left her ill-starred abode than speech breaks from her bare breast and with prelude of blows and long-drawn keenings she begins: 'It was not thus, my son, that I hoped to follow you attended by a throng of Argive dames nor so in my foolish prayers did I imagine your earliest years; nothing cruel was in my thoughts. For indeed at your time of life how in my ignorance should I fear war and Thebes for you? Which of the High Ones did it please to commence battle with our blood? Who for warfare[13] vowed this crime? But your house, Cadmus, is not yet in dole, no infant is mourned among the Tyrian folk. I bore the first fruit of tears and untimely death before trumpet and sword, as caring but lazily I believed in a nurse's trusty bosom and handed over my suckling.[14] But why not? She told me how she had saved her father by cunning and kept her hands innocent. Look at her, this woman who we are to think abjured the deadly covenant, alone immune from the madness of her fellow Lemnians; this woman who thus dared (and you believe her[15]), this woman, so strong in her devotion, undutifully cast off in a lonely field—I say not king or master but another's child, just that, and left him on a track in an ill-famed wood. No frightful snake—what need, alas, for such a mass of death?—but merely a breeze blowing strong or

as Håkanson thought, an inversion, *mando ubera* (sc. *infanti*) for *uberibus* (sc. *eius*) *mando infantem.*

[15] Sometimes taken as a question. Housman, reading *ausae*, paraphrases: 'and do you believe the story, now that you see what she has dared?' But *ausa* refers to the Lemnian history and *creditis* is sarcastic—Eurydice does not believe a word of it.

impulsaeque Noto frondes cassusque valeret
exanimare timor. nec vos incessere luctu
160 orba habeo; fixum matri immotumque manebat
hac altrice nefas. atquin et blandus ad illam,
nate, magis, solam nosse atque audire vocantem
ignarusque mei. nulla ex te gaudia matri.
illa tuos questus lacrimososque impia risus
165 audiit et vocis decerpsit murmura primae.
illa tibi genetrix semper dum vita manebat,
nunc ego. sed miserae mihi nec punire potestas
sic meritam! quid dona, duces, quid inania fertis
iusta rogis? illam (nil poscunt amplius umbrae),
170 illam, oro, cineri simul excisaeque parenti
reddite, quaeso, duces, per ego haec primordia belli,
cui peperi; sic aequa gemant mihi funera matres
Ogygiae.' sternit crines iteratque precando:
'reddite, nec vero crudelem avidamque vocate
175 sanguinis: occumbam pariter, dum vulnere iusto
exsaturata oculos unum impellamur in ignem.'
talia vociferans alia de parte gementem
Hypsipylen (neque enim illa comas nec pectora servat)
agnovit longe et socium indignata dolorem:
180 'hoc saltem, o proceres, tuque o, cui pignora nostri
proturbata tori, prohibete; auferte supremis
invisam exsequiis. quid se funesta parenti
miscet et in nostris spectatur et ipsa ruinis?
cui luget complexa suos?' ait atque repente
185 concidit abruptisque obmutuit ore querelis.

---

161 ad Pψ: et ω   181–83 sic fere P (sed auferte om., fecisse
pro funesta): ω apud Hill requiras
184–85 om. P, damnavit O. Mueller

leaves shaken by the wind or idle terror might have been
enough to cause his end. Nor can I accuse you warriors in
my grievous loss; with such a nurse a mother's tragedy
stood fixed and immutable. And yet, my child, you were
fonder of her, her only you knew and heard when she
called, me you ignored, your mother had no joy of you.
She, the undutiful, heard your plaints and tearful laughter,
she culled the murmurs of your earliest speech. She was
your mother always while you lived; I now. But woe is me! I
do not even have the power to punish her as she deserves.
Captains, why do you bring gifts to the pyre, why these
vain rites? Her—the shades demand no more—her, I beg,
give back, captains, to the ashes and the parent she has destroyed, I beseech you by these beginnings of war, the war
for which I gave birth. So may Ogygian mothers mourn
deaths matching mine.' She strews her hair and again in
supplication: 'Give her back, nor call me cruel and blood-
thirsty. I shall die with her, so I but sate my eyes with the
just stroke and we be thrown on the same pyre.' Thus
crying, she recognized Hypsipyle from afar lamenting in
another place—for she was not sparing hair or breast.
Indignant that her grief should be shared: 'This at least
forbid, you nobles and you[16] for whose sake the pledge of
our marriage bed has been thrust forth. Take that hateful
woman away from the funeral rites. Why does she mingle
her accursed self with his mother? Why is she too on view
in *our* tragedy? For whom does she mourn as she embraces
her own?' So she spoke, then suddenly collapsed and
breaking off her plaints fell silent. As when a bull calf

---

[16] Polynices. Understood of Lycurgus, *cui . . . tori* makes no
sense. *Nostri* = 'mine and my husband's.'

185b   sic ait abruptisque immutuit ore querelis.
     non secus ac primo fraudatum lacte iuvencum,
     cui trepidae vires et solus ab ubere sanguis,
     seu fera seu duras avexit pastor ad aras;
     nunc vallem spoliata parens, nunc flumina questu,
190   nunc arbusta movet vacuosque interrogat agros;
     tunc piget ire domum, maestoque novissima campo
     exit et oppositas impasta avertitur herbas.
       At genitor sceptrique decus cultusque Tonantis
     inicit ipse rogis, tergoque et pectore fusam
195   caesariem ferro minuit sectisque iacentis
     obnubit tenvia ora comis, ac talia fletu
     verba pio miscens: 'alio tibi, perfide, pacto,
     Iuppiter, hunc crinem voti reus ante dicaram
     si pariter virides nati libare dedisses
200   ad tua templa genas; sed non ratus ore sacerdos,
     damnataeque preces; ferat haec, quae dignior, umbra.'
     iam face subiecta primis in frondibus ignis
     exclamat; labor insanos arcere parentes.
       Stant iussi Danaum atque obtentis eminus armis
205   prospectu visus interclusere nefasto.
     ditantur flammae; non umquam opulentior illis
     ante cinis: crepitant gemmae, atque immane liquescit
     argentum, et pictis exsudat vestibus aurum;
     nec non Assyriis pinguescunt robora sucis,
210   pallentique croco strident ardentia mella,
     spumantesque mero paterae verguntur et atri
     sanguinis et rapto gratissima cymbia lactis.

190 armenta Pω (*Wakefield; cf. 5.334*)
206 illic Pω: illo ψ (*SB*[2])
212 rapti Pω (*Alton*)

whose strength is tremulous, his vigour drawn only from the udder, is cheated of his first milk, carried off by a wild beast or a shepherd for the cruel altar; now the robbed mother stirs valley and rivers and trees with her complaint, questioning the empty fields; then she cares not to go home, she is last to leave the sad meadow, and turns away unfed from the grass before her.

But the father with his own hand hurls his sceptre's pride and the Thunderer's emblems on the pyre and clips with steel the hair that falls down his back and breast, covering the tiny face of the dead babe with the severed tresses and mingling with parental tears such words as these: 'Far otherwise, perfidious Jupiter, had I once consecrated these locks to you, due to discharge[17] the vow should you have granted me to offer my son's youthful cheeks along with them at your temple. But your priest's words were not ratified, his prayer was denied. Let this shade take them who deserves them more.' The torch is put, the fire in the lowest branches cries aloud, it is a task to keep back the demented parents.

Danai stand as ordered with levelled shields barring vision afar from unlawful view. The flames are enriched. No ash was ever wealthier than they.[18] Gems crack, silver melts in mass, gold sweats from embroidered fabrics. Logs fatten with Assyrian juices, burning honey hisses with pale saffron, foaming bowls of wine are tipped and cups of black

[17] Lycurgus had vowed to dedicate his hair and his son's beard to Jupiter if his son grew to manhood. *Voti reus* goes with *si . . . dedisses*.

[18] The flames are equated with the ash they produce.

tunc septem numero turmas (centenus ubique
surgit eques) versis ducunt insignibus ipsi
215 Graiugenae reges, lustrantque ex more sinistro
orbe rogum et stantes inclinant pulvere flammas.
ter curvos egere sinus, illisaque telis
tela sonant, quater horrendum pepulere fragorem
arma, quater mollem famularum bracchia planctum.
220 semianimas alter pecudes spirantiaque ignis
accipit armenta; hic luctus abolere novique
funeris auspicium vates, quamquam omina sentit
vera, iubet: dextri gyro et vibrantibus hastis
hac redeunt, raptumque suis libamen ab armis
225 quisque iacit, seu frena libet seu cingula flammis
mergere seu iaculum summae seu cassidis umbram.
[multa gemunt extra raucis concentibus agri,
et lituis aures circum pulsantur acutis.
terretur clamore nemus: sic Martia vellunt
230 signa tubae, nondum ira calet, nec sanguine ferrum
irrubuit, primus bellorum comitur illo
vultus, honoris opus. stat adhuc incertus in alta
nube quibus sese Mavors indulgeat armis.]
    Finis erat, lassusque putres iam Mulciber ibat
235 in cineres; instant flammis multoque soporant
imbre rogum, posito donec cum sole labores
exhausti; seris vix cessit cura tenebris.
    Roscida iam novies caelo dimiserat astra
Lucifer et totidem Lunae praevenerat ignes
240 mutato nocturnus equo (nec conscia fallit
sidera et alterno deprenditur unus in ortu):
mirum opus accelerasse manus! stat saxea moles,
templum ingens cineri, rerumque effictus in illa

blood and cups of milk—most grateful to the lost one.
Then the Grecian kings in person lead seven squadrons (to
each one mount a hundred riders) with insignia reversed.
Leftward in due form they circle the pyre and bend the rising flames with their dust. Thrice they wind their ring,
weapons clash on weapons, four times shields beat out a
fearsome din,[19] four times handmaidens' arms a soft slap-
ping. Another fire receives half-dead sheep and breathing
cattle. At this point the prophet bids cancel the mourning
and the auspice of strange calamity, though he knows the
omens speak true. Rightward they return wheeling with
quivering spears and each throws an offering snatched
from his arms, be it bridle or belt he chooses to sink in the
flames or javelin or the crest that shades his helmet.

It was the end. Already weary Mulciber was subsiding
into crumbling ash. They attack the flames and put the
pyre to sleep with copious water, till their labours are exhausted along with the setting sun. Hardly does their duty
yield to tardy darkness.

Nine times now had Lucifer dismissed the dewy stars
from the sky and as often nocturnal on his changed horse
had he heralded the lunar fire—nor does he deceive the
stars; they know, and in his alternate rising detect him
as one.[20] 'Twas a marvel how swiftly the work was done.

---

[19] Before the first round and after each of the three. Then, at
the prophet's command (223), they make the circle in reverse.

[20] The morning and the evening star, Lucifer (Phosphoros)
and Hesperos, being one and the same (the planet Venus).

227–33 *non* habent Pω, *damnant plerique*
231 ille *O. Mueller*   243 effectus Pω (ς)

ordo docet casus: fessis hic flumina monstrat
245 Hypsipyle Danais, hic reptat flebilis infans,
    hic iacet, extremum tumuli circum asperat orbem
    squameus; exspectes morientis ab ore cruenta
    sibila, marmorea sic volvitur anguis in hasta.
        Iamque avidum pugnas visendi vulgus inermes
250 (fama vocat cunctos) arvis ac moenibus adsunt
    exciti; illi etiam quis belli incognitus horror,
    quos effeta domi, quos prima reliquerat aetas,
    conveniunt: non aut Ephyraeo in litore tanta
    umquam aut Oenomai fremuerunt agmina circo.
255   Collibus incurvis viridique obsessa corona
    vallis in amplexu nemorum sedet; hispida circum
    stant iuga, et obiectus geminis umbonibus agger
    campum exire vetat, longo quem tramite planum
    gramineae frontes sinuataque caespite vivo
260 mollia non subitis augent fastigia clivis.
    illic conferti, iam sole rubentibus arvis,
    bellatrix sedere cohors; ibi corpore mixto
    metiri numerum vultusque habitusque suorum
    dulce viris, tantique iuvat fiducia belli.
265 centum ibi nigrantes, armenti robora, tauros
    lenta mole trahunt; idem numerusque colorque

---

246 orbes *C. Mueller*   259 frontes P: frondes ω

---

21 To take *tumuli* as the boy's tomb makes havoc of the narrative, which has problems enough anyway. In 246f. he seems to be
lying on a mound (the *tumulus*?) around which the snake is coiled;
but in 247f. the snake is dying, coiled around the spear that kills
him, whereas in 5.575–78 he dies inside Jupiter's temple. The
torturous file (*Silvae* 4.7.26) was badly needed here.

344

BOOK 6

There stands a mass of stone, a great temple for the ashes, and therein a sculptured series tells the story: here is Hypsipyle showing the stream to the weary Danai, here crawls the poor babe, here he lies while the circling scaly one rasps the round edge of the knoll.[21] You might expect bloody hisses from his dying mouth, so coils the snake about the marble spear.

And now comes a multitude eager to see mock battles (Rumour summons them all[22]), roused from field and street. Even those who know not the horror of war, whom age exhausted or incipient had left at home,[23] come flocking. Hosts so great never clamoured on Ephyre's shore or Oenomaus' ring.

A valley sits embraced by woods amid a green circle of winding hills. Shaggy ridges stand around and an interposing mound with double bosses forbids the plain's exit. This, a long, level strip, is raised by grassy brows and gentle slopes, curving with living lawn in a smooth incline.[24] There assembled, when the fields were already rosy with the sun, the warrior troop took their seats. They were fain to measure the number and faces and bearing of their comrades in the mixed body and were gladdened by confidence in so great an armament. There they drag in slow bulk one hundred black bulls, the strength of the herd;

[22] *Cunctis* makes an unlikely homoeoteleuton, which should not have been recognized in my *Homoeoteleuton in Latin Dactylic Poetry* (Stuttgart: Teubner, 1996), p. 94. Statius was particularly intolerant of such.   [23] Men of military age would be in the army.   [24] The description is hard to make out. With hesitation I take *planum* as referring to the level top of the mound rather than to the plain below. It accommodates spectators, who look down a slope onto the flat where the sports are held (cf. 929).

matribus et nondum lunatis fronte iuvencis.
exin magnanimum series antiqua parentum
invehitur, miris in vultum animata figuris.
270 primus anhelantem duro Tirynthius angens
pectoris attritu sua frangit in ossa leonem.
haud illum impavidi quamvis et in aere suumque
Inachidae videre decus. pater ordine iuncto
laevus harundineae recubans super aggere ripae
275 cernitur emissaeque indulgens Inachus urnae.
Io post tergum, iam prona dolorque parentis,
spectat inocciduis stellatum visibus Argum.
ast illam melior Phariis erexerat arvis
Iuppiter atque hospes iam tunc Aurora colebat.
280 Tantalus inde parens, non qui fallentibus undis
imminet aut refugae sterilem rapit aëra silvae,
sed pius et magni vehitur conviva Tonantis.
parte alia victor curru Neptunia tendit
lora Pelops, prensatque rotas auriga natantes
285 Myrtilos et volucri iam iamque relinquitur axe.
et gravis Acrisius speciesque horrenda Coroebi
et Danaë culpata sinus et in amne reperto

---

25 Not, I think, Hercules' bones, which goes less well with
pectoris attritu.

26 On all fours, as a cow.

27 At the date of the sculpture: narrator's comment. Aurora =
the Orient.

28 Given him by the god.

cows too and steers not yet crescent-browed in number
and colour the same. Then an ancient line of great-hearted
ancestors is borne in, wonderfully figured with living faces.
First the Tirynthian, crushing the gasping lion and breaking it into its own bones[25] by the harsh friction of his breast.
Not without fear did the sons of Inachus see him, though in
bronze and their own glory. Father Inachus is next beheld
reclining leftward on the mound of his reedy bank and
giving free course to the pouring urn. Behind him Io,
already prone[26] and her father's grief, watches Argus,
starred with eyes that never set. But Jupiter in kinder
mood had raised her up in the Pharian land and already
Aurora was worshipping her guest.[27] Then father Tantalus
is borne, not he who hangs over the delusive waters or
catches at the barren air of retreating branches, but the
good Tantalus, dinner guest of the great Thunderer. In another part Pelops in his victorious car stretches Neptune's
reins,[28] while Myrtilos the charioteer clutches at the wobbling wheels and the swift axle is even now abandoning
him.[29] There too is stern Acrisius and the fearsome form of
Coroebus and Danaë of culprit lap and Amymone,[30] sad by

[29] Statius appears to be confusing the death of Myrtilos
(thrown into the sea by Pelops later on according to the usual
account) with that of Oenomaus. The wobbling wheels evidently
allude to Myrtilos' sabotage of Oenomaus' chariot. See SB[2]. The
language here suggests a relief (cf. 272) rather than a group of
sculptures (note *parte alia*).

[30] Daughter of Danaus. After arriving in Argos he sent her to
look for water. Attacked by a Satyr, she called on Neptune for
help. He had his way with her and brought water out of the
ground, ending a drought as she had asked him. She gave him a
son, Nauplius.

347

tristis Amymone, parvoque Alcmena superbit
Hercule tergemina crinem circumdata luna.
290 iungunt discordes inimica in foedera dextras
Belidae fratres, sed vultu mitior astat
Aegyptus; Danai manifestum agnoscere ficto
ore notas pacisque malae noctisque futurae.
mille dehinc species. tandem satiata Voluptas
295 praestantesque viros vocat ad sua praemia Virtus.
     Primus sudor equis. dic incluta, Phoebe, regentum
nomina, dic ipsos; neque enim generosior umquam
alipedum collata acies, ceu praepete cursu
confligant densae volucres aut litore in uno
300 Aeolus insanis statuat certamina ventis.
     Ducitur ante omnes rutilae manifestus Arion
igne iubae. Neptunus equo, si certa priorum
fama, pater; primus teneri laesisse lupatis
ora et litoreo domitasse in pulvere fertur,
305 verberibus parcens; etenim insatiatus eundi
ardor et hiberno par inconstantia ponto.
saepe per Ionium Libycumque natantibus ire
interiunctus equis omnesque assuerat in oras
caeruleum deferre patrem; stupuere relicta
310 Nubila, certantesque Eurique Notique sequuntur.
nec minor in terris bella Eurysthea gerentem
Amphitryoniaden alto per gramina sulco
duxerat, illi etiam ferus indocilisque teneri.
mox divum dono regis dignatus Adrasti

293 notas P: nefas ω
303 teneris Pω (*Garrod*)

348

the river she discovered, and Alcmena, with triple moon[31] about her hair, takes pride in little Hercules. The brethren sons of Belus join right hands of strife in a covenant of hate; but Aegyptus stands by with gentler mien, while on Danaus' dissembling face the marks of an evil pact[32] and the night to come are plain to recognize. Follow a thousand forms. At length Pleasure is satisfied and Valour calls men of mark to her prizes.

First toil is for the horses. Tell, Phoebus, the drivers' famous names, tell the horses themselves. For never met a nobler array of coursers. 'Twas as though a swarm of birds were to compete in rapid career or Aeolus to set up a race for the wild winds on one shore.

Before them all Arion is led, conspicuous by the fire of his ruddy mane. Neptune was the horse's father, if our elders' tale be true. He is said to have been the first to bruise the youngling's mouth with the bit and break him in on the sand of the shore, sparing the lash; for indeed there was no satisfying the horse's passion to be moving and he was as changeful as a winter sea. Often he was wont to go in harness with the swimming steeds through Ionian or Libyan deep, carrying his caerulean father to every coast. Outstripped, the Clouds were amazed, East and South Winds emulously follow. Nor less was he on land, bringing Amphitryon's son through deep-furrowed meadows as he fought Eurystheus' battles; even for him he was wild and unmanageable. Later by gift of the gods he deigned

[31] In memory of the triple night of Hercules' conception.
[32] Of marriage between the fifty sons of Aegyptus and the fifty daughters of Danaus. Aegyptus and Danaus were brothers, sons of Belus. Aegyptus' sons were murdered by Danaus' daughters.

315 imperia et multum mediis mansueverat annis.
tunc rector genero Polynici indulget agendum
multa monens, ubi fervor equo, qua suetus ab arte
mulceri, ne saeva manus, ne liber habenis
impetus. 'urge alios,' inquit, 'stimulisque minisque;
320 ille ibit, minus ipse voles.' sic ignea lora
cum daret et rapido Sol natum imponeret axi,
gaudentem lacrimans astra insidiosa docebat
nolentesque teri zonas mediamque polorum
temperiem: pius ille quidem et formidine cauta,
325 sed iuvenem durae prohibebant discere Parcae.
        Oebalios sublimis agit, spes proxima palmae,
Amphiaraus equos; tua furto lapsa propago,
Cyllare, dum Scythici diversus ad ostia Ponti
Castor Amyclaeas remo permutat habenas.
330 ipse habitu niveus, nivei dant colla iugales,
concolor est albis et cassis et infula cristis.
quin et Thessalicis felix Admetus ab oris
vix steriles compescit equas, Centaurica dicunt
semina: credo, adeo sexum indignantur, et omnis
335 in vires adducta Venus; noctemque diemque
assimulant maculis internigrantibus albae:
tantus uterque color, credi nec degener illo
de grege, Castaliae stupuit qui sibila cannae
laetus et audito contempsit Apolline pasci.
340 ecce et Iasonidae iuvenes, nova gloria matris
Hypsipyles, subiere iugo, quo vectus uterque,

---

33 Betokening his priestly status.
34 Centaurs, who lived in Thessaly, being wild and warlike
creatures.   35 Sexual.

to obey king Adrastus; and in the years between he had grown much tamer. On this occasion the ruler lets son-in-law Polynices drive him, with many an admonition: when the horse would get excited, with what art he was wont to be soothed, not to handle him harshly nor yet to let him speed free of the rein. 'Urge others,' he said, 'with goads and threats. *He* will go, and faster than you wish.' So when the Sun gave his child the fiery thongs and placed him in the rapid car, with tears he taught the happy youth of treacherous stars and zones unwilling to be trodden and the temperate region between the poles; loving was he and cautious in his fear, but the cruel Parcae would not suffer the young man to learn.

Amphiaraus, next favourite for the palm, drives aloft Oebalian horses, your offspring, Cyllarus, dropped by stealth, while Castor sojourned far away at the mouth of Scythian Pontus, exchanging his Amyclaean reins for an oar. He himself wears snow white, snowy are the coursers that give their necks to the yoke, his helm and fillet match his white[33] plume. Fortunate Admetus too from the land of Thessaly scarce controls his barren mares—Centaur's seed[34] they say and I believe; so do they scorn their sex, turning all their passion[35] into strength. They were like night and day, white with black spots, so strong was either colour, worthy to be believed to come from the herd that listened in joyous rapture to the whistling of the Castalian reed,[36] despising pasture when they heard Apollo play. And see, the young sons of Jason, new glory of their mother Hypsipyle, come to a chariot on which both

[36] Played by Apollo when he served Admetus as shepherd and horsekeeper.

nomen avo gentile Thoas atque omine dictus
Euneos Argoo. geminis eadem omnia: vultus,
currus, equi, vestes, par et concordia voti:
345   vincere vel solo cupiunt a fratre relinqui.
it Chromis Hippodamusque, alter satus Hercule magno,
alter ab Oenomao: dubites uter effera presset
frena magis. Getici pecus hic Diomedis, at ille
Pisaei iuga patris habet, crudelibus ambo
350   exuviis diroque imbuti sanguine currus.
     Metarum instar erat hinc nudo robore quercus,
olim omnes exuta comas, hinc saxeus umbo,
arbiter agricolis; finem iacet inter utrumque
quale quater iaculo spatium, ter harundine, vincas.
355   Interea cantu Musarum nobile mulcens
concilium citharaeque manus insertus Apollo
Parnasi summo spectabat ab aethere terras.

       *   *   *   *   *

orsa deo, nam saepe Iovem Phlegramque suique
anguis opus fratrumque pius cantarat honores.
360   tunc aperit quis fulmen agat, quis sidera ducat
spiritus, unde animi fluviis, quae pabula ventis,
quo fonte immensum vivat mare, quae via solis
praecipitet noctem, quae porrigat, imane tellus
an media et rursus mundo succincta latenti.

344 voti ω: -is P
351 erant *Slater*   *versum ante 358 excidisse vidit Housman*
358 deo P, *Housman* deum ω   362 vivat ωΣ: bibat P, *unde immensum quo fonte bibat mare Phillimore*

---

[37] Either of the twins being the other's alter ego, a chariot occupied by one contained both (SB[2]).

rode:[37] Thoas—family name from his grandfather—and Euneos,[38] called from Argo's omen. Twins, they had everything the same: face, chariot, horses, dress, nor less concord in their prayers; each wishes to win or to be outrun only by his brother. Chromis and Hippodamus run, one born of great Hercules, the other of Oenomaus; you might doubt which of the two pressed wilder reins. One has the animals of Getic Diomedes, the other the team of his Pisaean father.[39] Both chariots displayed cruel trophies and were stained with gruesome gore.

For turning posts there stood at one end a bare oak trunk long stripped of all its foliage, at the other a stone block, the farmers' umpire. Between either mark was a space that might be mastered four times with a javelin, three with an arrow.

Meanwhile Apollo was soothing the noble company of the Muses with his song, and with hands upon his lyre watched the earth from Parnassus' ethereal summit. * * *[40]—for often had he piously sung of Jupiter and Phlegra and the serpent, his own achievement, and the praises of his brothers. Then he expounds who drives the thunderbolt, what spirit leads the stars, where rivers get their boldness, winds their food, from what fountain lives the vast sea, what path the sun takes to shorten night and what to draw it out, whether earth lies at the bottom or in the centre, girt around again by a world unseen. It was

[38] 'He of the good ship' (reference to Argo).

[39] Oenomaus.   [40] Reading *deo*, Housman convincingly suggests the loss of a verse such as *caelicolum meritas* (better *primo?*) *non longa sonantia laudes*: 'the god's song was first in praise of the sky-dwellers, not lengthy.'

353

365 finis erat, differt avidas audire Sorores,
dumque chelyn lauro textumque illustre coronae
subligat et picto discingit pectora limbo,
haud procul Herculeam Nemeen clamore reductus
aspicit atque illic ingens certaminis instar
370 quadriiugi. noscit cunctos, et forte propinqui
constiterant Admetus et Amphiaraus in arvo.
tunc secum: 'quisnam iste duos, fidissima Phoebi
nomina, commisit deus in discrimina reges?
ambo pii carique ambo; nequeam ipse priorem
375 dicere. Peliacis hic cum famularer in arvis
(sic Iovis imperia et nigrae volvere Sorores),
tura dabat famulo nec me sentire minorem
ausus; at hic tripodum comes et pius artis alumnus
aetheriae. potior meritis tamen ille; sed huius
380 extrema iam fila colu. datur ordo senectae
Admeto serumque mori; tibi nulla supersunt
gaudia, nam Thebae iuxta et tenebrosa vorago.
scis miser, et nostrae pridem cecinere volucres.'
dixit, et os fletu paene inviolabile tinctus
385 extemplo Nemeen radiante per aëra saltu
ocior et patrio venit igne suisque sagittis.
ipse olim in terris, caelo vestigia durant,
claraque per Zephyros etiamnum semita lucet.
    Et iam sortitus Prothous versarat aëna

370 propinquo Pω (*Imhof*)

---

41 Statius seems to have overlooked the fact that this was no
semblance (*instar*) or approximation but an actual race; whereas
in 351 *metarum instar* the two objects were not turning posts
made for the purpose but only served as such.

over, and he puts off the Sisters eager to listen. While he binds the lyre and the bright fabric of his garland to a laurel bush and ungirds his breast of the embroidered cincture, not far away, drawn by the cheering, he sees Hercules' Nemea and there the vast semblance[41] of a chariot race. He knows them all, and by chance Admetus and Amphiaraus stood close together[42] in the field. Then to himself: 'Who is the god that has joined the two kings, Phoebus' most faithful names, in rivalry? Both are pious, both beloved; I could not say myself which stands first. One, when I was a serf in Pelion's fields (so Jove's commands and the dark Sisters[43] would have it), gave incense to his thrall and dared not feel me his inferior; the other is companion of tripods and pious disciple of ethereal skill. Yet the first has preference by his deserts; but the other's thread is at the distaff's end. To Admetus is given old age's course and a late death; for you no joys are left, for Thebes is at hand and the dark chasm. You know it, unhappy one, and our birds have long so sung.' He spoke and almost[44] his inviolable face was stained with tears. Straightway with a leap that shone through the air he came to Nemea, more swiftly than his father's flame and his own arrows. He himself is already long on land, but his traces linger in the sky and a bright track still gleams through the Zephyrs.

And now Prothous has shaken the lots in a brazen hel-

[42] Reading *propinqui*. I hardly think that *propinquo in arvo* can be so understood, as argued by Håkanson; that should mean 'in a nearby field,' but near to what? The relevant point is that Apollo saw them together.

[43] The Fates, sinister in this context.

[44] Gods were not supposed to weep (Ovid, *Metamorphoses* 2.621f.), but sometimes do, e.g. at 5.270.

390   casside, iamque locus cuique est et liminis ordo.
    terrarum decora ampla viri, decora aequa iugales,
    divum utrumque genus, stant uno margine clausi,
    spesque audaxque una metus et fiducia pallens.
    nil fixum cordi: pugnant exire paventque,
395   concurrit summos animosum frigus in artus.
    qui dominis, idem ardor equis; face lumina surgunt,
    ora sonant morsu, spumisque et sanguine ferrum
    uritur, impulsi nequeunt obsistere postes
    claustraque, compressae transfumat anhelitus irae.
400   stare adeo miserum est, pereunt vestigia mille
    ante fugam, absentemque ferit gravis ungula campum.
    circumstant fidi, nexusque et torta iubarum
    expediunt firmantque animos et plurima monstrant.
    insonuit contra Tyrrhenum murmur, et omnes
405   exsiluere loco. quae tantum carbasa ponto,
    quae bello sic tela volant, quae nubila caelo?
    amnibus hibernis minor est, minor impetus igni,
    tardius astra cadunt, glomerati tardius imbres,
    tardius e summo decurrunt flumina monte.
410   Emissos videre atque agnovere Pelasgi,
    et iam rapti oculis, iam caeco pulvere mixti
    una in nube latent, vultusque umbrante tumultu
    vix inter sese clamore et nomine noscunt.
    evolvere globum, et spatio quo quisque valebat
415   diducti; delet sulcos iterata priores

---

403 plura ministrant *Pollack*   408 glomerantur Pω (*SB*)

---

45 So *monstrant* must be rendered. In their excitement the
grooms shower advice on the animals as though they could understand.

met and each has his place and starting order. The men, splendid ornaments of the earth, the horses, ornaments no less splendid, both of race divine, stand behind one barrier, and with them hope and audacious fear and anxious confidence. In their hearts nothing is firm-fixed. They fight to go forth and are afraid; courageous chill courses all through their limbs. The horses are as ardent as their masters. Their eyes swell fiery, their mouths loudly champ, foam and blood corrode their bits, the posts and bars cannot withstand their push, the pant of stifled rage smokes through. To stand still is torture; a thousand paces are wasted before the start, the heavy hoof strikes the absent flat. Trusty attendants straighten the tangled patches in their manes, encourage them, give many words of counsel.[45] Opposite sounded the Tyrrhenian blare and all leapt from their stations. What canvass on sea, what weapons fly so in battle, what clouds in the sky? Not so swift the rush of winter rivers, not so swift the rush of fire. More slowly fall stars, more slowly balled rains,[46] more slowly run torrents down from a mountaintop.

The Pelasgi saw them as they shot out and recognized; and already, snatched from vision and mingled in blinding dust, they are hidden in a single cloud and as confusion obscures their faces they barely know each other by shout of names. They unroll the pack, separated by intervals matching the strength of each. A second track deletes

---

[46] Cf. Livy 1.31.2 *grandinem venti glomeratam in terras agunt*. Attempts to explain *glomerantur* without reference to hail are futile, and I cannot believe that even Statius could have it mean *glomerati cadunt*.

orbita. nunc avidi prono iuga pectore tangunt,
nunc pugnante genu et pressis duplicantur habenis.
colla toris crinita tument, stantesque repectit
aura iubas, bibit albentes humus arida nimbos.
420 fit sonus immanisque pedum tenuisque rotarum:
nulla manu requies, densis insibilat aër
verberibus; gelida non crebrior exsilit Arcto
grando, nec Oleniis manant tot cornibus imbres.
    Senserat adductis alium praesagus Arion
425 stare ducem loris, dirumque expaverat insons
Oedipodioniden; iam illinc a limine discors
iratusque oneri solito truculentior ardet.
Inachidae credunt accensum laudibus; ille
aurigam fugit, aurigae furiale minatur
430 efferus, et campo dominum circumspicit omni,
ante tamen cunctos. sequitur longeque secundus
Amphiaraus agit, quem Thessalus aequat eundo
Admetus; iuxta gemini, nunc Euneos ante
et nunc ante Thoas, cedunt vincuntque, nec umquam
435 ambitiosa pios collidit gloria fratres.
postremum discrimen erant Chromis asper et asper
Hippodamus, non arte rudes, sed mole tenentur
cornipedum; prior Hippodamus fert ora sequentum,
fert gemitus multaque umeros incenditur aura.
440 speravit flexae circum compendia metae
interius ductis Phoebeius augur habenis

427 solito P: ins- ω

---

47 At the turning posts.
48 Passing from the drivers to the horses.

358

the previous furrows. Now eagerly they touch the yoke with sloping chests, now they bend double[47] with striving knees and hard-drawn reins. Muscles swell on hair-strewn necks,[48] the breeze combs back erected manes, the dry ground drinks white showers. There is thunder of hooves, a sharper sound of wheels. Hands have no respite, the air hisses with multitudinous lashes. Not thicker leaps hail from the icy Bear, nor stream so many rains from Olenian horns.[49]

Prescient Arion had sensed that another driver stood pulling the reins and in his innocence had dreaded the fell son of Oedipus. Right from the starting line he was at odds with his burden and angry, more truculent in his ardour than of wont. The children of Inachus think him fired by desire for glory, but it is the driver he flees, the driver he threatens in his wild fury as he looks around for his master all over the field; yet he is ahead of them all.[50] Amphiaraus follows, driving a distant second, with Admetus of Thessaly running neck and neck. Close together come the twins, now Euneos in front, now Thoas; they yield, they lead, nor ever does ambition for glory cause these loving brothers to clash. Last in the race were fierce Chromis and fierce Hippodamus, no novices they, but retarded by their horses' bulk. Hippodamus is ahead and feels the mouths of his pursuers, feels their gasps, his shoulders are hot with their heavy breath. Phoebus' augur hoped to take first place by pulling in his reins as he shaves the curving goal.

[49] Cf. on 3.25.

[50] The usual punctuation with period after *omni* was rightly impugned by Håkanson. It puts Amphiaraus in the lead (after the lone horse Arion); but he and Admetus were neck and neck.

anticipasse viam; nec non et Thessalus heros
spe propiore calet, dum non cohibente magistro
spargitur in gyros dexterque exerrat Arion.
445 iam prior Oeclides et iam non tertius ibat
Admetus, laxo cum denique ab orbe reductus
aequoreus sonipes premit evaditque parumper
gavisos; subit astra fragor, caelumque tremescit,
omniaque excusso patuere sedilia vulgo.
450 sed nec lora regit nec verbera pallidus audet
Labdacides: lassa veluti ratione magister
in fluctus, in saxa ruit nec iam amplius astra
respicit et victam proiecit casibus artem.
      Rursus praecipites in recta ac devia campi
455 obliquant tenduntque vias, iterum axibus axes
inflicti, radiisque rotae; pax nulla fidesque.
bella geri ferro levius, bella horrida, credas;
is furor in laudes. trepidant mortemque minantur,
multaque transversis praestringitur ungula canthis.
460 nec iam sufficiunt stimuli, non verbera; voce
nominibusque cient Pholoën Admetus et Irin
funalemque Thoën, rapidum Danaeius augur
Ascheton increpitans meritumque vocabula Cycnum.
audit et Herculeum Strymon Chromin, Euneon audit
465 igneus Aëtion; tardumque Cydona lacessit
Hippodamus, variumque Thoas rogat ire Podarcen.
solus Echionides errante silentia curru
maesta tenet trepidaque timet se voce fateri.
      Vixdum coeptus equis labor, et iam pulvere quarto

446 cum tandem ab PωΣ (*Hill*: cum vix t- *Watt*)
459 campis Pω (*SB²*)
465 aethion PωΣ (*Housman*)

The Thessalian hero too burns with a closer hope as Arion,
unchecked by his master, scatters in rings, straying out to
the right. Now Oecles' son was ahead and Admetus no
longer running third, when finally back from a wide circuit
the horse of the sea presses and passes both; short-lived
their joy. A roar goes up to the stars, the sky trembles and
every seat shows bare as the multitude jumps to its feet.
But the scion of Labdacus pales, neither governing the
reins nor daring to use his whip. Even as a helmsman
whose science is weary rushes on waves, on rocks, nor any
more regards the stars; his skill overborne by chance, he
has flung it away.

Again headlong over the plain straight or straying they
swerve and stretch their courses, axles once more collide
with axles, wheels with spokes. No truce, no trust. You
would think war was a-waging, cruel war, only without
steel;[51] so mad are they for glory. They tremble and they
threaten death and many a hoof is scraped by tires[52]
athwart. Goads and lashes are no longer enough, they
urge by voice and name. Admetus calls on Pholoë and Iris
and trace horse Thoë, the Danaëian augur chides swift
Aschetus and Cycnus that deserved his name.[53] Strymon
hears Hercules' son Chromis, fiery Aëtion hears Euneos;
Hippodamus taunts slow Cydon, Thoas begs piebald
Podarces to take off. Only the scion of Echion keeps
gloomy silence in his errant car, fearing to give himself
away by a quavering voice.

The horses' ordeal was scarce begun and already they

---

[51] I take *ferro levius* as equivalent to *ferro minus*.
[52] *Canthis*, replacing the senseless *campis*.
[53] 'Headstrong' and (white) 'Swan.'

470 campum ineunt, iamque et tepidis sudoribus artus
effeti, et crassum rapit eiectatque vaporem
cornipedum flammata sitis, nec iam integer illis
impetus, et longi suspendunt ilia flatus.
hic anceps Fortuna diu decernere primum
475 ausa venit. ruit, Haemonium dum fervidus instat
Admetum superare, Thoas, nec pertulit ullam
frater opem. velit ille quidem, sed Martius ante
obstitit Hippodamus mediasque immisit habenas.
mox Chromis Hippodamum metae interioris ad orbem
480 viribus Herculeis et toto robore patris
axe tenet prenso; luctantur abire iugales
nequiquam frenosque et colla rigentia tendunt.
ut Siculas si quando rates tenet aestus et ingens
Auster agit, medio stant vela tumentia ponto.
485 tunc ipsum fracto curru deturbat et isset
ante Chromis; sed Thraces equi ut videre iacentem
Hippodamum, redit illa fames, iam iamque trementem
partiti furiis, ni frena ipsosque frementes
oblitus palmae retro Tirynthius heros
490 torsisset victusque et collaudatus abisset.
        At tibi promissos iamdudum Phoebus honores,
Amphiaraë, cupit. tandem ratus apta favori
tempora pulverei venit in spatia horrida circi,
cum iam in fine viae, et summum victoria nutat;
495 anguicomam monstri effigiem, saevissima visu

476 praetulit Pω (ς, *Baehrens*)

---

54 The first three laps went 'in a flash.'
55 *Suspendunt*, lit. 'hold in suspense.'

start the course on a fourth dusty lap.[54] Their limbs are exhausted with steaming sweat, the flaming thirst of the racers catches and expels thick vapour, their forward rush is no longer total, drawn-out pantings rack[55] their flanks. Here first came Fortune, long in doubt, with courage to decide. As he eagerly presses to pass Haemonian Admetus, Thoas crashes, nor did his brother bring him any aid; willingly he would, but Martian Hippodamus[56] blocked his way, driving his car between. Then Chromis at the circuit of the inner goal[57] clutches Hippodamus' axle and holds it with the strength of Hercules, the whole might of his sire; in vain the horses strive to get away, stretching bridles and straining necks. So it may hap that a tide holds fast Sicilian ships while a mighty South Wind urges them on; the swelling sails stand in mid sea. Then Chromis hurls the driver from the shattered car and would have passed ahead. But when the Thracian horses see Hippodamus lying on the ground, the old hunger returns and in their furies they would have torn him apart trembling there and then, had not the Tirynthian hero, forgetful of the palm, dragged bridles and horses away. He withdrew, a popular loser.

But Phoebus this long while has desired for you the honour he promised,[58] Amphiaraus. Thinking the time at last ripe for favour, he enters the rough[59] spaces of the dusty course, now that the tracks are ending and final victory wavers. The figure of a monster with snaky hair, a

---

[56] His father Oenomaus was a son of Mars.

[57] Cf. *meta ulterior* in Sidonius, *Poems* 23.361.

[58] As implied in 372–83.

[59] Churned up by the chariots. Not 'grim' or 'sans pitié.'

ora, movet sive ille Erebo seu finxit in astus
temporis, innumera certe formidine cultum
tollit in astra nefas. non illud ianitor atrae
impavidus Lethes, non ipsae horrore sine alto
500   Eumenides vidisse queant, turbasset euntes
Solis equos Martisque iugum. nam flavus Arion
ut vidit, saliere iubae, atque erectus in armos
stat sociumque iugi comitesque utrimque laboris
secum alte suspendit equos. ruit ilicet exsul
505   Aonius nexusque diu per terga volutus
exuit: abripitur longe moderamine liber
currus; at hunc putri praeter tellure iacentem
Taenarii currus et Thessalus axis et heros
Lemnius obliqua, quantum vitare dabatur,
510   transabiere fuga. tandem caligine mersum
erigit accursu comitum caput aegraque tollit
membra solo, et socero redit haud speratus Adrasto.
    Quis mortis, Thebane, locus, nisi dura negasset
Tisiphone, quantum poteras dimittere bellum!
515   te Thebe fraterque palam, te plangeret Argos,
te Nemea, tibi Lerna comas Larisaque supplex
poneret, Archemori maior colerere sepulcro.
    Tum vero Oeclides, quamquam iam certa sequenti
praemia, cum vacuus domino praeiret Arion,
520   ardet adhuc cupiens vel inanem vincere currum.
dat vires refovetque deus; volat ocior Euro,

496 astus P: -u ω: *anne* usus?

---

60 Amphiaraus, Admetus, and Euneus.
61 Or 'not as hoped' (= *haud ita speratus*)?
62 Like Opheltes, Polynices would have been deified (cf.

dreadful visage, he either moved from Erebus or framed as
a device for the nonce; certain it is that he raised this
abomination decked with countless terrors into the upper
world. The janitor of black Lethe could not look upon it
unafraid, nor the Eumenides themselves without deep
horror; it would have shocked the horses of the Sun and
Mars' team in their courses. When golden Arion saw it, his
mane leapt, he rears into his shoulders and stands, sus-
pending from above his yoke-fellow and the partners in
their labour on either side along with himself. The Aonian
exile straightway plunges and sprawls for a space on his
back, till he frees himself from the ties; the chariot, released from guidance, is swept afar. As for him, as he lies
on the sandy earth the Taenarian car and the wheels of
Thessaly and the Lemnian hero[60] fly past him, swerving to
avoid him as best they could. At last his companions run
up, he raises his head, sunk in darkness, and lifts his
injured limbs from the ground, and returns unhoped-for[61]
to Adrastus his wife's father.

What a chance to die, Theban, had not harsh Tisiphone
denied! What a war you could have banished! Thebes and
your brother would have mourned you in public, and
Argos and Nemea; for you Lerna and Larisa would prayer-
fully have sacrificed their hair.[62] Your grave would have
had more worship than Archemorus'.

Then Oecles' son, albeit sure of the prize had he followed, since Arion in front was masterless, yet still burns
with desire to beat the car, empty though it be. The god
gives strength and revival. Swifter than the East Wind he

5.751) and vows made to him throughout Argolis (cf. 193–201,
610, 633f.).

ceu modo carceribus dimissus in arva solutis,
verberibusque iubas et terga lacessit habenis
Ascheton increpitansque levem Cycnumque nivalem.
525 nunc saltem, dum nemo prior, rapit igneus orbes
axis, et effusae longe sparguntur harenae.
dat gemitum tellus et iam tum saeva minatur.
forsitan et victo prior isset Arione Cycnus,
sed vetat aequoreus vinci pater: hinc vice iusta
530 gloria mansit equo, cessit victoria vati.
huic pretium palmae gemini cratera ferebant
Herculeum iuvenes: illum Tirynthius olim
ferre manu sola spumantemque ore supino
vertere, seu monstri victor seu Marte, solebat.
535 Centauros habet arte truces aurumque figuris
terribile: hic mixta Lapitharum caede rotantur
saxa, faces aliique iterum crateres; ubique
ingentes morientum irae; tenet ipse furentem
Hylaeum et torta molitur robora barba.
540 at tibi Maeonio fertur circumflua limbo
pro meritis, Admete, chlamys repetitaque multo
murice: Phrixei natat hic contemptor ephebus
aequoris et picta tralucet caerulus unda;
in latus ire manus mutaturusque videtur
545 bracchia, nec siccum speres in stamine crinem;
contra autem frustra sedet anxia turre suprema
Sestias in speculis, moritur prope conscius ignis.

524 Ascheton *om.* Pω (ϛ)   increpitans caecum P: i-
sc(a)erum ω (ϛ)
538 ferentem *Heinsius, fort. recte*
544 manu *Markland*

flies, as though the barriers had just been lifted and he discharged into the open, chiding nimble Aschetos and snowy Cycnus, plying the whip on their manes and the reins on their backs. Now if not before, now when none is ahead, the fiery axle tears along the wheels, the sand is churned and scattered afar. The earth groans and threatens angrily—even then![63] Perhaps Cycnus would have gone ahead and Arion lost, but his father the sea god will not let him lose. So in fair division the horse kept his glory, victory went to the seer. Two young men bore him the palm's reward, Hercules' bowl, that the Tirynthian used once to bear in one hand and tilt foaming into his upturned mouth, victor over a monster or in war. It has Centaurs fierce by art and gold in shapes of terror. On its surface are hurled stones and torches and again other bowls[64] mingling in the slaughter of the Lapithae, everywhere is the mighty wrath of the dying; he himself holds raging Hylaeus, twisting the beard and plying his club. But for you, Admetus, is brought for your deserts a mantle with flowing Maeonian border, dyed deep with purple over and over. Here swims the youth[65] who despised Phrixus' sea, gleaming bluish in the coloured water. His hands seem to move sideways, he seems about to alternate his arms, you would think his hair in the thread would not be dry. Opposite sits the maid of Sestos anxious on her towertop, watching in vain; nearby the accomplice flame is dying. These riches Adrastus or-

---

[63] Later it was to swallow him up.

[64] The bowls of the banqueters in relief.

[65] Leander, swimming the Hellespont to reach Hero on the European side. Phrixus had once crossed it on the ram with the golden fleece.

THEBAID

has Adrastus opes dono victoribus ire
imperat; at generum famula solatur Achaea.
550   Sollicitat tunc ampla viros ad praemia cursu
praeceleres: agile studium et tenuissima virtus,
pacis opus, cum sacra vocant, nec inutile bellis
subsidium, si dextra neget. prior omnibus Idas,
nuper Olympiacis umbratus tempora ramis,
555 prosilit; excipiunt plausu Pisaea iuventus
Eleaeque manus. sequitur Sicyonius Alcon,
et bis in Isthmiaca victor clamatus harena
Phaedimus, alipedumque fugam praegressus equorum
ante Dymas, sed tunc aevo tardante secutus.
560 multi et, quos varii tacet ignorantia vulgi,
hinc atque hinc subiere. sed Arcada Parthenopaeum
appellant densique cient vaga murmura circi.
nota parens cursu; quis Maenaliae Atalantes
nesciat egregium decus et vestigia cunctis
565 indeprensa procis? onerat celeberrima natum
mater, et ipse procul fama iam notus inermes
narratur cervas pedes inter aperta Lycaei
tollere et emissum cursu deprendere telum.
tandem exspectatus volucri super agmina saltu
570 emicat et torto chlamydem diffibulat auro.
effulsere artus, membrorumque omnis aperta est
laetitia, insignes umeri, nec pectora nudi
deteriora genis, latuitque in corpore vultus.
ipse tamen formae laudem aspernatur et arcet

572 nudis Pω (SB)

66 As at games like these.
67 The reading and interpretation were settled conclusively

368

ders bestowed upon the victors. His son-in-law he consoles with an Achaean handmaiden.

Then he invites the fleet of foot to ample rewards; a quest of agility, where valour has small part, a work of peace when religion calls,[66] yet in war an aid not useless, failing the right arm. First of all Idas leaps forth, his temples lately shaded by Olympian branches; the men of Pisa and the bands of Elis greet him with applause. Alcon of Sicyon follows, and Phaedimus, twice hailed victor on Isthmian sand, and Dymas, who once outstripped the flight of wing-foot horses but now follows slowed by age. And many others, whom the ignorance of the motley multitude passes over in silence, come forward from here and there. But wandering murmurs of the packed circus call Arcadian Parthenopaeus by name and summon him. His mother is famous for her running. Who would not know of Maenalian Atalanta's peerless beauty and the prints that no suitor could overtake? The mother's renown burdens the son and already far-famed he is reported as slaying on foot the deer in the open spaces of Lycaeus and intercepting a flying dart as he runs. At last to expectation he dashes out, leaping lightly over the crowds and unpins the twisted gold upon his mantle. His limbs shine, the joy of them is all revealed, his splendid shoulders and chest in his nakedness no less comely than his cheeks; his face was lost to view in his body.[67] Himself, however, rejects praise of his beauty and keeps admirers at bay. Then, no novice, he con-

for all who will listen by Housman from Plato's *Charmides* (154d): 'If the lad were to take off his clothes, he would be faceless; so entirely beautiful is the shape of him'—from which Statius may well have picked up the idea.

575 mirantes; tunc Palladios non inscius haustus
incubuit pinguique cutem fuscatur olivo.
hoc Idas, hoc more Dymas aliique nitescunt.
sic ubi tranquillo perlucent sidera ponto
vibraturque fretis caeli stellantis imago,
580 omnia clara nitent, sed clarior omnia supra
Hesperus exercet radios, quantusque per altum
aethera, caeruleis tantus monstratur in undis.
proximus et forma nec multum segnior Idas
cursibus atque aevo iuxta prior; attamen illi
585 iam tenuem pingues florem induxere palaestrae,
deserpitque genis nec se lanugo fatetur
intonsae sub nube comae. tunc rite citatos
explorant acuuntque gradus, variasque per artes
instimulant docto languentia membra tumultu:
590 poplite nunc sidunt flexo, nunc lubrica forti
pectora collidunt plausu, nunc ignea tollunt
crura brevemque fugam necopino fine reponunt.
    Ut ruit atque aequum summisit regula limen,
corripuere leves spatium, campoque refulsit
595 nuda cohors: volucres isdem modo tardius arvis
isse videntur equi; credas e plebe Cydonum
Parthorumque fuga totidem exsiluisse sagittas.
non aliter, celeres Hyrcana per avia cervi
cum procul impasti fremitum accepere leonis,
600 sive putant, rapit attonitos fuga caeca metusque
congregat, et longum dant cornua mixta fragorem.
effugit hic oculos rapida puer ocior aura
Maenalius, quem deinde gradu premit horridus Idas
inspiratque umero, flatuque et pectoris umbra

581 exertat *Schrader*

centrates on Pallas' draughts,[68] darkening his flesh with rich oil. In like fashion Idas glistens and Dymas and the rest. So when the stars shine in a tranquil sea and the semblance of the spangled sky quivers in the waters, all brightly gleam but brighter than all Hesperus plies his rays, showing as large in the dark-blue waves as in the high heavens. Next to him in beauty and not much slower in speed is Idas, close in age but older; for him, however, the oil of the wrestling ground had already brought a faint down, the growth steals over his cheeks, surreptitious beneath the cloud of his unshorn hair. Then they duly set their steps in motion, testing and sharpening, and by various devices arouse their languid limbs to artificial commotion; now they sink on bended knee, now vigorously slap their slippery chests with flat of hand, now lift ardent legs, laying a brief sprint to rest with a sudden stop.

When the bar fell, offering a level threshold, they nimbly devoured the space, the naked troop shone upon the flat. The swift horses seem to have moved less fast a while ago over the same terrain. You might think that so many arrows had leapt forth from a Cydonian crowd or a flight of Parthians.[69] Not otherwise when swift stags in the Hyrcanian wilderness hear at a distance the roar of a hungry lion, or think they hear, blind flight sweeps them in panic and fear crowds them together; their mingling horns clash long and loud. The boy of Maenalus flees vision, swifter than the rapid wind. Rough Idas presses upon him, breathing on his shoulder, and strikes his back with his

---

[68] The olive being sacred to Minerva.
[69] Shooting behind them as they retreated.

605 terga ferit. post ambiguo discrimine tendunt
Phaedimus atque Dymas, illis celer imminet Alcon.
flavus ab intonso pendebat vertice crinis
Arcados; hoc primis Triviae pascebat ab annis
munus et, Ogygio victor cum Marte redisset,
610 nequiquam patriis audax promiserat aris.
tunc liber nexu lateque in terga solutus
occursu Zephyri retro fugit et simul ipsum
impedit infestoque volans obtenditur Idae.
inde dolum iuvenis fraudique accommoda sensit
615 tempora; iam finem iuxta, dum limina victor
Parthenopaeus init, correpto crine reductum
occupat, et longe primus ferit ostia portae.
  Arcades arma fremunt, armis defendere regem,
ni raptum decus et meriti reddantur honores,
620 contendunt totoque parant descendere circo.
sunt et quis Idae placeat dolus. ipse regesta
Parthenopaeus humo vultumque oculosque madentes
obruit, accessit lacrimarum gratia formae.
pectora nunc maerens, nunc ora indigna cruento
625 ungue secat meritamque comam; furit undique clamor
dissonus, ambiguumque senis cunctatur Adrasti
consilium. tandem ipse refert: 'compescite litem,
o pueri! virtus iterum temptanda; sed ite
limite non uno, latus hoc conceditur Idae,
630 tu diversa tene; fraus cursibus omnis abesto.'

605 premit Pω (SB²)   612 fluit *Bentley*
613 obtenditur ψ: ost- Pω   617 longe Pψ: -gae ψ

---

[70] The finishing line.   [71] 'I do not think *longe* means
more than that Idas was the indisputable victor' (Håkanson). But

panting and the shadow of his chest. Then Phaedimus and
Dymas strain in doubtful rivalry, fast Alcon is on their
heels. The Arcadian's blond hair hangs from his unshorn
head: he used to tend it from earliest years as a gift for
Trivia and had boldly promised it (in vain) to his native altars when he returned victorious from Ogygian warfare.
Now, free of bond and flowing at large over his back, it flees
behind him as it meets the Zephyr, hindering himself and
flying in threatening Idas' face. Hence that young man saw
a trick, opportunity for a foul. Already near the finish, as
Parthenopaeus is crossing the threshold[70] victorious, the
other seizes his hair and pulls him back, taking his place,
and strikes the mouth of the gate with a fine lead.[71]

The Arcadians roar 'To arms,' with arms they hasten
to defend their king unless the stolen prize and merited
honour be restored, and make to come down on all the
track. Others approve Idas' trick. Parthenopaeus himself
throws back earth, covering his face and wet eyes; the appeal of tears adds to his beauty. In his distress he tears with
bloody nails now his chest, now his undeserving face and
guilty hair; from all sides rages discordant clamour, and old
Adrastus' judgment delays in doubt. At last he speaks:
'Boys, cease your quarrel. Your prowess must be tested a
second time. But go not on a single track. This side is given
to Idas, do you keep the other. Let there be no cheating in
the race.'

perhaps there is a touch of irony: in fact the lead was minimal, but
in effect it was as big as you please. *Longae* is often read, to no purpose. Whether *longe* in 617 and/or *Aeneid* 2.711 (cf. R. F. Thomas,
Virgil and the Augustan Reception, Cambridge, 2001, pp. 214ff.)
are relevant I am not sure.

Audierant, dictoque manent. mox numina supplex
affatu tacito iuvenis Tegeaeus adorat:
'diva potens nemorum (tibi enim hic, tibi crinis honori
debitus, eque tuo venit haec iniuria voto),
635 si bene quid genetrix, si quid venatibus ipse
promerui, ne, quaeso, sinas hoc omine Thebas
ire nec Arcadiae tantum meruisse pudorem.'
auditum manifesta fides: vix campus euntem
sentit, et exilis plantis intervenit aër,
640 raraque non fracto vestigia pulvere pendent.
irrumpit clamore fores, clamore recurrit
ante ducem prensaque fovet suspiria palma.
finiti cursus, operumque insignia praesto.
Arcas equum dono, clipeum gerit improbus Idas,
645 cetera plebs Lyciis vadit contenta pharetris.
    Tunc vocat, emisso si quis decernere disco
impiger et vires velit ostentare superbas.
it iussus Pterelas et aënae lubrica massae
pondera vix toto curvatus corpore iuxta
650 deicit; inspectant taciti expenduntque laborem
Inachidae. mox turba ruunt, duo gentis Achaeae,
tres Ephyreiadae, Pisa satus unus, Acarnan
septimus; et plures agitabat gloria, ni se
arduus Hippomedon cavea stimulante tulisset
655 in medios, lateque ferens sub pectore dextro
orbem alium: 'hunc potius, iuvenes, qui moenia saxis
frangere, qui Tyrias deiectum vaditis arces,
hunc rapite: ast illud cui non iaculabile dextrae

---

[72] The hair I vowed to you.

[73] His steps are so rapid that the air hardly has time to come in
between them.

They heard and obey his word. Then the lad of Tegea silently addresses deity in suppliant prayer: 'Goddess, lady of the forests, for to you, to your honour, this hair is owed and from your vow[72] comes this disgrace: if my mother, if I myself, have deserved any favour by our hunts, do not allow me, I pray you, to go to Thebes with this omen, nor to earn such shame for Arcady.' Proof manifest that he was heard, the track scarce feels his passage, meagre the air that comes between his feet,[73] his steps are poised wide apart over[74] the dust and do not break it. With a shout he bursts through the doors, with a shout runs back before the chief and grasps the palm and comforts his sighs. The race is over, the badges of achievement ready. The Arcadian is given a horse, shameless Idas bears a shield, the rest of the field depart content with Lycian quivers.

Next he invites any brisk fellow who may wish to try conclusions hurling the disk and show off his proud strength. Pterelas comes at command and bending his whole body barely manages to throw the slippery weight of the bronze mass down close by. The children of Inachus watch in silence and estimate the feat. Then a crowd rushes in, two of Achaean race, three sons of Ephyre, one born of Pisa, the seventh an Acarnanian; and hope of glory was stirring yet more, had not tall Hippomedon betaken himself into their midst, spurred by the spectators. Bearing at his right side another broad round: 'This one rather, men,' he cried, 'you that are on your way to break walls with rocks and cast down the Tyrian towers, take this: as for

[74] *Pendent* implies that his feet barely touch the ground.

pondus?' et arreptum nullo conamine iecit
660 in latus. absistunt procul attonitique fatentur
cedere; vix unus Phlegyas acerque Menestheus
(hos etiam pudor et magni tenuere parentes)
promisere manum; concessit cetera pubes
sponte et adorato rediit inglorius disco.
665 qualis Bistoniis clipeus Mavortis in arvis
luce mala Pangaea ferit solemque refulgens
territat incussaque dei grave mugit ab hasta.
    Pisaeus Phlegyas opus incohat et simul omnes
abstulit in se oculos: ea viso corpore virtus
670 promissa. ac primum terra discumque manumque
asperat, excusso mox circum pulvere versat,
quod latus in digitos, mediae quod certius ulnae
conveniat, non artis egens: hic semper amori
ludus erat, patriae non tantum ubi laudis obiret
675 sacra, sed alternis Alpheon utrumque solebat
metari ripis et, qua latissima distant,
non umquam merso transmittere flumina disco.
ergo operum fidens non protinus horrida campi
iugera, sed caelo dextram metitur, humique
680 pressus utroque genu collecto sanguine discum
ipse super sese rotat atque in nubila condit.
ille citus sublime petit similisque cadenti
crescit in adversum, tandemque exhaustus ab alto
tardior ad terram redit atque immergitur arvis.

659 arreptum ψ: abr- Pω   675 utrumque P: utrim- ω
676 metari P: metiri ω

75 *Etiam* (= *etiamnum*).
76 As seen from either bank. Or *utrimque* may be right.

that weight, what arm could not throw it?' and effortless he caught it up and cast it to one side. They stand away awe-struck and confess themselves outmatched. Only Phlegyas and keen Menestheus—shame and great parentage kept them still[75] in the contest—reluctantly promised their hands. The rest of the young men willingly gave in and re-turned inglorious, making obeisance to the disk; even as in Bistonian fields the shield of Mars strikes Pangaeus with an evil glare and shining back affrights the sun and deeply booms with the impact of the god's spear.

Phlegyas of Pisa begins the work, drawing all eyes upon himself; such prowess his body's aspect promises. First he roughens the disk and his hand with earth, then shaking off the dirt turns it round and round to see which side suits his fingers, which more surely the middle of his forearm. Skill he does not lack. This sport was ever his passion, not only when he attended the ceremonies of his country's glory— he was wont to measure either Alpheos[76] on alternate banks and where they are furthest apart to cross the river with a disk that never sank. Therefore confident in his workmanship, he measures to begin with, not the rough[77] acres of the flat, but his arm with the sky;[78] crouching on the ground with either knee, he collects his strength and whirls the disk above him and sends it to hide in the clouds. Swiftly it seeks the height and as though falling gathers speed as it goes, till at length exhausted it returns from aloft to earth with less velocity[79] and plunges into the

[77] As though the rough ground would slow down the flight of the disk? [78] The distance the disk travelled upwards would assess the strength of the thrower's arm.

[79] In double defiance of the law of gravity.

377

685 sic cadit, attonitis quotiens avellitur astris,
Solis opaca soror; procul auxiliantia gentes
aera crepant frustraque timent, at Thessala victrix
ridet anhelantes audito carmine bigas.
collaudant Danai, sed non tibi molle tuenti,
690 Hippomedon, maiorque manus speratur in aequo.
    Atque illi extemplo, cui spes infringere dulce
immodicas, Fortuna venit. quid numina contra
tendere fas homini? spatium iam immane parabat,
iam cervix conversa, et iam latus omne redibat:
695 excidit ante pedes elapsum pondus et ictus
destituit frustraque manum demisit inanem.
ingemuere omnes, rarisque ea visa voluptas.
inde ad conatus timida subit arte Menestheus
cautior, et multum te, Maia crete, rogato
700 molis praegravidae castigat pulvere lapsus.
illa manu magna et multum felicior exit,
nec partem exiguam circi transvecta quievit.
fit sonus, et fixa signatur terra sagitta.
tertius Hippomedon valida ad certamina tardos
705 molitur gressus; namque illum corde sub alto
et casus Phlegyae monet et fortuna Menesthei.
erigit assuetum dextrae gestamen, et alte
sustentans rigidumque latus fortesque lacertos
consulit ac vasto contorquet turbine, et ipse
710 prosequitur. fugit horrendo per inania saltu
iamque procul meminit dextrae servatque tenorem

689 te molle tuente *Guyet*
699 create P: nate ω (*Schrader*)
700 praegravidae ω (*cf. Val. Fl. 8.98*): praevali- P
707 gestamen ωΣ: certa- P

378

fields. So falls the dark sister of the Sun when plucked away from the astonished stars; the people beat bronze to aid and idly fear, but the woman of Thessaly, her spell heard, laughs victorious at the panting steeds.[80] The Danai applaud (with no kindly look from Hippomedon) and a mightier throw is hoped for on the level.

To him forthwith comes Fortune, who loves to shatter hopes too high. How may man strive against the gods? Already he was preparing a mighty distance, already his neck was turned, already all his side was moving back: the weight slipped and fell before his feet, frustrating his effort and letting his hand drop empty. All groaned, and only a few enjoyed the sight. Then Menestheus advances to the attempt with timorous skill. More cautious, with many a prayer to you, son of Maia, he corrects with dirt the lubricity of the ponderous mass. With powerful hand and much better luck it goes forth and comes to rest after traversing no small part of the track. There is noise,[81] and an arrow is fixed to mark the spot. Third, Hippomedon comes with slow, ponderous tread to the trial of strength. Deep in his heart the fate of Phlegyas and the fortune of Menestheus warn him. He raises the load that his hand knows well and holding it high tests his rigid side and powerful arms, then swings it round with a tremendous whirl and himself follows through. The disk flies through the void with a fearsome bound and already far away remembers the hand that sent it and keeps course, passing vanquished

[80] 'Eclipses of the moon were believed to be caused by Thessalian witches, who were thought to have the power of drawing it down to earth; the steeds are those of the chariot of the moon' (Mozley).   [81] From the crowd.

discus, nec dubia iunctave Menesthea victum
transabiit meta: longe super aemula signa
consedit viridesque umeros et opaca theatri
715 culmina ceu latae tremefecit mole ruinae:
quale vaporifera saxum Polyphemus ab Aetna
lucis egente manu tamen in vestigia puppis
auditae iuxtaque inimicum auro exegit Ulixen.
[sic et Aloidae, cum iam calcaret Olympum
720 desuper Ossa rigens, ipsum glaciale ferebant
Pelion et trepido sperabant iungere caelo.]
    Tum genitus Talao victori tigrin inanem
ire iubet, fulvo quae circumfusa nitebat
margine et extremos auro mansueverat ungues.
725 Cnosiacos arcus habet et vaga tela Menestheus.
'at tibi,' ait, 'Phlegya, casu frustrate sinistro,
hunc, quondam nostri decus auxiliumque Pelasgi,
ferre damus, neque enim Hippomedon inviderit, ensem.
nunc opus est animis: infestos tollite caestus
730 comminus; haec bellis et ferro proxima virtus.'
    Constitit immanis cerni immanisque timeri
Argolicus Capaneus, ac dum nigrantia plumbo
tegmina cruda boum non mollior ipse lacertis
induitur, 'date tot iuvenum de milibus unum
735 huc,' ait, 'atque utinam potius de stirpe veniret
aemulus Aonia, quem fas demittere leto,
nec mea crudelis civili sanguine virtus.'
obstipuere animi, fecitque silentia terror.
tandem insperatus nuda de plebe Laconum
740 prosilit Alcidamas: mirantur Dorica regum
agmina, sed socii fretum Polluce magistro
norant et sacras inter crevisse palaestras.
ipse deus posuitque manus et bracchia finxit

Menestheus to no doubtful or adjacent goal; far beyond
the rival mark it comes down and with a crash, as of a great
mass of falling masonry, sets the green shoulders and
shady tops of the theatre a-tremble. Like the rock that
Polyphemus propelled from smoky Aetna with sightless
hand, yet on the track of the ship (he heard it) and close to
his enemy Ulixes.

Then Talaus' son orders an empty tiger be presented to
the victor, shining with surrounding tawny edge where the
claw tips are tamed with gold. Menestheus gets a Cnosian
bow and wandering shafts. 'But to you, Phlegyas,' he says,
'foiled by unlucky chance, I give this sword to wear, once
the pride and stay of our Pelasgus, nor will Hippomedon
grudge it. Now 'tis time for courage. Raise the fighting
gloves face to face. Here is valour at its nearest to battle
and steel.'

Argive Capaneus took his stand, monstrous to view,
monstrous to fear, and as he puts gloves of rawhide black
with lead on his arms, he no softer than they, 'Give me
here' he says 'one from so many thousands of warriors—
and would that my rival came rather from Aonian race
whom it were no sin to send to his death, and my valour
might not be cruel with a countryman's blood.' Their
minds were numbed and terror made silence. At length,
unlooked-for, Alcidamas of the naked Laconian folk leaps
forth. The hosts of the Dorian kings marvel, but his comrades knew that he relied on his master Pollux and grew
up among the sacred wrestling grounds. The god himself
placed his hands and moulded his arms, love of his

719–21 *in paucis codd. recc. repertos damnant plerique*

(materiae suadebat amor); tunc saepe locavit
745 comminus, et simili stantem miratus in ira
sustulit exsultans nudumque ad pectora pressit.
illum indignatur Capaneus ridetque vocantem,
ut miserans, poscitque alium; tandemque coactus
restitit, et stimulis iam languida colla tumescunt.
750   Fulmineas alte suspensi corpora plantis
erexere manus; tuto procul ora recessu
armorum in speculis, aditusque ad vulnera clausi.
hic, quantum Stygiis Tityos consurgat ab arvis,
si torvae patiantur aves, tanta undique pandit
755 membrorum spatia et tantis ferus ossibus exstat.
hic paulo ante puer, sed enim maturius aevo
robur, et ingentes spondet tener impetus annos,
quem vinci haud quisquam saevo neque sanguine tingi
malit, ut erecto timeant spectacula voto.
760   Ut sese permensi oculis et uterque priorem
speravere locum, non protinus ira nec ictus:
alternus paulum timor et permixta furori
consilia; inclinant tantum contraria iactu
bracchia et explorant caestus hebetantque terendo.
765 doctior hic differt animum metuensque futuri
cunctatus vires dispensat: at ille nocendi
prodigus incautusque sui ruit omnis et ambas
consumit sine lege manus atque irrita frendit
insurgens seque ipse premit. sed providus astu
770 et patria vigil arte Lacon hos reicit ictus,
hos cavet; interdum nutu capitisque citati

759 et (*SB*)   timeant ψ: -at Pω

material[82] persuading, then often set him opposite, wondering at him as he stood in wrath like his own, and lifted him up in triumph and pressed him naked to his chest. Capaneus counts him unworthy, laughing at his challenge as though in pity, and demands another opponent. At last perforce he takes his stand, his slackened neck already swelling at the provocation.

Poised tall on their feet they raised hands like thunderbolts. Their faces are held far back watching from their shoulders, all approach to wounds barred. The one displays from every angle the spaces of his limbs, standing fierce with mighty bones, large as Tityos rising from Stygian fields, if the grim birds would let him. The other was a boy not long ago, but his strength is riper than his years and youthful impulse gives promise of a great future. None would wish to see him worsted or cruelly bloodied, so that[83] they fear the spectacle in prayerful expectancy.

They measured each other with their eyes, both hoping for the first opening. Not at once came anger or blow. For a space each feared the other and plan mingled with rage. They only spar with opposing arms and test their gloves, dulling them as they rub. The one, a better boxer, delays his impulse, holds back, husbanding his strength and fearing the future. The other, lavish of harm and careless of himself, rushes all out, spending both hands without restraint, rises gnashing his teeth to no purpose, pressing upon himself. But the Laconian, with crafty foresight and watchful with his country's skill, parries the blows or avoids them. Sometimes with a nod of his swift, obedient head he

[82] The boy's body.　　　[83] With *et* the following subjunctive has to be by attraction to *malit*.

integer obsequio, manibus nunc obvia tela
discutiens, instat gressu vultuque recedit:
saepe etiam iniustis collatum viribus hostem
775 (is vigor ingenio, tanta experientia dextrae est)
ultro audax animis intratque et obumbrat et alte
assilit. ut praeceps cumulo salit unda minantes
in scopulos et fracta redit, sic ille furentem
circumit expugnans; levat ecce diuque minatur
780 in latus inque oculos, illum rigida arma caventem
avocat ac manibus necopinum interserit ictum
callidus et mediam designat vulnere frontem:
iam cruor, et tepido signantur tempora rivo.
nescit adhuc Capaneus subitumque per agmina murmur
785 miratur; verum ut fessam super ora reduxit
forte manum et summo maculas in vellere vidit,
non leo, non iaculo tantum indignata recepto
tigris: agit toto cedentem fervidus arvo
praecipitatque retro iuvenem atque in terga supinat,
790 dentibus horrendum stridens, geminatque rotatas
multiplicatque manus. rapiunt conamina venti,
pars cadit in caestus; motu Spartanus acuto
mille cavet lapsas circum cava tempora mortes
auxilioque pedum, sed non tamen immemor artis
795 adversus fugit et fugiens tamen ictibus obstat.
    Et iam utrumque labor suspiriaque aegra fatigant:
tardius ille premit, nec iam hic absistere velox,
defectique ambo genibus pariterque quierunt.
sic ubi longa vagos lassarunt aequora nautas

---

84 The gloves (*rigida arma*), by anticipation—breathless narrative, with the words tumbling over one another. Alternatively,

comes unscathed, now disperses the opposing weapons
with his hands or advances with his feet while retreating
with his face. Often too he engages the foe whose strength
is greater than his own (so lively his wit, so practised his
hand), boldly attacking him, getting inside, overshadow-
ing, bounding at him in the air. As a wave gathers and leaps
in a rush at threatening rocks, then returns broken, so he
circles his angry adversary, storming his defence. See, he
raises his rigid weapons,[84] long he threatens, the side, the
eyes. As the other guards against them, he distracts him
and cunningly slips in a sudden blow between his hands,
marking the middle of his brow with a gash; now there is
blood, a warm stream stains the temples. Capaneus does
not know it yet and wonders at the sudden noise in the
crowd, but when he chanced to draw a weary hand back
across his face and saw spots on the leather, no lion was
ever so indignant at a javelin's stroke, no tiger. In a passion
he pushes the retreating youth all over the field, driving
him headlong rearward, bending him back; horribly he
grinds his teeth, doubling and multiplying his whirling
fists. The winds snatch his efforts, part falls against the
gloves. With sharp jerks and the help of his feet the Spartan avoids a thousand deaths that fall about his hollow
temples; but he remembers his skill and flees facing the foe
and fleeing yet counters with blows.

And now both are wearied with toil and distressful
panting. The one presses more slowly, the other is no
longer nimble to evade. Both fail at the knees and rest
alike. So when long seas have tired wandering sailors, at a

an unexpressed object (*manus*) has to be understood with *levat*,
which hardly seems possible.

800   et signum de puppe datum, posuere parumper
      bracchia: vix requies, iam vox citat altera remos.
      ecce iterum immodice venientem eludit et exit
      sponte ruens mersusque umeris: effunditur ille
      in caput, assurgentem alio puer improbus ictu
805   perculit eventuque impalluit ipse secundo.
      clamorem Inachidae, quantum non litora, tollunt,
      non nemora. illum ab humo conantem ut vidit Adrastus
      tollentemque manus et non toleranda parantem:
      'ite, oro, socii, furit, ite, opponite dextras,
810   festinate, furit, palmamque et praemia ferte!
      non prius, effracto quam misceat ossa cerebro,
      absistet, video; moriturum auferte Lacona.'
      nec mora, prorumpit Tydeus, nec iussa recusat
      Hippomedon; tunc vix ambo conatibus ambas
815   restringunt cohibentque manus ac plurima suadent:
      'vincis, abi; pulchrum vitam donare minori.
      noster et hic bellique comes.' nil frangitur heros,
      ramumque oblatumque manu thoraca repellit
      vociferans: 'liceat! non has ego pulvere crasso
820   atque cruore genas, meruit quibus iste favorem
      semivir, infodiam, mittamque informe sepulcro
      corpus et Oebalio donem lugere magistro?'
      dicit; at hunc socii tumidum et vicisse negantem
      avertunt, contra laudant insignis alumnum
825   Taygeti longeque minas risere Lacones.
         Iamdudum variae laudes et conscia virtus
      Tydea magnanimum stimulis ingentibus angunt.

    801 citat PψΣ: ciet ω
    820 iste favorem ω: ista iuventa P
    827 ingentibus Pω: urg- P *ante corr.*

sign from the poop they drop their arms for a space, but hardly have they rested when a second cry rouses the oars. See, again Alcidamas eludes his enemy's furious attack, evading by a deliberate plunge with head in shoulders. Capaneus is thrown head foremost and as he rises the presumptious lad strikes him another blow and himself turns pale at his success. The sons of Inachus raise a shout, no shore or forest the like. When Adrastus saw him struggling from the ground lifting his hands and purposing the unbearable: 'Go, I beg you, comrades, he is mad; go, oppose your hands, hurry, he is mad! Bring the palm and the prizes. He will not stop till he mingles bone with shattered brain, I see it. Take the Laconian away or he dies.' Promptly Tydeus rushes forward, nor does Hippomedon refuse the order. Then with their joint efforts they manage to fasten his hands behind him and restrain, with much persuasion: 'You win, leave it. 'Tis a fine thing to spare the loser's life. He too is one of ours, a war comrade.' The hero is nowise mollified. He pushes away the branch and the proffered corselet, bellowing: 'Let me go! These cheeks with which the half-man won favour,[85] shall I not gouge with clotted dirt and blood, shall I not send his maimed body to the grave and give it to his Oebalian master to mourn?' He spoke, but his comrades turn him away swollen with ire and denying that he has won; whereas the Laconians laud the nursling of illustrious Taygetus and at a distance laugh at the threats.

This while have the various achievements of others and his conscious valour tormented great-souled Tydeus with

---

[85] Of the crowd. Håkanson (*semiviri foedem*) missed the fact that Pollux was the active partner. But the text remains in doubt.

ille quidem et disco bonus et contendere cursu,
nec caestu bellare minor, sed corde labores
830 ante alios erat uncta pale. sic otia Martis
degere et armiferas laxare assueverat iras
ingentes contra ille viros Acheloia circum
litora felicesque deo monstrante palaestras.
ergo ubi luctandi iuvenes animosa citavit
835 gloria, terrificos umeris Aetolus amictus
exuitur patriumque suem. levat ardua contra
membra Cleonaeae stirpis iactator Agylleus,
Herculea nec mole minor, sic grandibus alte
insurgens umeris hominem super improbus exit.
840 sed non ille rigor patriumque in corpore robur:
luxuriant artus, effusaque sanguine laxo
membra natant; unde haec audax fiducia tantum
Oenidae superare parem. quamquam ipse videri
exiguus, gravia ossa tamen nodisque lacerti
845 difficiles. numquam hunc animum Natura minori
corpore nec tantas ausa est includere vires.
    Postquam oleo gavisa cutis, petit aequor uterque
procursu medium atque hausta vestitur harena,
dum madidos artus alterno pulvere siccant,
850 collaque demersere umeris et bracchia late
vara tenent. iam tunc astu deducit in aequum
callidus et celsum procurvat Agyllea Tydeus,
summissus tergo et genibus vicinus harenae.
ille autem, Alpini veluti regina cupressus
855 verticis urguentes cervicem inclinat ad Austros

842 unde P: inde ω   849 tum Pω (*Håkanson*)
855 urguentes ω: -ti P, *Imhof*   ad austros ψ: in a- Pω: ab
Austro *Imhof*

mighty goads. He was good with the disk and at running, nor less so in the glove fight, but before all other sports he loved oiled wrestling. So was he wont to spend respites from war and relax armed angers against giant opponents around the shores of Achelous and the sports grounds happy in the teacher god.[86] So when courageous ambition of wrestling summoned the warriors, the Aetolian stripped from his shoulders their fearsome covering, his native boar. Against him Agylleus boasting Cleonaean stock raises his tall limbs; nor is he less than Hercules in build, so high he rises with his huge shoulders towering unconscionable above mortal measure; but he lacks that rigour, his father's strength of body. His limbs luxuriate, they spread and swim, slack their vigour. Hence Oeneus' son's bold confidence of beating so big an opponent. He himself was small indeed to look upon, but heavy-boned, his muscles tightly knotted. Never did Nature dare enclose such a spirit in a lesser frame nor force so great.

After their skins had rejoiced in oil, both run into the middle of the ground and clothe themselves with handfuls of sand, each drying wet limbs with alternate dust,[87] and sink their necks in their shoulders and hold their arms curved wide. Already crafty Tydeus artfully brings Agylleus down to level and bends his height forward, stooping his own back, knees close to the sand. Like the cypress, queen of the Alpine summit, that inclines her neck in the

[86] Achelous; cf. 9.481 *deus*.

[87] In turn they throw sand at each other, as in Ovid, *Metamorphoses* 9.35f. (Håkanson).

vix sese radice tenens, terraeque propinquat,
iamdudum aetherias eadem reditura sub auras:
non secus ingentes artus praecelsus Agylleus
sponte premit parvumque gemens duplicatur in hostem.

860 et iam alterna manus frontemque umerosque latusque
collaque pectoraque et vitantia crura lacessit.
interdumque diu pendent per mutua fulti
bracchia, nunc saevi digitorum vincula frangunt.
non sic ductores gemini gregis horrida tauri

865 bella movent; medio coniunx stat candida prato
victorem exspectans, rumpunt obnixa furentes
pectora, subdit amor stimulos et vulnera sanat:
fulmineo sic dente sues, sic hispida turpes
proelia villosis ineunt complexibus ursi.

870 vis eadem Oenidae; nec sole aut pulvere fessa
membra labant, riget arta cutis durisque laborum
castigata toris. contra non integer ille
flatibus alternis aegroque effetus hiatu
exuit ingestas fluvio sudoris harenas

875 ac furtim rapta sustentat pectora terra.
instat agens Tydeus fictumque in colla minatus
crura subit; coeptis non evaluere potiri
frustratae brevitate manus, venit arduus ille
desuper oppressumque ingentis mole ruinae

880 condidit. haud aliter collis scrutator Hiberi,
cum subiit longeque diem vitamque reliquit,
si tremuit suspensus ager subitumque fragorem
rupta dedit tellus, latet intus monte soluto

876 fictum ψ: ictum Pψ

urging South Wind, scarce holding herself by the root, and nears the earth, presently to return to the air on high the same as before, not otherwise does towering Agylleus of his own will lower his huge limbs bending double with a groan against his little foe. And now with hands, each in turn, they challenge forehead and shoulder and flank and neck and chest and evading legs. Sometimes they hang a long while supported by each other's arms, now they fiercely break the fingers' grip. Not so savagely do two bulls, chiefs of the herd, make grim warfare, while the fair consort stands in mid meadow expecting the victor; furiously they break straining breasts, love applies his goads and heals their wounds.[88] Thus boars with lightning tusks, thus ugly bears join bristling conflict with their shaggy embraces. The strength of Oeneus' son is constant,[89] his limbs do not fail, weary with sun or dust, his skin is tight and rigid, disciplined[90] by the hard sinews of toil. Whereas the other is not unimpaired; exhausted by breathings out and in, he gapes distressed, shedding the sand heaped on his body with a stream of sweat, and furtively clutches the ground to support his chest. Tydeus is upon him, harrying. Feinting at the neck, he catches at the legs; but to no avail, for his hands are too short to gain their object. His tall adversary comes down on him and crushes him from sight beneath the huge collapsing mass. Like the searcher of an Iberian[91] hill, when he has gone below and left daylight and life afar; if the suspended ground trembles and the ruptured earth comes down with a sudden crash, he hides

[88] Makes them painless.
[89] In contrast to his opponent. Not 'so violent is Oinides.'
[90] I.e. tightened.   [91] Spain was rich in mines.

obrutus, ac penitus fractum obtritumque cadaver
885 indignantem animam propriis non reddidit astris.
acrior hoc Tydeus, animisque et pectore supra est.
nec mora, cum vinclis onerique elapsus iniquo
circumit errantem et tergo necopinus inhaeret,
mox latus et firmo celer implicat ilia nexu;
890 poplitibus genua inde premens evadere nodos
nequiquam et lateri dextram insertare parantem
improbus (horrendum visu!), [ac] mirabile pondus,
sustulit. Herculeis pressum sic fama lacertis
terrigenam sudasse Libyn, cum fraude reperta
895 raptus in excelsum, nec iam spes ulla cadendi,
nec licet extrema matrem contingere planta.
fit sonus, et laetos attollunt agmina plausus.
tunc alte librans inopinum sponte remisit
obliquumque dedit, procumbentemque secutus
900 colla simul dextra, pedibus simul inguina vinxit.
deficit obsessus soloque pudore repugnat.
tandem pectus humi pronamque extensus in alvum
sternitur, ac longo maestus post tempore surgit,
turpia signata linquens vestigia terra.
905 palmam autem dextra laevaque nitentia dono
arma ferens Tydeus: 'quid si non sanguinis huius
partem haud exiguam (scitis) Dircaeus haberet
campus, ubi hae nuper, Thebarum foedera, plagae—'
haec simul ostentans quaesitaque praemia laudum
910 dat sociis, sequitur neglectus Agyllea thorax.

892 ac *secl., ita dist-* SB

92 Agylleus.

inside, buried by the fallen mountain, nor does the corpse, utterly smashed and crushed, return his indignant spirit to its proper stars. All the more vigorous for this, Tydeus is on top in spirit and heart. In a trice he has slipped from the bonds, the unconscionable load, and circles the other as he moves uncertain. Suddenly he is clinging to his back, then twines side and groin in a firm hold. Next, squeezing knees between thighs, as he[92] vainly struggles to escape the knots and thrust his hand in the other's side, irrepressible Tydeus (dreadful to see and wonderful) lifted the weight. So, as the story goes, sweated the Libyan son of earth[93] gripped in Hercules' arms, when his trick was discovered and he snatched into the air; no hope now of falling and he cannot touch his mother with the tip of his toe. A roar goes up, the host shouts glad applause. Then, balancing him on high, Tydeus suddenly lets him go and fall sideways; following as he plunges, he simultaneously grasps his neck with his right hand and his groin with his feet. Thus hemmed in, the other grows faint and only shame makes him fight back. Finally he sprawls at length on the ground, prone on his chest and belly. After a long time he rises dejected, leaving ugly traces marking the ground. Tydeus bears the palm in his right hand and the gift of shining arms in his left: 'What if no small part of this blood of mine (you all know it) were not on Dirce's plain, where lately these scars, my pact with Thebes—'showing them[94] as he spoke; and he gives his comrades the prizes his glory has won. An unprized corselet follows Agylleus.

[93] Antaeus. His trick was to draw strength from bodily contact with Earth his mother.   [94] *Haec* agrees with *foedera* = *plagas*; cf. 7.541 *bona foedera gesto / pectore in hoc.*

Sunt et qui nudo subeant concurrere ferro:
iamque aderant instructi armis Epidaurius Agreus
et nondum Fatis Dircaeus agentibus exsul.
dux vetat Iasides: 'manet ingens copia leti,
915 o iuvenes! servate animos avidumque furorem
sanguinis adversi. tuque o, quem propter avita
iugera, dilectas cui desolavimus urbes,
ne, precor, ante aciem ius tantum casibus esse
fraternisque sinas (abigant hoc numina!) votis.'
920 sic ait, atque ambos aurata casside ditat.
tum generum, ne laudis egens, iubet ardua necti
tempora Thebanumque ingenti voce citari
uictorem: dirae recinebant omina Parcae.
      Ipsum etiam proprio certamina festa labore
925 dignari et tumulis supremum hunc addere honorem
hortantur proceres ac, ne victoria desit
una ducum numero, fundat uel Lyctia cornu
tela rogant, tenui vel nubila transeat hasta.
obsequitur gaudens, viridique ex aggere in aequum
930 stipatus summis iuvenum descendit; at illi
pone levues portat pharetras et cornua iussus
armiger: ingentem iactu transmittere circum
eminus et dictae dare vulnera destinat orno.
      Quis fluere occultis rerum neget omina causis?
935 Fata patent homini, piget inservare, peritque
venturi praemissa fides: sic omina casum
fecimus, et vires hausit Fortuna nocendi.

---

922 thebarum Pω (*Alton*)   923 recinebant P: reti- ω

---

95 He would be proclaimed 'Polynices of Thebes.' The omen
may be simply the word 'Theban,' associating Thebes with victory.

BOOK 6

Some too come forward to fight with the naked sword. Already Epidaurian Agreus and the Dircaean exile, whose doom is not yet upon him, stood in arms. The royal scion of Iasus forbids: 'Young sirs, great plenty of death remains. Keep your high hearts and mad greed for adversary blood. And you, on whose account we have left desolate our ancestral acres and beloved cities, do not, I pray, before the fray let chance and your brother's vows (the gods forfend!) have so much power.' So he spoke and enriches both with a gilded helm. Then he orders that his son-in-law's tall temples be wreathed, lest he go short of glory, and that he be proclaimed victor in stentorian tone: Theban.[95] The fell Parcae echoed back the omen.

The leaders urge him also to dignify the festal contests with a feat of his own, adding this final honour to the tomb. And lest one victory be lacking to the number of the chiefs, they ask him to shoot Lyctian arrows from a bow or cross the clouds with a light spear. Happily he complies and from the green mound descends to the level surrounded by the foremost warriors. His armour-bearer at orders carries behind light quivers and bows. He plans to cross the great circus from a distance with a shot and wound a designated ash tree.

Who would deny that omens flow from the hidden causes of things? The Fates lie open to man, but he cares not to observe and the foreshown assurance of the future is wasted. So of omens we have made chance, and Fortune has drawn power to harm.[96]

But Polynices had not in fact defeated his adversary and that too might be ominous, foreshadowing his duel with Eteocles. See SB². [96] Introductory to what follows.

Campum emensa brevi fatalis ab arbore tacta
(horrendum visu!) per quas modo fugerat auras,
940 venit harundo retro versumque a fine tenorem
pertulit, et notae iuxta ruit ora pharetrae.
multa duces errore serunt: hi nubila et altos
occurrisse Notos, adversi roboris ictu
tela repulsa alii. penitus latet exitus ingens
945 monstratumque nefas: uni remeabile bellum
et tristes domino spondebat harundo recursus.

Quickly measuring the flat, the fateful shaft touched the tree and then (awful to see!) came back through the air through which it had just flown and maintained the reverse course from the target, falling close to the mouth of its familiar quiver. The leaders make much talk astray. Some say clouds and winds on high met the arrow, others that it was repelled by the shock of the fronting wood. Deep lies the mighty outcome, the evil revealed. The shaft promised its master a war from which he alone would return, a sad homecoming.

LIBER VII

Atque ita cunctantes Tyrii primordia belli
Iuppiter haud aequo respexit corde Pelasgos,
concussitque caput motu quo celsa laborant
sidera proclamatque adici cervicibus Atlans.
5   tunc ita velocem Tegees affatus alumnum:
'i, medium rapido Borean illabere saltu
Bistonias, puer, usque domos axemque nivosi
sideris, Oceano vetitum qua Parrhasis ignem
nubibus hibernis et nostro pascitur imbri.
10   atque ibi seu posita respirat cuspide Mavors,
quamquam invisa quies, seu, quod reor, arma tubasque
insatiatus agit caraeque in sanguine gentis
luxuriat: propere monitus iramque parentis
ede, nihil parcens. nempe olim accendere iussus
15   Inachias acies atque omne quod Isthmius umbo
distinet et raucae circumtonat ira Maleae:
illi, vix muros limenque egressa iuventus,

> 1 atque ea Pω (*Damsté*)
> 12 habet Pω (*SB²*: avet *Schrader*)

---

1 Arcadian Callisto, i.e. Ursa Major.

2 Håkanson favours *(h)avet*, but Garrod's objection stands: action is needed to balance inaction, not desire for action.

BOOK 7

With no kindly heart did Jupiter regard the Pelasgi as they thus delayed the outset of the Tyrian war, and shook his head; at that motion the high stars tremble and Atlas cries that the weight is heavier on his shoulders. Then he thus addressed the swift nursling of Tegea: 'Go, boy, and glide with rapid leap to the mid north, as far as the Bistonian dwellings and the axis of the snowy star, where the Parrhasian[1] feeds her fire forbidden to Ocean with winter clouds and my rain; and there, whether Mars has laid his spear aside and draws breath, though rest he hates, or, as I think, plies[2] arms and trumpets insatiate, revelling in the blood of the people he loves, speedily deliver his parent's angry commands and spare naught. Long ago, I believe, he was ordered to kindle Inachian armies and all that the Isthmian hump holds apart and the wrath of raucous Malea thunders round.[3] Their host has scarce passed beyond their boundary walls and they are at worship! One

---

[3] I.e. the entire Peloponnese, but the wording is open to exception. The Isthmus separates two seas but links (rather than separates) the peninsular and the rest of Greece, and the waters surrounding the peninsula are not very happily summed up as 'the wrath of Malea.' Statius tries again in *Achilleid* 1.407f. with no better success.

sacra colunt; credas bello rediisse, tot instant
plausibus, offensique sedent ad iusta sepulcri.
20 hicne tuus, Gradive, furor? sonat orbe recusso
discus et Oebalii coeunt in proelia caestus.
at si ipsi rabies ferrique insana voluptas
qua tumet, immeritas cineri dabit impius urbes
ferrum ignemque ferens, implorantesque Tonantem
25 sternet humi populos miserumque exhauriet orbem.
nunc lenis belli nostraque remittitur ira.
quod ni praecipitat pugnas dictoque iubentis
ocius impingit Tyriis Danaa agmina muris
(nil equidem crudele minor), sit mite bonumque
30 numen et effreni laxentur in otia mores,
reddat equos ensemque mihi, nec sanguinis ultra
ius erit: aspiciam terras pacemque iubebo
omnibus; Ogygio sat erit Tritonia bello.'
     Dixerat, et Thracum Cyllenius arva subibat;
35 atque illum Arctoae labentem cardine portae
tempestas aeterna plagae praetentaque caelo
agmina nimborum primique Aquilonis hiatus
in diversa ferunt: crepat aurea grandine multa
palla, nec Arcadii bene protegit umbra galeri.
40 hic steriles delubra notat Mavortia silvas
horrescitque tuens, ubi mille Furoribus illi
cingitur averso domus immansueta sub Haemo.
ferrea compago laterum, ferro apta teruntur
limina, ferratis incumbunt tecta columnis.
45 laeditur adversum Phoebi iubar, ipsaque sedem

43 apta P (cf. 3.16): arta ω

might suppose they were back from war, so busy are they clapping, sitting at the rites of an offended tomb. In this your rage, Gradivus? The disk sounds with recoiling circle[4] and Oebalian gloves meet in combat. But if he himself has the frenzy, the wild delight in battle that he is so proud of, he will ruthlessly give guiltless cities to ash with steel and fire and strew peoples on the ground as they implore the Thunderer and exhaust the hapless world. But now he is mild in warfare and my anger relaxes him. But unless he speeds the fighting and flings the Danaan host against the Tyrian walls quicker than my word of command—I threaten nothing cruel; let him be a gentle, kindly deity, let his wild ways slacken into peace, let him give me back horses and sword, nor any more shall he have power over blood. I shall look upon the earth and order universal peace. Tritonia shall cope with[5] the Ogygian war.'

He spoke and the Cyllenian was nearing the land of Thrace. As he glided down from the Bear's polar gate, he was carried this way and that by the tempest endemic to the region, the racks of rain clouds spread over the sky, and the first gapings of Aquilo's mouth. His golden mantle rattles with pouring hail and the shady Arcadian hat[6] gives scant cover. Here he marks barren woods, Mars' shrine, and shudders as he looks. There under distant Haemus is the god's ungentle house, girt with a thousand Rages.[7] The sides are of iron structure, the trodden thresholds are fitted with iron, the roof rests on iron-bound pillars. Phoebus' opposing ray takes hurt, the very light fears the

---

[4] As it hits the ground.   [5] Or 'suffice for.'

[6] The *petasos*, a felt hat with a broad brim.

[7] A seemingly careless anticipation of 47ff.

lux timet, et durus contristat sidera fulgor.
digna loco statio: primis salit Impetus amens
e foribus caecumque Nefas Iraeque rubentes
exsanguesque Metus, occultisque ensibus astant
50 Insidiae geminumque tenens Discordia ferrum.
innumeris strepit aula Minis, tristissima Virtus
stat medio, laetusque Furor vultuque cruento
Mors armata sedet; bellorum solus in aris
sanguis et incensis qui raptus ab urbibus ignis.
55 terrarum exuviae circum et fastigia templi
captae insignibant gentes: caelataque ferro
fragmina portarum bellatricesque carinae
et vacui currus protritaque curribus ora,
paene etiam gemitus: adeo vis omnis et omne
60 vulnus. ubique ipsum, sed non usquam ore remisso
cernere erat: talem divina Mulciber arte
ediderat; nondum radiis monstratus adulter
foeda catenato luerat conubia lecto.

Quaerere templorum regem vix coeperat ales
65 Maenalius, tremit ecce solum et mugire refractis
corniger Hebrus aquis; tunc quod pecus utile bello
vallem infestabat, trepidas spumare per herbas,
signa adventantis, clausaeque adamante perenni
dissiluere fores. Hyrcano in sanguine pulcher
70 ipse subit curru, diraque aspergine latos
mutat agros, spolia a tergo flentesque catervae.
dant silvae nixque alta locum; regit atra iugales
sanguinea Bellona manu longaque fatigat
cuspide. deriguit visu Cyllenia proles

---

[8] Effect of earthquake. Rivers are commonly conceived of as

dwelling and a harsh glare glooms the stars. The guard is worthy of the place. Wild Impulse leaps from the outer gates and blind Evil and ruddy Angers and bloodless Fears. Treachery lurks with hidden swords and Strife holding two-edged steel. The court resounds with countless Threats, Valour most sombre stands in the centre, and joyful Rage and armed Death with bloodstained countenance there sit. On the altars is blood of wars, that only, and fire snatched from burning towns. Trophies from many lands and captured peoples marked the temple's sides and top, and fragments of iron-wrought gates and warship keels and empty chariots and heads by chariots crushed, groans too almost. Every violence truly, every wound. Everywhere himself was to be seen, but nowhere with easy look; thus had Mulciber portrayed him with his divine art. Not yet had he been revealed an adulterer by sunbeams and expiated a shameful union in a chained bed.

Scarce had the winged Maenalian begun to look for the king of the temple when, see, the ground quakes and horned Hebrus bellows as his waters are broken back.[8] Then the beasts useful in war[9] that infested the valley foamed in the quivering grasses, sign of his coming, and the closed gates of everlasting adamant flew open. Himself arrives in his car, handsome in Hyrcanian blood, and changes the broad fields with the dire spatter. Spoils and weeping crowds are at his back. Woods and deep snow yield passage. Black Bellona governs the team with bloody hand and harasses them with her long spear. Cyllene's son

bulls or part-bulls. Homer's Scamander bellows *like* a bull (*Iliad* 21.237).

9 Horses.

403

75 summisitque genas: ipsi reverentia patri,
si prope sit, dematque minas nec talia mandet.
'quod Iovis imperium, magno quid ab aethere portas?'
occupat Armipotens, 'neque enim hunc, germane, sub axem
sponte venis hiemesque meas, cui roscida iuxta
80 Maenala et aestivi clementior aura Lycaei.'
ille refert consulta patris. nec longa moratus,
sicut anhelabant, iuncto sudore volantes
Mars impellit equos, resides in proelia Graios
ipse etiam indignans. vidit pater altus et irae
85 iam levior tardo flectebat pondere vultum.
ut si quando ruit debellatasque relinquit
Eurus aquas, pax ipsa tumet pontumque iacentem
exanimis iam volvit hiems: nondum arma carinis
omnia, nec toto respirant pectore nautae.
90   Finierat pugnas honor exsequialis inermes;
necdum aberant coetus, cunctisque silentibus heros
vina solo fundens cinerem placabat Adrastus
Archemori: 'da, parve, tuum trieteride multa
instaurare diem, nec saucius Arcadas aras
95 malit adire Pelops Eleaque pulset eburna
templa manu, nec Castaliis altaribus anguis,
nec sua pinigero magis annatet umbra Lechaeo.
nos te lugenti, puer, infitiamur Averno,
maestaque perpetuis sollemnia iungimus astris,
100 nunc festina cohors. at si Boeotia ferro
vertere tecta dabis, magnis tunc dignior aris,

---

⁸² volentes *coni. Hill*   ⁸⁴ ira Pω (*Peyrared*)

---

¹⁰ Poetic licence; Pelops' *shoulder* was ivory.
¹¹ I.e. 'may you visit your Nemean festival no less gladly than

froze at the sight and dropped his eyes. The Father himself
would be awed were he at hand, would retract his threats
nor send such a message. The Lord of Arms speaks first:
'What command of Jove do you bring, what from the great
ether? For you come not of your own will, my brother, to
this clime, to my blizzards, you that live by dewy Maenalus
and the mild breeze of summer Lycaeus.' The other repeats the Father's decree. Mars does not tarry long but
drives his flying horses, panting as they are, in continued
toil, he too indignant at the battle-torpid Greeks. The
Father on high saw and eased his wrath, slowly and ponderously he changes countenance; as when the East Wind
plunges, leaving the vanquished waters, the very calm is
tumid and the exhausted storm now rolls a flattened sea;
ships do not yet have all their rigging and sailors do not
breathe freely quite.

   The funeral celebration had ended weaponless fights
but the assemblage was not yet gone. All were silent while
the hero Adrastus poured wine upon the ground, appeas-
ing Archemorus' dust: 'Grant, little one, that we may renew your day at many a triennial. Let not wounded Pelops
more desire to approach Arcadian altars or knock with
ivory hand[10] at Elean temples, nor the snake glide more
willingly to the Castalian shrine, nor its shade swim to
pine-clad Lechaeum.[11] We, O boy, deny you to Avernus'
mourning and link our sad observance to the everlasting
stars. Now we are a host in haste, but if you grant us to
overturn the Boeotian dwellings with our steel, then shall a

Pelops, Python, and Palaemon visit the other three' (unfortunately, the Pythian was not in *honour* of Python!). *Malit = magis
velit.*

tunc deus, Inachias nec tantum culta per urbes
numina, captivis etiam iurabere Thebis.'
dux ea pro cunctis, eadem sibi quisque vovebat.
105   Iam pronis Gradivus equis Ephyraea premebat
litora, qua summas caput Acrocorinthos in auras
tollit et alterna geminum mare protegit umbra.
inde unum dira comitum de plebe Pavorem
quadripedes anteire iubet: non alter anhelos
110   insinuare metus animumque avertere veris
aptior. innumerae monstro vocesque manusque
et facies quamcumque velit; bonus omnia credi
auctor et horrificis lymphare incursibus urbes.
si geminos soles ruituraque suadeat astra,
115   aut nutare solum aut veteres descendere silvas,
a! miseri vidisse putant. tunc acre novabat
ingenium: falso Nemeaeum pulvere campum
erigit; attoniti tenebrosam a vertice nubem
respexere duces; falso clamore tumultum
120   auget, et arma virum pulsusque imitatur equorum,
terribilemque vagas ululatum spargit in auras.
exsiluere animi, dubiumque in murmure vulgus
pendet: 'ubi iste fragor? ni fallimur aure. sed unde
pulvereo stant astra globo? num Ismenius ultro
125   miles? ita est: veniunt. tanta autem audacia Thebis?
an dubitent, age, dum inferias et busta colamus?'
haec Pavor attonitis; variosque per agmina vultus

110 animumque . . . veris ω: -moque vires P

[12] Or with P's reading 'steal strength from the mind' (or 'from
courage'). But the following lines are about Panic's powers of de-
ception.

great altar add you dignity, then shall you be a god, deity worshipped not only in Inachian cities; in captive Thebes also you shall be invoked.' So prayed the leader on behalf of all, and each the same for himself.

Now Gradivus was treading Ephyre's shore with his thrusting horses, where Acrocorinthos lifts his head into the topmost airs and covers the twin sea with his alternating shadow. Thence he bids Panic, one of his dire crew of companions, go before his steeds. None better suited to instil panting fears and turn the mind from reality.[12] The monster has countless voices and hands and whatever face he pleases; on his authority all things are credible, he can drive cities crazy with his terrifying onslaughts. If he persuades them of two suns or of stars about to plunge or ground wobbling or ancient forests descending, why, the poor souls think they have seen it. Then he bethought him of something new and clever. He raises false dust on the plain of Nemea. The leaders gaze astounded at a dark cloud above their heads. He swells the tumult with false clamour, imitating men's arms and horses' gallop, scattering a fearsome yell upon the wandering winds. Their hearts leapt and the multitude hangs doubtful and murmuring: 'Where this noise?—unless our ears deceive us. But why stand the stars in a ball of dust? Is it the Ismenian army challenging us? So it is. They come. But is Thebes so bold? Well, are they to wait, look you, while we attend to funerals and sepulchres?' Thus Panic speaks[13] to their bewilderment. He takes on various guises as he goes through

13 The questions and answers are the army's, but Panic inspires them.

induitur: nunc Pisaeis e milibus unus,
nunc Pylius, nunc ore Lacon, hostesque propinquos
130 adiurat turmasque metu consternat inani.
nil falsum trepidis. ut vero amentibus ipse
incidit et sacrae circum fastigia vallis
turbine praevectus rapido ter sustulit hastam,
ter concussit equos, clipeum ter pectore plausit:
135 arma, arma insani sua quisque ignotaque nullo
more rapit, mutant galeas alienaque cogunt
ad iuga cornipedes; ferus omni in pectore saevit
mortis amor caedisque, nihil flagrantibus obstat:
praecipitant redimuntque moras. sic litora vento
140 incipiente fremunt, fugitur cum portus; ubique
vela fluunt, laxi iactantur ubique rudentes;
iamque natant remi, natat omnis in aequore summo
ancora, iam dulcis medii de gurgite ponti
respicitur tellus comitesque a puppe relicti.
145   Viderat Inachias rapidum glomerare cohortes
Bacchus iter; gemuit Tyriam conversus ad urbem,
altricemque domum et patrios reminiscitur ignes,
purpureum tristi turbatus pectore vultum:
non crines, non serta loco, dextramque reliquit
150 thyrsus, et intactae ceciderunt cornibus uvae.
ergo ut erat lacrimis lapsoque inhonorus amictu
ante Iovem (et tunc forte polum secretus habebat)
constitit, haud umquam facie conspectus in illa
(nec causae latuere patrem), supplexque profatur:
155 'exscindisne tuas, divum sator optime, Thebas?
saeva adeo coniunx? nec te telluris amatae
deceptique laris miseret cinerumque meorum?

---

[14] Mars.   [15] A favouring wind.

the host, now one of Pisa's thousands, now a Pylian, now a Laconian by the look of him, and swears that the enemy are close, confounding the troops with vain alarm. To the frightened nothing is false. But when he[14] comes upon the maddened army in his own person, when, carried around the heights of the sacred valley in a rapid whirl, he thrice lifts his spear, thrice strikes his steeds, thrice slaps shield against chest, in wild disorder each man snatches arms, arms, whether his own or a stranger's; they change helmets and drive horses into yokes not theirs. Fierce love of death and slaughter rages in every breast and nothing stands in their passion's way; they plunge, making up for their delay. So shores resound as the wind[15] rises and men flee the harbour; everywhere sails are streaming, everywhere loose tackle is tossing, and now oars float, every anchor floats on the water's surface, now from mid sea they gaze back at sweet land and the comrades they have left astern.

Bacchus had seen the Inachian cohorts mass their rapid march. Turning to the Tyrian city he groaned, remembering the home that fostered him and his father's fires,[16] sad at heart, his shining face distraught. His hair and garlands were disordered, the wand left his hand, the grapes fell from his horns untouched. So, as he was, inglorious in tears and dishevelled raiment, he stood before Jupiter, who chanced to be alone in his heavenly dwelling, never before seen in such guise (nor was the reason any secret to his sire), and suppliant speaks: 'Most excellent begetter of the gods, are you razing your Thebes? Is your lady so cruel? Have you no pity for the beloved land, the hearth you

---

[16] The lightning that destroyed Semele, also indicated in 157 *cinerumque meorum* and 158–60 and 191.

THEBAID

esto, olim invitum iaculatus nubibus ignem,
credimus: en iterum atra refers incendia terris,
160 nec Styge iurata, nec paelicis arte rogatus.
quis modus? an nobis pater iratusque bonusque
fulmen habes? sed non Danaeia limina talis
Parrhasiumque nemus Ledaeasque ibis Amyclas.
scilicet e cunctis ego neglectissima natis
165 progenies. ego nempe tamen qui dulce ferenti
pondus eram, cui tu dignatus limina vitae
praereptumque uterum et maternos reddere menses.
adde quod imbellis rarisque exercita castris
turba meas acies, mea tantum proelia norunt,
170 nectere fronde comas et ad inspirata rotari
buxa: timent thyrsos nuptarum et proelia matrum.
unde tubas Martemque pati, qui fervidus ecce
quanta parat? quid si ille tuos Curetas in arma
ducat et innocuis iubeat decernere peltis?
175 quin etiam invisos (sic hostis defuit?) Argos
eligis! o ipsis, genitor, graviora periclis
iussa: novercales ruimus ditare Mycenas!
cedo equidem. quo sacra tamen ritusque peremptae
gentis, et in tumulos si quid male feta reliquit
180 mater, abire iubes? Thracen silvasque Lycurgi?
anne triumphatos fugiam captivus ad Indos?
da sedem profugo. potuit Latonia frater
saxa (nec invideo) defigere Delon et imis

---

[167] uterum *Barth*: iter Pω   [176] elicis Pω (ς, *Markland*)
[177] ruimus ω: lu- P

---

[17] Home of Callisto.   [18] After Semele's death Jupiter
carried the fetal Bacchus in his thigh till birth.

410

tricked, my ashes? So be it, once you hurled fire from the clouds against your will, we believe it. Behold, a second time you bring black conflagration on the earth, though not sworn by Styx nor besought by the art of a paramour. How far will you go? You are my father, angry but kind; for me do you have your thunderbolt? But you will not visit Danaëan thresholds in such fashion nor the Parrhasian forest[17] nor Leda's Amyclae. It seems that of all your sons I am the least esteemed. And yet I am he (am I not?) whom you carried,[18] sweet burden, to whom you deigned restore life's threshold, the womb that was snatched away, and my mother's months. Add that the unwarlike throng, rarely practised in camps, know only *my* armies, *my* battles—to bind their hair with leaves and whirl to the blowing of pipes; they fear the wands of brides and the battles of mothers.[19] How are they to suffer trumpets and Mars? And see what work fiery Mars is preparing. What if he were to lead your Curetes to arms and bid them try the issue with their harmless bucklers? And you choose hated Argos[20]—was there no other enemy? More grievous, sire, are your commands than the danger itself. Do we fall to make my stepmother's Mycenae rich? For my part I yield. But where are the slaughtered people's sacraments and rites to go and whatever the mother who conceived me to her sorrow left for burial?[21] Shall I flee to Thrace and Lycurgus' forests or to the Indians over whom I triumphed to become their prisoner? Give the fugitive a place to dwell. My brother (and I grudge him not) could fix Delos

19 Reveling Bacchanals. 20 Hated as Juno's favourite.
21 Her ashes.

commendare fretis; cara summovit ab arce
185 hostiles Tritonis aquas; vidi ipse potentem
gentibus Eois Epaphum dare iura, nec ullas
Cyllene secreta tubas Minoave curat
Ida: quid heu tantum nostris offenderis aris?
hic tibi (quando minor iam nostra potentia) noctes
190 Herculeae placitusque vagae Nycteidos ardor,
hic Tyrium genus et nostro felicior igne
taurus: Agenoreos saltem tutare nepotes.'
    Invidiam risit pater, et iam poplite flexum
sternentemque manus tranquillus ad oscula tollit
195 inque vicem placida orsa refert: 'non coniugis ista
consiliis, ut rere, puer, nec saeva roganti
sic expostus ego: immoto deducimur orbe
Fatorum; veteres seraeque in proelia causae.
nam cui tanta quies irarum aut sanguinis usus
200 parcior humani? videt axis et ista per aevum
mecum aeterna domus quotiens iam torta reponam
fulmina, quam rarus terris hic imperet ignis.
quin etiam invitus magna ulciscendaque passis
aut Lapithas Marti aut veterem Calydona Dianae
205 expugnare dedi: nimia est iactura pigetque

205 mea est Pω: meaque est ψ (*Phillimore*)

---

22 The floating island, birthplace of Apollo, who stabilized it.
23 In a contest with Neptune Minerva repelled his waters from
the Athenian acropolis.
24 Birthplace of Mercury.
25 In Crete. Minos was Jupiter's son.
26 Jupiter's other children are not disturbed in their favourite
localities, so why Bacchus in Thebes? *Tubas* = war trumpets.
27 Antiope, mated by Jupiter in the form of a Satyr.

fast, Latona's rock,[22] and commend her to the depth of the seas, the Tritonian removed hostile waters from her dear citadel,[23] I myself have seen potent Epaphus ruling the races of the East, neither does hidden Cyllene[24] or Minoan Ida[25] trouble for trumpets. Why, ah why, are you offended only by *my* altars?[26] Here, since my influence now counts for little, you have your nights of Hercules and your chosen love of the wandering daughter of Nycteus,[27] here the race of Tyre and the bull more fortunate[28] than my fire; at least protect Agenor's progeny.'

The Father smiled at his reproach. Calmly he raised him for a kiss as he knelt with hands outstretched and in turn gave tranquil answer: 'My lad, this is not by my wife's counsels as you suppose nor am I so subject to her fierce demands. Our lot is spun by the changeless wheel of the Fates. Ancient and belated are the causes that lead to the war. For whose anger rests so readily, who more sparing to take human blood? Heaven and these halls, immortal as myself throughout the ages, are my witness how often I put back the thunderbolt already whirling, how seldom this fire gives earth my commands. It was unwillingly even that I gave the Lapiths to Mars[29] to destroy or ancient Calydon to Diana, though they had suffered great wrongs that cried for vengeance. The loss is too great and it irks me to shift so

[28] Jupiter had better luck with Europa than with Semele. The Thebans were descended from Jupiter through Cadmus and Agenor but not through Cadmus' sister Europa. None the less she seems to be regarded as their ancestor, as in 11.212—14. Cf. 279.

[29] According to a late version of the legend, Mars took offence at not being invited to Pirithous' wedding feast, so made the Centaurs drunk, causing their fight with the Lapiths.

tot mutare animas, tot reddere corpora vitae.
Labdacios vero Pelopisque a stirpe nepotes
tardum abolere mihi; scis ipse (ut crimina mittam
Dorica) quam promptae superos incessere Thebae;
210   te quoque–sed, quoniam vetus excidit ira, silebo.
non tamen aut patrio respersus sanguine Pentheus,
aut matrem scelerasse toris aut crimine fratres
progenuisse reus, lacero tua lustra replevit
funere: ubi hi fletus, ubi tunc ars tanta precandi?
215   ast ego non proprio diros impendo dolori
Oedipodionidas: rogat hoc tellusque polusque
et pietas et laesa fides Naturaque et ipsi
Eumenidum mores. sed tu super urbe moveri
parce tua: non hoc statui sub tempore rebus
220   occasum Aoniis, veniet suspectior aetas
ultoresque alii: nunc regia Iuno queretur.'
his ille auditis mentemque habitumque recepit;
ut, cum sole malo tristique rosaria pallent
usta Noto, si clara dies Zephyrique refecit
225   aura polum, redit omnis honos, emissaque lucent
germina, et informes ornat sua gloria virgas.

    Nuntius attonitas iamdudum Eteoclis ad aures
explorata ferens longo docet agmine Graios
ire duces, nec iam Aoniis procul afore campis;
230   quacumque ingressi, tremere ac miserescere cunctos
Thebarum; qui stirpe refert, qui nomine et armis.

223 pallent *ω*: pendent *ex* pund- P

---

30 Not bodies but souls are returned to life, in new bodies
(*Aeneid* 6.751, perhaps misunderstood).

many souls and return so many bodies to life.[30] But the progeny of Labdacus and Pelops it is high time for me to abolish from the root. You know yourself (to say nothing of Dorian offences) how prompt is Thebes to assail the High Ones. You too—but since the old anger is forgotten, I shall be mute.[31] And yet Pentheus, who was not stained with his father's blood nor guilty of defiling his mother's bed or the crime of begetting brothers, filled your wilds with his lacerated corpse. Where were these tears then, where such elaborate entreaty? But I do not sacrifice the fell sons of Oedipus to my private wrath. Earth and heaven demand it, and piety and violated faith and Nature and the very morals of the Eumenides. But be not troubled for your city. I have not decreed an end to Aonian history at this time, a more dangerous hour shall come and other avengers.[32] For now queen Juno shall complain.' So hearing, Bacchus regained his mind and mien. So rose beds fade,[33] scorched by a harmful sun and an unkind South Wind, but if the day clears and Zephyr's breeze revive, the sky, all the beauty returns, the buds open and gleam, the formless twigs are adorned in their glory.

A messenger has this while past brought sure tidings to Eteocles' stunned ears that Grecian leaders are marching in lengthy column and will soon be no great distance from Aonian fields; wherever they enter, all tremble and pity Thebes. He reports who they are by lineage and name and

31 Jupiter is about to say 'took vengeance on Pentheus,' but pulls himself up. Then he says it.

32 The Epigoni, sons of the Seven, who captured Thebes in the next generation.

33 *Pendent* ('droop') could be right, but see Håkanson.

ille metum condens audire exposcit et odit
narrantem: hinc socios dictis stimulare suasque
metiri decernit opes. exciuerat omnem
235 Aoniam Euboeamque et Phocidos arua propinquae
Mars, ita dulce Iovi. longe fugit ordine velox
tessera: propellunt acies, seseque sub armis
ostentant; subeunt campo qui proximus urbi
damnatus bellis patet exspectatque furores.
240 nondum hostes contra, trepido tamen agmine matres
conscendunt muros, inde arma nitentia natis
et formidandos monstrant sub casside patres.
    Turre procul sola nondum concessa videri
Antigone populis teneras defenditur atra
245 veste genas; iuxtaque comes quo Laius ibat
armigero; nunc virgo senem regina veretur.
quae sic orsa prior: 'spesne obstatura Pelasgis
haec vexilla, pater? Pelopis descendere totas
audimus gentes: dic, o precor, extera regum
250 agmina; nam video quae noster signa Menoeceus,
quae noster regat arma Creon, quam celsus aëna
Sphinge per ingentes Homoloidas exeat Haemon.'
sic rudis Antigone, senior cui talia Phorbas:
'mille sagittiferos gelidae de colle Tanagrae
255 promovet ecce Dryas; hic, cui nivea arma tridentem
atque auro rude fulmen habent, Orionis alti
non falsus virtute nepos: procul, oro, paternum
omen et innuptae vetus excidat ira Dianae.

236 longe P: -go ω
246 tunc Pω (SB)
248 totas ω: tantas P ante corr.

arms. The other, hiding his fear, demands to be told and hates the teller. Then he decides to urge on his allies with a speech and to measure his own power. Mars had stirred up all Aonia and Euboea and the fields of neighbouring Phocis, such was Jupiter's pleasure. The swift signal flies far in its sequence. They march forth their ranks and show themselves in arms. They enter a plain that spreads close to the city, doomed to battles and awaiting war's madness. The enemy does not yet face them, but mothers mount the walls in an anxious throng and thence show their children the shining armour and their fathers, figures of fear under their helms.

Distant on a lonely tower Antigone, whom the people are not yet allowed to see, defends her tender cheeks with a black cloth. Beside her in attendance is Laius' onetime armour-bearer; now the royal maiden reveres him, an old man. She speaks first: 'Father, is there hope that these banners will withstand the Pelasgi? We hear that all Pelops' races are descending upon us. Tell me, I pray, of the foreign kings and their troops. For I see what standards our Menoeceus commands, what arms our Creon, how tall with brazen Sphinx Haemon goes out through the great Homoloid gates.' So in her ignorance Antigone, to whom thus old Phorbas replies:[34] 'See, Dryas brings up a thousand archers from cold Tanagra's hill. His snow-white shield bears a trident and a rude thunderbolt in gold. He is the grandson (and his valour attests it) of tall Orion. Far, I pray, be the ancestral omen and may virgin Diana forget

---

[34] With the following list of Boeotian places cf. Pliny, *Natural History* 4.25f.

iungunt se castris regisque in nomen adoptant
260 Ocalee Medeonque et confertissima lucis
Nisa Dionaeisque avibus circumsona Thisbe.
proximus Eurymedon, cui pastoralia Fauni
arma patris pinuque iubas imitatur equinas,
terribilis silvis: reor et Mavorte cruento
265 talis erit. dites pecorum comitantur Erythrae,
qui Scolon densamque iugis Eteonon iniquis,
qui breve litus Hyles Atalantaeamque superbi
Schoenon habent notique colunt vestigia campi;
fraxineas Macetum vibrant de more sarisas
270 saevaque difficiles excludere vulnera peltas.
ecce autem clamore ruunt Neptunia plebes
Onchesti, quos pinigeris Mycalesos in agris
Palladiusque Melas Hecataeaque gurgite nutrit
Gargaphie, quorumque novis Haliartos aristis
275 invidet et nimia sata laeta supervenit herba.
tela rudes trunci, galeae vacua ora leonum,
arborei dant scuta sinus. hos regis egenos
Amphion en noster agit (cognoscere pronum,
virgo), lyra galeam tauroque insignis avito.
280 macte animo iuvenis! medios parat ire per enses
nudaque pro caris opponere pectora muris.

262 cui ω: qui P   271 plebes Pω: proles *vel* pubes ψ

---

35 According to late legend, Orion was born from the urine of
Jupiter, Neptune, and Mercury; hence the trident and thunder-
bolt on his grandson's shield. A great hunter, he gave offence to
Diana; as to how, accounts vary.

36 Venus' doves. Thisbe is called 'of many doves' in the Homeric catalogue (*Iliad* 2.502).

418

her ancient wrath.[35] Ocaleë and Medeon and Nisa thick with woods and Thisbe echoing with Dione's birds[36] have joined our forces and take service in our king's name. Next is Eurymedon with the pastoral arms of his father Faunus and pine to imitate a horsehair crest, terrible to the woods; such, I think, will he be in bloody combat. Erythrae, rich in flocks, bears company, and they that inhabit Scolos and Eteonos, thick with rugged ridges, and the brief shore of Hyle and the proud dwellers in Atalanta's Schoenos who cultivate the traces of her famous field;[37] they brandish ashen pikes after the Macedonian fashion and bucklers scarce able to keep out cruel wounds. But see, the Neptunian folk of Onchestus rush on shouting; they that Mycalesos nurtures in her pine-covered fields and Palladian Melas and Hecate's Gargaphie with her waters and they whose young harvest Haliartos grudges, growing over the flourishing crop with too-abundant grass.[38] Their weapons are rude trunks, their helmets the hollow faces of lions, treefolds[39] provide their shields. As they lack a king, see, our Amphion[40] leads them (he is easy to recognize, maiden), his helm conspicuous with lyre and ancestral bull. Bravo, young man! He means to go through the midst of swords and protect the walls he loves with his bare

[37] Race track. If Statius gave any thought to the matter, he must have imagined Atalanta as having at some point moved from Boeotia to Arcadia.   [38] 'Grassy' in *Iliad* 2.503. But who are 'they'?   [39] Bark.   [40] Son of the musician, who with his brother tied Dirce to a bull, thus avenging her ill-treatment of their mother Antiope. But *avito* clearly indicates Europa's bull (Jupiter), though she had nothing to do with Amphion except as putative ancestor of the Thebans.

vos etiam nostris, Heliconia turba, venitis
addere rebus opem; tuque, o Permesse, canoris
et felix Olmie vadis, armastis alumnos
285 bellorum resides. patriis concentibus audis
exsultare gregem, quales, cum pallida cedit
bruma, renidentem deducunt Strymona cycni.
ite alacres, numquam vestri morientur honores,
bellaque perpetuo memorabunt carmine Musae.'

290   Dixerat, et paulum virgo interfata loquenti:
'illi autem, quanam iunguntur origine fratres?
sic certe paria arma viris, sic exit in auras
cassidis aequus apex; utinam haec concordia nostris!'
cui senior ridens: 'non prima errore videndi
295 falleris, Antigone: multi hos (nam decipit aetas)
dixerunt fratres. pater est natusque, sed aevi
confudere modos: puerum Lapithaona Nymphe
Dercetis expertem thalami crudumque maritis
ignibus ante diem cupido violavit amore
300 improba conubii; nec longum, et pulcher Alatreus
editus, ac primae genitorem in flore iuventae
consequitur traxitque notas et miscuit annos.
et nunc sic fratres mentito nomine gaudent,
plus pater: hunc olim iuvat et ventura senectus.
305 tercentum genitor totidemque in proelia natus
exercent equites: hi deseruisse feruntur
exilem Glisanta Coroniamque feracem,
messe Coroniam, Baccho Glisanta colentes.

284 Olmie Σ *ad 282 et 287*: hormie Pω
290 loquenti P: doce -ω
298 maritis ψΣ: -ti Pω

breast. You too, Heliconian throng, come to aid our fortunes; and you, Permessus and Olmius, happy in your
tuneful waters,[41] have armed your nurslings though they
hang back from war. You hear the company exult in their
native choirs, like swans escorting bright Strymon when
pale winter yields. Go you in good cheer, never shall your
praises die and the Muses shall celebrate your wars in
perpetual song.'

He spoke and the maiden briefly interposed: 'Those
brothers now, what origin unites them? Thus surely their
arms match and equal helmet crests rise into the air.
Would that mine agreed so well!' The old man smiled: 'You
are not the first your eyes deceive, Antigone. Many (for
their years mislead) have called them brothers. They are
father and son, but they have confounded the fashions
of age. The Nymph Dercetis in ardent desire for union
shamelessly violated the boy Lapithaon before his time,
who knew nothing of the marriage bed, unripe for conju-
gal flames. 'Twas no long while before fair Alatreus was
born; he overtook his father in the flower of youth, took on
his traits and mingled the years. And now, thus brothers,
they rejoice in the false name, the father more: he takes
pleasure also in old age one day to come.[42] The father mar-
shals three hundred horse for battle, the son as many. They
are said to have left meagre Glisas and fertile Coronia; they
cultivate Coronia with the harvest, Glisas with the vine.

[41] Rising on Mt Helicon, these rivers were sacred to the
Muses.
[42] A cryptic saying that has been food for debate. Perhaps the
implication is simply that the son was too young for such thoughts.

sed potius celsos umbrantem hunc aspice late
310 Hypsea quadriiugos; clipei septemplice tauro
laeva, ter insuto servantur pectora ferro,
pectora: nam tergo numquam metus. hasta vetustum
silvarum decus, emissae cui pervia semper
armaque corporaque et numquam manus irrita voti.
315 Asopos genuisse datur, dignusque videri
tunc pater, abreptis cum torrentissimus exit
pontibus, aut natae tumidus cum virginis ultor
flumina concussit generum indignata Tonantem.
namque ferunt raptam patriis Aeginan ab undis
320 amplexu latuisse Iovis: furit amnis et astris
infensus bellare parat (nondum ista licebant
nec superis); stetit audaces effusus in iras,
conseruitque manum, nec quem imploraret habebat,
donec vix tonitru summotus et igne trisulco
325 cessit. adhuc ripis animosus gurges anhelis
fulmineum cinerem magnaeque insignia poenae
gaudet et Aetnaeos in caelum efflare vapores.
talem Cadmeo mirabimur Hypsea campo,
si modo placavit felix Aegina Tonantem.
330 ducit Itonaeos et Alalcomenaea Minervae
agmina, quos Midea et quos uvida suggerit Arne,
Aulida qui Graeanque serunt viridesque Plataeas,
et sulco Peteona domant, refluumque meatu
Euripum, qua noster, habent teque, ultima tractu
335 Anthedon, ubi gramineo de litore Glaucus
poscentes irrupit aquas, iam crine genisque
caerulus, et mixtos expavit ab inguine pisces.

331 mide et ω: medon P *ex* medion (?) (*Dubner*)   vivida P:
(h)umida ω (ς, *Heinsius*)

422

But rather look at Hypseus here as he broadly overshadows his tall team. His left hand is guarded by the sevenfold bullshide of his shield, his breast by triply woven steel—his breast; for he never fears for his back. His spear is an ancient glory of the woods; discharged, it ever breaches arms and bodies, and his hand never fails of his aim. Asopos is given as his father, worthy to seem so when he goes forth at his most torrential, sweeping bridges away, or when in vengeance for his virgin daughter he swelled and churned his stream in wrath against his Thunderer son-in-law.[43] For they say Aegina was snatched from her father's water and hid in Jupiter's embrace. The river rages and makes to go to war against the stars (not yet were such acts permitted even to the High Ones). He stood in a fit of bold fury and joined battle with none to ask for aid,[44] until finally thunder and triple fire dislodged him and he gave way. Even yet the valiant stream with panting banks rejoices to breathe out thunderbolt ash and Aetnaean vapours upon the sky, signs of his great chastisement. Such shall we wonder at Hypseus in the plain of Cadmus, if only happy Aegina has appeased the Thunderer. He leads the men of Itone and Minerva's Alalcomenaean columns, whom Midea supplies and grapy Arne, them that sow Aulis and Graea and green Plataeae and that tame Peteon with the furrow and hold Euripus, ebbing and flowing, where Euripus is ours, and you, Anthedon, sited last of all, where Glaucus plunged from the grassy strand into the summoning sea, already cerulean in hair and beard, and was shocked to see the fish

[43] Extended use of *gener*, as often.

[44] He could not appeal to Jupiter, the usual recourse of the wronged.

glandibus et torta Zephyros incidere funda
cura: Cydoneas anteibunt gaesa sagittas.
340 tu quoque praeclarum forma, Cephise, dedisses
Narcissum, sed Thespiacis iam pallet in agris
trux puer; orbata florem, pater, alluis unda.
quis tibi Phoebeas acies veteremque revolvat
Phocida? qui Panopen, qui Daulida, qui Cyparisson,
345 et valles, Lebadia, tuas et Hyampolin acri
subnixam scopulo, vel qui Parnason utrumque
aut Cirrham tauris Anemorianque supinant
Coryciumque nemus propellentemque Lilaean
Cephisi glaciale caput, quo suetus anhelam
350 ferre sitim Python amnemque avertere ponto:
omnibus intextas cono super aspice laurus
armaque vel Tityon vel Delon habentia, vel quas
hic deus innumera laxavit caede pharetras.
Iphitus asper agit, genitor cui nuper ademptus
355 Naubolus Hippasides, tuus, o mitissime Lai,
hospes; adhuc currus securaque lora tenebam,
cum tua subter equos iacuit convulsa cruentis
ictibus (o utinam nostro cum sanguine!) cervix.'
   Dicenti maduere genae, vultumque per omnem
360 pallor iit, vocisque repens singultus apertum
intercepit iter; refovet frigentis amicum
pectus alumna senis; redit atque exile profatur:
'o mihi sollicitum decus ac suprema voluptas,
Antigone! seras tibi demoror improbus umbras,
365 fors eadem scelera et caedes visurus avitas,
donec te thalamis habilem integramque resignem:

351 immixtas Pω (ς, *Bentley*)   353 innumera ψ: -as Pω
354 asper P: acer ω   356 tenebam P: -at ω

mingling from his groin. Their care is to cut the Zephyrs with bullets and twisted sling; their javelins will outfly Cydonian arrows. You too, Cephisus, would have given fair Narcissus, but already the pitiless boy is pale in Thespiae's fields; his father washes the flower with desolate wave. Who should rehearse for you the troops of Phoebus and ancient Phocis, the men of Panope and Daulis and Cyparissos and your valleys, Lebadia, and Hyampolis, leaning against a jagged crag; or those who with bulls upturn twin Parnassus or Cirrha and Anemoria and the Corycian forest and Lilaea that sends forth the icy fount of Cephisus, whither Python was wont to carry his panting thirst and turn the river from the sea? Behold the laurels twined about every helm and the shields imaging Tityos[45] or Delos or the quivers that the god emptied here in uncounted slaughter.[46] Fierce Iphitus leads them, who lately lost his father Naubolus son of Hippasus, your host, most gentle Laius. I still held the chariot and the reins with no thought of harm when your neck lay under the horses mangled by cruel blows. Would that my blood too had flowed there!'

As he spoke his cheeks grew moist and a pallor went through all his face, a sudden sobbing interrupted the passage of his voice. His nursling revives the chilled ancient's loving heart. He returns and weakly speaks: 'Antigone, my anxious pride and last pleasure, all too long do I delay for your sake my belated end (perhaps to see the same crimes and ancestral deeds of blood), waiting to give you up ready

[45] Shot by Apollo.

[46] Of Niobe's children. 'Here' = in Thebes. The alternative reading *innumeras* is equally hyperbolical.

hoc satis, et fessum vita dimittite, Parcae.
sed dum labor iners, quanti (nunc ecce reviso)
transabiere duces: Clonin atque in terga comantes
370 non ego Abantiadas, non te, saxosa Caryste,
non humiles Aegas altumque Capherea dixi.
et iam acies obtunsa negat, cunctique resistunt,
et tuus armatis iubet ecce silentia frater.'
   Vix ea turre senex, cum rector ab aggere coepit:
375 'magnanimi reges, quibus haud parere recusem
ductor et ipse meas miles defendere Thebas,
non ego vos stimulare parem (nam liber in arma
impetus, et meritas ultro iurastis in iras),
nec laudare satis dignasque rependere grates
380 sufficiam (referent superi vestraeque subacto
hoste manus): urbem socia de gente subistis
tutari, quam non aliis populator ab oris
belliger externave satus tellure, sed hostis
indigena assultat, cui castra adversa regenti
385 hic pater, hic genetrix, hic iunctae stirpe sorores,
hic erat et frater. cerne en ubicumque nefandus
excidium moliris avis: venere volentes
Aoniae populi, nec sum tibi, saeve, relictus.
quid velit ista cohors et te sentire decebat:
390 reddere regna vetant.' sic fatus et omnia rite
disponit, qui bella gerant, qui moenia servent,
quas in fronte manus, medio quas robore sistat.
perspicuas sic luce fores et virgea pastor
claustra levat, dum terra recens; iubet ordine primo
395 ire duces, media stipantur plebe maritae;

---

47 The past tense (*erat*) may imply that Polynices is no longer
one of the family.

for wedlock and unharmed. That is enough; and discharge me, Parcae, from the life I am weary of. But while I sink helpless, what mighty leaders (now I see them again, look!) have passed by! I said naught of Clonis and the long-haired sons of Abas, naught of you, rocky Carystos, nor of low-lying Aegae and lofty Caphereus. And now my dull eyes refuse and they all stay still and your brother, see, orders the army silent.'

So the old man on the tower; scarce had he ended when from the platform the ruler begins: 'Great-hearted kings, whom I your leader would not refuse to obey and as a common soldier myself defend my Thebes: I would not make to spur you on, for free is your rush to arms and of your own will you have sworn to fight for my just wrath. Nor could I praise you enough or return you worthy thanks; the High Ones will repay, and your own hands when the enemy is vanquished. You have come hither to protect a city of allied race. No warlike ravager from other shores, no child of a foreign soil, but a native foe assails her, one that rules a hostile camp when his father, his mother, his sisters joined in blood were here, here too his brother.[47] Behold, villain, wherever you are, plotting destruction to your ancestors! The peoples of Aonia have come of their own free will and I have not been left at your mercy, ruffian. What this army wills, even you should have recognized. They forbid me to return the throne.' So he spoke and duly orders all: who should fight, who keep the walls, what force he puts in the van, what in the centre strength. So the shepherd raises the doors and wattle barriers when the light shines through, while the earth is fresh; he bids the leaders go first, the flock of ewes is packed in the middle; he himself

ipse levat gravidas et humum tractura parentum
ubera, succiduasque apportat matribus agnas.
    Interea Danai noctemque diemque sub armis,
noctem iterum rursusque diem (sic ira ferebat)
400   ingeminant: contempta quies, vix aut sopor illis
aut epulae fecere moram; properatur in hostem
more fugae. nec monstra tenent, quae plurima nectit
prodigiale canens certi fors praevia fati.
quippe serunt diros monitus volucresque feraeque
405   sideraque adversique suis decursibus amnes,
infestumque tonat pater et mala fulgura lucent;
terrificaeque adytis voces clausaeque deorum
sponte fores; nunc sanguineus, nunc saxeus imber,
et subiti manes flentumque occursus avorum.
410   tunc et Apollineae tacuere oracula Cirrhae,
et non adsuetis pernox ululavit Eleusin
mensibus, et templis Sparte praesaga reclusis
vidit Amyclaeos (facinus!) concurrere fratres.
Arcades insanas latrare Lycaonis umbras
415   nocte ferunt tacita, saevo decurrere campo
Oenomaum sua Pisa refert; Acheloon utroque
deformem cornu vagus infamabat Acarnan.
Perseos effigiem maestam exorantque Mycenae
confusum Iunonis ebur; mugire potentem
420   Inachon agricolae, gemini maris accola narrat
Thebanum toto planxisse Palaemona ponto.

---

396 iuvat *Imhof*   tractura Pψ: tac- ω   405 adv- *cod.*
Paris. saec. X: av- Pω, *vulg.*   420 incola Pω (*Schrader*)

---

48 As remarked by Eden, *aversi* would indicate flooding, not
the common prodigy of reverse flow.

raises the pregnant ones and the udders of parents like to trail the ground and brings the stumbling lambs to their dams.

Meanwhile the Danai add night to day under arms, and night again and day again; so their wrath willed it. Rest they despised, hardly did sleep or food make them pause. They hurry to meet the enemy as though in flight. Nor do prodigies detain them, though sure Fate's harbinger chance, prophesying portent-wise, links them in plenty. For birds and beasts give dire warnings, and stars, and rivers turned contrary to their downward courses.[48] The Father thunders balefully and evil lightnings flash. Terrifying voices come from sanctuaries and temple doors shut on their own. It rains now blood, now stones, ghosts appear suddenly and weeping ancestors confront. Then the oracles of Apollo's Cirrha were silent, Eleusis howled all night out of season, and prophetic Sparta saw the brothers of Amyclae[49] (oh enormity!) meet in conflict in their opened temple. Arcadians say that Lycaon's mad shade barked in the silence of the night, his Pisa reports Oenomaus racing over the cruel flat, a wandering Acarnanian slanderously told of Achelous maimed of both his horns.[50] Mycenae propitiates Perseus' gloomy image and Juno's troubled ivory. Rustics tell of potent Inachus bellowing. A dweller by the double sea[51] says that Theban Palaemon lamented all over the waters. The Pelopean

[49] Castor and Pollux.

[50] He had lost only one of them in his fight with Hercules. *Acarnan* is not Tydeus (an Aetolian) or the eponymous hero of Acarnania but an anonymous Acarnanian (SB[1]).

[51] I.e. in the Isthmus of Corinth.

haec audit Pelopea phalanx, sed bellicus ardor
consiliis obstat divum prohibetque timeri.
    Iam ripas, Asope, tuas Boeotaque ventum
425   flumina. non ausae transmittere protinus alae
hostilem fluvium; forte et trepidantibus ingens
descendebat agris, animos sive imbrifer arcus,
seu montana dedit nubes, seu fluminis illa
mens fuit obiectusque vado pater arma vetabat.
430   tunc ferus Hippomedon magno cum fragmine ripae
cunctantem deiecit equum, ducibusque relictis
gurgite de medio frenis suspensus et armis,
'ite viri,' clamat, 'sic vos in moenia primus
ducere, sic clausas voveo perfringere Thebas.'
435   praecipitant cuncti fluvio puduitque secutos.
ac velut ignotum si quando armenta per amnem
pastor agit, stat triste pecus, procul altera tellus
omnibus et late medius timor: ast ubi ductor
taurus init fecitque vadum, tunc mollior unda,
440   tunc faciles saltus, visaeque accedere ripae.
     Haud procul inde iugum tutisque accommoda castris
arva notant, unde urbem etiam turresque videre ⟨est⟩
Sidonias; placuit sedes fidique receptus
colle per excelsum patulo quem subter aperto
445   arva sinu, nullique aliis a montibus instant
despectus; nec longa labor munimina durus
addidit: ipsa loco mirum natura favebat.
in vallum elatae rupes devexaque fossis
aequa et fortuito ductae quater aggere pinnae;

442 videre est Ϛ: -re ω: -ri Pψ

phalanx hears these things, but warlike ardour opposes the counsels of the gods and forbids that they be feared.

Now they have reached your banks, Asopos, and Boeotian streams. The squadrons dared not ford the hostile river forthwith; as it happened he was coming down in spate through the affrighted fields. Did rainbow or mountain cloud give him courage or was it the stream's own purpose and did the father[52] interpose his waters forbidding their arms? Then fierce Hippomedon forced his hesitant mount down together with a great piece of bank and leaving the leaders behind cried from mid river holding harness and arms above his head: 'Come, men. Thus do I vow to be first to lead you into the walls and break through closed Thebes.' They all plunge into the current, ashamed to have been behind. So when a herdsman is driving cattle through an unknown river, the herd stand dismayed; to all the other bank seems far away and wide the fear between; But when the leader bull goes in and makes a ford, then the water is gentler, the leaps easy, and the banks seem to draw closer.

Not far from thence they mark a ridge, ground suitable for a safe encampment, from which they can even see the city with her Sidonian towers. The station pleased them, offering secure reception: a hill with spreading top, beneath which an open slope of fields, not overlooked by other heights. Nor did hard toil add long lines of fortification; its own nature favoured the spot to a marvel. Rocks rose to form a rampart, the slopes were as good as ditches, and four merlons were raised by chance mounds. The rest

[52] Perhaps without special reference, as in 2.217f. *pater . . . Inachus* et sim. Or was the fate of Asopos' son Hypseus in mind?

450 cetera dant ipsi, donec sol montibus omnis
    erepsit rebusque dedit sopor otia fessis.
        Quis queat attonitas dictis ostendere Thebas?
    urbem in conspectu belli suprema parantis
    territat insomnem nox atra diemque minatur.
455 discurrunt muris; nil saeptum horrore sub illo,
    nil fidum satis, invalidaeque Amphionis arces.
    rumor ubique alius pluresque annuntiat hostes
    maioresque timor; spectant tentoria contra
    Inachia externosque suis in montibus ignes.
460 hi precibus questuque deos, hi Martia tela
    belligerosque hortantur equos, hi pectora fletu
    cara premunt miserique rogos et crastina mandant
    funera. si tenuis demisit lumina somnus,
    bella gerunt. modo lucra morae, modo taedia visae
465 attonitis; lucemque timent lucemque precantur.
    it geminum excutiens anguem et bacchatur utrisque
    Tisiphone castris; fratrem huic, fratrem ingerit illi,
    aut utrique patrem: procul ille penatibus imis
    excitus implorat Furias oculosque reposcit.
470   Iam gelidam Phoeben et caligantia primus
    hauserat astra dies, cum iam tumet igne futuro
    Oceanus lateque novo Titane reclusum
    aequor anhelantum radiis subsidit equorum:
    ecce truces oculos sordentibus obsita canis
475 exsangues Iocasta genas et bracchia planctu
    nigra ferens ramumque oleae cum velleris atri
    nexibus, Eumenidum velut antiquissima, portis
    egreditur magna cum maiestate malorum.

    451 derepsit *Heinsius*
    457 alios P: altus ω (*Heinsius*)   pluresque Pω: -res ψ

they themselves supply, until all sun crept from the hills and sleep gave rest to weariness.

Who could portray in words the shock of Thebes? In sight of war like to be the end of them black night terrifies the sleepless city and threatens day. They run about the walls. In that terror nothing is truly guarded and secure, Amphion's towers are feeble. Everywhere is a different rumour and fear announces more and greater enemies. They see the Inachian tents confronting them and stranger fires in their hills. Some call upon the gods with prayer and plaint, others exhort their martial weapons and warhorses, others again tearfully press beloved breasts and sorrowfully commission funeral pyres for the morrow. If a light sleep droop their eyes, they are fighting; dazed as they are, delay seems now a gain, now a weariness; they fear the light and for the light they pray. Tisiphone shakes her twin serpents and runs riot in both armies. She thrusts his brother upon one and his brother upon the other, or their father on both. He afar in the depths of the palace is roused and invokes the Furies and reclaims his eyes.[53]

Now dawn had swallowed chill Phoebe and the glooming stars. Ocean now swells with coming fire and the wide waters opened up by the new Titan subside with the rays of his panting steeds. See, Jocasta goes forth from the gates in all the majesty of her sorrows. Her fierce eyes are covered with unkempt white hair, her cheeks bloodless, her arms dark with beating. She carries an olive branch with twines of black wool like the eldest of the

[53] In order to see the coming carnage.

433

hinc atque hinc natae, melior iam sexus, aniles
480   praecipitantem artus et plus quam possit euntem
sustentant. venit ante hostes, et pectore nudo
claustra adversa ferit tremulisque ululatibus orat
admitti: 'reserate viam! rogat impia belli
mater; in his aliquod ius exsecrabile castris
485   huic utero est.' trepidi visam expavere manipli
auditamque magis; remeat iam missus Adrasto
nuntius: excipiunt iussi mediosque per enses
dant iter. illa duces ut primum aspexit Achivos
clamorem horrendum luctu furiata resolvit:
490   'Argolici proceres, ecquis monstraverit hostem
quem peperi? quanam inveniam, mihi dicite, natum
sub galea?' venit attonitae Cadmeius heros
obvius, et raptam lacrimis gaudentibus implet
solaturque tenens, atque inter singula matrem,
495   matrem iterat, nunc ipsam urguens, nunc cara sororum
pectora, cum mixta fletus anus asperat ira:
'quid molles lacrimas venerandaque nomina fingis,
rex Argive, mihi? quid colla amplexibus ambis
invisamque teris ferrato pectore matrem?
500   tune ille exsilio vagus et miserabilis hospes?
quem non permoveas? longae tua iussa cohortes
exspectant, multoque latus praefulgurat ense.
a miserae matres! hunc te noctesque diesque
deflebam? si verba tamen monitusque tuorum
505   dignaris, dum castra silent suspensaque bellum
horrescit pietas, genetrix iubeoque rogoque:
i mecum patriosque deos arsuraque saltem

Furies. On either side her daughters, now the better sex,[54] support her as she hastens her aged limbs and moves faster than she can. Coming in face of the foe, she strikes the opposing bars with her naked bosom, then begs for admittance with tremulous wails: 'Unbar my way! The impious mother of the war asks it. In this camp this womb has a right—an abominable right.' Seeing her the soldiers trembled in terror, hearing her yet more. A messenger was sent to Adrastus, and now returns. On orders they let her in and give passage through the swords. At first sight of the Achaean leaders, maddened with grief she let loose a dreadful cry: 'Nobles of Argos, will anyone show me the enemy I bore? Under what helmet, tell me, shall I find my son?' The Cadmean hero comes to the distracted woman and takes her, filling her with tears of joy, comforting as he holds her and repeating between this and that 'Mother, mother,' now pressing her to his breast, now his dear sisters. But the aged one embitters her weeping with a dash of anger: 'Argive king, why feign you tender tears and reverend names for me? Why circle my neck with embraces and hug your hated mother with iron-clad breast? Are you the wandering exile, the pitiable guest? Whom would you not stir to compassion? Long columns await your orders, many swords flash at your side. Ah, unhappy mothers! Is this you that I wept for day and night? Yet if you have any respect for the words and counsel of your folk, I who bore you command and beg, while the armies are silent and piety in suspense shudders at war: come with me and at least look upon your country's gods and the dwellings about to

[54] Contrary to the norm.

435

tecta vide, fratremque (quid aufers lumina?), fratrem
alloquere et regnum iam me sub iudice posce:
510   aut dabit, aut ferrum causa meliore resumes.
anne times ne forte doli, et te conscia mater
decipiam? non sic miseros fas omne penates
effugit: vix Oedipode ducente timeres.
nupsi equidem peperique nefas, sed diligo tales
515   (a dolor!) et vestros etiamnum excuso furores.
quod si adeo perstas, ultro tibi, saeve, triumphum
detulimus: religa captas in terga sorores,
inice vincla mihi: gravis huc utcumque feretur
et pater. ad vestrum gemitus nunc verto pudorem,
520   Inachidae, liquistis enim parvosque senesque
et lacrimas has quisque domi: sua credite matri
viscera! si vobis hic parvo in tempore carus
(sitque precor), quid me, oro, decet quidve ista, Pelasgi,
ubera? ab Hyrcanis hoc Odrysiisve tulissem
525   regibus, et si qui nostros vicere furores.
annuite, aut natum complexa superstite bello
hic moriar.'
         Tumidas frangebant dicta cohortes,
nutantesque virum galeas et sparsa videres
fletibus arma piis. quales ubi tela virosque
530   pectoris impulsu rabidi stravere leones,
protinus ira minor, gaudentque in corpore capto
securam differre famem: sic flexa Pelasgum
corda labant, ferrique avidus mansueverat ardor.
    Ipse etiam ante oculos nunc matris ad oscula versus,

---

509 posce ω: -es P

burn and your brother (why do you look away?), speak to your brother and claim the throne with me now as arbiter. Either he will give it or you will pick up the sword again with a better cause. Or are you afraid of some trick, and that I, your mother, may be in it to deceive you? Not so has all morality fled our unhappy house. If Oedipus were leading you, you would scarce have to fear. I married and gave birth to sin, 'tis true, but I love you both as you are (oh the pain!) and even now excuse your madness. But if you persist, we have brought you, cruel one, a triumph unasked: take your sisters prisoner and bind their hands behind them, lay chains on me. Your father too, who irks you, shall be brought here, no matter how. Now, sons of Inachus, I turn my sorrows to your sense of right. For each of you has left little ones and elders and tears like mine at home. Trust a mother with her flesh and blood. If this young man here is dear to you in so short a time, and I pray he is, what, I beg, befits me, what these breasts, Pelasgi? I should have won this boon from Hyrcanian or Odrysian kings and from those, if such there be, whose madness outdid ours. Consent, or I shall die here with my son in my arms and the war shall survive me.'

Her words soften the proud troops. You might see warriors' helmets nodding and arms scattered with pious tears. As when raging lions by impact of their breasts have strewn men and weapons on the ground, their anger all at once diminishes and they are happy to defer their hunger sure of satisfaction on a captured body: so the hearts of the Pelasgi were turned and waver, their eager passion for battle grew milder.

He himself before their eyes turns to kiss his mother,

535 nunc rudis Ismenes, nunc flebiliora precantis
    Antigones, variaque animum turbante procella
    exciderat regnum: cupit ire, et mitis Adrastus
    non vetat; hic iustae Tydeus memor occupat irae:
    'me potius, socii, qui fidum Eteoclea nuper
540 expertus, nec frater eram, me opponite regi,
    cuius adhuc pacem egregiam et bona foedera gesto
    pectore in hoc. ubi tunc fidei pacisque sequestra
    mater eras, pulchris cum me nox vestra morata est
    hospitiis? nempe haec trahis ad commercia natum.
545 duc illum in campum, vestro qui sanguine pinguis
    spirat adhuc pinguisque meo. tu porro sequeris,
    heu nimium mitis nimiumque oblite tuorum?
    scilicet infestae cum te circum undique dextrae
    nudabunt enses, haec flebit et arma quiescent?
550 tene ille, heu demens, semel intra moenia clausum
    possessumque odiis Argiva in castra remittet?
    ante haec excusso frondescet lancea ferro,
    Inachus ante retro nosterque Achelous abibit.
    sed mite alloquium et saevis pax quaeritur armis:
555 haec quoque castra patent, necdum meruere timeri.
    an suspectus ego? abscedo et mea vulnera dono.
    intret: et hic genetrix eadem mediaeque sorores.
    finge autem pactis evictum excedere regnis,
    nempe iterum reddes?' rursus mutata trahuntur
560 agmina consiliis: subito ceu turbine caeli

---

55 *Rudis* ('pure' Lasueur). Mozley's 'plain of speech' is echoed
by Melville ('blunt Ismene'). But in 253 *rudis Antigone* is 'artless
Antigone.'

56 Probably with a double meaning: 'Your friends' (such as
myself) and 'your kin' (Eteocles,' i.e. his treacherous character).

now innocent[55] Ismene, now Antigone as she entreated
with yet more copious tears. A various tempest confused
his mind and the throne was forgotten. He desires to go,
and gentle Adrastus does not gainsay. Here Tydeus, mindful of just wrath, forestalls: 'Me rather, comrades, that
lately sampled Eteocles' good faith (and I was not his
brother!), set *me* to face the king, whose remarkable peace
and honest covenant I still bear on this breast. Where were
you then, mother, broker of peace and faith, when your
people's night detained me with such splendid hospitality?
Such is the commerce, I suppose, to which you drag your
son. Lead him to the field that still steams fat with your
Theban blood and fat with mine. And you, will you follow?
You are too gentle, too little mindful of your folk.[56] When
all around you hostile hands bare swords, will she weep,
forsooth, and the weapons rest? Will he, O fool, send you
back to the Argive camp once you are shut inside the walls
and in the power of his hate? Sooner shall this lance shake
off its iron and grow leaves, sooner shall Inachus and our
Achelous flow backwards. But gentle converse and peace
to fierce arms is what they seek: well, this camp too is open
and has not yet deserved to be feared. Or am *I* suspect? I
leave, and waive my wounds. Let him come in. Here too
are mother and sisters to mediate, the same. But suppose
him worsted, suppose he vacates the covenanted throne:
will you give it back again?'[57] Once more the army
changes, swayed by his counsel; as with a sudden revolu-

[57] I.e. 'even if Eteocles goes peacefully, the situation will only
repeat itself when it is your turn to retire. Best resolve it once
for all.'

obvius adversum Boreae Notus abstulit aequor.
arma iterum furiaeque placent; fera tempus Erinys
arripit et primae molitur semina pugnae.
     Errabant geminae Dircaea ad flumina tigres,
565 mite iugum, belli quondam vastator Eoi
currus, Erythraeis sed nuper victor ab oris
Liber in Aonios meritas dimiserat agros.
illas turba dei seniorque ex more sacerdos
sanguinis oblitas atque Indum gramen olentes
570 palmite maturo variisque ornare corymbis
curat et alterno maculas interligat ostro.
iamque ipsi colles, ipsa has (quis credat?) amabant
armenta, atque ausae circum mugire iuvencae;
quippe nihil grassata fames: manus obvia pascit,
575 exceptantque cibos fusoque horrenda supinant
ora mero, vaga rure quies; si quando benigno
urbem iniere gradu, domus omnis et omnia sacris
templa calent, ipsumque fides intrasse Lyaeum.
has ubi vipereo tactas ter utramque flagello
580 Eumenis in furias animumque redire priorem
impulit, erumpunt non agnoscentibus agris.
ceu duo diverso pariter si fulmina caelo
rupta cadant longumque trahant per nubila crinem:
non aliter cursu rapidae atque immane frementes
585 transiliunt campos aurigamque impete vasto,
Amphiaraë, tuum (nec defuit omen, eriles
forte is primus equos stagna ad vicina trahebat)

581 argis P *ex* antris, ω (ς, *Bentley*)

tion in the sky South Wind meets North Wind and takes the adverse sea. Once again arms and madness are in favour. The fierce Erinys seizes her moment and sets in place the seeds of battle's beginning.

Two tigresses were straying by Dirce's waters, a gentle pair, once the ravaging chariot of eastern warfare, but lately Liber, victor from Erythraean shores, had discharged them for retirement in Aonian fields. The god's votaries and aged priest care of wont to adorn them, forgetful of bloodshed and fragrant of Indian herbage, with ripe vine shoots and varied clusters, interlacing their markings[58] with bands of purple. And now the very hills, the very herds (who would believe it?) loved them and heifers dared to low around them. For no hunger made them murderous; hands come to feed them, and they take their victuals, wine is poured and they bend back their fearsome heads. Quietly they roam over the countryside and if ever they enter a town with kindly tread, every house and all the temples warm with sacrifice, Lyaeus himself is believed to have come in. The Fury touched each of them thrice with her snaky whip and drove them to return to their mad mood of yore. They break out and the fields know them not; as though two thunderbolts bursting together from the distant sky were falling, dragging their long hair through the clouds. Not otherwise with rapid rush and hideous roar they bound across the plain and with a vast spring seize upon your charioteer, Amphiaraus. Nor lacked an omen, for he first chanced to be leading his master's horses to the nearby pool.[59] Then they attack

[58] Cf. 2.129.   [59] Foreshadowing that Amphiaraus would be first of the Seven to die.

corripiunt; mox Taenarium (qui proximus) Idan
Aetolumque Acamanta premunt: fuga torva per agros
590   cornipedum, visa donec flammatus Aconteus
strage virum, cui sueta feras prosternere virtus
(Arcas erat), densis iam fida ad moenia versas
insequitur telis, multumque hastile resumens
ter, quater adducto per terga, per ilia telo
595   transigit. illae autem longo cum limite fusi
sanguinis ad portas utrimque exstantia ducunt
spicula semianimes, gemituque imitante querelas
saucia dilectis acclinant pectora muris.
templa putes urbemque rapi facibusque nefandis
600   Sidonios ardere lares, sic clamor apertis
exoritur muris; mallent cunabula magni
Herculis aut Semeles thalamum aut penetrale ruisse
Harmoniae. cultor Baccheus Acontea Phegeus
iam vacuum telis geminoque in sanguine ovantem
605   comminus ense petit; subeunt Tegeaea iuventus
auxilio tardi: iam supra sacra ferarum
corpora maerenti iuvenis iacet ultio Baccho.
    Rumpitur et Graium subito per castra tumultu
concilium; fugit exsertos Iocasta per hostes
610   iam non ausa preces; natas ipsamque repellunt
qui modo tam mites, et praeceps tempore Tydeus
utitur: 'ite age, nunc pacem sperate fidemque!

602 tumulum *Gronovius*
609 exertos P: externos ω: erectos *Watt*

---

60 There is a hiatus in the narrative, whether by the poet's fault
or through the loss of a passage telling us how the fighting moved

Taenarian Idas, who came next, and Aetolian Acamas.
Grim was the flight of the horses through the fields, until
Aconteus, whose valour was wont to lay wild beasts low
(he was an Arcadian), inflamed at the sight of slaughtered
men, pursues them as they turn toward their trusty walls
with showers of darts and picking up spear after spear
drives weapons three times and four through their backs
and flanks. With a long trail of streaming blood they bring
bolts standing out on either side to the gates, but half
alive, and uttering groans that sounded human lean their
wounded breasts against the walls they love. You might
think that temples and city were being sacked and
Sidonian homes aflame with wicked torches, such clamour
rises from the opened walls. They had rather the cradle of
great Hercules or Semele's bower or Harmonia's inner
chamber had collapsed. Bacchus' worshipper Phegeus attacks Aconteus, now out of weapons and triumphing in the
couple's blood, with sword face to face. The men of Tegea
come to his rescue, but they are too slow. Already the
young man lies on the sacred bodies of the beasts, avenging Bacchus' sorrow.

The council of the Greeks is interrupted by a sudden
tumult in the camp.[60] Jocasta flees through manifest enemies, no longer daring to entreat. They, lately so gentle,
thrust her and her daughters away and Tydeus is quick to
use his opportunity: 'Go then, hope now for peace and

from the gates of Thebes (606f.) to the Argive camp now under assault. Moreover in 612–14 Tydeus implies that Eteocles knew of
Jocasta's mission and that the attack was a violation of good faith;
in 613 he calls it an atrocity (*nefas*); cf. 505f. The reader has been
told nothing of this, only of Jocasta's setting out (474ff.) (SB[2]).

num saltem differre nefas potuitve morari,
dum genetrix dimissa redit?' sic fatus aperto
615   ense vocat socios. saevus iam clamor et irae
hinc atque inde calent; nullo venit ordine bellum,
confusique duces vulgo, et neglecta regentum
imperia; una equites mixti peditumque catervae
et rapidi currus; premit indigesta ruentes
620   copia, nec sese vacat ostentare nec hostem
noscere. sic subitis Thebana Argivaque pubes
conflixere globis; retro vexilla tubaeque
post tergum et litui bellum invenere secuti.
tantus ab exiguo crudescit sanguine Mavors!
625   ventus uti primas struit intra nubila vires,
lenis adhuc, frondesque et aperta cacumina gestat,
mox rapuit nemus et montes patefecit opacos.

　　Nunc age, Pieriae, non vos longinqua, sorores,
consulimus, vestras acies vestramque referte
630   Aoniam; vidistis enim, dum Marte propinquo
horrent Tyrrhenos Heliconia plectra tumultus.

　　Sidonium Pterelan sonipes male fidus in armis
rumpentem frenos diversa per agmina raptat
iam liber, sic fessa manus. venit hasta per armos
635   Tydeos et laevum iuveni transverberat inguen
labentemque affigit equo. fugit ille perempto

---

624 ab exiguo ω: in ambi- P   625 intra P: inter ω
634 armos ω: ambos P *ante corr.*

---

61 As specified in 585–607.   62 Cf. *OED* diversus 7. But
in 612–23 the fighting is described as a confused melee.

63 The scholiast explains *rumpentem* as 'pulling back, so that
he might be thought (*crederetur*) to be breaking the reins by

good faith! Could he not at least defer the villainy and wait until we let his mother go and she returned?' So saying he draws his sword and summons his comrades. Fierce now the clamour, anger grows hot on either side. The war comes in confusion. Officers are mingled with men, commanders' orders neglected. Horse and foot and swift chariots are mixed up, an indiscriminate horde presses upon them as they run, there is no time to show oneself or to recognize an enemy. Thus the men of Thebes and Argos clash in sudden groupings. Standards and trumpets are in the rear and clarions follow the fighting to find it. So great a battle rages high from so little blood![61] As when the wind builds up early strength within the clouds; gentle still, it carries leaves and open treetops, but then sweeps the forest away and lays bare the shaded hills.

Come now, Pierian sisters, we ask you not of distant doings, tell us of your own warfare, your Aonia. For you saw it, as Helicon's quills shuddered at Tyrrhenian bray, close to the battle.

Sidonian Pterelas' steed betrayed him in the fray, carrying him through the enemy host[62] as he made to break the reins,[63] now out of his control, so weary the driver's hand. Tydeus' spear runs through the horse's[64] shoulders and transfixes the young man's left groin, nailing him to his mount as he falls. The animal flees, pinned to his slain mas-

excessive effort'—which does not go very well with weary hands. What follows too is not easy to decipher.

[64] *Ambos* or *armos*? Hill chooses the former, leaving much in doubt. With *armos* the spear can (with some effort) be routed as entering the horse's right shoulder, just missing the rider, and running through at a downward angle till it emerges in his left groin.

consertus domino, nec iam arma aut frena tenentem
portat adhuc: ceu nondum anima defectus utraque
cum sua Centaurus moriens in terga recumbit.
640 certat opus ferri: sternunt alterna furentes
Hippomedon Sybarin, Pylium Periphanta Menoeceus,
Parthenopaeus Ityn: Sybaris iacet ense cruento,
cuspide trux Periphas, Itys insidiante sagitta.
Caeneos Inachii ferro Mavortius Haemon
645 colla rapit, cui dividuum trans corpus hiantes
truncum oculi quaerunt, animus caput; arma iacentis
iam rapiebat Abas: cornu deprensus Achiva
dimisit moriens clipeum hostilemque suumque.
     Quis tibi Baccheos, Eunaee, relinquere cultus,
650 quis lucos, vetitus quibus emansisse sacerdos,
suasit et assuetum Bromio mutare furorem?
quem terrere queas? clipei penetrabile textum
pallentes hederae Nysaeaque serta coronant,
candida pampineo subnectitur instita pilo,
655 crine latent umeri, crescunt lanugine malae,
et rubet imbellis Tyrio subtemine thorax,
bracchiaque in manicis et pictae vincula plantae
carbaseique sinus, et fibula rasilis auro
Taenariam fulva mordebat iaspide pallam,
660 quam super a tergo velox gorytos et arcus
pendentesque sonant aurata lynce pharetrae.
it lymphante deo media inter milia longum

646 iacentis Pψ: -ti ω

65 For the madness of war. One is tempted to translate *Bromii*,
'the madness of Bromius to which you are accustomed,' but this is
probably a Statian twist.

446

ter, and bears him on though no longer holding shield
or reins, as a Centaur not yet failing of both his lives
sinks dying on his own back. The work of rival steel goes
forward. They rage by turns: Sybaris is brought down
by Hippomedon, Pylian Periphas by Menoeceus, Itys
by Parthenopaeus; Sybaris falls by bloody sword, fierce
Periphas by spear, Itys by treacherous arrow. Mavortian
Haemon sweeps off the neck of Inachian Caeneus with his
blade; across the body's division the gaping eyes seek the
trunk, the spirit seeks the head. Abas was already seiz-
ing his arms as he lay, but caught by an Achaean shaft he
dropped in death his enemy's shield and his own.

Who persuaded you, Eunaeus, to leave Bacchus' worship and the groves away from which his priest must not
pass a night and to change a madness used to Bromius?[65]
Whom could you frighten? Nysaean garlands of pale ivy
wreathe the penetrable texture of your shield and a white
ribbon binds your vine-wood javelin, your shoulders are
hidden by your hair, your cheeks grow with down, your
unwarlike corselet blushes with Tyrian thread, your arms
are sleeved, the sandals on your feet embroidered,[66] you
are swathed in linen, and a smooth golden clasp bites
your Taenarian[67] cloak with a tawny jasper while up at
the back of it clatter a swift bow case[68] and a bow and
hanging quiver of gold-figured lynx hide. Frenzied by the
god, he moves among the thousands crying and crying:

[66] *Pictae* by hypallage (*picta sunt tibi vincula plantae*).

[67] Laconian purples were well known.

[68] Containing a bow that shot swift arrows. But *gorytos* is usually a quiver, as in 4.269 and 9.730.

447

vociferans: 'prohibete manus, haec omine dextro
moenia Cirrhaea monstravit Apollo iuvenca;
665 parcite, in haec ultro scopuli venere volentes.
gens sacrata sumus: gener huic est Iuppiter urbi
Gradivusque socer; Bacchum haud mentimur alumnum
et magnum Alciden.' iactanti talia frustra
turbidus aëria Capaneus occurrit in hasta.
670 qualis ubi primam leo mane cubilibus atris
erexit rabiem et saevo speculatur ab antro
aut cervum aut nondum bellantem fronte iuvencum,
it fremitu gaudens; licet arma gregesque lacessant
venantum, praedam videt et sua vulnera nescit:
675 sic tum congressu Capaneus gavisus iniquo
librabat magna venturam mole cupressum.
ante tamen, 'quid femineis ululatibus,' inquit,
'terrificas, moriture, viros? utinam ipse veniret
cui furis! haec Tyriis cane matribus!' et simul hastam
680 expulit; illa volans, ceu vis non ulla moretur
obvia, vix sonuit clipeo et iam terga reliquit.
arma fluunt, longisque crepat singultibus aurum,
eruptusque sinus vicit cruor. occidis audax,
occidis Aonii puer altera cura Lyaei.
685 marcida te fractis planxerunt Ismara thyrsis,
te Tmolos, te Nysa ferax Theseaque Naxos
et Thebana metu iuratus in orgia Ganges.
    Nec segnem Argolicae sensere Eteoclea turmae,

683 vitiat *Haupt*

---

69 The Delphic oracle told Cadmus to follow the first cow he
saw on leaving the shrine and build a city at the spot where she lay
down.

'Hands off! With fair omen Apollo showed these walls with his Cirrhaean heifer.[69] Spare them; willing rocks came of themselves to make them. We are a hallowed race. Jupiter is son-in-law to this city, Gradivus father-in-law.[70] Bacchus we call our nursling, nor lie, and great Alcides.' As he thus idly boasts, stormy Capaneus confronts him with his sky-scraping spear. As a lion rouses his first fury at daybreak in his dark lair and spies from his grim cavern a stag or a steer with brow not yet for fighting; off he goes joyously roaring, though arms and bands of hunters challenge, sees his prey and knows not of his wounds: so then Capaneus rejoicing in the unequal encounter poises the mighty weight of his cypress for its journey. But before the cast he cries: 'Why do you scare men, doomed wight, with your womanish howls? Would that he whom your madness serves might come himself! Sing your song to Tyrian mothers!' With the words he flung his spear. It flew as though no opposing force might stay it, scarce sounding on the shield before it left the back. His arms drop, the gold rattles with his lengthy sobs, blood breaks out, surpassing his bosom.[71] You die, bold lad, you die, second love of Aonian Lyaeus.[72] Drooping Ismara mourned you with broken wands, and Tmolus and fertile Nysa and Theseus' Naxos and Ganges, pledged by terror to Theban mysteries.

The Argive squadrons found Eteocles no sluggard, but

[70] Through Semele and Harmonia respectively.

[71] I.e. of a deeper red than the cuirass (656) over which it flows (Håkanson).   [72] The first was a boy, Ampelos ('Vine'); cf. Ovid, *Fasti* 3.409–14. So Housman (after Jortin). Otherwise understood of the tigers (cf. 607 *maerenti . . . Baccho*) or of Phegeus (603, which makes no mention of his death); but *cura* is not *dolor*.

449

parcior ad cives Polynicis inhorruit ensis.
690 eminet ante alios iam formidantibus arva
Amphiaraus equis ac multo pulvere vertit
campum indignantem: famulo decus addit inane
maestus et extremos obitus illustrat Apollo.
ille etiam clipeum galeamque incendit honoro
695 sidere; nec tarde fratri, Gradive, dedisti
ne qua manus vatem, ne quid mortalia bello
laedere tela queant: sanctum et venerabile Diti
funus eat. talis medios aufertur in hostes
certus et ipse necis, vires fiducia leti
700 suggerit; inde viro maioraque membra diesque
latior et numquam tanta experientia caeli,
si vacet: avertit morti contermina Virtus.
ardet inexpleto saevi Mavortis amore
et fruitur dextra atque anima flagrante superbit.
705 hicne hominum casus lenire et demere Fatis
iura frequens? quantum subito diversus ab illo
qui tripodas laurusque sequi, qui doctus in omni
nube salutato volucrem cognoscere Phoebo!
innumeram ferro plebem, ceu letifer annus
710 aut iubar adversi grave sideris, immolat umbris
ipse suis: iaculo Phlegyan iaculoque superbum
Phylea, falcato Clonin et Chremetaona curru
comminus hunc stantem metit, hunc a poplite sectum,
cuspide non missa Chromin Iphinoumque Sagenque
715 intonsumque Gyan sacrumque Lycorea Phoebo
(invitus: iam fraxineum demiserat hastae
robur et excussis apparuit infula cristis),

---

73 Editors read *laetior* ignoring *latior* in P. But the heavens expanded because the prophet's eye took in more of them (or would

450

Polynices' blade was more sparing and shuddered to be used against his countrymen. Prominent above the rest is Amphiaraus, though his horses already fear the ground, and turns up the indignant plain in copious dust. Grieving Apollo gives hollow glory to his servant, shedding a splendour on his final passing, firing his shield too and helmet with starry lustre. Nor were you slow, Gradivus, to grant your brother that no hand, no mortal weapon, have power to harm the prophet in the fray; let his death go hallowed, for Dis to reverence. Such is he borne into the midst of the enemy, certain himself of doom; assurance of death gives him strength. Hence his limbs are larger, the daylight wider,[73] never before so ample his survey of heaven—if he but had the time. Valour, close neighbour to death, distracts him. He burns with insatiate love of savage war, revels in his right hand, pride in his fiery soul. Is this he that so often softened human affliction and took their prerogative from the Fates? How different of a sudden from the follower of tripod and laurel, skilled to salute Phoebus and recognize the bird in every cloud! Like a season of plague or the grievous ray of a hostile star, with his steel he immolates a numberless multitude to his own shade. With javelin he slays Phlegyas, with javelin proud Phyleus, with scythed chariot mows down Clonis and Chremetaon (one standing to face him, the other severed from the knee), Chromis with a spear thrust and Iphinous and Sages and unshorn Gyas and Lycoreus sacred to Phoebus (him unwilling; he had already plunged the strength of his ashen spear when the crest was shaken off and the fillet came to

have done if he had had time to observe); see SB[2]. *Tanta* rather than *tanti* is in Statius' manner.

Alcathoum saxo, cui circum stagna Carysti
et domus et coniunx et amantes litora nati.
720   vixerat ille diu pauper scrutator aquarum,
decepit tellus; moriens hiemesque Notosque
laudat et experti meliora pericula ponti.
    Aspicit has longe iamdudum Asopius Hypseus
palantum strages ardetque avertere pugnam,
725   quamquam haud ipse minus curru Tirynthia fundens
robora; sed viso praesens minor augure sanguis:
illum armis animisque cupit. prohibebat iniquo
agmine consertum cunei latus; inde superbus
exseruit patriis electum missile ripis,
730   ac prius: 'Aonidum dives largitor aquarum,
clare Giganteis etiamnum, Asope, favillis,
da numen dextrae: rogat hoc natusque tuique
quercus alumna vadi; fas et me spernere Phoebum,
si tibi collatus divum sator. omnia mergam
735   fontibus arma tuis tristesque sine augure vittas.'
audierat genitor: vetat indulgere volentem
Phoebus, et aurigam iactus detorquet in Hersen.
ille ruit: deus ipse vagis succedit habenis,
Lernaeum falso simulans Haliacmona vultu.
740   tunc vero ardenti non ulla obsistere temptant
signa, ruunt solo terrore, et vulnera citra
mors trepidis ignava venit, dubiumque tuenti
presserit infestos onus impuleritne iugales.
sic ubi nubiferum montis latus aut nova ventis

---

74 Destroyed by Jupiter's thunderbolts; cf. 324–27.
75 The spear.
76 The god's massive body in the chariot (750f.) and the speed

view), Alcathous with a stone, who had home and wife and
shore-loving children by the pools of Carystos. Long had
he lived a poor searcher of the waters; land tricked him,
and in death he praises storms and winds and the kinder
perils of the sea he knew.

This while past Asopian Hypseus views from afar the
carnage of his scattered comrades and is eager to deflect
the battle, although himself in no less measure routing
Tirynthian forces with his chariot. But when he saw the augur, he thought little of bloodshed to hand; him he desires
with weapon and will. A serried wedge of enemy warriors
barred his way. Then proudly he took out a missile culled
from his father's banks, and first: 'Rich donor of Aonian
streams, Asopos, famous yet for ashes as of Giants,[74] give
deity to my right hand. Your son asks this and the oak[75]
nursling of your stream. I too may despise Phoebus if the
Father of the gods was matched with you. I shall sink all
the arms in your waters and the fillets sad without their
augur.' His father heard and would fain have given him
his wish, but Phoebus forbids and turns the cast upon
the charioteer Herses, who plunges; the god himself takes
over the straying reins, simulating Lernaean Haliacmon
with false countenance. Then indeed no standards try to
check his ardent course, they fall from mere fright and a
coward's death without a wound comes to the tremblers.
An onlooker might wonder whether the horses onrushing
were burdened by their load or urged on.[76] So when a
cloudy mountainside is loosened by the winds of a new

of the horses would seem contradictory—was Apollo a load or a
driving force? For *infestis* cf. Livy 25.18.13 *infestis equis con-
currerunt.*

745 solvit hiems aut victa situ non pertulit aetas,
desilit horrendus campo timor, arva virosque
limite non uno longaevaque robora secum
praecipitans, tandemque exhaustus turbine fesso
aut vallem cavat aut medios intercipit amnes.
750 non secus ingentique viro magnoque gravatus
temo deo nunc hoc, nunc illo in sanguine fervet.
ipse sedens telis pariterque ministrat habenis
Delius, ipse docet iactus adversaque flectit
spicula fortunamque hastis venientibus aufert.
755 sternuntur terra Melaneus pedes, Antiphus alto
nil defensus equo, genitusque Heliconide Nympha
Aëtion, caesoque infamis fratre Polites,
conatusque toris vittatam attingere Manto
Lampus: in hunc sacras Phoebus dedit ipse sagittas.
760 et iam cornipedes trepidi ad moribunda reflantes
corpora rimantur terras, omnisque per artus
sulcus et incisis altum rubet orbita membris.
hos iam ignorantes terit impius axis, at illi
vulnere semineces (nec devitare facultas)
765 venturum super ora vident; iam lubrica tabo
frena, nec insisti madidus dat temo, rotaeque
sanguine difficiles, et tardior ungula fossis
visceribus: tunc ipse furens in morte relicta
spicula et e mediis exstantes ossibus hastas
770 avellit, strident animae currumque sequuntur.
    Tandem se famulo summum confessus Apollo
'utere luce tua longamque,' ait, 'indue famam,
dum tibi me iunctum Mors irrevocata veretur.
vincimur: immites scis nulla revolvere Parcas

760 trepidi ac P: -da ac ω (*Hill*)

454

winter or its age fordone by decay can no longer give
support, it leaps down upon the plain, a horrific terror,
sweeping with it fields and men and ancient timber in
more swathes than one; and at last exhausted in its weary
rush either hollows out a valley or blocks rivers in mid flow:
not otherwise does the car, weighed down by huge warrior
and great god, grow hot in blood now here now there. The
Delian himself sits ministering at once with weapons and
reins, himself instructs the casts and turns enemy darts
aside, robbing the spears of fortune as they come. Melaneus on foot is stretched on the ground, as is Antiphus,
whom his tall horse does not defend, and Aëtion, born of
the Nymph Heliconis, and Polites, ill-famed for a brother's
killing, and Lampus, who tried to lie with fillet-bearing
Manto; against him Phoebus himself gave sacred arrows.[77]
And now the horses snort in alarm at dying bodies and sniff
the ground; every furrow runs through limbs, every wheel
track reddens deep with severed members. Some already
unconscious the impious axle grinds, others half-dead
from their wounds see it coming over their faces and have
no power to evade. Now the harness is slippery with gore
and the pole too wet for treading, the wheels are clogged
with blood and the hooves slowed by trampled entrails.
Then he himself madly plucks out darts left in the dead and
spears sticking out of bones; the ghosts screech and pursue
the chariot.

At length Apollo for the last time acknowledges himself
to his servant: 'Use the light you have and take on length of
renown while irrevocable death fears me in your company.
We are overborne. You know that the merciless Parcae

---

[77] Special arrows, not part of the chariot stock? Cf. 752f.

775 stamina; vade diu populis promissa voluptas
Elysiis, certe non perpessure Creontis
imperia aut vetito nudus iaciture sepulcro.'
ille refert contra, et paulum respirat ab armis:
'olim te, Cirrhaee pater, peritura sedentem
780 ad iuga (quis tantus miseris honor?) axe trementi
sensimus; instantes quonam usque morabere manes?
audio iam rapidae cursum Stygis atraque Ditis
flumina tergeminosque mali custodis hiatus.
accipe commissum capiti decus, accipe laurus,
785 quas Erebo deferre nefas. nunc voce suprema,
si qua recessuro debetur gratia vati,
deceptum tibi, Phoebe, larem poenasque nefandae
coniugis et pulchrum nati commendo furorem.'
desiluit maerens lacrimasque avertit Apollo:
790 tunc vero ingemuit currusque orbique iugales.
non aliter caeco nocturni turbine Cauri
scit peritura ratis, cum iam damnata sororis
igne Therapnaei fugerunt carbasa fratres.
    Iamque recessurae paulatim horrescere terrae
795 summaque terga quati graviorque effervere pulvis
coeperat; inferno mugit iam murmure campus.
bella putant trepidi bellique hunc esse fragorem
hortanturque gradus; alius tremor arma virosque
mirantesque inclinat equos. iam frondea nutant
800 culmina, iam muri, ripisque Ismenos apertis
effugit; exciderunt irae, nutantia figunt
tela solo, dubiasque vagi nituntur in hastas

---

78 Apollo knows the future.
79 Alcmaeon. Amphiaraus too sees the future.

never wind back their threads. Go, delight long promised to the people of Elysium. At least you will not suffer Creon's command and lie naked and forbidden burial.'[78] He answers, taking breath awhile from fighting: 'Long have I felt you by the swaying axle, Cirrhaean father, as you sit at the doomed yoke (wherefore such honour to the unfortunate?). How long shall you delay the death at hand? Already I hear the flow of swift Styx, the black rivers of Dis, the triple gape of the evil guardian. Take the laurels committed to adorn my head, which 'twere sacrilege to bring to Erebus, take them. Now with my final utterance, if any grace be due to your departing prophet, Phoebus, I commend to you my cheated hearth and the punishment of my wicked wife and the noble madness of my son.'[79] Apollo leapt down grieving and turned away his tears. Then did the chariot and the orphaned team make moan. Not otherwise does a ship at night in a northwester's blind turmoil know that she will perish when the brethren of Therapnae have fled sails doomed by their sister's fire.[80]

And now the earth began gradually to shiver prior to giving way. The surface quakes and denser dust boils up. Now the plain rumbles with subterranean din. Alarmed the warriors think it is battle, that this is the noise of battle, and urge their steps; a different tremor bends arms and men and marvelling horses. Now the leafy summits nod, now the walls, and Ismenos flees through opening banks. Wrath is forgotten, they fix their nodding weapons in the ground or wandering lean on their unsteady spears as they

[80] Helen's star was considered baneful to shipping, those of her brothers benign; cf. *Silvae* 3.2.8–12 and Pliny, *Natural History* 2.101.

comminus inque vicem viso pallore recedunt.
sic ubi navales miscet super aequora pugnas
805 contempto Bellona mari, si forte benigna
tempestas, sibi quisque cavent, ensesque recondit
mors alia, et socii pacem fecere timores.
talis erat campo belli fluitantis imago.
sive laborantes concepto flamine terrae
810 ventorum rabiem et clausum eiecere furorem,
exedit seu putre solum carpsitque terendo
unda latens, sive hac volventis machina caeli
incubuit, sive omne fretum Neptunia movit
cuspis et extremas gravius mare torsit in oras,
815 seu vati datus ille fragor, seu terra minata est
fratribus: ecce alte praeceps humus ore profundo
dissilit, inque vicem timuerunt sidera et umbrae.
illum ingens haurit specus et transire parantes
mergit equos; non arma manu, non frena remisit:
820 sicut erat, rectos defert in Tartara currus,
respexitque cadens caelum, campumque coire
ingemuit, donec levior distantia rursus
miscuit arva tremor lucemque exclusit Averno.

come face to face and both draw back seeing each other's pallor. So when Bellona mingles naval battles on the waters, contemning the sea, if a kindly[81] storm arises, each looks to himself and a different death sheathes their swords and shared fears make peace. Such was the picture of wavering war upon the plain. Did the earth in labour with wind in her womb expel a raging blast, a prisoned fury? Or did hidden water erode the crumbling soil and sap it by abrasion? Or did the fabric of the rolling sky bear down this way? Or did Neptune's spear move all the sea and hurl a heavier ocean upon the fringing coasts? Or was that commotion for the prophet's sake? Or did earth threaten the brothers? See, the ground becomes a precipice, springing asunder in a deep chasm, stars and shades fear in turn. Him a huge cavern swallows, sinking the horses as they are about to cross. He did not let the arms go from his hand or the reins. As he was, he brought the chariot upright down to Tartarus and falling looked back at the sky and groaned to see the plain meet, until a fainter tremor mingled again the sundered fields and shut off the daylight from Avernus.

[81] Because it interrupts the fighting.

D1207227

PROGRAMMABLE
LOGIC CONTROLLERS

James A. Rehg • Glenn J. Sartori

IN PARTNERSHIP WITH THE NJATC

Taken from:
Programmable Logic Controllers
by James A. Rehg and Glenn J. Sartori

PEARSON
Custom
Publishing

PEARSON
Prentice
Hall

Cover image courtesy of Jim Pickerell/Jupiter Images

Taken from:

Programmable Logic Controllers
by James A. Rehg and Glenn J. Sartori
Copyright © 2007 by Prentice-Hall, Inc.
A Pearson Education Company
Upper Saddle River, New Jersey 07458

This special edition published in cooperation with Pearson Custom Publishing.

Printed in the United States of America

10 9 8 7 6 5 4 3 2 1

ISBN 0-536-39651-5

2007520004

EM/MJ

Please visit our web site at *www.pearsoncustom.com*

PEARSON CUSTOM PUBLISHING
501 Boylston Street, Suite 900, Boston, MA 02116
A Pearson Education Company

Preface

INTRODUCTION

The 1970s witnessed the birth of two types of computers that changed the world and the way business is conducted. The Apple II, introduced in 1976, was the world's first widely used micro-computer. Today's multibillion-dollar personal computer industry is an outgrowth of this small computer company started by two young entre-preneurs in a garage.

The second computer, created in 1972 by Richard Morley and now called a *programmable logic controller* (PLC), does not have the instant name recognition of the personal computer, but it has had an equally significant impact in man-ufacturing. The PLC is often called the personal computer for the factory floor.

PLCs are the de facto standard used to control automation systems in every industry across the globe. Control applications range from a single machine to an entire production facility with pro-cesses that have both analog and discrete con-trol requirements. This textbook addresses the application, operation, programming, and trou-bleshooting of PLCs used in automation and con-trol applications.

IMPORTANT FEATURES

The text has the following salient features:

- The text is divided into two parts. Part 1, Chapters 1 through 9, introduces the reader to fundamental PLC concepts and the basic operation and programming format for the commonly used instructions in most PLC applications. If you learn the instructions in Part 1 you will be able to program and inter-pret 90 percent of the ladder rungs used in automation control. Part 2, Chapters 10 through 17, addresses the advanced instruc-tions, covers four of the languages (Ladder Diagram, Function Block, Sequential Function Chart, and Structured Text) in the IEC 61131 PLC standard, and provides a practical intro-duction to industrial networks. Goals and learning objectives are provided at the begin-ning of every chapter.
- The presentation format includes a descrip-tion of programming and PLC instructions for all three Allen-Bradley PLCs, PLC 5, SLC 500, and ControlLogix, with the SLC 500 system used most often in the example problems.

- Standard ladder logic building blocks are developed for PLC instructions in Chapters 4 through 11, 13, 15, and 16. The standards start with a description of the automation control requirement and then present the ladder rung options used for a solution. Example problems show how these standard rungs are grouped for a total automation solution.
- The operation and programming for two generations of PLC software—rack/slot-based addressing and variable- or tag-based addressing systems—is discussed.
- Text content is sequenced to support a laboratory with a class lecture.
- Laboratory exercises are provided at the Prentice Hall Web site *www.prenhall.com*. To access supplementary materials online, instructors need to request an instructor access code. Go to *www.prenhall.com*, click the Instructor Resource Center link, and then click Register Today for an instructor access code. Within 48 hours after registering, you will receive a confirming e-mail including an instructor access code. Once you have received your code, go to the site and log on for full instructions on downloading the materials you wish to use.
- Troubleshooting is integrated into every chapter.
- The text is written in a direct, clear, and easy-to-read style that is designed for students with no prior PLC experience.
- Real-world control problems are used in illustrated programming examples.
- A pneumatic robot material handler and a process tank control problem are used in Chapters 3, 4, 7, 11, 13, 15, and 16 to illustrate PLC control of a sequential machine and process system. The control solution for each problem changes as new PLC instructions are introduced in the chapters.
- The text includes a generous number of example problems at varying levels of difficulty and a large number of descriptive figures.
- A CD-ROM with reference material from Allen-Bradley is provided with the text.
- The text content and organization permits teachers to adjust the chapter sequence to fit a current syllabus.
- A glossary of terms is provided in an appendix.
- A description of the five IEC 61131 programming languages with detailed coverage of the four supported in Allen-Bradley PLCs is given.

FOR THE STUDENTS

An increasing number of graduates of engineering and engineering technology programs are working in manufacturing automation because production systems have become increasingly complex and highly automated. As a result, students need to understand the theory and operation of PLCs used in the control of production systems. Our primary goal for this book is to create a clear and comprehensive text for students to use to learn programmable logic controllers. Every effort is made to present the material in a logical order, to express the concepts in a writing style that a first-time user of PLCs can understand, and to keep the needs of the student foremost in every part of the text development. Texts often include technical terms when describing new concepts that have not been previously defined or that are not common knowledge for the students. A special effort is made in this text not to use any term or technical language that is not introduced or defined earlier in the text.

In addition, the text is written as both a learning tool and as a future reference resource. If you work in automation, you will have to use PLCs or PLC-like controllers. The information presented in the text describes PLCs clearly for the student learner, and the broad coverage of topics serves as an ideal resource when the student graduate is working with industrial controls.

STUDENT CD-ROM INCLUDED WITH TEXT

The text comes with a student CD-ROM with valuable resources for learning to operate and program programmable logic controllers. Reference material from Allen-Bradley is included on the

CD-ROM. The material provides quick access to technical data related to Allen-Bradley PLCs.

The text integrates all three of the Allen-Bradley PLC processors (PLC 5, SLC 500, and ControlLogix) throughout the text. The SLC 500, however, is used for the majority of the examples and is the processor described when an instruction operates in the same way in all three processors. When operation differs for the three processors or where different instructions are present, each process is covered in a separate section. Because the operation of the PLC 5 is similar to the SLC 500 in many cases, these two are frequently covered in the same section. However, the chapter organization permits an instructor to separate the SLC 500 and PLC 5 processors from the ControlLogix if the course requires just one type of PLC content.

The text is organized in two parts. Part 1 introduces PLCs and covers in detail the programming instructions used to write a large number of the PLC programs used in industry. Part 2 is written to support additional topics in an introductory course, a second course in PLCs, or an advanced PLC offering as illustrated in the previous table.

VENDOR RESOURCES OR A PLC TEXTBOOK?

A review of PLC texts indicates that many add little new information from what is available online directly from the vendors that manufacture the devices. Vendor reference and resource material is a valuable aid to the PLC application engineer or technician when device-specific information is needed. This text is designed to complement vendor resources by providing concepts and content not provided by the vendors. For example, thirteen of the chapters have standard application solutions for instructions with comments on how an instruction can be used most effectively. In addition, information on troubleshooting and programming not provided by the vendors is included.

The writing style of this text differs from the industry material as well. Industry resources are written for an industry audience and assume a certain minimum knowledge base on the subject.

This text makes no such assumption and describes the technology so that students can learn PLCs with no previous experience in PLCs or discrete and analog system control. The text does make good use of vendor resources so that students learn how to use the material, which will be their source of PLC information in the future.

CHAPTER CONTENT

Part 1, titled *Programmable Logic Controller—Fundamental Concepts*, includes nine chapters written to support a first course in programmable logic controllers. Chapter 1 and all subsequent chapters start with chapter goals and objectives. In addition, this chapter defines a PLC and covers a brief history of PLCs, a description of the system and components, an introduction to vendor systems, a description of PLC types and types of input and output modules, and a comparison between relay ladder logic and PLC ladder logic. Every chapter ends with general chapter questions, Web and data sheet questions, and problems divided into general, PLC 5, SLC 500, ControlLogix, and challenge groups.

Chapter 2 focuses on discrete input devices and output actuators and describes the operation of the most frequently used input devices and output actuators in automation control systems. Devices covered include manual and mechanically operated switches, transducers and sensors including proximity and photoelectric devices, interfacing switches and sensors, input wiring, field device current sourcing and current sinking concepts, electromagnetic output and solenoid-controlled devices, control relays, contactors, motor starters, pilot lights, alarms, interfacing output devices, and output wiring.

Chapter 3 covers an introduction to PLC programming with the following topics: decimal, octal, and binary number systems, ladder logic fundamentals, addressing rack/slot and tag-based systems, examine if closed and examine if open inputs selection and applications, retentive and non-retentive coil outputs, virtual or internal relays, scan time, multiple inputs, standard input logic, sealing contacts, multiple outputs, latched outputs, and using internal memory bits. In

addition, empirical program design is introduced along with programming devices and software. Troubleshooting techniques for PLC-controlled systems and program design are also covered.

Chapter 4 covers programming timers, and the standard ladder logic used for timers. Topics include mechanical and electronic timing relays, and PLC timer instructions, such as on-delay timers, off-delay timers, retentive timers, and the reset instruction. In addition, cascaded timers, empirical design of timer ladders, and troubleshooting of timer ladders and input/output modules are addressed. The use of timers in pneumatic robot control is also described.

Chapter 5 describes the counter function present in PLCs, and the standard ladder logic used for counters. Topics include counter instructions, such as up counters, down counters, up/down counters, and cascade counters; using counter output bits; programming counter instructions; and counter applications. In addition, the reset instruction and one-shot function are covered along with programming and application issues.

Chapter 6 focuses on arithmetic and move instructions available in the PLC instruction set, and the standard ladder logic used for these instructions. Topics include instructions and format for addition, subtraction, multiplication, division, square root, and move instructions; programming these instructions; and application of math and move instructions.

Chapter 7 describes the binary-coded decimal (BCD) and the hexadecimal numbering systems and covers the conversion and comparison instructions. In addition, the standard ladder logic used for these instructions is covered. The instructions for converting to and from BCD numbers are presented. The comparison instructions covered include equal to, not equal to, less than, greater than, less than or equal to, and greater than or equal to. In addition, programming and application of the comparison instructions are addressed.

Chapter 8 focuses on instructions that change the flow of the program execution and covers some special-purpose instructions. In addition, the standard ladder logic used for these instructions is covered. The program flow instructions described include master control and zone control instructions, jump instructions, subroutines, and immediate input and output instructions. In addition, the clear instruction is covered along with programming and application issues.

Chapter 9 is the last chapter in Part 1 of the text. The addressing modes discussed include direct, indirect, indexed, and indexed indirect. Typical applications for the addressing modes are included to indicate how each mode is used.

Part 2 of the text, titled *Advanced PLC Instructions and Applications*, includes Chapters 10 through 17. The content of Part 2 could be used selectively to enhance a first course in PLCs or it could be used for a second, more advanced PLC offering.

Chapter 10 covers instructions related to data handling and shift register applications. In addition, the standard ladder logic used for these instructions is covered. Topics include the copy and fill instructions, the FIFO, LIFO, and FAL functions, bit patterns in a register, changing a register bit status, shift register functions, programming FIFO, LIFO, and shift register instructions.

Chapter 11 addresses the programming and operation of PLC sequencers, and the standard ladder logic used for sequencers. Topics include electromechanical sequencing, the basic PLC sequencer function, PLC sequencer with timing, cascading sequencers, and programming applications for the sequencer function.

Chapter 12 covers analog PLC applications. The concepts covered include analog sensors and actuators, types of PLC analog modules and systems, PLC analog input and output data, programming analog instructions, and analog applications.

Chapter 13 introduces the first of the new IEC 61131 programming languages, Function Block Diagram (FBD). The Allen-Bradley FBD instruction format is used in the description, which includes programming examples and application information. In addition, the standard ladder logic used for these instructions is covered.

Chapter 14 describes how the analog principles from Chapter 12 and FBD instructions from Chapter 13 are applied to the control of on-off

and continuous processes. The topics include on-off control, two-position control, floating control, PID principles, fuzzy logic, and programming the PID function.

Chapter 15 introduces the second of the new IEC 61131 programming languages, Structured Text (ST). The Allen-Bradley ST instruction format is used in the description, which includes programming examples and application information. In addition, the standard ladder logic used for these instructions is covered.

Chapter 16 introduces the third of the new IEC 61131 programming languages, Sequential Function Chart (SFC). The Allen-Bradley instruction format is used in the description, which includes programming examples and application information.

Chapter 17 addresses industrial networks and distributive control. The network topics include PLC network architecture, Ethernet/IP, DeviceNet, ControlNet, remote I/O, Data Highway Plus, DH 485, Modbus, and Profibus. In addition, wireless networks and the human-machine interface (HMI) are covered.

ACKNOWLEDGMENTS

The authors would like to thank the many people that helped to make this text possible. First we want to thank the following individuals from industry who supplied valuable content oversight and application information. The industry participants included Don Cox and Dave Mayewski.

We would also like to acknowledge the support received from Allen-Bradley for software and systems that permitted us to verify the code presented in the text. A special thanks to John Sjolander for assistance above and beyond the call of duty.

We would like to thank Kate Linsner, Lara Dimmick, and Rex Davidson at Prentice Hall, and Jean Findley at Custom Editorial Productions. Thanks to Marci Rehg for copy editing. A special thanks to the reviewers that provided valuable feedback and suggestions to improve the content, chapter sequences, and concepts that should be modified and added. The reviewers include:

* Tom Cunningham, Baker College, Owosso
* Daniel Green, Sinclair Community College
* Sam Guccione, Eastern Illinois University
* Gregory Harstine, Stark State College of Technology
* Jude Pearse, University of Maine
* Eduard Plett, Kansas State University
* Dave Setser, Johnson County Community College
* Cree Stout, York Technical College
* Ken Swayne, Pelissippi State Technical Community College
* Marc Timmerman, Oregon Institute of Technology
* Edward Troyan, Lehigh Carbon Community College

In addition, we want to thank the teachers, staff, and students at Penn State Altoona for helping us understand how PLCs should be taught and learned.

Finally, we would like to thank you for adopting the text for your class and for providing us feedback on what you see as beneficial changes to the content and sequencing of the material. We invite you to email us with your comments and suggestions.

James A. Rehg (james@rehg.org)
Glenn J. Sartori (rg492@sbcglobal.net)

Contents

Dedicated to my wonderful wife Marci, my sons James and Richard, their loving wives Dorothy and Lorri, and my delightful grandchildren. Also to the thousands of students whose insightful questions have taught me so much during my 39 years in the classroom.

—James Rehg

Dedicated to my family: my loving wife Rosanne and her sister Chris, who are two of my biggest cheerleaders. And to my two sons Michael and Jeffrey, who with their thriving families offer me loving support.

—Glenn Sartori

Programmable Logic Controllers— Fundamental Concepts

GOAL

The goal for the first half of the text is to introduce you to the fundamental concepts associated with the operation and programming of programmable logic controllers (PLCs). In every programming language a large percentage of the programs developed use a small subset of the language instructions and functions available in the language. Therefore, the goal of Part 1, Chapters 1 through 9, is for you to master the instructions and formats used most frequently in PLC program development, thus preparing you to write control programs for a large number of automation control applications.

OBJECTIVES

After completing Part 1 you should be able to:

- Identify a PLC and have an appreciation for the history behind the technology.
- Identify and interface standard automation control input and output devices to PLC input and output modules.
- Use data in and convert data between the following number systems: binary, octal, decimal, binary-coded decimal, and hexadecimal.
- Write automation control programs using instructions from the following categories: inputs, outputs, timers, counters, arithmetic and move operations, comparison operations, program control, and data addressing modes.

CAREER INSIGHT

The following career insight provides some information on the careers available to students who master the content of Part 1 of the text. Read the career insight to get a general feel for the career opportunities in PLCs. If you enjoy the technology and problems covered in Part 1, then there are numerous career paths that you can follow in the PLC area.

There are many opportunities associated with programmable logic controllers (PLC). The PLC has become the de facto standard for control of discrete industrial processes, and is moving into the process control areas as well. On the factory floor the PLC plays the same role that the microcomputer has in the office, namely a program-controlled device for problem solution. The PLC has both a hardware and software component, so both aspects of the machine must be addressed for a successful solution. Therefore, there are opportunities on both the hardware and software sides of this technology.

From the hardware viewpoint, you could work for PLC vendors in jobs ranging from designing new hardware to interfacing with customers in a technical sales capacity. You could work for automation vendors who represent the PLC manufacturers and provide design and technical sales assistance to the end users. Numerous additional opportunities exist at system houses (companies that design automation systems for end users) where the complete design of an automation system is performed, including the integration of a PLC for control.

Every hardware solution demands a software solution as well. PLC programmers are required from PLC vendors to end users. The PLC vendors, automation vendors, system houses, and end users all must employ PLC programmers to either develop new programs or maintain existing programs. At present the programming is primarily ladder logic, but as the new programming

languages defined in the IEC 61131 PLC standard are embraced, the programming will include five different programming options. The skills needed for this new standard are similar to the skills needed to learn and use high-level text-based languages, such as C+, or graphic languages, such as LabView.

The opportunities are numerous for individuals who have mastered the PLC technology. Students who like the programming aspect of the device can find careers that are focused primarily on programming. Students with an interest in hardware can find jobs that are focused primarily on that area of PLCs. Finally, there are opportunities that require an integration of both the hardware and software sides. If you enjoy this technology, it is a wonderful and rewarding career area.

CHAPTER 1

Introduction to Programmable Logic Controllers

1-1 GOALS AND OBJECTIVES

Chapters 1, 2, and 3 introduce the reader to the programmable logic controller (PLC) technology and the industrial control devices used in automation. As a result, you will find that these chapters cover numerous concepts that prepare the reader for the specific PLC instructions that begin in Chapter 4. The first three chapter's topics are varied, but they all focus on an understanding of the hardware and software in a PLC system. Therefore, the primary goal of this chapter is to introduce programmable logic controllers (PLC) to the student who has no knowledge of this technology. A secondary goal is to show how PLCs fit into the general control needs present in automation.

After completing this chapter you should be able to:

- Write the definition of a PLC.
- Describe the similarities and differences between PLC ladder logic and relay ladder logic.
- Describe the function of all of the component parts of a PLC system.
- Describe the difference between programmable logic controllers and personal computers.

- Define the three types of PLCs currently available: rack/slot address-based, tag-based, and soft PLCs.
- Draw a PLC input and output interface for a typical application.
- Create a simple ladder logic program.
- Describe the electrical safety issues associated with working on PLC systems and the actions to take for an electrical shock victim.

1-2 THE PLC INDUSTRY TODAY

Dick Morley conceived the programmable controller on January 1, 1968. When his new company, Modicon, installed the first model 084 PLC at the Oldsmobile Division of General Motors Corporation and the Landis Company in Landis, Pennsylvania, in 1970, the PLC evolution began. Today the 6.5 billion dollar PLC business is growing at 20 percent per year; however, few people beyond those working in manufacturing automation know it exists. The PLC has been a strong silent partner in promoting manufacturing automation around the globe. A search of the Thomas Register, an online automation manufacturers data base, found 110 listings under the heading of programmable controller vendors, and over 1000 vendors

offering PLC add-in boards and other peripherals. In addition, over 2000 companies are developing PLC solutions. This industrial strength microcomputer controls a wide variety of industrial processes, from automobile assembly to stamping out Oreo cookies. The study of PLCs begins with definitions of a programmable logic controller.

1-2-1 PLC Definitions
PLCs are defined as follows:

PLCs are special-purpose industrial computers designed for use in the control of a wide variety of manufacturing machines and systems.

Or

A PLC is a specialized electronic device based on one or more microprocessors that is used to control industrial machinery.

The definitions state that PLCs are industrial computers, where the term "industrial" implies that PLCs are computers designed to operate in the harsh physical and electrical noise environments present in production plants. They are also specialized electronic devices, so they are not just personal computers that have been moved to the factory floor. Figure 1-1 provides a look at several configurations of Allen-Bradley's Logix systems.

PLC control applications vary from the on/off control of a pump motor using a liquid level switch to control of a conveyor system used to sort packages based upon destination zip codes. Because PLCs are computers, they must be programmed using a programming language. Although most PLCs in the United States use a vendor-specific programming language, called *ladder logic*, there are five standard programming languages that are available for programming new applications.

In 1979 the International Electrotechnical Commission (IEC) established a working group to look at the standardization of PLCs. The PLC standard, called IEC 1131 (changed later to IEC 61131), has six parts. Part 3 is of most interest for this text and is the one that defines the following new languages present in the standard.

- Ladder Diagrams (LD)
- Function Block Diagrams (FBD)
- Structured Text (ST)
- Instruction List (IL)
- Sequential Function Charts (SFC)

The PLC language preferences in specific countries is quite varied. Developers in Europe and Asia, for example, embrace a variety of PLC

FIGURE 1-1: Allen-Bradley Logix systems.

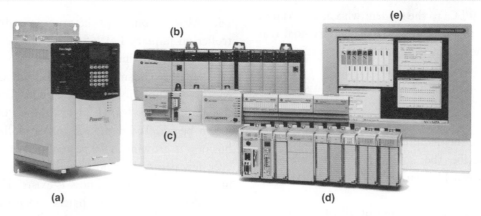

(a) DriveLogix
(b) ControlLogix
(c) FlexLogix
(d) CompactLogix
(e) SoftLogix

Courtesy of Rockwell Automation, Inc.

languages compared to the U.S. market, where ladder logic is used most often. In some applications, such as process and motion control, function block diagrams are used, and in some sequential machine control the SFC language is used. Allen-Bradley, the most commonly used PLC vendor in the United States, offers ladder logic, function block diagrams, sequential function charts, and structured text. These new languages are addressed fully in Part 2 of the text. However, in Part 1, ladder logic is used for the introduction to PLCs.

The reader may notice a similarity between the definition of a PLC and the operation of the personal computer used in offices and homes. The differences between these two technologies are addressed in the next section.

1-2-2 PC versus PLC

The original design for the programmable logic controller was called a *programmable controller*, or PC. The PC abbreviation caused no confusion until the personal computer became widely used and also adopted the PC abbreviation. To avoid confusion, the programmable controller industry added the word *logic* in the title, producing the new term *programmable logic controller*, or PLC. To avoid confusion, this text uses the term programmable logic controller, or PLC. The abbreviation PC will refer to a personal computer.

The PC and PLC have some things in common and many things that make them different. The architecture of the PC and PLC systems are similar, with both featuring a *motherboard*, *processor*, *memory*, and *expansion slots*. Figure 1-2 illustrates the PLC's *central processing unit* (CPU) composed of a microprocessor, often an 8051 integrated circuit, and the computer-type architecture. The PLC processor has a *microprocessor* chip linked to *memory* and *I/O* (input/output) chips through parallel *address*, *data*, and *control* buses. Generally, PLCs do not have removable or fixed storage media such as floppy and hard disk drives, but they do have solid-state memory to store programs. PLCs do not have a monitor, but a human machine interface (HMI) flat screen display is often used to show process or production machine status. PCs do many jobs in homes and offices, but PLCs

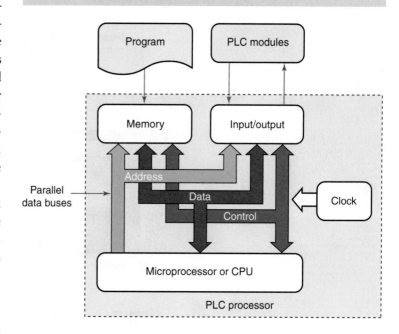

FIGURE 1-2: Processor architecture for PLC.

perform only one task, the control of manufacturing machines and processes.

Will PC and PLC technologies converge? According to vendors such as Allen-Bradley and Siemens the answer is someday, but the PC will never replace the PLC. PCs are performing PLC-type control in some applications using software, such as SoftLogic, that allows the PC to simulate the actions of a PLC. Technical differences notwithstanding, the PC and PLC industries are beginning to look more alike; and in manufacturing automation, both are replacing relay ladder logic.

1-3 RELAY LADDER LOGIC

Industrial automation began with relays used to control the sequence of operations in machines. These sequential control systems, called *relay ladder logic,* were the control standard for industry. The early PLCs were designed to eliminate the relay logic used for sequential control applications. To understand how PLCs accomplished this task, it is important to understand the operation of relays and relay ladder logic. Figure 1-3 illustrates five types of relays and identifies all of the parts of this electromechanical device.

FIGURE 1-3: Electromechanical relays.

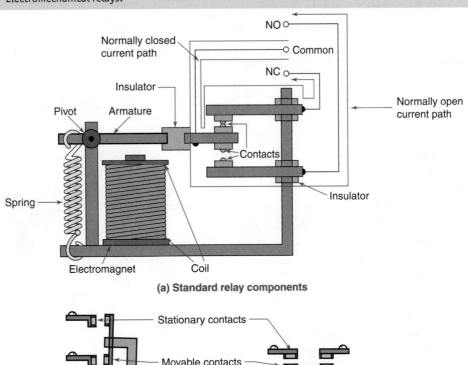

NO

Normally closed
current path

Common

Insulator

NC

Pivot   Armature

Normally open
current path

Contacts

Spring

Insulator

Electromagnet   Coil

(a) Standard relay components

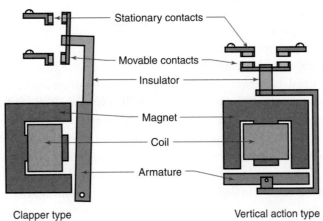

Stationary contacts

Movable contacts

Insulator

Magnet

Coil

Armature

Clapper type   Vertical action type

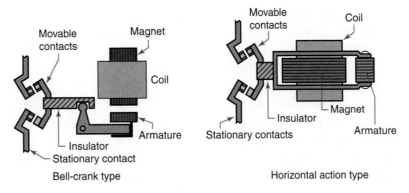

Movable
contacts   Magnet

Coil

Movable
contacts   Coil

Armature   Magnet

Insulator   Insulator   Armature

Stationary contact   Stationary contacts

Bell-crank type   Horizontal action type

(b) Relay configurations

Source: Kraebber and Rehg, Computer Integrated Manufacturing, *Third Edition, © 2005, p. 503, reprint by permission of Prentice Hall, Upper Saddle River, NJ; and Rehg and Sartori,* Industrial Electronics, *First Edition, © 2006, p. 69, reprinted by permission of Prentice Hall, Upper Saddle River, NJ.*

FIGURE 1-4: Relay.

Courtesy of Square D/Schneider Electric.

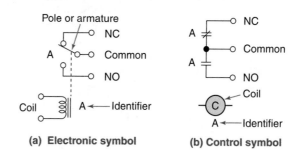

(a) Electronic symbol   **(b) Control symbol**

1-3-1 Electromagnetic Relay

Joseph Henry, developer of the electromagnet in 1831, built the first relay-type device in 1836. After nearly 170 years of service, the relay illustrated in Figure 1-3(a) still has the same three components:

1. The *electromagnet* is a magnet, which is created by passing a current through wire wound around a steel core.
2. The *armature*, called a *clapper*, is a hinged metal plate that is pulled toward the coil by the electromagnet when the coil is energized and pulled away from the coil by the spring when the coil is de-energized.
3. The *contacts*, which create one electrical path through the *normally closed* (NC) contacts when the coil is not energized (armature up) and a second path through the *normally open* (NO) contacts when the coil is energized (armature down).

This *single pole double throw* (SPDT) configuration in Figure 1-3(a) has one common contact (*single pole* or *armature*) and two positions (NC and NO) called *throws*. When the coil is not energized, the spring holds the armature in the up position (pulls down on the opposite side of the pivot point). In this position a near zero resistance connection is established between the common armature contact and the NC contact. When the coil is energized, the armature pivots down so contact with the NC contact is broken.

In this position, a near zero resistance connection is established between the common armature contact and the NO contact. *Insulators* are used in the armature to isolate the electrical switching contacts of the relay from the rest of the relay components. Figure 1-3(b) shows four other relays with a *single pole single throw* (SPST) relay configuration.

Figure 1-4 shows a Square D relay with contacts like the vertical action in Figure 1-3. Figure 1-5 illustrates two different schematic representations for the relays in Figures 1-3 and 1-4. The relay contact symbols used for electronic circuit schematics are often different from those used in control-type schematics.

Compare the NO and NC conduction paths in Figure 1-3(a) with the electronic and control schematics in Figure 1-5(b). The NO contact symbol has two parallel lines, indicating an open circuit, and the NC symbol has the same two parallel lines with a line across them to indicate closed contacts.

Relays are available in a variety of sizes with a number of contact configurations. Figure 1-6(a) illustrates a SPST relay with the electronic (left) and control symbol (right). Figures 1-6(b) and (c) illustrate symbols for a *two pole double throw* (2PDT) and a *three pole double throw* (3PDT) device. The relay symbols in Figure 1-6(b) identify a device with double break contacts that does not have a common pole for the NC and NO contacts. All four of the relays in Figure 1-3(b) have this *double break* contact configuration. The terms *double*

FIGURE 1-6: Relays with multiple poles and throws.

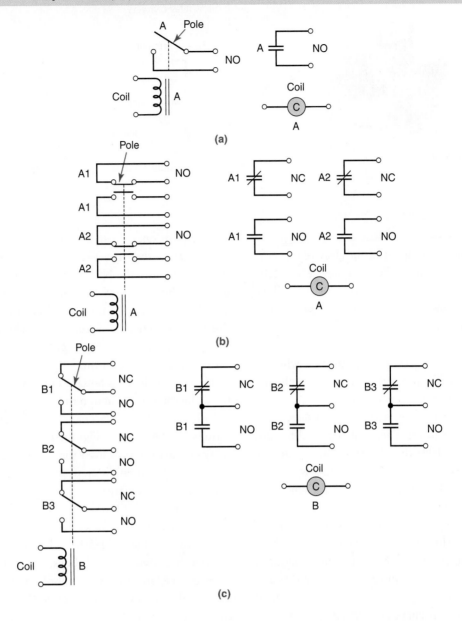

(a)

(b)

(c)

pole and *triple pole* are often used instead of two pole and three pole, respectively. The dashed lines indicate that the relay coil activates *all* sets of NO and NC contacts in unison. With the operation of the relay established, a relay control circuit example is used to introduce basic sequential logic control.

1-3-2 Relay Control Systems

To illustrate how relays are used in machine control, consider the following simple control problem. A tank, illustrated in Figure 1-7(a), is filled through an electrically operated valve and emptied by a motor-driven pump. Control of the valve and pump must satisfy the following logic:

1. The pump can operate only when the input valve to the tank is open.
2. The input valve can be opened when the pump is either operating or not operating.

The *electronic schematic* in Figure 1-7(b) illustrates a solution to the control problem. The same solution is represented in Figure 1-7(c)

FIGURE 1-7: Process tank control systems.

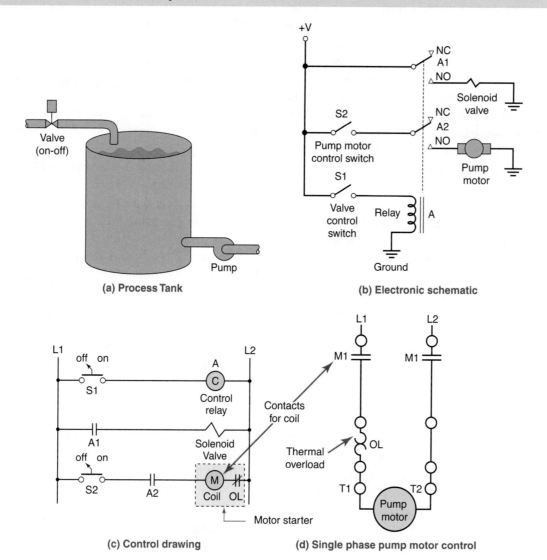

(a) Process Tank

(b) Electronic schematic

(c) Control drawing

(d) Single phase pump motor control

using control schematic symbols in a control drawing. The control drawing is also called a *relay ladder logic diagram* or a *two-wire diagram*. Let S1 close and verify that the outputs in both schematics satisfy the logic required for this control problem. Next, change S2 from open to close and note how the outputs react.

The circuits work as follows:

1. Switch S1 is closed manually and causes the electromagnetic relay A to be energized.
2. When the relay is energized in Figure 1-7(b), the A1 and A2 poles move from the normally closed (NC) positions to the normally open (NO) positions. In Figure

1-7(c), A1 and A2 contacts are closed and power flow results.
3. In Figure 1-7(c), the change in contact A1 energizes the input valve and allows liquid to flow into the tank.
4. The change in contact A2 causes no immediate action.
5. Switch S2 is closed manually and causes the pump to operate.

For the pump to operate when the pump switch is activated, the NO relay contact A2 has to close. If the valve switch S1 is opened manually while the pump is operating, the pump motor stops because the relay is not energized (The NO contacts no longer have power flow).

The control diagram in Figure 1-7(c) provides the same control as the circuit in Figure 1-7(b) but it uses control-type symbols for the components in a configuration called a *relay ladder logic diagram*. It is called this because it uses relays, looks like a ladder, and satisfies the logic control requirements specified for control of the output device. Standard control drawing symbols are used to represent the different input and output devices, such as mechanical switches, sensors, magnetic contactors and relays, and electrical contacts.

These diagrams have a vertical line at the left (marked L1) and right (marked L2) sides. The left vertical line, sometimes called the *left power rail*, usually represents the positive, hot, or high side of the power source; the right vertical line, called the *right power rail*, represents the power return, neutral, or ground. All the circuits containing the switches, sensors, and output actuators used to operate a machine are drawn between these two vertical lines. These types of drawings are sometimes called *two-wire* or *three-wire diagrams*; however, this is an older description and the relay ladder logic identification is a better choice.

In Figure 1-7(b) the motor is connected directly to the switch and relay contacts, but this is only done in industrial control applications when a small factional horsepower motor is used. The control schematic, Figure 1-7(c), indicates the preferred solution, which is to use a specialpurpose motor relay (identified with an M), called a *motor starter*, to switch the power for the pump motor. Starters can switch the high voltage and current associated with large motors. Figure 1-7(d) shows the starter's normally open M1 contacts in the motor power lines. There is one set of *overload*, OL, contacts to protect the motor. The thermal overloads are drawn between the contacts and the motor in Figure 1-7(d), and the starter overloads are shown in the ladder rung between the coil (M) and the L2 power rail. By convention, only one OL contact is shown in the rung, but there would be a contact for every overload relay. Later in this chapter this relay ladder is converted to a PLC solution; however, some PLC terminology and basic operation must be covered first. This preparation for PLC program development starts in the next section with the elements of a PLC system and components used.

1-4 PLC SYSTEM AND COMPONENTS

Figure 1-8 illustrates and names the many modules in the block diagram for a PLC system. These components and modules are described in Sections 1-4-1 through 1-4-6, and the PLC system diagram in Figure 1-8 is referenced often in these sections. Put a bookmark at this figure's page for ease in flipping back to the PLC block diagram.

The heart of the PLC is the PLC processor. The processor is surrounded by input modules on the left, output modules on the right, and a power supply above. Programming is performed by either a handheld programmer, by a directly connected personal computer, or through a computer with a network connection. The processor communicates with input and output devices through input and output modules. Note the variety of input and output devices that interface with the input and output modules (see Figure 1-12).

The processor frequently interfaces with a variety of local area networks (LANs), with the most commonly used networks and sub-networks listed in the upper left and lower right of the figure. In most cases, *network communications* and *sub-network scanner* modules are used to build a data exchange with external systems. Seven commonly used data interfaces (Ethernet/IP to SERCOS interface) are shown and each is described in detail in the following sections.

For the larger systems, the PLC blocks in Figure 1-8 are mounted in a *rack* as illustrated in Figure 1-9(a). The rack provides mechanical support and all the electrical interconnections plus the data interface between all of the PLC modules using the backplane bus structure. In smaller PLC systems, the component modules are integrated into a single unit like in the Allen-Bradley Pico model. The rack illustrated in Figure 1-9(b) is for the Allen-Bradley SLC 500 series PLCs. The PLC in Figure 1-9(a) is a ControlLogix system. The pictured sensors or actuators, called *field devices*, are covered in Chapter 2.

FIGURE 1-8: PLC system block diagram.

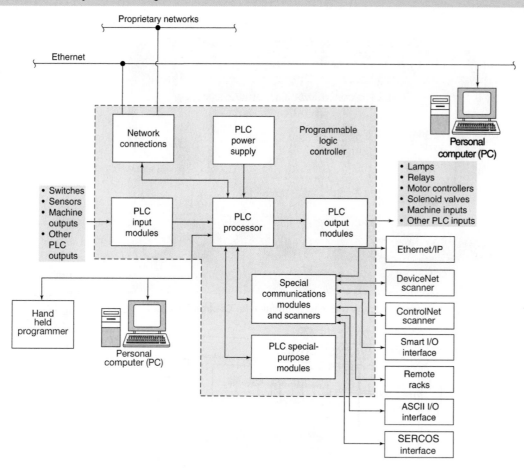

1-4-1 Backplane

The power and data interface for the modules is provided by the *backplane* in the rack in Figure 1-9(b). The backplane has copper conductors, called *lands*, that deliver power to the modules and also provide a data bus to exchange data between the modules and the processor. Modules slide into the rack and engage connectors on the backplane to access the backplane's power and data buses. The number of slots in the rack is determined by the number and type of modules required for the control application. The SLC 500 series PLC racks are available in 4, 7, 10, and 13 slot models. A discussion of each component in Figure 1-8 follows.

1-4-2 Processor and Power Supply

The center box in Figure 1-8, called the *PLC processor*, is the central processing unit (CPU) that handles all logical operations and performs all the mathematical computations. The proces-

sor occupies the fourth slot position in the ControlLogix rack illustration in Figure 1-9(a) and is in slot zero for the SLC 500 system in Figure 1-9(b). In older systems the processor must be in slot zero, but in the new PLC models, one or more processors can be in any slot in the rack. In addition, multiple processors can be used in a single rack to enhance performance in models like the Logix family of PLCs. A picture of an Allen-Bradley ControlLogix processor is shown in Figure 1-10.

Figure 1-9(a and b) illustrates a *PLC power supply* in the left-most box in the rack. The power supply provides power to the processor and to the modules plugged into the rack.

1-4-3 Programming Device

The programming devices connected to the processor in Figure 1-8 are used to enter and download programs or to edit existing programs in the PLC. PCs and a handheld programmer are

FIGURE 1-9: PLC racks and view of the backplane.

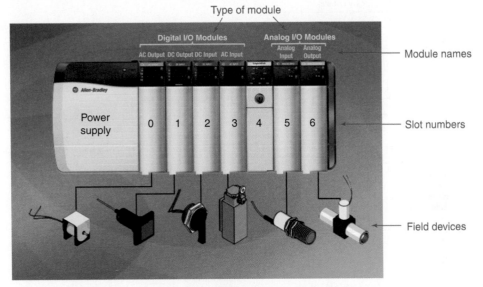

(a) Front panel and rack with seven modules for ControlLogix PLC

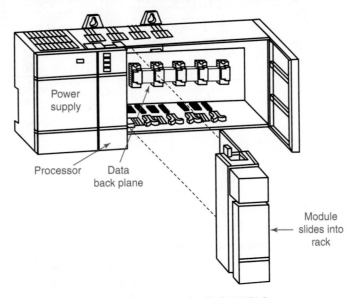

(b) Module and rack interface for SLC 500 PLC

Courtesy of Rockwell Automation, Inc.; and Rehg and Sartori, Industrial Electronics, *First Edition, © 2006, p. 568, reprint by permission of Prentice Hall, Upper Saddle River, NJ.*

shown in the block diagram. Figure 1-11 shows a handheld programmer for the SLC 500 system.

1-4-4 Input and Output Interface

The input and output (I/O) interface used in PLCs can take two forms: *fixed* or *modular*. The fixed type is associated with the small or micro PLC systems where all of the features are inte-

grated into a single unit. The number of I/O ports is fixed within each model and cannot be changed. The modular types, like Figure 1-9, use a rack to hold the I/O modules so the number and type of I/O modules can be varied.

The input interface provides the link between the PLC processor and the external devices that measure the conditions in the production area. The input devices used most often include

FIGURE 1-10: ControlLogix processor.

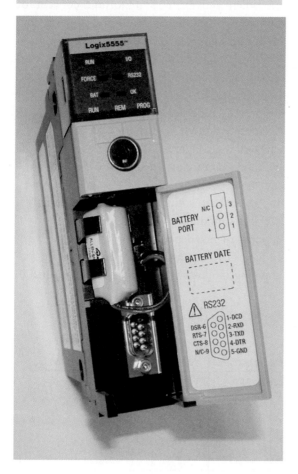

switches, sensors, machine outputs, or other PLC outputs. These input devices are often called *field devices*, indicating that they are not a part of the PLC hardware. The PLC input modules are both a *physical interface* for the connection of wires and an *electrical/data interface* to determine the on/off state or voltage level from the attached field device. In addition, they act as *signal conditioners* changing the many different types of input voltages to the 0 to 5 volt DC voltage levels used in the PLC processor.

The fixed and modular output modules provide the interface between the PLC processor and the external devices or actuators, such as lamps, relays, motor and heater contactors, solenoid valves, and machine inputs. The term *field device* is also used to address the wide range of output devices attached to a PLC system. The output module is both a location for termination of wiring and a signal conditioner to provide the proper voltage and output drive power required by the output field devices.

As a *signal conditioner* for the PLC, the many different input and output modules match the large variety of field devices to the processor's input and output. Figure 1-12 lists some of Allen-Bradley's input and output modules

FIGURE 1-11: Handheld programmer for SLC 500.

(a) Handheld programmer

(b) Programmer keyboard

available—note the range of I/O points (points is another term for input terminals) and the supported input and output signal types.

Selecting input and output modules requires a through analysis of the input and output field devices. The voltage and current characteristics of the modules must be matched to the specifications of the field device. Voltage type (AC or DC) and levels must be considered. Also, system surge and continuous current levels at turn on and minimum current levels for turn off must be matched to a module with equal capability. There are numerous input and output modules because of the variety of input and output field devices and the voltage and current requirements present.

DC modules can be either *current sourcing* (current flows out from the module when active)

or *current sinking* (current flows into the module when active). This important concept of sourcing and sinking current for modules is covered in this chapter for the PLC modules and in Chapter 2 for the field devices. Figure 1-9(a) shows several I/O modules in the Control-Logix's rack.

Interface modules are available for PLCs with a combination of inputs and outputs on the same module. Figure 1-12 illustrates some of the combination modules for the SLC 500 system.

Input current sinking and sourcing circuits. DC input modules are current sourcing, current sinking, or not dependent on the current orientation. The current flow for input sinking and sourcing modules is illustrated and described in

FIGURE 1-12: Allen-Bradley SLC 500 discrete I/O modules.

	ID Code	Voltage Category	Category Number	Input/Output	I/O Points	Module Description
AC Modules	100	100/120V AC	1746-IA4	Input	4	120V AC Input
	300	100/120V AV	1746-IA8	Input	8	120V AC Input
	500	100/120V AC	1746-IA16	Input	16	120V AC Input
	101	200/240V AC	1746-IM4	Input	4	240V AC Input
	301	200/240V AC	1746-IM8	Input	8	240V AC Input
	501	200/240V AC	1746-IM16	Input	16	240V AC Input
	2703	100/120V AC	1746-OA8	Output	8	120/240V AC Output
	2903	100/120V AC	1746-OA16	Output	16	120/240V AC Output
	2803	120/240V AC	1746-OAP12(1)	Output	12	High Current 120/240V AC Output
DC Modules	306	24V DC	1746-IB8	Input	8	Current Sinking DC Input
	506	24V DC	1746-IB16	Input	16	Current Sinking DC Input
	706	24V DC	1746-IB32(1)	Input	32	Current Sinking DC Input
	519	24V DC	1746-ITB16	Input	16	Fast Response DC Sinking Input
	509	48V DC	1746-IC16	Input	16	Current Sinking DC Input
	507	125V DC	1746-IH16	Input	16	Current Sinking DC Input
	320	24V DC	1746-IV8	Input	8	Current Sinking DC Input
	520	24V DC	1746-IV16	Input	16	Current Sinking DC Input
	720	24V DC	1746-IV32(1)	Input	32	Current Sinking DC Input
	518	24V DC	1746-ITV16	Input	16	Fast Response DC Sourcing Input
	515	5V DC/TTL	1746-IG16(2)	Input	16	Current Sourcing TTL Input
	2619	24V DC	1746-OB6EI	Output	6	Isolated Sourcing DC Output
	2713	24V DC	1746-OB8	Output	8	Current Sourcing DC Output
	2913	24V DC	1746-OB16	Output	16	Current Sourcing DC Output
	2920	24V DC	1746-OB16E(1)(3)	Output	16	Current Sourcing DC Output
	3113	24V DC	1746-OB32(1)	Output	32	Current Sourcing DC Output
	3120	24V DC	1746-OB32E(1)	Output	32	Current Sourcing DC Output
	2721	24V DC	1746-OBP8(3)	Output	8	High Current Sinking DC Output
	2921	24V DC	1746-OBP16(1)	Output	16	High Current Sinking DC Output
	2714	24V DC	1746-OV8	Output	8	Current Sinking DC Output
	2914	24V DC	1746-OV16	Output	16	Current Sinking DC Output
	3114	24V DC	1746-OV32(1)	Output	32	Current Sinking DC Output
	2922	24V DC	1746-OVP16(1)	Output	16	High Current Sinking DC Output
	2915	5V DC/TTL	1746-OG16(2)	Output	16	Current Sinking TTL Output
AC/DC Modules	510	24V AC/DC	1746-IN16	Input	16	24V AC/DC Input
	2500	AC/DC Relay	1746-OW4(1)	Output	4	Relay (Hard Contact) Output
	2700	AC/DC Relay	1746-OW8(1)	Output	8	Relay (Hard Contact) Output
	2900	AC/DC Relay	1746-OW16(1)	Output	16	Relay (Hard Contact) Output
	2701	AC/DC Relay	1746-OX8(1)	Output	8	Isolated Relay Output
	800	In-120V AC, Out-Relay	1746-IO4(1)	Input/Output	2 In, 2 Out	Combination Input/Output
	1100	In-120V AC, Out-Relay	1746-IO8(1)	Input/Output	4 In, 4 Out	Combination Input/Output
	1500	In-120V AC, Out-Relay	1746-IO12(1)	Input/Output	6 In, 6 Out	Combination Input/Output
	1512	In-24V DC, Out-Relay	1746-IO12DC(3)	Input/Output	6 In, 6 Out	Combination Input/Output

(1) Certifed for Class 1, Division 2 hazardous location by CSA only.
(2) Not CE marked.
(3) These modules carry the C-UL mark and are certified by UL per CSA only.

An application has the following input field devices that must be interfaced to the SLC 500 PLC. For each combination of field devices select the appropriate combination of input modules from Figure 1-12 to interface them with a PLC.

  a. Seventeen 120 VAC inputs, five 5 VDC inputs are sourcing, which require a sinking module, and three 24 VDC inputs are sinking, which require a sourcing module.

SOLUTION

Use one 1746-IA16 AC module and one 1746-IA4 AC module with 16 and 4 AC inputs, respectively, to handle the seventeen inputs. Use one 1746-IG16 5V TTL sourcing module with 16 I/O points for the five DC inputs, and one 1746-IB8 sinking module with 8 I/O points for the three 24 VDC inputs.

For each combination of the following field devices, select the appropriate combination of output modules from Figure 1-12 to interface them with a PLC.

  a. Ten 90 VAC output field devices that require isolation and twenty-one 12 to 20 VDC current sinking output field devices.
  b. Twenty-eight pneumatic valves that require 28 VDC, ten 24 VDC control signals for a CNC machine with sourcing inputs, and three 120 VAC motors with continuous currents less than 1 amp and starting surge currents less than 10 amps.

SOLUTION

  a. Use one 1746-OW16 (16 outputs) relay output module to isolate loads and one 1746-OV32 (32 outputs) 24 VDC sinking module for the 12 to 20 VDC signals. Whenever inductive loads, like the solenoid valves, are switched in control applications, surge suppressive circuits should be used to reduce the voltage spikes produced.
  b. Use two 1746-OW16 (16 relay type outputs) modules for 28 VDC loads. Use one 1746-OB16 (16 output) 24 VDC sourcing module for the 24 VDC CNC signals. Finally, use a 1746-OAP12 (12 outputs) 120 VAC high current output module for the three motors.

Figures 1-13(a) and (b). Read the description in these figures before continuing. Note the direction of conventional current flow for each type in the drawings.

The current flows *into* the input terminals of sinking DC input modules [Figure 1-13(a)] and flows *out of* the terminals of sourcing DC input modules [Figure 1-13(b)]. When you wire the interface, you must be sure that the power supply polarity orientation supports the current direction required by the module and field device. Verify in the figure that the current flow is out of the positive battery terminal (conventional current flow) and into the sinking module. The current is out of the sourcing module. Note in the figures that a sinking DC input module requires that the field device has a sourcing type of output. If the input module is sourcing, then the field device must be the opposite.

The interface in Figure 1-13(c) illustrates that AC input modules can interface to an AC field device or to either a sinking or sourcing DC field device. Descriptions of the operation are provided in the figure.

Output sinking and sourcing circuits. DC output modules are current sourcing, current sinking, or not dependent on the current orientation. The current flow for DC output sinking and sourcing modules is illustrated and described in Figures 1-14(a) and (b).

The current flows *into* the output terminals of sinking DC output modules [Figure 1-14(a)] and flows *out of* the terminals of sourcing DC modules [Figure 1-14(b)]. You must verify that the power supply polarity orientation supports the current direction required by the module and field device. Note in the figures that a sinking

FIGURE 1-13: Input module interfaces.

Input Interface Description	Input Module Interface
(a) DC Input Module (Current Sinking) Most DC modules are either current **sinking** or current sourcing, but some will work with either current mode. The sinking input modules have a current flow into the module input terminal when the input is active. Therefore, the current must be flowing out of the field device, so the sensor or switch is current sourcing. This configuration has a single module common terminal, while others have both a signal and common for each input port.	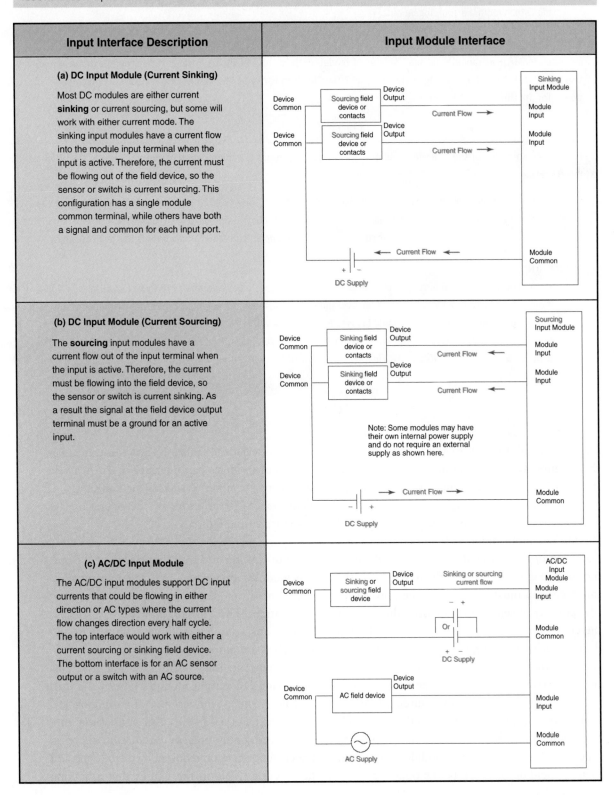
(b) DC Input Module (Current Sourcing) The **sourcing** input modules have a current flow out of the input terminal when the input is active. Therefore, the current must be flowing into the field device, so the sensor or switch is current sinking. As a result the signal at the field device output terminal must be a ground for an active input.	
(c) AC/DC Input Module The AC/DC input modules support DC input currents that could be flowing in either direction or AC types where the current flow changes direction every half cycle. The top interface would work with either a current sourcing or sinking field device. The bottom interface is for an AC sensor output or a switch with an AC source.	

FIGURE 1-14: Output module interfaces.

Output Interface Description	Output Module Interface
(a) DC Output Module (Current Sinking) The **sinking** output modules have a current flow into the module output terminal when the output is active. For compatibility, the field device or actuator must have a **sourcing** (current flowing out) type of input. The commons for all field devices are connected to a positive DC supply and the supply common is connected to the module common terminal.	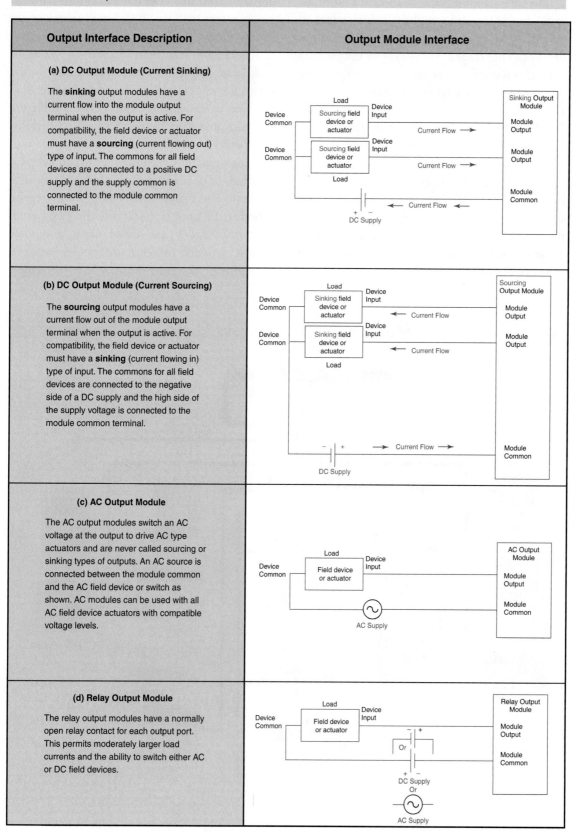
(b) DC Output Module (Current Sourcing) The **sourcing** output modules have a current flow out of the module output terminal when the output is active. For compatibility, the field device or actuator must have a **sinking** (current flowing in) type of input. The commons for all field devices are connected to the negative side of a DC supply and the high side of the supply voltage is connected to the module common terminal.	
(c) AC Output Module The AC output modules switch an AC voltage at the output to drive AC type actuators and are never called sourcing or sinking types of outputs. An AC source is connected between the module common and the AC field device or switch as shown. AC modules can be used with all AC field device actuators with compatible voltage levels.	
(d) Relay Output Module The relay output modules have a normally open relay contact for each output port. This permits moderately larger load currents and the ability to switch either AC or DC field devices.	

output module requires that the field device is a sourcing type. If the output module is sourcing, then the field device must be the opposite.

The interface in Figures 1-14(c) and (d) illustrates that AC output modules can interface to an AC field device, and that a relay output device can interface to either type of output field device, sinking or sourcing. Descriptions of the operation are provided in the figure.

1-4-5 Special Communications Modules and Network Connections

Communications modules and networks are introduced here and are covered in greater detail in Chapter 17. While Figure 1-15 includes many different networks, PLC systems rarely have all network options present. The figure is used to show you what is possible but not to imply that it is a typical implementation.

The special communication modules listed in Figure 1-8 provide a link for the PLC processor to other computer-controlled machines and devices that must share data and control requirements with the PLC. Seven examples are listed: *DeviceNet*, *ControlNet*, *Ethernet/IP*, *SERCOS interface*, *Smart I/O interface*, *Remote racks*, and *ASCII I/O interface*. In addition, the network connections box indicates that the PLC is linked to information level networks like the Ethernet and vendor-specific networks called proprietary networks. The use of these communications modules permits the PLC to act as a data hub or data concentrator for these six subnetworks and a gateway or link to the enterprise Ethernet. In some applications the PLCs from the same vendor are linked using a vendor-specific network called a *proprietary network* (Figure 1-8). The Allen-Bradley *data highway* is

FIGURE 1-15: Communication network options for PLC control systems.

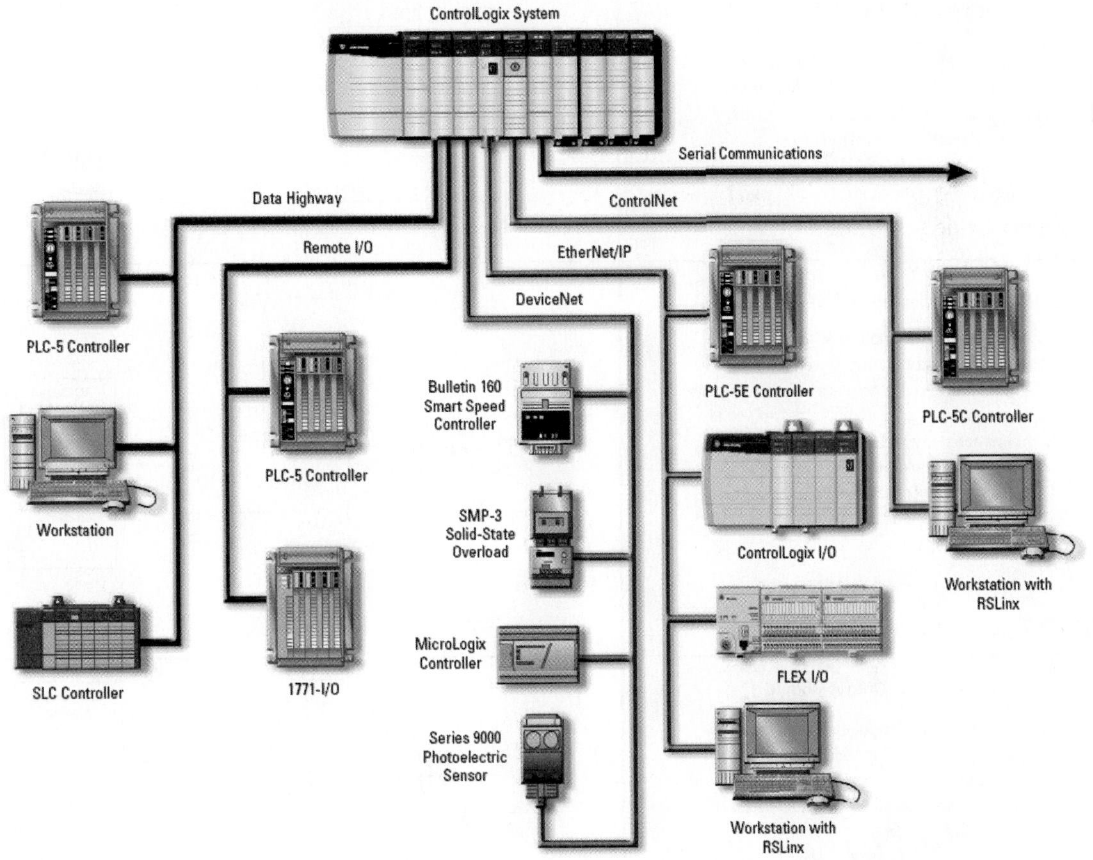

Courtesy of Rockwell Automation, Inc.

an example of this type of vendor-specific network. A brief overview of these network technologies is provided here so you understand the control and network capability of current PLC systems.

- **DeviceNet:** DeviceNet, Figure 1-15, is a low-cost communications network that connects *smart* or intelligent input and output field devices, such as sensors and actuators, to the PLC. A *smart* field device is one that has an embedded microprocessor so that it can communicate over a network, thus eliminating costly hardwiring. Find the DeviceNet in Figure 1-15 and review the range of device types connected to the network.
- **ControlNet:** ControlNet is another open network standard that is one level above DeviceNet in the control hierarchy. While the primary function of DeviceNet is the networking of input and output devices, ControlNet uses the *producer/consumer* network model to efficiently exchange time-critical application information in control systems. Find the ControlNet in Figure 1-15 and look at the type of systems attached.
- **Ethernet/IP:** Ethernet/IP (IP stands for industrial protocol) is an open industrial networking standard that takes advantage of commercial off-the-shelf Ethernet communication devices and physical media. Find the Ethernet/IP in Figure 1-15 and look at the type of systems attached.

Study the three levels of network control illustrated in Figure 1-15. One can see that plantfloor architecture has flattened into three layers: Ethernet/IP, ControlNet, and DeviceNet. The highest level, Ethernet/IP, provides the information layer for plant-wide data collection and program maintenance. The middle level, ControlNet, supports the automation and control layer with input and output control where data cannot be lost and with message passing between systems. The lowest level, DeviceNet, supports a device layer for cost-effective integration of individual input and output field devices. Some overlap in the network layers exists since

sensors and actuators are interfaced to each depending upon the application.

PLCs located in this network architecture often use *smart I/O interfaces*, *remote racks*, and *serial communications* to further distribute data communications to remote control locations. A description of the last four special communication modules follows.

- **SERCOS Interfaces:** This special communications module is a Serial Realtime Communications System, or SERCOS for short. SERCOS is a digital motion control network that interfaces the motion control module in the PLC with the servo motor drive through a fiber optic cable.
- **Smart I/O Interfaces:** PLC vendors have proprietary network protocols to allow all their devices to communicate. One common application for a proprietary network is the use of *smart I/O devices*. The Allen-Bradley Data Highway in Figure 1-15 is an example of a proprietary network used to place Allen-Bradley devices on a network. In the figure it is used to connect two PLC models and a programming station. Find the Data Highway in Figure 1-15 and compare the type of systems attached to it and to the other networks.
- **Remote Racks:** In an effort to distribute the control capability across a large automation system, the PLC vendors provide *remote rack* capability. The rack, similar to the rack illustrated in Figure 1-9, uses the standard I/0 modules for control of machines and processes; however, the processor module is replaced with a remote rack communications module. The processor in the main PLC rack sends control instructions over the single network cable to the communication module in the remote rack and then to the I/O modules included in the remote rack.
- **ASCII I/O Interface:** The last special communications module is the ASCII I/O interface. This serial communication resource is either built into the processor module or comes as a separate module. In both cases, the ASCII interface permits serial data

communication using several standard interfaces, such as RS-232 and RS-422.

1-4-6 PLC Special-Purpose Modules

The final element in the PLC system block diagram, Figure 1-8, is labeled *PLC special-purpose modules*. This term represents a broad collection of modules developed by PLC vendors for PLC control of a variety of automation devices. Examples of Allen Bradley modules include analog input and output, temperature measurement and control (thermocouple and resistance temperature device), multiple PID loop control, servo motor control, stepper motor control, high-speed counter, and hydraulic ram control.

Systems from most PLC vendors conform to the block diagram in Figure 1-8 and have similar operational modes. With the introduction of the basic PLC system completed, a detailed study of the three types of PLC systems is presented in the next section.

1-5 PLC TYPES

PLCs are grouped into three operational classifications, namely *rack* or *address-based systems*, *tag-based systems*, and *soft PLCs* or *PC-based control*. The first type, rack or address-based control, was implemented in the initial PLC systems and is still the type used most frequently. The Allen-Bradley PLC-5 and SLC 500 systems use versions of this system.

1-5-1 Rack/Slot Address Based

The PLC system illustrated in Figure 1-9(b) is a rack/slot address-based system because the slot location of the input and output (I/O) modules in the rack establishes the PLC address for the input or output signal attached to the module. The modules placed in the rack to the right of the processor, Figure 1-9(b), are most often some type of input or output module. The type of field device that is connected to the PLC and the type of signal, such as AC, DC, discrete, analog, voltage, or current, dictate the type of I/O card required. While numerous types of I/O modules are used (see Figure 1-12 for some from Allen-Bradley), each has two functions:

1. They provide the interface terminals to which field device wires are attached.
2. They provide an electronic signal conditioning circuit that interfaces the type of signal present with the PLC.

The signal level presented at each input is represented inside the PLC by a variable, which is the letter I followed by an address reference number. While each PLC vendor of rack/slot address-based systems has a different addressing scheme, the address is determined by the type of module present (input or output), the rack/slot number occupied by the module, and the terminal number used for the connection. For example, the following syntax is used to address discrete inputs on an Allen-Bradley SLC 500 system.

I : (rack/slot number) / (terminal number)

The slot number in the PLC rack in which the input module is placed and the terminal number on the input module to which the field device wiring is attached determines the input address for the SLC 500 system. The letter I indicates that it is an input; the colon (:) is a delimiter separating the module type letter (I or O) and the module slot number. The back slash (/) is a delimiter between the module slot number and terminal number. Examples 1-3 and 1-4 illustrate this addressing concept.

1-5-2 Tag Based PLCs

Tag-based systems are used in all of the new models of PLCs, such as the Allen-Bradley's ControlLogix family and PLCs from Telemecanique and Siemens. The tag name used in these systems is the same as a variable declared in high-level programming languages such as BASIC and C. In this type of addressing system, field device inputs and outputs are assigned *variable names* at the time the control system design is performed. Allen-Bradley uses the term *tag* instead of the term *variable*. Later the variable name or tag is assigned to an I/O module and a specific terminal number. The tag is the only reference used when the program is developed with

An Allen-Bradley SLC 500 system uses a rack like the one illustrated in Figure 1-9(b). Determine the address for a discrete input signal attached to terminal 5 of the DC input module in slot 2.

SOLUTION

The address for the discrete DC input would be

I:2/5

The letter I indicates an input, the 2 indicates that the DC input module is in slot 2, and 5 indicates that the discrete field device input signal wire is connected to terminal 5.

The addressing for discrete output modules would be similar to the input module except that the letter I would be replaced by the letter O. The following example illustrates the rack/slot address scheme for outputs.

EXAMPLE 1-4

An Allen-Bradley SLC system uses a rack like the one illustrated in Figure 1-9(b). Determine the address for a discrete output field device attached to terminal 12 of the AC output module in slot 5.

SOLUTION

The address for the discrete AC output would be

O:5/12

The letter O indicates that it is an output, the 5 indicates that the AC output module is in slot 5, and the 12 indicates that the output field device wire is connected to terminal 12.

the PLC's ladder logic program. When the tags or variables are defined, the type of data to be represented by the tag is declared.

1-5-3 Soft PLCs or PC-Based Control

A PC-based control system, called Soft PLC by Allen Bradley, is an emulation of a PLC using software on a PC. This implementation uses an industrial PC, an input/output card in the PC for an interface to the field devices, and application software that makes the PC operate like a PLC.

A second implementation uses a standard PLC with an industrial PC module placed in one of the PLC rack slots. This version puts the PC on the PLC backplane and gives the soft PLC application running in the PC access to all of the I/O modules in the PLC rack. Soft PLC solutions use one of these two implementations.

When is a Soft PLC the optimum solution? In general, on and off control of machine outputs with few numerical calculation requirements would be an application for a rack-type PLC solution. However, if large data storage and extensive mathematical manipulation is required along with sequential or process control, then a Soft PLC implementation is the better choice. If the power of the PC can be utilized, such as in data storage and numerical processing or in displaying graphics of the process, then the higher cost associated with a Soft PLC solution is justified.

1-6 PLC LADDER LOGIC PROGRAMMING

Ladder logic is a PLC graphical programming technique that was introduced with the first PLCs more than 35 years ago. The relay logic solution to the pump control problem in Figures 1-16(a) and (b) is similar to the PLC ladder logic program for the same problem. However, the subtle differences between the two systems often create confusion for the new user of PLCs. After developing the PLC solution those differences are explored.

FIGURE 1-16: Process tank control systems.

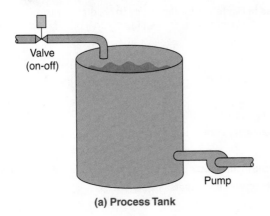

(a) Process Tank

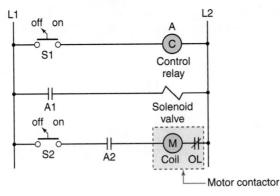

(b) Control drawing

1-6-1 PLC Solution

When the ladder logic solution for the tank control in Figure 1-16(a) is replaced by a PLC program, the field devices remain but the mechanical relay is eliminated. A *field device* is a general term for all input devices and all output actuators. Output actuators in PLC systems are mechanical, pneumatic, hydraulic, or electrical devices that produce a mechanical motion in response to an electrical input signal. Figure 1-17(a) illustrates how the switches and actuators are interfaced to the PLC. Note that the input switches (illustrated using the standard symbol for a selector switch) are connected to the PLC input module, and the actuators are wired to the output module. The terminations at the input and output modules are identified by terminal numbers. For example, the switches are connected to terminals 1 and 2 on the input module and the valve and pump are connected to similar ter-

minal numbers on the output module. The illustration indicates that the PLC processor and program are located between the input and output modules.

The PLC ladder logic program that would provide the same logical control as the circuit in Figure 1-16(b) is illustrated in Figure 1-17(b). Compare Figures 1-16(b) and 1-17(b) to identify similarities and differences. They include:

- The control circuit in Figure 1-16(b) exists in the form of physical components and wire, but the ladder logic program in Figure 1-17(b) exists only as a set of instructions and logical statements in the PLC memory.
- The mechanical relay in the relay logic has been replaced by a software or virtual relay (CR1) in the PLC ladder logic. The software or virtual relay exists only in the PLC memory.
- The PLC rung output [-( )-] is called a coil in some literature but should not be used when referring to PLC ladder outputs. A better term is *discrete output instruction*, which is a bit that exists only in memory.
- Each rung of the PLC ladder logic represents a logical statement executed in software with inputs on the left and outputs on the right. If the inputs are true, then the output is true or active. For example, if input instruction I1 is true (continuity is present), then output CR1 will be active. Keep in mind that this is virtual power flow, no actual current flow is present. If CR1 is active then the input instruction with address CR1 in rung 01 is true and output O1 will be active. Input instruction I1 will be true if switch S1 is closed and a voltage is present at terminal 1 of the input module. If output O1 is active, then terminal 1 of the output module has a ground present to turn on the solenoid valve.
- The number of virtual relays, output instructions, and referenced input instructions in the PLC ladder logic is only limited by the size of the PLC memory, while the number of contacts for the mechanical relay is limited to the number of poles present on the relay selected.

- The input and output instructions in the PLC ladder logic do not represent the switches and actuators directly. The PLC input instructions are logical symbols associated with the input signals (voltages) at the input module terminals. The output symbol is associated with the signal (voltage) that will be presented to the actuator connected to the output module.
- The input and output devices have separate power sources that are isolated from the power for the PLC processor.

The solution in Figure 1-17 is used to emphasize that a PLC solution has field devices interfaced to PLC input and output modules and the PLC program logically connects the input devices to the output actuators through the ladder logic program. In the future, only the field device wiring and the ladder logic program are presented for a solution. The PLC ladder logic inputs are called *instructions* and not *contacts* because the input instructions only represent the value of a binary bit in the PLC memory. In summary, all the symbols in the relay logic diagram represent actual components and contacts present in the control system, but the input (-| |-) and output (- ( ) -) instruction symbols in the PLC ladder logic represent only data values stored in the PLC memory.

FIGURE 1-17: PLC solution to the pump control problem in Figure 1-16.

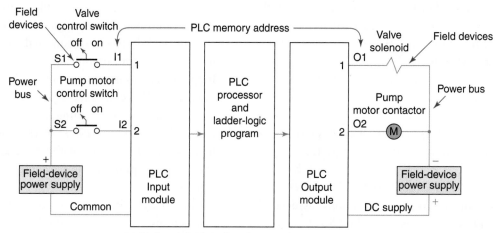

(a) PLC and field device interface for one pump

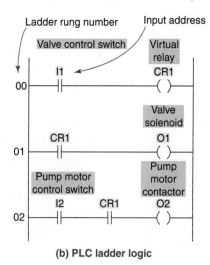

(b) PLC ladder logic

1-6-2   Ladder Logic Operation

The PLC solution in Figure 1-17(b) has three rungs with input instructions on the left and output instructions on the right. The input instructions in rungs 00 and 02 have data addresses of I1 and I2, so the voltage at input terminals 1 and 2 determines if these instruction states are true (continuity) or false (no continuity). The input terminal voltages are set by the position of external switches S1 and S2 in Figure 1-17(a). The input instruction in rung 01 is controlled by the condition of the virtual relay, CR1.

The output instructions in rungs 01 and 02 have data addresses of O1 and O2, so their state, true or false, determines the state, on and off, of the output devices connected to output terminals 1 and 2. For example, if O1 output is active, then the valve solenoid is turned on. The output in rung 00, CR1, is a virtual relay with input instructions referenced to it in rungs 01 and 02. If the output CR1 is active then all the instructions associated with that virtual relay are true. The operation of the ladder logic is summarized as follows.

- Rung 00: Output instruction CR1 is active because input instruction I1 is true (input terminal 1 has a voltage present because switch S1 is closed). If CR1 is active then both of the input instructions associated with CR1 in rungs 01 and 02 are true.

FIGURE 1-18: Alternate ladder logic solution to the single-pump problem.

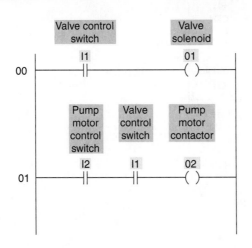

- Rung 01: Output instruction O1 is active because input instruction CR1 is true. If O1 is active then the valve solenoid is on and the inflow valve is open.
- Rung 02: Output instruction O2 is active only if input instructions CR1 and I2 are both true. If output O2 is active then the pump motor contactor connected to output terminal 2 is on and the pump is running. Thus the pump operation requires that output CR1 is true (switch S1 is closed and the input valve is open) AND switch S2 is closed (pump control switch is on).

Study the operation of the program and PLC interface in Figure 1-17 until you are familiar with the notation and operation. In summary, a PLC solution requires that:

- Input field devices, switches and sensors, are wired to terminals on the input module.
- Output field devices are connected to terminals on the output module.
- Input instructions with addresses for each input field device are placed on the left side of the ladder logic rung, and output instructions with addresses for each output field device are placed on the right side of the rung. Outputs can be paralleled on the same rung.
- Virtual relays and combinations of input instructions are placed on the ladder rungs to provide the desired control of the outputs.

1-6-3   An Alternate Solution

Figure 1-18 illustrates an alternate solution to the ladder logic in Figure 1-17(b). Note that the virtual relay, CR1, has been removed and multiple input instructions with the address I1 have been used to achieve the same logical control. In the relay ladder logic solution, Figure 1-16(b), the field device selector switch for the valve had only one set of contacts. This single contact had to control two different devices so a relay was necessary with two switching contacts (2PST). In contrast, the I1 instruction in the PLC ladder logic is not a physical contact but a virtual one created in memory. The single contact of valve control switch, S1, establishes the input condi-

tion at terminal 1 (voltage present or no voltage present). A nearly unlimited number of I1 instructions can be used in the PLC ladder logic, and each will be true if the S1 switch is on. The number of these instructions is limited by PLC memory size. This alternate solution illustrates that multiple solutions to control problems exist, but only one solution is optimum. With only two rungs in the alternate solution, less memory is used and the program runs faster. Verify that the solutions in Figure 1-18, and Figure 1-17 work equally well.

1-6-4   PLC Advantages

In the PLC solution, the only physical wires in the system are the interfaces between the input and output field devices and the PLC input and output modules. All the elements on the ladder program rungs, namely the virtual relays, virtual relay instructions, field device input instructions, and output instructions, exist only in software in the PLC memory. As a result, the PLC ladder logic has many advantages when compared to conventional relay logic. Understanding these advantages is best illustrated by Example 1-5.

Although both systems satisfy the control requirements, the new relay logic requires extensive changes to the physical system compared to the PLC implementation. Both diagrams in Figure 1-19 are notated with an *M* to indicate modified wiring and an *N* for new wiring in the relay logic. The relay ladder logic requires five

modifications and five new wires. In contrast, the new PLC solution has no modifications and just new wiring for the second pump motor contactor and selector switch. The relay logic solution has the wiring for the new components plus extensive wiring changes because the original relay and pump switch had to be replaced. The replacement was necessary because the number of poles on the original relay was not sufficient for the new control requirement. There are extensive changes in the ladder logic program for the PLC solution; however, these are implemented in software so it is both faster and performed at much lower cost.

Figure 1-20(b) is an alternate solution to the ladder in Figure 1-20(a) and does not use any virtual control relays. Verify that the ladder logic in Figure 1-20(a and b) would provide the same control for the tank problem.

It is clear from this example why PLCs are the choice for sequential control over relay logic in industrial automation. In addition, the similarity between the PLC ladder logic program and the control diagram [Figure 1-7(c)] used for relay ladder logic provides an easy transition to PLCs for electricians, technicians, and design engineers who must work with both.

Other advantages of PLCs include:

- **Reliability:** Relays are electro-mechanical devices, and physical wear in relay logic controls occurs every time the devices are turned on. PLCs have reliability inherent in all

---

EXAMPLE 1-5

The tank control system illustrated in Figures 1-7 and 1-17 has a second pump added to drain the tank. This second pump should be on if the following conditions are true: (1) the inlet valve is open, (2) pump 1 is on, and (3) the new pump 2 selector switch is closed. Determine the changes required in the relay logic solution in Figure 1-7 and in the PLC solution in Figure 1-17.

SOLUTION

The second pump and pump selector switch must be added in both the PLC and relay logic solution. No other changes to the physical system are necessary for the PLC solution shown in Figure 1-19(a). However, Figure 1-19(b) shows the three major changes required in the relay logic solution: (1) a new relay with three double throw poles, (2) replacement of the original single pole pump number one control switch with a double pole type, and (3) extensive modifications to the relay control wiring. Compare the new relay ladder logic solution illustrated in Figure 1-19(b) and the PLC ladder logic solution shown in Figure 1-20(a). Review both solutions and then read the analysis of the changes in each.

FIGURE 1-19: Two-pump solution using PLC and relay ladder logic.

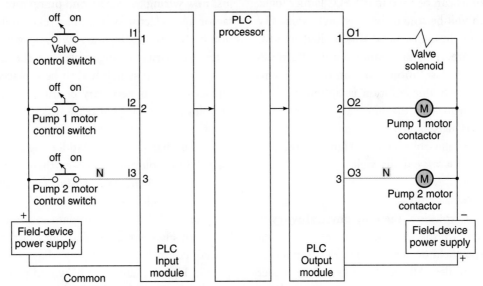

(a) PLC and field device interface for two pumps

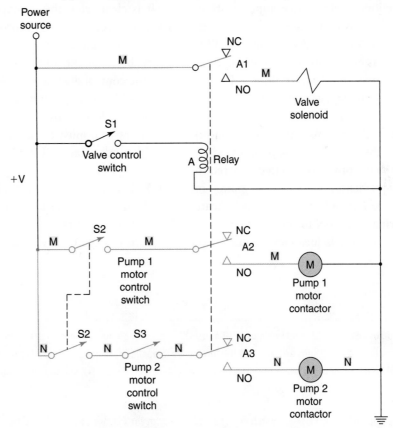

(b) Relay ladder logic solution for two pumps

electronic devices. The mean time between failure (MTBF), a statistical analysis of failure potential, is typically very large for PLCs.

- **Improved maintenance and troubleshooting:** If a problem occurs in any PLC module or in the processor, the module or processor can be changed in a matter of minutes without any changes in wiring. The PLC also makes troubleshooting the entire control system easier because a technician or engineer can check the status of each input or use software to force a change in outputs to identify the input or output device causing the problem.

- **Off-line programming:** In the past, PLCs could be programmed only with special programming terminals supplied by the vendor; however, the present systems use microcomputers (PCs) as programming terminals. The new programming software allows PLC program development on the PC to be tested with emulator software to find problems before the software is used in the control system. The new programming software allows downloads directly to the PLC, through a serial connection, or over the Internet. In most situations, the application programming is performed using only PC hardware and software resources while the PLC is running the process. This process, called *off-line programming*, allows new program development and current program modifications without taking the PLCs out of the production process. In contrast, installing and modifying relay logic circuits often takes days or weeks with considerable lost production as the control circuits are interfaced to the production system.

- **On-line programming:** On-line programming allows the programmer to edit ladder logic rungs while the PLC is executing a production program. The changes are made in a special on-line mode and when change is complete the new ladder logic is made an active part of the current ladder program. This is a large dollar savings in production line industries, such as automotive assembly, where any time the production line is halted,

FIGURE 1-20: Two-pump PLC ladder logic solutions.

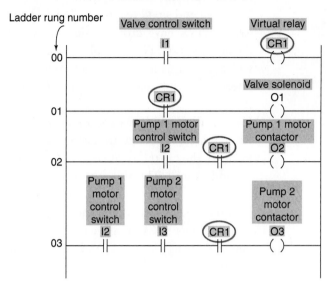

(a) PLC ladder logic solution for two pumps

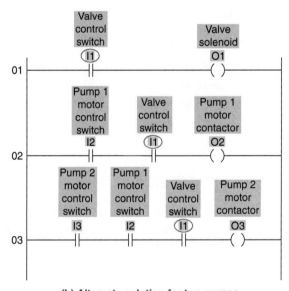

(b) Alternate solution for two pumps

thousands of dollars are lost. Also, changes to variable values and set points are performed while the processor is in the production mode.

- **Broad application base:** PLC software supports a broad range of discrete and analog applications in numerous industries. With only program and module changes, a PLC can be moved from control of an assembly

cell to control of liquid level and temperature in a process control system.

- **Low cost and small footprint:** The cost and size of PLCs have dropped significantly in the last 10 years. For example, a microPLC, which would fit in the palm of your hand, offers powerful machine control for less than $300.
- **High-end control grows exponentially:** Although cost and size are dropping on the low end, the capability of large PLC systems expand as well. The ability to network and distribute the control using numerous proprietary and international network standards permits PLCs to take control of entire manufacturing systems and production plants.

The comparison between relay ladder logic and PLC programs illustrates the enormous advantage to using PLC in automation control. However, the move from relay logic to PLC control does not diminish the need for good and safe practices when working on electrical systems. The next section reviews the requirements for electrical safety.

1-7 ELECTRICAL AND PLC SAFETY

It is important to have a healthy respect for the energy sources encountered everyday, like electrical power, but there is no need to fear them. The key is to respect energy sources and know how to work with them safely; this section introduces safety related to electrical energy. The important components of electrical safety include:

- Electrical shock—how the body reacts
- The nature of electrical shock
- Safe electrical practices
- Response to shock victims

Each component is covered in the following sections.

1-7-1 Electrical Shock—How the Body Reacts
When electric current flows through the body, the resistance in the tissue converts most of the energy into heat. When the current is high, the amount of heat generated is sufficient to burn the body tissue. Although the effect is similar to a burn caused by an open flame, it is more serious because the damaged tissue is often beneath the skin and may include internal organs. In addition, electrical shock may cause significant damage to the central nervous system. The primary effect is to overload the electrical signals in the nervous system and take control of the muscles away from the brain. For example, all forearm muscles contract when a large shock or current flows through the forearm muscle. Muscles that both close and open the fingers are present in the forearm, and the muscles that close the fingers are stronger than those used to open them. As a result, the fingers will close strongly and the brain will not be able to command them to open. If the shock or electrical current is a result of the hand touching an electrical energy source, the hand will close on the source and be unable to release it. Involuntary muscle contraction, called *tetanus*, is only stopped by removing the current. The victim may still need to be physically pulled from the shock source, after the electrical source is de-energized, because muscle control is not immediately restored. Internal muscles, such as the diaphragm and heart, can also be immobilized by a DC current so that breathing and/or blood pumping is stopped.

A second problem, called *fibrillation*, produced by a small AC current, causes the heart to flutter rather than beat so blood flow through the body ceases. Direct current (DC) has the tendency to induce *muscular tetanus*, whereas alternating current (AC) causes fibrillation. In either case, electric currents high enough to cause involuntary muscle action are dangerous and should be avoided.

1-7-2 The Nature of Electrical Shock
Electrical shock occurs when some part of the body becomes a current carrying part of an elec-

trical circuit. In Figure 1-21 the path from one hand to the other is passing current because the right hand is in contact with a voltage source and the left hand is touching a ground for the voltage source. In this case the left hand is holding a water pipe with a portion buried in the ground and the energy source has its negative terminal connected to a grounding rod driven into the earth. A similar shock would occur if the victim were to accidentally grab the wires on each side of the load. A shock of this type is dangerous because the current is passing through the chest where the diaphragm (used for lung action) and heart muscles are located. A shock occurs whenever any part of the body becomes a conductor between a point of higher electrical potential and a point of lower electrical potential (i.e., one hand on each side of the load). If the potential is high enough to overcome the contact resistance of the skin, then the current flowing through the body will cause damage to nerves and/or tissue. Table 1-1 indicates the level of current (all values are in milliamps) necessary to stimulate different bodily

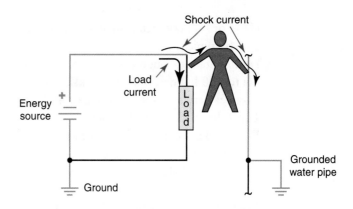

FIGURE 1-21: Electrical shock across the chest.

responses. Note that the current levels are different for men and women, and AC current is dangerous at much lower current levels than DC.

The level of current that flows under shock conditions is dependent on the resistance that the body presents to the electrical source. Research conducted on contact resistance between parts of the human body and points of

TABLE 1-1: Bodily response to electrical shock.

Bodily Effect	Gender	Direct Current dc	Alternating Current 60 Hz ac	Alternating Current 10K Hz ac
Slight sensation felt	Men	1.0	0.4	7.0
at hands	Women	0.6	0.3	5.0
Threshold of	Men	5.2	1.1	12
perception	Women	3.5	0.7	8.0
Painful, but maintained	Men	62	9.0	55
voluntary muscle control	Women	41	6.0	37
Painful, unable to let go	Men	76	16	75
of wires	Women	51	10.5	50
Severe pain, difficulty	Men	90	23	94
breathing	Women	60	15	63
Possible heart fibrillation	Men	500	100	
after 3 seconds	Women	500	100	

contact with electrical circuits provides the following data:

- Hand or foot contact, insulated with rubber: 20 MΩ typical
- Foot contact through leather shoe sole: 100 kΩ to 500 kΩ dry, 5 kΩ to 20 kΩ wet
- Contact between wire and finger: 40 kΩ to 1 mΩ dry, 4 kΩ to 15 kΩ wet
- Wire held by hand: 15 kΩ to 50 kΩ dr, 3 kΩ to 5 kΩ wet
- Metal pliers held by hand: 5 kΩ to 10 kΩ dry, 1 kΩ to 3 kΩ wet
- Contact with palm of hand: 3 kΩ to 8 kΩ dry, 1 kΩ to 2 kΩ wet
- 1.5-inch metal pipe grasped by one hand: 1 kΩ to 3 kΩ dry, 500 Ω to 1.5 kΩ wet
- Hand immersed in conductive liquid: 200 Ω to 500 Ω
- Foot immersed in conductive liquid: 100 Ω to 300 Ω

IMPORTANT: The resistance values between parts of the body and an electrical conductor are presented as examples obtained in one research study. They may not be the same for every person. You should **never** intentionally make contact between some part of your body and dangerous levels of electrical energy based on the assumed contact resistances listed here. Approved safety devices are required when handling dangerous levels of electrical energy.

Safety data for bodily response to current was obtained from tests conducted by The Massachusetts Institute of Technology and the nominal body resistance values were determined by tests conducted by the Lawrence Livermore National Laboratory.

1-7-3 Safe Electrical Practices

Whenever possible, work on all industrial systems should be performed when the system is in a *zero energy state*. In this state all sources of energy are removed to minimize the possibility of injury for persons working on the system. This concept applies to all energy sources. Some examples of energy sources include:

- Voltage sources
- Compressed springs
- High pressure fluids
- High pressure air
- Potential energy from suspended weight
- Chemical energy (flammable and reactive substances)
- Nuclear energy (radioactivity)

Systems that are controlled by a PLC often have multiple power sources. The PLC is usually powered from 110 volts AC, and the input and output modules can have AC and DC sources with a wide range of voltages from 5 volts DC to 440 volts AC. In addition, the system often controls valves that switch high pressure air and fluid. It is often not possible to work or troubleshoot a PLC system in the zero energy state, so good practices should be used to avoid electrical shock. Contact with high pressure air and fluid should also be avoided, and attention paid to the pneumatic and hydraulic devices powered by these energy sources. Deep cuts can be produced by small streams of high pressure air and liquid.

The primary safety process used throughout industry is a *lock-out/tag-out* procedure. This technique is normally not used in instructional laboratories but is quite common in industry. In the PLC laboratory is it good practice to check for the presence of voltage with a meter before actually touching any conductors in the circuit. This is especially important when AC voltage is present or when a DC voltage greater than 5 volts is used. Many industry safety manuals include the following three-step procedure when measuring a voltage:

1. Verify that that the meter is working by measuring a known voltage source.
2. Use the meter to test the circuit you plan to touch for the presence of a voltage.
3. Verify again that that the meter is working by measuring a known voltage source.

This may seem excessive, but avoiding accidental contact with dangerous voltage levels is important, and this is a proven technique for preventing electrical shock.

EXAMPLE 1-6

Determine the electrical DC potential necessary to produce pain with loss of muscle control in men when a wire is held in the dry hand. Minimum resistance values should be used.

SOLUTION

Ohms law is used to calculate the electrical DC source value as follows:

$$DC\ source = contact\ resistance\ x\ current\ level$$
$$= 15\ k\Omega\ x\ 76\ mA$$
$$= 1140\ volts$$

This level of DC voltage is not common in most cases.

EXAMPLE 1-7

Determine the electrical AC potential necessary to produce fibrillation in women when a wire is held in the wet hand. Minimum resistance values should be used.

SOLUTION

Ohms law is used to calculate the electrical AC source value as follows:

$$DC\ source = contact\ resistance\ x\ current\ level$$
$$= 3\ k\Omega\ x\ 100\ mA$$
$$= 300\ volts$$

This level of voltage is common in motor control circuits. Also, if the skin is penetrated by an arc or wire, then the resistance drops sharply and the voltage necessary for a dangerous shock is reduced accordingly.

EXAMPLE 1-8

Determine the level of bodily response if a 28 VAC 60 Hz source is touched by pliers held in the wet hands. Use minimum resistance values.

SOLUTION

Ohms law is used to calculate the electrical AC current value as follows:

$$DC\ source = \frac{AC\ source}{contact\ resistance}$$
$$= \frac{28\ VAC}{1k\Omega}$$
$$= 28\ mA$$

This level of discomfort falls between severe pain/difficulty in breathing and fibrillation for both men and women. A large number of control circuits in PLC systems have 28 VAC sources, so the possibility of shock should be an incentive for safe electrical practices.

A final precaution is to make initial contact with the conductor(s) with the back of one hand or fingers before grasping it between the fingers. If voltage is present when the back of the hands or fingers contact the conductor, then the natural muscle reaction will throw the fingers away from the conductor. This is a final precaution and should never be done to determine if a conductor has voltage present. Another suggestion often stated when working around high power circuits is to work with one of your hands in your pocket. This is just a way of emphasizing that you never want to permit shock current to pass through the chest region. If you follow

good practices electrical energy is safe to work with, and you never need to fear it or experience an electrical shock.

1-7-4 Response to Shock Victims

Electrical shock need not occur, but if it does you should know what actions must be taken to reduce the likelihood of a serious injury. When a person is in contact with an electrical conductor and is unconscious or unable to release the electrical circuit, the first step is to quickly remove power from the circuit. If you make direct contact with victim, then it is possible that you will also receive the same level of electrical shock. After the energy source has been removed, the breathing and pulse of the victim may have to be restored, so CPR is often necessary while waiting for the arrival of 911 emergency medical teams.

1-8 WEB SITES FOR PLC MANUFACTURERS

A search in Google using the words *PLC* or *programmable logic controller* will produce hundreds of responses. The list will include companies that make PLCs, ones that design automation systems using PLCs, others that make peripheral devices to support PLCs, and organizations that support the PLC industry. The following list of PLC manufacturers and their URLs represents some of the more frequently used PLCs in North American industrial applications. The list also includes some produced in Europe and Japan, since many machines used in U.S. industries are manufactured there. The URLs are often links to the company's home page; links to the PLC products should be selected. Also, URLs frequently change, so use a search engine with the company name if the URL provided is no longer active.

- Allen-Bradley: *http://www.ab.com*
- AutomationDirect: *http://web2.automationdirect.com/adc/Home/Home*
- GE—Fanuc: *http://www.geindustrial.com/cwc/gefanuc/ctrlio.html*
- Mitsubishi Electric: *http://www.mitsubishi-automation.de/products.html*
- Omron Electronics LLC: *http://oeiweb.omron.com/*
- Panasonic: *http://www.mew-europe.com/*
- Parker: *http://www.parker.com/ead/cm1.asp?cmid=307*
- Rockwell Automation: *http://www.automation.rockwell.com/*
- Schneider Electric: *http://www.us.telemecanique.com/*
- Siemens: *http://www2.automation.siemens.com/meta/index_76.htm*

CHAPTER 2

Input Devices and Output Actuators

2-1 GOALS AND OBJECTIVES

The primary goal of this chapter is to present the description and operation of typical mechanical and electrical input devices and output actuators that interface with a Programmable Logic Controller (PLC). A secondary goal is to introduce the student to input and output wiring techniques, which are important in connecting these devices to a PLC. Finally, troubleshooting tips are provided to give the student some insight into typical failure modes of input and output devices.

After completing this chapter you should be able to:

- Identify and describe various manually operated switches such as toggle switches, push button switches, selector switches, and push wheels.
- Identify and describe various mechanically operated switches such as limit switches, flow switches, level switches, pressure switches, and temperature switches.
- Identify, describe, and make an application selection for proximity sensors and photoelectric sensors.

- Identify and describe the following output devices: solenoids, relays, contactors, motor starters, lamps, and alarms.
- Describe methods for powering and connecting input and output devices to a PLC.
- Develop control diagrams that use relay ladder logic which describes the operation of the sequential control system using various input and output devices.
- Troubleshoot input switches and sensors and output actuators and indicators.

2-2 MANUALLY OPERATED INDUSTRIAL SWITCHES

Manually operated switches that are connected to a PLC as input devices perform a simple on-off function, where the term *manually operated* implies that a person physically moves the switching mechanism. All on-off switches share similar contact configurations; however, their appearance, size, and mounting methods are often quite different.

The most common manually activated switches that interface to PLCs are the toggle switch, push button switch, selector switch, and push wheel, all of which are discussed in the fol-

lowing subsections. Before we discuss these manually operated switches, let's review the following terms that are used to describe switches and contact configurations.

- **Pole:** The term *pole* refers to an internal conductor in the switch that is moved by the switching mechanism. Switches can have any number of poles, but most switches used as PLC input devices have from one to three.
- **NC and NO:** The abbreviation *NC* stands for *normally closed* and refers to switch contacts that are in the closed position when the switch is off. Similarly, *NO* stands for *normally open* and refers to switch contacts that are not closed when the switch is off. The term *normally* implies that the switch operator has a nominal starting on or off position.
- **Throw:** There are usually just two terms, *single throw* and *double throw*, associated with a switch's throw specification. When a switch has both an NC and NO contact it has a double throw; if only an NO contact is present,

then it has a single throw. Some double throw switches have a center off position and as a result both of the contacts are NO.

- **Operator:** The *operator* is the mechanical mechanism that is moved to cause a change in the switch contacts. Operators are manually moved or mechanically operated by linking to a movement in the production process or to a human operator.

2-2-1 Toggle Switches

Toggle switches are illustrated in Figure 2-1, and contact configurations in Figure 2-2. Note that the pole and throw specifications are combined to describe switch contact configurations; for example, single pole double throw (SPDT). The dotted lines connecting the poles indicate that they are all a part of a single switch, and all poles are changed by a single operation of the switch operator. In order to prevent inadvertent switch activation, some toggle switches requiring a two-step operation are used. First, the lever handle of the toggle switch must be pulled out, and then it must be moved to the desired position.

EXAMPLE 2-1

Select a switch configuration and draw a solution for the following control problem. A single switch should start a 110 VAC motor and control two 28 VDC indicator lamps. An illuminated red lamp indicates that the motor is not powered and an illuminated green lamp indicates that the motor has power applied.

SOLUTION

The solution requires a single switch to control a 110 VAC motor and two 28 VDC lamps so a two pole switch is needed (one pole for the lamps and one for the motor). Only one lamp should be on at a time, so a double throw action is necessary. The circuit in Figure 2-3 provides the necessary control. The switch has a double pole double throw contact configuration, and the dashed line between the poles indicates that the same operator changes both poles.

Other switch configurations are the *double break* contacts and the *make before break* contacts. Referring to the SPST switch in Figure 2-2, note that one end of the pole of the switch always maintains contact while the other end of the pole moves between an open and a closed position. In switches with double break contacts, however, both ends of the pole move when the switch is activated. Figure 2-4 illustrates the contact schematic for an SPST and SPDT double

break selector switch. Note that *DB* is added to the abbreviation (SPSTDB) to indicate that a double break contact is present. Example 2-2 illustrates how double break contacts are used in a control circuit.

The SPDT switch operations that we have discussed have the NC contacts opening before the NO contacts can close. In this case, the pole is not in contact with either the NC or NO contacts for a few milliseconds. This operation is classified as

FIGURE 2-1: Electronic circuit toggle switches.

(a) Toggle switches

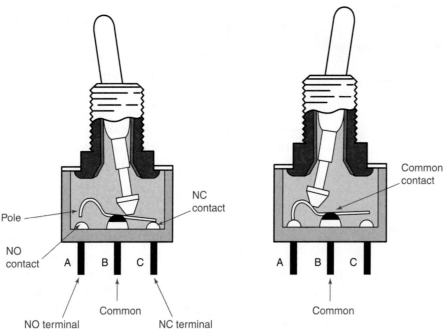

(b) Cutaway view of a toggle switch

Photo courtesy of NKK Switches—www.nkkswitches.com; and Rehg and Sartori, Industrial Electronics, *1ˢᵗ Edition, © 2006. Reprinted by permission of Pearson Education, Inc., Upper Saddle River, NJ.*

EXAMPLE 2-2

Draw the circuit for the following control problem using double break and non-double break contacts. Power to a 110 VAC motor and a 28 VDC lamp must be controlled so that the motor is powered when the switch is on and the red light is on when the switch is off.

SOLUTION

An SPDTDB switch contact is used for this application because the switched voltage for each device is different. The double break contacts permit different voltages to be switched by the NC and NO contacts. If a DB configuration were not available, then a DPDT switch would have to be used with a circuit similar to Figure 2-3. Note that the SPDT switch shown in Figure 2-2 could not be used because the pole has a common terminal for the NC and NO contacts, and as a result the single pole could not be used to switch two different voltages.

FIGURE 2-2: Contact configurations.

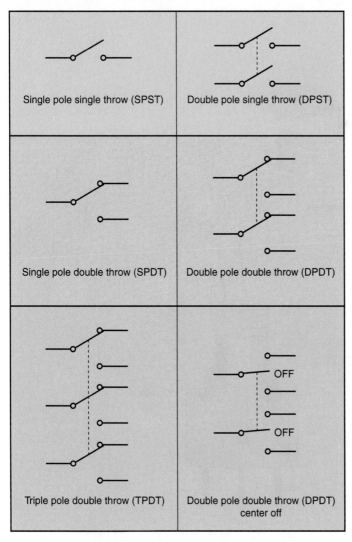

Single pole single throw (SPST)	Double pole single throw (DPST)
Single pole double throw (SPDT)	Double pole double throw (DPDT)
Triple pole double throw (TPDT)	Double pole double throw (DPDT) center off

Rehg and Sartori, Industrial Electronics, 1st Edition, © 2006. Reprinted by permission of Pearson Education, Inc., Upper Saddle River, NJ.

a *break before make*, which is the most common type of contact transfer. However, in some control circuits a problem can result if the switched device is not connected to either contact during the switching operation. The *make before break* contact transfer solves this problem. In this type of transfer, the NO contacts close before the NC contacts open. The make before break configuration is frequently used in rotary switches.

2-2-2 Push Button Switches

Push button switches, like toggle switches, are available in many different configurations, as Figure 2-6 illustrates. Most push buttons are of the momentary contact type, so that the on condition requires the button to be held in the down position. In a maintain contact push button switch, the button is pressed once to close the NO contacts, and then pressed a second time to return the NO contacts to their open condition.

Industrial push button switches are available in four styles: *no guard, full guard, extended guard,* and *mushroom button.* No guard or extended head switches have the button extending beyond the enclosing cylinder, as shown in Figure 2-6(b). Fully guarded or flush head switches have the button flush with the enclosing cylinder, as shown in Figure 2-6(a), and extended guard switches have the button below the enclosing cylinder, as shown in Figure 2-6(c). *Mushroom* switches are shown in Figure 2-6(d), (e), and (f), and are so named because the button has a large, circular, mushroom-shaped surface. Mushroom switches are most commonly used for applications where a device must be easily and quickly turned off, like an emergency stop control. The guarded switches are used where an application is turned on, so the guard prevents device activation if an object accidentally leans against the switch.

Momentary contact mushroom push buttons typically have the down position as the momentary contact, while the spring returns the button out to the normal position. Maintain contact push buttons have two configurations. One is a push-pull button that is shown in Figure 2-6(d). When the button is pressed it remains depressed until the button is pulled out to return the switch to the normal position. In some models, such as that shown in Figure 2-6(f), the mushroom button must be rotated before it will return to the normal position. Another maintain contact option requires the button to be pressed once to turn the switch on and pressed a second time to turn the switch off.

The style shown in Figure 2-6(g) has two push buttons interlocked so that one button turns the switch on and the second returns the switch to the normal position. Switch vendors offer both illuminated and non-illuminated buttons in a variety of terminal configurations. The abbreviation most often used to identify a push

FIGURE 2-3: Motor and lamp control circuit.

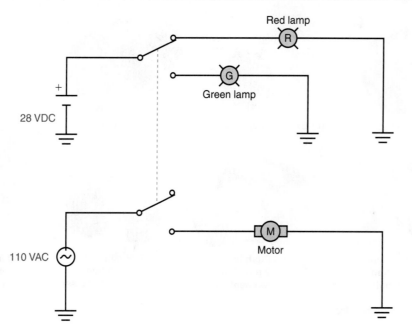

Rehg and Sartori, Industrial Electronics, 1st Edition, © 2006. Reprinted by permission of Pearson Education, Inc., Upper Saddle River, NJ.

FIGURE 2-4: Double break switch contacts.

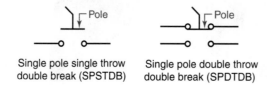

Single pole single throw
double break (SPSTDB)   Single pole double throw
double break (SPDTDB)

Rehg and Sartori, Industrial Electronics, 1st Edition, © 2006. Reprinted by permission of Pearson Education, Inc., Upper Saddle River, NJ.

FIGURE 2-5: Example of DB control circuit.

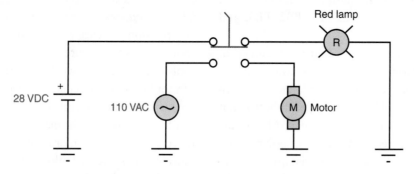

Switch drawn in off condition

Rehg and Sartori, Industrial Electronics, 1st Edition, © 2006. Reprinted by permission of Pearson Education, Inc., Upper Saddle River, NJ.

FIGURE 2-6: Push button switch operators.

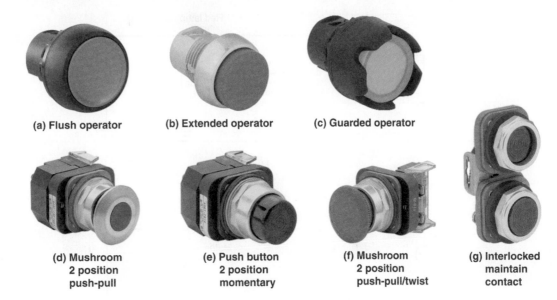

(a) Flush operator   (b) Extended operator   (c) Guarded operator

(d) Mushroom
2 position
push-pull

(e) Push button
2 position
momentary

(f) Mushroom
2 position
push-pull/twist

(g) Interlocked
maintain
contact

Courtesy of Rockwell Automation, Inc.

FIGURE 2-7: Selector switches.

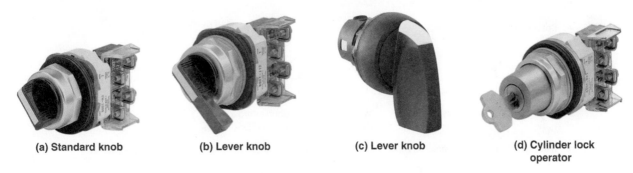

(a) Standard knob   (b) Lever knob   (c) Lever knob   (d) Cylinder lock
operator

Courtesy of Rockwell Automation, Inc.

button switch is PB. If multiple push buttons are used they are identified as PB1, PB2, PB3, and so on.

Two other switch types that are included in the push button category are tactile switches and membrane switches. Tactile push button switches operate like a standard push button but with a much lower operating force. Membrane switches are created using layers of polycarbonate or polyester insulating material and conductive links. As a result, the switches can be integrated directly into a machine panel or instrument faceplate.

2-2-3 Selector Switches

Selector switches are typically two-, three-, and four-position switches with a number of different knob options (see Figure 2-7). The larger winged knob is designed for workers with gloves. The selector knob can be replaced with a keyed cylinder for key switch operation as shown in Figure 2-7(d). Selectors offer the maintain contact option at every switch position or momentary contact in many of the switch positions. The abbreviation most often used to identify a selector switch is SS. If multiple selector switches are used they are identified as SS1, SS2, SS3, and so on. Clockwise or

FIGURE 2-8: Switch symbols.

PUSH BUTTONS							
Momentary Contact					Maintained Contact		Illuminated
Single Circuit		Double Circuit	Mushroom Head	Wobble Stick	Two Single Ckt.	One Double Ckt.	
N.O.	N.C.	N.O. & N.C.					

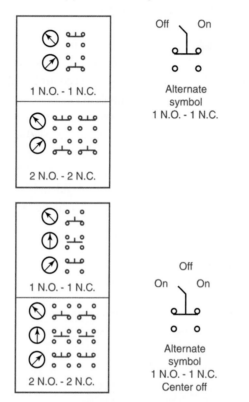

(a) Push-button symbols

1 N.O. - 1 N.C.

2 N.O. - 2 N.C.

Off   On

Alternate symbol
1 N.O. - 1 N.C.

1 N.O. - 1 N.C.

2 N.O. - 2 N.C.

Off

On   On

Alternate symbol
1 N.O. - 1 N.C.
Center off

(b) Selector symbols

Rehg and Sartori, Industrial Electronics, *1ˢᵗ Edition, © 2006. Reprinted by permission of Pearson Education, Inc., Upper Saddle River, NJ.*

counterclockwise rotation is used to change the condition of the switch contacts. All of the standard contact configurations, such as SPST, SPDT, DPST, and DPDT, are available in both push button and selector switches.

Figure 2-8 illustrates the standard drawing symbols used for push button and selector switches. The push button symbols, Figure 2-8(a), are illustrated for momentary and maintained contact. The symbol for *wobble* lever (four-way toggle) represents a switch that has a handle. The handle triggers a change in contacts when the handle is moved up and down or left and right. The illuminated push button allows the switch face to be illuminated. The selector symbols are shown in Figure 2-8(b).

2-3 MECHANICALLY OPERATED INDUSTRIAL SWITCHES

Mechanically operated industrial switches are automatically opened or closed by a process parameter such as position, pressure, or temperature. The

FIGURE 2-9: Limit switches shown in five configurations.

switch contacts open or close when a predetermined process set point is reached. The following subsections discuss the mechanically operated switches typically interfaced with a PLC.

2-3-1 Limit Switches

The *limit switch* is the most commonly used mechanically operated industrial switch. Limit switch contacts are typically activated with a cam that rotates a lever, by depressing a plunger, or by tripping a wobble lever. Figure 2-9 shows five different limit switch configurations: (a) adjustable roller lever, (b) plunger, (c) standard roller lever, (d) wobble lever, and (e) adjustable rod lever.

Figure 2-10 illustrates the standard schematic symbols and control symbols for limit switches. The symbols in Figure 2-10(a) through (d) indicate that the switch is a momentary contact, and the symbol in Figure 2-10(e) indicates a maintained contact switch. The symbols in Figure 2-10(a) and (b) illustrate NO and NC contacts on the top and NO held closed and NC held open on the bottom. Machine schematics are normally drawn with the

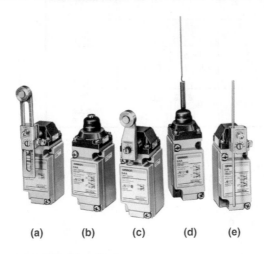

| (a) | (b) | (c) | (d) | (e) |

(a) Adjustable roller lever
(b) Plunger
(c) Standard roller lever
(d) Wobble lever
(e) Adjustable rod lever

Courtesy of Omron Electronics LLC.

FIGURE 2-10: Schematic symbols for limit switches—momentary and maintained contacts.

Limit				
Normally open	Normally closed	Neutral position		
			Actuated	Maintained position
Held closed	Held open	NP	NP	

| (a) | (b) | (c) | (d) | (e) |

(a) – (d) Momentary contact types
(e) Maintained contact type

Rehg and Sartori, Industrial Electronics, *1st Edition, © 2006. Reprinted by permission of Pearson Education, Inc., Upper Saddle River, NJ.*

FIGURE 2-27: Photoelectric sensor lens.

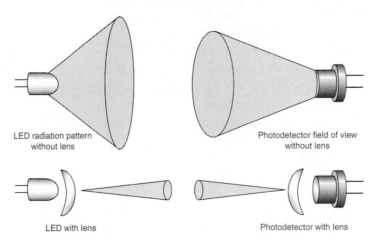

LED radiation pattern
without lens

Photodetector field of view
without lens

LED with lens

Photodetector with lens

Courtesy of Rockwell Automation, Inc.

FIGURE 2-28: Comparison of photoelectric sensor output devices.

Output Type	Strengths	Weaknesses
Electromechanical Relay *AC or DC switching*	• Output is electrically isolated from supply power • Easy series and/or parallel connection of sensor outputs • High switching current	• No short circuit protection possible • Finite relay life
FET *AC or DC switching*	• Very low leakage current • Fast switching speed	• Low output current
Power MOSFET *AC or DC switching*	• Very low leakage current • Fast switching speed	• Moderately high output current
TRIAC *AC switching only*	• High output current	• Relatively high leakage current • Slow output switching
NPN or PNP Transistor *DC switching only*	• Very low leakage current • Fast switching speed	• No AC switching

Courtesy of Rockwell Automation, Inc.

can be difficult. However, when a wider field of view is required, then the sensor has a shorter overall range.

- **Logic circuit:** modulates the LED light source, amplifies the signal from the light detector, and determines if the output state should be changed.
- **Output device:** signals a PLC that a change has occurred. Figure 2-28 provides a comparison between the various output devices; study the table until you can name the options.

Photoelectric sensor operating modes. Photoelectric sensors operate in the following different sensing modes:

- **Through beam** or transmitted beam has the light source and receiver packaged in separate housings.
- **Retroreflective** or reflex has both the light source and receiver in one housing.
- **Polarized retroreflective** has polarizing filters in front of the light source and receiver that are 90 degrees out of phase with each other.

through the wall the liquid must have a significantly higher dielectric constant than the material used for the bin, and the bin wall must be thin. In the third level-detection application, an ultrasonic sensor is used to detect the level of the liquid in the tank. In the last two applications, Figure 2-25(c) and (e), sensors are use to verify the presence of products. In the first, three capacitive sensors verify that cookies are packaged in the box. Note that the sensors look through the box lid to check for the cookies. In the second application ultrasonic sensors, set for discrete mode operation, determine that the box is properly filled with cans. Study the applications until you understand how these sensors are being used.

2-4-2 Photoelectric Sensors

Photoelectric sensors are used in many applications and industries to provide accurate detection of objects without physical contact. Two components present in all photoelectric sensors are *a light source* and a *receiver* used to detect the presence of the light source. In its most basic form, a photoelectric sensor is just like a limit switch, where a beam of light replaces the limit switch's mechanical actuator. Photoelectric devices sense the presence of an object or part when the part either breaks a light beam or reflects a beam of light to a receiver. The change in light could be the result of the presence or absence of the object, or as the result in a change of the size, shape, reflectivity, or color of an object. Photoelectric sensors operate over distances from 5mm (0.2 in) to over 250 m (820 ft). Some laser devices can operate at ranges of 304.5 m (1000 ft).

Understanding the operation of photo sensors is the first step in using and troubleshooting them effectively. Photoelectric sensors are comprised of some or all of the following:

- **Light source:** typically a light emitting diode (LED). The LED configuration used in photo sensors is illustrated in Figure 2-26, showing that infrared generates the most light and the least heat of any LED color. In many applications, a visible red beam of light is used, but other colors, such as visible red, blue, and yellow, are used in special applications where specific colors or color contrasts are important. When long distances between the

FIGURE 2-26: LED photoelectric sensors.

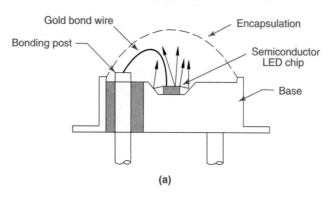

(a)

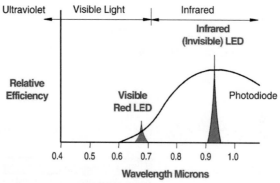

The invisible (infrared) LED is a spectral match for this silicon phototransistor and has much greater efficiency than a visible (red) LED.

(b)

Courtesy of Rockwell Automation, Inc.

source and receiver are necessary, sensors use lasers as a light source. In those applications distances of 304.5 m (1000 ft) are possible. The laser is usually a red color so that alignment between the light source and receiver is enhanced.

- **Light detector:** the component used to detect the presence of the light source. It produces a change in current directly proportional to the amount of light falling on the light detector. Photodiodes or phototransistors are the robust solid-state components that are most often used for the light detector. The wavelengths of the light for the source and receiver are often matched to improve sensing efficiency.
- **Lenses:** used with LED light sources and photo detectors to narrow or focus the light beam area (Figure 2-27) and increase the sensor's range. When the source and receiver beams or fields of view are narrow, alignment

the sensors are used to check for the presence of a part in manufacturing. In Figure 2-24(d) the sensor detects parts that are not oriented properly, and in Figure 2-24(f) the limits of travel of the surface grinding plate are detected. Study the applications until you understand how these sensors are being used.

Capacitive and ultrasonic proximity sensor applications are illustrated in Figure 2-25. The first three applications, Figure 2-25(a) through (c), use a capacitive proximity sensor, while the last two, Figure 2-25(d) and (e), use an ultrasonic sensor. There are three level-detection applications illustrated in Figure 2-25(a), (b), and (d). In the first two, capacitive sensors are used with the sensor placed through the wall of the bin to sense the granular material and looking through the bin wall in the liquid application. To sense the liquid

FIGURE 2-25: Capacitive and ultrasonic proximity sensor applications.

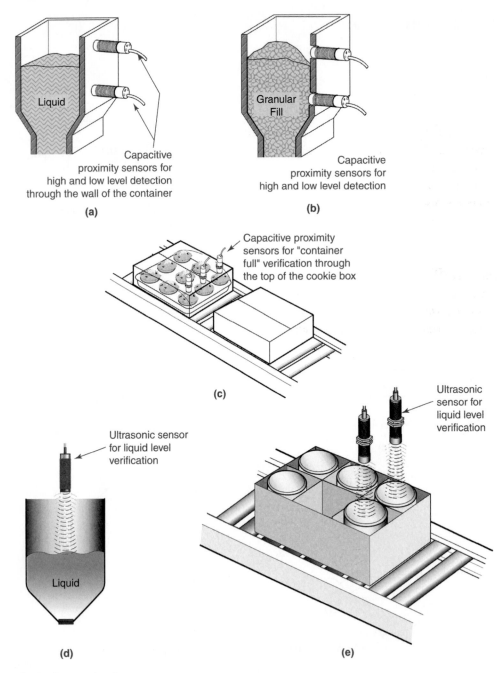

Courtesy of Rockwell Automation, Inc.

tance or height of the target. Highest performance is achieved under the following conditions:

- Ideal target objects have a flat, smooth surface. Sensing distance is reduced when the object is rounded or uneven.
- Objects must be inside the ultrasonic pulse cone, which is 4 degrees or less from the center axis.
- Soft materials, such as foam or fabric, are difficult to detect because they don't reflect the sound waves adequately.

- Reflective surfaces must be positioned to reflect the ultrasonic waves back to the receiver.
- Object temperatures must be less than 100° C.

Any environmental conditions that deaden sound, such as disturbances in the air, can reduce the effectiveness of the sensor.

Proximity sensor applications. Inductive proximity sensor applications are shown in Figure 2-24. In Figure 2-24(a), (b), (c), and (e),

FIGURE 2-24: Inductive sensor applications.

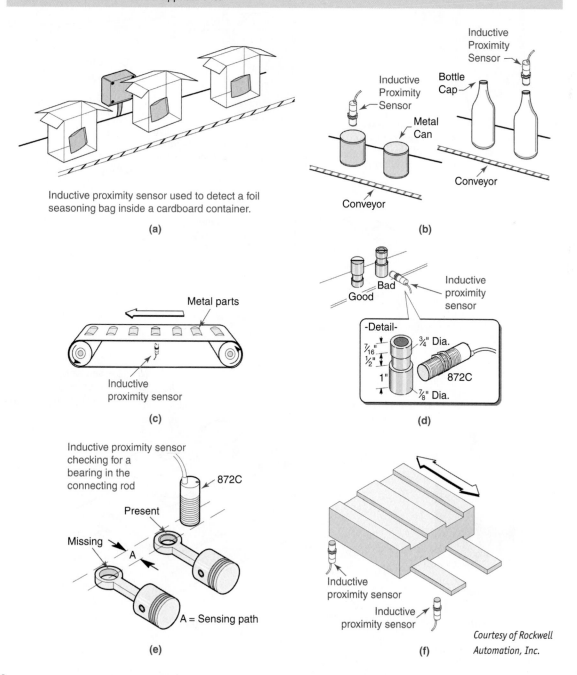

Inductive proximity sensor used to detect a foil seasoning bag inside a cardboard container.

(a)

(b)

(c)

(d)

(e)

(f)

Courtesy of Rockwell Automation, Inc.

FIGURE 2-22: Target movement with respect to the inductive proximity sensor.

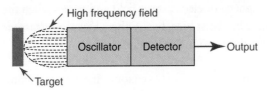

FIGURE 2-23: Capacitive proximity sensor block diagram.

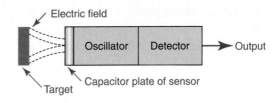

integrated into the sensor (see Figure 2-20) or a shield produced by the metal in which the sensor is mounted. In either case the shielding causes the field to be more focused; in other words, the shielded sensor has a smaller sensing range than the unshielded sensor.

The movement of a target with respect to an inductive proximity sensor is illustrated in Figure 2-22. If a target enters the high frequency magnetic field, eddy currents are induced on the target material. This transfer of energy to the target causes the oscillation amplitude to drop. The detector recognizes the decrease in amplitude and produces an output. Based on the operation of the inductive sensor circuit, the performance characteristics of the sensor include:

- Detection of all materials that are electrical conductors.
- Detection not limited to magnetic materials.
- Detection of stationary and moving objects.
- Preferred target is a flat, smooth object.
- Energy levels are low so that they do not create radio frequency interference or generate heat in the target.

Capacitive proximity sensors. Capacitive proximity sensors operate under the electrical principle of *capacitance* and detect the presence of a part when an object of any material type comes within the electric field established by the capacitor plate(s) in the sensor. Capacitive sensors sense both metallic and nonmetallic objects and are commonly used in the food packaging industry to check product inside containers and to validate fluid and solid levels inside tanks. However, the lower cost and high reliability of inductive sensors makes them the first choice for industrial automation over the capacitive types.

Capacitive proximity sensors use a changing dielectric to change the value of a capacitor in the sensor's oscillation circuit. Recall that the capacitance of a capacitor is determined by the size of the plates, plate separation distance, and the dielectric between the plates. Figure 2-23 provides a block diagram of a capacitive proximity sensor. Note that the target acts as the capacitor's second plate. As an approaching target interacts with the electrostatic field created by the sensor, the capacitance of a capacitor inside the sensor is changed. As the oscillation amplitude increases, the oscillator output voltage increases, causing the output of the detector to change.

Capacitive proximity sensors can sense conducting materials farther away than nonconducting, and the larger the target mass, the farther the sensing distance. Capacitive sensors are more sensitive to changes in temperature and humidity than the inductive sensor and have the following performance characteristics:

- Detected materials include conductors, insulators, plastics, glass, ceramics, oils and greases, water, and all materials with a high moisture content or dielectric constant greater than 1.2.
- Detection of stationary and moving objects.
- Preferred target is a flat, smooth object.
- Operation at low energy levels so that it does not create radio frequency interference or generate heat in the target.

Ultrasonic proximity sensors. Ultrasonic proximity sensors bounce sound waves off a target object and measure the time it takes for the sound waves to return, similar to sonar. The measured time is directly proportional to the dis-

internal receiving device. If a hole is present, the beam goes though the hole (sensor position A) and does not return. If a hole is not present, the beam bounces back (sensor position B).

A vast number of sensors are available with unique combinations of sensing performance, output characteristics, and mounting options. Individual sensors are often used to sense and control a single machine function. In other applications, numerous sensors are used to control every operation of an automated system. Sensing devices fall into two categories:

- Contact devices, which physically touch the parameter being measured.
- Non-contact devices, which sense or measure the process parameter without physically touching it.

The non-contact sensor is a solid-state sensor with no moving parts, unlike the mechanical contact sensor, and it is faster and more reliable than the mechanical device. Contact and non-contact sensors have either a *discrete sensing capability*, which provides on and off states and is discussed in this section, or an *analog sensing capability*, which measures a range of input conditions and is discussed in Chapter 12.

Discrete sensors have a single trigger point and provide two states—*on* and *off*. The sensor depicted in Figure 2-19 is a discrete sensor. Another example of this type of switch is the thermostat that controls the heating systems in homes. A single temperature level (72° F) is set, and the heating system cycles on and off as the house temperature moves below and above the thermostat temperature setting. Discrete solid-state sensors use electronic circuits to perform the sensing function, and provide the on and off output states through a variety of output contacts and circuits.

Typical discrete contact sensors are those switches that were discussed in Section 2-3. Discrete non-contact sensors fall primarily into two categories: *proximity sensors* and *photoelectric sensors*.

2-4-1 Proximity Sensors

As the name implies, *proximity sensors* measure conditions without physically touching the part. Proximity sensors are used to automate discrete part production in manufacturing systems. Proximity sensors operate with an *inductive* or *capacitive* sensing capability, which generates a magnetic or electrostatic field and senses when the field has been breached. Others have an *ultrasonic* capability to make measurements.

Inductive proximity sensors. Inductive proximity sensors operate under the electrical principle of *inductance* and detect the presence of a ferrous or nonferrous metal part when it comes within the magnetic field generated by the sensor's coil. The only requirement for the part material is that it can conduct a current. Inductive proximity sensors are available in various package types with 70 percent of all sensors used falling into the cylindrical threaded barrel type. The shape of the part to be sensed and the sensing application dictate the type of package shape for best operation. Figure 2-20 shows two barrel inductive sensors.

Inductive proximity sensors are comprised of a coil, oscillator, and a detector, which generate an output as shown in the block diagram in Figure 2-21. The coil and the oscillator produce a magnetic field, and the shape of the field is determined by two factors: the core of the coil, which is made from highly permeable ferrite material, and the degree of shielding around the coil. The shield can be either an internal shield

FIGURE 2-20: Barrel inductive proximity sensors.

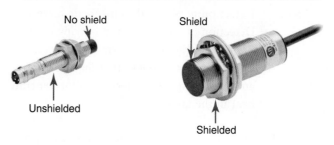

Courtesy of Rockwell Automation, Inc.

FIGURE 2-21: Inductive proximity sensor block diagram.

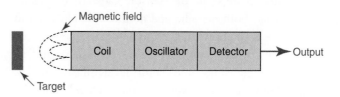

EXAMPLE 2-5

Draw the ladder rung that turns on a motor contactor and a green pilot lamp for the following limit switch conditions: LS1 or LS2 are true and LS3 or LS4 are not true. Remember that the term *true* or *active* means a switch is activated and *not true* or *not active* means it is in the normal position. All switches are double pole double throw.

SOLUTION

The ladder rung solution is shown in Figure 2-18. Note that the switch contacts are considered inputs (left side of the rung) and the contactor and pilot lamp are considered outputs (right side of the rung). The parallel-series connection is the AND/OR function. In other words, the input is true if you have (LS1 OR LS2) AND (NOT LS3 OR NOT LS4). All switches have NO and NC contacts as they are double throw types. Since either switch LS1 or LS2 must be activated or switched to make the outputs true, the NO contacts are used in the ladder rung. Because either switch LS3 OR LS4 must be in its normal condition, the NC contacts are used in the ladder rung. Note that there are two parallel sets of limit switches and two outputs, a green pilot lamp and a motor contactor. When multiple outputs are present on a single rung, they are always in parallel.

FIGURE 2-18: Solution for Example 2-5.

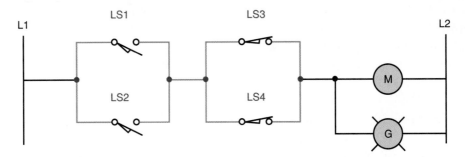

Rehg and Sartori, Industrial Electronics, *1st Edition, © 2006. Reprinted by permission of Pearson Education, Inc., Upper Saddle River, NJ.*

FIGURE 2-19: Hole inspection with sensor.

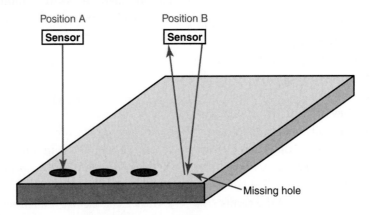

Rehg and Sartori, Industrial Electronics, *1st Edition, © 2006. Reprinted by permission of Pearson Education, Inc., Upper Saddle River, NJ.*

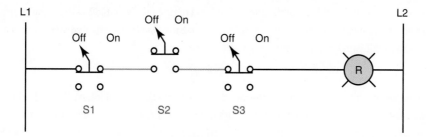

EXAMPLE 2-4

Draw a ladder rung to turn on a solenoid valve when the flow switch (FL1) is activated or when the selector switch (S1) is activated. All contacts are single pole double throw.

SOLUTION

The ladder rung solution is shown in Figure 2-17. Note that the switch contacts are considered inputs (left side of the rung) and the solenoid valve is considered an output (right side of the rung). The parallel connection is considered the OR function. In other words, the input is true if you have FL1 OR S1. All devices have NO and NC contacts as they are double throw types. The normal condition for the contacts is float set point is not reached (no flow) so the NO contacts are open, and the selector is in the off position with NO contacts open. The output should be active (on) when the flow is present OR the selector is turned on.

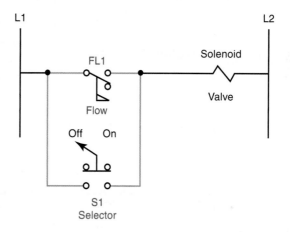

diagrams, relay ladder logic, motor control diagrams, two-wire diagrams, and *three-wire diagrams.* When each is used depends on the type of system that the drawing represents. For example, systems that include only relays are called relay ladder logic, but when they describe the control provided by a PLC they are called just ladder logic or ladder diagrams. Let's take a look at three examples of ladder diagrams using the switches that have been discussed (Examples 2-3, 2-4, and 2-5).

At the present time the use of the terms *true* and *active* (for the on condition) or *not true* and *not active* (for the off condition) for devices is not used because the operation of the electrical circuit is understood with just the *on* and *off* ref-

erence. However, PLC operation will be discussed where the switch condition is separated from the ladder logic representation. Therefore, starting to use these terms here prepares you for the next sections.

2-4 INDUSTRIAL SENSORS

Industrial sensors are the eyes, ears, and tactile senses of the PLC in an automated system. Strategically mounted sensors provide the automation system with the same data that an operator gathers using the five human senses. For example, in Figure 2-19 a sensor verifies that a part has the proper number of holes prior to insertion of a mating part into the holes. The sensor in the figure bounces a light beam off of the object back to an

FIGURE 2-15: Pressure and temperature control symbols.

Symbol		Description
Pressure controls	**Temperature controls**	
Automatic operation		
		Single pole double throw — automatically opens or closes on rise or fall.
		Single pole double throw — slow-acting contact with no snap action. Contacts close on rise and close on fall with an open circuit between contact closures.
		Single pole single throw, normally closed — closes on rise.
		Single pole single throw, normally closed — opens on rise.
		Single pole single throw, normally open — closes on rise.
		Single pole single throw, normally closed — opens on rise.
		Two circuit, single pole single throw, normally open — a common terminal is connected to two separate contacts that close on rise.
		Two circuit, single pole single throw, normally closed — a common terminal is connected to two separate contacts that open on rise.
Manual reset		
		Single pole single throw, normally open — contacts open at a predetermined setting on fall and remain open until system is restored to normal run conditions, at which time contacts can be manually reset.
		Single pole single throw, normally closed — contacts open on rise and remain open until system is restored to normal run conditions, at which time contacts can be manually reset.
		Single pole double throw, one contact normally closed — contact opens on rise and remains open until system is restored to normal run condition, at which time contact can be manually reset. A second contact closes when the first contact opens.
		Single pole single throw, normally closed — contacts close on fall and remain closed until system is resorted to a higher predetermined setting.

FIGURE 2-13: Differential pressure switch.

Contact Arrangement	Contact Symbol
1 N.O. - 1 N.C.	

(a)   (b)

Courtesy of Square D/Schneider Electric.

FIGURE 2-14: Temperature switch.

Bellows
Housing
(Plated
Steel)

Cylinder
(#304
Stainless
Steel)

Capilliary
(Plated Copper)

End Plug
(Brass)

Courtesy of Square D/Schneider Electric.

increased temperature. As the stainless steel cylinder is heated the fluid expands, increasing the pressure against every surface in the sealed chamber. As a result, the bellows expands with the increased pressure and causes electrical contacts to change state.

Figure 2-15 illustrates the symbols and contact configurations for the pressure switches and temperature switches; a description of each of the symbols is also provided.

2-3-6 Control Diagrams

A control diagram is a type of symbolic language that describes the electrical/electronic operation of an industrial system. Control diagrams have numerous names such as *ladder logic, ladder*

EXAMPLE 2-3

Draw a ladder rung to turn on a red pilot lamp when three selector switches have the following conditions: switch S1 is off, switch S2 is on, and switch S3 is off. All switches are single pole double throw.

SOLUTION

The ladder rung solution is shown in Figure 2-16. Note that the switch contacts are considered inputs (left side of the rung) and the pilot lamp is considered an output (right side of the rung). The series connection produces the AND function. In other words, the input is true if you have S2 AND NOT S1 AND NOT S3. All switches have NO and NC contacts as they are double throw types. Because the output is active when S1 and S3 are off, the NC contacts on those switches must be used. Switch S2 is on for an active output, so the NO contact on that switch is used. Continuity through the input logic is achieved only when S1 and S3 are off (not true) and S2 is on (true), which results in turning on the lamp.

FIGURE 2-12: Level-activated lever switches.

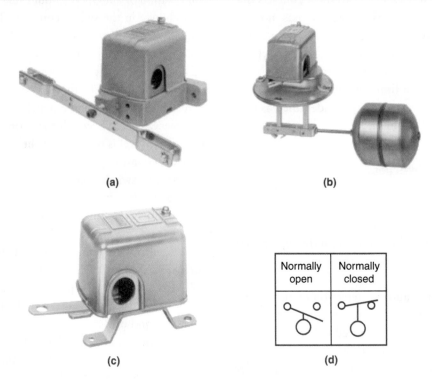

(a)

(b)

(c)

Normally open	Normally closed

(d)

Courtesy of Square D/Schneider Electric.

2-3-4 Pressure Switches

Discrete pressure switches change the open or close condition of a contact based on the pressure applied to the device by water, air, or another fluid such as oil. Pressure switches are either absolute (trigger at a specific pressure value) or differential (trigger on the difference between two pressures). A common application for a pressure switch is to control the air pressure in a tank by turning on an air compressor motor whenever the tank pressure falls below a set value. Switches are available with fixed switching pressures or with an adjustable trigger level.

Pressure switches have two primary components: a *movable component* that is displaced by applied fluid pressure and a set of *snap-action contacts*. The fluid pressure is usually applied to the inside of a closed bellows or on one side of a bellows-shaped diaphragm, causing the ends of the bellows to expand or the diaphragm to displace. In other switches a piston is used to provide the displacement from the applied pressure. The electrical contacts are mechanically linked to the moving component so at a specific displace-ment the contacts change states (open to close or close to open). The contacts have a snap action so that when the trigger level is reached they rapidly move from the current state to the opposite state. The pressure switch in Figure 2-13(a) is a non-adjustable differential device. Differential switches trigger on the difference between two applied pressures. The schematic symbol for the pressure switch is illustrated in Figure 2-13(b), along with a typical contact configuration. Figure 2-15 shows additional contact symbols for pressure switches.

2-3-5 Temperature Switches

Discrete temperature switches, often called *thermostats,* cause electrical contacts to change state at a specific temperature. This contact change on a temperature switch is triggered by the expansion of a fluid inside a sealed chamber. Figure 2-14 illustrates a temperature switch where the sealed chamber includes the exterior capillary tubing and stainless steel cylinder along with a bellows inside the switch body. The fluid that fills this chamber has a high coefficient of expansion with

machine in the off or starting condition, so the latter two symbols are used to show contacts that are activated when the machine has not yet started. The symbol in Figure 2-10(c) is a center neutral contact with the top contact held closed in Figure 2-10(d). The abbreviation most often used to identify a limit switch is LS. If multiple limit switches are used they are identified as LS1, LS2, LS3, and so on.

2-3-2 Flow Switches

Flow switches are used to detect a change in the flow of a liquid or a gas in a pipe or duct. The switch illustrated in Figure 2-11(a) is activated when the flow of liquid through the pipe moves the operator suspended in the flow. Switches are available for liquids with varying viscosities flowing in pipes and for detection of air and gas movement in ducts. The schematic symbol used for flow switches is illustrated in Figure 2-11(b). The abbreviation used for the flow switch is FL. If multiple flow switches are used, then they are identified by FL1, FL2, FL3, and so on.

2-3-3 Level Switches

Level switches or float switches are discrete switches used for control of liquid and granular material levels in tanks and bins. Level switches,

like the three shown in Figure 2-12, use the vertical position of a float on a liquid surface to trigger a change in the switch contacts. The switch includes a snap action mechanism that provides quick-make and quick-break contact operation and adds hysteresis at the trigger point. *Hysteresis* is a separation between the activation point and the deactivation point of the switch. With hysteresis present, once the switch turns on, it remains on until the level is moved past the turn on point to the deactivation point. Hysteresis is needed to keep the level switch from cycling between on and off at a single activation point due to shock, vibration, or a varying level. Hysteresis is sometimes referred to as a dead band. Think of the thermostat in your home. If you set the temperature to 72 degrees, the heater typically turns on at 71 and off at 73, thus providing a dead band, which prevents the thermostat from rapidly cycling on and off.

Level switches are available in two configurations: *open tank*, Figure 2-12(a) and (c), and *closed tank*, Figure 2-12(b). Open tank models are used with tanks that are not sealed and are open to atmospheric pressure. Closed tank models are used in applications where the tank is sealed and could be pressurized. Figure 2-12(d) illustrates the NO and NC schematic symbols for the float switch.

FIGURE 2-11: Flow switch in liquid flowing through a pipe.

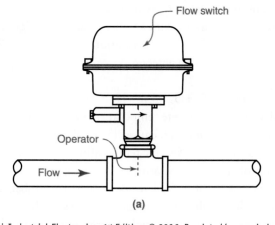
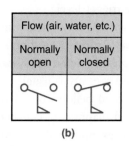

(a) (b)

machine in the off or starting condition, so the latter two symbols are used to show contacts that are activated when the machine has not yet started. The symbol in Figure 2-10(c) is a center neutral contact with the top contact held closed in Figure 2-10(d). The abbreviation most often used to identify a limit switch is LS. If multiple limit switches are used they are identified as LS1, LS2, LS3, and so on.

2-3-2 Flow Switches

Flow switches are used to detect a change in the flow of a liquid or a gas in a pipe or duct. The switch illustrated in Figure 2-11(a) is activated when the flow of liquid through the pipe moves the operator suspended in the flow. Switches are available for liquids with varying viscosities flowing in pipes and for detection of air and gas movement in ducts. The schematic symbol used for flow switches is illustrated in Figure 2-11(b). The abbreviation used for the flow switch is FL. If multiple flow switches are used, then they are identified by FL1, FL2, FL3, and so on.

2-3-3 Level Switches

Level switches or float switches are discrete switches used for control of liquid and granular material levels in tanks and bins. Level switches,

like the three shown in Figure 2-12, use the vertical position of a float on a liquid surface to trigger a change in the switch contacts. The switch includes a snap action mechanism that provides quick-make and quick-break contact operation and adds hysteresis at the trigger point. *Hysteresis* is a separation between the activation point and the deactivation point of the switch. With hysteresis present, once the switch turns on, it remains on until the level is moved past the turn on point to the deactivation point. Hysteresis is needed to keep the level switch from cycling between on and off at a single activation point due to shock, vibration, or a varying level. Hysteresis is sometimes referred to as a dead band. Think of the thermostat in your home. If you set the temperature to 72 degrees, the heater typically turns on at 71 and off at 73, thus providing a dead band, which prevents the thermostat from rapidly cycling on and off.

Level switches are available in two configurations: *open tank*, Figure 2-12(a) and (c), and *closed tank*, Figure 2-12(b). Open tank models are used with tanks that are not sealed and are open to atmospheric pressure. Closed tank models are used in applications where the tank is sealed and could be pressurized. Figure 2-12(d) illustrates the NO and NC schematic symbols for the float switch.

FIGURE 2-11: Flow switch in liquid flowing through a pipe.

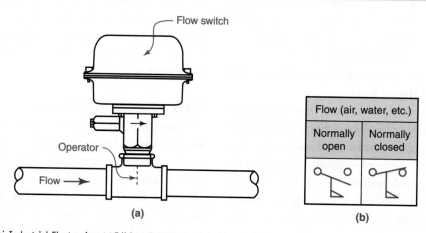

the sensors are used to check for the presence of a part in manufacturing. In Figure 2-24(d) the sensor detects parts that are not oriented properly, and in Figure 2-24(f) the limits of travel of the surface grinding plate are detected. Study the applications until you understand how these sensors are being used.

Capacitive and ultrasonic proximity sensor applications are illustrated in Figure 2-25. The first three applications, Figure 2-25(a) through (c), use a capacitive proximity sensor, while the last two, Figure 2-25(d) and (e), use an ultrasonic sensor. There are three level-detection applications illustrated in Figure 2-25(a), (b), and (d). In the first two, capacitive sensors are used with the sensor placed through the wall of the bin to sense the granular material and looking through the bin wall in the liquid application. To sense the liquid

FIGURE 2-25: Capacitive and ultrasonic proximity sensor applications.

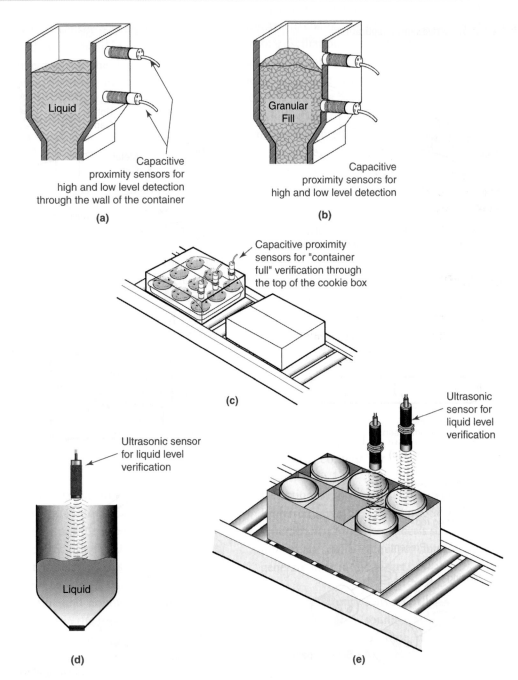

Courtesy of Rockwell Automation, Inc.

through the wall the liquid must have a significantly higher dielectric constant than the material used for the bin, and the bin wall must be thin. In the third level-detection application, an ultrasonic sensor is used to detect the level of the liquid in the tank. In the last two applications, Figure 2-25(c) and (e), sensors are use to verify the presence of products. In the first, three capacitive sensors verify that cookies are packaged in the box. Note that the sensors look through the box lid to check for the cookies. In the second application ultrasonic sensors, set for discrete mode operation, determine that the box is properly filled with cans. Study the applications until you understand how these sensors are being used.

2-4-2   Photoelectric Sensors

Photoelectric sensors are used in many applications and industries to provide accurate detection of objects without physical contact. Two components present in all photoelectric sensors are *a light source* and a *receiver* used to detect the presence of the light source. In its most basic form, a photoelectric sensor is just like a limit switch, where a beam of light replaces the limit switch's mechanical actuator. Photoelectric devices sense the presence of an object or part when the part either breaks a light beam or reflects a beam of light to a receiver. The change in light could be the result of the presence or absence of the object, or as the result in a change of the size, shape, reflectivity, or color of an object. Photoelectric sensors operate over distances from 5mm (0.2 in) to over 250 m (820 ft). Some laser devices can operate at ranges of 304.5 m (1000 ft).

Understanding the operation of photo sensors is the first step in using and troubleshooting them effectively. Photoelectric sensors are comprised of some or all of the following:

- **Light source:** typically a light emitting diode (LED). The LED configuration used in photo sensors is illustrated in Figure 2-26, showing that infrared generates the most light and the least heat of any LED color. In many applications, a visible red beam of light is used, but other colors, such as visible red, blue, and yellow, are used in special applications where specific colors or color contrasts are important. When long distances between the

FIGURE 2-26: LED photoelectric sensors.

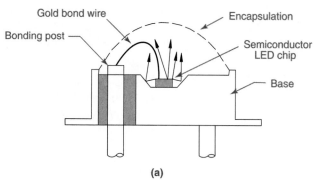

(a)

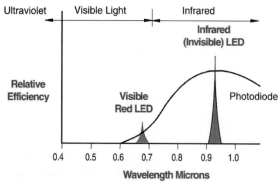

The invisible (infrared) LED is a spectral match for this silicon phototransistor and has much greater efficiency than a visible (red) LED.

(b)

Courtesy of Rockwell Automation, Inc.

source and receiver are necessary, sensors use lasers as a light source. In those applications distances of 304.5 m (1000 ft) are possible. The laser is usually a red color so that alignment between the light source and receiver is enhanced.

- **Light detector:** the component used to detect the presence of the light source. It produces a change in current directly proportional to the amount of light falling on the light detector. Photodiodes or phototransistors are the robust solid-state components that are most often used for the light detector. The wavelengths of the light for the source and receiver are often matched to improve sensing efficiency.

- **Lenses:** used with LED light sources and photo detectors to narrow or focus the light beam area (Figure 2-27) and increase the sensor's range. When the source and receiver beams or fields of view are narrow, alignment

FIGURE 2-27: Photoelectric sensor lens.

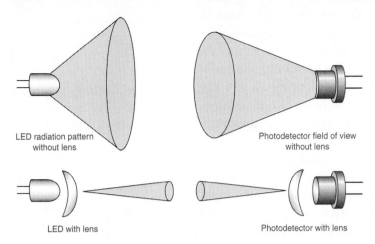

LED radiation pattern
without lens

Photodetector field of view
without lens

LED with lens

Photodetector with lens

Courtesy of Rockwell Automation, Inc.

FIGURE 2-28: Comparison of photoelectric sensor output devices.

Output Type	Strengths	Weaknesses
Electromechanical Relay *AC or DC switching*	• Output is electrically isolated from supply power • Easy series and/or parallel connection of sensor outputs • High switching current	• No short circuit protection possible • Finite relay life
FET *AC or DC switching*	• Very low leakage current • Fast switching speed	• Low output current
Power MOSFET *AC or DC switching*	• Very low leakage current • Fast switching speed	• Moderately high output current
TRIAC *AC switching only*	• High output current	• Relatively high leakage current • Slow output switching
NPN or PNP Transistor *DC switching only*	• Very low leakage current • Fast switching speed	• No AC switching

Courtesy of Rockwell Automation, Inc.

can be difficult. However, when a wider field of view is required, then the sensor has a shorter overall range.

- **Logic circuit:** modulates the LED light source, amplifies the signal from the light detector, and determines if the output state should be changed.
- **Output device:** signals a PLC that a change has occurred. Figure 2-28 provides a comparison between the various output devices; study the table until you can name the options.

Photoelectric sensor operating modes. Photoelectric sensors operate in the following different sensing modes:

- **Through beam** or transmitted beam has the light source and receiver packaged in separate housings.
- **Retroreflective** or reflex has both the light source and receiver in one housing.
- **Polarized retroreflective** has polarizing filters in front of the light source and receiver that are 90 degrees out of phase with each other.

- **Diffused** or photo proximity has the light source and receiver in the same package like the retroreflective mode; however, it uses the detected part to reflect the light beam back to the receiver.

In the *through beam mode* the light source and receiver are packaged in separate housings. These two units are positioned opposite each other so that the light from the source (S) shines directly on the receiver (R) as shown in Figure 2-29. Targets must break or block the beam between the light source and the receiver. Through beam sensors

provide the longest sensing distances and the highest level of operating margin. In photoelectric sensors the term *margin* is used to describe the light level reaching the receiver. With a margin of one, the receiver has the minimum level of light needed to detect that a beam is present. A graph of distance versus margin is included in the sensor figures. When an application dictates the use of photoelectric sensors, a margin greater than one is used.

In the *retroreflective mode* as shown in Figure 2-30 both the light source and receiver are packaged in a single housing. The light beam

FIGURE 2-29: Photoelectric sensor—through beam mode.

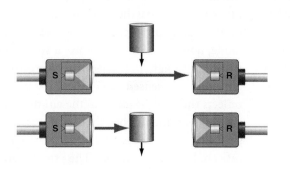

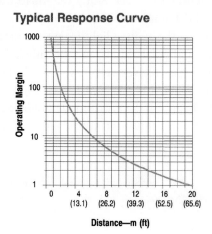

Courtesy of Rockwell Automation, Inc.

FIGURE 2-30: Photoelectric sensor—retroreflective mode.

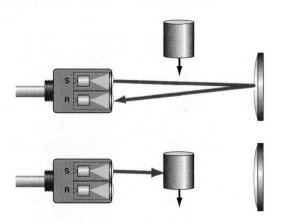

Courtesy of Rockwell Automation, Inc.

emitted by the light source is reflected by a special reflective device, called a *target*, back to the receiver where it triggers a change in the output device. The object is detected when it breaks this light beam and the output device changes states. Special reflectors or reflective tapes with special glass beads or corner-cube reflective surfaces are used for the retroreflective target; as a result, the target does not have to be aligned perfectly perpendicular to the sensor. Misalignment of a reflector or reflective tape of up to 15 degrees will not significantly reduce the operating margin of the sensing system.

In the *polarized retroreflective mode* the sensors have polarizing filters in front of the light source and receiver that are 90 degrees out of phase with each other. Study the illustration in Figure 2-31 until the filter orientation is clear, noting that the emitted light from the source has a horizontal polarization, and the only light that can reach the receiver *must* have a vertical polarization. When a highly polished or shiny object breaks the beam, the horizontally polarized light

from the emitter is reflected back toward the receiver. The receiver's vertical filter blocks the light from reaching the receiver, so the receiver is not triggered. As a result, the sensor's output device is off. When no object is present, the emitted horizontally polarized light is reflected back by the special target in a nonpolarized condition. Some of the nonpolarized light passes through the vertical polarizing filter at the receiver and the receiver is activated. This causes the output device to turn on.

Access to both sides of the object to be sensed is required for transmitted beam and retroreflective sensors to establish a beam that can be interrupted by the passing object. It is often not possible to obtain access on both sides of an object. In these applications, a *diffused mode* is the only photoelectric sensor choice. Diffused mode sensors have the light source and receiver in the same package like the retroreflective mode; however, they do not use a special target to reflect the light beam back to the receiver. The object to be sensed becomes the target that reflects the light beam from the emitter back to the receiver. Light from the source striking the surface of the sensed object is scattered or reflected at all angles. The small portion reflected back to the sensor is detected by the receiver and used to trigger the output device. This is called a *standard diffused mode* and is illustrated in Figure 2-32.

Detecting targets positioned close to reflective backgrounds can be particularly challenging, and may require a special type of diffused mode sensor. There are five additional types of diffused mode sensors offered by vendors for automation control. Other types include *sharp cutoff diffused, fixed focus diffused, wide angle diffused, background suppression diffused,* and *distance measurement diffused.*

While many applications can be handled by any of these sensing modes, each offers specific strengths and weaknesses. The typical application plus advantages and cautions are summarized in Figure 2-33. Note that there are transmitted beam (through beam), two types of retroreflective, five types of diffused, and fiber optics sensors that operate in all modes. In some photoelectric sen-

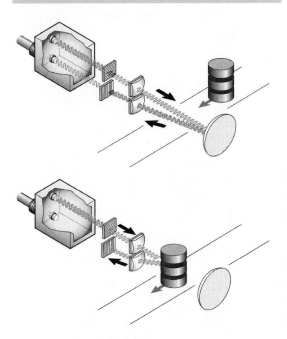

FIGURE 2-31: Photoelectric sensor—polarized retroreflective mode.

Courtesy of Rockwell Automation, Inc.

FIGURE 2-32: Photoelectric sensor—standard diffused mode.

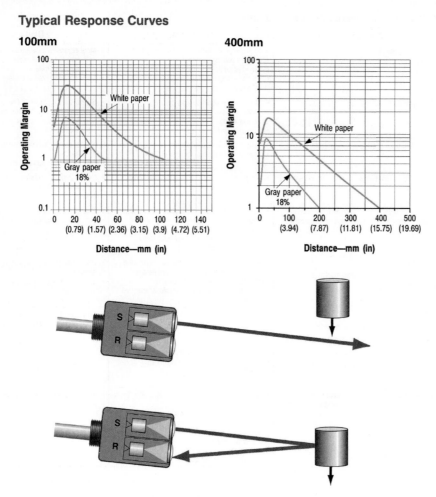

Typical Response Curves

Courtesy of Rockwell Automation, Inc.

sor applications, specialized lighting is often required where imaging of an object is difficult.

Photoelectric sensor functions. All the photoelectric sensors function in the same basic manner, with a light source and the light detector; however, the electronics associated with the sensors have the following operational options:

- **Light ON–Dark ON:** Light ON occurs when the output becomes high or active when the source illuminates the receiver. Dark ON works in the opposite mode. These modes are selected using either a switch or through output terminal selection.

- **Output Control:** Sensors are available in a variety of output circuits which match the interfacing needs of the automation controllers. The modes of operation vary widely as well. The table in Figure 2-33 lists the photoelectric sensor modes, their typical application area, and their advantages and disadvantages.

- **On and Off Delay Timers:** Delay timers provide a variable delay to a change in the output after the input stimulus triggers an output change. The delay occurs as the sensor is changing from on to off so that the off condition is delayed by the selectable value.

FIGURE 2-33: Comparison of photoelectric sensor modes.

Photoelectric Sensing Modes Advantages and Cautions

Sensing Mode	Applications	Advantages	Cautions
Transmitted Beam	General purpose sensing Parts counting	• High margin for contaminated environments • Longest sensing distances • Not affected by second surface reflections • Probably most reliable when you have highly reflective objects	• More expensive because separate light source and receiver required, more costly wiring • Alignment important • Avoid detecting objects of clear material
Retroreflective	General purpose sensing	• Moderate sensing distances • Less expensive than transmitted beam because of simpler wiring • Ease of alignment	• Shorter sensing distance than transmitted beam • Less margin than transmitted beam • May detect reflections from shiny objects (use polarized instead)
Polarized Retroreflective	General purpose sensing of shiny objects	• Ignores first surface reflections • Uses visible red beam for ease of alignment	• Shorter sensing distance than standard retroreflective • May see second surface reflections
Standard Diffuse	Applications where both sides of the object cannot be accessed	• Access to both sides of the object not required • No reflector needed • Ease of alignment	• Can be difficult to apply if the background behind the object is sufficiently reflective and close to the object
Sharp Cutoff Diffuse	Short-range detection of objects with the need to ignore backgrounds that are close to the object	• Access to both sides of the object not required • Provides some protection against sensing of close backgrounds • Detects objects regardless of color within specified distance	• Only useful for very short distance sensing • Not used with backgrounds close to object
Background Suppression Diffuse	General purpose sensing Areas where you need to ignore backgrounds that are close to the object	• Access to both sides of the target not required • Ignores backgrounds beyond rated sensing distance regardless of reflectivity • Detects objects regardless of color at specified distance	• More expensive than other types of diffuse sensors • Limited maximum sensing distance
Fixed Focus Diffuse	Detection of small targets Detects objects at a specific distance from sensor Detection of color marks	• Accurate detection of small objects in a specific location	• Very short distance sensing • Not suitable for general purpose sensing • Object must be accurately positioned
Wide Angle Diffuse	Detection of objects not accurately positioned Detection of very fine threads over a broad area	• Good at ignoring background reflections • Detects objects that are not accurately positioned • No reflector needed	• Short distance sensing
Fiber Optics	Allows photoelectric sensing in areas where a sensor cannot be mounted because of size or environment considerations	• Glass fiber optic cables available for high ambient temperature applications • Shock and vibration resistant • Plastic fiber optic cables can be used in areas where continuous movement is required • Insert in limited space • Noise immunity • Corrosive areas placement	• More expensive than lensed sensors • Short distance sensing

Courtesy of Rockwell Automation, Inc.

Photoelectric sensor applications. The applications in Figure 2-34 illustrate many of the photoelectric sensor operating modes described in the table in Figure 2-33. The sensors used in Figure 2-34(a) and (f) are operating in the diffused mode. In Figure 2-34(a) *fiber optic units* extend the diffused sensor some distance from the amplifier out to the sensing point in the application. Here the presence of part of a product and an installed cork are checked as the bottle passes a point on the conveyor. In Figure 2-34(f) a self-contained sensor is used with two different types of transparent objects. The application in Figure 2-34(b) uses a retroreflective mode sensor to determine when the paper rolls have reached the desired diameter. The applications in Figure 2-34(c) and (d) both use the through beam mode with a light source in one leg of the sensor and the receiver in the other leg. The sensor in Figure 2-34(d) uses a sensor controller from the sensor manufacturer to provide process control based on the sensor response. The final application in Figure 2-34(e) uses two sensors to measure the difference in the height of two surfaces on a part. Note that a standard discrete diffused sensor is used to indicate when the part is in position and then the sensor controller records the two distance measurements from the sensors.

At this point the type of non-contact sensor (proximity or photoelectric) and the sensing mode (inductive, capacitive, through beam, retroreflective beam, or diffused beam) has been discussed. So let's take a look at selecting the sensor type and mode of operation based on some typical applications.

FIGURE 2-34: Photoelectric sensor applications.

Detecting presence of cork

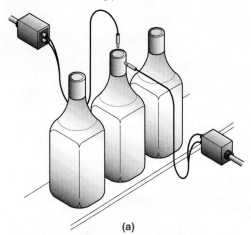

(a)

Detecting diameter of paper roll

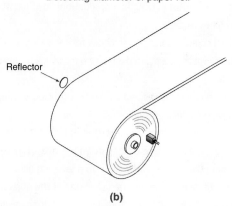

Reflector

(b)

Detecting edge of material to activate cutter

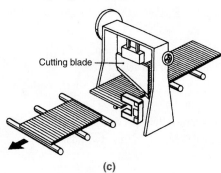

Cutting blade

(c)

Detecting marks on packaging film to adjust roller and cutter speed

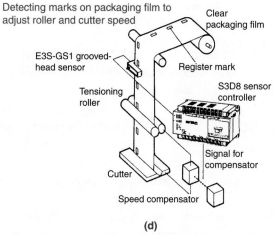

Clear packaging film

E3S-GS1 grooved-head sensor

Register mark

Tensioning roller

S3D8 sensor controller

Signal for compensator

Cutter

Speed compensator

(d)

Measuring height difference

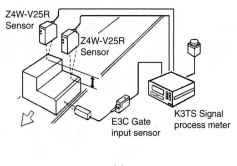

Z4W-V25R Sensor

Z4W-V25R Sensor

E3C Gate input sensor

K3TS Signal process meter

(e)

Sensing of transparent objects

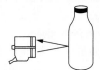

Typical examples
(1) Sensing of transparent or translucent objects.
(2) Sensing of transparent greases, film, or plastic plates.
(3) Sensing of the liquid level.

Sensing of objects through a transparent cover

Typical examples
(1) Sensing of the contents in a transparent case.
(2) Sensing of the position of meter pointer.

(f)

Courtesy of Rockwell Automation, Inc.

EXAMPLE 2-6

Select a sensor type and sensing method or mode for each of the following application situations.

    a. Count boxes (18 inches square) on a 24-inch conveyor belt with complete access to both sides of the conveyor.

    b. Count shiny thermos bottles moving in a production machine. Access to both sides of the conveyor is permitted, but sensor must be 18 inches from parts.

    c. Detect small metal screws coming from a bowl feeder on a pair of metal rails.

    d. Detect a small black relay on a printed circuit board with a highly reflective surface. Sensor must be located 6 inches above the relay and board.

    e. The level of shampoo must be verified as the clear plastic bottles move down a conveyor. The only sensor location is 0.5 inches from one side of the passing bottle.

    f. Suggest an alternate sensor for the application in Figure 2-34(a).

    g. Detect the leading edge of a plate moving down a conveyor. Access is available only from the top.

    h. Detect shiny round plastic cans at the input to a labeling machine. The sensor must be mounted 1.5 inches from the can, and a reflector could be mounted on the other side of the object.

    i. Detect the presence of a metal slug at the input to a forging machine. There is a single side access restriction, but the sensor can be mounted as close to the slug as necessary.

SOLUTION

    a. Use a through or transmitted beam since it is the first choice when access to both sides of the object is available.

    b. The transmitted beam is not used since reflections could reduce reliability. Use a polarized retroreflective for reliable detection.

    c. The metal rails prevent the use of an inductive proximity. Use a fixed focus diffused with the focus placed on the screws. Wide angle diffused cannot be used because of all the other hardware that would be in the field of view.

    d. The main problem is the highly reflective background, nonmetallic object, single-side access, and the 6-inch sensing distance. Distance is too long for capacitive, so background suppression diffused must be used.

    e. The clear plastic bottle would permit either a capacitive or diffused sensor to be used. However, the close sensing distance eliminates the diffused because of the blind zone in a diffused sensor. A second fixed focus diffused would be used to verify a bottle was present by detecting the cap, and then the level could be verified.

    f. Two capacitive proximity sensors could be used in this application as an alternate solution.

    g. Transmitted beam and fixed focus diffused are the sensors of choice for edge detection. With access from only one side the fixed focus diffused must be used.

    h. The application could support a retroreflective sensor, except that the close mounting distance would place the cans in the blind zone. Therefore a wide angle diffused is the best sensor for this application.

    i. An inductive proximity is the best choice for this application.

2-5   INTERFACING INPUT FIELD DEVICES

Interfacing input field devices to the PLC involves the physical connection of the device, the powering of the device, the sizing of the wiring to ensure adequate current carrying capability, and the routing of the wiring to minimize electrical interference and safety. The term *field* is used to designate that the device is not part of the PLC. The PLC inputs are generally configured into two types—inputs share a common return or input pairs are totally isolated. Both types are typically otpo-isolated from the input field devices.

2-5-1   Powering Input Field Devices

Sensors typically have the following power voltage ratings: 10–30 VDC, 20–130 VAC, 90–250 VAC, and 20–250 VAC/DC. These values bracket the supply voltages available on the factory floor. AC sensors power the load and sensor from the same power source, but most DC sensors require

a separate DC supply that isolates the sensor electronics from the AC power line.

Two-wire and three-wire sensor outputs. Sensors outputs are commonly divided into two categories: two-wire and three-wire. Two-wire devices have an output switch that is placed in series with the PLC and the power source. Figure 2-35(a) illustrates the two-wire switch. Note that when the switch is closed, the current flows into the PLC input, through the PLC electronics, and returns to the power source via the PLC common. Figure 2-35(b) illustrates the three-wire switch. The three-wire switch operates as a two-wire switch but has a third wire that is connected to the PLC common. Generally, the three-wire switch is only for electronic sensors that have an output wire plus two power wires.

2-5-2 Input Wiring

The PLC input is both a *physical interface* for the connection of wires and an *electrical/data interface* to determine the on/off state or level of the signal from the attached field device. PLC input circuitry (covered in Chapter 1) varies with the manufacturers of the equipment, but generally the input circuitry signal conditions the input voltage before it's fed into an opto-isolator integrated circuit. The purpose of the opto-isolator is to isolate the incoming voltage and grounds from the rest of the PLC circuitry. Figure 2-36 depicts PLC input opto-isolators for a DC input and for an AC input. The series resistor limits the current into the PLC input from the switch or sensor connected to the input. For the DC unit, the input polarity must be observed for the opto-isolator to turn on. For the AC unit, the opto-isolator will turn on with either polarity. This AC unit is typically designated as an AC/DC-type of PLC input module and is used for both AC and DC inputs because the input polarity does not matter. However, caution should be taken when dealing with the hot and neutral lines of an AC input. In general a PLC input module has either all inputs isolated from each other with no common input connection or groups of inputs share a common connection. For example, inputs are grouped in fours so

FIGURE 2-35: Two-wire and three-wire sensors.

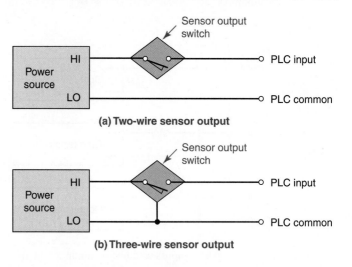

(a) Two-wire sensor output

(b) Three-wire sensor output

FIGURE 2-36: PLC opto-isolator inputs.

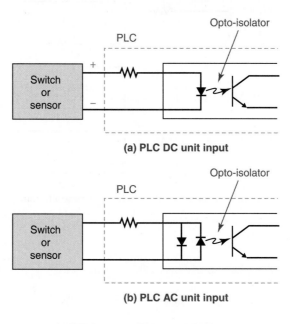

(a) PLC DC unit input

(b) PLC AC unit input

every four inputs has a common ground. Figure 2-37 illustrates both these input module configurations. Figure 2-37(a) shows PLC input circuits connected to a common terminal, and Figure 2-37(b) shows PLC totally isolated input circuits.

The input wiring for a sensor and PLC input is illustrated in Figure 2-38. In this interface, current flows out of the PLC input (a sourcing input), and into the sensor output terminal (a sinking output). Note the direction of current flow as specified by the arrow. The PLC input and the

FIGURE 2-37: PLC inputs with common terminal configurations.

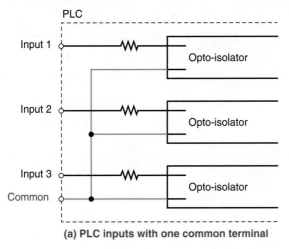

(a) PLC inputs with one common terminal

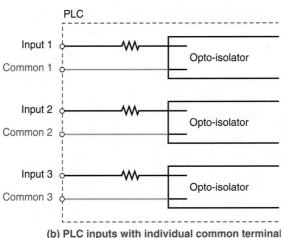

(b) PLC inputs with individual common terminal

sensor output can be either current sourcing (current flows out from from the terminal when active) or current sinking (current flows into the terminal when active). Let's examine this important concept of current sinking and current sourcing.

2-5-3 Current Sinking and Current Sourcing Devices

When wiring a sensor to the PLC input, these rules must be followed:

- Current sinking sensors must be matched to current sourcing PLC inputs.
- Current sourcing sensors must be matched with current sinking PLC inputs.

Reread the rules until you have them memorized. If you interface a sensor to a PLC and do not follow the rule, the interface will not function, and damage may result for the sensor and/or the PLC input circuitry.

When applied to DC type sensors, an NPN is a sinking transistor, which is shown in Figure 2-38, and a PNP is used for sourcing. Referring to Figure 2-38, the NPN (sinking) sensor output has the emitter connected to the return of a power supply and the collector to the PLC input; thus current flows out of the PLC and into the sensor.

FIGURE 2-38: Sensor and PLC input interface.

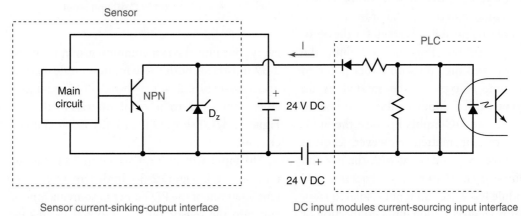

Sensor current-sinking-output interface   DC input modules current-sourcing input interface

Rehg and Sartori, Industrial Electronics, *1st Edition, © 2006. Reprinted by permission of Pearson Education, Inc., Upper Saddle River, NJ.*

When a PNP (sourcing) sensor output is used, the emitter is connected to a positive voltage of a power supply and the collector to the PLC input; thus current flows out of the sensor and into the PLC. In both cases, when the sensor is off, no current flows through the PLC. Read Appendix B for additional PLC module interface circuitry information.

2-6 ELECTROMAGNETIC OUTPUT ACTUATORS

An *electromagnetic actuator* is any device that contains a magnetic winding or coil that converts electrical energy into mechanical movement. The common types of these actuators driven by a PLC are solenoids, relays, contactors, and motor starters. Discussions of these types of actuators and their electrical symbols are found in the following subsections.

2-6-1 Solenoid-Controlled Devices

Before we discuss devices let's first look at solenoids. *Solenoids* convert electrical energy directly into linear mechanical motion. The basic DC solenoid illustrated in Figure 2-39 has two components: a *coil of wire* and an *iron core*

plunger. In the de-energized case, Figure 2-39(a), the only force acting on the iron core is the spring pushing it out of the coil. When the switch is closed, Figure 2-39(b), current through the coil creates an electromagnet with a magnetic flux that flows from the top of the coil into the bottom of the coil. This magnetic field pulls the iron core into the coil because the magnetic force is greater than the spring force. The stroke is the difference between the de-energized and energized positions of the core.

AC-powered solenoids are more common in industry and include a third component called a *frame*. Figure 2-40(a) illustrates a cutaway view for each of three time intervals of solenoid operation; the solenoid schematic symbol is shown in Figure 2-40(b). Study the cutaway of the AC solenoid until you recognize all the parts and the three time intervals: (1) just after the coil is energized, (2) as the plunger, called an *armature*, is closing, and (3) fully energized when the armature is pulled in.

A very common solenoid-controlled device is the valve. A *solenoid valve* is an electromechanical device that is used to control the flow of air or fluids such as water, inert gas, light oil, and refrigerants. Solenoid valves are the simplest output device and are used extensively in industrial

---

FIGURE 2-39: Basic solenoid.

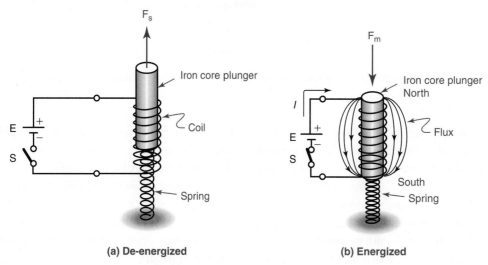

(a) De-energized   (b) Energized

Rehg and Sartori, Industrial Electronics, *1st Edition, © 2006. Reprinted by permission of Pearson Education, Inc., Upper Saddle River, NJ.*

FIGURE 2-40: AC solenoid.

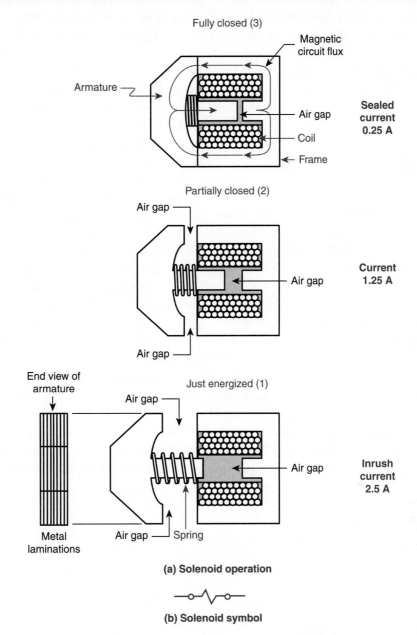

Fully closed (3)

Magnetic circuit flux

Armature

Air gap

Coil

Frame

Sealed current 0.25 A

Partially closed (2)

Air gap

Air gap

Air gap

Current 1.25 A

End view of armature

Just energized (1)

Air gap

Air gap

Inrush current 2.5 A

Metal laminations

Air gap — Spring

(a) Solenoid operation

(b) Solenoid symbol

control systems. Figure 2-41 illustrates the basic construction of a normally closed, two-position solenoid valve. A cutaway view and an exploded view are depicted. The spring that is wrapped around the plunger exerts a force on the pilot valve, holding it in position and allowing no flow through the valve body, inlet to outlet. This is the de-energized condition. When the coil is energized, a magnetic field is generated, moving the plunger, pilot valve, and piston assembly, allowing flow through the valve body. The magnetic field overcomes the spring force, which is pushing in the opposite direction of the magnetic field. The most common fluid controlled by this valve type is oil in a hydraulic cylinder or air in a pneumatic cylinder. Also available in the marketplace are solenoid valves in the normally open position, which close when the coil is energized.

Solenoid valves are generally limited to small-diameter pipes and are not applicable for direct

FIGURE 2-41: Solenoid valve.

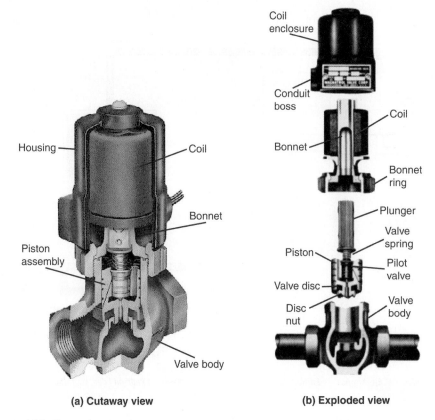

(a) Cutaway view   **(b) Exploded view**

Courtesy of Magnatrol Valve Corporation.

control of fluid through large-diameter pipes. However, the solenoid valve is used as a pilot or lead valve to control the flow to a pneumatic-actuated valve, which controls the flow through the large-diameter pipe. Pneumatic- or air-assisted control valves are opened and closed by an electrical signal that is converted to air pressure (3–15 psi), allowing the valve opening to be anywhere between full open and full closed. These valves are mainly used to control the flow of liquid through large-diameter pipes and in explosive atmosphere applications such as chemical processing and spray painting. Figure 2-42 illustrates a pneumatic-assisted control valve—a three-way, two-position smaller solenoid valve controls a larger pneumatic-actuated valve. Note the solenoid valve symbol pictures the de-energized state as indicated by the arrows, indicating that the exhaust is connected to the piping system, and by a T symbol indicating the inlet is closed. When the solenoid is energized, the exhaust is closed and the inlet is connected to the piping system, and air flows to

the diaphragm housing. The diaphragm compresses the spring, opening the main valve and allowing air to flow through the pipe. The air pressure in the diaphragm is let out through the exhaust port when the solenoid is de-energized, and the spring inside the diaphragm closes the main valve. This is a discrete application of a smaller valve switching 3 to 15 psi on and off to a larger control valve.

2-6-2   Control Relays

Control relays are remotely operated switches that are one of the oldest control devices still in common use. They are the combination of electromagnets and solenoids with switch contact configurations. There are numerous relay models to satisfy every control requirement. Industrial control relays are shown in Figure 2-43.

Relays have two primary functions: (1) control of a large current and/or voltage with a small electrical signal and (2) isolation of the power used to control the action from the power that must be

FIGURE 2-42: Pneumatic-assisted control valve.

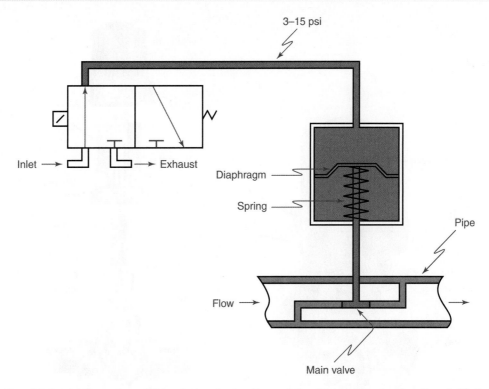

3–15 psi

Inlet →

→ Exhaust

Diaphragm

Spring

Pipe

Flow →

Main valve

Rehg and Sartori, Industrial Electronics, *1st Edition, © 2006. Reprinted by permission of Pearson Education, Inc., Upper Saddle River, NJ.*

FIGURE 2-43: Industrial control relays.

Rehg and Sartori, Industrial Electronics, *1st Edition, © 2006. Reprinted by permission of Pearson Education, Inc., Upper Saddle River, NJ.*

switched to cause some action. Usually relay coil currents are typical well below 1 amp, whereas contact ratings for industrial relays are at least 10 amps. In effect, a relay acts as a binary (on or off) amplifier. This binary amplifier effect is illustrated by the control circuit example in Figure 2-44. In the example, a relatively small electronic switch located in a PLC at some distance from the relay controls the switching of a 24 VDC source across the coil of the relay located at the site of the load. When the relay coil is energized the contacts switch the large voltage and current to the load. Eliminating the relay and using the electronic switch in the PLC to accomplish this is not possible because of the high AC voltage and current that would have to be routed to and switched by the PLC. The second function is illustrated in the example as well. The control voltage is DC, and controlled voltage is AC with both of the sources and grounds isolated from each other. Study the circuit until the operation and advantage of the relay is clear.

Relay Contact Ratings

The most important consideration when selecting relays, or relay outputs on a PLC, is the *rated voltage and current.*

- **Rated voltage:** the suggested operation voltage for the coil. If the voltage is too low the relay may fail to operate and voltages too

high can shorten the relay's life. PLC output modules have a wide voltage range to work with most relay voltage requirements.

- **Rated current:** the maximum current before contact damage, such as welding or melting, occurs.

The contact ratings for a typical industrial control relay are illustrated in Figure 2-45. Note the large variation between allowable DC and AC load currents for approximately the same voltage.

Referring to Figure 2-45, the 120 VAC has the break contact current maximum at 6 amps, whereas at about the same DC voltage the maximum break current is 0.55 amps. The primary reason for this wide variation is the small air gap between open contacts, which is not adequate to break a sustained DC arc from an inductive load. However, this lower limit is adequate for the control logic applications where this type of relay is generally used. Occasionally the required load on

relay contacts may be slightly higher than their nominal rating. Current capacity is increased by connecting contacts in parallel, and arc suppression is improved by connecting multiple contacts in series. The parallel contacts must be on the same relay so that the parallel contacts close and open at the same time.

Relay contact configurations. The contact configuration and terminology covered in the first part of the chapter for switches applies equally well to relay contacts. The two primary specifications that transfer to relays are number of poles and contact condition—normally open (NO) or normally closed (NC). A relay armature may actuate more than one set of contacts, so as in switches the relay could be a multiple pole device. Relays typically have one to eight poles. Contacts are normally open, normally closed, or a combination of the two. As with switches, the "normal" state of a relay's contacts is the condition present when

FIGURE 2-44: Relay control circuit.

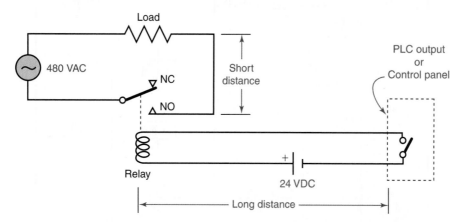

Rehg and Sartori, Industrial Electronics, *1st Edition, © 2006. Reprinted by permission of Pearson Education, Inc., Upper Saddle River, NJ.*

FIGURE 2-45: Control relay contact ratings.

Contact Ratings

AC Ratings								DC Ratings				
Volts	Inductive 35% Power Factor						Resistive 75% Power Factor	Volts	Inductive			
	UL Rating	Make		Break		Cont. Amps	Make, Break & Cont. Amps		UL Rating	Make & ▲ Break Amps	Cont. Amps	
		Amps	VA	Amps	VA							
120	A600	60	7200	6	720	10	10	125	Q600	0.55	2.5	
240		30	7200	3	720	10	10	250		0.27	2.5	
480		15	7200	1.5	720	10	10	600		0.10	2.5	
600		12	7200	1.2	720	10	10					

▲ 69 VA maximum up to 300 volts.

Courtesy of Square D/Schneider Electric.

FIGURE 2-46: Relay schematic symbols.

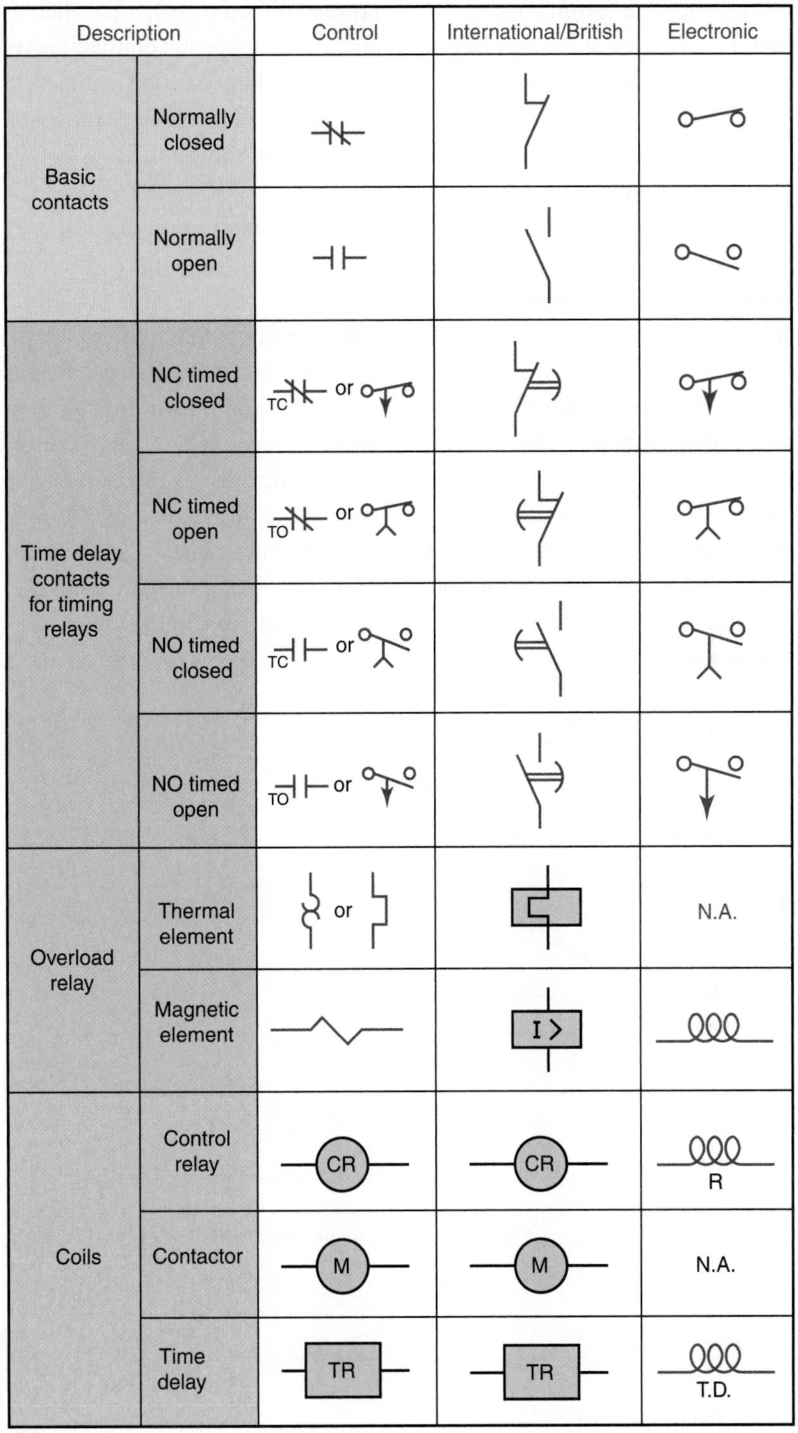

Description		Control	International/British	Electronic
Basic contacts	Normally closed			
	Normally open			
Time delay contacts for timing relays	NC timed closed	TC or		
	NC timed open	TO or		
	NO timed closed	TC or		
	NO timed open	TO or		
Overload relay	Thermal element	or		N.A.
	Magnetic element		I >	
Coils	Control relay	CR	CR	R
	Contactor	M	M	N.A.
	Time delay	TR	TR	T.D.

the coil is de-energized, just as it comes in the box from the manufacturer. In Figure 2-44, the relay is shown in the de-energized condition and the states of the contacts are labeled. The symbols used in schematics to identify relay coils and contacts are different for an electronic schematic versus a control wiring drawing. In addition, the international standard has another representation. The table in Figure 2-46 lists the symbols used for each type of circuit schematic.

Holding contacts. *Holding* or *seal-in contacts* provide a method of maintaining current flow after a momentary switch has been pressed and released. The holding contacts carry the full power of the rung output. In general, a holding contact is connected in parallel with the momentary switch as shown in Figure 2-47. When the NO start push button PB1 is pressed, current flows through the NC stop push button PB2 to the motor starter M. The auxiliary contact M1 of the starter is connected in parallel with PB1, keeping the starter coil energized after PB1 is released.

2-6-3 Latching Relays

The *latching relay* is a relay whose contacts remain open and/or closed even after power has been removed from the coil. Thus, if a relay position must be maintained in an automated process after power is removed, the latching relay provides that function. The latching relay has a latch coil and an unlatch coil. Figure 2-48 depicts a latching relay with two coils labeled coil A and coil B. Energizing coil A produces a magnetic field,

which opposes the magnetic field of the permanent magnet in circuit A, and is great enough to break the armature free and snap into a closed position. The armature remains in that position upon removal of power from coil A, but it will snap back upon energizing coil B. Because the operation depends upon cancellation of a magnetic field, the polarity indicated in the figure must be applied to the coils.

Figure 2-49 illustrates the control diagram for a latching relay in the unlatched state. In this state the solenoid SOL1 is de-energized. When the push button PB1 is momentarily pressed, the latch coil L is energized, setting the relay in the latched position. The relay contact is closed, thus completing the circuit and energizing SOL1. When the push button PB2 is momentarily pressed, the unlatch coil U is energized, setting the relay in the unlatched position. The relay contact is open, thus opening the circuit and de-energizing SOL1.

2-6-4 Contactors

Contactors, shown in Figure 2-50, are relays designed to switch large currents from large voltage sources. Contactors have multiple contacts so that both lines of a single-phase source and all three lines of a three-phase source can be switched. In addition to the contacts used to switch the primary voltage, there are usually one or more contacts, called *auxiliary contacts*, for use in the contactor control circuit. These auxiliary contacts are often limited to 120 VAC and may be either normally open or normally closed.

FIGURE 2-47: Seal-in contact.

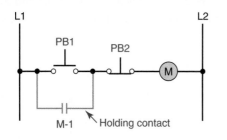

FIGURE 2-48: Latching relay operation.

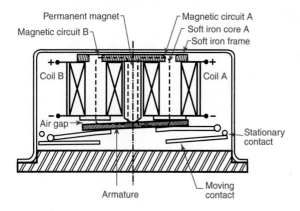

Courtesy of Teledyne Relays.

FIGURE 2-49: Latching relay control diagram.

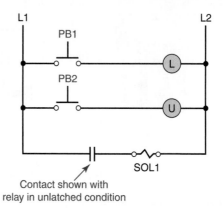

FIGURE 2-50: Contactors.

Courtesy of Square D/Schneider Electric.

Contactors also have an *arc-quenching system* to suppress the arc formed when the contacts carrying inductive current open. Contactors for AC and DC loads are quite different in design because of the need to prevent arcing when contacts open. DC contactors are designed to handle DC current, as well as the greater difficulty of breaking a DC arc.

2-6-5 Motor Starters

A typical motor starter includes contacts, which were discussed in the previous subsection, an *overload block* or thermal unit, which provides over-current protection for the motor with a thermal *overload contact*, which is opened when an overload is detected. The thermal unit resets to its normal state when the overload is removed. Most thermal units are manufactured to operate in one of the following three basic overload methods.

- **Eutectic Alloy Overload Method** uses a eutectic alloy, which is similar to solder but with a lower melting point, to control a ratchet-pivot assembly that controls the overload contacts.
- **Bimetallic Overload Method** uses two dissimilar metals, bonded together, to provide the movement that opens the overload contacts.
- **Phase-loss Sensitivity Overload Method** is similar to the bimetallic overload method except that the difference in current in any of the phases is used to trip the trip-bar assembly, activating the overload and cutting off current flow to the motor.

Figure 2-51 shows a motor starter and a cutaway showing one set of contacts and the ther-

FIGURE 2-51: Starter operation.

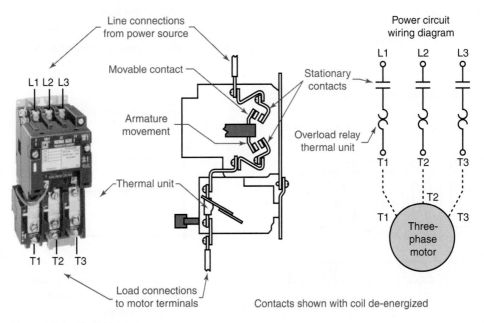

Courtesy of Square D/Schneider Electric.

EXAMPLE 2-7

Draw the control diagram with relay ladder rungs for controlling the movement of a container on a conveyor where

- The depression of a start button starts a motor, which starts a conveyor moving.
- The motor stops when the container reaches a specific position or when the stop button is depressed.
- A red lamp indicates that the conveyor is stopped, and a green lamp indicates that the conveyor is moving.

SOLUTION

Refer to Figure 2-52, the control diagram, as you read the following description.

1. The depression of the start button PB1 energizes the control relay CR if the normally closed limit switch LS is not activated and the stop button PB2 is not depressed.
2. The CR-1 contact closes, sealing in CR even if PB1 is released.
   - The CR-2 contact opens, turning off the red lamp.
   - The CR-3 contact closes, turning on the green lamp.
   - The CR-4 contact closes, energizing the motor contactor M, which starts the motor, moving the container as the conveyor moves.
3. The (NC) limit switch LS is activated (contacts open) when the container reaches the specified position, de-energizing CR, which opens contact CR-1.
   - The CR-2 contact closes, turning on the red lamp.
   - The CR-3 contact opens, turning off the green lamp.
   - The CR-4 contact opens, de-energizing the motor contactor, which stops the motor, the conveyor, and the container.

FIGURE 2-52: Solution for Example 2-7.

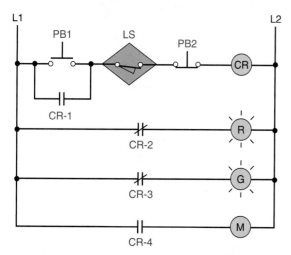

motor. The contacts are normally open so that the power is broken whenever the motor starter's coil is not energized.

2-7 VISUAL AND AUDIO OUTPUT DEVICES

In addition to driving output actuators, the PLC turns on various visual and audio devices to indicate a specific condition and/or warning. For example, if a process parameter has been exceeded a lamp could be illuminated, or if an unplanned event occurs a flashing light and an audible alarm could be initiated. These devices have been briefly mentioned previously, but they are discussed in detail in the following subsections.

2-7-1 Pilot Lamps

Pilot lamps are industrial grade lamps used in control panels and machine front panels to indicate events and conditions in the system. The variety of lamp models is as varied as the applications that use them. Figure 2-53 shows two types and the schematic symbols for each. Both models permit testing of the lamp. The top lamp

mal unit. The incoming three-phase AC power, typically 480 volts or higher for motors 1 horsepower or greater, is connected to L1, L2, and L3 in the figure. The motor attaches to the other end at T1, T2, and T3. The motor starter contacts and a thermal overload unit separate the power lines from the motor. The coil and armature inside the motor starter close all three contacts to start the

FIGURE 2-53: Pilot lamp types.

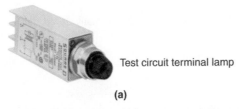

Push to test lamp

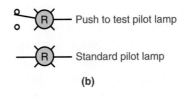 Push to test pilot lamp

Standard pilot lamp

Test circuit terminal lamp

(a)

(b)

Courtesy of Square D/Schneider Electric.

has a push to test switch that is activated by applying pressure to the lens face. The second has test terminals at the rear that can be wired to a test switch to activate the lamp. Lamp voltages include 6.3, 28, and 120 volts, and the lens cap color options include clear, red, green, amber, and yellow. The letter (first letter of the color, for example, R for red) inside the schematic symbol indicates the lens color.

2-7-2 Horns and Alarms

Industrial horns are available in several different sizes that offer a large range of sound output levels—from localized to broad-scale—to alert operators of machine conditions almost anywhere on the plant floor. Figure 2-54 illustrates a typical horn and the schematic symbol for the horn. The horn in the figure is available in sizes from 3-inch to 7-inch cubes, where the size is a function of the output sound level capability—the larger the horn the higher the sound level capability. Input voltages typically fall within the ranges of 10 to 24 VDC or 24 to 240 VAC. Horn features include multi-tone capability, tone selection, and volume control, allowing users to assign different tones to various alarm situations. Using selectable tone options, users can select a tone and frequency that contrasts with ambient noise in the external environment, helping to ensure that the alarm signal can be clearly distinguished. For

FIGURE 2-54: Industrial horns.

Symbol

Courtesy of Rockwell Automation, Inc.

example, users can select a lower decibel sound with a high contrasting frequency for maximum distinctness and minimal noise. The multi-tone/circuit feature also allows a single horn to produce up to three different tones for three different conditions, essentially acting as three horns in a single housing. For applications requiring greater visibility, the light and horn combination has a strobe light option that can be combined for effective visual and audio signaling.

FIGURE 2-55: Industrial panel alarms.

Courtesy of Rockwell Automation, Inc.

FIGURE 2-56: PLC relay outputs with common terminal.

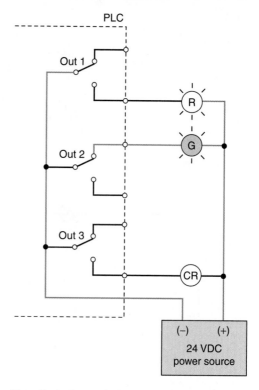

Note: Out1, Out2, and Out3 are relay contacts

Figure 2-55 illustrates a variety of panel-mounted *industrial alarms*, and the schematic symbol for an alarm. These alarms can provide sound outputs in the range of 80 to 105 dB and are available in 12 VAC/DC, 24 VAC/DC, 120 VAC, and 240 VAC. Alarm features include continuous or pulsing sound outputs, a flashing or steady LED lamp, and a strobe light version. Horns and alarms are ideal for applications where operators monitor and maintain multiple pieces of equipment.

2-8 INTERFACING OUTPUT FIELD DEVICES

Interfacing output devices to a PLC generally involves a PLC output module with either a relay or a solid-state output to which the field device is attached. Relay outputs are used for high-current requirements in the one- to two-ampere range or for power isolation, whereas solid-state outputs are used to control low-power DC circuitry with transistors or low-power AC circuitry with triacs. As with the interface to PLC inputs, PLC outputs are available with a common terminal or totally isolated.

2-8-1 Powering Output Field Devices

Typically, the power for output field devices is not supplied by the PLC but provided separately, allowing the wide range of requirements to be satisfied. The power includes solenoid and relay coil voltage, motor voltage (single-phase and three-phase), and the power for lamps, horns, and alarms. Vendor device specifications detail the power requirements for the field devices. The user must ensure that the current requirements of the devices are compatible with the PLC output capability.

2-8-2 Output Wiring

Using the *PLC relay outputs* involves wiring to relays that share a common terminal or connecting to relays that are totally isolated. Relay outputs that share a common terminal are shown in Figure 2-56. Note that the common terminal is connected to the wiper of all the relays, and each relay has an NC and an NO contact, which are available for wiring to a field device. Note the 24 VDC power source is connected to all

FIGURE 2-57: PLC relay outputs with isolated common terminals.

FIGURE 2-58: PLC current sinking and current sourcing outputs.

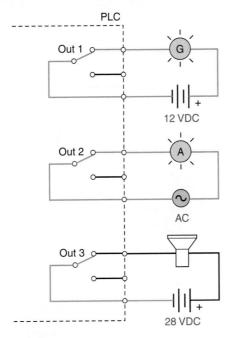

Note: Out1, Out2, and Out3 are relay contacts

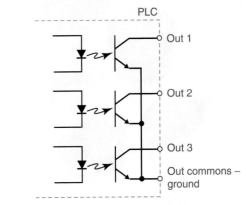

(a) PLC solid state outputs-current sinking type

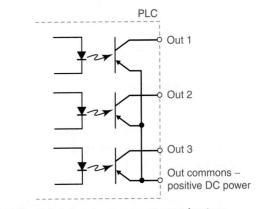

(b) PLC solid state outputs-current sourcing type

Note: Outputs are driven by transistors - NPN for the sinking and PNP for the sourcing

the field devices plus the PLC common terminal. Observe that the PLC relays are in the de-energized state and the red lamp and the relay CR are connected to NO contacts and are off, but the green lamp is connected to an NC contact and is on.

PLC output relays that are totally isolated from each other are illustrated in Figure 2-57 and show the field devices that they are driving. Note each relay output controls a different device, each with its own power source. Output 1 is connected to a DC voltage-powered lamp, output 2 is connected to an AC voltage-powered lamp, and output 3 is connected to a DC voltage-powered alarm. Observe that when the PLC relays are de-energized, both lamps are on and the horn is off.

The PLC solid-state outputs are for the most part driven by transistors or logic elements and generally share a common terminal, although triac outputs to switch AC loads are available in the totally isolated configuration. As with the transistor PLC input, the transistor PLC output is either current sinking or current sourcing, as shown in Figure 2-58. Note that the transistors are driven by an opto-isolator and that they share a common terminal. Let's examine Figure 2-59,

FIGURE 2-59: Field devices connected to PLC outputs.

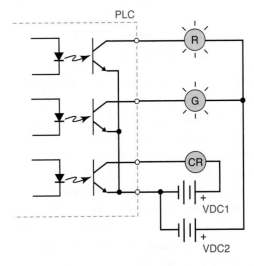

Note: Outputs are driven by NPN transistors

which depicts field devices connected to the PLC solid-state outputs. Note that the two lamps are powered by the same power source, whereas the relay coil is powered from a different source. However, the commons of both power supplies are connected to the common of the transistor outputs. Each of field devices remains off until the transistor driver turns on.

2-8-3 Current Sinking and Current Sourcing Devices

When wiring a field device to a DC voltage PLC output, these rules must be followed:

- **Sinking outputs:** current must flow through the field device and into the current sinking PLC output to ground.
- **Sourcing outputs:** current must flow out of the current sourcing PLC output and through the field device to ground.

For the current sinking output (an NPN transistor), the negative side of the power source must be connected to the PLC output common terminal. For the current sourcing output (a PNP transistor), the positive side of the power source must be connected to the PLC output common terminal. Reread these rules until you have them committed to memory. Additional PLC module interface circuitry is discussed in Appendix B.

2-9 TROUBLESHOOTING INPUT AND OUTPUT DEVICES

Every minute a production system is not producing due to a problem, the company is losing money. That is why competent system troubleshooters are worth their weight in gold. The best way to make your mark in a career is to demonstrate that you can solve problems, especially troubleshooting machine and system failures.

The primary message is that you must have a troubleshooting game plan because random and unrelated actions to solve the problem are seldom successful. In general, to troubleshoot a problem, you work from the outside of the machine or system and work your way inside.

This implies a series of steps. It is tempting to jump quickly to a conclusion as to the problem, and occasionally you may be correct. The methodical process may appear to take longer, but it leads to a correct solution more often. Also, the more experience you have following a plan, the more often you are correct when you decide to make an intuitive guess. Here is a suggested plan.

1. Outside analysis comes first. Take an overall look at the system and note all the symptoms. Get symptom reports from more than one person if you cannot observe the symptoms in person. Determine if the problem is in the machine or system or in the users of the hardware. Most PLCs have indicator lights on the input/output modules to aid in troubleshooting.

2. Analyze the interfaces. The places where mechanical and electrical systems come together are often the places where they fail. Inputs, outputs, control devices, and power supplies are often interfaces where problems occur. Check those that could relate to the symptoms recorded.

3. Start to move into the system following an electrical path or signal flow from an interface using techniques to isolate problems to individual sections, circuits, or components using a combination of system outputs, test equipment, and an experienced engineering sense (a high level of common sense).

4. Identify the most likely component for the problem. When you have a high degree of confidence that you have identified the malfunctioning component or interface, then it is often faster to just replace it to verify your suspicion.

5. Identify the cause of the failure. Finding the problem is only half of the task for a competent troubleshooter. Identifying why the failure occurred is the second part. It may just be component life expectancy, but it is important to determine if anything from a user or system standpoint shortened the device's life.

6. Verify that the fix is permanent. The system should be taken to the limits of its operation over a test period to verify that the problem is truly fixed. The length of time and limits used depends on the problem that was removed.

2-9-1 Troubleshooting Switches

All of the switches covered in this chapter have a common troubleshooting approach. Switch problems can be grouped into two categories: *operator problems* and *contact problems.*

Operators such as a switch handle or push button are the mechanical elements that force the contacts from their normal position to the opposite state. Often the operator will change positions from on to off but the contacts may not move. When operators fail, the contacts may remain in either the normal position or the opposite one. Operator problems usually affect all the contacts in the multipole multi-throw configuration.

Contact problems on switches include always open, always closed, or excessive resistance for closed contacts. If a contact is forced to carry excessive current or has arced, the contacts fuse together and never open. The same switching conditions can cause the contacts to be burned, and the resistance when closed becomes much higher than normal.

When a switch is suspected for the system problem the following procedures can be used.

- If a contact should be open, then the voltage measured across the contacts should be the voltage being switched.
- If a contact should be closed, then the voltage measured across the contacts should be near zero. A higher reading indicates excessive contact resistance or open.
- If excessive contact resistance is suspected, then one of the switch wires should be removed and resistance measured with an ohmmeter.
- If a switch is not closing a contact, then the jumper across the contacts will test to see if the problem is fixed.
- If a switch is not opening, then removal of one of the switched wires will verify that problem.

2-9-2 Troubleshooting Relays

Relay problems can be grouped into the two categories just described for switches plus a third category, *relay coil hum.* The operator for a relay is the electromagnetic coil or solenoid plus the mechanical linkage to the contact poles. All of the problems and troubleshooting procedures discussed for switch operators and contacts apply to relays as well.

Because relay contacts are switched by the action of a solenoid or electromagnet, improper drive currents to the coil can cause some problems. A specified minimum amount of current through the coil, called the *pull-in current,* is required to positively "pull in" the armature to actuate the contact(s). After the armature is pulled in it takes less magnetic field flux and less coil current to hold it there. As a result, a value of coil current significantly lower than the pull-in value must be reached before the armature "drops out" to its normal state. This current level is called the *dropout* current. If the improper drive currents are present relays may not pull in completely, causing higher contact resistance and overheating of the coils. Armatures that do not fully close AC relays cause coil overheating due to the lower coil reactance values, resulting in higher sustained coil currents. Also, relays may fail to drop out if the coil current is not falling into the drop-out range.

Devices using AC solenoids will have one or more single turn coils, called shading rings, embedded in the face of their magnetic armature assembly. Without this coil the armature would tend to drop out whenever the AC voltage drops toward zero, and then be pulled in as the voltage and magnetic field reverses. This produces a humming noise in AC relays. The shading ring, which minimizes this noise, produces an induced magnetic field that is out of phase with that of the applied power. This holds the armature in between power reversals. Over time, shading rings tend to crack from the pounding of the armature faces. When this happens, the solenoid will become very noisy, coil current will increase, and premature failure will result.

2-9-3 Troubleshooting Proximity Sensors

The following tips may be helpful if the problem appears to be in the sensor or sensor amplifier. Sensors from different vendors have different operating characteristics, so the first requirement is to know how the sensors in the system operate. In fact, some sensors have adjustment screws to set switching points with details in vendor literature. The following order does not indicate a preferred sequence. Review all the tips and consider those that apply to the current sensor problem.

- Verify that the sensor has power in the specified range. Checking other operating equipment connected to the same power bus is a method for testing for power.
- Verify that all the amplifier settings are correct. Many sensor amplifiers have a sensitivity adjustment, so make sure that the protective seal is still in place.
- Verify that all switch settings are correct.
- Use the operation indicator on the sensor or sensor amplifier to determine if the sensor electronics recognize that a part is present. An on condition for the operation indicator usually indicates that the output transistor or relay is operating. Some devices with the output set to the normally open (NO) operation will have the operation indicator on when an object is sensed. The opposite is true for an NC setting. A testing method is to move the part toward the sensor along the same path used in the process and determine how close the required sensing distance is to the maximum value.
- Verify that a foreign object is not creating a problem on one of the sensing heads.

- Verify that the velocity of the parts past the sensor does not exceed the frequency response of the unit.
- Verify that the sensing distance was not reduced due to a change in the ambient temperature or supply voltage.

2-9-4 Troubleshooting Photoelectric Sensors

The following tips may be helpful if the problem appears to be in the sensor or sensor amplifier. The first rule is to know the operation of the sensor in the system.

- Verify that the sensor has power in the specified range. Verifying power to other operating equipment connected to the same power bus is one method for testing for power.
- Verify that all the amplifier settings are correct. Many sensor amplifiers have a sensitivity adjustment, so make sure that the protective seal is still in place. Verify that all switch settings are correct.
- Use the operation indicator on the sensor or sensor amplifier to determine if the sensor electronics recognize that a part is present. An on condition for the operation indicator usually indicates that the output transistor or relay is operating. Some devices that have the output set to light ON mode have the operation indicator on when light is striking the sensor. The opposite is true for a dark ON mode setting.
- Verify that the lenses are clean and free of foreign objects.
- Verify that the velocity of the parts past the sensor does not exceed the rise and fall time for the unit.
- Verify that the sensing distance was not reduced due to a change in the ambient temperature or supply voltage.

CHAPTER 3

Introduction to PLC Programming

3-1 GOALS AND OBJECTIVES

Chapter 3, like Chapter 1, covers numerous PLC topics that are necessary to know before specific PLC instructions are introduced. One goal of this chapter is to cover topics that focus on how the PLC operates, such as number systems, bit/word addressing, memory allocations, input and output addressing, and scanning cycle. A second goal is to cover topics that focus on PLC programming. The final goal is to introduce the three Allen-Bradley processors—PLC 5, SLC 500, and ControlLogix—by grouping the PLC 5 and SLC 500 topic together where they are similar but keeping the ControlLogix separate because it is quite different from the other two. Although the topics may appear to be unrelated, they are all operational concepts needed in Chapters 4 through 16 when programs are built with the many PLC instructions.

After completing this chapter you should be able to:

- Convert to and from hexadecimal, decimal, octal, and binary numbers.
- Describe the input, output, internal relay, and status addressing format for rack/slot-based PLC 5 and SLC 500 and tag-based Logix PLC processors from Allen-Bradley.

- Describe PLC scan time and the use of examine if closed and examine if open instructions.
- Write PLC programs and interpret PLC programs with the following logic combinations: AND, OR, AND/OR, and OR/AND.
- Describe the function of sealing instructions.
- Describe the operation of standard and latched PLC outputs.
- Describe PLC memory organization, data types, and use of internal binary bits, bytes, and words.
- Develop ladder logic programs with input instructions and output coil combinations.
- Describe and use program design techniques to develop a PLC program.

3-2 NUMBER SYSTEMS

Everyday tasks, like buying gasoline or groceries, employ the decimal or base 10 number system. This system is also used in manufacturing automation to input parameter values or to display the value of system variables. In addition to decimal, four other number systems are used in automation: *binary, octal, binary coded decimal (BCD),* and *hexadecimal*. It is important to understand all the number systems if you work with a process controlled by a PLC; however, hexadecimal is used

most often. Number systems are introduced in the text at the beginning of the chapter in which they are used for a PLC instruction. As a result, binary, octal, and decimal are at the start of this chapter, binary arithmetic is in Chapter 6, and BCD and hexadecimal are in Chapter 7.

3-2-1 Number System Basics

All number systems have a *base* or *radix*. In the decimal system the base is 10, which means that 10 symbols (0 through 9) are used to represent decimal numbers. In addition to the base, the quantity specified by a number is a function of the place or position of the digits in the number. For example, 1 represents a quantity of one and 100 represents a quantity of one hundred. In the first number, the 1 occupies the zero position, and it has a value of 1×10^0 or 1×1 or just 1. Note that any non-zero number raised to the zero power is equal to 1. In the second number, the 1 is in the two's position, and it has a value of 1×10^2 or 1×100 or 100. The other two positions that hold zeros do not change the final value because they will contribute 0×10^0 or 0 and 0×10^1, which is also 0. Therefore, the number value is 100. The value of a decimal number depends on the digits that make up the number and the place or position value of each digit. The *position values* are illustrated by the number 4562.6 in Figure 3-1. Locate the position values, the base, and the digit values in the figure.

Note that the position values increase from right to left, and the zero position is to the left of the decimal point. Figure 3-1 also illustrates how the value of a decimal number is determined by adding the product of the *digits* and their *position weight values*. Note in the figure that the sum of the products is 4562.6_{10}, which is read as "four thousand five hundred and sixty-two point six base 10." The 10 in the subscript indicates the base or radix for the number. This discussion of decimal notation is used to generalize the conversion of a number from any base to base 10. The formula is:

$$\text{Number}_{10} = \text{the summation of all positions digits} \times \text{Base}^{\text{Position value of the digit}}$$

The formula is the summation of all position digits times the given number's base raised to the power of the position value of the digit. Using Figure 3-1, verify that the demonstrated conversion process employs this general formula. Although engineers use the decimal system, the computer uses the binary number system for all of its internal operation.

3-2-2 Binary System

Computers and PLCs make logical decisions and perform mathematical calculations using electronic circuits. The easiest and least expensive electronic circuits are *discrete designs* that have two states: on or off. The number system used in these electronic systems has two digits, 0 and 1, has a base of 2, and is called a *binary number system*. The binary system must be able to use just two digits to represent every numerical value required by a control system.

FIGURE 3-1: Weight values and position values.

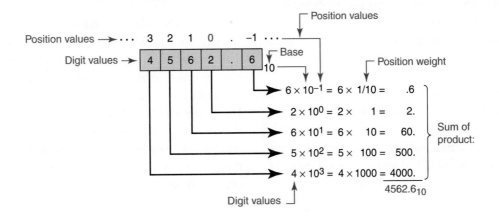

Figure 3-2 compares the binary system (base 2) to the decimal system (base 10), demonstrating how the base 2 system counts from 0 to 18_{10}. The base of a number is indicated by placing the base as a subscript on the least significant digit. For example, the 18_{10} in the previous sentence means 18 in the base 10 number system.

The two systems are identical for the decimal numbers, 0 and 1. However, after 1, the binary system runs out of digits. Therefore, a 2 in base 10 is a one zero in the base 2 system. Another distinction between the systems is that 10 in the binary system is pronounced "one zero base two" and not "ten." The binary for 18_{10} is 010010_2 and is pronounced "one zero zero one zero base two" and not "ten thousand ten." Note that leading zeros are normally not identified when reading the value. Also, the "base two" at the end is usually dropped.

Binary and decimal conversion. The PLC works in binary and the world works in decimal, so knowing how to convert numbers between the two systems is critical. Figure 3-3 illustrates the conversion process from binary to decimal. Find the location of the position values, digit values, and position weight for the binary number in the figure.

The digit value in position 0 in the figure is a 1. Each digit value produces a number that is part of the sum of products in Figure 3-3. The digit value of 1 in position 0 contributes a 1 to the sum of products. The digit value of 1 in position 1 produces a 2 in the sum of products. Observe the digit values for the rest of the positions and note the value produced in the sum of products.

The conversion process in Figure 3-3 indicates that the values in the sum of products column results from multiplying the digit value by the digit weight. For example, for position 0 the sum of products value is $1 \times 1 = 1$, and for position 3 it is $0 \times 8 = 0$. So if the digit value is a 0 the sum of products value is always a 0, but if the digit value is a 1 then the position weight value determines the sum of products value. The position weight is the base 2 raised to the power of the position value. Study the figure for the conversion of each digit value so you see that 10110111_2 is equal to 183_{10}. In summary, each digit value is multiplied by its position weight and then added to get the decimal equivalent.

On the other hand, conversion from decimal to binary, illustrated in Figure 3-4, uses a series of divisions by 2, the binary base value. Study

---

FIGURE 3-2: Decimal and binary number systems.

Decimal$_{10}$		Binary$_2$						Octal$_8$ ← Base	
1	0	5	4	3	2	1	0	1	0
0	0	0	0	0	0	0	0	0	0
0	1	0	0	0	0	0	1	0	1
0	2	0	0	0	0	1	0	0	2
0	3	0	0	0	0	1	1	0	3
0	4	0	0	0	1	0	0	0	4
0	5	0	0	0	1	0	1	0	5
0	6	0	0	0	1	1	0	0	6
0	7	0	0	0	1	1	1	0	7
0	8	0	0	1	0	0	0	1	0
0	9	0	0	1	0	0	1	1	1
1	0	0	0	1	0	1	0	1	2
1	1	0	0	1	0	1	1	1	3
1	2	0	0	1	1	0	0	1	4
1	3	0	0	1	1	0	1	1	5
1	4	0	0	1	1	1	0	1	6
1	5	0	0	1	1	1	1	1	7
1	6	0	1	0	0	0	0	2	0
1	7	0	1	0	0	0	1	2	1
1	8	0	1	0	0	1	0	2	2

Position values →

(a) Comparison of number systems

FIGURE 3-3: Conversion from binary to decimal.

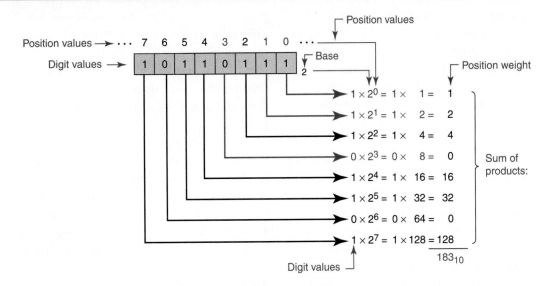

FIGURE 3-4: Conversion from decimal to binary.

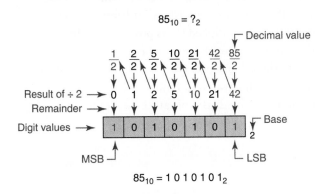

the process in the figure until you can see where the result of the division and the remainder are placed.

The remainder of the first division (1 in the figure) is the least significant bit (LSB) value of the binary conversion, and the remainder of the last division (1 in the figure) is the most significant bit (MSB) value. The result of each division (i.e., 42 in the first division) is used for the next division (i.e., 42/2 in the figure). A review of the Figure 3-4 indicates that 85_{10} is equal to 1010101_2.

3-2-3   Octal Number System

The octal number system, shown in Figure 3-2, has a base or radix of 8, which means that eight symbols, 0 through 7, are used to represent octal

numbers. As a result of not using digits 8 or 9, the digits in the zero position value increases from 0 to 7, then repeat after 7. Octal numbers, like their binary counterpart, are pronounced in a special manner. For example, the octal number 7261 is pronounced "seven two six one base 8" and not "seven thousand two hundred sixty-one." The octal number system, popular in the early days of computers and PLCs, easily converts from binary to octal and back to binary.

Octal conversions. Octal numbers can easily be converted to binary using the method illustrated in Figure 3-5(a). Each octal digit, 0 through 7, in the number 2713_8 is replaced with its three-bit binary equivalent. Review the binary values for octal digits 0 through 7 in Figure 3-2. The three-bit binary groups are appended together to form the binary equivalent, 010111001011_2, of the octal value. Conversion from binary back to octal, also illustrated in Figure 3-5(a), is equally straightforward. One can see that the binary number is partitioned into groups of three bits, starting at the least significant bit end of the binary value. Leading zeros are added if necessary to obtain the final group of three. Then each partition of three-bit binary numbers is converted to its equivalent 0 through 7 octal value, using the chart in Figure 3-2. Study the conversion for the values in Figure 3-5(a) until conversion between octal and binary numbers is

FIGURE 3-5: Octal conversion.

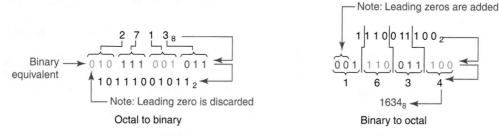

(a) Octal to binary and binary to octal conversions

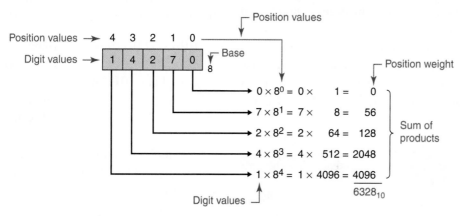

(b) Octal to decimal conversion

understood and the binary values for 0 through 7 are committed to memory.

Conversion from octal to decimal, illustrated in Figure 3-5(b), uses the formula introduced earlier for binary numbers.

$$\text{Number}_{10} = \sum \text{position digits} \times 8^{\text{Position value of the digit}}$$

This formula evaluates as the summation of all position digits times the radix (8) raised to the power of the position value. The conversion of 15_8 is performed as follows:

$$\text{Number}_{10} = 1 \times 8^1 + 5 \times 8^0 = 1 \times 8 +$$
$$5 \times 1 = 8 + 5 = 13_{10}$$

This result is verified in Figure 3-2 where $13_{10} = 001101_2 = 15_8$. Conversion from base 10 to base 8 can be performed by first converting from decimal to binary and then converting the binary value into octal.

A knowledge of number systems is necessary to understand the operation of some PLC instructions, and binary notation is used throughout the text when referring to Boolean (on and off) signals.

3-3 HEXADECIMAL NUMBER SYSTEM

3-3-1 Introduction

The binary number system requires many digits to represent a large value, for example, to represent the decimal value 202 requires eight binary digits. Note that the decimal number 202 is only three digits and, thus, represents numbers much more compactly than does the binary numbering system. However, decimal numbers are not usable in computer systems.

When dealing with large values, binary numbers quickly become too unwieldy. A shorthand method of expressing large values is the hexadecimal (hex) numbering system, which is a popular numbering system in the PLC. Hexadecimal numbers offer the following two features:

- Hex numbers are very compact
- It is easy to convert from hex to binary and binary to hex.

As in the binary system, which uses the base 2, and the octal system, which uses the base 8, and the decimal system, which uses the base 10, the

hexadecimal system uses the base 16. These 16 digits are represented by the numbers 0 through 9 and the letters A, B, C, D, E, and F.

Hexadecimal numbers are used extensively in PLC comparison instructions and instructions that incorporate masks. Therefore, a good grasp of the conversions described in this Section are necessary to evaluate the comparison actions and the instruction results.

3-3-2   Comparison of Numbering Systems

The following table lists the decimal numbers 0 through 16 and the binary, octal and hexadecimal equivalents. Note that a lower case "b" is appended to the binary number, a lower case "q" is appended to the octal number and a lower case "h" is appended to the hexadecimal number.

Decimal	Binary	Octal	Hex
00	0000b	00q	00h
01	0001b	01q	01h
02	0010b	02q	02h
03	0011b	03q	03h
04	0100b	04q	04h
05	0101b	05q	05h
06	0110b	06q	06h
07	0111b	07q	07h
08	1000b	10q	08h
09	1001b	11q	09h
10	1010b	12q	0Ah
11	1011b	13q	0Bh
12	1100b	14q	0Ch
13	1101b	15q	0Dh
14	1110b	16q	0Eh
15	1111b	17q	0Fh
16	10000b	20q	10h

This table provides all the information that is needed to convert from one number base into any other number base for the decimal values from 0 to 16.

3-3-3   Binary to Hex Conversion

Conversion from a binary number to hex number is accomplished by the following two steps:

1. Break the binary number into 4-bit sections from the LSB to the MSB.
2. Convert each 4-bit binary number to its hex equivalent.

For example, the binary value 1010 1111 1011 0010 is broken into 4-bit sections starting from the LSB and continuing toward the MSB, and then it is converted into the hex number AFB2.

- 1010111110110010   (Binary number to be converted)
- 1010 1111 1011 0010   (Binary number in 4-digit sections)
-    A   F   B   2   (Hex number)

Let's look at another example, where the binary value 10010011001011 is converted into the hex number 24CD.

- 10 0100 1100 1101
- 2   4   C   D

Note that there are only 2 digits in the most significant section, and it is not unusual to have less than 4 digits in the most significant section. That is why it is important that when breaking the binary number into 4-bit sections, you start from the LSB.

3-3-4   Hex to Binary Conversion

It is also easy to convert from a hex number to a binary number and is accomplished by the following two steps:

1. Convert the hex number to its 4-bit binary equivalent.
2. Combine the 4-bit sections by removing the spaces.

For example, the hex value AFB2 will be written:

- A   F   B   2   (Hex number to be converted)
- 1010 1111 1011 0010   (Binary equivalent)
- 101011110110010   (Binary digits combined)

3-3-5 Hex to Decimal Conversion

The conversion from a hex number to a decimal number is accomplished by the following four steps:

1. Multiply each hex digit by its weighted value
2. Convert the hex digits to their decimal equivalent
3. Convert the hex weighted values to decimals and complete the multiplication
4. Add all the values.

Let's use the hex number AFB2h from a previous example and convert it to its decimal equivalent of 44,978.

- $A \times 16^3 + F \times 16^2 + B \times 16^1 + 2 \times 16^0$ (Weighted values)
- $10 \times 16^3 + 15 \times 16^2 + 11 \times 16^1 + 2 \times 16^0$ (Decimal equivalents)
- $10 \times 4096 + 15 \times 256 + 11 \times 16 + 2 \times 1$ (Conversion)
- $40,960 + 3,840 + 176 + 2 = 44,978$ (Multiplications & result)

3-3-6 Decimal to Hex Conversion

The conversion of a decimal number to a hex number is slightly more difficult. The typical method to convert from decimal to hex is repeated division by 16. While repeated subtraction by the weighted position value is another method, it is more difficult for large decimal numbers.

3-3-7 Repeated Division Method

For this method, divide the decimal number by 16, and convert the remainder to a hex number, which is the least significant digit of the final hex number. This process is continued by dividing the quotient by 16 and converting its remainder until the quotient is 0. When performing the division, begin as the least significant digit (right) and each new digit is the next more significant digit (the left) of the previous digit.

This method can be clarified by reviewing the following table, which provides an example of the repeated division by 16 method. Let's use the number 44,978, and verify that the equivalent hex number is AFB2h.

Division	Quotient	Remainder	Hex Digit
44978/16	2811	2	2
2811/16	175	11	B
175/16	10	15	F
10/16	0	10	A

Arranging the hex digits from right to left yields the number AFB2h. Review this example until you understand the method. Having introduced the number system, we now address the storage of numbers in the PLC.

3-4 BITS, BYTES, WORDS, AND MEMORY

Binary numbers have special notations, as illustrated in Figure 3-6. A single binary digit is a *bit*, and eight bits are a *byte*, pronounced like the word *bite*. Two bytes or 16-bits is a *word*, and two words or 32 bits represents a *double word*.

PLC memory is organized using either bytes, single words, or double words. For example, most older PLCs use 8-bit or 16-bit memory words, and newer systems, like ControlLogix from Allen-Bradley, use double word (32 bits) as the default. The memory block, introduced in Figure 1-2, indicates that the memory has three binary interfaces: *data*, *control*, and *address*. A general description of each interface states that the data bus carries parameter values and PLC instructions, the control bus provides the logical control for movement of instruction and data, and the address bus carries the binary address number for all the binary values stored in memory.

FIGURE 3-6: Bits, bytes, and words.

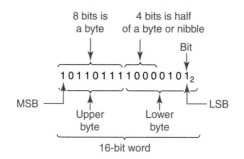

Memory is organized into blocks of consecutive bytes or words. Figure 3-7 shows a 16-bit 1K memory layout, where 1K memory represents 1024 locations. Each memory location has a number like the street address number of a house, and points to a specific word in memory. The address numbers for the 1K memory layout in the figure are 0 to 1023_{10} or 0000000000_2 to 1111111111_2. Each of the 1024 16-bit words has a unique 10-bit address. When the address bits are increased to 11 the addressable memory increases to 2024 16-bit words. This relationship between the memory size and the required number of address bits is present as the memory grows to the size used in current PLCs. The following are some examples of PLC memory limits.

- Automation Direct D4-450 processors: 60-kilobyte models
- Allen-Bradley ControlLogix processors: 2-, 4-, and 8-megabyte models
- Modicon Quantum processors: up to 8 megabytes available

- Siemens Samitac S7 processors: up to 20 megabytes available

Many PLCs are organized using memory words in a structure called a register. An understanding of the register structure is useful when PLC instructions are used in a program.

3-5 PLC MEMORY AND REGISTER STRUCTURE

Although knowledge of the details of the PLC memory technology is not necessary to program and implement PLCs, an understanding of program and data storage and the location of processor status bits is important. For example, when a program is created, one must know where the PLC places input and output data and where the CPU saves operational status information. This text presents the memory organization for the Allen-Bradley PLC 5, SLC 500, and ControlLogix processors models.

FIGURE 3-7: PLC 1K memory block.

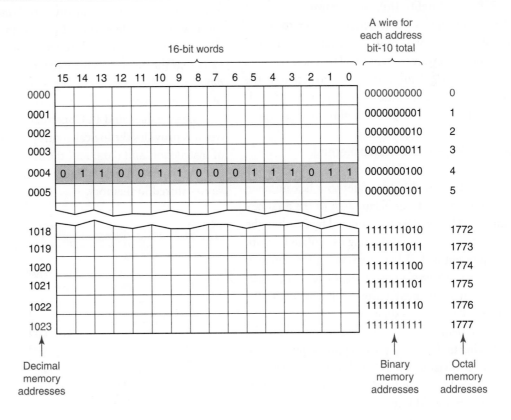

Since it is necessary to learn one vendor's PLC system well, the Allen-Bradley (AB) PLCs, which represent the largest share of U.S. installations, are the primary focus of this text. With a good knowledge of the three AB systems, it is not difficult to learn a second manufacturer's PLC system.

3-5-1 Allen-Bradley Memory Organization

Allen-Bradley PLCs have two distinctly different memory structures identified by the terms *rack-based systems* and *tag-based systems*. The rack address-based system, introduced in Chapter 1, has it roots in the early PLC systems.

Rack-based memory. Figure 3-8 represents the common memory structure for most rack/slot address–based PLCs, like the PLC 5 and SLC 500, as a two-drawer filing cabinet. An examination of the figure shows that one drawer is for *program* files and the second is for *data* files.

Each of the two file groups (data and program) in the figure is subdivided into instruction-specific files and file types.

Data files. The data files are subdivided into 9 (0 to 8) *designated* file types and 247 (9 to 255) *user-defined* file types. Continuing the file drawer analogy, a data file drawer contains folders (the 9 designated folders and 247 user-defined folders) with data in each folder. Each folder has bits of memory in rows that are 8-, 16-, or 32-bits wide. The number of bytes, words, or double words present depends on the type of folder examined. For example, folder 0 (Output File)

FIGURE 3-8: Rack/slot-based memory.

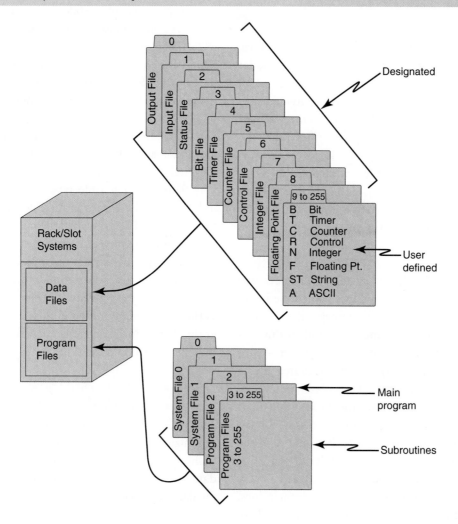

may have 37 words used to store output data status. Folder 7 (Integer File) may have 1000 words used to store data in an integer format. The memory map depicted in Figure 3-8 has blocks of 16-bit words assigned to files 0 through 8. With this memory allocation technique, output data is assigned a specific part of memory, input is assigned another, and all the files have specific locations where their values are stored. Therefore, in order to know the status of a field device connected to an input module, one must know the specific memory location in which to look for that data.

A separate block of memory is designated as *user-defined* space. In this location, the programmer has the option to designate what type of data (i.e., timers, counters, integer values, or any of the designated file types) will be stored. User-defined space is important when the available memory assigned to a file has been consumed.

Program files. In Figure 3-8 the program files, a part of processor memory, store the ladder logic programs. Two program file types, *system* and *program,* exist. They are subdivided into *system functions* (file 0 and 1), *main program* (file 2), and *subroutine programs* (files 3 through 255). File 2 is the default location for the main program, and files 3 through 255 are available for subroutines called from the main program. The size of data and program memory is determined by the size of the memory in the PLC.

Tag- or variable-based systems. The new generation of Allen-Bradley PLCs, called the Logix series, uses a different memory organization, called a *tag-based* memory system. In this system all data (i.e., output status, input status, integer values, or any of the designated file or data types) are assigned a variable name called a tag. In Logix systems the program data is stored in a tag, so it is not necessary for the programmer to know where that data is stored in memory. A program can be developed using only tag names, and the processor tracks where all tag values are stored. The programmer does, however, assign input and output terminals to

input and output tags before the program is executed.

With the two types (rack-based or tag-based) of PLC memory systems defined, the memory organization for each of the Allen-Bradley processors can be introduced. The PLC 5 is addressed first, followed by the SLC 500 and then the ControlLogix.

3-5-2 Allen-Bradley PLC 5 Memory Organization

The PLC 5 divides processor information into the two file groups, program and data, as described in the previous section. The data files area stores processor information obtained from input modules, results sent to output modules, and other system data. The PLC 5 is a rack/group-based memory allocation system with specific memory allocated for I/O data based on the rack and group assigned to the I/O module. In PLC 5 notation the place where modules are loaded is called a *chassis* (the unit into which modules are placed) instead of a rack, because a rack may not be limited to one chassis. The structure of the data files 0 through 999 are illustrated in Table 3-1. Study the table carefully and then continue.

Data file content. Table 3-1 shows the 16 data files (numbers 0 through 8 and 3 to 999) used in the PLC 5, as well as the user-defined file numbers 9 to 999. Each file type has an identifier indicated by the letters in the File Type Indentifier column. The associated file number is listed plus the number of words used to store the data. Some file types use structures, which are groups of memory words. For example, there are 1000 timer structures permitted. This means that 1000 timers are permitted in a ladder logic program. Each timer or timer structure requires three words to hold the timer data.

3-5-3 Allen-Bradley SLC 500 Memory Organization

The SLC 500 is similar to the PLC 5 in memory organization. The SLC also divides information in the processor into two file groups, program and data, with the same type of information stored in the data files. The structure of data files 0 through 255 is illustrated in Table 3-2.

TABLE 3-1 PLC memory organization.

File Type	File Type Identifier	File Number	Maximum Number of 16 bit Words or Structures
Output image	O	0	32 words[1]
Input image	I	1	32 words[1]
Status	S	2	12 words[1]
Bit (binary)	B	3	1000 words
Timer	T	4	1000 structures (3000 words)[2]
Counter	C	5	1000 structures (3000 words)[2]
Control	R	6	1000 structures (3000 words)[2]
Integer	N	7	1000 words
Floating point	F	8	1000 structures (2000 words)[2]
ASCII	A	3 to 999	1000 words
BCD	D	3 to 999	1000 words
Block transfer	BT	3 to 999	1000 structures (6000 words)[2]
Message	MG	3 to 999	585 structures (32760 words)[2]
PID	PD	3 to 999	399 structures (32718 words)[2]
SFC status	SC	3 to 999	1000 structures (3000 words)[2]
ASCII string	ST	3 to 999	780 structures (32769 words)[2]
User defined	–	9 to 999	6

1. This is the number for a PLC 5/11 and 5/20. The number increases for PLC 5/30 through 5/80.
2. The structure value indicates the number of these file types that are permitted. Structures require multiple words to store the files data.

The table shows 10 ten data files (numbers 0 through 9) used in the SLC series and the user-defined file numbers 9 through 255. Compare Tables 3-1 and 3-2 to understand the differences between the PLC 5 and SLC 500 systems.

Data file content. Data files are organized by the type of data they contain using the SLC 500 instruction and processor notation. The files commonly used on all SLC PLCs include the following:

- Output (file 0): This file stores the on or off condition at the output terminals for the output module associated with this memory register.
- Input (file 1): This file stores the on or off condition at the input terminals for the input module associated with this memory register.

- Status (file 2): This file stores controller information used for troubleshooting controller and program problems.
- Bit (file 3): A bit consists of one binary digit and is often referred to as a Boolean type of data element. Bit files are used most often for bit (relay logic)-type program development.
- Timer (file 4): This file stores the data for each timer used in a program. The data includes timer accumulator and preset values, plus all status and output bits.
- Counter (file 5): This file stores the data for each counter used in a program. The data includes counter accumulator and preset values, plus all status and output bits.
- Control (file 6): This file stores the length, pointer position, and status bits for specific PLC instructions.

TABLE 3-2 SLC memory organization.

File Type	File Type Identifier	File Number	Maximum Number of 16 bit Words or Structures
Output image	0	0	31 words[1]
Input image	I	1	31 words[1]
Status	S	2	164 words[1]
Bit (binary)	B	3	256 words
Timer	T	4	256 structures (768 words)[1]
Counter	C	5	256 structures (768 words)[1]
Control	R	6	256 structures (768 words)[1]
Integer	N	7	1000 words
Floating point	F	8	256 structures (512 words)[1]
Network	x[2]	9	256 words
User Defined	x[3]	9 to 255	247 words

1. The structure value indicates the number of these file types that are permitted. Structures require three words to store the file data.
2. If non SLC 500 devices exist on the Allen Bradley DH–485 network link, use this area for network transfer. You can use either binary (B) or integer (N) file types by specifying the appropriate letter for x. Otherwise, you can use file 9 for user-defined files.
3. Use this area when you need more binary, timer, counter, control, integer, floating-point, or network files that will fit in the reserved files. You can use binary (B), timer (T), counter (C), control (R), integer (N), floating-point (F), or transfers (B and/or N) file types by specifying the appropriate letter for x. You cannot use this area for output image, input image, and/or status files.

- Integer (file 7): This file typically includes 256 16-bit words for the storage of unsigned or signed integer values. The storage elements can be addressed at the word and bit level. The range of stored signed integer values is –32,768 to +32,767, and the range for unsigned values is 0 to 65,635.
- Floating point (file 8): This file stores single precision non-extended 32-bit numbers that include their whole and decimal components. The range of values stored is $+/- 1.1754944 \times 10^{-38}$ to $+/- 3.4028238 \times 10^{+38}$. Some PLCs reserve 64-bit memory locations for even larger scientific notation values.
- User-defined (files 9–255): These files can be used to create any file type from 3 through 8. They are used to expand the number of data files available to the programmer.

This chapter describes the output (0), input (1), and bit (3) file types in detail and indicates the type of processor data stored in the status file (file 2). The remaining file types are covered in Chapters 4 through 11.

Program file content. Program files contain controller information, the main ladder program, interrupt subroutines, and all subroutine programs. These files in the SLC system are:

- System Program (file 0): This file contains various system-related information and user-programmed information, such as processor type, I/O configuration, processor file name, and password.
- Reserved (file 1): This file is reserved.
- Main Ladder Program (file 2): This file contains the main ladder logic program.

- Subroutine Ladder Program (files 3 to 255): Subroutines are ladder logic programs called from the main ladder logic program. All subroutine programs are placed in this program area.

The memory organization for the ControlLogix processor is the final processor covered.

3-5-4 Allen-Bradley Logix System Memory Organization

Variable- or tag-based systems are used in all of today's new PLC models, such as the Allen-Bradley's Logix family of processors. In this type of addressing system, field device inputs and outputs, internal relays, and data values are assigned variable names, like the variables used in programming languages such as BASIC or C. Instead of the term *variable,* Allen-Bradley uses the term *tag* and defines it as follows.

A tag is a text-based name for an area of the controller's memory where data is stored.

In the ControlLogix controller, tags are a mechanism for allocating memory, referencing data in programs, and monitoring data. The minimum memory allocation for a tag is 4 bytes (16 bits).

At some point in the design, tags that represent input and output field devices are assigned to an I/O module and a specific module terminal number. When the variables are defined, a wide assortment of data types are available.

Variable data types. The most frequently used ControlLogix data types are divided into five groups: *Boolean, integer, real, strings,* and *user defined.* The Boolean group has only one data type defined, but other groups, such as integer, have eight definitions of integer data that are available for selection by the programmer. In the user-defined category, the system gives the automation designer and PLC programmer the option of creating a unique data type specific to the process being controlled. The tag data can be *restricted* to the local program or can be *global* so it is available for all programs and tasks within the controller. Input and output data types are all global.

There are two predefined data types: *basic data types* and *structured data types.* Table 3-3 lists and specifies the more commonly used basic data types, including discrete (or Bool), integer, and real. Note the description, size, and range for each of the commonly used types.

Structured data types are created for predefined functions and instructions used in ladder logic. As seen in the list of the structured data types in Table 3-4, commonly used instructions such as timers and counters are a specific data type. Note the names of each group and the data stored.

ControlLogix program organization. In the rack/group- or rack/slot-based systems, the programmer assigns the data from an input field device to an input instruction on a ladder rung by specifying the memory location for the data.

TABLE 3-3 Data types for IEC language variables.

Data Type	Bits						
	31	16	15	8	7	1	0
Bool	not used						0 or 1
Sint	not used				−128 to +127		
Int	not used		−32,768 to +32,767				
Dint	−2,147,483,648 to +2,147,483,647						
Real	-3.40282347E^{38} to −1.17549435E^{-38} (negative values) 0 1.17549435E^{-38} to 3.40282347E^{38} (positive values)						

TABLE 3-4 Tag-based system-structured data types.

Structure Data Type	Type of Data Stored
Counter	Control structure for the counter instructions
Timer	Control structure for the timer instructions
Control	Control structure for the array instructions
Motion Instructions	Control structure for the motion instructions
Motion Group	Control structure for the motion group
PID	Control structure for the PID instructions
Axis	Control structure for an axis
Message	Control structure for the message instructions

Therefore, the programmer must know the input module and terminal number for the field device because the address is based on that information.

In the tag-based system, the allocation of variable names for program values is not tied to specific memory locations in the memory structure. For example, in the ControlLogix system, the programmer has three options in creating tags:

1. Leave the ? in the tag location in the ladder and then define a tag at a later time.
2. Define all of the tags for the programming project before the program is developed.
3. Define the tags as the program is entered.

After tags are defined, those that represent input or output field devices are assigned the input or output terminal where the field device is attached. In addition, the programmer must be familiar with the memory structure used in the Logix system. The memory structure for the ControlLogix PLC is illustrated in Figure 3-9.

This memory structure uses the following terms:

Project: A *project* (the large white project box in Figure 3-9) is a collection of all of the program's elements. When a project is created the new controller dialog box requests the following information:

- Controller model and software revision number
- Project name and description
- Rack size and slot location of the processor
- File folder name into which the program is stored

Task: A *task,* associated with a program, has two functions. First, it holds the information necessary to schedule the program's execution. Second, it sets the execution priority for one or more programs. ControlLogix supports up to 32 tasks. Two types of tasks are used: *continuous* and *periodic.*

- Continuous tasks execute non-stop. At the creation of a new project, a continuous task (white task box in Figure 3-9) is created.
- Periodic tasks interrupt the continuous task and execute for a fixed length of time at specific time intervals. Whenever the time period for the task expires, the task executes one last time. The periodic rate can be from 1 ms to 2000 s with a default of 10 ms. For example, a periodic task, like the one in Figure 3-10, is used to store production information at regular fixed intervals.

Program: Although each task requires at least one *program* (white program box inside white task box in Figure 3-9), a task can have as many as 32 separate programs. Only one program in a task can execute at any one time.

Routine: *Routines* provide the executable code for the project, using a specific programming language such as ladder logic.

Main routine: When a program executes, its main routine executes first. The main routine is used to call (execute) other routines (subroutines).

Subroutine: A subroutine is any routine other than the main routine.

FIGURE 3-9: Tag-based program structure for ControlLogix.

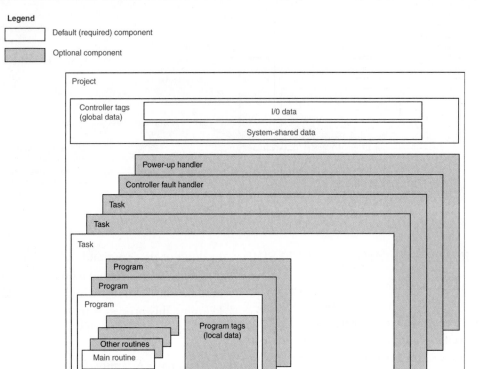

FIGURE 3-10: Periodic and continuous tasks.

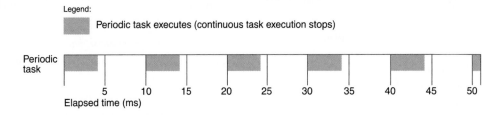

Program tags: The *program tags* (blue box in Figure 3-9) area is a memory location in which to save variable information such as the local tag names and data types.

Controller tags: The *controller tags* (white box in project box in Figure 3-9) area is a memory location in which to save global variable information.

The program structure illustrated in Figure 3-9 is represented in the RSLogix 5000 software as shown in Figure 3-11. The first folder, Controller, appended with the project name

(Controller_1 in the figure), includes global tags and system data. The next folder, Tasks, has all of the program code including tasks, programs, and routines. In addition, the program tags are saved in this area.

This section of the text described the memory and register structures used in the three Allen-Bradley processors. The PLC 5 and SLC 500 had similar structures but the ControlLogix used tags in place of specific memory locations. The next step is to introduce the addressing format for the three PLC processors based on the memory and register structure.

FIGURE 3-11: Program structure and RSLogix 5000 left panel.

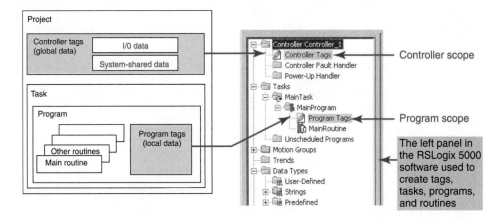

3-6   INPUT AND OUTPUT ADDRESSING

An engineer or technician must be familiar with both rack-based and tag-based addressing schemes because all three Allen Bradley PLC processors are frequently found in automation control schemes. As a result, all three are covered starting with the PLC 5.

3-6-1   PLC 5 Rack/Group-Based Addressing

Input and output (I/O) addressing connects the physical location of a field device at a terminal on an I/O module to a bit location in the processor memory. Therefore, before creating a PLC 5 program using RSLogix 5, the system is configured by performing the following pre-program tasks:

1. Select input and output modules.
2. Determine field device terminations to the modules.
3. Define the memory address of field devices and data.

The PLC 5 uses a rack and group number, called *rack/group addressing*.

Defining terminals, groups, and racks. The main purpose of a PLC is to control output field devices, like valves, using inputs from switches and sensors. To use field device data in a program, the condition of input and output devices must be saved in memory. The part of processor memory that saves input and output addresses is the *input image table*, called file I, and *the output image table*, called file O (see Table 3-1).

Each bit of the input and output image tables is associated with a terminal on an input or output module that can be wired to a field device. Learning this process starts with defining *terminals, groups,* and *racks* for the PLC 5.

Terminals: A *terminal* is an attachment point for field devices on PLC input and output modules and is associated with specific space in processor memory. Terminals are sometimes called I/O points.

Groups: A *group* includes 16 input terminals and 16 output terminals. Therefore, a group consists of one input word (16 bits) and one output word (16 bits).

Logical rack: A *logical rack* is a set of 8 groups (numbered 0 to 7). Since a group is one input word and one output word, a logical rack has 8 input words and 8 output words, or 128 input terminals (8 words, 16 bits each) and 128 output terminals (8 words, 16 bits each). PLC 5 processors can support up to 24 racks with the zero rack in the PLC 5 system reserved for the processor.

In summary, the terminal numbers increase from zero *counting in octal* to the maximum number for the module. Every input and output terminal has a corresponding input and output bit in the input word and output word. A group is composed of an input word and an output word. A rack represents 8 groups (numbers 0 to 7) and may or may not be the same as the physical chassis in which the modules are inserted.

PLC 5 Modes and memory allocation. Usually group 0 is associated with the slot 0 in the chassis, and group 7 is a slot toward the right end. The PLC 5 is configured using three addressing modes: *half-slot, one- or single-slot,* and *two-slot* addressing. These addressing modes are defined as:

Half-slot: In *half-slot addressing* the PLC is configured with two groups to a slot, so that the slot can accept a module that has two input words (32 terminals) and two output words (32 terminals) for field device attachment. One group (16 inputs and 16 outputs) fills one-half of the slot.

One- or single-slot: In *one-slot addressing* the PLC is configured with one group to a slot, so that the slot can accept a module that has one input word (16 terminals) and one output word (16 terminals) for field device attachment. Since one group (16 inputs and 16 outputs) fills the slot, the slot number and the group number are the same.

Two-slot: In *two-slot addressing* the PLC is configured with one group distributed over two adjacent slots, so that the adjacent slots can accept a module that has one input

word (16 terminals) and one output word (16 terminals) for field device attachment. One group (16 inputs and 16 outputs) fills two slots.

As Figure 3-12 indicates, the chassis is configured by setting switches. In the PLC 5, the relationship between the slot locations and the group number is determined by two factors: (1) the number of input and output terminals on the module placed into the slot, and (2) the selected addressing mode for the chassis. Single-slot addressing is the only one described and used in this text because when 16-terminal or point input or output modules are used in this mode, the group and slot numbers are the same. This characteristic makes addressing easier to understand. Figure 3-13 illustrates an example of 16-terminal input and output modules using single-slot addressing. Note that the slot numbers at the top match the group number at the bottom.

Chassis slots 6 and 7: In Figure 3-13, slot 6 has a 16-point input module and slot 7 has a 16-point output module. With single-slot addressing, group 6 (slot 6) and group 7 (slot 7) identify the bits for these I/O points. As a result, word 6 in the input image table and word 7 in the

FIGURE 3-12: PLC 5 slot addressing mode switch setting.

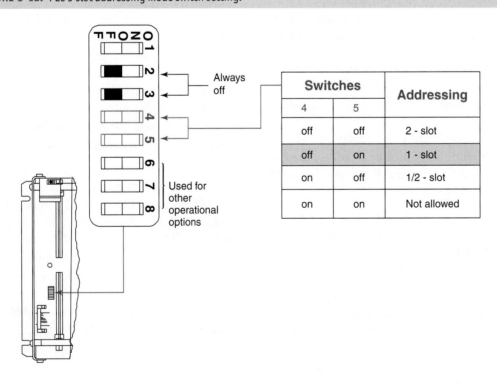

Switches		Addressing
4	5	
off	off	2 - slot
off	on	1 - slot
on	off	1/2 - slot
on	on	Not allowed

FIGURE 3-13: PLC 5 single-slot addressing mode.

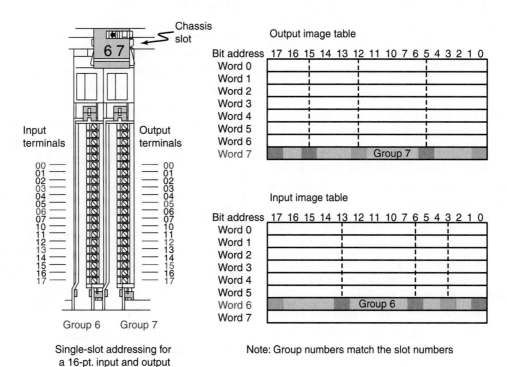

Single-slot

Single-slot addressing for
a 16-pt. input and output

Note: Group numbers match the slot numbers

output image table are allocated to group 6 and group 7, respectively. Each group can have both an input word and an output word, but these modules are just an input and output type. As a result, word 7 in the input image table and word 6 in the output image table are not used.

With the input and output memory organization covered for the PLC 5 system, the addressing format for input and output bits is discussed next.

PLC 5 Rack/Group I/O addressing. The PLC 5 system with single-slot addressing, illustrated in Figure 3-14, has the following format for addressing I/O.

The structure starts with either an I for inputs or an O for outputs, and uses a colon (:) as a delimiter or separator. The next two digits are the rack number, which is followed by the I/O group number. The forward slash (/) separates the final two digits, which are the terminal numbers or input or output image table bit numbers.

The illustration in Figure 3-14 shows a single-slot addressing scheme with 16-point input and output modules located in adjacent slots 4 and 5 in rack 01. Because single-slot addressing is used, the slot number is also the group and word number used in the address. The addresses on the ladder rung below the figure use the format previously described for PLC 5 systems. Note that the RSLogix 5 ladder logic programming software places the bit number below the rung and the rest of the address above the line. All numbers in the address are in the *octal* number system.

3-6-2 SLC 500 Rack/Slot-Based Addressing

The addressing of I/O in the SLC model PLC is similar to the PLC 5 single-slot addressing previously described. However, the SLC uses slots and PLC 5 uses groups. The programming software used for the SLC system is RSLogix 500.

SLC 500 series input and output addressing. Input and output addressing for SLC 500 was introduced in Chapter 1 and is expanded upon

FIGURE 3-14: PLC 5 address syntax for inputs and outputs.

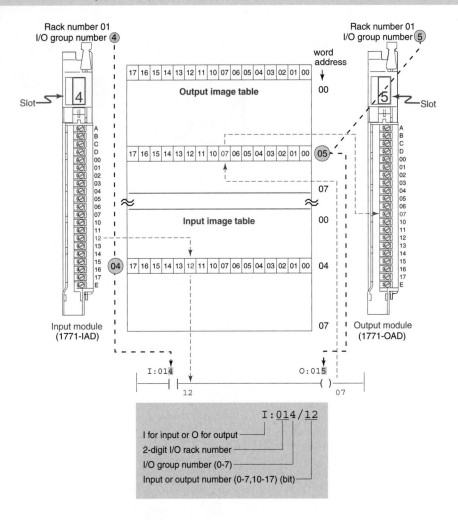

I for input or O for output ————
2-digit I/O rack number ————
I/O group number (0-7) ————
Input or output number (0-7,10-17) (bit) ————

I:014/12

EXAMPLE 3-1

Determine the input and output addresses for the bits with light blue blocks in Figure 3-13. Assume the modules are in rack 01.

SOLUTION

a. Figure 3-13 output: **0:017/0**—rack 01, group 7, and bit 0

b. Figure 3-13 output:**0:017/12**—rack 01, group 7, and bit 12

c. Figure 3-13 input: **I:016/3**—rack 01, group6, and bit 3

d. Figure 3-13 input: **I:016/17**—rack 01, group 6, and bit 17

Note that the octal number system is used for the terminal numbers on the PLC 5 modules.

---

here. The illustrations in Figure 3-15(a) through (d) provide the required information for learning the SLC rack/slot addressing process. Note that the PLC rack in the figure has four slots, with the processor in slot 0 and an input module in slot 1. The module has 16 inputs (IN0 to IN15) and three field devices connected to input terminals 2 (momentary push button switch), 6 (NO limit switch held closed), and 12 (a three-wire proximity sensor). In order to reference the

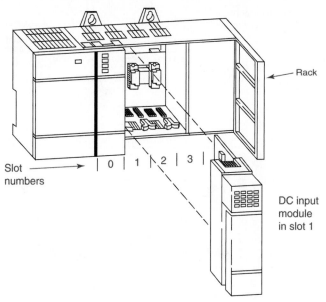

Slot numbers

DC input module in slot 1

(a) SLC 500 four slot rack

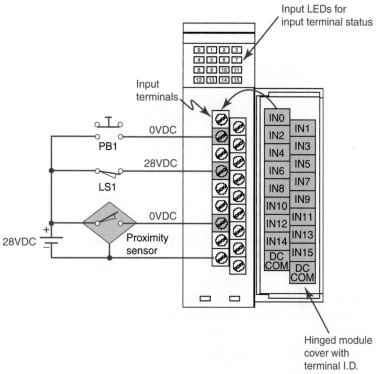

Input LEDs for input terminal status

Input terminals

(b) SLC 500 input module

Hinged module cover with terminal I.D.

FIGURE 3-15: (Continued).

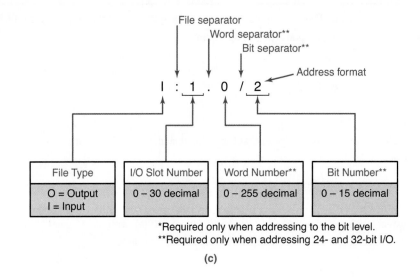

(c)

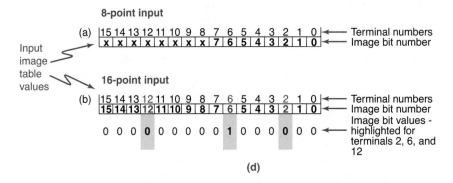

(d)

three field devices in a ladder program, their addresses must be known. The following address format description is illustrated in Figure 3-15(c).

The structure begins with either an I for inputs or an O for outputs and uses a colon (:) as a delimiter or separator. The next digit, the slot number, is followed by the period (.) delimiter. The next digit, the word number (only needed if the addressed word is not 0), is followed by the forward slash (/) delimiter, which separates the word number from the final two digits for the terminal number.

The values used for the address in Figure 3-15(c) are for the momentary pushbutton switch connected to terminal IN 2 in Figure 3-15(b).

Two input register or image table examples are illustrated in Figure 3-15(d): an 8-point input module and a 16-point input module. If the number of

inputs exceeds 16, the address must include the word number (0 for inputs 0 to 15 and 1 for inputs 16 and higher). The module in Figure 3-15(b) is a 16-point input module. Note that the input image table values (0s and 1s) for the field devices in Figure 3-15(b) are displayed in Figure 3-15(d). The open push button and proximity sensor have 0 volts at the terminal, so the register value is 0. The limit switch has 28 volts present, so its register value is 1.

The illustrations in Figure 3-15(a) through (d) are for an input module in slot 1, but a similar approach is used when an output module is added to the PLC. For example, if an output module is placed in slot 2, the I in the address in Figure 3-15(c) changes to an O, and the slot changes from 1 to 2. The output terminal to which the field device is connected determines the bit number. Again, a word number is necessary only if the number of outputs exceeds 16. Examples 3-2, 3-3, and 3-4 illustrate this addressing concept.

EXAMPLE 3-2

An Allen-Bradley SLC system uses a rack like the one illustrated in Figure 3-15(a), with the 16-point input DC module in slot 3. Determine the address for a discrete input signal attached to terminal 5 of the module.

SOLUTION

The address for the discrete DC input would be

$$I:3/5$$

The letter I indicates that it is an input, the 3 indicates that the DC input module is in slot 3, and the 5 indicates that the discrete field device input signal wire is connected to terminal 5.

EXAMPLE 3-3

An Allen-Bradley SLC system uses a rack like the one illustrated in Figure 3-15(a), with the 24-point input DC module in slot 2. Determine the address for a discrete input signal attached to terminal 19 of the module.

SOLUTION

The address for the discrete DC input would be

$$I:2.1/3$$

The letter I indicates that it is an input, the 2 indicates that the DC input module is in slot 2, and the 1 indicates that it is the second word. Two words are needed because there are more than 16 terminals. Because terminal 16 is bit 0 in word 1, terminal 19 is bit 3 in the second word. Figure 3-16 illustrates the relationship between terminals and register bits for input and output modules in the SLC 500 system. Find bit 3 in word 1 and verify that it is terminal 19 on the module.

EXAMPLE 3-4

An Allen-Bradley SLC system uses a rack like the one illustrated in Figure 3-15(a), with an 8-terminal DC output module in slot 1. Determine the address for the field device attached to terminal 7 of the module.

SOLUTION

The address for the discrete DC output would be

$$O:1/7$$

The letter O indicates that it is an output, the 1 indicates that the module is in slot 1, and the 7 indicates that the field device output signal wire is connected to terminal 7.

FIGURE 3-16: Addressing 32-point input and output modules for the SLC 500 PLC.

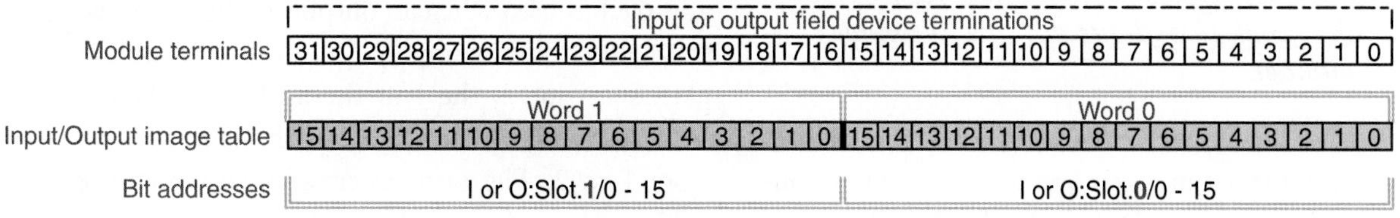

Allen Bradley SLC 500 addressing for a 32-point input or output module

---

I/O Addressing. The display of the input and output registers for an SLC 500 controller is illustrated in Figure 3-17. Note that output slot 5 and input slot 1 have 32-point modules installed. The output words are O:5.0 and O:5.1, and the inputs are I:1.0 and I:1.1. The addressing options when single and multiple words are present are illustrated in the output register data file. The address O:8/14 indicates that the field device is attached to terminal 14, and the module is in slot 8. No word (O:8.0/14) element is present since the 0 word is assumed if none is entered.

If two words are present, then the elimination of the word element is still an option. For example, the bit addressed O:5.1/4 indicates that the bit is in locaton 4 of word 1 for the module in slot 5. On the module's word 1 location 4 is terminal number 20, since numbering of terminals starts at 0 and goes to 31. As a result, a second addressing option would be O:5/20 with the word element eliminated and the bits numbered 0 to 31, identical to the terminals. Bits in word 0 are numbered 0 to 15 and in word 1 they are numbered 16 to 31. If additional words are present they would continue to count in this fashion. It is clear from this discussion that using memory locations for program files offers a number of disadvantages in data addressing. For example, inputs and outputs cannot be given a variable name associated with their field device, and all I/O wiring address assignments must be completed before programming for the PLC can begin.

3-6-3 Other Vendors' Rack/Slot PLC Addressing

Most companies standardize automation control to a single PLC vendor to make programming and troubleshooting of the system controller easier.

FIGURE 3-17: SLC 500 input and output registers.

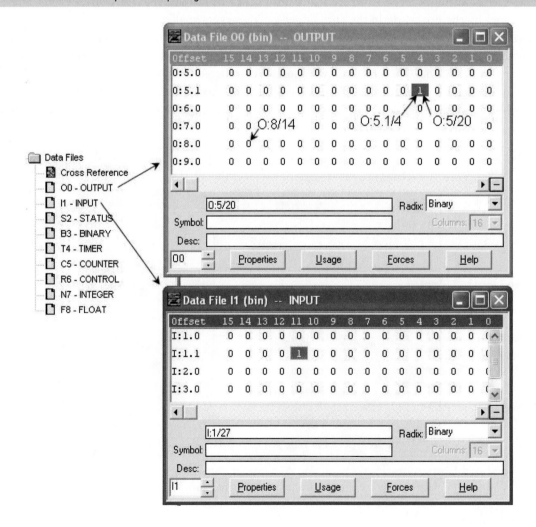

Unfortunately, this does not mean that only one type of PLC is used. Many automation systems purchased from vendors use a PLC as the imbedded machine controller. The PLC used is often one selected by the system builder and cannot be changed. One must be familiar with the operation and programming language of that PLC in order to troubleshoot machine problems. Therefore, someone working in manufacturing automation will need to know several PLC systems. No two PLC manufacturers have identical programming formats, but PLC procedures and instructions are similar to the Allen-Bradley languages covered in this text. When one is learned well, the others can be learned quickly.

3-6-4 Tag-Based Addressing

In the previous sections the older rack/group and rack/slot formats for addressing inputs and outputs was described. In each case, the programmer was obligated to use an address that was mapped to the specific memory location where that data was stored by the processor. In the current generation of PLCs, like AB's ControlLogix, the programmer assigns a *tag name* in the RS Logix 5000 software for field devices, process data, and most other ladder logic instructions. The type of tag needed—for example, Boolean (on or off), integer, real, timer, counter, or control—is specified by assigning a *data type* to the tag name. Review some of the examples of basic and structured data types described in Section 3-5-4 and listed in Tables 3-3 and 3-4.

With this approach, the storage location of the Boolean input or output tag no longer is required; instead, the programmer creates a tag to represent the data. All program development proceeds with just the tag names and the data types assigned. Later, input and output variables are matched with the pin number on the respective modules where the field devices are connected.

Creating tags in the tags window. The tags window is used to create program tags as the ladder logic is developed. Figure 3-18 provides an example of a tags window. Compare the data element, tag name, and type of data listed under those column headings.

Note that the tag names identify by name or describe the data that the tag represents, and the data types are like those listed earlier in the chapter in Tables 3-3 and 3-4. The tags have the same form for all types of data, which is a major benefit offered by this new generation of PLCs.

As shown in Figure 3-19(a), the tag window is opened from either the Controller tags or

FIGURE 3-18: Program tags window for creating tags.

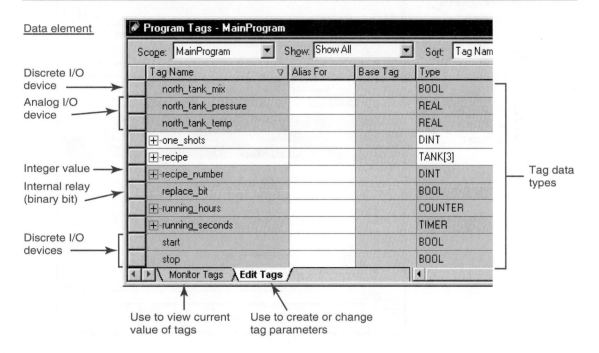

FIGURE 3-19: Creating tags and setting the alias.

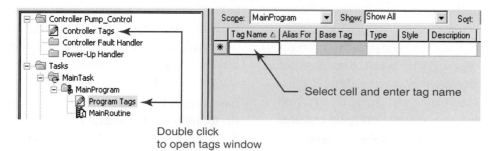

Double click
to open tags window

(a) Opening the tag window

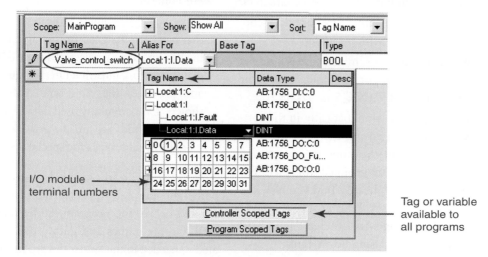

(b) Assigning I/O terminal numbers and address

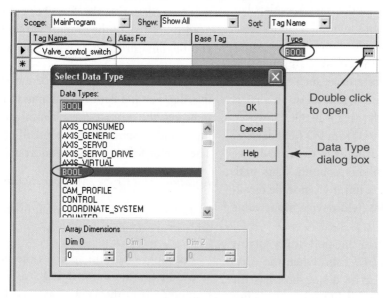

(c) Assigning data types

Program Tags file listing. Each of the four visible columns—Tag Name, Alias For, Base Tag, and Type—is described next.

Tag Name: A *tag name* is assigned to an area of the controller memory where data is stored. The name is entered by selecting the open cell in the tag name column and typing the tag. Note the following requirements and good practices:

- Tags can only include numbers, letters (not case sensitive), and single underscores (_) with a maximum length of 40 characters.
- Tags must begin with a letter or underscore but cannot end with an underscore.
- When entering tags, mixed case is used for ease of reading, for example, Tank_1 or Tank1 and not TANK_1 or TANK1.
- Tags are sorted alphabetically in the software; therefore, using the same word to start tags from the same manufacturing area keeps them grouped together. For example, Tank1_heater, Tank1_mixer, and Tank1_ sensor will be grouped in that order in the tag window. See Figure 3-18 for an example using north_tank.

Alias For: *Alias for* is a tag that references memory defined by another tag. The Alias For column links the data's internal memory location to the descriptive name for the value listed in the Name Tag column. In general, if a tag is an internal reference, such as a binary bit for an internal or virtual relay, an alias is not necessary, and the area is blank. However, if tags represent values from I/O field devices, a path through the module to the field device must be created in this column. This path gives the processor a link to a module terminal point where the field device input value is present.

In Figure 3-19(b), a pull-down arrow appears after *Local:1:I.Data* when the Alias For cell is selected. The dialog box has the address locations for all I/O modules. When *Local:1:I* is expanded two files appear: *Local:1:I.Fault* and *Local:1:I.Data*. When *Local:1:I.Data* is selected, a second drop-down arrow appears. This arrow displays a dialog box [Figure 3-19(b)] for all of the terminal numbers on the input module located at the address *Local:1:I.Data*. Next, the tag name (Value_control_switch) used in the program is linked to the input terminal number 1 where the field device represented by the tag name is connected. This step makes the logical address, called the tag name, an alias for the physical address located in *Local:1:I.Data.1*.

Base Tag: A *base tag* is a tag that represents the location where the data is stored in memory. In most cases, the address entry in the Base Tag column is the same as the entry in the Alias For column.

Type: The *Type* column indicates the data type that has been assigned to the tag name. When the heading Type is selected, Figure 3-19(c), the dialog box link illustrated in the figure is active and produces the data type dialog box as shown. The commonly used data types listed in Tables 3-3 and 3-4 are present, along with a long list of data types for special applications.

In the solution to a control problem, the tag name and tag data type can be identified and entered before the program ladder logic is created. Or, tag names and data types can be created as needed in the ladder design. In either case, identification of the physical addresses for the tags (completion of the Alias For column) is not needed until all of the module wiring is finished, and the final program is ready for field testing.

Alias and base tag address format. A study of the Alias For and Base Tag columns in Figure 3-21 indicates the format for physical addresses of input and outputs in the ControlLogix system. The format for the physical address is:

Location : Slot : Type . Member . Submember . Bit

The terms used in the format for the physical address are defined as follows:

Location: Location specifies the network location for the data. If LOCAL is used, the module is in the same chassis or DIN rail as the controller. If ADAPTER_NAME is used, it identifies the remote communication adapter, such as a DeviceNet remote I/O block or bridge module.

Slot: Slot specifies the slot number of the I/O module in its chassis or DIN rail.

Create tag names, data types, and aliases in a tag window for the tank control problem described in Chapter 1 [Figure 1–7(a) and Figure 1–17] using the PLC configuration and field device wiring illustrated in Figure 3-20.

SOLUTION

Study the solution in Figure 3-21. Note how tag names were chosen to represent the input and output field devices and how the choice of names caused similar data to be grouped together. Also, one tag, Valve_control_tag, is an internal memory bit used like the control relay in the original solution in Chapter 1.

Two additional columns, Style and Description, are displayed. In the Style column, the programmer indicates the desired number system radix for display of variable values. In the optional Description column each tag is described. This description appears above the instruction in the ladder logic if that display option is selected.

FIGURE 3-20: PLC configuration for Example 3-5.

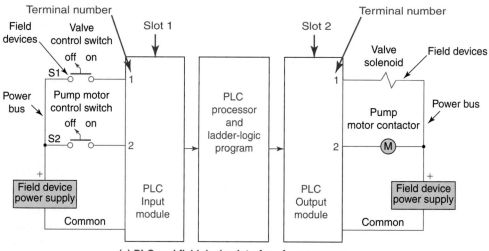

(a) PLC and field device interface for one pump

FIGURE 3-21: Tag window for pump control—Examples 3-5 and 3-6.

Pump control tag data

Tag Name	△	Alias For	Base Tag	Type	Style	Description
Pump_motor_control_switch		Local:1:I.Data.2(C)	Local:1:I.Data.2(C)	BOOL	Decimal	Start switch for pump motor
Pump_motor_starter		Local:2:O.Data.2(C)	Local:2:O.Data.2(C)	BOOL	Decimal	PLC output bit for pump motor...
Valve_control_bit				BOOL	Decimal	Internal relay for valve control
Valve_control_switch		Local:1:I.Data.1(C)	Local:1:I.Data.1(C)	BOOL	Decimal	Start switch for valve solenoid
Valve_solenoid		Local:2:O.Data.1(C)	Local:2:O.Data.1(C)	BOOL	Decimal	PLC output bit for valve conta...

Scope: MainProgram   Show: Show All   Sort: Tag Name

Type: Type specifies four types of data: *I* for input, *O* for output, *C* for configuration, and *S* for status.

Member: Member specifies the type of data that the module can store. For digital modules a DATA member usually stores the input or output bit values, and for an analog module a

Channel member (CH#) usually stores the analog channel values.

Submember (optional): Submember is specific data related to a member.

Bit (optional): Bit specifies the specific terminal on a digital I/O module.

EXAMPLE 3-6

Define each term for the base tag associated with the Valve_control_switch and the Valve_solenoid in Figure 3-21.

SOLUTION

a. The base tag or physical address for the tag Valve_control_switch is Local:1:I.Data.2(C). Local indicates that the module is in the same rack as the processor, 1 indicates that the module is in slot 1 in the rack, I indicates that the module is an input, Data indicates that it is a digital input, 2 indicates that the selector switch is attached to terminal 2 on the module, and C indicates that it is a controller tag with global access.

b. The base tag or physical address for the tag Valve_solenoid is Local:2:O.Data.2(C). Local indicates that the module is in the same rack as the processor, 2 indicates that the module is in slot 2 in the rack, O indicates that it is an output module, Data indicates that it is a digital output, 2 indicates that the valve solenoid is attached to terminal 2 on the module, and C indicates that it is a controller tag with global access.

Two types of delimiters, colons (:) and periods (.), are used to separate the information presented in the physical memory call-out. Note that bits are not delimited by a slash (/) as in the PLC 5 and SLC 500. If the address is a control-type tag, a (C) is placed at the end of the address to indicate a controller tag with global scope.

After comparing all of the base tags in Figure 3-21 with the physical memory address format, one should be able to identify all parts of the physical address.

3-7 INTERNAL CONTROL RELAY BIT ADDRESSING

Relay ladder logic uses control relays to represent the binary values in the logical solution of control problems. Review the operation of the relay ladder logic in Figure 1-7 in order to see how control relays are used in the tank control problem. The number of poles on the mechanical relays is determined by the number of contacts needed in other rungs. PLC Ladder logic uses internal memory bits as internal relays, which are sometimes called *virtual control relays*. Since virtual relays are just internal memory bits, the number of virtual relays used and therefore the number of instructions with the virtual relay addresses in other rungs is limited only by the PLC memory size. Addressing these internal memory bits in a rack/slot-based system will use a format similar

to that required for field devices. Internal relays in a tag-based system require only the identification of the tag name and the setting of the data type to Boolean. The following sections cover each type.

3-7-1 PLC 5 and SLC 500 Binary Bit Addressing

Review the memory layout for the Allen-Bradley PLC 5 and SLC 500 family of processors introduced earlier in Tables 3-1 and 3-2, respectively. Note that file 3, the bit file, is designated by the letter *B* in the address. The format for addressing bit files in both of these PLC systems is illustrated in Figure 3-22(a).

The binary bit address starts with a *file letter*, *B*, to indicate that a binary bit or word is referenced. The value after the file letter is the *file number*, which indicates the block of memory designated for use in storing binary bit data. File number 3 is the default binary bit file in both the PLC 5 and SLC 500 PLC. The only difference is the number of addressable bits available in file 3 for each processor. The SLC 500 has 256 (numbers 0 to 255) 16-bit words and the PLC 5 has 1000 (0 to 999) 16-bit words in file 3. Additional storage is available for binary bits when the default locations are full.

The colon is a file delimiter or separator between the file number and element or word number. The forward slash separates the word number from the bit address or the *bit number*.

FIGURE 3-22: Binary bit addressing in SLC 500 PLCs.

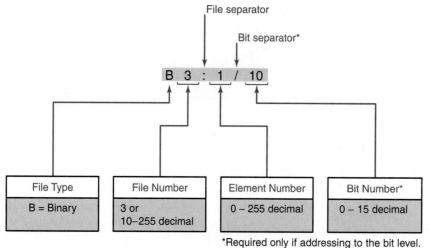

(a) Binary bit addressing syntax

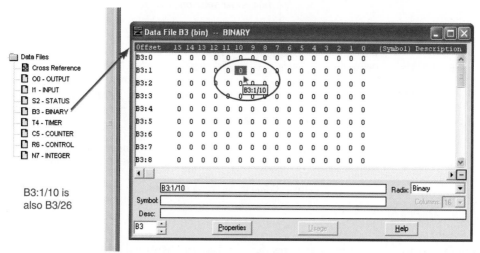

(b) RSLogix 500 view of file 3 data

EXAMPLE 3-7

Convert the PLC ladder logic solution for the tank problem in Figure 1-17(b) to a solution using an Allen-Bradley SLC system. Obtain module slot and terminal numbers from Figure 3-20. Let bit zero of word zero in file 3 be used for the internal relay.

SOLUTION

Study the solution in Figure 3-23(a). PLC input and output instructions replace the field devices in the relay ladder logic solution. The internal relay replaces the control relay, and the binary address for the internal relay is used to reference the output coil in rung 0 and the input instructions in rungs 1 and 2. Figure 3-23(b) describes the address notation for input and output instructions and for internal bits. Note how the ladder has been documented with a ladder description, rung descriptions, and instruction descriptions. All PLC programs should have instruction descriptions, rung comments, and ladder file titles. Some of the solutions in this book do not have this full documentation in order to reduce figure size.

Review input, output, and binary bit addressing for an understanding of how the generic addresses and the ladder from Chapter 1 were converted to the SLC 500 addressing format using slot and terminal numbers.

FIGURE 3-23: Solution for Example 3-7.

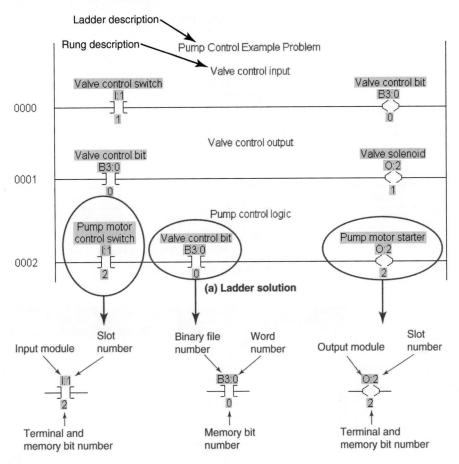

(a) Ladder solution

(b) SLC 500 ladder rung notation

The bit number, 0 to 15, references the specific bit in the 16-bit word. If the forward slash and this last bit field is omitted, the address references the entire word.

For another addressing option, omit the element or word number so that the address format would be

B3/ [bit number]

Because the word or element number (0 to 255) is omitted, the bits of the 256 words are numbered consecutively from 0 to 4095. This format is used less frequently than the format described in Figure 3-22(a).

Figure 3-22(b) illustrates a binary bit file for the SLC 500 PLC. The first nine words (B3:0 to B3:8) are displayed with their value, 0 or 1, for each bit. Each row begins with the first three fields of the internal bit address (B3:0, for example); to complete the address one adds a forward slash and the bit location in the word. An example, B3:1/10 (bit 10 in word 1), is highlighted. The alternate address for this example is B3/26 (binary bit 26 out of the possible 4096 bits).

A *radix* drop-down box in the lower-right corner is used to change the display's radix value. The radix selected for display is usually decimal or binary, depending upon how the data is used in the PLC program.

Examples of PLC 5 and SLC 500 binary bit addressing are provided in Figure 3-24. Note that an example with the element or word number

FIGURE 3-24: PLC 5 and SLC 500 internal relay address examples.

Allen Bradley – PLC 5 and SLC 500 System	
B3:5/14	Bit 14, word or element 5 – File 3 (0 to 255 words) is reserved for binary bit data.
B3:240/7	Bit 7, word or element 240 – File 3 (0 to 255 words) is reserved for binary bit data.
B15:0/14	File 15 (user defined), Bit 14 and word or element 0 – User defined file 15 word 0 is defined as a binary bit file by the B prefix.
B3:9	Bits 0 to 15, word or element 9 – Since the bit field is omitted, the address references all the bits in word or element 9.
B3/157	Bit 13, word or element 10 – Since the word field is omitted, the bit address is the bit location when counted consecutively from bit zero in word zero. The bit number for the number 15 bit in any consecutive word is equal to (the word number $\times$ 16) −1. For this example, the 15th bit in word 10 is (10 $\times$ 16) −1 = 159, so the 13th bit is 157.

omitted is provided for bit addressing. A formula and process for finding the value of the bit for this format are also provided.

3-7-2 ControlLogix Binary Bit Addressing

An internal control relay is created in the ControlLogix system by creating a tag (either program or controller type or scope) and assigning a Boolean type to the tag. The Valve_control _bit tag, created for the pump control problem and illustrated in Figure 3-21, is an example of an internal memory bit or control relay in the Logix system.

EXAMPLE 3-8

Convert the PLC ladder logic solution for the tank problem in Figure 1-17(b) to a solution, using an Allen-Bradley ControlLogix system. Obtain tag names and base tag addresses from Figure 3-21.

SOLUTION

Figure 3-25 presents another solution for the tank system in Figures 1-7 and 3-20. Note that the binary address for the internal relay is used to reference both the output coil in rung 0 and the input instructions in rungs 1 and 2. Compare this solution with the SLC 500 ladders described earlier and verify that it operates the same. Note also how much more descriptive the solution becomes when tag names are used in place of the memory addresses in the SLC solution.

The virtual relays used in the last two examples used non-retentive memory bits. A second type, called retentive memory, is also available and is discussed next.

3-7-3 Retentive and Non-retentive Memory

Retentive memory retains the memory state (0 or 1) when the PLC is cycled from on to off and back to on. Non-retentive memory locations are reset to 0 whenever the PLC is turned on. All PLCs offer both types of memory for the binary bits. Allen-Bradley PLC software provides both retentive [-(L)- and –(U)-] and non-retentive [-( )-] coil instructions as a programming option. Non-retentive memory permits an output bit to become true when the rung is true and then return to a false state when the rung is false or the PLC is turned off. The retentive bit is set when the rung is true and remains set when the rung is false or when the PLC power is removed. Retentive memory is used when a *warm restart* must be a part of the system operation. In a warm restart situation the automation must maintain the value of some variables if the PLC or automation system is shut down by a power failure or system fault. Retentive memory permits the system to be restarted with memory locations holding the values that were present when the execution was halted.

Retentive memory for control of process machinery components, such as conveyors, pneumatic and hydraulic actuators, and motors, may present safety hazards. For example, when a latched output bit turns on a conveyor motor, that motor is in the on condition until the bit is unlatched. If conveyor power is lost, the conveyor stops; however, when power is restored the conveyor motor immediately turns on and the conveyor starts moving. Operators or maintenance technicians who are unaware that the conveyor motor is controlled by a retentive memory bit could be injured if they are working on

FIGURE 3-25: Solution for Example 3-8.

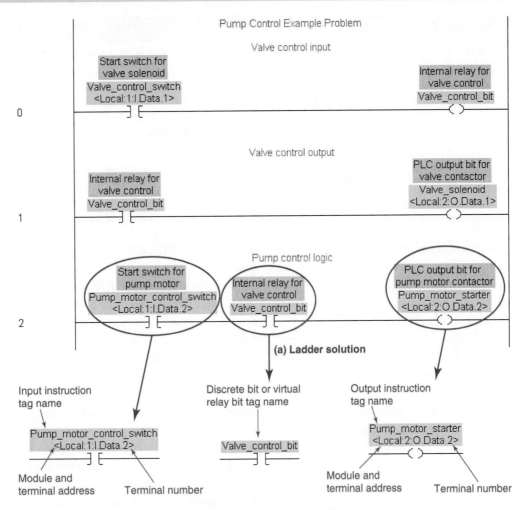

the motor and conveyor drive or if they are near the conveyor belt when the system starts to move at the restoration of power.

PLCs have a third type of stored memory information called *status data*, which is discussed next.

3-8 STATUS DATA ADDRESSING

Most PLCs have a *status memory* allocation that stores important data related to the operation of the processor. In the PLC 5 and SLC 500 models, instructions can set or reset processor status bits; in other cases, a program error during execution will set error bits in the status memory area. In some cases, the programmer may access status data and use that data to modify the program execution. Generally, the program-

mer does not use the status bits or words in the course of programming most applications. It is important, however, to be aware that this processor status data is available and accessible when specific control situations demand its use. The PLC 5 and SLC 500 have status memory allocations and the ability to address some status data.

3-8-1 PLC 5 and SLC 500 Status Data Addressing

The SLC 500 PLC saves status data in 163 words of memory. In some cases a single word will have 16 bits of different status data. In others, blocks of words are used to store data from a single event, such as the *Global Status File* of network data stored in words 100 to 163. Figure 3-26

FIGURE 3-26: SLC 500 status memory addressing of first pass bit.

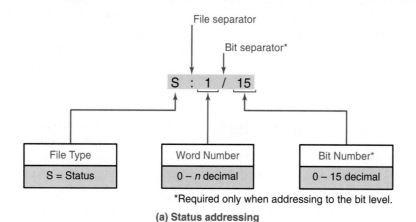

File separator

Bit separator*

S : 1 / 15

File Type	Word Number	Bit Number*
S = Status	0 – *n* decimal	0 – 15 decimal

*Required only when addressing to the bit level.

(a) Status addressing

First-Pass Bit   S:1/15

Use the bit to initialize your program as the application requires. When this bit is set by the processor, it indicates that the first scan of the user program is in progress (following power up in the RUN mode or entry into a REM Run or REM Test mode). The processor clears this bit following the first scan.

When this bit is cleared, it indicates that the program is not in the first scan of a REM Test or REM Run mode.

(b) First-pass bit definition

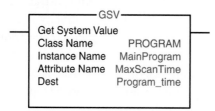

```
┌──────────GSV──────────┐
│ Get System Value       │
│ Class Name     PROGRAM │
│ Instance Name  MainProgram │
│ Attribute Name MaxScanTime │
│ Dest           Program_time │
└────────────────────────┘
```

(c) ControlLogix command to get status information

illustrates the format for addressing data in the PLC 5 and SLC 500 status file.

One should recognize the format used for file addressing in the both PLC systems. Figure 3-8 indicates that file 2 is the status file, and the delimiters in Figure 3-26(a) continue to be a colon between file type and word, with a forward slash to separate the word from the bit. Figure 3-26(b) illustrates a typical status file that is often used in programs. The status bit, addressed by S:1/15, is called the *first pass bit*. Its definition and operation can be studied in Figure 3-26(b).

The information presented thus far covers the first four address files (0 – outputs, 1 – inputs, 2 – status, and 3 – binary bits) in the PLC 5 and SLC 500 system. Later chapters describe the remaining files (files 4 through 8).

3-8-2   Logix System Status

Unlike the PLC 5 and SLC 500 models, the Logix models have no status file. Instead they use two instructions, *GSV (Get System Value)* and *SSV (Store System Value)*, to get and set controller status data that is stored in objects. The class names used in the instructions include *AXIS, CONTROLLER, CONTROLLERDEVICE, CST, DF1, FAULTLOG, MESSAGE, MODULE, MOTIONGROUP, PROGRAM, ROUTINE, SERIALPORT, TASK,* and *WALLCLOCKTIME.*

When the GSV instruction is used in a program, it retrieves the specified status information stored as an attribute under the object name. For example, Figure 3-26(c) shows a GSV instruction that will retrieve the longest program execution time from a variable named *PROGRAM*.

MainProgram.MaxScanTime. Note that the object has three parts listed in the figure: Class Name, Instance Name, and Attribute Name. The GSV instruction moves the longest program execution time to a tag called Program_time specified as the destination (Dest).

3-9 ALLEN-BRADLEY INPUT INSTRUCTIONS AND OUTPUT COILS

In the PLC ladder logic solutions presented thus far, only the *examine if closed* (-||-) input XIC instruction and the output energized (-( )-) output OTE instruction have been used. A second instruction (XIO) and symbol (-|/|-) called *examine if open*, is often required for the input field devices in ladder logic. Also, two retentive output instructions, OTL and OTU, *output latch* (-(L)-) and *output unlatch* (-(U)-), respectively, are required for the ladder outputs. Figure 3-27 presents information on the two inputs, and Figure 3-30 covers the three outputs. This information applies equally to PLC 5, SLC 500, and ControlLogix processors and programming.

3-9-1 Examine if Closed and Examine if Open Instructions

The names *examine if closed* and *examine if open* plus the shorthand notation XIC and XIO, used for Allen-Bradley (AB) PLCs, are used in this text. Figure 3-27 lists a number of other terms that are widely used to describe these two logic symbols and input instructions. The figure also indicates the address format used most often for all three AB PLCs. Read the descripitons in the figure again and review the ladder rung in Figure 3-28.

The rung in Figure 3-28 has an XIC (-||-) input and an output energize symbol (-( )-) shown. For the output to be *true (activated)*, the input XIC instuction must provide *continuity* or *power flow*. In relay ladder logic, the input contacts apply a voltage and pass a current to a relay coil at the output. Since PLC ladder logic is only a logical representation, no real current flows. However, the concept of power flow or continuity through the XIC instructions is still used. Row 5 in Figure 3-27 focuses on the conditions that produce continuity and power flow through the XIC and XIO instructions in a PLC ladder rung, and row 6

describes the conditions that interrupt continuity and power flow through the same instructions.

The XIC's input image table or register bit must be a 1 to produce continuity, but for continuity in XIO the bit must be a 0. The bit is a 1 if the input field device connected to the input terminals has a closed contact; it is a 0 if the contact of the field device is open. Thus a true XIC instruction needs continuity in the field device contact, and a true XIO instruction needs no continuity or an open in the field device contact. The XIO and XIC can also have an address from another internal reference such as an output bit address or an internal relay bit address. Again, if the XIC's address bit is a 1 then continuity is present, and the XIO's reference bit must be a 0 for continuity. Review row 5 until the conditions that produce continuity are clear.

Row 6 describes the conditions necessary to *interrupt* continuity. These conditions are just the opposite of what is required to produce continuity. If the input field device contact is open, then the XIC has no continuity or no logical power flow. Similarly, if the input field device for the XIO instruction has a closed contact, then no continuity is present and the instruction has no logical power flow. Again, review row 6 until the conditions that interrupt continuity are clear.

You may wonder how current sinking and sourcing input modules affect the operation of the XIC and XIO instructions just discussed. The type of input has no effect since a closed field device contact makes both a current sinking and current sourcing input active (a 1 is placed in the input image table). Likewise, an open field device contact makes both types of module inputs not active (a 0 is placed in the input image table).

Field device contacts versus PLC instructions. An important distinction must be made between the normally open (NO) and normally closed (NC) physical contacts used in input and output field devices, such as the contacts of a push button switch and the ladder input logic symbols XIC (-||-) and XIO (-|/|-) Input field devices, like switches, have physical contacts that present a voltage or a ground to the input module of the PLC. The symbols used for both the NO and NC physical switch contacts and the XIC and XIO ladder logic symbols are identical.

FIGURE 3-27: Ladder contacts—Examine if closed and examine if open.

	Symbol	—⊢⊦—	—⊦/⊦—
1	Allen Bradley names	Examine If Closed	Examine If Open
2	Abbreviation	XIC	XIO
3	Other names used	Examine On Examine If On Open Contact Symbol Normally Open Contact	Examine Off Examine If Off Closed Contact Symbol Normally Closed Contact
4	Possible addresses	**PLC 5 and SLC 500** Input image table bit address, i.e., I:2/3. Output image table bit address, i.e.,, O:3/12. Any internal relay bit address, i.e., B3:5/8. Any bit level address. **ControlLogix** Any tag with a Boolean data type. Any tag associated with an input module terminal.	**PLC 5 and SLC 500** Input image table bit address, i.e., I:2/3. Output image table bit address, i.e., O:3/12. Any internal relay address, i.e., B3:5/8. Any bit level address. **ControlLogix** Any tag with a Boolean data type. Any tag associated with an input module terminal.
5	Continuity, power flow, true, active, closed contacts, or highlighted if	Input field device contacts are closed. The input image table bit is a 1. The reference address (i.e., B3:5/8 or O:3/12) is true (1).	Input field device contacts are open. The input image table bit is a 0. The reference address (i.e., B3:5/8 or O:3/12) is false (0).
6	No continuity, no power flow, false, not active, open contacts, or not highlighted if	Input field device contacts are open. The input image table bit is a 0. The reference address (i.e., B3:5/8 or O:3/12) is false (0).	Input field device contacts are closed. The input image table bit is a 1. The reference address (i.e., B3:5/8 or O:3/12) is true (1).
7	Operational comments	• The symbol looks like a normally open relay contact, but no current flows since the ladder rung is just a logical representation of the input logic necessary to activate the output. • To evaluate the condition of this logic symbol we ask the processor to EXAMINE IF (the field device is) CLOSED. If it is, then this symbol has continuity. If the field device is OPEN, then no continuity is present. • The address or memory bit location associated with this symbol applies the condition of that address or bit to the symbol. If the address is true, or 1, then this symbol has continuity. If it is false, or 0, there is no continuity.	• The symbol looks like a normally closed relay contact, but no current flows since the ladder rung is just a logical representation of the input logic necessary to activate the output. • To evaluate the condition of this logic symbol we ask the processor to EXAMINE IF (the field device is) OPEN. If it is, then this symbol has continuity. If the field device is CLOSED, then no continuity is present. • The address or memory bit location associated with this symbol applies the condition of that address or bit to the symbol. If the address is false, or 0, then this symbol has continuity. If it is true, or 1, there is no continuity.

FIGURE 3-28: Continuity and power flow in a ladder logic rung.

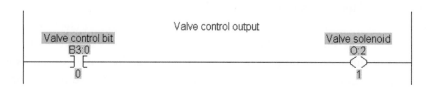

However, the input logic symbols in PLC ladders are virtual contacts or logic symbols because they are created in software and represent Boolean memory values. Therefore, they are called *instructions* and not *contacts*. Frequently, PLC literature refers to XIC (-| |-) and XIO (-|/|-) instructions as normally open or normally closed contacts or just contacts in general. To avoid confusion, this text uses the term *contact* for field devices and the term *instruction* for any input XIC or XIO symbol addressed by a PLC memory bit.

Linking field devices with XIC and XIO instructions. Figure 3-29 shows the interface between an input field device (limit switch) and XIC and XIO instructions in a ladder logic rung. A study of the figure indicates that the limit switch has normally open (NO) contacts when not actived and closed contacts when activated by the automation process.

An *input image table*, also called an input memory register, has a bit associated with each terminal of the input module. The image table or register bit is a 0 when when the limit switch is in the normally open position, and it is a 1 when the field device contacts are held closed. Figure 3-29(a) depicts this convention in the XIC example.

Two choices for the instruction placed in the ladder logic rungs are examine if closed (XIC) and examine if open (XIO). The XIC instruction symbol (-| |-) looks like a normally open set of contacts, and from a virtual power flow analogy it works accordingly. When its memory address bit or image table bit is a 0, continuity is *not* present. However, when these bits are a 1, the instruction produces continuity. Figure 3-29(a) illustrates these two conditions. When an instruction produces continuity the RSLogix software grays the symbol to indicate an active state with continuity.

The XIO ladder logic instruction symbols (-|/|-) look like a normally closed set of contacts. Note that continuity is present when the input image table bit is a 0 and the field device contacts are open. However, when the field device contact closes and the image table bit is a 1, the XIO instruction is not true and no continuity is present. Figure 3-29(b) illustrates both of these con-

ditions. Note that the symbol is grayed out, indicating continuity and power flow when the input image table bit is a 0.

A ladder input instruction and the input field device are linked in the instruction address by the input module terminal where the field device is attached. Since the ladder instruction in Figure 3-29 has an address of 1:3/10, it is the input module in slot 3 and terminal 10 (SLC 500 notation). The figure shows that the condition of the ladder instruction, either active or not active, is determined by the bit value in the input module register for that terminal, either 1 or 0, respectively. In Figure 3-29, shading is used to indicate the instructions producing continuity. The use of the terms *examine if closed* and *examine if open* is confusing but necessary because these instructions represent PLC memory bits, not switch contacts. Review Figure 3-29 again to be sure you understand how field devices and input instruction bits interact.

Ladder logic terminology. This text uses the terms *true, active or continuity* and *false, not active or no continuity* to describe the conditions of the XIC and XIO instructions. In other reference material additional terms for continuity include *power flow, contacts closed,* and *highlighted.* For no continuity terms include *no power flow, contacts open,* and *not highlighted.* These terms merely indicate that the input instruction condition is either allowing logical power flow or interrupting it.

3-9-2 Output Energize, Output Latch, and Output Unlatch Instructions

Figure 3-30 provides information on three of the most commonly used output instructions: output energize (OTE), output latch (OTL), and output unlatch (OTU). The OTE output is similar to a relay coil in relay ladder logic, and the OTL and OTU instructions are like a latching relay (described in Chapter 2) with a latch and unlatch coil.

Allen-Bradley output energize—OTE instruction. Column 1 in Figure 3-30 lists the OTE basics. The address of an output is usually a reference to an output field device connected to an

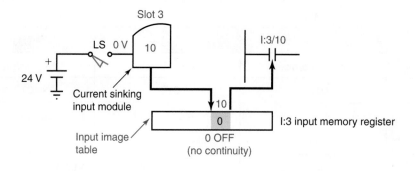

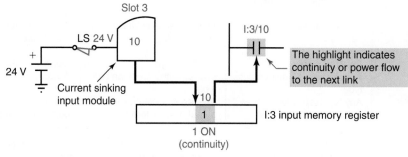

(a) Examine if closed example

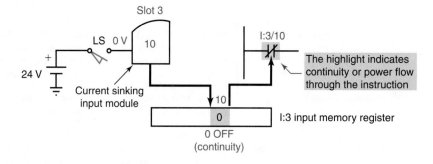

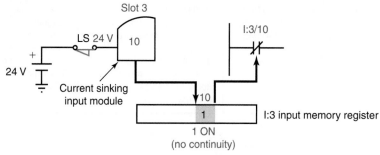

(b) Examine if open example

Source: Rehg and Sartori, Industrial Electronics, © 2006, p. 583. Reprinted by permission of Prentice Hall, Upper Saddle River, NJ.

	1	2	3
Symbol	—( )—	—(L)—	—(U)—
Allen Bradley names	Output Energize	Output Latch	Output Unlatch
Abbreviation	OTE	OTL	OTU
Other names used	Output Coil Output Instruction	Retentive Coil Retentive Memory	Retentive Coil Retentive Memory
Possible addresses	**PLC 5 and SLC 500** Output image table bit address, i.e., O:3/12. An internal relay bit address, i.e., B3:5/8. **ControlLogix** Any tag with a Boolean data type. Any tag associated with an output module terminal.	**PLC 5 and SLC 500** Output image table bit address, i.e., O:3/12. An internal relay bit address, i.e., B3:5/8. **ControlLogix** Any tag with a Boolean data type. Any tag associated with an output module terminal.	**PLC 5 and SLC 500** Output image table bit address, i.e., O:3/12. An internal relay bit address, i.e., B3:5/8. **ControlLogix** Any tag with a Boolean data type. Any tag associated with an output module terminal.
The output symbol is true, active, or highlighted and the bit in the output image table is true or a 1 if:	The input logic is true. The rung segment to the left of the symbol is true.	The input logic sets the retentive bit for this Output Latch to true or 1.	The input logic is true. When the Output Unlatch is true the retentive bit for this address is reset to false or 0.
Operational comments	• The OUTPUT ENERGIZE symbol is analogous to a relay coil in relay ladder logic. However, here it represents the output field device connected to the output module. • The output image table bit for this energized OUTPUT instruction is set to 1 when the ladder rung is TRUE. • The output image table bit for this energized OUTPUT instruction is set to 0 when the ladder rung is FALSE.	• The OUTPUT LATCH is analogous to a latching coil for a latching relay in relay ladder logic. However, here it is a command that sets a retentive memory bit to 1. • This retentive output is set when the rung input logic is true and remains set until a rung with an OUTPUT UNLATCH instruction with the same address becomes true. • The precautions described in Section 3-7-3 on retentive memory apply to this instruction as well.	• The OUTPUT UNLATCH is analogous to a unlatching coil for a latching relay in relay ladder logic. However, here it is a command that clears a retentive memory bit to 0. • The OUTPUT UNLATCH command has the same output image table address as the OUTPUT LATCH command that set the retentive bit. • Retentive memory instructions should be used cautiously because of the safety issues described in Section 3-7-3.

output module. Therefore, it could be any valid output address used in the PLC 5, SLC 500, or ControlLogix systems. Read the information and review the sample addresses for each of the outputs in the figure.

The output instructions are true or active if the input logic instructions provide power flow or continuity to the output. Therefore a path must exist from the left power rail (vertical bar)

through rung links that are true and input instructions that are grayed out. Figure 3-31 provides a visual picture of how power flow occurs and how it forces the output instruction to a true state.

Note that link 1 connected to the left power rail is always true. The remaining links (2, 3, and 4) are true if the instructions to the left of them are true. Ultimately, the output is true if the link to

FIGURE 3-31: Ladder rung power flow.

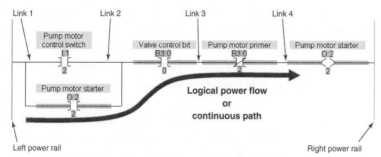

(a) Rung power flow or continuity example

Instruction address	Instruction type	Status	Register bit value	Condition	Instruction highlight
I:1/2	XIC	False	0	No power flow	Clear
O:2/2	XIC	True	1	Power flow	Gray
B3:0/0	XIC	True	1	Power flow	Gray
B3:0/2	XIO	True	0	Power flow	Gray

(b) Contact information

FIGURE 3-32: OTL and OTU instructions.

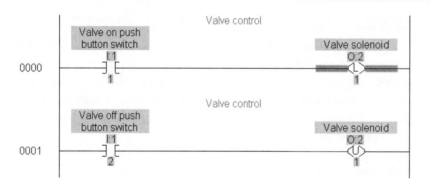

its left (link 4 in the figure) is true. When an XIC instruction is true, the bit value in its input register or image table is a 1, power flow is present, and the instruction is highlighted. In contrast, if the bit value in the XIO's register is a 0, the instruction has power flow and is highlighted. The OTE instruction is implemented with the same format used in all of the Allen-Bradley processors.

Allen-Bradley output latch and unlatch— OTL and OTU instruction. The OTL and OTU instruction information is listed in the last two columns in Figure 3-30. These two instructions perform like the latching relay described in Chapter 2.

The output latch turns on the output image table bit for this output when the OTL instructions are true. That bit remains true (1) until it is cleared (set to a 0) by the action of another rung, using an OTU instruction. These instructions have *retentive memory registers* that remain in their current state (0 or 1) until changed by another instruction.

As illustrated in Figure 3-32, the OTL and OTU instruction sequence is used when the automation system requires an output to remain on after a momentary field device input switch has cycled from close to open or remain on after a power loss is restored.

Note in the figure that the solenoid valve output is true (latched), but the input instruction

(I:1/1) has no power flow (not highlighted). If input I:1/2 in rung 2 becomes true, then the valve is turned off by the OTU instruction. The addresses for the OTL and OTU instructions must be the same, such as O:2/1 in this example. All of the Allen-Bradley processors implement the OTL and OTU instructions with the same format.

Output latch versus sealing instructions. The latch and unlatch output instructions are retentive, which means that the state of those outputs is unchanged even when power is removed from the processor. The safety issues associated with retentive memory in PLCs was addressed earlier in this chapter. An alternate approach to the use of latching outputs is the use of *sealing instructions.* Figure 3-33 illustrates a sealing instruction implementation for an SLC 500 program. Note that the figure uses the address of the output for an input instruction that is across the start instruction. Many references use the term *sealing contact* instead of *sealing instruction.*

The ladders in Figures 3-32 and 3-33 perform the same control. A valve is turned on with one depression of a push button and turned off with the depression of a second push button. The rung in Figure 3-33 shows the condition after the valve on push button switch is pressed and released. At the start, all instructions, except I:1/2, are false (no power flow). When I:1/1 is pressed the OTE output is true (power flow through I:1/1 and I:1/2). If the OTE is true (1), then the instruction O:2/1 (valve solenoid sealing instruction) is true because it uses the address of the OTE output. This instruction *seals around* the momentary push button, so that I:1/1 can return to a false state (no power flow), and the output is held in the true condition.

The output returns to the false state (0) when the push button I:1/2 is pressed because the instruction I:1/2 becomes false (no power flow). Therefore, the OTE output bit is false (0), and the sealing instruction returns to the no power flow state. This rung has no inherent safety issues because it is built without retentive memory bits. Accordingly, when power is lost in the processor all of the input and output bits clear to a false (0) state. When power is restored the valve solenoid is off and must be turned on with the push button.

3-10 INPUTS, OUTPUTS, AND SCAN TIME

The operation of input instructions and output coil instructions was addressed in the last section. The elapsed time from a change in an input field device to the resulting change in the output field device is dictated by the PLC *scan* and *scan time.* Therefore, it is important to understand these concepts.

3-10-1 Scan Time

PLC ladder logic programs have multiple rungs; therefore, a process must be used to coordinate the changes in input instructions on all of the rungs and on the associated changes in the outputs. The process used is a *PLC scan,* which is illustrated in Figure 3-34 and described next.

1. *Read the status of all input field devices* by transferring a 0 or a 1 to the input registers, based on the open or closed condition of the field device and voltage level present at the input module terminals. This concept was introduced in Figure 3-29.

FIGURE 3-33: Sealing instruction operation.

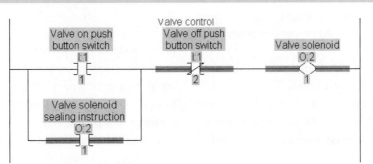

FIGURE 3-34: PLC scan cycle.

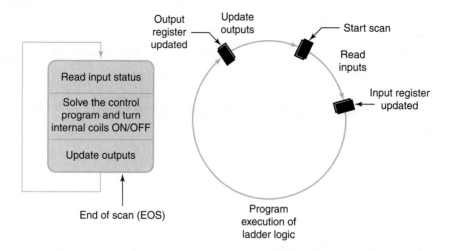

2. Perform the following four steps:
   a. Change the highlight condition of all input instruction symbols to reflect the condition of their bits in the input register.
   b. Evaluate the Boolean logic present on each rung starting with rung 0.
   c. Determine the condition of the ladder link (true or false) connected to the output.
   d. Set the output instruction true (1) if the link is true (input logic on the rung is true) or set it false (0) if the link is not true (input logic on the rung is false).
3. Update the output bit addressed by the ladder output instruction in the output register. This bit either controls an output field device connected to an output module terminal or controls an internal relay.

If the output coil is true, then its output register bit is a 1, and the output module turns on the output field device attached to that terminal. If the output coil is false, then the associated register bit is a 0, and the output module turns off the output field device attached to that terminal.

The time required for a scan, called *scan time*, is not constant, but it is affected by the number of rungs in the program, or the amount of memory used to store the program. A good rule of thumb is 1 millisecond per 1000 bytes of program memory used. Scan time is also affected by the varying time required to execute some of the program instructions. Scan times can vary from 0.2 $\bar{\mu}$s to 50 ms.

3-10-2 Linking Inputs and Outputs

Figure 3-35 illustrates the complete operation of a PLC from input field device to output field device. This figure also illustrates the scan steps described in Figure 3-34, displaying four views of field device input data moving through the PLC during a scan to the ouput field device.

The figure's four parts indicate the flow of information during a full PLC scan.

Start scan and read inputs: Figure 3-35(a) indicates the condition of the system prior to the start of a scan. Note that the normally open (NO) limit switch (LS) wired to terminal 10 is held closed by the process, but the input register is still false (0) and does not reflect that change. All input terminals are scanned.

Input register update: In Figure 3-35(b), the 16-bit input register is updated. In this example, bit 10 changes from a 0 to a 1.

Program execution of ladder logic: In Figure 3-35(c), the ladder logic program is executed by first updating all instructions on the input side of the rungs. Here the input instruction logic is evaluated to determine if power flow from the left rail to the output is present. All true rungs will have the output instruction changed from false to true. In this example,

FIGURE 3-35: Scan cycle—sequence of operation.

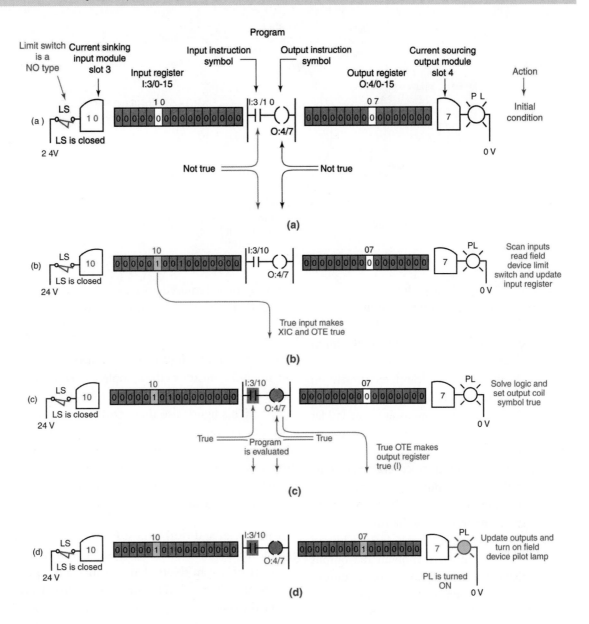

the XIC instruction, 1:3/10, becomes true (continuity is present, and power flow occurs). Because the link connected to the output instruction coil, O:4/7, is true, the output instruction becomes true (highlighted).

Update output register and outputs: Figure 3-35(d) illustrates how the output register is updated, and bit 7 changes from a 0 to a 1. This change in the output register causes the output module in slot 4 to turn on the pilot lamp connected to output terminal 7.

Although Figure 3-35 has the register notation for an Allen-Bradley SLC 500, the scan cycle described applies to all Allen-Bradley PLCs. It is assumed that the field devices and the input and output modules have been matched using the current sinking and current sourcing techniques outlined in Chapters 1 and 2. At this point, you should be able to determine the condition (true or false) of an output field device given a ladder logic program and the condition and type of the input field device.

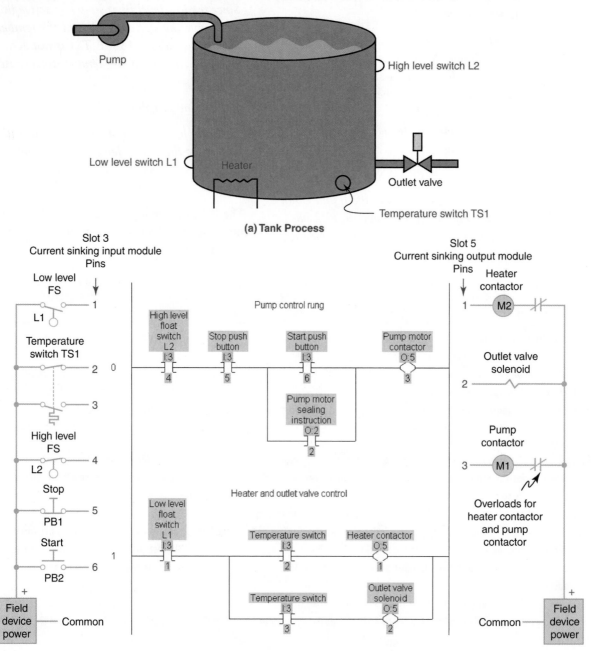

(a) Tank Process

(b) PLC Interface and Program

3-10-3 Process Tank Application

The system in Figure 3-36, a process tank with an input pump, heater, and drain valve, is used for liquid heating applications commonly found in the chemical and food processing industries.

The input field devices include:

- Two float switches: a low level (L1) that is normally open (NO) and a high level (L2) that is normally closed.

- A temperature switch: one switch (TS1) with a trigger value of 185° F that has one normally closed (NC) contact and one NO contact.

- Two momentary push button switches: an NC stop (PB1) and an NO start (PB2).

The output field devices include:

- Two contactors with overloads: one for the heater and one for the pump.

- A solenoid operated outlet valve.
- The following description of the operation refers to Figure 3-36:

The mixing tank shown in the figure is used to heat a liquid. Note the location of the field devices just described. A start push button, PB2, is used to initiate the processes, and a stop push button, PB1, is used to interrupt it. The three outputs are turned on based on the following logic:

$$\text{Fill pump} = \text{PB2 AND NOT L2}$$

The start PB is pressed, and the liquid is not above the high level float switch. PB2 has a sealing instruction because it has momentary contacts.

$$\text{Heater contactor} = \text{L1 AND NOT TS1}$$

Since the low level float switch is active (liquid above the switch level) and the temperature is not above 185° F, TS1 is not active. The NC contact of the temperature switch is used.

$$\text{Outlet valve} = \text{L1 AND TS1}$$

Since the low level float switch is active (liquid above the switch level) and the temperature is above 185° F, TS1 is active. The NO contact of the temperature switch is used.

The PLC ladder logic in Figure 3-36 implements these three logic equations in rungs 0 and 1. Note that rung 1 has two outputs.

EXAMPLE 3-9

The ladder logic in Figure 3-36 provides the control for the heater tank. Given the following condition of the input field devices before a scan, determine the condition of the three outputs.
- Liquid is above L2.
- The temperature is at 200° F.

Use the ladder logic program in Figure 3-36 to predict what output field devices will be on at the end of the scan.

SOLUTION

First, translate the given process conditions to the status of the field devices. For example, with liquid above L2 both level swithes are active, and with the temperature above 185° F the temperature switch is active. The best way to see how these actions change the ladder logic is to build a table that starts with the condition of field devices and progresses down to the condition of the rung link before the output instruction. The following table displays the results.

A study of the system status and the table indicates that the two normally closed field device contacts on L2 and TS1 are forced open when the devices are active. The open condition of the field device contacts makes the XIC instruction with that address false. Therefore, rung 0 is false, and the rung link after I:3/2 is false. This result forces the pump motor and heater contactors to the off condition.

Conversely, I:3/1 and I:3/3 XIC instructions are both true since their controlling field contact is closed. As a result, there is continuity from the left rail of the ladder logic to the outlet valve solenoid. Therefore, the outlet valve is open, and the tank is draining.

System Parameters	Input Field Devices and Logic Rung Status			
Field devices	L1 (NO)	L2 (NC)	TS1 (NO)	TS1 (NC)
Input module pin number	1	4	3	2
Field device condition	Active	Active	Active	Active
Field device contacts	Closed	Open	Closed	Open
Input device address	I:3/1	I:3/4	I:3/3	I:3/2
Rung link status	True	False	True	False

With an understanding of the scan cycle and of the technique for linking inputs and outputs in a PLC, one can easily evaluate ladder logic programs. Understanding the PLC scan process is also useful for troubleshooting problems in PLC-controlled systems. The design of a ladder logic program for a specific system, however, is more difficult. The next section describes the selection of the correct ladder logic instructions (XIC or XIO), given input and output field device configurations and the required system operation.

3-11 PLC PROGRAM DESIGN AND RELAY LADDER LOGIC CONVERSION

The need for design skills in ladder logic programming has two origins:

- *Many relay ladder logic control systems still exist in industry and need to be converted to a PLC solution.* One needs to connect the field devices to PLC input and output modules and then design a PLC ladder logic program that replicates the existing control in the relay ladder logic.
- The PLC has become the de facto standard device for the sequential control of production machines and for an increasing number of process control applications. As a result, one needs to know how to design PLC ladder logic programs for new applications.

A process change must produce a specific response from the process control system. In the Figure 3-36 example, when the liquid in the tank reaches the high-level mark, the fill pump must turn off. The designer must work with three elements to achieve control:

1. The input field device
2. The PLC program
3. The output field device

The input field device can be either a switch or a sensor and can have either normally open or normally closed contacts. The type of contacts used affects the design. The PLC program can use either XIC or XIO input instructions and OTE or latch-type output instructions. The output field device can be either *direct acting* (if the OTE is true, then the field device is on) or *inverse acting* (if the OTE is true, then the field device is off). In many cases, the type of input field device, the contact configuration, and the action of the output field device are fixed by the process equipment. Therefore, the designer concentrates on selecting the correct PLC input instructions in order to achieve the proper operation.

3-11-1 Examine if Closed and Examine if Open Selection

Students learning PLCs are often confused when selecting the correct XIC or XIO input instructions for the PLC ladder rung. An input field device with an NC contact configuration does not necessarily have an examine if open (-|/|-) instruction type representing it in the PLC rung. PLC input rung instructions must be selected using a process that looks at the input field device contact type (NO or NC) and its operational condition (activated or not activated). In addition, the input rung instruction selected, XIC or XIO, is affected by the requirement for the output field device to be either on or off. Therefore, learning a process that will *always* work is critical.

The selection table in Figure 3-37 illustrates a selection strategy. Design statements usually begin with a statement describing how system outputs should respond when input switches and sensors change states. For example, in Figure 3-36 the liquid continues to heat after the liquid reaches the maximum level, and the pump is turned off. When the liquid temperature is higher than the set point, the temperature switch is activated (the NO contact of the TS1 temperature switch is held closed), and the outlet valve is turned on or opened. When the design is performed, the temperature switch has an instruction on a ladder rung using either an XIC or XIO instruction. The instruction type selected, XIC or XIO, depends on how the control statement relates the action of the temperature switch to the desired action of the drain valve. In addition, the type of contacts present on the input field device affect the input instruction. The chart leads students through the selection process based on these factors. The process of using the chart is the same for all Allen-Bradley processors and is enumerated below.

FIGURE 3-37: XIC and XIO selection guide.

0	1	2	3	4	5	6
Row number	Input field device type	Input field device actuation	Field device contact condition	Output field device condition	Ladder logic OTE output instruction condition	Ladder logic input contact
1	NO	Not actuated	Open contacts	Off	Not true	Examine if closed XIC (⊣⊢)
2	NO	Not actuated	Open contacts	On	True	Examine if open XIO (⊣/⊢)
3	NO	Actuated	Closed contacts	Off	Not true	Examine if open XIO (⊣/⊢)
4	NO	Actuated	Closed contacts	On	True	Examine if closed XIC (⊣⊢)
5	NC	Not actuated	Closed contacts	Off	Not true	Examine if open XIO (⊣/⊢)
6	NC	Not actuated	Closed contacts	On	True	Examine if closed XIC (⊣⊢)
7	NC	Actuated	Open contacts	Off	Not true	Examine if closed XIC (⊣⊢)
8	NC	Actuated	Open contacts	On	True	Examine if open XIO (⊣/⊢)

1. Identify the input field device and determine the contact type (NO or NC) used. In column 1 of the chart, find the four corresponding rows, NO or NC, for that contact type.

   Tank example: The NO contacts of the TS1 temperature switch are used for control of the drain valve so rows 1 to 4 in the chart are selected.

2. Determine if the input field device is actuated or not actuated for the desired change in the output field device. From the four rows chosen in step 1, find the two rows in column 2 of the chart that correspond to this condition.

   Tank example: The temperature switch must be activated (NO contacts held closed) for the outlet valve to be on or opened. Rows 3 and 4 are selected because they represent NO contacts with an activated field device. Note in column 3 that an active NO switch has closed contacts, which sets the input register bits to 1.

3. Determine the desired condition, on or off, for the output field device in column 4. Locate the corresponding row from the two rows selected in step 2.

   Tank example: Since the outlet valve must be turned on (column 4) or opened, the parameters across row 4 describe the operation of the input and output field devices for this problem. For example, an active NO input field device is turning on the ladder output OTE instruction, so that the output field device is on. Therefore, the 24 volts appled to the input pin must make the rung true.

4. From column 6 select the ladder rung input instruction type that satisfies this application.

   Tank example: The rung input instruction must be examine if closed or XIC (-| |-) for this application. The XIC instruction is true when the input terminal is high (+24 volts) and the input register bit is a 1. This true XIC instruction allows power flow to the output coil, which energizes the outlet valve.

Although the process was demonstrated using input and output field devices, it works equally well with internal input bits and internal output bits. After working through several examples, the process for picking XIC and XIO instructions becomes clear and dependence on the chart in Figure 3-37 diminishes.

3-11-2 Multiple Inputs

Most PLC programs, like the example ladder logic in Figures 3-31 and 3-36, have more than one power flow path in the rung and have more than one input per rung. The logic in these multiple input rungs falls into these six categories: *AND, OR, AND/OR, OR/AND, INVERSION, and FEEDBACK logic*. Figure 3-38 shows the relay ladder equivalent circuit, ladder logic equivalent program, gate logic equivalent, and Boolean equation for the six types. A brief description of each follows.

AND logic: All inputs must be true for the rung to be true [Figure 3-38(a)].

OR logic: If any input is true, then the rung is true [Figure 3-38(b)].

OR/AND logic: If all inputs in at least one AND group are true, then the rung is true [Figure 3-38(c)].

AND/OR logic: If at least one input in all OR groups is true, then the rung is true [Figure 3-38(d)].

INVERSION logic: The state of a rung with an XIC instruction is the inverse of the state of the address of the XIC instruction [Figure 3-38(e)].

FEEDBACK logic: The feedback from the output in the form of a sealing instruction holds the output in the true state [Figure 3-38(f)].

Multiple input instruction rungs are not difficult to understand. For example, the logic equation for the AND logic in Figure 3-38(a) is $X = AB$ and is read as X is true if A AND B are true. One can see from the relay schematic that both switches must be on for the output to be on. The same logic is represented in the ladder logic. Equations with AND logic are usually written in two forms, which are $X = AB$ or $X = A \cdot B$. The AND function is assumed if two letters are placed next to each other or if a dot ($\cdot$) is used between the terms.

A second example, Figure 3-38(b), shows an OR logic equation, $X = A + B$. This equation is read as X is true if either A OR B are true. Note that the plus sign ($+$) is used to indicate that the OR function is used between the terms. The relay schematic shows this relationship electrically. The light is on if either LS1 OR LS2 is closed or active.

EXAMPLE 3-10

An application must use a normally closed (NC) sensor to turn off an output field device (output image table bit is a 0) when the sensor is not activated (NC contact in normal position). Determine the type of ladder logic instruction symbol required for this application.

Solution

The chart in Figure 3-37 is used to find the logic instruction by selecting rows in the following order (Note: the shaded area is for the previous example):

1. Rows 5 to 8 for the NC contacts on the field device (column 1).
2. Rows 5 and 6 for the not activated field device (NC contacts – closed) requirement (column 2).
3. Row 5 because the output device must be off (column 4).
4. Therefore, the ladder rung instruction symbol (row 5 and column 6) is examine if open XIO (-|/|-)

Verify the operation. The not activated NC field device contact puts a 1 in the input image table and causes the XIO instruction to be false. A false XIO does not have continuity or power flow, and the output is false. A false output turns off the associated output field device. This results in the desired operation.

When a person just learning PLC programming reads this more complex problem statement, it is not immediately clear that an XIO instruction would be used. The selection chart leads the programmer through the selection process. After a short time using the chart and selecting input instructions for the eight combinations, the chart can be discarded as no longer necessary.

FIGURE 3-38: Logic configurations.

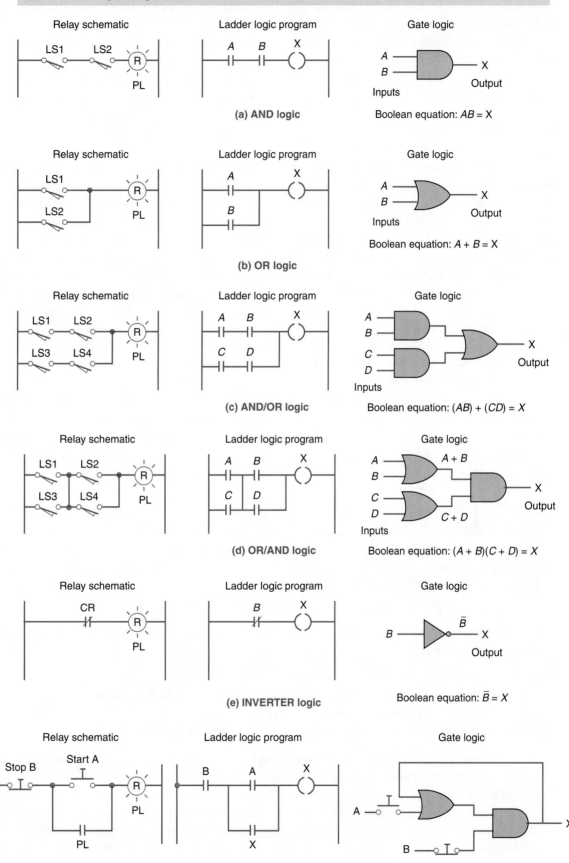

Relay schematic · Ladder logic program · Gate logic

(a) AND logic — Boolean equation: $AB = X$

(b) OR logic — Boolean equation: $A + B = X$

(c) AND/OR logic — Boolean equation: $(AB) + (CD) = X$

(d) OR/AND logic — Boolean equation: $(A + B)(C + D) = X$

(e) INVERTER logic — Boolean equation: $\bar{B} = X$

(f) Feedback logic

EXAMPLE 3-11

Write the Boolean equation for the Y output rung in Figure 3-39(a).

SOLUTION

Instructions A, B, C, D, and E are an OR/AND configuration, F is an AND, and G and H are an OR type. The equation is

$$Y = [(\text{not } A \bullet B \bullet C) + (D \bullet \text{not } E)]F \bullet (\text{not } G + H)$$

EXAMPLE 3-12

Determine the condition of the input switches (activated or not activated) for power flow in Figure 3-39(a). The sensor contact configurations are as follows: A is NO, B is NC, C is NO, D is NO, E is NC, F is NO, G is NC, and H is NO.

SOLUTION

Use the table in Figure 3-37 to solve this problem, beginning with input instruction A (NO contacts) in the ladder logic in Figure 3-39(a).

1. Find the four rows in column 1 that agree with the input contacts. Instruction A is NO, so rows 1 to 4 are selected.
2. Find the two rows from rows 1 to 4 that agree with the ladder rung instruction type in column 6. Instruction A is an XIO instruction, so the two rows are rows 2 and 3.
3. Find the one row from rows 2 and 3 that has the output true in column 5. Instruction A is highlighted, so power flow is present and the output is true. Thus row 2 describes the operation of this instruction and can be used to find the condition of the NO field device. In this case the field device is *not active* (column 2).

Use this process to step through the solution for the remaining instructions. Verify results with the following answers.

The input condition for the remaining switches is as follows: B field device is not activated, C field device is activated, D field device is activated, E field device is not activated, F field device is activated, G field device is activated, and H field device is activated.

Take each of the remaining examples in Figure 3-38, beginning with the relay schematic, and determine what limit switches must be closed (active) for the light to be illuminated. Then see if that agrees with the logic equation given in the last column. The input logic combinations described in this section apply to the PLC 5, SLC 500, and ControlLogix processors.

Figure 3-39 illustrates the many variations on these standard configurations. Four power flow combinations are presented because of different combinations of active input instructions. The power flow path follows highlighted instructions. An unbroken path of these instructions from the left rail to the output instruction causes the output to be true.

FIGURE 3-39: Multiple input power flow example (Note: Bold contacts have continuity.).

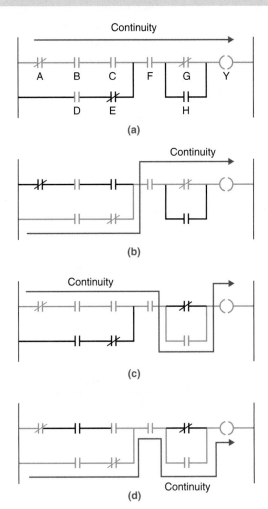

Note: Blue contacts have continuity

The combination of NC or NO field device switch contacts, XIC or XIO rung instructions, and a rung power flow requirement for a true output makes the selection of sensor activation conditions difficult to determine. The selection table (Figure 3-37) helps to provides correct answers. However, it also helps you see how all of the variables interact, so that dependance on the chart is eventually eliminated.

3-11-3 Multiple Outputs
PLCs also can have branches at the output side of the rung. Figure 3-40 illustrates several multiple output configurations. Note that the illustrations in Figure 3-40(a) and (b) use SLC 500 addressing, but the format could be used by any Allen-Bradley PLC processor. The ControlLogix processor permits both the older format and the addition of multiple outputs linked on the same ladder rung, as shown in Figure 3-40(c). In this figure all outputs are OTE, but any PLC output instruction could be used in place of the OTE instructions. Review the ladders in Figures 3-38, 3-39, and 3-40 for the many different instruction configurations.

3-11-4 Empirical Program Design
Programmable logic controller programming is accomplished using two techniques: *empirical* and *structured*. The empirical programming approach is frequently used with ladder logic programs; the structured technique is used with higher-level PLC programming languages such as Structured Text and Sequential Function Charts. The empirical approach is described here and structured approaches are presented in the second part of the text.

The empirical approach, the solution technique used most often for PLC ladder logic program design, develops the ladder solution one rung at a time. The frustration for designers is that this design approach yields numerous solutions that will all work. It is not easy to determine if the solution generated is the optimal solution available. Any design procedure is just a guideline, and the designer has many options for the implementation. The options selected are dictated by company preferences and designer experience. The design of the ladder logic for the process problem in Figure 3-36 is used to illustrate how the empirical process works, using the following seven steps:

1. As completely as possible, write a description of the problem and process control sequence. PLC ladder logic is best suited for process problems in which a

---

FIGURE 3-40: Multiple ladder outputs.

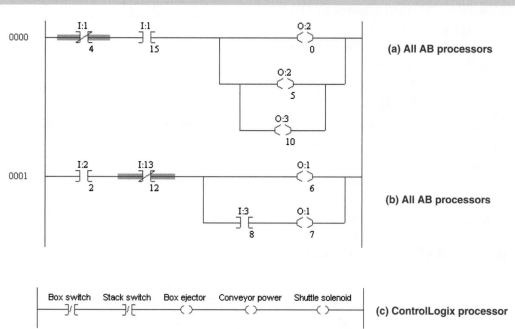

(a) All AB processors

(b) All AB processors

(c) ControlLogix processor

sequence of events must be controlled. The following problem statement describes the process in Figure 3-36:

Example problem statement: A mixing tank like the one shown in Figure 3-36(a) is used to heat a liquid. Note the location of all devices. A start push button is used to initiate the processes, and a stop push button is used to stop the pump. The inlet pipe's pump delivers fluid to the tank. Two level switches, L1 [low level float switch (FS)] and L2 [high level float switch (FS)], control the fill and empty cycles in the process. When the start switch is pressed the fill pump is activated. Liquid rises in the tank until the L2 FS is activated and stops the fill cycle. The heater is activated in the fill cycle when the liquid activates the L1 FS. The heater turns off when the process liquid exceeds the set point temperature (185° F) and makes temperature sensor TS1 active. Due to the temperature of the input liquid, the set point temperature is not reached until after the tank has finished filling. When the tank is full and the liquid is at the desired temperature, TS1 is active, the output valve is turned on (opened), and the tank empty cycle starts. The output valve is closed at the end of the empty cycle when the liquid level is below L1 FS.

2. Make a list of all output devices and all input devices with the type of contact used (manual input switches, process switches, and sensors).

Example output and input device list: The process has three output devices: pump contactor, heater contactor, and outlet solenoid valve. The process has five input devices: stop momentary push button PB1 (NC), start momentary push button PB2 (NO), float switch Ll (NO), float switch L2 (NC), and temperature switch TS1 (NO contacts close when the temperature is above 185° F) . Because the switches are all single pole double throw, one set of NC and NO contacts is available. The contact type listed is connected to the input module as illustrated in Figure 3-36. *Note that*

only the NO contact from the TS1 temperature switch is used in this design.

3. Use the process description to write a logic equation that makes each output device active (on). Indicate the input conditions that make the output active.

Example output logic equations: The logic equations for the three outputs are:

Pump motor contractor = NOT PB1 AND PB2 (sealed with output instruction) AND NOT L2

The pump motor contactor is true (pump is running) when the start switch is pressed (NO contact is held closed) and sealed by the pump output OTE instruction, *AND* when the stop switch is not active (NC contact is closed), *AND* when the high level float switch L2 is not active (fluid is below high level switch, and so NC contact is closed).

Heater contractor = LI AND NOT TSI

The heater contactor is true (liquid is heating) when the low level float switch L1 is active (fluid is above low switch level, so the NO contact is held closed), *AND* the temperature switch TS1 is not active (fluid temperature is below 185° F, so the NO contact is open).

Outlet solenoid value = LI AND TSI

The outlet valve solenoid is true (valve is open) when the low level float switch L1 is active (fluid is above the low level switch, so the NO contact is held closed) *AND* when the temperature switch TS1 is active (temperature is above 185° F, so the NO contact is held closed).

4. For a PLC 5 or SLC 500 design, one must complete a wiring diagram for input and output devices, illustrating their connection to the input and output modules. Ladder logic input instruction addresses must include module terminal numbers for these PLC modules. If a CompactLogix system is used, then the tag names for all field device components and contacts

must be identified. Assigning input and output alias addresses for module terminal numbers can be performed at the same time, but the ladder logic programming is not dependent upon it.

Example input and output wiring diagram solution: Figure 3-41 illustrates the wiring for the input and output field devices. Wire labeling and numbering that adheres to company policy can be added at this time to the diagram.

5. Enter the SLC 500 ladder logic diagram by creating the rung(s) for each logic equation. Use the ladder instruction selection guide in Figure 3-37 to select an XIC or an XIO instruction for each input field device contact. Because Allen-Bradley ladders execute left to right and top to bottom, the rungs are created and listed in the execution order used by the sequential process. Also, this arrangment makes the program easier to read and understand. Finally, the finished ladder logic is documented and annotated.

Example ladder logic solution: The ladder logic in Figure 3-41 produces the control required for the problem statement. Study this solution to the problem and compare it to the ladder logic solution for the same problem in Figure 3-36. Both work equally well, but the solution in Figure 3-36 uses both the NO and NC contacts on the temperature switch. As a result, an XIO instruction is needed for this solution in rung 1 for the heater contactor. The sealing instruction, O:5/3, opens after pump power is removed by liquid above the high level float switch so the pump does not restart during the drain cycle.

6. Test the solution to see if it meets the control requirements specified in step 1. If changes are needed, modify or add rungs to fix any problems.

Example ladder modification: A serious problem not discussed in the original Figure 3-36 solution requires additional ladder modifications. When the NO contacts of the liquid temperature switch (TS1) are closed by a liquid temperature greater than 185° F the heat output (O:2.0) is false

because the XIO instruction (I:1/1) in the heater rung is false (no power flow). A temperature greater than 185° F also opens the drain valve because TS1 causes the I:1/1 XIC instruction in the valve rung to be true. However, the liquid temperature likely will drop below 185° F as the liquid drains, causing TS1 NO contacts to open, so that the heater turns back on and the outlet valve closes. When the liquid temperature is again at the proper level, the drain cycle continues. This cycling will occur until L1 (low level float switch) is open and the tank is empty. This cycling of the heater is not a problem because it holds the liquid at the proper temperature; however, the closing of the outlet valve is a problem. The outlet valve rung must be modified by placing a sealing instruction with the outlet valve address around the XIC instruction in the valve rung. Now when the temperature drops below 185° F the valve is sealed on, and the TS1 instruction no longer controls the valve rung. Figure 3-42 illustrates this modified rung.

7. Document the solution based on company standards. Add rung comments and instruction descriptions that would give an engineer or technician who is not familiar with the design sufficient information to troubleshoot any production or control system problems.

The empirical approach described by the seven-step process works well for small ladder logic applications. However, as the control problem gets more complex, the designer's ability to predict all of the interaction amoung the rungs is limited, and numerous fixes and patches are necessary during design testing. As a result, everyone except the original designer finds the program more difficult to read and understand. Compare the fix added to the solution in Figure 3-42 with the original solution in Figure 3-41. Also, compare this design solution with the original solution in Figure 3-36 and with the relay ladder logic solution in Chapter 1.

Another problem created by this approach is the nonsequential nature of the program structure. Although the PLC scans the program from the first rung down to the last, turning on out-

FIGURE 3-41: Empirical design for tank control example.

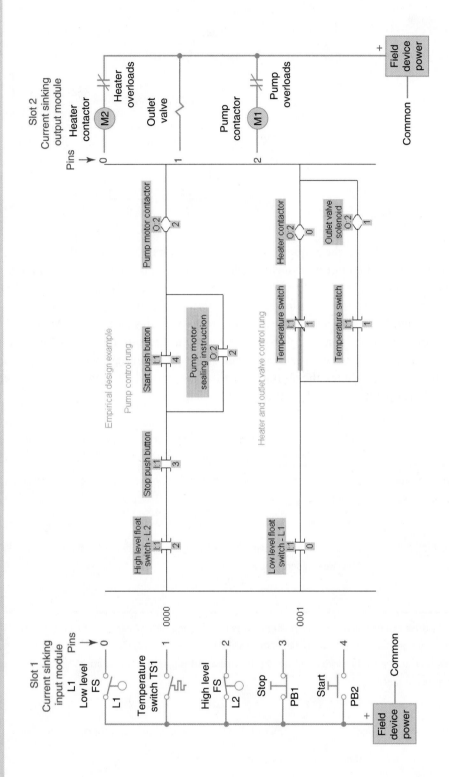

FIGURE 3-42: Fix to tank control design.

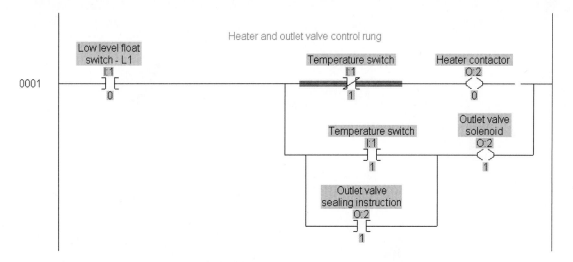

puts based on the input logic, the sequential change in the output states does not necessarily follow in that order. For example, the output on the last rung may turn on first and be followed by another output somewhere else in the ladder. It is not uncommon for a large system control problem to have a ladder program with several thousand rungs present. Determining the output sequence and machine operation in such a large

system is more difficult if the program was developed using this empirical technique.

The previous example, as well as the next two, refer to the SLC 500 processor. If the PLC 5 were used, addresses would be adjusted for the single slot addressing mode and for rack number. If the ControlLogix were used, tag names with appropriate data types would be used for addressing.

EXAMPLE 3-13

Design a ladder logic system to provide two-handed control for a production machine, so that the operator uses both hands to initiate the start cycle of the machine.

SOLUTION

Figure 3-43 illustrates the circuit that satisfies this control requirement. The necessary logic equation is Machine on = AND PB2. Note that a simple AND logic statisfies the need for two-handed control.

EXAMPLE 3-14

Design a ladder logic system to drive two pneumatic actuators through the part-loading cycle illustrated in Figure 3-44(a). The two pneumatic actuators and the gripper have sensors (NO contacts) to indicate the end positions of the actuators. A cycle is started when the start selector switch is on and when the pickup sensor indicates that a part is in the pickup location. Use the limit sensors to control actuator and gripper sequences.

SOLUTION

Figure 3-44(b) illustrates the circuit satisfying the control requirement. The logic equations necessary for control are:

$$\text{Axis X down} = \text{SEL1 AND PTS AND YIN AND GOP}$$

$$\text{Gripper close} = \text{XDN (sealed by GRV) AND NOT YOUT}$$

$$\text{Axis Y out} = \text{YUP AND GCL}$$

Where YIN and YOUT are Y axis in and out sensors, XUP and XDN are X axis up and down sensors, GOP and GCL are gripper open and close sensors, and GRV is the gripper valve. Verify that the Boolean equation for each output is implemented in Figure 3-44(b) ladder logic. Move the robot through its cycle starting at the home position, letting the end-of-axis sensors change and verifying that the ladder logic provides a good solution. Note that the two-axis pneumatic robot is driven by the end-of-axis sensors so that optimum speed is attained.

Note that not GCL is used for GOP and Not GOP is used for GSL in the final design. The Not GCL makes sure that the gripper is fully closed before the X axis starts back up. The Not GOP makes sure that the gripper is fully opened before returning to the home position.

FIGURE 3-43: Ladder logic for two-handed control.

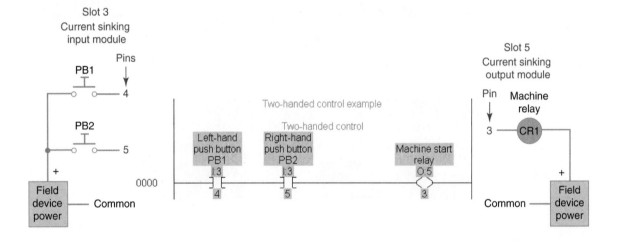

FIGURE 3-44: Two-axis robot part loader.

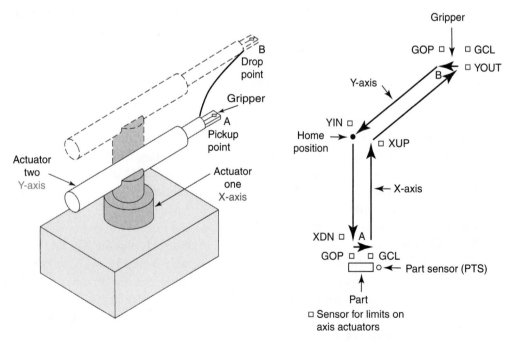

(a) Two-axis robot motion

FIGURE 3-44: (Continued).

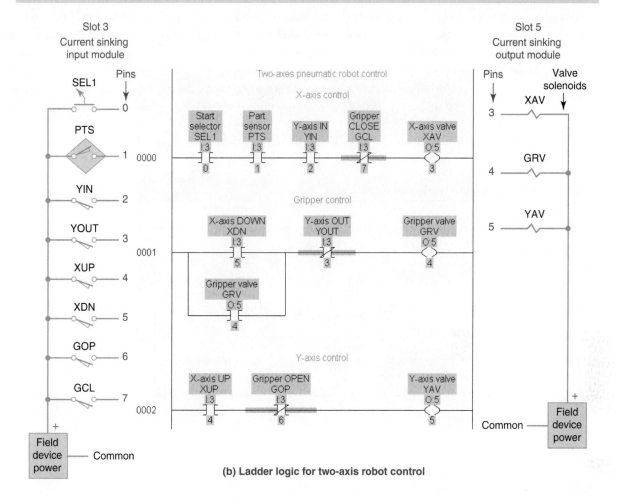

(b) Ladder logic for two-axis robot control

3-11-5 Converting Relay Logic to PLC Solutions

In addition to developing new PLC design, engineers and technicians are often asked to convert existing relay ladder logic to a PLC solution. The following technique is used:

1. Study the relay ladder logic for an understanding of how the control system functions. Write logic equations for each rung, in order to define the input logic for an active output condition.

2. Circle all of the elements on the relay ladder logic that are physical input field devices or output field devices. Note whenever multiple contacts on an input field device were used. Also, record the type of input contact (NO or NC) and condition (active or not active) when the output is on.

3. Select input and output modules whose voltages and current ratings are consistent with the input and output field devices.

4. Draw the input and output interface for all input and output field devices. Connect only one contact for each input field device to the input module.

5. Create a ladder logic rung for every relay logic rung. Replace every output device with an OTE instruction. If the output was a control relay, replace it with a binary bit (virtual relay).

6. Use the control requirements established in step 1, plus the XIC and XIO selection table in Figure 3-37, to create the rung input logic for all input field devices and virtual relay instructions.

7. Check the logic to verify that the PLC ladder logic performs exactly like the original relay ladder logic.

EXAMPLE 3-15

Convert the relay ladder logic in Figure 3-45(a) to a PLC implementation.

SOLUTION

1. Study the relay ladder logic for an understanding of how the control system functions. Write logic equations for each rung to define the input logic for an active output condition. Note that only the NO contact of the LS8 limit switch is used.

$$\text{Outputs CR1 and PL3} = (\text{PB14 OR CR1}) \text{ AND LS7}$$

$$\text{Outputs SOL3 UP and CR2} = (\text{PS7 AND CR1}) \text{ AND SOL}$$

$$\text{Outputs SOL4 FWD} = \text{LS8 AND NOT LS9 AND CR2}$$

$$\text{Outputs SOL5 DWN, CR3, and PL4} = [\text{PB1 OR (NOT LS8 AND CR3)}] \text{ AND NOT PB2 AND NOT CR2}$$

2. Circle all the elements on the relay ladder logic that are physical input field devices or output field devices [See Figure 3-45(b)]. Note whenever multiple contacts on an input field device were used. Also, record the type of input contact (NO or NC) and condition (active or not active) when the output is active or on. Multiple contacts were used on LS8, but the solution uses only a NO contact from LS8.

PB1	NO	active
PB2	NC	not active
PB14	NO	active
LS7	NO	active
LS8	NO	active for one rung and not active for another rung
PS7	NO	active
SOL	NO	active

FIGURE 3-45: Relay ladder logic for converstion to ladder logic.

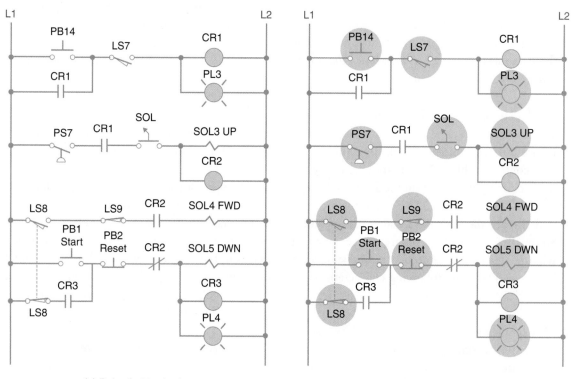

(a) Relay ladder logic   (b) Field devices marked

---

3. Select input and output modules with voltages and current ratings consistent with the input and output field devices. Input and output modules are 120 VAC.
4. Draw the input and output interface for all input and output field devices. Connect only one contact for each input field device to the input module. See Figure 3-46 for the interface solution.
5. Create a ladder logic rung for every relay logic rung. Replace every output device with an OTE instruction. If the output was a control relay, replace it with a binary bit. Using both the control requirements established in step 1 and the XIC and XIO selection table in Figure 3-37, create the rung input logic for all input field devices and internal relay instructions. See Figure 3-46 for the ladder logic solution.
6. A check of the logic verifies that the PLC ladder logic performs exactly like the original relay ladder logic.

3-12 TROUBLESHOOTING LADDER LOGIC CONTROL SYSTEMS

The PLC's reliability record is unmatched when compared with other microprocessor-controlled devices. For example, the statistically calculated mean time between failure rate is close to 5 years for some Allen-Bradley PLC products. Even with this great record, failures in the total automation system do occur and must be corrected. The system includes all of the input and output field devices, the PLC processor and modules, the ladder logic or other type of automation programs, and other devices and actuators present in the system. To locate the fault, an organized approach must be implemented.

3-12-1 System Troubleshooting Tools
Such an organized approach requires tools. The three important ones are *system block diagrams*, *bracketing*, and *signal flow analysis*.

Block diagrams. A block diagram is a set of rectangles used to describe all the parts of a system. Figure 3-47 illustrates a block diagram for the tank control problem. Note that each field device is a block, input and output modules are blocks, and the PLC is a block. The parts of the program that impact the signal flow also are included. Study the system in the figure and compare it with the description of process tank operation in Section 3-11-4. The following characteristics of block diagrams are evident from the figure.

- Complex systems are represented by a series of simple rectangles.
- Information flows from left to right through the rectangles.

- Systems, subsystems, and program structures can be represented.

Because the system block diagrams are not provided by the equipment vendor, in most cases the engineer must create one for troubleshooting requirements. A block diagram is easily generated as follows:

1. Make a list of all of the system components that would be replaced in the advent of a failure.
2. Arrange the list of system components with inputs at the top and outputs at the bottom. The remaining items that are between inputs and outputs should be arranged in the order that signals or information flows through them.
3. Put all of the block diagram components into rectangles and connect the blocks with signal flow lines, based on the system operation.

A troubleshooting tool, called bracketing, is used with the block diagram to isolate a fault.

Bracketing. Bracketing is a technique that uses markers to identify the portion of the system block diagram in which the fault exists. The brackets are used initially on the system block diagram, but they can be moved to a schematic diagram when the fault is narrowed down to a single circuit. A three-step process is used to establish the initial location for the brackets.

1. *Record and study all system symptoms.* List all conditions that vary from normal operation.

FIGURE 3-46: PLC ladder logic for relay ladder logic.

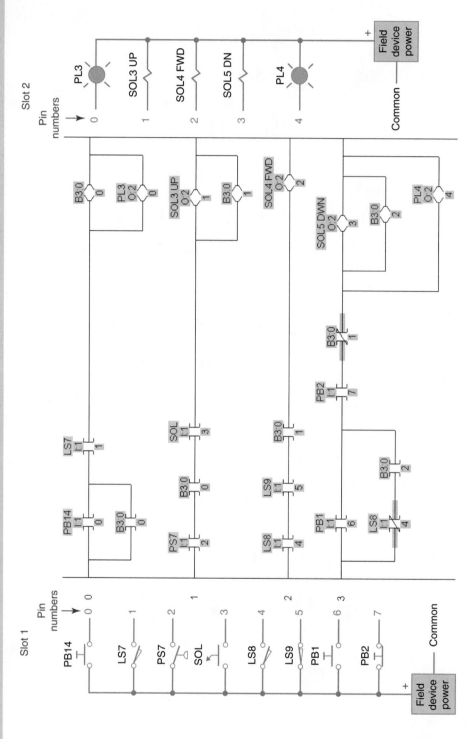

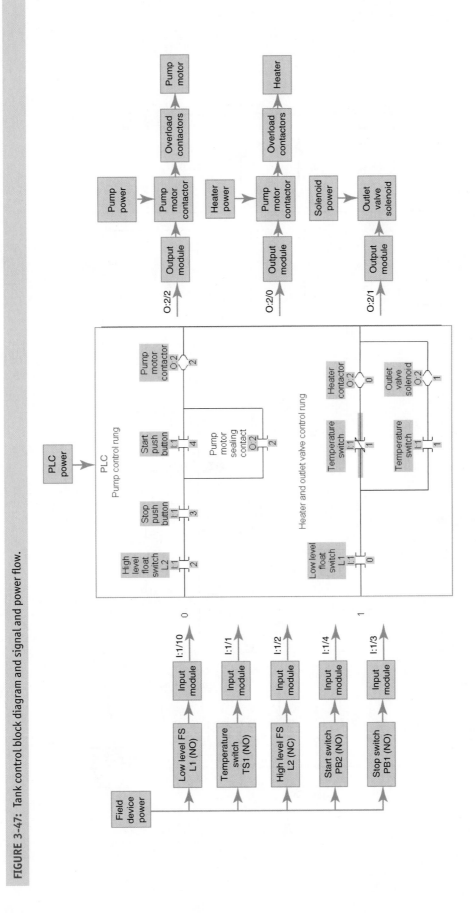

FIGURE 3-47: Tank control block diagram and signal and power flow.

2. *Locate points on the system block diagram where abnormal operation is occurring.* Place a right bracket ( ]) after each abnormal block. Note that the signal flow on the block diagrams is from left (inputs) to right (outputs). In general, the right brackets are placed on the right side of output blocks that are not operating.

3. *Along the signal flow path, move to the left from each bad bracket until normal operation is observed.* Place a left bracket ([ ) to the right of the block where a normal output was detected. In general, the left bracket initially is placed with a minimum of detailed testing or only with easily performed tests.

The application of the brackets to the system block diagram is often just a mental process for experienced troubleshooters. However, the beginner should physically mark them on the block until all the troubleshooting techniques are fully internalized. The brackets tell us that the fault is somewhere in the system between the left and right brackets. Before proceeding with additional checks on the faulty system, it is important to learn the concepts associated with signal flow in the block diagrams.

Signal flow. Signal flow is generally divided into two groups, called *power* and *information*. Power flow illustrates how power is delivered to all the components in the system, and information flow indicates how information or data flows from source(s) to destination(s).

The five distinct types of signal flow topologies are *linear, divergent, convergent, feedback,* and *switched*. The user must recognize each type of path because a unique troubleshooting approach is associated with each of the topologies. A description of each type follows.

Linear: The linear signal path is a series connection of blocks, like the input and output blocks in Figure 3-47.

Divergent: A divergent signal path is present when a single block feeds two or more blocks or when a path on the left divides into two or more paths going to the right. In Figure 3-46

the power flow options in rung 1 of the ladder logic program illustrate the divergent type of signal and power flow.

Convergent: A convergent signal path is present when signals from two or more blocks feed into a single block or when two or more paths on the left merge into one path going to the right.

Feedback: A feedback signal flow is created when part of the output signal is diverted back to the system input and added to the input signal. All of the sealing instructions are examples of this type of signal or power flow.

Switched paths: Switched signal flow paths include linear, divergent, and convergent paths, with switches present to change the flow of the signal.

Every system has a signal flow block diagram that is a combination of these five topologies. Topology analysis speeds the troubleshooting process.

Signal flow analysis. The five topologies (linear, divergent, convergent, feedback, and switched) introduced in the previous section have rules that can be used to speed the search for the faulty system component. The topology rules that cause bracket movement follow.

Linear rule: When brackets enclose a linear set of system blocks to be tested, the first test point should be at or just before the midpoint of the bracketed area. If the signal is faulty, then the right bracket ( ]) moves to that point because the fault is to its left. If the signal is valid, however, then the left bracket ([ ) moves to that point because the fault is in the blocks to the right of this point. Application of this *divide-and-conquer rule* eliminates half of the components with a single check. In the PLC signal flow the ladder logic is included in the flow path. Although tests in the middle of the ladder are not possible, the concept can still be applied.

Divergent rule: When brackets enclose system blocks with a divergent path, the stage before the divergence is fault-free if any of the divergent paths are normal. For example, assume

that brackets ([ ]) enclose the power supply that provides power to three other blocks in the diagram. If one can verify that power is being delivered to one of the system blocks, then the power supply is not the problem. As a result, the left bracket ([ ) is moved to the output side of the power supply.

Convergent rule: When brackets enclose system blocks with a convergent path, the following two rules must be applied:

- Rule 1: If all convergent inputs are required to produce a valid output, then a valid output indicates that all input paths are fault-free.
- Rule 2: If only one convergent input is required to produce a valid output, then each input must be checked to verify that the input paths are fault-free.

Feedback rule: When brackets enclose system blocks with a feedback path, a change or modification to the feedback path is used to indicate normal operation of the closed-loop system.

Switched rule: If brackets contain linear, divergent, or convergent topologies that are changed by a switch setting, it is necessary to observe the system when the switch is moved to another position. If the trouble disappears, then the problem is in the signal flow path of the previous switch position. Switched paths are some of the easiest to troubleshoot.

3-12-2 Troubleshooting Sequence

A general set of steps can be developed for use on system faults. The sequence is as follows:

1. *Define the problem*: Gather all of the symptom data for the failure, as well as information on the state of the system when the fault occurred.
2. *Decide what needs to be tested*: Put the brackets on the system block diagram (physically or mentally) in order to narrow the search for the fault to that part of the system where faulty operation has been verified.
3. *Decide what type of test to perform*: Initially, apply tests that do not require measurements inside system boxes. Start with changes in the signal flow path in order to perform broad system tests that will eliminate some of the suspect units between the brackets. As the brackets narrow the type of test becomes more precise with increased use of test equipment. When tests fail to provide any new information on the location of the fault, move to the next level of more precise tests.
4. *Correct the problem*: After the faulty unit or component is identified, the problem is corrected by adjustment or replacement of the unit or component.
5. *Verify correct operation*: After a problem is corrected, thoroughly test the system in order to verify that the applied fix corrected all of the system problems.
6. *Determine the cause of the failure*: getting the system back into operation is only half of the solution.

The first three steps in the sequence are repeated as often as necessary until the fault is located. Symptoms are studied, possible faulty units are bracketed, and the easiest possible changes in the signal flow are applied to eliminate some suspected units. As the brackets move closer together, the tests on suspected units introduce more precise test equipment. Throughout the process, symptoms continue to be analyzed. The analysis includes time to think about the problem in order to reflect on results of previous tests and possible future tests. If possible, determine what caused the unit or component to fail and recommend system changes that would prevent a similar failure in the future.

3-12-3 Troubleshooting Input and Output Modules

The general troubleshooting approach introduced in Section 3-12 allows the technician and engineer to view the system as a series of process elements or boxes. Figure 3-48(a) depicts the linear signal flow from the high level float switch L2 to the pump motor. The flow is repeated in

FIGURE 3-48: Signal flow path.

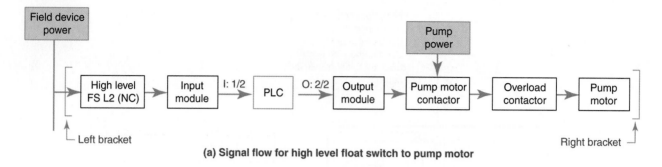

(a) Signal flow for high level float switch to pump motor

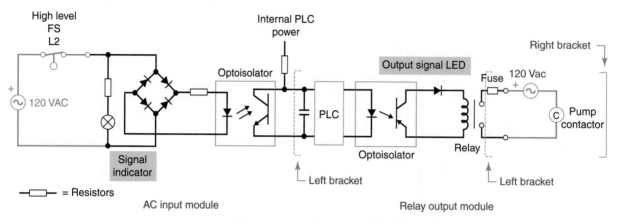

(b) Input and output module schematics

Figure 3-48(b), with typical internal circuits for an input module and an output module inserted into the boxes. Note PLC input and output modules have circuit indicators that are on if a signal is present. Each I/O point displays an indicator on the module's face. Figure 3-49 shows the front of a module with the 16 indicators grouped near the top. In the illustration only the numbers for ports 0, 3, 12, and 15 are present, but all are present on actual modules. These indicators are ideal for troubleshooting PLC system problems. The following troubleshooting sequence for the tank control solution in Figures 3-41 and 3-47 illustrates this point:

• The fill pump does not respond when the start push button is pressed, and the tank is empty. It was verified that the start switch is operating properly and that the source power to all devices is present. Therefore, the problem is located in a module between the left and right brackets on the signal flow in Figure 3-48(a).

• Because the indicator for input 2 on the input module is on, the NC float switch is closed and a voltage is present at terminal 2 of the module. The left bracket moves to the output of the input module. (See new dashed bracket.)

• Because the indicator for output 2 on the output module is on, the PLC logic made O:2/2 active. The left bracket moves to the right side of the output relay contacts in Figure 3-48(b). (See new dashed bracket.)

At this point, more than half of the control circuit has been removed from the troubleshooting problem by using signal indicators on the PLC modules. Some output modules that use fuses to protect the output circuits may have a blown fuse indicator [Figure 3-49(b)]. If the module's fuse is blown, then the indicator is on. If individual ports are fused then the module must be removed to check for a bad output point fuse. Note that the NO output relay contacts in Figure 3-48(b) are fused.

FIGURE 3-49: LED indicators on I/O modules.

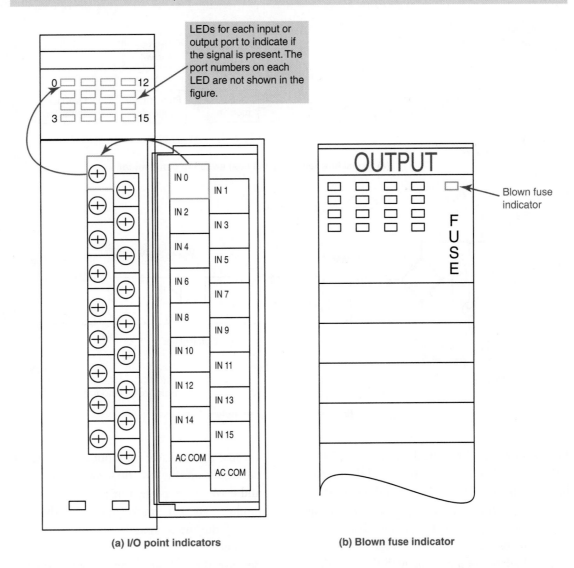

LEDs for each input or output port to indicate if the signal is present. The port numbers on each LED are not shown in the figure.

Blown fuse indicator

(a) I/O point indicators   **(b) Blown fuse indicator**

- After the output module is removed, it is determined that the fuse for output 2 is bad. After a good fuse is installed the system operates normally.
- Other techniques to troubleshoot I/O modules efficiently include:
  - If the module appears to be the problem, swap a similar module from another slot in order to see if the problem is solved or merely moves to a new location in the PLC rack.

- If an individual I/O point is suspect, change the field device termination to another I/O point. Change the program and test to see if the problem has been corrected.
- Use the forcing function. Turn on or off an input or rung from the programming console in order to see how the system responds. Inputs can be forced regardless of the state of the input field device.

CHAPTER 4

Programming Timers

4-1 GOALS AND OBJECTIVES

There are two principal goals of this chapter. The first goal is to provide the student with information on the operation and functions of hardware timers—both mechanical and electronic. The second goal is to show how the programmable timer instructions are applied in Allen-Bradley PLCs that are used in industrial automation systems.

After completing this chapter you should be able to:

- Describe the operation of a mechanical timing relay.
- Explain the differences between timed contacts and instantaneous contacts of a timing relay.
- Describe the difference between mechanical and electronic timing relays.
- Compare and contrast retentive timers to non-retentive timers.
- Describe the operation of TON, TOF, and RTO timer instructions.
- Describe the operation of cascading timers.
- Develop ladder logic solutions using timer instructions for the Allen-Bradley PLC 5, SLC 500, and ControlLogix series of PLCs.
- Convert relay ladder logic timer rungs to their PLC equivalent.

- Troubleshoot system problems associated with I/O modules and ladder rungs with timer instructions.

4-2 MECHANICAL TIMING RELAYS

Mechanical timing or time delay relays, as the name implies, have *fixed* or *variable* delay incorporated into their design that suspends the movement of the contacts when the coil is energized, de-energized, or both. Timers are a critical part of industrial automation and are necessary in sequential processes where a machine follows a set operational sequence with some steps assigned a specific time span. In relay ladder logic the timers are called *timing relays* because a contact closure is associated with the timing function. Knowledge of timing relays is important because relay ladder logic implementations continue to be used in small control applications and where higher current levels must be switched. In addition, relay ladder logic program with mechanical timers must be converted to a PLC implementation; as a result, an understanding of mechanical timer operation is necessary for a successful conversion. The schematic symbols for the four basic types of timing relays are illustrated in Figure 4-1.

FIGURE 4-1: Schematic symbols for timing relays.

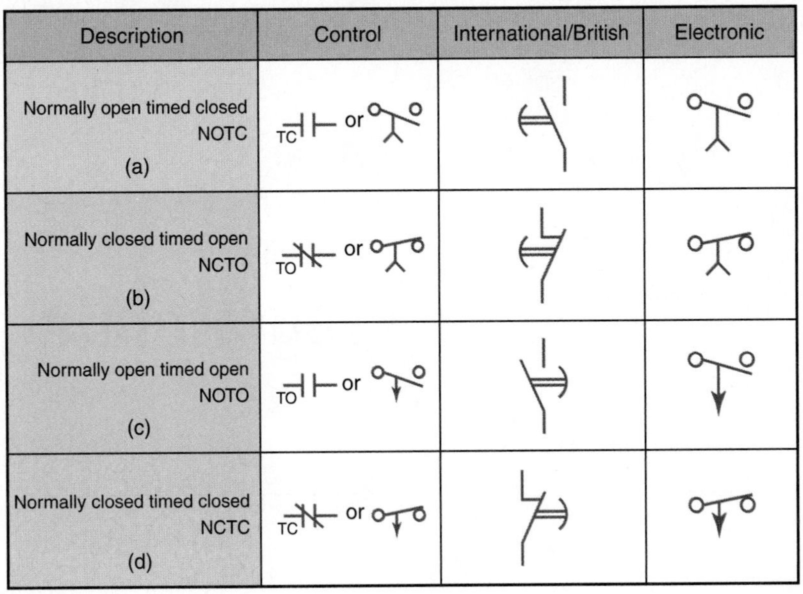

Description	Control	International/British	Electronic
Normally open timed closed NOTC (a)			
Normally closed timed open NCTO (b)			
Normally open timed open NOTO (c)			
Normally closed timed closed NCTC (d)			

Rehg and Sartori, Industrial Electronics, 1st Edition, © 2006, Reprinted by permission of Pearson Education, Inc., Upper Saddle River, NJ

Mechanical timing relays use pneumatics to develop the time delay by the controlled release of air through an orifice during the expansion or compression of a bellows. The time delay period is set by positioning a needle valve to vary the amount of orifice restriction. The pneumatic timing relay provides *on-delay* and *off-delay* timing options with a range of 0.05 to 180 seconds and an accuracy of plus or minus 10 percent of the set time. However, pneumatic timers tend to drift over time, thus requiring periodic adjustment. Both AC and DC switching types are available with a typical switching current range of 6 to 12 amps and a voltage range of 120 to 600 volts. The continuous current is typically 10 amps.

4-2-1 Timed Contacts

Timed contacts have a *fixed* or *adjustable* delay action set by the pneumatic timing process. Time delay relay contacts are specified as either normally open (NO) or normally closed (NC), with the additional requirement that the delay operates in the direction of closing or in the direction of opening. The four basic types of time delay relay contacts fall into two groups: on delay and off delay.

On-delay timing relays. The normally open and normally closed timed contacts for *on-delay*

timing relays have special names. The normally open are called *normally open, timed close* (NOTC) contacts, and the normally closed are called *normally closed, timed open* (NCTO) contacts. The two types of contacts operate as follows:

Normally open, timed closed (NOTC): The control and electronic symbols and the timing diagram for *normally open, timed closed* on-delay timing relays are shown in Figures 4-1(a) and 4-2(a), respectively. After the relay coil is energized, the timed normally open (NO) contacts remain open until after the time delay value. After the time delay (5 seconds in the figure), the timed contacts change state (NO contacts close) and remain in that new state as long as the coil is energized. When the coil is de-energized, the timed contacts immediately return to their initial state (NO contacts open).

Normally closed, timed open (NCTO): The symbols and timing diagram for *normally closed, timed open* on-delay time delays are shown in Figures 4-1(b) and 4-2(b), respectively. After the relay coil is energized, the timed normally closed (NC) contacts remain closed until after the time delay value. After

the time delay (5 seconds in the figure), the timed contacts change state (NC contacts open) and remain in that new state as long as the coil is energized. When the coil is de-energized, the timed contacts immediately return to their initial state (NC contacts closed).

The action of the NOTC and NCTO contacts could also be described as the action of an NO and an NC contact on an on-delay time relay.

Off-delay timing relays. The normally open and normally closed timed contacts for *off-delay* timing relays also have special names. The normally open are called *normally open, timed open* (NOTO) contacts, and the normally closed are called *normally closed, timed closed* (NCTC) contacts. The two types of contacts operate as follows:

Normally open, timed open (NOTO): The control and electronic symbols and the timing diagram for *normally open, timed open* off-delay timing relays are shown in Figures 4-1(c) and 4-2(c), respectively. After the relay coil is energized, the timed NO contacts immediately close and remain in that new state as long as the coil is energized. When the coil is de-energized, the timed contacts remain in the changed state (the NO contacts close) until the set time delay value is reached. At the end of the time delay (5 seconds in the figure), the timed contacts return to their initial state (NO contacts open). Note that

the delay starts after power is removed from the coil.

Normally closed, timed close (NCTC): The symbols and timing diagram for *normally closed, timed closed* off-delay timing relays are shown in Figures 4-1(d) and 4-2(d), respectively. After the relay coil is energized, the timed NC contacts immediately open and remain in that new state as long as the coil is energized. When the coil is de-energized, the timed contacts remain in the changed state (NC contacts open) until the set time delay value is reached. At the end of the time delay (5 seconds in the figure), timed contacts return to their initial state (NC contacts closed). Note that the delay starts after power is removed from the coil.

The action of the NOTO and NCTC contacts could also be described as the action of an NO and an NC contact on an off-delay time relay. In addition to the timed contacts on timing relays, *instantaneous* contacts are also present.

4-2-2 Instantaneous Contacts

Instantaneous contacts operate independently from the timing process, like standard control relay contacts. When the coil is energized the contacts change states; when the coil is de-energized they return to their normal states. An illustration of the instantaneous contact on each type of delay is provided in Figure 4-2; the schematic symbols are the same as a basic relay contact. Note that the contact state change coincides with the waveform of the coil voltage.

EXAMPLE 4-1

Draw the relay ladder diagram for an application where a motor is started 10 seconds after a start momentary push button is depressed and is stopped when a stop momentary push button is depressed.

SOLUTION

Figure 4-3 illustrates the solution, where TMR1 is the NOTC time delay coil, contact TMR1-1 is an instantaneous contact, and contact TMR1-2 is a timed contact. The instantaneous contact seals in the momentary start push button after it's released, and the normally open, timed closed contact activates the motor after the 10-second delay. Both TMR1 contacts are associated with one timer.

FIGURE 4-2: Timing relay timing diagrams.

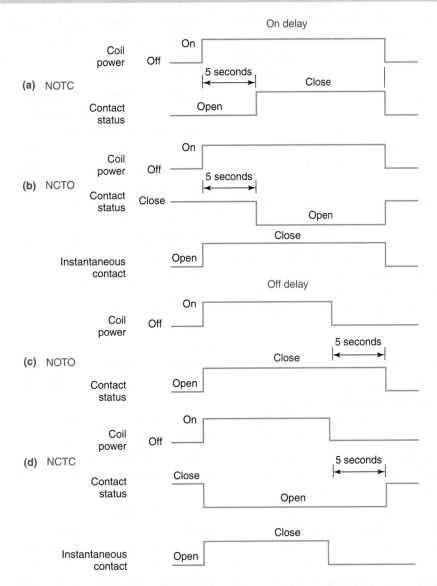

Rehg and Sartori, Industrial Electronics, 1st Edition, © 2006, Reprinted by permission of Pearson Education, Inc., Upper Saddle River, NJ

FIGURE 4-3: Relay ladder diagram for Example 4-1.

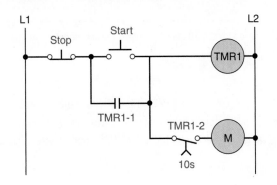

4-2-3 Timing Relay Operation

The operation is based on the pneumatic control illustrated in Figure 4-4. Study the drawing until all the components are familiar, and refer to the figure as you read the following description.

- When the solenoid plunger (10) is retracted from the push rod (11), it allows the spring (3) located inside the synthetic rubber bellows (1) to push the timing mechanism plunger (4) upward.
- As the plunger rises, it causes the over-center toggle mechanism (5) to move the snap-action

FIGURE 4-4: Pneumatic timing mechanism.

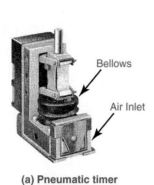

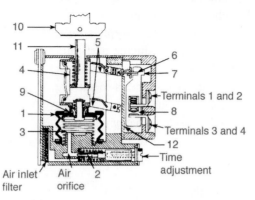

(a) Pneumatic timer   (b) Cutaway of pneumatic timer

Source: (a) Courtesy of Square D/Schneider Electric and (b) Courtesy of Rockwell Automation, Inc.

toggle blade (6) upward, which in turn picks up the push plate (7), which carries the movable contacts (8).

- The speed with which the bellows can expand is determined by the setting of the needle valve (2). If this needle valve is nearly closed, a maximum length of time will be required for air to pass it and permit the bellows to expand. The needle valve setting determines the time interval that must elapse between the release of the solenoid actuator and expansion of the bellows to switch the contact.
- When the push rod (11) is again depressed by the solenoid plunger (10), it forces the timing mechanism plunger (4) to the lower position, exhausting the air through the release valve (9) and resetting the timer almost instantaneously.

4-2-4   Selecting Timing Relays

Timing relays are selected based on the following operational characteristics:

- Length of time delay required
- Range of timing values required for the machine or process
- Timing options required for the process
- Repeatability and accuracy of the timed delay required for the process
- Current rating, configuration, and quantity of timed contacts and/or instantaneous contacts required for the control

4-3   ELECTRONIC TIMING RELAYS

Electronic timing relays are more accurate and repeatable than pneumatic timing relays, plus they provide an economical solution for applications requiring basic timing functions. Figure 4-5(a) depicts a typical electronic timing relay, and Figure 4-5(b) depicts a multifunctional timing relay. The typical timing relays provide the timing functions as described in the previous section and operate with a supply voltage in the 24 to 48 VDC range or the 24 to 240 VAC range. The solid-state electronics provide timing settings from 0.05 seconds to 60 hours with a timing accuracy of plus or minus 5 percent of the set time and an excellent repeatability of plus or minus 0.2 percent.

The multifunction electronic timing relay is typically microprocessor controlled and provides 10 or more timing functions, which are variations of the on-delay and off-delay timed outputs plus

FIGURE 4-5:   Timing relays.

(a) Electronic timing relay   (b) Multifunction timing relay

Courtesy of Rockwell Automation, Inc.

some pulsed output options. With the variety of timing functions and ranges available, the multifunction relay eliminates the need for additional auxiliary relays in complex applications, saving installation time and reducing parts and labor costs. Go to the Allen-Bradley Web site at http://www.ab.com and select timers to see the numerous output combinations that are available for electronic timers. These electronic timing relays are stand-alone devices and not a part of a PLC.

4-4 PLC TIMER INSTRUCTIONS

Timer instructions are important in PLC applications where the time for a machine's cycle times is critical, or when some time delay is needed between process sequences. PLC timers are *output instructions* that provide the same functions as on-delay and off-delay mechanical timing relays and electronic time delay relays.

PLC timers offer numerous advantages over their mechanical and electronic counterparts. PLC time settings can be easily changed and the quantity of timers can be changed through programming without wiring modifications. In addition, the PLC timer is highly accurate and repeatable because its time delays are generated in the PLC processor. The accuracy of the timed event may be affected, however, if the program has a large number of rungs and therefore a long scan time.

4-5 ALLEN-BRADLEY TIMER INSTRUCTIONS

The timer instructions for the Allen-Bradley (AB) PLC 5, SLC 500, and Logix processors operate in nearly identical fashion. Therefore, most of the example solutions in this chapter use the SLC 500 instructions; however, PLC 5 and ControlLogix instructions are used in a few examples to illustrate the differences in the three systems.

AB has three timer instructions discussed in this chapter: timer on-delay (TON), timer off-delay (TOF), and retentive timer on-delay (RTO). The next sections prepare for the discussion of these instructions by introducing the timer ladder logic symbol, timer parameters, and the function of the timer Boolean bits and integer registers.

FIGURE 4-6: PLC timer block.

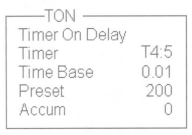

(a) Allen Bradley

(b) Mitsubishi

4-5-1 Allen-Bradley Timer Symbol and Parameters

All three AB timer instructions are represented as blocks in the ladder logic with three (ControlLogix) or four (PLC 5 and SLC 500) data parameters. Figure 4-6(a) shows the TON timer instructional block for the PLC 5 and SLC 500. In other PLC brands the timer uses a symbol like that in Figure 4-6(b), and in some cases they use the symbol of a timing relay discussed in Section 4-2. Each PLC manufacturer represents the data inside the block slightly differently, but the parameters generally include the same information. The timer blocks for the PLC 5 and SLC 500 are illustrated in Figure 4-7 and the block for the ControlLogix processor is illustrated in Figure 4-8. The four parameters required for a timer include *timer number, time base, preset value,* and *accumulator value.* Refer to Figures 4-7 and 4-8 as you read the following descriptions.

• Timer Number and Tag Name: The Allen-Bradley PLC 5 and SLC 500 timer instructions, Figure 4-7(a) and (b), use a timer file, T4, for all timers and attach a unique number to identify the specific timer. For example, T4:0, T4:1, and T4:2 are three timers numbered 0, 1, and 2. The colon (:) is a delimiter used to separate the file number and the timer number. The number of timers allowed in file T4 is 256 (numbers 0 to 255); if more timers

FIGURE 4-7: PLC 5 and SLC 500 TON timer instructions.

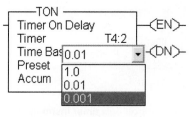

(a) SLC 500 timer instruction

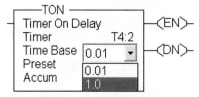

(b) PLC 5 timer instruction

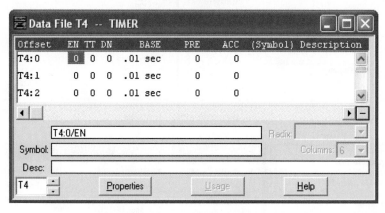

(c) Timer date file for SLC 500 and PLC 5

are needed files T10 through T255 can be used, with each holding 256 timers. The timer database file is shown in Figure 4-7(c) with the current value of all parameters displayed for each timer. Timer parameters can be entered directly into the timer instructions or into this database file dialog box.

The Logix processors, Figure 4-8(a), use a tag name for the timers, such as Pump_timer. The descriptive tag name makes it easier to know what function the timer serves in the control system. Any valid tag name (see Chapter 3 for tag name rules) can be used, but the name must be declared using the programming software tag properties dialog boxes illustrated in Figure 4-8(b). The tag name typed into the timer instruction appears at the top of the dialog box when the tag is validated. The description (optional), tag type, and data type are added to complete the validation. The description can be any text desired, and the tag type used most often is *Base*. The data type, *TIMER*, must be selected or typed. A pop-up Select Data Type dialog box appears when the selection box button at the right of the data type line is double-clicked.

The timer tag database is shown in Figure 4-8(c). The database is accessed by double-clicking the Program Tags file in the file menu. This dialog box offers two views of the timer database: monitor tags or edit tags. To view tag values the monitor tags tab is selected at the lower left of the dialog box and the display in Figure 4-8(c) is displayed. The values for all timer variables are displayed. Note that the Logix system has some additional variables compared to the PLC 5 and SLC 500

FIGURE 4-8: ControlLogix timer instruction.

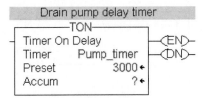

(a) ControlLogix timer instruction

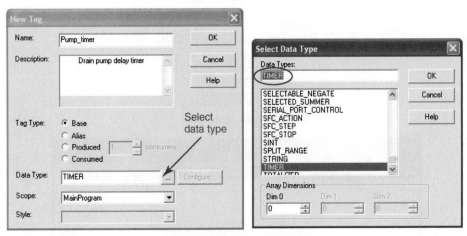

(b) Tag properties dialog boxes

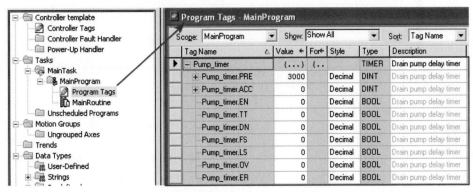

(c) ControlLogix timer tag database file

systems. If the other tab, edit tags, is selected then changes to the timer database are entered.

- **Time Base:** PLC timers increment from 0 to a preset value in time segments of 1, 0.1, 0.01, and 0.001 seconds. The *time base* indicates the incremental change in the accumulator value when the timer instruction is active. For example, if the preset holds 1000 and the time base is 0.01, then the time delay is configured for 10 seconds (1000 × 0.01). Figure 4-7(a) illustrates the time base options for the SLC 500 and Figure 4-7(b) shows the options for

the PLC 5. Note that the SLC 500 has a time base value of 0.001 seconds listed, but it is not supported and cannot be used.

The ControlLogix timer, Figure 4-8(a), has two variations from the PLC 5 and SLC 500 models. First, the *time base* selection field is absent since it has a *fixed time base* of 0.001 seconds, and second, the timer number is replaced by a tag name.

- **Preset Value (PRE):** This integer value is the number of time increments that the timer must accumulate to reach the desired time

delay. For example, if the time base is 0.01 and the preset value is 200, then the time delay is 2 seconds (0.01 × 200). The range of preset value for the PLC 5 and SLC 500 timers is from 0 to +32,767. If a timer preset value is a negative number, a runtime error occurs.

The preset value for the ControlLogix timer in Figure 4-8(a) and (c) is 3000. The timer time is 3 seconds (3000 × 0.001) since the time base is fixed at 0.001 seconds for each increment of the accumulator. The range for the ControlLogix preset value is −32,768 to +32,767 for integers, but it is in the +/− 2 million range for double integers.

- **Accumulator Value (ACC):** The accumulator value indicates the number of increments that the timer has accumulated while the timer rung and instruction are active. The ranges of values permitted for the accumulator are the same as those given for the preset value. The accumulator value is reset to zero when the timer is reset, and the non-retentive timers are reset when the rung and instruction are false.

Configuring a timer includes: selecting the timer number or tag name, selecting a time base (SLC 500 and PLC 5 only), and entering a preset value for the time delay required. In rare situations an accumulator value other than zero is entered. The three timer bits used in timer ladder logic control are described next.

4-5-2   Allen-Bradley Timer Bits

The three AB timer models (PLC 5, SLC 500, and Logix) and all three Allen Bradley timer types have the same three Boolean bits for ladder logic control. Their names and descriptions follow.

- **Timer Enable Bit (EN):** The enable bit is true when the rung input logic is true, and the enable bit is false when the rung input logic is false. When the EN bit is true the timer accumulator is incrementing at the rate set by the timer time base.
- **Timer Timing Bit (TT):** The timer timing bit is true only when the accumulator is incrementing. TT remains true until the accumulator reaches the preset value. When the accumulator value is equal to or greater than

the preset value, the timer timing bit is returned to a false condition. In other words, the TT bit indicates when timing action is occurring and can be used to control timed events in automation applications.
- **Timer Done Bit (DN):** The DN bit signals the end of the timing process by changing states from false to true or from true to false depending on the type of timer instruction used.

4-5-3   Allen-Bradley TON, TOF, and RTO Instructions

The three types of Allen-Bradley timer instructions include: *on-delay timer* (TON), *off-delay timer* (TOF), and *retentive timer* (RTO). The truth tables in Table 4-1 describe the conditions that cause a true or false state on the timer output bits (EN, TT, and DN) for each timer type. This truth table applies to timers from all three Allen-Bradley processors. Read the truth table before continuing.

The action of the timer enable bit is the same for all three types; namely, it is true if the timer instruction rung logic is true and false if the logic is false. However, the timer action created by the enable varies with the three different timer types. Review Table 4-1 to verify this operation.

The timer timing (TT) bits of TON and RTO are true when the accumulator (ACC) is less than the preset value AND the timer is enabled. The TOF has the same operation except that the enable bit is false. All three of the timers have a different logic requirement for the TT to be false. Also, the done bit on each timer has unique true and false conditions. Review TT and DN bit operation in the table.

The most frequently used timer instruction, TON, has an active DN bit if the ACC is equal to or greater than the preset (PRE) value AND the timer enable bit remains true. Compare this with the logic for the other two.

The timing diagrams of the TON, TOF, and RTO timers are illustrated in Figure 4-9. Study each timer in the figure and note the condition of the TT and DN bits as the EN bit transitions from false to true and back to false. Compare the operation illustrated in the timing diagram with the description of the output bit operation in Table 4-1. Note the operation of the TT and DN bits if the EN

TABLE 4-1 Timer output bit truth table.

On-delay timer output bits	are TRUE if	are FALSE if
Timer enable	Timer rung is true.	Timer rung is false.
Timer timing	Timer rung is true AND the accumulator value is less than the preset value.	Timer rung is false OR the accumulator value is equal to or greater than the preset value OR the timer done bit is true.
Timer done	Timer rung is true AND the accumulator value is equal to or greater than the preset value.	Timer rung is false OR the timer rung is less than the preset value.

(a) Truth table for the on-delay timer output bits (TON)

Off-delay timer output bits	are TRUE if	are FALSE if
Timer enable	Timer rung is true.	Timer rung is false.
Timer timing	Timer rung is false AND the accumulator value is less than the preset value.	Timer rung is true OR the accumulator is equal to or greater than the preset value OR the done bit is false.
Timer done	Timer rung is true OR the timer timing bit is true.	Timer rung is false AND the accumulator value is equal to or greater than the preset value.

(b) Truth table for the off-delay timer output bits (TOF)

Retentive timer output bits	are TRUE if	are FALSE if
Timer enable	Timer rung is true.	Timer rung is false.
Timer timing	Timer rung is true AND the accumulator value is less than the preset value.	Timer rung is false OR the accumulator value is equal to or greater than the preset value.
Timer done	The accumulator value is equal to or greater than the preset value.	Reset instruction is initiated OR the timer rung is true but the accumulator is less than the preset value.

(c) Truth table for the retentive timer output bits (RTO)

bit changes before the preset value is reached by the accumulator.

A summary of the general operation of a TON, TOF, and RTO timer with a 15-second preset value follows. The description applies to timers from all three Allen-Bradley processors. Refer to Table 4-1 and Figure 4-9 as you read each timer's description.

On-delay Timer. The *on-delay timer* (TON) in Figure 4-9(a) starts timing (15 second delay) when the timer's ladder rung becomes true. The true rung forces the enable (EN) bit to true, causes the accumulator to start incrementing by the values set in the time base, and makes the timer timing (TT) bit true. The done

FIGURE 4-9: Timing diagrams.

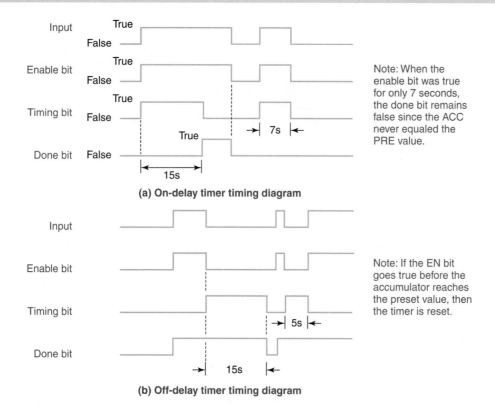

Input

Enable bit

Timing bit

Done bit

Note: When the enable bit was true for only 7 seconds, the done bit remains false since the ACC never equaled the PRE value.

(a) On-delay timer timing diagram

Input

Enable bit

Timing bit

Done bit

Note: If the EN bit goes true before the accumulator reaches the preset value, then the timer is reset.

(b) Off-delay timer timing diagram

(DN) bit becomes true when the accumulator value reaches the preset time value. The DN bit remains true until the timer's rung returns to the false state, making the EN bit false. This reset action also returns the accumulator to a zero value. The condition of the timer instruction is determined by the input logic on the rung; therefore, timer operation is controlled by the associated input field device(s). If the EN bit returns to a false condition before the accumulator reaches the preset value [the 7 second pulse in Figure 4-9(a)], then the timer is reset and the DN bit remains false (no change).

A photocopier is an example of an on-delay timing function. When the print button is pressed, the operation of the photocopier is not started for some time period (an on-delay) to permit the copier to heat up before starting to make copies.

Off-delay Timer. For the off-delay timer (TOF) in Figure 4-9(b), the done bit is true and the accumulator is set to zero when the ladder rung and enable bit are true. No changes in the timer bits occur until the ladder rung and enable bit return to the false state in Figure 4-9(b). At this point the accumulator starts incrementing toward the 15 second preset value with the increment set by the time base. When the accumulator value equals the preset value, the timer done bit goes from true to false. If the EN bit returns to a true condition, [the 5 second pulse in Figure 4-9(b)], before the accumulator reaches the preset value, then the timer is reset and the DN bit remains true (no change).

As an example of an off-delay timing function, think about the light in an automatic garage door opener. When the garage door opener is activated, the light comes on when the door starts to open. The door motor turns off when it is open, but the light remains on (an off-delay) a preset period of time before it is extinguished.

Retentive Timer. The retentive timer, RTO, accumulates time whenever it is active, which means that the timer retains the accumulated

FIGURE 4-9: (Continued).

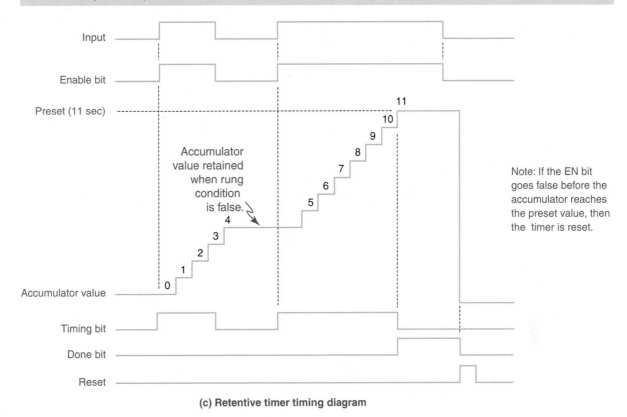

Note: If the EN bit goes false before the accumulator reaches the preset value, then the timer is reset.

(c) Retentive timer timing diagram

time even if the rung is not active or power to the PLC is lost. As a result, the accumulator retains the current time value and starts incrementing from that value when the ladder rung and enable bit once again go true. The time base sets the time increment for the accumulator change and the preset value indicates the desired time delay. The done bit goes true and the timer timing bit goes false when the accumulator value is equal to or greater than the preset value. The retentive timer retains its current time when power is lost or when the timer rung is false. The only method of resetting a retentive timer is by a *reset instruction* that has the address as the timer.

Figure 4-9(c) illustrates the operation of a retentive timer with a preset value of 11 seconds. When the timer rung becomes active, the enable bit is true and the timer accumulator (ACC) begins to increment. When the rung is false, the ACC holds the current value, which is 4 in the figure. When the input returns to a true state, the ACC begins incrementing from 4 until it reaches the preset value of 11. At the preset value, the ACC stops incrementing and the retentive timer done bit (DN) is true. The figure shows how a reset (RES) instruction is used to reset the ACC to zero and return the timer done bit to a false state.

The accumulator of the retentive timer operates like the trip mileage indicator on the instrument panel in your car. As you drive, the indicator displays your accumulated miles. When you stop for gas the display holds the number. It then continues accumulating as you start driving again. When you finish the trip, you manually reset the display to zero.

With the operation of the TON, TOF, and RTO timer instruction covered, the next section describes how each timer parameter and bit is addressed.

4-6 ALLEN-BRADLEY TIMER PARAMETER AND BIT ADDRESSING

The timer parameters and control bits described in the last two sections are stored in the processor memory. The format for storing the PLC 5 and SLC 500 parameters is the same, but is quite different for the Logix family of processors.

4-6-1 PLC 5 and SLC 500 Timer Memory Map

The PLC 5 and SLC 500 processors use three words in memory to store control bit values and operational parameters. Figure 4-10 illustrates how the timer memory for these processors is organized. Each block of words is identified with the timer number; for example, a three-word block would be addressed as T4:5. This three-word block holds the data for timer 5.

Word 0 is the control word with the control or timer output bits (EN, TT, and DN) stored in the three most significant bits. These output bits are Boolean data types, so their values in the timer memory map are either 0 or 1. The preset value is stored in word 1 and the accumulator value is stored in word 2. Figure 4-10 illustrates the layout of the three bits (EN, TT, and DN) and two words (PRE and ACC) that can be addressed for system control.

The address structure for timers in the PLC 5 and SLC 500 processors uses the following format:

Tf:e.s/b

Each element in the timer address format is defined in the following table.

Element	Description	
T	The T indicates that the address is a timer file.	
f	The default value for f is 4. File 4 supports 256 timer instructions (T4:0 to T4:255). If more than 256 timers are needed in a program, then additional files (9 to 255) are available. Each of these files supports 256 timers (T9:0 to T9:255).	
:	Element delimiter	
e	Element number, e, is the number of the timer.	For file 4, e has a range of 0 to 255 timers. The same range is used for e if files 9 to 255 are used.
.	Word delimiter	
s	Word number, S, indicates one of the three timer words.	The value of S ranges from 0 to 2 because each timer has three addressable words.
/	Bit delimiter	
b	Bit number, b, is the bit location in the timer words.	The range is 0 to 15 for all three timer words, but bits 13, 14, and 15 are the only ones used for word 0.

Example timer data addresses are listed in the following table. Study the timer address structure (Tf:e.s/b) and the description of each address element in the previous table, and then verify that you understand what timer data is being addressed by each of the following examples.

T4:0/15 or T4:0/EN	Enable bit of timer number 0
T4:2/14 or T4:2/TT	Timer timing bit of timer number 2
T4:15/13 or T4:15/DN	Done bit of timer number 15
T4:5.1 or T4:5.PRE	Preset value of timer number 5
T4:10.2 or T4:10.ACC	Accumulator value of timer number 10
T4:20.1/0 or T4:20.PRE/0	Bit 0 of the preset value of timer number 20
T4:3.2/11 or T4:3.ACC/11	Bit 11 of the accumulator value of timer number 3
T4:25/DN	The done bit for timer 25 in timer file 4
T4:255/TT	The timer timing bit for the last timer (255) in timer file 4
T9:0.ACC	The accumulator word for timer 0 in timer file 9
T9:255.PRE	The preset word for the last timer (255) in timer file 9
T255:255/EN	The enable bit for last available timer in the system

FIGURE 4-10: Timer output bit image map.

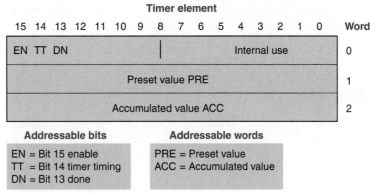

Timers are 3-word elements. Word 0 is the control word, word 1 stores the preset value, and word 2 stores the accumulated value.

These addressing examples indicate all of the possible addressing modes that are available for PLC 5 and SLC 500 timers. Note that parameters are addressed based on the bit or word number or with the mnemonic for that bit or word. For example, in the first example bit 15 is also the enable (EN) bit. Also, in the fourth example the preset is addressed as a .1 for word 1 or as .PRE for preset word. These bit and word addresses are used in any other PLC instruction where a timer bit or word address is permitted. For example, in Chapter 6, move instructions will use the corresponding word addresses which are used with counters to transfer preset values to counters.

4-6-2 ControlLogix Timer Addressing

The format for addressing ControlLogix timers is simplified with the use of tag names for each timer. Figure 4-11 illustrates how the data for timer, *running_seconds*, is displayed in the Program Tags dialog box. Note that the Edit Tags tab is selected at the bottom of the dialog box, so this box could be used to enter parameter data. The Monitor Tags tab could be selected to examine the value of timer bits and words.

The ControlLogix timers have the EN, TT, and DN output bits and PRE and ACC parameter words found in the PLC 5 and SLC 500 PLCs plus the four other data values displayed in Figure 4-11.

FIGURE 4-11: ControlLogix output bit and parameter addressing.

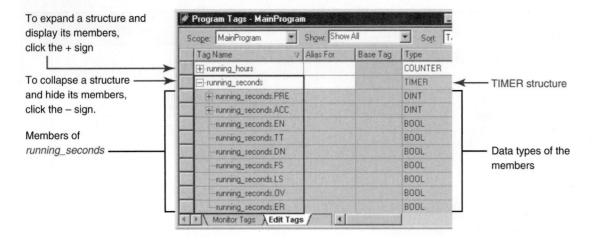

To expand a structure and display its members, click the + sign

To collapse a structure and hide its members, click the − sign.

Members of *running_seconds*

TIMER structure

Data types of the members

4-6-3 Timer Contacts versus PLC Instructions

An important distinction was made in Chapter 3 between the normally open and normally closed physical contacts on input field devices, and the XIC and XIO instructions used for ladder input logic. This distinction is also carried over to the timers. Mechanical timing relays have physical contacts and electronic timers have either physical contacts or solid-state switches to control output devices. However, the virtual timers in PLCs are created in software; as a result, they have memory bit outputs and the PLC timer is called an instruction.

There is, however, a relationship between the mechanical and electronic timers and their PLC counterparts. The PLC TON timer is the same as an on-delay timing relay, and the TOF timer is the same as the off-delay timing relay. The TON done bit is like a normally open, timer closed timing relay contact, and the TOF done bit is like the normally open, timed opened relay contact. The instantaneous contacts on the timing relays are equivalent to the enable bit on both types of PLC timers.

4-7 PROGRAMMING ALLEN-BRADLEY TON AND TOF TIMER LADDER LOGIC

Sections 4-5 and 4-6 presented an overview of timer instructions, including setting timing parameters and addressing timer data. This section uses that information to develop timer lad-

der logic for machine and system control. The first section looks at six ladder configurations that are used to build most timer ladder logic. Learning this standard timer ladder logic is important because most timer ladder solutions are just variations from these six standard ladder configurations.

The second half of this section covers a number of example problems that demonstrate how the three Allen-Bradley timer instructions are used for automation control.

4-7-1 Standard Ladder Logic for Allen-Bradley TON Timers

Automation programs that include timers use a standard set of timer ladder logic configurations. Learning these common timer ladder solutions is a great way to start the study of timer applications. The standard TON solutions for common control problems are listed in Figure 4-12.

The first set of standard rungs, Figure 4-12(a) through (d), illustrates timer ladder configurations triggered by field device switches with momentary or continuous types of contacts. This set also covers the different output options for TON timers. Read the description of the timer operation in the figure as you study the standard timer ladder logic. It is clear that the simplest timer applications require two rungs, one for the timer instruction and one for the output device being controlled. In addition, a maintain contact input for the timer is the simplest to implement. The momentary contact inputs

FIGURE 4-12: Standard ladder logic rungs for TON timers.

Application	Standard Ladder Logic Rungs for TON Timers
Turn on an output device for a set time period when a maintain contact input device changes states. The input field device is a NO selector switch. If the switch is closed, then the timer rung, EN bit, and TT bit are true because instruction I:1/1 is true. Therefore, the T4:1/TT instruction has continuity and the O:3/0 output is true. The TT bit and output are on for the preset time value.	I:1 ⊣ ⊢ 1 ┌─── TON ───────────────┐ ⟨EN⟩ │ Timer On Delay │ │ Timer T4:1 │ │ Time Base 1.0 │ ⟨DN⟩ │ Preset 30< │ │ Accum 0< │ └───────────────────────┘ T4:1 O:3 ⊣ ⊢ ⟨ ⟩ TT 0 **(a)**
Turn on an output device after a set time period when a maintain contact input device changes states. The input field device is a NO selector switch. If the switch is closed, then the timer rung, EN bit, and TT bit are true because instruction I:1/1 is true. After the preset time value the done bit is true. Therefore, the T4:1/DN instruction has continuity and the O:3/0 output is true. The output is on until the timer input rung goes false.	I:1 ⊣ ⊢ 1 ┌─── TON ───────────────┐ ⟨EN⟩ │ Timer On Delay │ │ Timer T4:1 │ │ Time Base 1.0 │ ⟨DN⟩ │ Preset 30< │ │ Accum 0< │ └───────────────────────┘ T4:1 O:3 ⊣ ⊢ ⟨ ⟩ DN 0 **(b)**
Turn on an output device for a set time period when a momentary contact input device changes states. The input field device is a NO push button switch. If the switch is closed, then the timer rung, EN bit, and TT bit are true because instruction I:1/1 is true. The active T4:1/TT bit seals the input instruction and makes the O:3/0 output true. The TT bit and output are on for the preset time value.	I:1 ⊣ ⊢ 1 T4:1 ⊣ ⊢ TT ┌─── TON ───────────────┐ ⟨EN⟩ │ Timer On Delay │ │ Timer T4:1 │ │ Time Base 1.0 │ ⟨DN⟩ │ Preset 30< │ │ Accum 0< │ └───────────────────────┘ T4:1 O:3 ⊣ ⊢ ⟨ ⟩ TT 0 **(c)**
Turn on an output device for one PLC scan after a set time period when a momentary contact input device changes states. The input field device is a NO push button switch. When the switch is closed, then the timer rung, EN bit, and TT bit are true because instruction I:1/1 is true. The active T4:1/TT bit seals the input instruction for the momentary switch. After the preset time value the done bit is true. Therefore, the T4:1/DN instruction has continuity and the O:3/0 output is true. One scan later, T4:1/TT goes false and the timer is reset. This causes the output, O:3/0, to be true for one scan time.	I:1 ⊣ ⊢ 1 T4:1 ⊣ ⊢ TT ┌─── TON ───────────────┐ ⟨EN⟩ │ Timer On Delay │ │ Timer T4:1 │ │ Time Base 1.0 │ ⟨DN⟩ │ Preset 30< │ │ Accum 0< │ └───────────────────────┘ T4:1 O:3 ⊣ ⊢ ⟨ ⟩ DN 0 **(d)**

FIGURE 4-12: (Continued).

Application	Standard Ladder Logic Rungs for TON Timers Pulse Generators
Turn on an output device with a pulse sequence where one half of the duty cycle has a variable time and the other has a time equal to the scan time of the ladder. The input field device is a NO selector switch. If the switch is closed, then the timer rung, EN bit, and TT bit are true because instruction I:1/1 is true and the pulse timer done bit is false. As a result, the timer is incrementing the ACC at a 1 second rate. When the ACC equals the preset (5 seconds), the timer DN bit is true. This makes the timer rung false because the XIO instruction has no power flow since the timer DN is true. Therefore, the timer resets, which makes the DN bit is true for only one scan, and the timer starts the timing process again. The pulse output timing diagrams for the two output options are illustrated below the ladder logic. The done bit is used to generate one waveform, and the timer timing bit is used to generate the other. Note that the outputs are virtual relays (memory bits) since most field devices could not respond fast enough for this narrow pulse. The pulse is used, however, for logic control in the program.	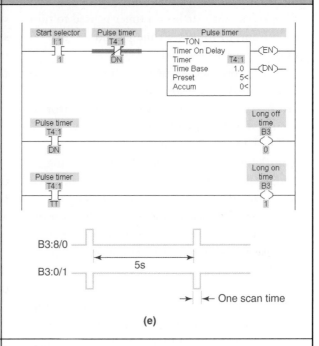
Turn on an output device with a pulse sequence where both halves of the duty cycle have a variable time. The input field device is a NO selector switch. If the switch is closed, then the T4:2 timer rung and the timers EN bit and TT bit are true because instruction I:1/1 is true. As a result, the timer is incrementing the ACC at a 1 second rate. When the T4:2 ACC equals the preset (4 seconds), the timer DN bit is true. This makes the T4:3 timer rung true, and that timer starts incrementing its ACC toward the preset value of 2 seconds. While the T4:3 ACC is incrementing, the output O:3/2 is true because the T4:2 done bit remains true. When the T4:3 timers ACC equals 2, the done bit of T4:3 becomes true. This resets both the T4:2 timer (XIO instruction in timer T4:2 rung is true) and the T4:3 timer held on by the T4:2 done bit. The output also returns to the false state when T4:3 ACC reaches 2 seconds. Note that the up time for the pulse is determined by the T4:3 since that timer determines how long the output is true. The pulse output timing diagram is illustrated below the ladder logic.	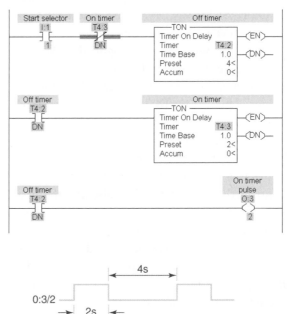

requires a sealing instruction because the TON timer instruction must be true until the timer reaches the preset value. The timer's TT bit is used to perform the required sealing of the input. The standard circuits in Figure 4-12(c and d) also demonstrate how a timer is used to turn on an output for a set time period or turn on one after a set time period.

The second set, Figure 4-12(e) and (f), features two configurations for using timers to create pulse generators. The pulse generator in Figure 4-12(e) is called a regenerative clock because it uses an output of the timer reset itself. The XIO instruction in the timer rung is addressed with the timer done to reset the timer whenever the done bit changes from false to true. The TON instruction is reset whenever the timer rung is false; as a result, the false done bit resets this regenerative circuit so the timer instruction done bit is true for only one scan time. This output pulse (one scan time wide) is too narrow to drive most field devices, so this ladder configuration is used most often for logic control within the PLC program. This configuration is used in the next two chapters for control of other PLC instructions.

The other pulse generator, Figure 4-12(f), provides a variable duty cycle that is a function of the preset values for the two timers. The done bit from the first timer, T4:2, is used to control the output, O:3/2, and to make the second timer, T4:3, active. T4:3 determines how long the output is on before it resets the system and timing sequence is restarted. Therefore, the second timer controls the on time for the pulse and the first timer controls the off time. This is a regenerative timer using two timer instructions. Note that other program rungs can be inserted between the timer rungs and the output rung. Read the description of the pulse generator operation in the figure as you study the standard pulse generator ladder logic.

The Allen-Bradley SLC 500 timer is used to create the example solutions in all six TON ladders. However, PLC 5 and ControlLogix timers could be used and the operation of the ladder logic would be unchanged. The only difference would be the addresses used for the input logic for the PLC 5 and the use of tags for the ControlLogix.

4-7-2 Standard Ladder Logic for Allen-Bradley TOF Timers

The standard TOF solutions used in control problems are listed in Figure 4-13. The standard rungs illustrate how the TOF timer performs with a selector switch for the input field device. The selector contacts, used in Figure 4-13(a), remain in the open position long enough for the timer to time out or complete the timing process. The field device in Figure 4-13(b) could be either a selector with maintain contacts or a push button with momentary contacts. The time duration for a true done bit is the sum of the time the input is held closed and the preset time value. The choice is dictated by the system control requirements. The timing diagrams are included because the operation of TOF timers is often more difficult to understand than their TON counterparts. Note that other program rungs can be inserted between the timer rung and the output rung. Read the description of the timer operation in the figure as you study the standard timer ladder logic.

The Allen-Bradley SLC 500 timer is used to create both TOF example solutions; however, PLC 5 and ControlLogix TOF timers could be used and the operation of the ladder logic would be unchanged. The only difference would be the addresses used for the input logic in the PLC 5 and the use of tags for the ControlLogix.

4-7-3 Allen-Bradley TON and TOF Timer Applications

This section includes a number of timer applications and example problems that demonstrate how TON and TOF timers for the three Allen-Bradley processors are used. The applications describe the use of a timer in a control requirement, and the examples show you how a control problem is stated and illustrate one workable solution.

In addition, the standard time ladder logic, which is the basis for the solution, is indicated. What becomes clear is that just a few timer configurations are used to solve most of the timer problems in automation control.

Pump delay control logic application. In some large pump applications power to the pump motor is delayed while auxiliary circuits open valves or initiate priming operations. The ladder logic in Figures 4-14(a and b) illustrates a pump

FIGURE 4-13: Standard ladder logic rungs for TOF timers.

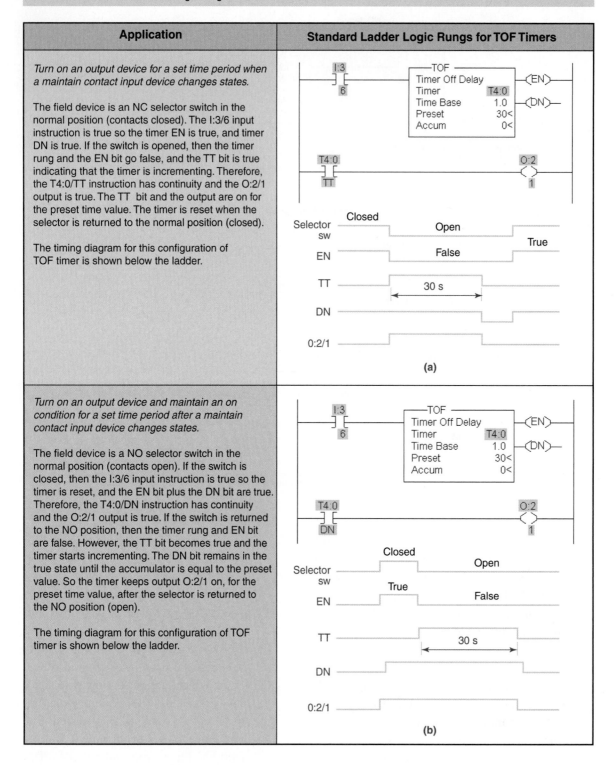

Application	Standard Ladder Logic Rungs for TOF Timers
Turn on an output device for a set time period when a maintain contact input device changes states. The field device is an NC selector switch in the normal position (contacts closed). The I:3/6 input instruction is true so the timer EN is true, and timer DN is true. If the switch is opened, then the timer rung and the EN bit go false, and the TT bit is true indicating that the timer is incrementing. Therefore, the T4:0/TT instruction has continuity and the O:2/1 output is true. The TT bit and the output are on for the preset time value. The timer is reset when the selector is returned to the normal position (closed). The timing diagram for this configuration of TOF timer is shown below the ladder.	(a)
Turn on an output device and maintain an on condition for a set time period after a maintain contact input device changes states. The field device is a NO selector switch in the normal position (contacts open). If the switch is closed, then the I:3/6 input instruction is true so the timer is reset, and the EN bit plus the DN bit are true. Therefore, the T4:0/DN instruction has continuity and the O:2/1 output is true. If the switch is returned to the NO position, then the timer rung and EN bit are false. However, the TT bit becomes true and the timer starts incrementing. The DN bit remains in the true state until the accumulator is equal to the preset value. So the timer keeps output O:2/1 on, for the preset time value, after the selector is returned to the NO position (open). The timing diagram for this configuration of TOF timer is shown below the ladder.	(b)

start delay timer using a TON PLC timer instruction and the associated timing diagram. When selector A, an input field device switch, is active the timer begins incrementing toward the preset value in 0.01 second increments. Two seconds later, when the preset value is reached (0.01 × 200 = 2 seconds), the timer done bit becomes active and the pump contactor is turned on. When SS1 is opened, the timer resets and the pump turns off. As in all TON timers, the accumulated value

FIGURE 4-14: On-delay timer diagrams.

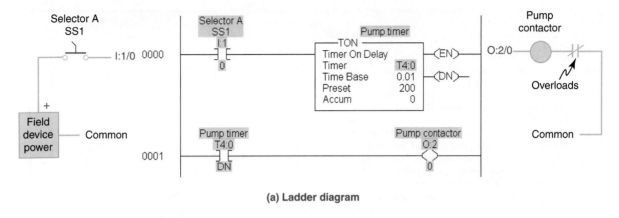

(a) Ladder diagram

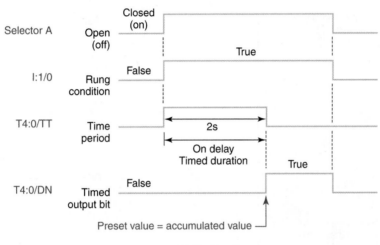

(b) Timing diagram

is automatically reset to zero when the enable bit goes from a 1 to a 0. Note that this timer example is the standard configuration shown in Figure 4-12(b). All of the timer applications are either one of the standard timer ladder logic configurations or some combination of those configurations.

Traffic Light Control Application. Figure 4-15 depicts a ladder diagram where the active and done bits from three on-delay timers are used to turn on and off traffic lights—the red light is on for 32 seconds, the green light is on for 27 seconds, and the amber light is on for 5 seconds. Note that the timers are numbered T4:0, T4:1, and T4:2; their preset times are 32, 27, and 5 seconds, respectively. Refer to Figure 4-15 as you read the following operation of the timers.

1. Before power is applied, all timer EN, TT, and DN bits are false, all examine if closed (XIC) instructions (-||-) are not active (no continuity), and all examine if open (XIO) instructions (-|/|-) are not active (continuity).

2. At power on the T4:2/DN bit is false, so the examine if open instruction in rung 0 is true, which makes the rung true. Since rung 0 is true, the T4:0/EN bit is true, and the T4:0/TT timing cycle is started. The two input instructions in rung 3 are true (T4:0/EN bit is true and the T4:0/DN false), so output O:2/0 is true and the red light is turned on.

3. After 32 seconds, the T4:0/DN done bit is a 1, making rung 3 and output O:2/0 false. When the address on an examine if open instruction is a 1, the instruction is false

FIGURE 4-15: Ladder diagram for traffic light control.

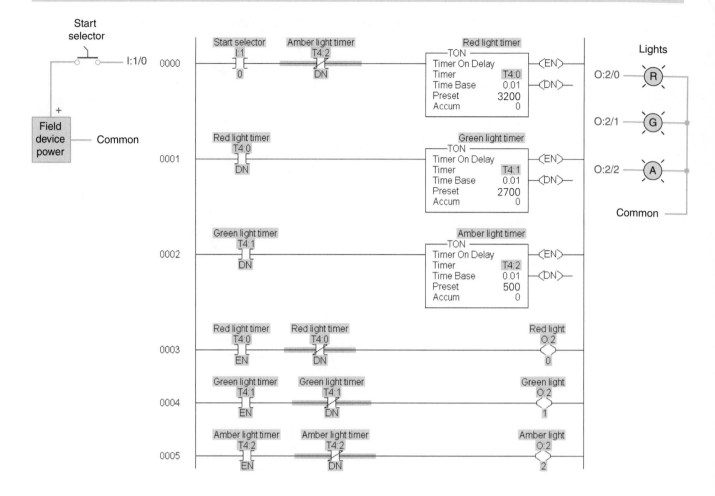

and continuity is removed, which turns off the red light. In addition, the T4:0/DN addressed XIC instruction in rung 1 is true, which starts the green light timer. Rung 4 is also true because the T4:1 timer enable bit is true and the T4:1 done bit is false. This makes output O:2/1 active and turns on the green light.

4. After an additional 27 seconds, the T4:1/DN bit goes true, making rung 4 false and extinguishing the green light. In addition, rung 2 is true, which starts the amber timer. As a result, rung 5 and the O:2/2 output are true, thus illuminating the amber light.

5. After an additional 5 seconds, the T4:2 done bit goes true, making rung 5 false and extinguishing the amber light. Also, the true T4:2/DN bit makes rung 0 and the T4:0 timer false. This causes the T4:0

done bit to go false, which makes rung 1 false, causing the T4:1 timer and T4:1/DN bit to go false. The change in T4:1/DN makes rung 2 and T4:2 false. With this change in T4:2 and an active start selector, rung 0 returns to the active state.

6. With rung 0 true again, the previous timing sequence is repeated.

All of the timers in this example are modifications of the standard timer ladder logic in Figure 4-12(b).

Machine guard lock and indicator application. Production machines often lock out the operator while the machine is processing parts plus a fixed time for the machine to come to a stop. The ladder logic in Figure 4-16(a) uses the selector switch, which starts the process and triggers a TOF timer. The timer controls an output that

FIGURE 4-16: Off-delay timer diagrams.

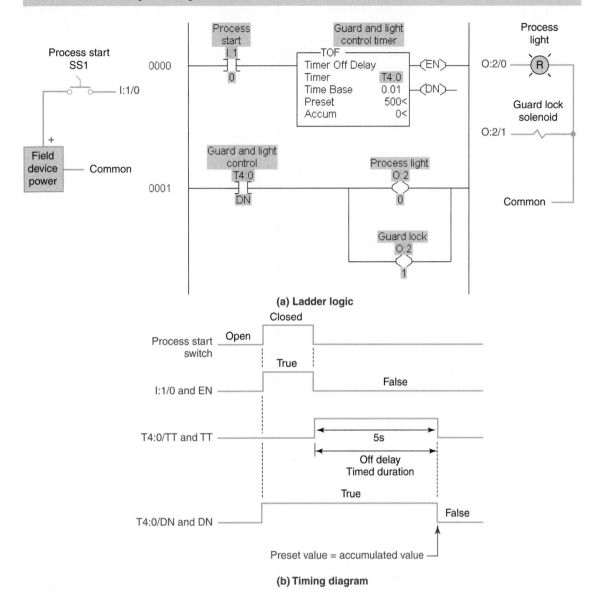

(a) Ladder logic

(b) Timing diagram

locks the machine doors at the start of the process and lights a doors locked indicator. The operator turns off the machine when the part is finished and the TOF timer keeps the doors locked for an additional 5 seconds for the motor to come to a stop. Figure 4-16(b) displays the timing diagram for this operation. When the NO selector switch is true, the *machine start* input instruction is true, the T4:0/EN and T4:0/DN bits are true, the accumulator value is reset to zero, and rung 0 becomes active. As a result, rung 1 is true because T4:0/DN is true and the machine door is locked and the process light is illuminated. When the machine is turned off, the

switch contacts return to the NO state, rung 0 returns to the false state, and the timer accumulator begins incrementing toward the preset value while T4:0/DN remains true. When the preset value is reached ($500 \times 0.01 = 5$ seconds), the timer output (T4:0/DN) becomes false and the door is unlocked and the process light is extinguished.

Note that this timer example is the standard configuration in Figure 4-13(b), but it has a maintain contact switch. Compare the ladder logic and the timing diagrams for the TOF timer in Figures 4-13(b) and 4-16 to see how the standard ladder logic was adapted to this application.

EXAMPLE 4-2

Draw a ladder diagram for a pumping system where the pump requires a 5-second delay before pumping; when the pump is shut off, it requires a 15-second delay before it can be restarted. Start and stop switches are NO momentary contact push buttons.

SOLUTION

Refer to Figure 4-17(a), the ladder solution, and 4-17(b), the timing diagram, as you read the following description.

The pump control is implemented with T4:0, an on-delay timer, and T4:1, an off-delay timer. The activation of the momentary start switch makes rung 0 true, which initiates the on-delay timer (T4:0/EN and T4:0/TT are true). Since the start switch is

FIGURE 4-17: Pumping system ladder diagram for Example 4-2.

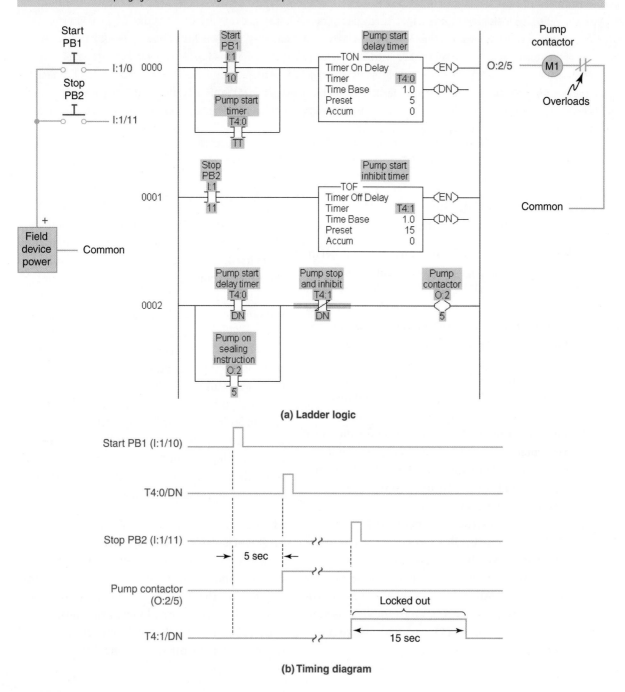

(a) Ladder logic

(b) Timing diagram

a momentary contact type, the I:1/10 instruction must be sealed with the T4:0 timer timing bit (T4:0/TT) to keep the rung active while the timer is incrementing the accumulator for the on-delay time of 5 seconds. Upon completion of the on-delay time of 5 seconds, the T4:0 timer done bit (T4:0/DN) is active, which makes the XIC instruction in rung 2 true. The XIO instruction in rung 2 is also true (continuity) because the T4:1 timer done bit (T4:0/DN) addressing the XIO instruction is false or 0. As a result, the pump output, 0:2/5, is true, so the pump starts 5 seconds after the start switch is pressed. The sealing instruction (0:2/5 around T4:0/DN in rung 2) is necessary because the T4:0/DN bit starts the pump after 5 seconds but is a 1 or true for only one scan. The sealing instruction in rung 2 keeps the pump on after the delayed start.

T4:0/DN is true for only one scan because the timer resets immediately after the preset time is reached. This occurs because T4:0/TT bit is used to seal the XIC start instruction in rung 0, which is a momentary start push button. At 5 seconds the timer timing bit becomes false, which makes the T4:0 timer rung false and the timer resets. As a result, one scan after the done bit is true it returns to the false or 0 state. Review the operation of the standard ladder logic in Figure 4-12(c), which is used for this pump delay timer.

Now when the stop PB is pressed, the I:1/11 instruction in rung 1 is true, and the T4:1/DN bit of the TOF timer in rung 1 is true. When the stop switch is released, the T4:1 TOF timer starts timing and keeps the T4:1/DN bit true for 15 seconds. Thus the initiation of the stop push button makes the XIO instruction in rung 2 false because the T4:1/DN output is true. This action stops the pump because output 0:2/5 false. Rung 2 is held in this false condition by the XIO instruction for the duration of the T4:1 time, so the start push button cannot restart the pump for 15 seconds. Upon completion of the off-delay time of 15 seconds, the T4:1/DN output becomes false, the XIO instructions returns to true state, and the pump can be restarted. Note that this example uses standard timer ladder logic from Figures 4-12(c) and 4-13(b).

4-8   ALLEN-BRADLEY RETENTIVE TIMERS

Review the operation of the retentive timer in Table 4-1(c) on page 158 and Figure 4-9(c). The retentive timer (RTO) operates the same as a TON timer, except the accumulator (ACC) is not reset when the timer enable returns to the false state. The accumulator will continue to increment from the previous value whenever the EN bit goes from false to true. When the ACC equals the PRE value the timer timing bit goes false and the done bit becomes true. The done bit remains in that state until a reset (RES) instruction for the timer is executed. The reset instruction is covered in the next section. Compare and study Table 4-1(c) and Figure 4-9(c) until you understand the logical operation of an RTO timer instruction.

The RTO instruction operates the same for all three Allen-Bradley processors. The RTO ladder logic symbol for the PLC 5, SLC 500, and ControlLogix systems is the same as their TON symbol. After the reset instruction is introduced in the next section, an example is used to illustrate how the RTO and RES instructions operate.

4-8-1   Reset Instruction for RTO Timer and Other Allen-Bradley Instructions

Since the retentive timer does not automatically reset itself, a reset instruction is used to return the timer accumulator to zero and turn off the done bit. The reset (RES) instruction must have the same program address as the timer you want to reset. The reset instruction can reset the timer at any time during its operation and is independent of the input conditions. The reset instruction is also used for the TON and TOF timers and with other Allen-Bradley instructions covered in later chapters. The operation of the reset instruction is the same for all three types of Allen-Bradley PLC processors. Example 4-3 illustrates the operation of an RTO and RES instruction in an automation system.

Heater sequential control application. In large furnaces the electric heaters are often turned on or off in a sequence to control the heating and cooling of the product. In this application three heaters come on at the same time and remain on as long as the momentary start switch is held. When the switch is released the heaters turn off in sequence at 30-second

EXAMPLE 4-3

The pumping system in Figure 4-17 from Example 4-2 has an additional requirement to shut the pump down and illuminate a red pilot lamp after four hours of operation. The illuminated pilot lamp indicates that it's time to check the pump since it moves very abrasive material. A NO momentary push button reset switch is used to reset the system when the maintenance is completed. Draw the new ladder diagram for the pumping system with these additional requirements.

SOLUTION

Refer to Figure 4-18 as you read the following description.

The operation of rungs 0, 1, and 2 are similar to the ladder logic in Example 4-2; the last three rungs are new. Every time the pump is running, output O:2/5 (rung 2) is active. This makes the XIC instruction (O:2/5) and the retentive timer (T4:2) in rung 3 active, which increments the accumulated time in T4:2. Note that the retentive timer preset value is 14,400 seconds, which is 4 hours. When the accumulated number equals 14,400 seconds, the retentive timer done bit (T4:2/DN) is true, which causes a true

FIGURE 4-18: Pumping system ladder diagram for Example 4-3.

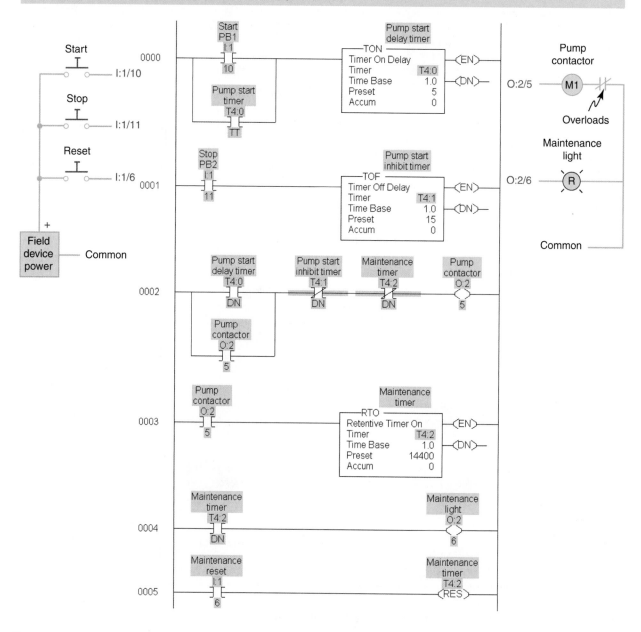

intervals. Figure 4-19(a) depicts a ladder diagram using the ControlLogix syntax where the done bits from three off-delay timers (TOF) are used to turn on three heaters and then sequentially turn them off at the 30-second interval rate. (Note that the arrowed lines in the ladder

FIGURE 4-19: Control of heaters with off-delay timers.

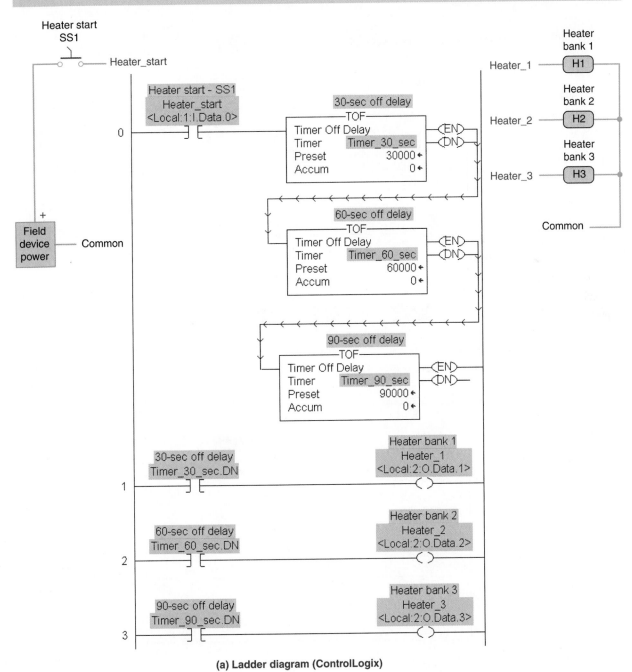

(a) Ladder diagram (ControlLogix)

FIGURE 4-19: (Continued).

Program Tags - MainProgram

Scope: MainProgram ▼   Show: Show All ▼   Sort: Tag Name ▼

Tag Name △	Alias For	Base Tag	Type	Style	Description
Heater_start	Local:1:I.Data.0(C)	Local:1:I.Data.0(C)	BOOL	Decimal	Heater start - SS1
+ Pump_timer			TIMER		Drain pump delay timer
+ Timer_30_sec			TIMER		30 sec off delay
+ Timer_60_sec			TIMER		60 sec off delay
+ Timer_90_sec			TIMER		90 sec off delay
Heater_1	Local:2:O.Data.1(C)	Local:2:O.Data.1(C)	BOOL	Decimal	Heater bank 1
Heater_2	Local:2:O.Data.2(C)	Local:2:O.Data.2(C)	BOOL	Decimal	Heater bank 2
Heater_3	Local:2:O.Data.3(C)	Local:2:O.Data.3(C)	BOOL	Decimal	Heater bank 3
*	▼				

(b) Tag database file (ControlLogix)

logic are part of the ControlLogix display format to indicate that the rung was too large to be displayed in a single horizontal line.) The timers are identified by their tag names, Timer_30_sec, Timer_60_sec, and Timer_90_sec. When the heater start switch, tag Heater_start, is held closed, all three TOF timer EN and DN bits transition to true, so the outputs (tags Heater_1, Heater_2, and Heater_3) in rungs 1, 2, and 3 are true. As a result, heater banks 1, 2, and 3 are turned on. After the start [normally open (NO) momentary selector] switch is released, all three timers start timing. Heater 1 turns off after 30 seconds, heater 2 turns off after 60 seconds, and heater 3 turns off after 90 seconds. This application uses the standard ladder logic described in Figure 4-13(b) with a momentary contact for the trigger.

This example illustrates the use of a TOF timer with an NO momentary contact field device. Since the TOF timing operation is triggered with a true to false transition of the timer rung, the momentary selector switch in this example makes it an ideal trigger for the TOF timer. The TOF timer done bit becomes true when the rung is true and remains true until the accumulator reaches the preset value. As a result, the combination of an NO momentary switch and the done bit of a TOF timer is ideal for this timed off control of an output. In comparison, if a TON timer is used, then the rung must

remain true until the preset value is reached. This requires a maintain contact switch or a sealing instruction if a momentary switch is used [see Figure 4-12(c) and (d)].

There are several changes in the ladder logic since the ControlLogix processor is used. The timer outputs can be placed in series on a single rung instead of having three parallel outputs. Also, tag names are used in place of the file number addresses used with the PLC 5 and SLC 500 systems. Finally, the aliases for the tag names are included to identify the input and output module racks, the slot numbers, and the terminal numbers. Review the solution's tag names and the information in the tag name database displayed in Figure 4-19(b). Each of the timer cells can be expanded (click on the + in front of the tag name) to display all the timer data. You may want to review this addressing format in Chapter 3, and then read this solution again.

4-9 CASCADED TIMERS

When one timer's output triggers another timer's input, those timers are referred to as *cascaded*. Cascaded timers are used when there is a need of a time delay that exceeds the maximum time delay capability of a single timer. Figure 4-20 illustrates cascaded timers used to achieve an extended time delay of 43,200 seconds, or 12 hours. The

FIGURE 4-20: Cascaded timers.

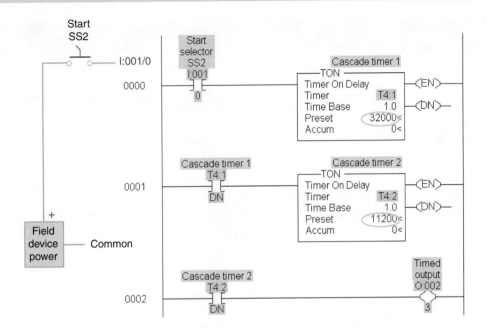

(a) Ladder diagram (PLC-5)

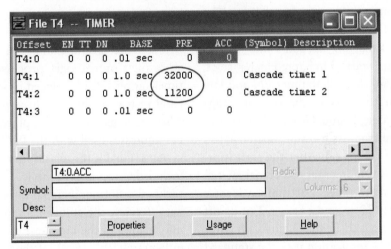

(b) Timer data file (PLC-5)

addressing format for the PLC 5 processor is used in this example solution.

Note that in Figure 4-20 the timer done bit (T4:1/DN) of timer 1 is used to make rung 1 active and start the second timer. The preset value of T4:1 is 32,000 (the maximum of this timer) and the preset value of T4:2 is 11,200. When the start switch is closed, I:001/0 is true, rung 0 becomes true, and T4:1 begins to increment the accumulator. After the T4:1 accumulator reaches 32,000, its done bit becomes true, causing the

T4:2 timer accumulator to begin to increment. When the T4:2 timer accumulator reaches 11,200, its done bit turns on O:002/3 and signals a time delay equal to 43,200 seconds. Figure 4-20 indicates that one timer's done bit is the input to another timer, hence these timers are cascaded.

Except for the input and output instruction addressing, the PLC 5 ladder logic is the same as the SLC 500 displayed in the earlier figures. The timer data file for the PLC 5 system is shown in Figure 4-20(b). Although four timers are

FIGURE 4-22: (Continued).

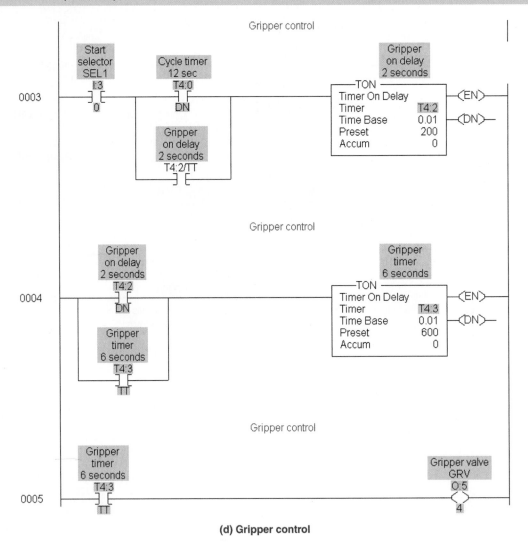

(d) Gripper control

4-11 CONVERSION OF RELAY LOGIC TIMER LADDERS TO PLC LOGIC

Conversion of relay ladder logic to an equivalent PLC ladder solution was introduced in Section 3-11-5 with relay ladders containing only input instructions and output coils. When mechanical or electronic timers are present in the relay ladders, they must be converted as well. The following conversion rules for timers are appended to the initial rule set in Section 3-11-5.

1. Replace the on-delay relay timer (NO timed closed type) with a TON PLC timer.

2. Replace the off-delay relay timer (NO timed open type) with a TOF PLC timer.

3. Select the time base so that the timing resolution meets the requirements of the application.

4. Set the preset value so that the product of the time base and the preset value equal the delay time value.

5. In an on-delay conversion, replace the NO timed contact with an XIC instruction addressed with the done bit of the PLC timer. If the NC relay timer contact is used, then replace it with an XIO instruction addressed with the done bit of the PLC timer.

6. In an off-delay conversion, replace the NO timed contact with an XIC instruction

FIGURE 4-22: (Continued).

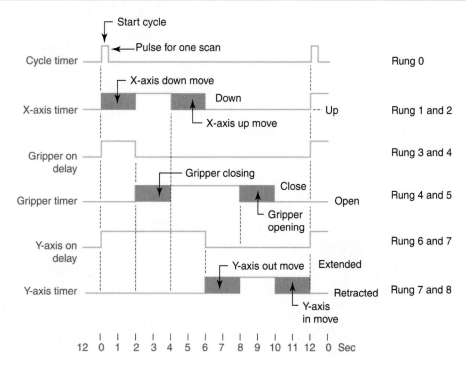

(b) Two-axis timing diagram

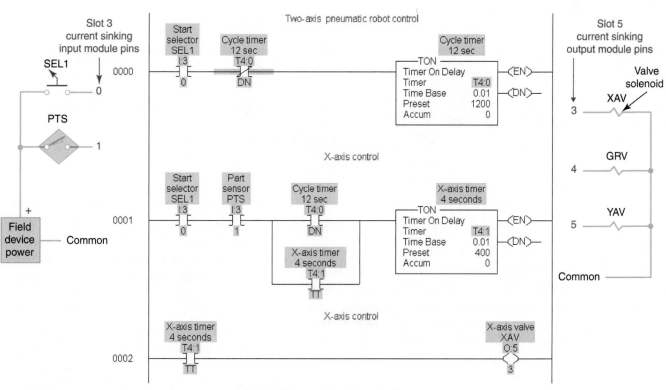

(c) Cycle timer and x-axis control

3. Start with the waveform for the initial sequential machine action and work through each step or stage in the machine operation. Sequential machines operate in steps and often the previous step triggers the following step.

In this example the process cycle timer is addressed first, then the motion of the X-axis, then the gripper, and finally the Y-axis. The completion of one timed operation triggers the next timer process.

4. Write the input Boolean logic equation to control the timer instruction and the output actuator. This is often a trial-and-error technique where you try a solution and then modify it.

In rung 1, for example, X-AXIS AND PTS AND (CYCLE TIMER DN sealed by X-AXIS TIMER TT). The sealing instruction is needed because the cycle timer done bit is only true for one scan.

5. Link the standard timer ladders together and verify that the solution satisfies the problem requirements.

For this example, see the robot control ladder in Figure 4-22(c) through (e).

The following comments summarize the operation of the robot control ladder solution.

- Rung 0 is a pulse generator (preset value establishes the time between cycle start pulses), and placing the done bit on an XIO instruction in the timer's input logic makes the pulse width equal to one scan.

- The Start selector switch, SEL1, is placed in the logic rung for each timer (rung 0, 1, 3, and 6) so that the system can be reset with that instruction.

- The instructions used to make the timer instruction active are all done bits (rungs 1, 3, 4, 6, and 7) that are only active for one scan. As a result, these timer activation bits are sealed with the timer timing bit to keep the instruction active until the accumulator is equal to the preset values.

FIGURE 4-22: Two-axis pneumatic robot control.

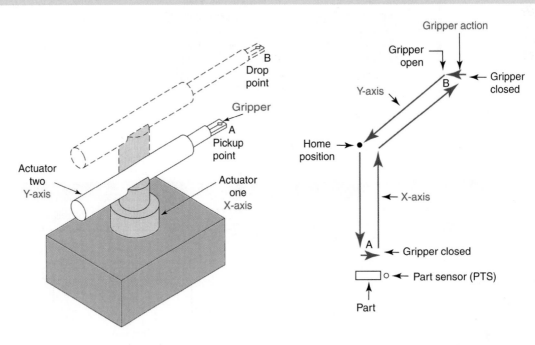

(a) Two-axis robot motion

FIGURE 4-21: Two-handed machine control with anti–tie down.

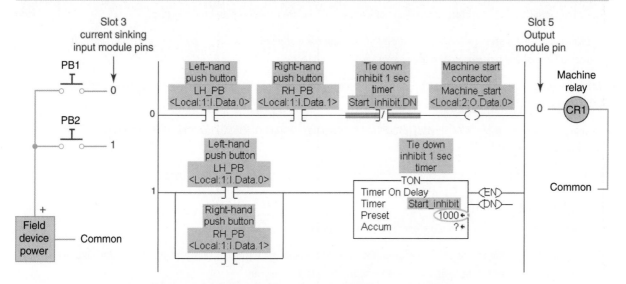

(a) Anti-tie down ladder logic

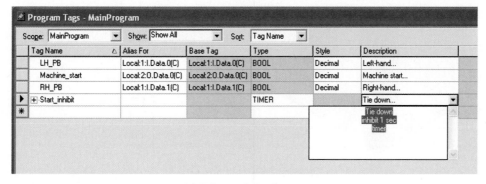

(b) Tag value dialog box

(c) Edit tag dialog box

machine is inhibited because the timer done bit, *Start_inhibit.DN,* becomes true and the XIO instruction addressed by this bit in rung 0 is then false. The two hand PBs must be in parallel in order that either can enable the timer so the logic equation is:

$$\text{Timer enable} = \text{LH\_PB OR RH\_PB}$$

The circuit for a ControlLogix processor satisfying the control requirement is illustrated in Figure 4-21(a). Review the ladder logic operation to verify that it satisfies the control description.

The tag dialog boxes are displayed in Figure 4-21(b) and (c). The TON timers in ControlLogix have a fixed 0.001 second time base so a preset of 1000 produces a 1-second delay (1000 × 0.001 s = 1 s). The tag data base in Figure 4-21(b) is in the monitor mode and shows the current value of all tags; as a result, the 1000 appears as the preset value. When the system is running all parameter can be monitored. Figure 4-21(c) illustrates the edit tag mode for the tag data base. Interface data is presented and the method used for entering instruction descriptions using a drop down text box is illustrated.

EXAMPLE 4-5

It is common in automation systems to use timers to set the extension and retraction time for a pneumatic actuator when the cylinder does not have end-of-travel sensors. The pneumatic robot in Figure 4-22(a) is used for material handling and the axes and gripper cylinders do not have end-of-travel sensors. Use 2 seconds for actuator extension and retraction and to open and close the gripper. A cycle is started when the start selector switch is on and when the pickup sensor indicates that a part is in the pickup location. Use the timing diagram in Figure 4-22(b) and the interface information in Figure 4-22(c).

SOLUTION

When empirical programming is used, there are numerous valid solutions to control problems of this type. One may be more efficient (less ladder rungs) than others, but all work equally well.

The cycle time for the robot is 12 seconds with the following sequence starting when the start selector and part sensor are true: X-axis down (4 seconds), gripper closes (6 seconds), X-axis up (2 seconds), Y-axis extends (4 seconds), Y-axis retracts (2 seconds). A study of the timing diagram reveals that some of the actions of the actuators overlap. For example, the X-axis is down for 4 seconds and the gripper closes during the last 2-seconds that the X-axis is down. Verify this overlap on the waveform. Also, there are three waveforms (X-axis timer, gripper timer, and Y-axis timer) that specify the motion of the actuators. However, there are two waveforms (gripper on delay and Y-axis on delay) that are just used to delay the start of those axes motions. For example, the gripper solenoid must be turned on (closed) 2 seconds after the start of the cycle, so a 2-second timer is used to achieve this delay and also to trigger the start of the gripper timer. The cycle is synchronized (cycle timer) with a pulse that occurs every 12 seconds. The axes and gripper waveforms are listed in Figure 4-22(b). Study these waveforms and the ladder logic in Figure 4-22(c) for the X-axis control, Figure 4-22(d) for the gripper control, and Figure 4-22(e) for the Y-axis control as you proceed.

The following steps are added to the empirical design process in Chapter 3 when timers are present.

1. *Draw a timing diagram for all outputs.* The first step in the discrete control of a sequential machine is to generate a timing diagram that shows the on/off sequence for each of the actuators and other field devices. If the timing of input switches and sensors is important, then they are included as well.

   The timing diagram for the robot in this example is displayed in Figure 4-22(b), and the ladder solution is shown in Figure 4-22(c), (d), and (e).

2. Use the timer operation descriptions in Table 4-1 and Figure 4-9 plus the standard timer ladder logics in Figures 4-12 and 4-13 to identify the type of timer ladder(s) to consider for each waveform. Each waveform requires the timer instruction in one rung and the timer output in a second rung.

   All the waveforms in this example could be produced with TON timers. The cycle timer ladder (rung 0) is found in the standard ladders logic, Figure 4-12(e). The standard ladder in Figure 4-12(d) is used for the output timers (rungs 1 and 2, 4 and 5, and 7 and 8) and the standard ladder in Figure 4-12(c) is used for the output on delay timers (rungs 3 and 4, and 6 and 7).

shown, only the two used in the program have the data illustrated. Timer data values can be changed using this pop-up file display. You may want to review the PLC 5 addressing format in Chapter 3, and then read this solution again.

4-10 EMPIRICAL DESIGN PROCESS WITH PLC TIMERS

The empirical design process, introduced in Section 3-11-4, is an organized approach to the design of PLC ladder logic programs. However, the term *empirical* implies that some rework of the design after it is finished is often necessary. If you tried some of the designs at the end of Chapter 3, then you may understand that the process often does not lead directly to a complete design. This troublesome aspect of the empirical process should become more obvious when timers are added into the design process.

4-10-1 Adding Timers to the Process

The first step in using timers in PLC ladder designs is to know the operation of the three types of timers summarized in Table 4-1 and Figure 4-9

and all the standard timer circuits illustrated in Figures 4-12 and 4-13. Stop now and review them if necessary.

When a timer is added to a ladder it affects two rungs: one rung that makes the timer instruction (TON, TOF, RTN) active, and a second rung that uses a timer output (EN, TT, or DN) to control a system parameter. The complete empirical process is listed in Section 3-11-4; modifications for timers follow and are listed in the solution to Example 4-5.

Step 1: (Write the process description): Include a complete description of time delay(s) required in the process. Note especially the trigger for the delay(s) that is required, the outputs that are delayed, and if it is an on-delay or an off-delay.

Step 2: (Write Boolean equations for all field devices): One of the Boolean expressions should indicate the logic necessary to enable the timer(s). Also, timer output bits should be added into the other Boolean expressions where timers are controlling process outputs.

Examples 4-4 and 4-5 demonstrate how timer ladder design is added into the design process.

EXAMPLE 4-4

Design a ladder logic system to provide two-handed control for a production machine. Two-handed control requires that the operator use both hands to initiate the start cycle of the machine. However, operators tape down one of the hand controls with duct tape so that they can load the machine with one hand and start it with the other. The safety demands a two-handed control circuit with anti-tie down capability. The left and right start push buttons must be operated within a half-second window or the machine will not start. A simpler solution without anti-tie down was developed in Example 3-13; review that before continuing.

Solution

As long as the second hand switch closes within 0.5 second after the first switch closure, then the machine would be allowed to start. If the two switch closures fall outside this 0.5-second window, the machine is off. A look at the standard timer ladder logic in Figure 4-12 indicates that circuit (b) could be used. However, rung 2 is changed as follows:

- The two push button start switches are added to rung 2.

- The XIC instruction addressed by the timer DN bit is changed to an XIO instruction.

The Boolean logic to start the machine is:

Machine on = LH_PB AND RH_PB AND NOT START_INHIBIT

The first push button contact that closes starts the 1 second timer. If the second push button's contact closes outside the 1-second window, then the timer opens the start circuit in rung 0 before the second push button contact can close and start the machine. The

---

3. Start with the waveform for the initial sequential machine action and work through each step or stage in the machine operation. Sequential machines operate in steps and often the previous step triggers the following step.

   In this example the process cycle timer is addressed first, then the motion of the X-axis, then the gripper, and finally the Y-axis. The completion of one timed operation triggers the next timer process.

4. Write the input Boolean logic equation to control the timer instruction and the output actuator. This is often a trial-and-error technique where you try a solution and then modify it.

   In rung 1, for example, X-AXIS AND PTS AND (CYCLE TIMER DN sealed by X-AXIS TIMER TT). The sealing instruction is needed because the cycle timer done bit is only true for one scan.

5. Link the standard timer ladders together and verify that the solution satisfies the problem requirements.

   For this example, see the robot control ladder in Figure 4-22(c) through (e).

   The following comments summarize the operation of the robot control ladder solution.

   - Rung 0 is a pulse generator (preset value establishes the time between cycle start pulses), and placing the done bit on an XIO instruction in the timer's input logic makes the pulse width equal to one scan.
   - The Start selector switch, SEL1, is placed in the logic rung for each timer (rung 0, 1, 3, and 6) so that the system can be reset with that instruction.
   - The instructions used to make the timer instruction active are all done bits (rungs 1, 3, 4, 6, and 7) that are only active for one scan. As a result, these timer activation bits are sealed with the timer timing bit to keep the instruction active until the accumulator is equal to the preset values.

FIGURE 4-22: Two-axis pneumatic robot control.

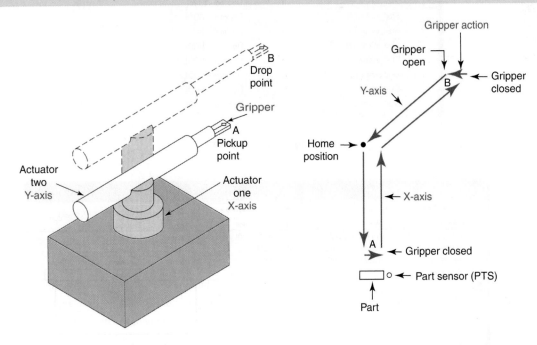

(a) Two-axis robot motion

FIGURE 4-22: (Continued).

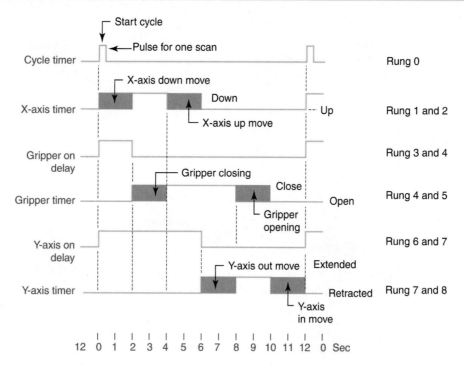

(b) Two-axis timing diagram

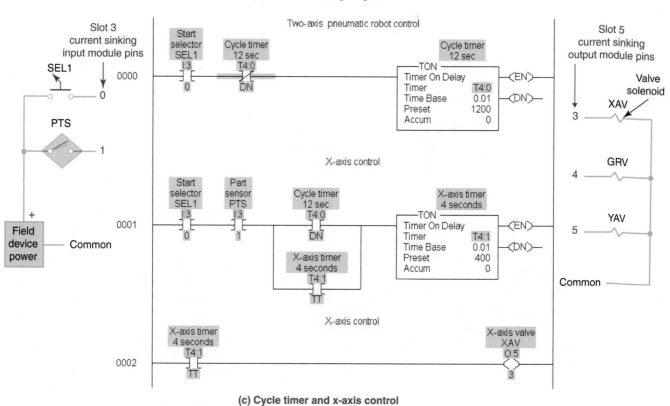

(c) Cycle timer and x-axis control

FIGURE 4-22: (Continued).

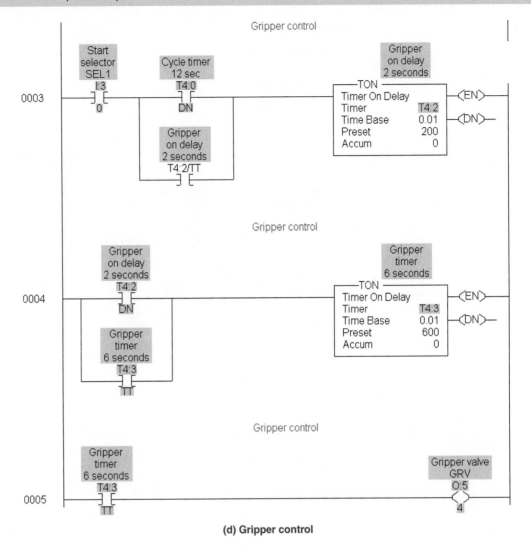

(d) Gripper control

4-11 CONVERSION OF RELAY LOGIC TIMER LADDERS TO PLC LOGIC

Conversion of relay ladder logic to an equivalent PLC ladder solution was introduced in Section 3-11-5 with relay ladders containing only input instructions and output coils. When mechanical or electronic timers are present in the relay ladders, they must be converted as well. The following conversion rules for timers are appended to the initial rule set in Section 3-11-5.

1. Replace the on-delay relay timer (NO timed closed type) with a TON PLC timer.
2. Replace the off-delay relay timer (NO timed open type) with a TOF PLC timer.

3. Select the time base so that the timing resolution meets the requirements of the application.
4. Set the preset value so that the product of the time base and the preset value equal the delay time value.
5. In an on-delay conversion, replace the NO timed contact with an XIC instruction addressed with the done bit of the PLC timer. If the NC relay timer contact is used, then replace it with an XIO instruction addressed with the done bit of the PLC timer.
6. In an off-delay conversion, replace the NO timed contact with an XIC instruction

FIGURE 4-22: (Continued).

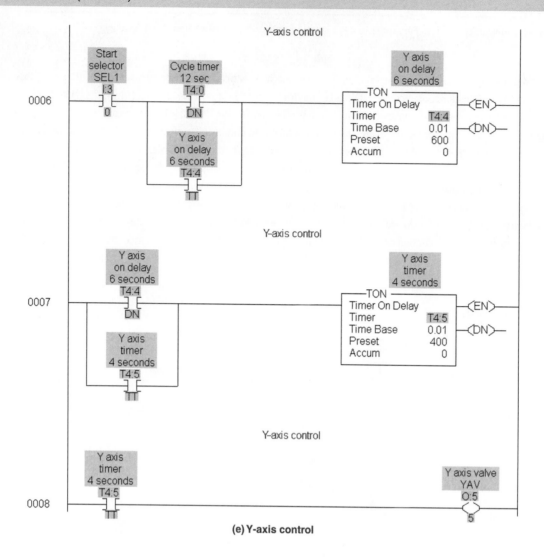

(e) Y-axis control

addressed with the done bit of the PLC timer. If the NC relay timer contact is used, then replace it with an XIO instruction addressed with the done bit of the PLC timer.

7. If an instantaneous NO contact on the mechanical or electronic time delay relay is used, then use an XIC instruction address with the enable bit from the PLC timer.

8. If an instantaneous NC contact on the mechanical or electronic time delay relay is used, then use an XIO instruction address with the enable bit from the PLC timer.

The conversion of input field devices—switches and sensors—plus output field devices—actua-tors, and contactors—follows the guidelines specified in Section 3-11-5.

4-12 TROUBLESHOOTING LADDER RUNS WITH TIMERS

Some guidelines and a systematic procedure for troubleshooting PLC systems were presented in Section 3-12. In this chapter the troubleshooting of the timer instruction is addressed.

4-12-1 Troubleshooting Timer Ladder Logic

The most difficult ladder timer programs to verify are those with multiple cascaded timers with small preset time values. Execution is often too

EXAMPLE 4-6

Convert the relay ladder timer circuit in Figure 4-3 to a PLC solution using a PLC 5 system from Allen-Bradley.

SOLUTION

Refer to Figures 4-3 and 4-23(a) as you read the solution. The TMR1 mechanical timer is an on-delay timer with an NO timed close contact (TMR1-2) and an NO instantaneous contact (TMR1-1). The TMR1 relay is replaced by a TON timer (T4:0). The TMR1-1 instantaneous contact is replaced by an XIC PLC instruction with the address T4:0/EN. The TMR1-2 NO timed closed contact is replaced by an XIC PLC instruction with the address T4:0/DN. The input contacts and output coil are replaced with PLC logic symbols as illustrated in Figure 4-23(a). Now the ladder is examined to determine if simplification is possible.

The solution in Figure 4-23(a) functions exactly like the wired relay ladder logic; however, the ladder logic can be simplified. The PLC ladder in Figure 4-23(b) works equally well but does not have the stop push button contact in rung 1. The stop instruction is not necessary because the timer is reset when the stop instruction in rung 0 is active. A timer reset makes the done bit 0, which turns off the motor.

The I/O Configuration dialog box for the PLC 5 is illustrated in Figure 4-23(c). Note that all the data necessary for addressing an instruction are provided. Double-clicking on the Chassis Type data opens the list of the modules present.

FIGURE 4-23: Relay ladder logic conversion.

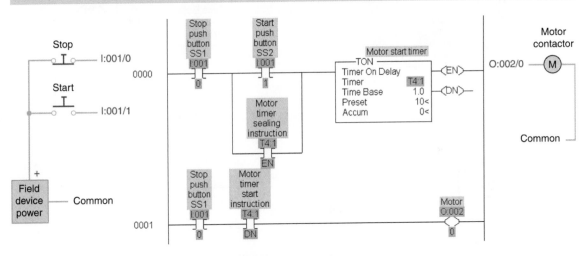

(a) Exact conversion

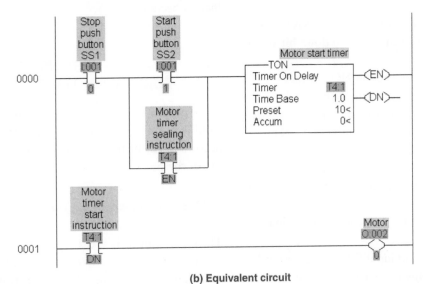

(b) Equivalent circuit

FIGURE 4-23: Relay ladder logic conversion.

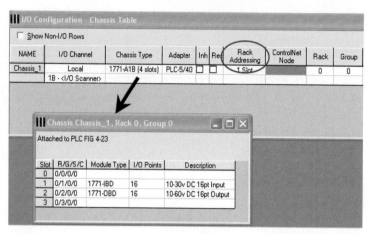

(c) PLC 5 I/O configuration

fast to determine if the syntax is correct. One or more of the following suggestions may help.

- Test the timers starting with the first in the sequence, and then add one timer at a time until the total sequence is operational.
- If the preset times are very small, increase all times proportionately to initially verify the correct sequential operation.
- Use the timer dialog boxes like those illustrated in Figure 4-20(b) for PLC 5 and SLC 500 and in Figure 4-21(b) for the Control-Logix timer instructions to track timer data as the program executes.

Often PLC programs cannot be tested on the manufacturing process, so the use of PLC simulators from Allen-Bradley for the three processors is necessary for program verification and troubleshooting. The simulator permits full execution of the ladder program in the off-line mode to verify that proper operation of the system was achieved in the ladder program.

4-12-2 Temporary End Instruction

The temporary end (TND) instruction is useful for troubleshooting any PLC program, but it is especially helpful for timers. The TND instruction is an output instruction and is shown in Figure 4-24 in rung 2. TND is used to progressively debug a program, or conditionally omit the balance of your current program file. It is placed as an output on the rung with input instruction logic. When the logic preceding this output instruction is true, TND stops the processor from scanning the rest of the program file, updates the I/O, and resumes scanning at rung 0 of the main program. If the TND instruction's rung is false, the processor continues the scan until the next TND instruction or the END statement.

The robot program in Figure 4-22(c) is modified by placing the TND instruction after rung 1. The modified program is shown in Figure 4-24. The done bit on the timer makes the TND rung true and program terminates after rung 1. This is a way to verify that the X-axis timer ladder logic is operating properly. The instruction could be moved through the program and an axis test added with each move down the ladder logic.

4-13 LOCATION OF THE INSTRUCTIONS

The location of instructions from this chapter in the Allen-Bradley programming software is indicated in Figure 4-25.

FIGURE 4-24: Temporary end instruction.

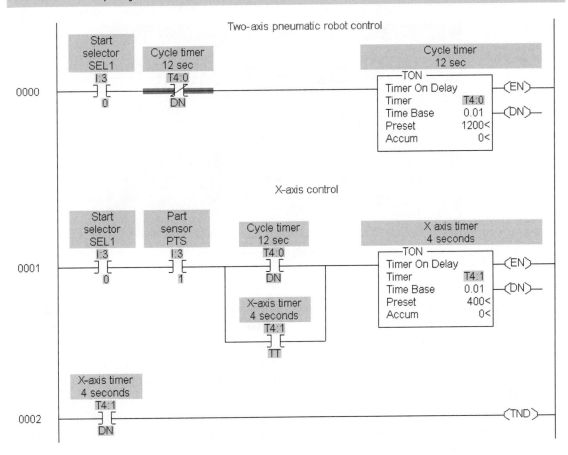

FIGURE 4-25: Location of instructions described in this chapter.

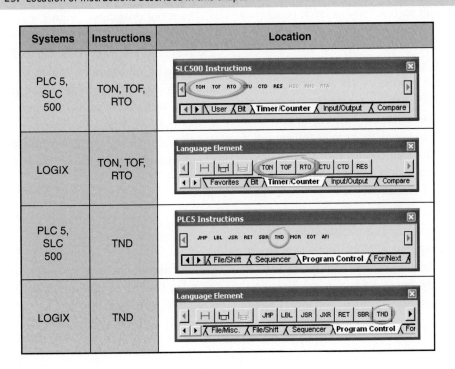

CHAPTER 5

Programming Counters

5-1 GOALS AND OBJECTIVES

There are two principal goals of this chapter. The first goal is to provide the student with information on the operation and functions of hardware counters—both mechanical and electronic. The second goal is to show how the programmable counter instructions are applied to the solution of automation problems using Allen-Bradley PLCs.

After completing this chapter you should be able to:

- Describe the operation of mechanical and electrical counters.
- Describe the program data used to define counter operation.
- Generate and analyze ladder diagrams for the up counter, down counter, and up/down counter in industrial applications.
- Implement cascade counters to achieve high counting requirements.
- Use the done bit, enable bit, and overflow/underflow bits to control automated systems.
- Develop ladder logic solutions using counter instructions for Allen-Bradley PLC 5, SLC 500, and Logix systems.

- Convert relay ladder logic counter rungs to their PLC equivalent.
- Describe troubleshooting techniques for counter ladder logic.

5-2 MECHANICAL AND ELECTRONIC COUNTERS

Mechanical counters, illustrated in Figure 5-1, use shaft rotations to increment or decrement numerical wheels, thus displaying an accumulated count. Counters are available with a push button reset, a lever reset, or no reset, and actuating the reset causes the counter display to indicate all zeros. The counter without a reset is typically used as an elapsed time meter.

Electronic counters, illustrated in Figure 5-2, have an LCD numerical readout and can count up, down, or up and down depending on the application. After selecting the operating mode and function, input pulses drive the counter's electronics, which in turn drive the LCD readout. Front panel reset, remote reset, or no reset styles are available.

A typical application of electronic counters is shown in Figure 5-3, where a photoelectric

FIGURE 5-1: Mechanical counters.

Courtesy of Redington Counters, Inc.

FIGURE 5-2: Electronic counters.

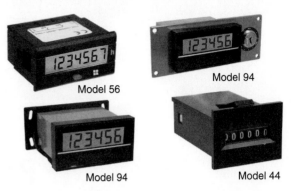

Model 56

Model 94

Model 94

Model 44

Courtesy of Redington Counters, Inc.

sensor in the through beam mode is used to count soft drink bottles moving along a conveyor. The output of the receiver is the input to an electronic counter.

5-3 INTRODUCTION TO ALLEN-BRADLEY COUNTERS

PLC counter instructions are an important industrial automation application. Allen-Bradley and other vendors have *up* and *down* counter instructions, with some vendors offering an *up/down* counter instruction as well. Allen-Bradley permits up/down counting through programming with individual up and down instructions. *Counters* are similar to timers, except counters accumulate the changes in an external trigger sig-

nal whereas timers increment using an internal clock. PLC counters are generally triggered by a change in an input field device that causes a false to true transition of the counter ladder rung. PLC counters are output instructions that serve the same function in control systems as mechanical and electronic counters. Specifically, counters turn on or turn off an output field device after the counter accumulator has reached a preset value.

PLC count settings can be easily modified and counters can be added to an application through the PLC software without wiring modifications. Since the PLC counters are virtual devices existing only in the PLC software, the number of counters available is large and is only limited by file number allocation. In addition, PLC counters have extremely high accuracy and repeatability

FIGURE 5-3: Application of electronic counter.

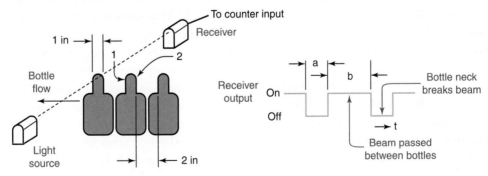

Source: Rehg and Sartori, Industrial Electronics, *1st Edition, © 2006, Reprinted by permission of Pearson Education, Inc., Upper Saddle River, NJ.*

because the counting function is implemented in software using microprocessor technology.

Allen-Bradley counters, illustrated in Figure 5-4, are schematically represented as a block with counter parameters displayed inside. Counter parameters include:

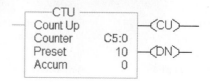

FIGURE 5-4: PLC counter block.

```
    CTU
    Count Up                 <CU>
    Counter       C5:0
    Preset          10       <DN>
    Accum            0
```

- **Counter Number:** This number identifies the counter file and data. Allen-Bradley PLC 5 and SLC 500 processors use a counter file, identified by the letter C, that has a default file number of 5. A numeric value is appended to the C5 file to indicate the counter number. For example, C5:0, C5:1, and C5:250 are three counters numbered 0, 1, and 250. These PLC 5 PLCs can support up to 1000 counters numbered 0 through 999 in the C5 file area. If additional counters are required, files 9 through 255 can be used for additional blocks of counters. The colon (:) is a delimiter used to separate the file number and the counter number.

  The Logix processors use a tag name for the counters, such as Product_count. This tag is then assigned a data type named *counter*. The counter tag or number must be unique and only one up or down counter can have that specific number or name symbol in a ladder solution.

- **Preset Value (PRE):** This is the count value or set point that the counter must accumulate before the counter output is active or true. In Allen-Bradley PLC 5 and SLC 500 systems, the PRE value has a range of −32,768 to +32,767. The values are stored in binary form with the negative number stored as a 2's complement. Signed numbers and 2's complement arithmetic are covered at the beginning of the next chapter. The ControlLogix system permits preset values between +2,147,483,647 or −2,147,483,648, which is the range of values for a double integer.

- **Accumulated Value (ACC):** This register or tag stores the accumulated number of counts or false to true transitions of the counter rung. The ACC is generally set to zero at the beginning of the count. In PLC 5 and SLC 500 systems the ACC values can range from

−32,768 to +32,767. Any value in that range can be loaded into the accumulator, but the accumulator value will always be zero when the counter is reset. The ControlLogix system permits the count value to reach +2,147,483,647 or −2,147,483,648, before an overflow indication bit is generated.

The PRE and ACC values are 16 bit integers stored in memory registers for the PLC 5 and SLC 500 systems. When they are referenced, the address must specify the integer word value for that parameter. For example, if the accumulator is addressed as *C5:6.ACC*, then that references the 16 bit integer register with the accumulator value for counter 6. An address such as *C5:4.PRE* would address the integer word with the preset value for the number 4 counter.

Tags are used in the ControlLogix processor to identify the counters. So an address such as *Counter_1.ACC* references the 32 bit accumulator value for the counter named *Counter_1*. A similar address for the preset value would be *Counter_1.PRE*.

As a result, the PRE and ACC values for all Allen-Bradley PLCs can be set or used by other PLC instructions by just referencing the address of these parameters. In later chapters, the ACC values are frequently referenced in other PLC input instructions for program control.

5-3-1 Counter Output Bits

The bits used to control program flow and to turn on and turn off output field devices in all Allen-Bradley processors include: *count up (CU) enable bit, count down (CD) enable bit, count up overflow (OV) bit, count down underflow (UN) bit,* and *done (DN) bit*. A truth table describing

TABLE 5-1 Counter truth table.

Up-counter bits	are TRUE if	are FALSE if
Counter enable	Counter rung is true.	Counter rung is false or reset instruction is initiated.
Counter overflow	Accumulated value wraps around from positive maximum value to negative maximum value.	Accumulated value is equal to or less than the positive maximum value.
Counter done	The accumulated value is equal to or greater than the preset value.	The accumulated value is less than the preset value.

(a) Truth table for the up-counter bits

Down-counter bits	are TRUE if	are FALSE if
Counter enable	Counter rung is true.	Counter rung is false or reset instruction is initiated.
Counter underflow	Accumulated value wraps around from negative maximum value to positive maximum value.	Accumulated value is equal to or greater than the maximum negative value.
Counter done	The accumulated value is equal to or greater than the preset value.	The accumulated value is less than the preset value.

(b) Truth table for the down-counter bits

counter output bit operation is illustrated in Table 5-1. Review that table and then read the following bit descriptions.

- **Count Up (CU) Enable Bit:** CU is active or true when the input logic on the counter rung makes the up counter rung true or active. The CU enable bit is off when the up counter rung is false or inactive.
- **Count Down (CD) Enable Bit:** CD is active or true when the input logic on the counter rung makes the down counter rung true or active. The CD enable bit is off when the down counter rung is false or inactive.
- **Count Up Overflow (OV) Bit:** OV is associated with an up counter and is active or true when the counter increments above the maximum positive value or +32,767 for

PLC 5 and SLC 500 processors. On the next up count the counter will wrap around to the maximum negative number, or −32,768 for these PLCs. For example, if the ACC is at +32,767, then the ACC will have a −32,768 value after the next false to true transition of the input logic. For all additional false to true transitions of the input the ACC will increment toward 0. The range for the counter accumulator is illustrated in Figure 5-5.

- **Count Down Underflow (UN) Bit:** UN is associated with a down counter and is active or true when the counter decrements below the maximum negative value, or −32,768 for PLC 5 and SLC 500 processors. On the next down count the counter will wrap around to the maximum positive number or 32,767 for

FIGURE 5-5: PLC 5 and SLC 500 accumulator range.

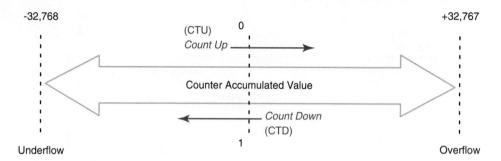

those Allen-Bradley PLCs. For example, if the ACC is at −32,768, then the ACC will have a +32,767 value after the next false to true transition of the input logic. For all additional false to true transitions of the input the ACC will decrement toward 0. Review Figure 5-5 for the range of the accumulator and values for the UN bit.

- Done (DN) Bit: DN is true or a 1 for all counters when the ACC value is equal to or greater than the PRE value. It is false or a 0 when the ACC is less than the PRE value.

Three PLC counter functions are introduced in the following sections of this chapter: the *up counter* (CTU), the *down counter* (CTD), and the *up/down counter,* which is a combination of the CTU and CTD. PLC counters are retentive, that is, whatever number is in the counter accumulator at power shutdown remains unchanged upon power-up. Also, the reset (RES) instruction sets the accumulator count to zero for the Allen-Bradley up and down counters.

5-4 ALLEN-BRADLEY COUNTER AND RESET INSTRUCTIONS

The counter instructions for the Allen-Bradley (AB) PLC 5, SLC 500, and Logix processors operate in nearly identical fashion. Therefore, most of the example solutions in this chapter use the SLC 500 instructions; however, PLC 5 and ControlLogix instructions are used in a few examples to illustrate the differences in the three systems.

AB PLCs have two counter instructions, count up (CTU) and count down (CTD). In addition,

the reset (RES) instruction is used to initialize both types of counters. The SLC 500 and MicroLogix PLCs also have a high-speed counter (HSC) instruction. Counter addressing for each of the Allen-Bradley processors is addressed in the next several sections.

5-4-1 PLC 5 and SLC 500 Counter and Reset Addressing

The counter instructions for the PLC 5 and SLC 500 processors use the same default address file, C5, and have the same instruction structure. The counter registers and control bits are located in three words, just as in the AB timer instructions. Review the bit and word layout illustrated in Figure 5-6. Note that word 0 contains the output bit data, word 1 is the preset value, and word 2 is the accumulator value. The addresses of all bits and registers are used by other instructions for logical control or for changing counter parameters.

Addressing counter registers and outputs. The address structure for counters in the PLC 5 and SLC 500 processors is like the format described in Chapter 4 for the timers and has the following format:

$$Cf:e.s/b$$

Figure 5-7 describes each element in this timer address format. The file number, f, is 5, but file numbers 9 through 255 are also available if the 256 counters in file 5 are not sufficient. The element number, e, is the counter identification number. Each file (5 and 9 through 255) has 256 (0 through 255) counters available. The counter word number, s, identifies which of the three

FIGURE 5-6: PLC 5 and SLC 500 three-word counter files.

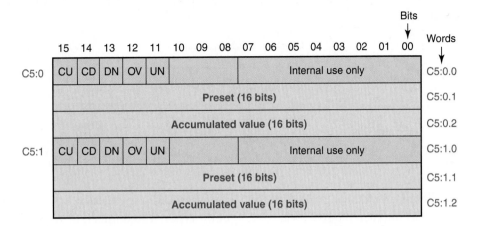

words (0, 1, or 2) in each counter file is being addressed. The first words for the two counters in Figure 5-6 are C5:0.0 and C5:1.0. The final entry in a counter address is the bit number, b, within the counter word. Each output bit is addressed using either the mnemonic letters, such as DN for the done bit, or the bit location in the register, for example, C5:0/13 for the done bit (Figure 5-6). Example counter data addresses are listed in Table 5-2. Study the counter address structure (Cf:e.s/b) and the description of each address element in Figure 5-7, and then verify that you understand what counter data is being addressed by each example in Table 5-2.

FIGURE 5-7: Counter address form for PLC 5 and SLC 500.

Element description

C	The C indicates that the address is a Counter.	
f	File number. For SLC 500 processors the default is 5. File 5 supports 256 counters (C5:0 to C5:255). If more than 256 counters are needed, then file numbers 9 to 255 are available. Each of these supports 256 counters (C9:0 to C9:255).	
:	Element delimiter	
e	Element number, e, is the number of the counter.	For file 5, e has a range of 0 to 255 counters. The same range is for e if files 9 to 255 are used. These are 3-word elements. The range is 0 to 255.
.	Word delimiter	
s	Word number, s, indicates one of the three counter words.	The value of s ranges from 0 to 2, because each counter has three addressable words.
/	Bit delimiter	
b	Bit number, b, is the bit location in the timer word.	The range is 0 to 15 for all 3 counter words, but bits 10, 11, 12, 13, 14, and 15 are the only ones used for word 0.

TABLE 5-2 Counter address format for PLC 5 and SLC 500.

Address Level	Address Format	Description
Bit	C5:0/15 or C5:0/CU	Count up enable bit – true if the counter rung is active
Bit	C5:0/14 or C5:0/CD	Count down enable bit – true if the counter rung is active
Bit	C5:0/13 or C5:0/DN	Done bit – true if the accumulator is equal to or greater than the preset value
Bit	C5:0/12 or C5:0/OV	Overflow bit – true if the accumulator is greater than +32,767
Bit	C5:0/11 or C5:0/UN	Underflow bit – true if the accumulator is less than –32,768
Word	C5:0.1 or C5:0.PRE	Preset value of the counter
Word	C5:0.2 or C5:0.ACC	Accumulated value of the counter
Bit	C5:0.1/0 or C5:0.PRE/0	Bit 0 of the preset value
Bit	C5:0.2/0 or C5:0.ACC/0	Bit 0 of the accumulated value

Figure 5-8(a) illustrates a PLC 5 and SLC 500 count up instruction, while Figure 5-8(b) illustrates the same parameter data in the counter data file dialog box. Compare the parameter data for counter 4 (C5:4) in both formats. The preset value is 25 for the count up instruction (CTU) and the instruction description is *Machine cycle counter*. When the PLC program is running, the current accumulator value is displayed in the instruction block and in the data file.

FIGURE 5-8: PLC 5 and SLC 500 counter instruction.

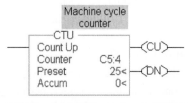

(a) PLC 5 and SLC 500 counter instruction

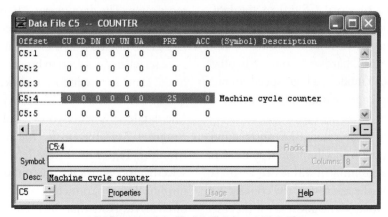

(b) Counter data file for PLC 5 and SLC 500

The count down instruction would have a similar display.

High-speed counter. The SLC 500 and MicroLogix processors have a high-speed counter (HSC) instruction built into the hardware. The HSC instruction counts high-speed pulses at a maximum pulse rate of 8k Hz. The HSC, a variation of the CTU counter, counts false to true transitions at input terminal I:0/0. The HSC is a hardware counter operating asynchronously or independent of the ladder program scan. As a result, the HSC does not count rung transitions. This means that the maximum pulse rate for the counter is not limited to the scan rate of the PLC. In contrast, the CTU counter instruction is a software instruction counting transitions (false to true) of the rung logic, so the maximum pulse rate is limited by the scan rate of the ladder program. The HSC's status or output bits and accumulator values are non-retentive, whereas the CTU instruction has retentive output bits and ACC values.

When the rung containing the HSC output instruction is enabled, the HSC instruction counts false to true transitions at input terminal I:0/0. A false input value interrupts the counting. Only fixed I/O controllers, like the MicroLogic system, that have 24 VDC inputs can use the HSC instruction, and only one HSC instruction is allowed per controller. To use the HSC with a fixed controller, a jumper in the controller must be clipped. The status bits, registers, and addressing for the HSC are the same as that used for the standard CTU counter. The HSC is always C5:0 and reads inputs on I:0/0. The HSC adds one additional status bit, called the update accumulator (UA), which is located in bit 10 of word C5:0.0 of the HSC counter data register. When the UA bit is true the accumulator register, C5:0.2, is updated to the count value in the HSC hardware counter. In other SLC 500 and PLC 5 models, a high-speed counter module is used to capture high-speed pulses.

Reset instruction. The reset (RES) instruction, introduced for timers in Chapter 4, is used to return counter accumulator values to zero. To perform this reset, the address of the counter, for example C5:3, is used as the address for the reset instruction. The overflow and underflow bits are also reset to zero when the accumulator value is reset to a value within the normal operating range. The done bit may also be reset depending on how the preset value compares with a zero accumulator value. It is important to remember that the ACC register and all output bits are held in the zero state as long as the RES instruction rung is true. The RES instruction releases the counter instruction to start counting when the reset instruction rung is false. Thus the counter is reset and disabled while the input logic of the reset rung remains true.

5-4-2 Logix Counter Instructions

The counter instruction for the ControlLogix PLC is the same as that illustrated for the PLC 5 and SLC 500 in Figure 5-8(a), except for the address format. For example, the SLC 500 counter number, such as C5:3, is replaced with a tag name such as Machine_cycle_counter. The tag name makes it easier to know the counter function in the control system. Figure 5-9(a) shows an RSLogix 5000 software ladder rung with two counters. Note that the multiple output counters are shown in series; this is another improvement offered by the 5000 software. When the input instruction Can_switch becomes active, the rung goes from false to true and both counters in the rung increment. Counters are named with any valid tag name (see Chapter 3 for tag name rules), then the Tag Properties dialog box illustrated in Figure 5-9(b) is used to assign a *COUNTER* data type to the tag. The tag name entered, for example *Total_count*, appears at the top, and the description, tag type, and data type must be added. The description can be any text desired and the default *base* type is used most often. The data type, *COUNTER*, must be selected or typed. A pop-up selection dialog box [see the dialog box on the right in Figure 5-9(b)] appears when the selection box button at the right of the Data Type window is clicked.

The counter database is shown in Figure 5-9(c). The database is accessed by double-clicking the *Program Tags* file in the file menu. With the Monitor Tags tab (lower left of illustration) selected, the values for all counter variables are displayed and parameter values can be entered or changed. Note that the preset values from the

FIGURE 5-9: Logix counter instruction.

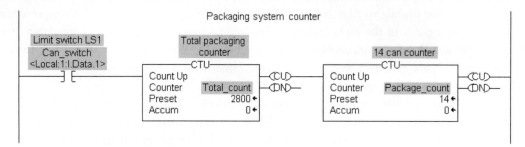

Packaging system counter

(a) RSLogix 5000 ladder with counters

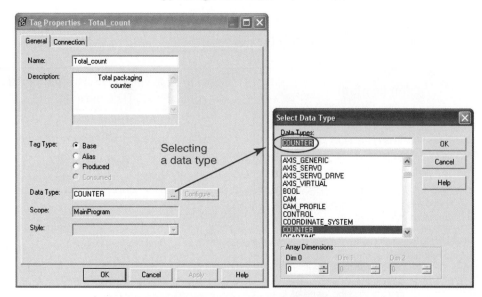

(b) Tag properties dialog box and data type list

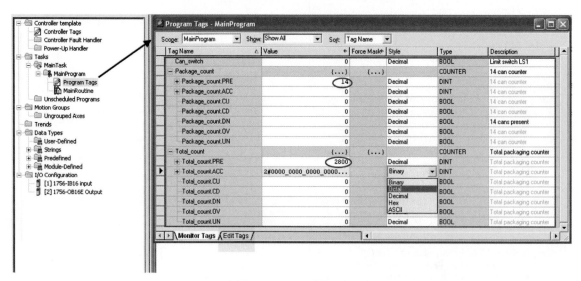

(c) Program tags dialog box

ladder display are visible. Also, the radix or base of the value is changed with the drop-down selection box (see blue highlight) that appears when you click the tag cell in the style column. The ACC display was changed from decimal to binary in the figure. Note that five radix values are offered for display of the register data. The ACC is for a double integer decimal value (two 16-bit words), so the binary representation must be 32-bit words, but the cell is not expanded. Thus only the upper 16 bits of the 32-bit word are visible.

A second input and output database is displayed when the Edit Tags tab at the bottom left of Figure 5-9(c) is selected. This representation is used to assign input and output pins for field devices, but it is not as important for internal instructions such as counters.

5-4-3 Standard Ladder Logic for Counters

Standard counter ladder logic configurations are used when counter instructions are necessary in a control program. Figure 5-10 illustrates four

FIGURE 5-10: Standard ladder logic rungs for CTU and CTD counters.

Application	Standard Ladder Logic Rungs for CTU and CTD Counters
Turn on an output field device after a preset number of false to true transitions of the input logic or turn off an output field device after a preset number of counter inputs. The input field devices are NO sensors. Every time the sensor becomes active, the counter rung and the CU bit transition from false to true and the counter accumulator increments up one count. When the ACC is equal to 10, the DN bit is set true. This causes output O:3/1 to become true and O:3/2 to become false. The counter ACC is reset to 0 when the RES instruction is true or active. The address of the RES instruction is the same as the counter. A CTU counter is shown but a CTD counter could be used for a count down application. Also, a SLC 500 format is presented, but the PLC 5 or ControlLogix could be used as well.	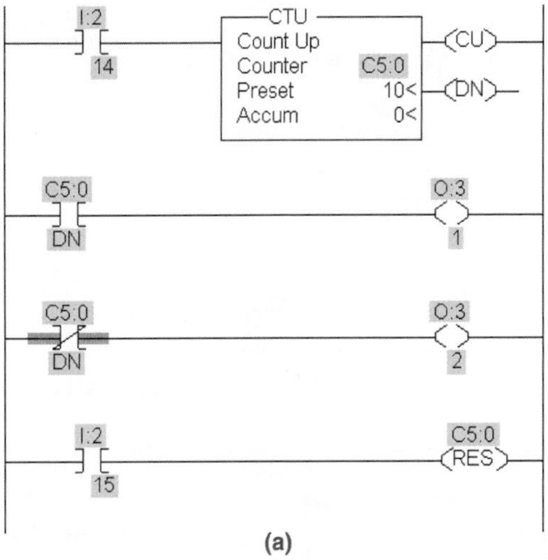 (a)
Turn on an output field device after a preset number of false to true transitions of the input logic or turn off an output field device after a preset number of counter inputs. Hold the ACC value at the PRE value when the ACC value equals the PRE value. The input field devices are NO momentary push button switches. Every time I:2/14 becomes active, the counter rung and the CU bit transition from false to true and the counter accumulator increments up one count. When the ACC is equal to 9, the DN bit is set true. This opens the counter input rung and freezes the ACC at 9. This also causes O:3/1 to become true and output O:3/2 to become false. The counter ACC is reset to 0 when the RES instruction is true or active. Note that the address of the RES instruction is the same as the counter. A CTU counter is shown but a CTD counter could be used for a count down application. Also, a SLC 500 format is presented, but the PLC 5 or ControlLogix could be used as well.	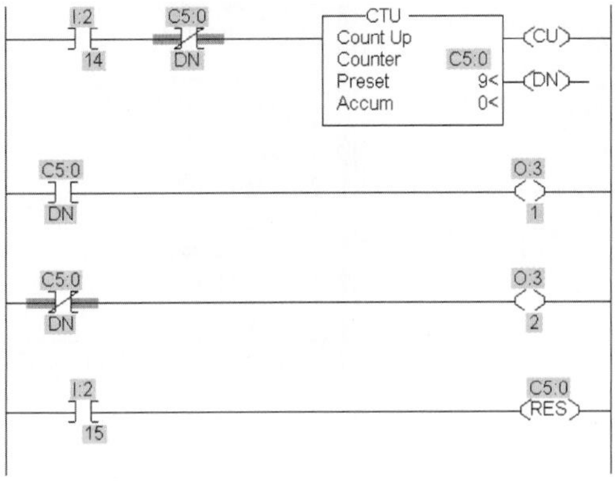 (b)

configurations with features that can be mixed and matched to solve most ladder logic requirements for counters. Read the description of the standard counter ladder configurations in the figure before continuing.

CTU/CTD Standard Ladder Logic: The application addressed in Figure 5-10(a) is for the discrete control of output field devices based on measuring the number of events that occur in a process. The counter in the figure records the number of false to true transitions of input instruction I:2/14 based on changes of an input field device. When the correct count is reached (ACC is equal to PRE), the counter done bit (DN) turns on or off field devices, depending

FIGURE 5-10: (Continued).

Application	Standard Ladder Logic Rungs for CTU and CTD Counters
Counter applications where a trigger signal pulse stretcher is needed, where trigger switch contact bounce is excessive, or where the sensor trigger signal may have several off to on transitions at the start or end of the trigger pulse. The field device is a NO sensor. When the sensor contacts close the I:2/13 instructions become true and starts the TON timer, the timer TT bit is true and increments the counter ACC by one count. The TT bit is true for 3 seconds because the TT bit is sealing I:2/13, holding the timer rung true. Changes in the input field device and I:2/13 are masked by the sealing instruction. Therefore, changes or instability of the I:2/13 trigger do not cause an unstable counter. After 3 seconds, the timer resets and the counter rung returns to the false state. In the second rung from the bottom, the counter DN bit is used to trigger an output field device after a count of 9. The counter is reset in the last rung with instruction I:2/12. A CTU counter is shown but a CTD counter could be used for a count down application. Also, a SLC 500 format is presented, but the PLC 5 or ControlLogix could be used as well.	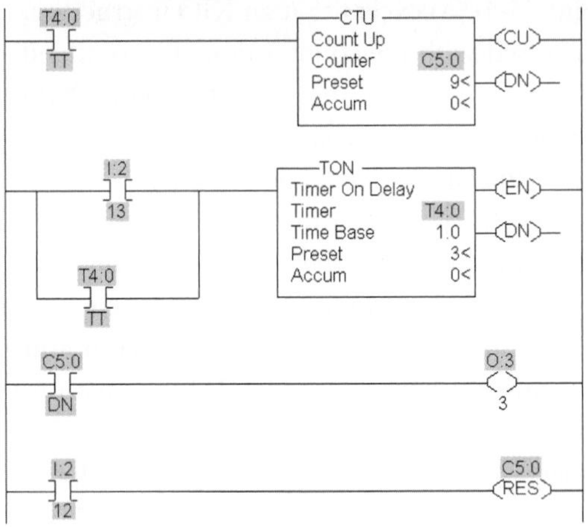 (c)
Applications where an up/down counter is required. The field devices are NO push button switches. When the switches are closed, their respective input rungs transition from false to true. I:2/10 increments the accumulator C5:1.ACC up and I:2/11 decrements the same accumulator down, creating an up/down counter. The DN bit drives output O:3/1 true when the ACC is equal to or greater than 10; output O:3/1 is false for values of the ACC below 10. Both counters are reset by the I:2/15 contact. A SLC 500 format is presented, but the PLC 5 or ControlLogix could be used as well.	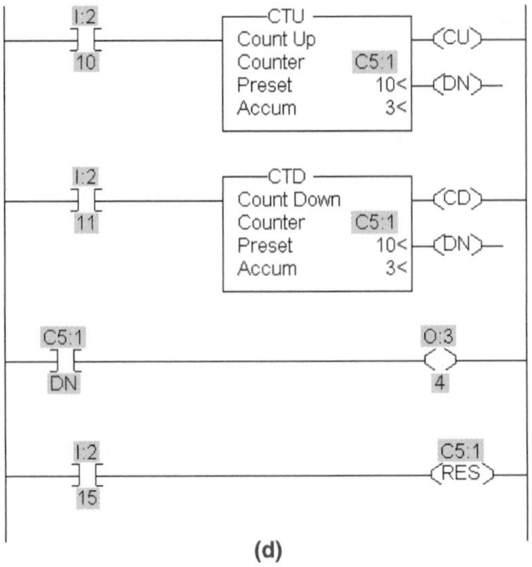 (d)

on how the output instruction rung is configured. In Figure 5-10(a) an XIC instruction is used to turn on output O:3/1, and an XIO instruction is used to turn off output O:3/2 when the preset count is reached. In this application the counter will continue to record changes in the field device after the PRE value is reached. In this and all the remaining examples, the RES instruction is used to reset the counter ACC to zero. The RES instruction has the same address as the counter that is being reset. An up counter is shown, but this ladder rung would work with a down counter as well.

The configuration in Figure 5-10(b) is like Figure 5-10(a) except that an XIO instruction, addressed with the counter done bit, is added to the input logic for counter. This XIO instruction permits changes of the input field device to transition the counter until the ACC is equal to the PRE value. At this point, the active DN bit makes the XIO instruction false and the rung can no longer cause the counter to increment. The ACC is reset to zero and counting is restored with the RES instruction. An up counter is shown, but this ladder rung would work with a down counter as well.

CTU/CTD Stretched Trigger Standard Ladder Logic: The ladder in Figure 5-10(c) solves an interesting process problem. Study the bottle counting application in Figure 5-3 where a sensor is used to detect the presence of a bottle. In applications like these, you often get an output from the sensor as illustrated in Figure 5-11(c) and (d). The multiple outputs at the start and end of the detection are a result of the bottle wobbling as the trigger starts and ends. The sensor beam is broken, then established, and then broken again as the bottle neck breaks the beam. The same scenario occurs when the bottle neck leaves the beam. As a result, you get three counting pulses [Figure 5-11(e)] where only one should have been present. Study Figure 5-11 to see how this is occurring.

The problem is solved in two ways. First, a sensor with hysteresis is used so that the oscillations at the trigger point are reduced. However, if the bottle oscillations are large, then sensor hysteresis will not fix the false count problem. The second solution is the ladder configuration in Figure 5-10(c). The first transition of the sensor starts a timer and the timer timing bit is used to trigger the counter instruction. Any oscillations of the bottle are ignored and

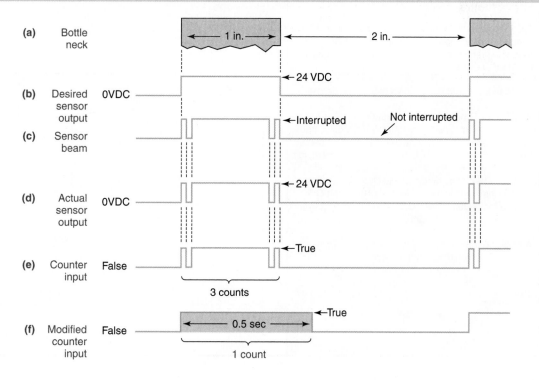

FIGURE 5-11: Sensor output for Figure 5-3.

the correct count is made. The timer preset must be large enough to cover the original sensor pulse, but less than the period for the sensor output, as shown in Figure 5-11(f). The ACC is reset to zero with the RES instruction. An up counter is shown, but this ladder rung would work with a down counter as well. Example 5-1 illustrates this point.

Study the solution in Figure 5-10(c) until it is clear how this standard counter ladder logic solves the problem of the bottle counter in this example.

CTU/CTD Up/Down Standard Ladder Logic: The standard counter in Figure 5-10(d) is an up/down counter configured from an up counter and a down counter. Each counter is triggered from a different bit in the input image table (I:2/10 and I:2/11 in the figure), but the up counter and down counter have the same address, C5:1. Since each counter changes the same counter accumulator register (C5:1.ACC), the accumulator increments with every false to true transition of I:2/10 and decrements with every false to true transition of I:2/11. Some PLC systems have an up/down counter instruction. In that case, the counter symbol has two input lines: one to increment, or count up, and one to decrement, or count down. Also, some PLCs have the reset action built into the counter instruction. In Figure 5-10(d), the counter is reset with a RES instruction in the fourth ladder rung.

Study the four standard counter configurations in Figure 5-10. Every counter application you encounter can be explained using some combination of the techniques present in these four basic counter circuits. Note that the ACC in the counter is reset to zero and that counting is restored with the RES instruction.

5-4-4 Allen-Bradley Up Counters

The AB up counter (CTU) is an output instruction that increases the accumulator value by one for every false to true transition of the counter's rung. The done bit is true when the accumulator reaches the value stored as the preset. The CTU operation is the same for all three Allen-Bradley PLCs.

The up counter application in Figure 5-12 turns a green light on and an amber light off after the accumulated value reaches 4. Review the ladder logic in Figure 5-12(a) and the timing diagram in Figure 5-12(b). When the push button switch PB1 closes, the I:1/0 bit of the input image table changes from a 0 to a 1. This makes the counter rung true and increments the accumulator in C5:0 CTU instruction. When the ACC is less than the PRE value, the amber light is on since the done bit address on the XIO instruction is false. When the ACC is equal to or greater than the PRE value (four or more transitions of PB1), the green light is turned on and the amber is extinguished. When the push button switch PB2 is pressed, the XIC instruction, I:1/1, activates the reset instruction, which forces the accumulated value to zero. Counting resumes when PB2 is released and PB1 is closed. Study the ladder logic and timing diagram until the operation of the up counter is understood.

The CTU applications in Examples 5-2 and 5-3 permit a comparison between the SLC 500 and ControlLogix versions of the count up instruction. Review the standard ladder logic for counters in Figure 5-10 since they are the basis for all counter ladder logic designs.

EXAMPLE 5-1

The bottles are moving at a rate of 3 inches per second in Figure 5-3. The ladder in Figure 5-10(c) is used to drive the bottle counter. Determine the delay for the pulse stretched timer in this application.

SOLUTION

Study the timing diagram for the problem shown in Figure 5-11. The bottles have a 3-inch separation from the front edge of one bottle to the front edge of the next bottle. If the bottles are traveling at a fixed rate of 3 inches per second, then it takes 1 second to cover those 3 inches of travel. Setting the PRE for the timer at 0.5 seconds (half of the total travel time) provides a single trigger pulse for the counter as each bottle passes.

FIGURE 5-12: Up counter application.

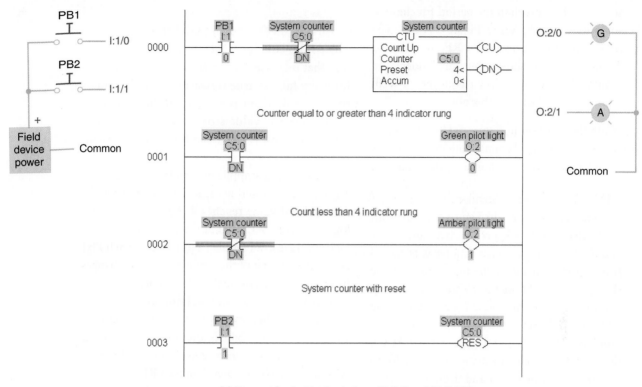

(a) Up counter ladder logic for a PLC 5 and SLC 500

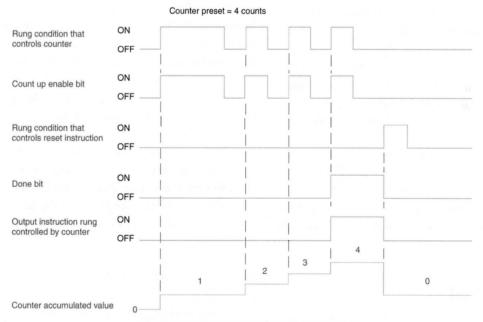

(b) Up counter timing diagram for ladder in (a)

EXAMPLE 5-2

Design the ladder logic for an industrial application that packages canned vegetables supplied by a conveyor. When 12 cans are detected by a current sourcing proximity sensor, a packaging operation is initiated. The production line must package 200 boxes of 12 cans per shift. When 200 packages have been completed, a red stack light is illuminated. While the system is packaging cans, a green stack light is illuminated. A total count of cans packaged per shift should also be recorded.

SOLUTION

Refer to the ladder logic in Figure 5-13 as you read the following solution.

When a can activates sensor S1, the XIC input instruction I:1/10 is true, which sends a false to true transition to counters C5:0 and C5:1. Note that the preset values of the counters are:

- C5:0 has a preset value of 3000, and records the maximum amount of cans on the conveyor per shift.
- C5:1 has a preset value of 12, which is the amount of cans per package.
- C5:2 has a preset value of 200, which is the maximum amount of packages that can be completed per shift.

The *unit total counter* done bit, C5:1/DN, drives three operations: (1) it increments C5:2, which is the package counter, (2) it turns on the *packaging operation* for the 12 cans just counted, and (3) it resets the C5:1 accumulator to zero, which prepares this CTU instruction to count the next set of 12 cans. CTU instruction C5:2 uses the false to true transition of the C5:1 done bit to count the number of packages completed per shift. When the C5:2/DN bit is false, the green stack light is on, indicating that 200 packages have not been completed. When C5:2 reaches 200, its done bit turns off the green light and turns on the red pilot light. Finally, push button switch PB1 initiates reset instructions for counters C5:0, C5:1; and C5:2 so that the packaging control is ready for the next shift.

ControlLogix solution for packaging automation. The SLC 500 solution for Example 5-2 is converted to the equivalent solution for the ControlLogix PLC and displayed in Figure 5-14. Compare the two solutions and notice that the Logix solution permits more than one output per rung, so the ladder logic appears less cluttered. In addition, the use of tag names for symbols and data values makes it easier to read and interpret the ladder logic solution. The operation of the two ladder solutions is identical. If the input logic of a rung makes the rung true, all outputs on the rung are active. Note only the red light is implemented and tag data is displayed in Figure 5-14(b).

EXAMPLE 5-3

Modify the ladder diagram for the packaging control solution in Figure 5-13 for Example 5-2 to detect an interruption of the can flow on the conveyor and then to:

- Turn off the can conveyor motor and green stack light.
- Turn on an amber stack light.

SOLUTION

Refer to Figure 5-15 as you read the following description.

The four additional rungs in Figure 5-15 are added to the automation application solution in Figure 5-13. Detection of a jam on the can conveyor is achieved by verifying that counter C5:1 increments every 3 seconds.

A standard start/stop rung is used with the addition of an internal relay bit, B3:0/0, addressing an XIO instruction in rung 0. The start/stop field devices are momentary push buttons, with the start an NO contact configuration

FIGURE 5-13: Ladder diagram for the packaging system—Example 5-2.

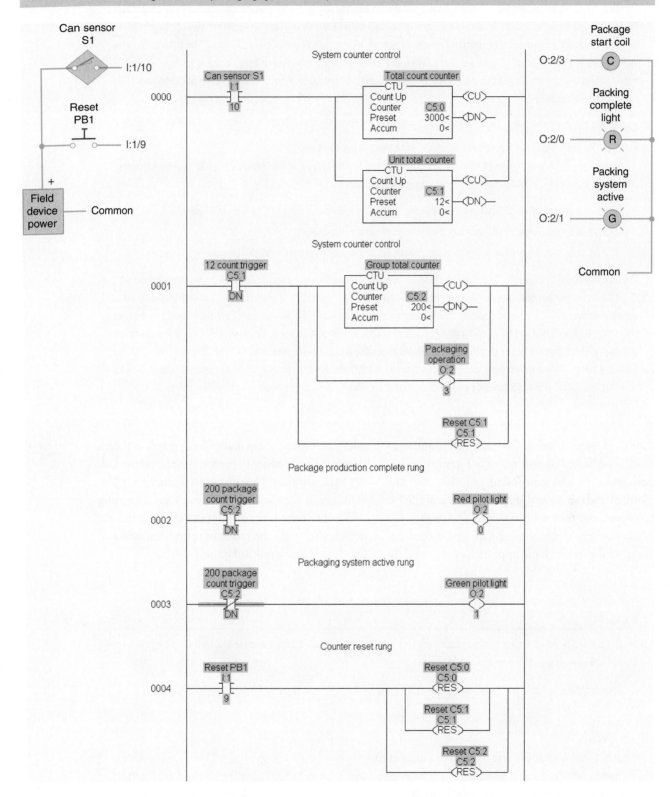

and the stop an NC contact. The virtual relay XIO instruction, B3:0/0, gives another rung the option of turning off the conveyor motor contactor. Note that for safety:

- The motor overloads are hardwired in series with the motor contactor coil.
- An auxiliary contact from the motor contactor is used as an input to provide a sealing instruction for the start push button.

Usually the start switch is sealed by an instruction with the address from the motor contactor OTE instruction (0:2/10 in Figure 5-15). However, the following description illustrates why this would produce an unsafe operating condition.

FIGURE 5-14: ControlLogix ladder for the can packaging system.

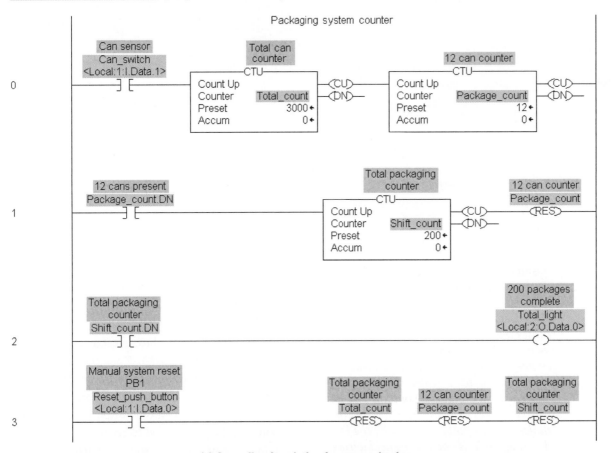

(a) ControlLogix solution for can packaging

(b) ControlLogix program tag dialog box data

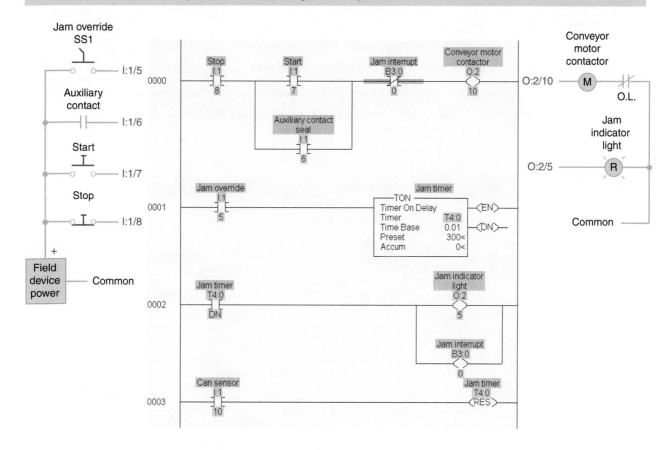

Assume that the sealing contact for the start I:1/7 is addressed to the O:2/10 output, and the conveyor is started by pressing the start PB. A jam on the conveyor causes the conveyor motor overload contacts to open the motor contactor field circuit, and the conveyor motor turns off. If the start switch is sealed by the O:2/10 address, then the O:2/10 output remains true. The field device contactor coil continues to have power applied by the ladder rung, but it is open in the field wiring. When the jam is removed and the overloads reset, the conveyor will start moving immediately and that could present a danger of injury to maintenance or machine operators.

The unsafe condition is removed by using an NO auxiliary contact from the motor contactor as an input field device, and assigning this address to the start PB sealing instruction. If the contactor overload contacts trip, the motor contactor turns off and the auxiliary contacts open. This forces output O:2/10 to a false state.

Thus when the jam is removed and the overloads are reset, the conveyor does not restart until the start PB is again depressed.

Four rungs are used to detect a conveyor jam, as shown in Figure 5-15. Rung 0 is a start/stop rung for the conveyor motor. This was always present, but it was not shown in the solution in Figure 5-13 because it did not play a part in that solution. Here it is used to control the conveyor contactor when the system is started with the start push button and also when the conveyor is halted by a jam. Rung 1 has a TON timer that is enabled by an NO start selector switch used to activate this jam detection logic. The timer has a 3-second preset value and is enabled by input I:1/5. If the timer is enabled for more than 3 seconds, then the done bit is true and rung 2 lights the jam indicator and turns off the conveyor motor. However, without a jam present, the can sensor, I:1/10, is true every 1.25 seconds and the can sensor instruction in rung 3 resets the timer at that time interval. This resets the timer accu-

mulator to zero, and the timing process restarts. If a jam is detected, the stack light output and the virtual relay B3:0/0 are true. The XIO instruction for the B3:0/0 bit makes the motor contactor output false and drops out the start circuit. The system will not restart until the start PB is pressed after the jam is cleared. Review the ladder logic and this description until you understand how the timer in this automation system acts as a *watch dog* timer.

5-4-5 Allen-Bradley Down Counters

The function of the *down counter* is to decrement its accumulated value on the false to true transitions of the counter rung. The operation of the down counter is identical to that of the up counter except that the value in the accumulator is decremented until the preset value is reached and the output becomes true. A down counter could be used to count the number of cans dispensed from a soft drink machine; when the machine is empty

the counter could turn on a sold out light. However, an up counter can be used in this application as well. The CTU would count every can sold with the preset number set to the maximum number of cans that the machine can hold. When the accumulator reaches the preset value the sold out light is turned on. In fact, a down counter is seldom used by itself; it's generally used with an up counter to form an up/down counter. The conditions to set and reset the output bits of a down counter are shown as a truth table in Table 5-1(b), and the timing diagram for the down counter is illustrated in Figure 5-16. Before you continue, review the table and timing diagram until you are familiar with the operation of the down counter output bits.

5-4-6 Allen-Bradley Up/Down Counters

Figure 5-17 illustrates the up/down counter timing diagram. The up/down counter in the figure provides an output as long as the count is equal to or greater than 4. The preset value is 4, and

FIGURE 5-16: Down counter timing diagram.

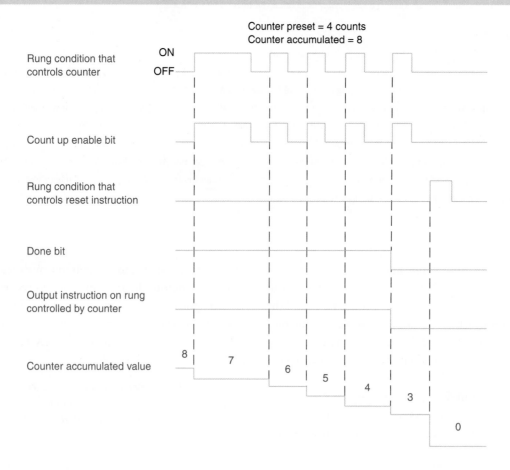

FIGURE 5-17: Up/down counter timing diagram.

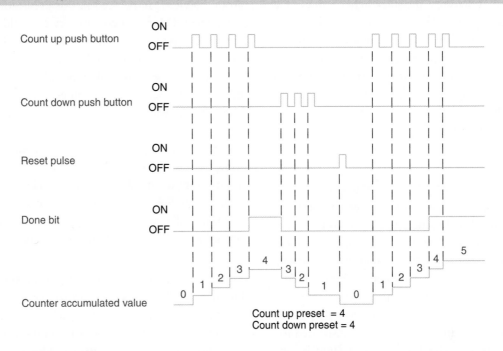

Count up preset = 4
Count down preset = 4

EXAMPLE 5-4

Draw the ladder diagram using counters to count the number of cars entering and leaving an airport parking garage. The parking garage can hold 308 cars; when it is full a red light is illuminated.

SOLUTION

Refer to Figure 5-18 as you read the following description.

When a car enters the garage, the limit switch on the entrance gate, LS1, is activated so rung 0 is true. The up counter increments when the rung cycles from false to true. In similar fashion, when a car exits the garage, the exit gate limit switch, LS2, is activated, and a similar false to true transition of rung 1 decrements the down counter by 1. Because the up counter and the down counter are the same counter number (C5:0), they are at the same program address and the accumulated value is the same for both. When the accumulated value reaches 308, the done bit C5:0/DN turns on the red full lot light. No reset rung is provided because the lot always has some cars present, so the ACC value will not be zero. Once a month management does an inventory late at night and uses the counter data dialog box, Figure 5-8(b), to update the ACC counter.

---

the accumulated value starts at 0. The count up pulses increment the counter by 1, the count down pulses decrement the counter by 1, and the reset returns the counter to 0. Note that the output is true when the count is greater than or equals 4 and false when the count is 3 or less.

5-4-7 Allen-Bradley One-Shot Instructions

One-shot instructions are used with numerous PLC instructions. They are used with counter reset instructions when the counter must start a new count before the reset input contacts return to their normal state. One-shot instructions are available on most PLC systems, but can be built using standard ladder logic on all PLCs. One-shot operation is defined as follows:

One-shot instructions make the rung output active for one scan even if the input instruction triggering it remains active for multiple scans.

FIGURE 5-18: Ladder diagram for parking lot counter—Example 5-4.

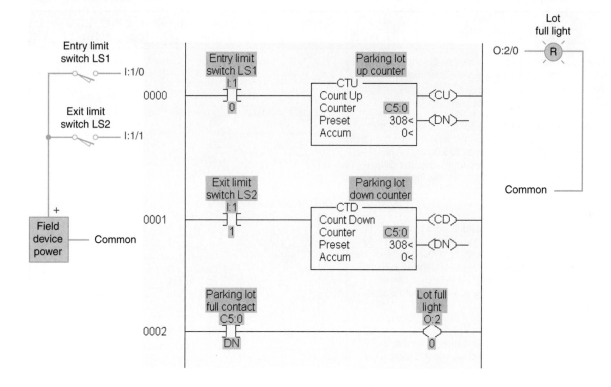

The three processors, PLC 5, SLC 500, and ControlLogix, use similar but not identical one-shot instructions. The standard ladder logic rungs for all Allen-Bradley's one-shot instructions are illustrated in Figures 5-19 (PLC 5), 5-21 (SLC 500), and 5-22 (ControlLogix). The timing diagrams in Figure 5-20 illustrate the pulse action for one-shot instructions. Read the descriptions for these example ladder rungs and study the timing diagrams before continuing.

PLC 5 ONS One-Shot instructions. Allen-Bradley has three one-shot instructions for the PLC 5 processor that are illustrated in Figure 5-19. The ONS one-shot instruction is illustrated in Figure 5-19(a), and this instruction is available on all PLC 5 processor models. The timing diagram for this one-shot instruction is shown in Figure 5-20(a). Note that the instruction format starts with standard input logic instruction(s), which is followed by the ONS instruction symbol and then the output instruction. The input can be any valid input instruction for the PLC 5, and the output instruction

can be any valid output instruction for the processor. The one-shot instruction is triggered by a false to true change in the input logic, so it is an input rising instruction. Remember it is a rising edge from the rung logic that triggers the ONS instruction regardless of the type of change that occurred in the field device. The address for the ONS symbol is either a binary or integer bit address, for example, B3:0/3 or N7:10/8. This address stores the previous value of the ONS instruction and cannot be used in any other ladder rung. The ONS instruction, which must be located on the rung directly next to the output instruction, makes the output true for only one scan regardless of how long the input logic is true.

PLC 5 OSR and OSF one-shot instructions. The OSR is a one-shot rising and the OSF is a one-shot falling instruction. Both are output instructions placed on the right end of the rung and operate in similar fashion. The OSR is triggered by a false to true change (rising or leading edge) in the input logic and the OSF by

FIGURE 5-19: Standard ladder logic rungs for PLC 5 one-shot instructions.

Application	Standard Ladder Logic Rungs for PLC 5 One Shot Instructions
Turn on an output instruction or a bit for one scan with either a rising or falling edge of an input instruction. **ONS** The ONS, one shot instruction, is used to make an output instruction (RES) true for one scan when the input logic on the rung goes from false to true. The ONS must be assigned a Boolean bit (B3:0/39) that is not used anywhere else in the program. Also, the ONS instruction is the final instruction for the input logic and cannot be in an OR branch. **OSR** The OSR, one shot rising instruction, is an output instruction (O:001) used to make an output bit true for one scan. The OSR is triggered by a rising edge on the ladder rung input logic (I:001/1) as illustrated in Figure 5-20(b). The OSR must be assigned a Boolean bit (word 17 and bit 7) that is not used anywhere else in the program. **OSF** The OSF, one shot falling instruction, is an output instruction used to make an output bit (O:002) true for one scan. The OSF is triggered by a falling edge on the ladder rung input logic (I:001/2) as illustrated in Figure 5-20(c). The OSF must be assigned a Boolean bit (word 18 and bit 4) that is not used anywhere else in the program.	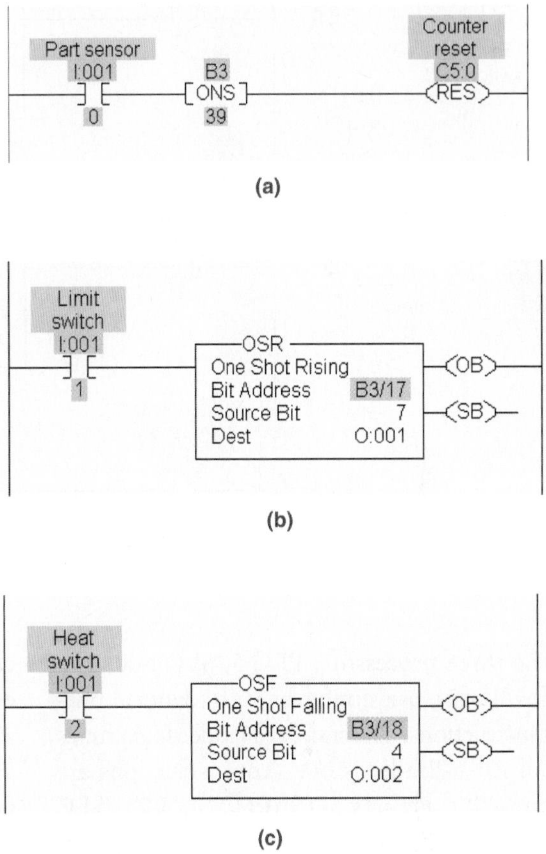 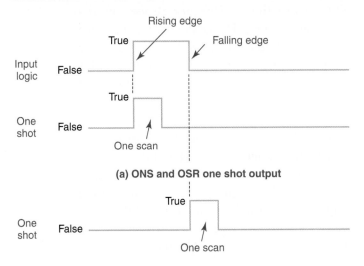

FIGURE 5-20: One-shot timing diagrams.

(a) ONS and OSR one shot output

(b) OSF one shot output

a true to false change (falling or trailing edge). These commands are available only on the enhanced model of the PLC 5. The standard ladder implementation of this instruction is illustrated in Figure 5-19(b) and (c). Note that the three parameters entered in the instruction are:

Bit Address: The bit address used to store the status of the one-shot instruction, such as B3/17.

Source Bit: The bit address of the output word address that will be true for one scan, such as bit7 in word O:001.

Dest: The destination or output word, such as O:001, that has the bit held true for one scan.

Application	Standard Ladder Logic Rungs for SLC 500 One Shot Instructions
Turn on an output instruction for one scan with the rising edge of an input instruction. **OSR** The OSR, one shot rising instruction is used to make an output instruction (RES) true for one scan when the input logic on the rung goes from false to true. The OSR must be assigned a Boolean bit (B3:2/12) that is not used anywhere else in the program. Also, the OSR instruction is the final instruction for the input logic.	Entry limit switch LS1 I:1 —] [— Counter reset 0 B3:2 —[OSR]— C5:1 —(RES)— 12

The timing diagrams for the OSR and OSF instructions are shown in Figure 5-20(a) and (b), respectively. The reset instruction used with timers, counters, and control instructions is illustrated in Figure 5-19(a).

SLC 500 OSR one-shot instructions. The OSR instruction is illustrated in Figure 5-21, and the timing diagram is displayed in Figure 5-20(a). This instruction is available on all SLC processor models, and the instruction format is identical to the ONS for the PLC 5. The input can be any valid input instruction for the SLC PLC, and the output instruction can be any valid output instruction for the processor. The one-shot instruction is triggered by a false to true change in the input logic, so it is an input rising instruction. The address for the OSR symbol is either a binary or integer bit; for example, B3:2/3 or N7:0/8. This bit stores the previous value of the OSR instruction and cannot be used in any other ladder rung. The OSR makes the output instruction true for one scan independent of the number of scans that the input is true.

ControlLogix ONS, OSR, and OSF one-shot instructions. The ControlLogix standard circuits are illustrated in Figure 5-22 and the timing diagrams are like those shown in Figure 5-20. The one-shot instructions in ControlLogix have the same ladder format as those in the PLC 5 with the exception of the addressing. The one-shot instructions in ControlLogix use tag names for all instruction and parameter addressing. In addition, the output bit uses a tag name in place of the output bit number and word number used in the PLC 5.

One-Shot applications with counters. One-shot instructions are often required in counter applications. An example describes this best, so review the counter ladder example in Figure 5-23. Assume that the counter is counting parts entering a production queue using a part detection sensor. When the queue has four parts present, the counter done bit, C5:1/DN, stops the part flow into the queue and triggers a machine loader that puts the four parts into a production machine. The machine then makes I:1/1 active to reset the counter for the next four-count sequence. This parts loaded signal from the machine keeps the reset instruction true for 5 seconds, and during that time parts continue to flow into the queue. However, the counter accumulator is held at 0 because the reset instruction is active for 5 seconds. If a new part enters the queue and activates the part detection sensor, I:1/0, while the machine reset instruction is true, then the part is not counted.

The problem is solved with the modified reset rung in Figure 5-24. Now the RES instruction is active for only one scan, which resets the counter in milliseconds. Even though I:1/1 is true for 5 seconds, the C5:1 can start counting one scan after the reset logic is active. Study this example of a one-shot application until it is clear how the ONS instruction is used.

Application	Standard Ladder Logic Rungs for ControlLogix One Shot Instructions
Turn on an output instruction or a bit for one scan with either a rising or falling edge of an input instruction. **ONS** The ONS, one shot instruction, is used to make an output instruction (Shift_count) true for one scan when the input logic on the rung goes from false to true. The ONS must be assigned a tag (One_shot) of the Boolean data type that is not used anywhere else in the program. Also, the ONS instruction is the final instruction for the input logic. **OSR** The OSR, one shot rising instruction, is an output instruction used to make an output tag (Output_1) with a Boolean data type true for one scan. The OSR is triggered by a rising edge on the ladder rung input logic as illustrated in Figure 5-2 (b). The OSR must be assigned a tag (Storage_bit_1) of the Boolean data type that is not used anywhere else in the program. **OSF** The OSF, one shot falling instruction, is an output instruction used to make an output tag (Output_2) with a Boolean data type true for one scan. The OSF is triggered by a falling edge on the ladder rung input logic as illustrated in Figure 5-2 (c). The OSF must be assigned a tag (Storage_bit_2) of the Boolean data type that is not used anywhere else in the program.	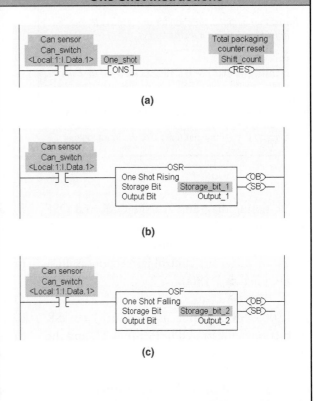

FIGURE 5-23: Machine queue parts counter.

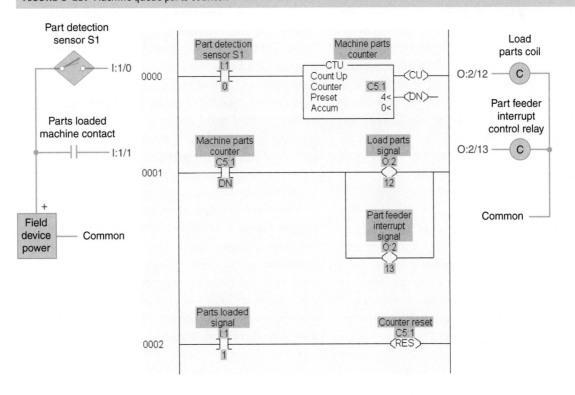

5-5 CASCADED COUNTERS

Some applications require the counting of events where the total number of events exceeds the maximum number allowable per counter. SLC 500 up counters, for example, have a maximum count of 32,767. *Cascaded counters* are used to extend the count to a value high than the individual counter maximum. As in cascaded timers, the output of one counter is the input to another. Figure 5-25 depicts a ladder diagram that illustrates cascaded counters, where a red light is turned on after 60,000 counts.

The first rung has C5:1 counting the input pulses generated by I:1/0. After C5:1 counts to 30,000, the C5:1 done bit goes true and performs two functions: it makes the rung for the C5:1 counter false so C5:1.ACC remains at 30,000, and it connects the second counter, C5:2, to the input instruction I:1/0. After C5:2 has counted to 30,000, the C5:2 done bit goes true. When the C5:1 and the C5:2 done bits are both true, the red light is on. The C5:2 ACC remains at 30,000 because C5:2/DN on the XIO instruction in the counter rung makes the counter instruction false.

5-6 EMPIRICAL DESIGN PROCESS WITH PLC COUNTERS

The empirical design process, introduced in Section 3-11-4, is an organized approach to the design of PLC ladder logic programs. However, the term *empirical* implies that some degree of trial and error is present. This troublesome aspect of the

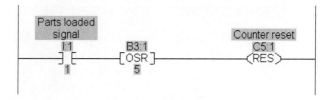

FIGURE 5-24: Modified ladder rung to fix timing problem on the machine queue parts counter.

empirical process should become more obvious when counters are added into the design process.

5-6-1 Adding Counters to the Process

The first step in using counters in PLC ladder design is to know the addressing and operation of the up, down, and up/down counters and all the standard counter circuits illustrated in Figure 5-10. In addition, the operation of the reset instruction, RES, must be clear and the operation of the one-shot instructions for the various processes must be learned. Stop now and review all of these if necessary.

When a counter is added to a ladder it affects three rungs: one rung to make the counter command (CTU or CTD) active, a second rung that uses a counter output (CU, CD, OV, UN, or DN) to control a system parameter (in most counter applications the DN bit is the only output bit used), and a third rung to reset the counter accumulator. The complete empirical process is listed in Section 3-11-4; the modifications for counters are as follows:

FIGURE 5-25: Cascade counters.

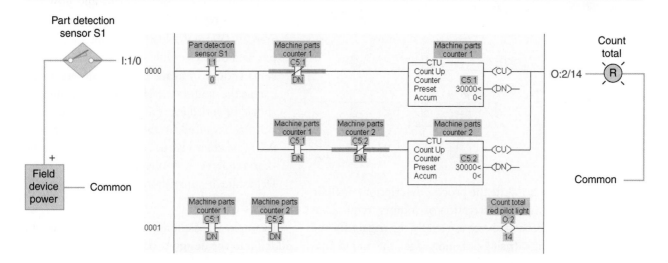

EXAMPLE 5-5

A conveyor system, illustrated in Figure 5-26, sorts boxes so that each chute receives 10 boxes. The operation is as follows:

- Gates 1 and 2 are up, sensor S1 counts 10 boxes for chute 1, and then gate 1 drops.
- Sensor S2 counts 10 boxes for chute 2 and then gate 2 drops.
- Sensor S3 counts 10 boxes for chute 3 and then gates 1 and 2 are raised and the process starts over.

With average conveyor speed, it takes 4 seconds for the boxes to enter the chute after the sensor detects them. Draw the PLC 5 ladder logic necessary for this control problem.

SOLUTION

Refer to Figure 5-26 as you read the empirical design process used. The empirical design is as follows:

- The operation of the system is described in the problem statement.
- The system inputs are sensors 1, 2, and 3 and the outputs are C5:0 (chute 1), C5:1 (chute 2), C5:2 (chute 3), gate 1 actuator, and gate 2 actuator.

Before the equations are written, study the standard ladder logic options for the PLC 5 system counters shown in Figure 5-10 The solution in Figure 5-10(b) is selected because the counter done bit remains active and can be used to control the gates.

The logic equations for the outputs are:

- C5:0 count input = sensor 1 AND NOT C5:0/DN
- C5:1 count input = sensor 2 AND C5:0/DN AND NOT C5:1/DN
- C5:2 count input = sensor 3 AND C5:1/DN AND NOT C5:2/DN
- T4:0 timer input = C5:2/DN AND NOT T4:0/DN
- RES = T4:0/DN (timer 0 has a preset value of 6 seconds). Note that the reset instruction resets all counters. The timer is reset by its own done bit.
- Gate 1 = C5:0/DN (counter 0 has a preset value of 10)
- Gate 2 = C5:1/DN (counter 1 has a preset value of 10)

The sensor and actuator wiring plus ladder logic solution is illustrated in Figure 5-27.

The timer is used to permit the tenth box to reach chute 3 before the system is reset and all gates are raised and the process is restarted.

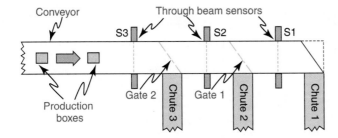

Step 1: (Write the process description): Include a complete description of count(s) required in the process. Note especially the trigger for the count(s) (rising or falling edge), the output con- trolled by the counter DN bit, and how the counter is reset.

Step 2: (Write Boolean equations for all output field devices): One of the Boolean expressions should indicate the logic necessary to enable the counter(s). The counter output bits should be added into the other Boolean expressions as required by the process description. Also, the reset instruction, RES, is an output that requires a Boolean equation as well. Determine if a one-shot is needed for the RES instruction.

Example 5-5 demonstrates how counters are added into the design process.

FIGURE 5-27: Box sorter ladder logic—Example 5-5.

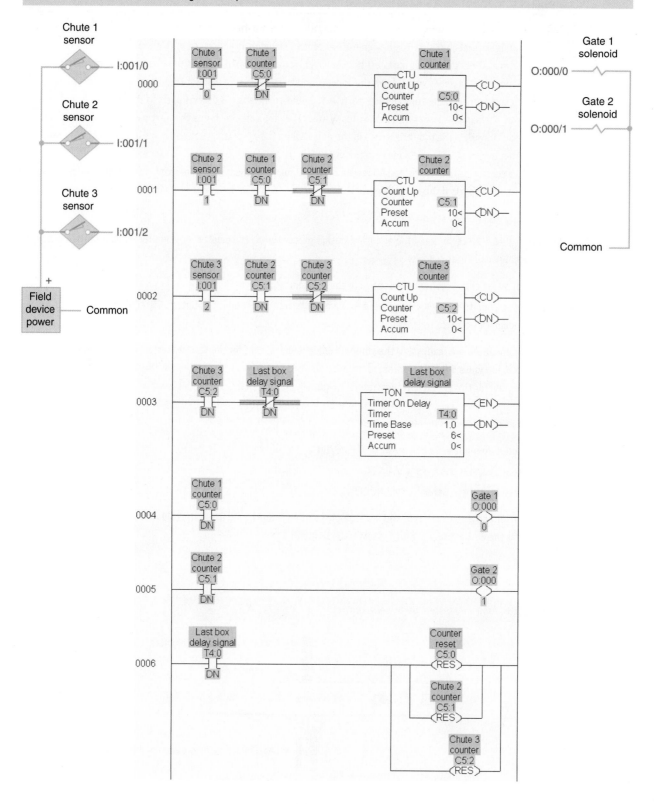

EXAMPLE 5-6

The assembly system in Figure 5-28 is typical of many used in automation systems. This system will be used for program design in several chapters. The design for two control elements is addressed in this example.

The pneumatic ejector pushes parts off the conveyor into a four-part queue. If the queue is full, then parts are passed to another assembly station down the conveyor. Sensor 1 detects a part for this assembly machine and triggers the ejection process. Sensor 2 detects parts in the hold area, sensor 3 detects parts in the stop area, and sensor 4 detects parts in the assembly machine ready area. The stop actuator holds the next part to be released, and the hold actuator holds the top three parts in the queue when the next part is released. The assembly system takes the part from the ready area and adds it to the product.

Design a control system using SLC 500 instructions that manages the queue by ejecting a part if the queue is less than 4 and passing parts if the queue is equal to 4. Draw the SLC 500 ladder logic necessary for this control problem.

SOLUTION

Refer to Figure 5-29 as you read the empirical design process used. The empirical design for managing the ejector and assembly queue is as follows:

- The operation of the system is described in the problem statement.
- The system inputs are sensors 1 and 4, and the outputs are C5:0 (count up counter), C5:0 (count down counter), and pneumatic actuator (ejector).

Before the equations are read, study the standard ladder logic options for the SLC 500 system counters, Figure 5-10. The solution in Figure 5-10(d) is selected because an up/down counter is required for this application. Also, the timing diagram for this problem is illustrated in Figure 5-17. Note that the done bit is active went the counter ACC is at 4.

The logic equations for the outputs are:

- C5:0 count up input = sensor 1 AND NOT C5:0/DN
- C5:0 count down input = sensor 4
- Pneumatic ejector = sensor 1 AND NOT C5:0/DN

The sensor and actuator wiring and ladder logic solution is illustrated in Figure 5-29. Review the last two examples so that the design process for counters is understood.

FIGURE 5-28: Assembly system part queue control.

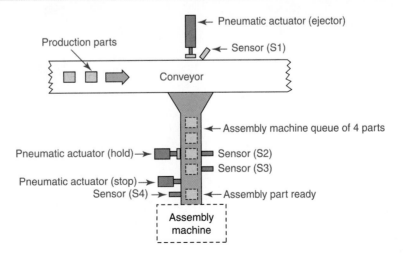

FIGURE 5-29: Queue control ladder logic—Example 5-6.

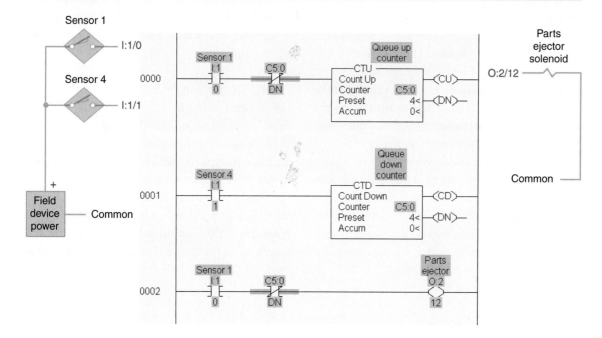

5-7 CONVERSION OF RELAY LOGIC COUNTER LADDERS TO PLC LOGIC

Conversion of relay ladder logic with contacts and timers to an equivalent PLC ladder solution was introduced in Chapters 3 and 4. When mechanical or electronic counters are present in the relay ladders, they must be converted as well. The following conversion rules for counters are appended to the initial rule set in Section 3-11-5.

1. Replace the mechanical or electronic counter operated as an up counter with the PLC up counter.
2. Replace the mechanical or electronic counter operated as a down counter with the PLC down counter.
3. Set the preset value so that the PLC instruction turns on the done bit at the same count value used in the mechanical or electronic relay ladder device.
4. Replace the mechanical counter contacts and electronic counter solid-state output with the PLC equivalent. For example, NO contacts in relay logic are replaced with an XIC instruction in the PLC output rung. If NC contacts are present use an XIO instruction. The controlled device

should be the same, but care must be taken to match the current sinking versus sourcing needs of the field device to the opposite specifications on the output module.

The conversion of input field devices—switches and sensors—plus output field devices—actuators and contactors—follows the guidelines specified in Section 3-11-5.

5-8 TROUBLESHOOTING COUNTER LADDER LOGIC

The most difficult counter programs to verify are those with multiple cascaded counters and one or more reset instructions. Use the following suggestions for troubleshooting counters.

- Test the counters starting with the first in the sequence, and then add one counter at a time until the total sequence is operational. Use the temporary end instruction, TND, described in Chapter 4.
- If the reset instructions are present, determine if all necessary process executions driven by

counter bits are performed before the counter is reset.

- Use the suspend instruction, SUS, to verify status values for all registers and bits at critical points in the ladder. The SUS instruction is described in the next subsection.
- If the count is inconsistent, then verify that the period (from a false to true transition to the next false to true transition) of the counter logic transition is not shorter than the scan time.
- Be aware of situations where counter values are used to update internal PLC memory bits and inhibit process actions, since the scan time and internal update time is much faster than most process events. The counter problem described in Section 5-8-2 illustrates this type of programming situation.

- Use the counter dialog boxes like those illustrated in Figure 5-8(b) for PLC 5 and SLC 500 and in Figure 5-9(c) for the ControlLogix counter to track changes in counter parameters and tags.

5-8-1 Suspend Instruction

The suspend instruction, SUS, is used to trap and identify specific conditions during system troubleshooting and program debugging. A program can have multiple suspend instructions, each controlled by a different input instruction address. The SUS is added to the cascade counter example in Figure 5-25 and redrawn in Figure 5-30. When true, this output instruction places the controller in the suspend or idle mode. The suspend ID, number 100 in the figure, must be

FIGURE 5-30: Ladder logic with SUS instruction.

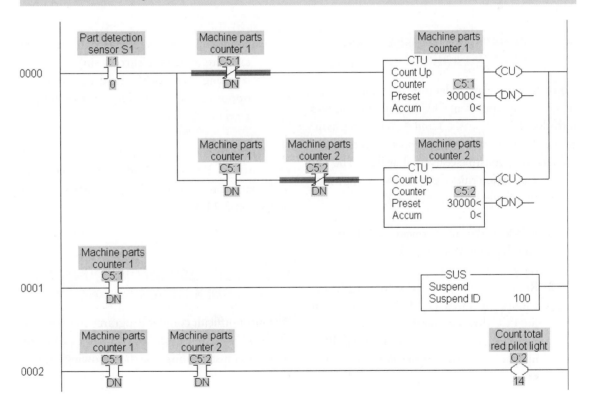

selected by the programmer and entered in the instruction. When the SUS instruction executes, the ID number is written in word 7 (S:7) of the status file. If multiple suspend instructions are present, then this will indicate which SUS instruction was active. The suspend file (program or subroutine number identifying where the executed SUS instruction resides) is placed in word 8 (S:8) of the status file. All ladder logic outputs are de-energized, but other status files have the data present when the suspend instruction is executed.

5-8-2 Process Speed versus Scan Time

Problems often occur where counter values are used to inhibit process actions because of the relative speed of the scan is usually much faster than the process event. The ladder logic from Example 5-6 in Figure 5-29 illustrates this situation. The following problem was observed as the program in Figure 5-29 was executing.

When the queue is at three parts and a fourth part arrives at ejector sensor 1, the count in the queue increases to 4 but the fourth part is not ejected into the queue.

Study the following two equations for the control and see if you can identify the problem.

C5:0 count up AND NOT C5:0/DN
Pneumatic AND NOT C5:0/DN

Note that both of those outputs (counter C5:0 and ejector) are triggered by the same logic and that a feedback is present since one of the input conditions, NOT C5:0/DN, is generated by counter C5:0, the output for that input logic.

Also, the time required for incrementing C5:0 is the scan rate, which is relatively fast (10 to 100 msec), and the time required for the ejector to extend and return is relatively long (>1500 msec) because it is a pneumatic system.

In the ladder solution the up counter is incremented from 3 to 4 when the fourth part makes sensor 1 active. Thus the queue indicates that four parts have arrived, and the C5:0/DN is now true. The pneumatic ejector output, O:2/12, is also true when the fourth part arrives at sensor 1. However, within one scan (10 to 100 seconds) the C5:0/DN bit is true, making the XIC instruction with the C5:0/DN address false so power flow to the pneumatic ejector output is present for only one scan. As a result, the ejector never moves because its response time is much larger. The solution is to add a timer using the standard ladder configuration in Figure 4-12(c) that turns on an output for a set period of time to drive the ejector. The following changes would be necessary: 1) change the parts ejector output in rung 2 to a binary bit B3:0/0; 2) Add the two rungs from the standard to the solution; 3) Change the I:1/1 XIC instruction in the standard to the binary bit B3:0/0; 4) Change the OTE output in the standard from O:3/0 to O:2/12 parts ejector. Now the ejector output is on for a set time for every part ejection.

5-9 LOCATION OF THE INSTRUCTIONS

The location of instructions from this chapter in the Allen-Bradley programming software is indicated in Figure 5-31.

FIGURE 5-31: Location of instructions described in this chapter.

Systems	Instructions	Location
PLC 5, SLC 500, LOGIX	CTU, CTD, RES	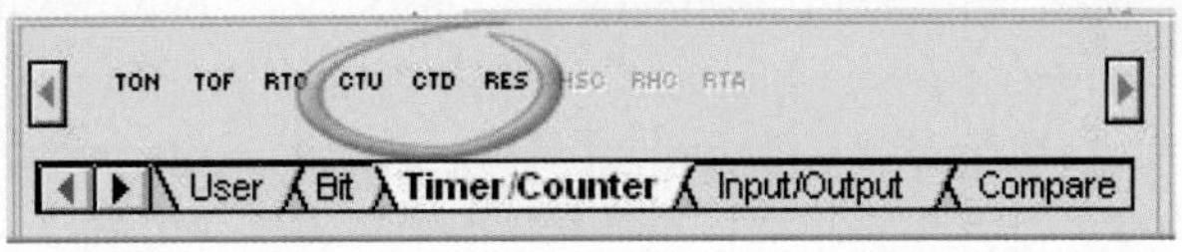 TON TOF RTO CTU CTD RES HSC RHC RTA User / Bit / **Timer/Counter** / Input/Output / Compare
PLC 5	ONS, OSR, OSF	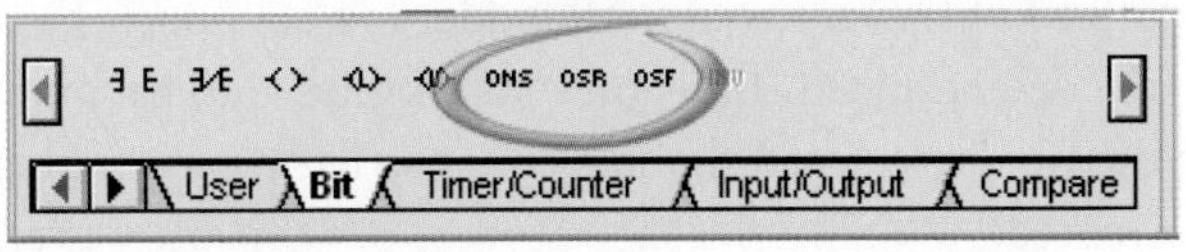 ⊣ ⊢ ⊣/⊢ <> <L> <U> ONS OSR OSF User / **Bit** / Timer/Counter / Input/Output / Compare
SLC 500	OSR	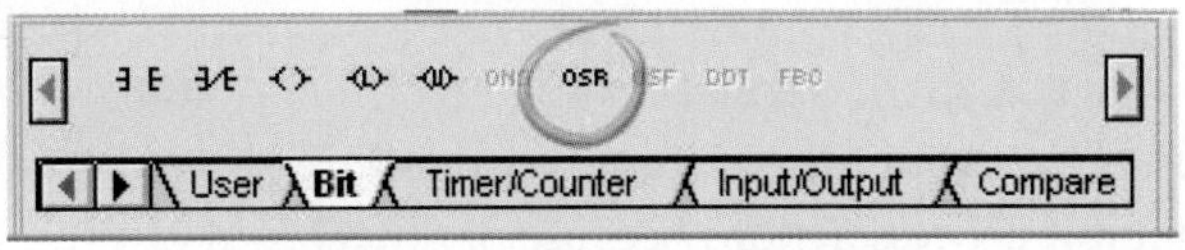 ⊣ ⊢ ⊣/⊢ <> <L> <U> ONS OSR OSF DDT FBC User / **Bit** / Timer/Counter / Input/Output / Compare
LOGIX	ONS, OSR, OSF	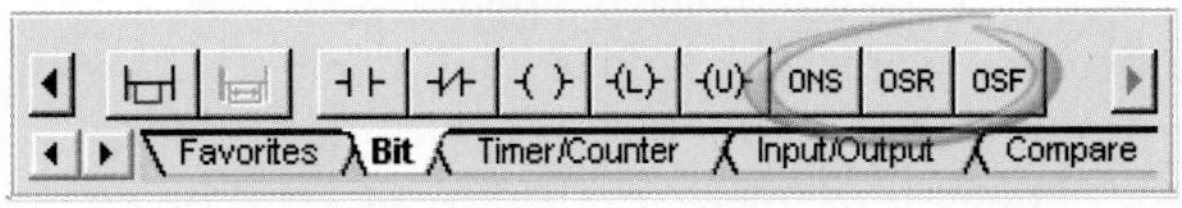 ⊣⊢ ⊣/⊢ ( ) (L) (U) ONS OSR OSF Favorites / **Bit** / Timer/Counter / Input/Output / Compare
PLC 5	TND	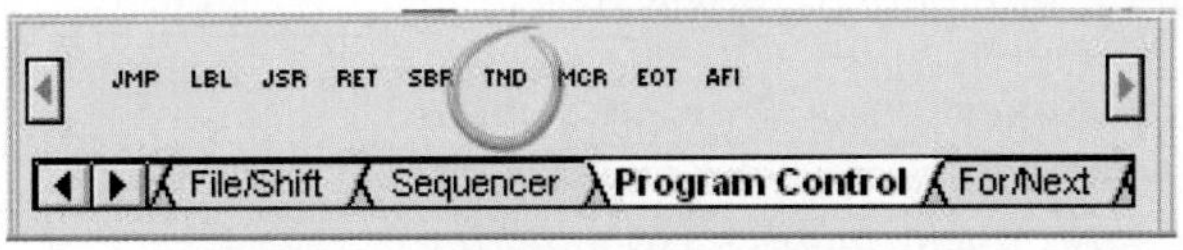 JMP LBL JSR RET SBR TND MCR EOT AFI File/Shift / Sequencer / **Program Control** / For/Next
SLC 500	TND, SUS	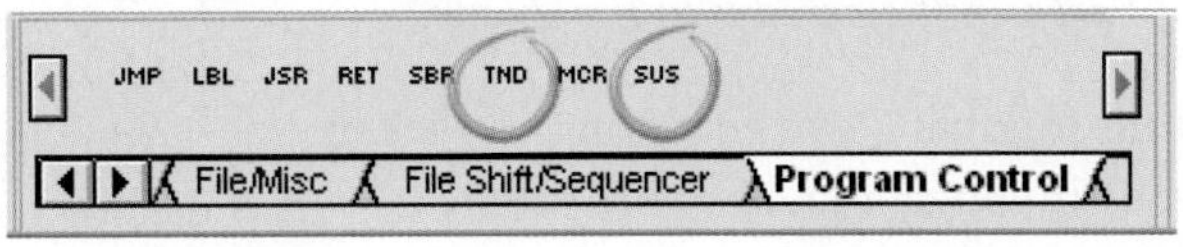 JMP LBL JSR RET SBR TND MCR SUS File/Misc / File Shift/Sequencer / **Program Control**
LOGIX	TND	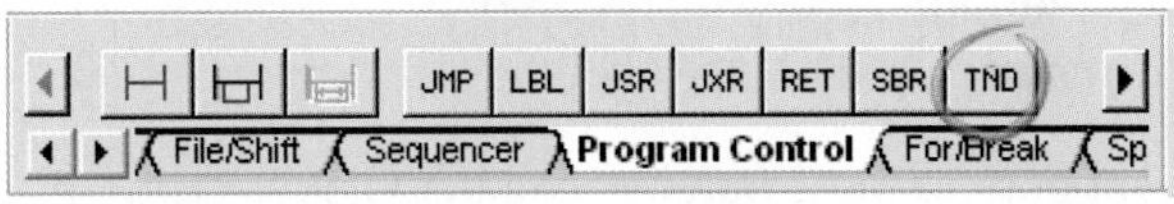 JMP LBL JSR JXR RET SBR TND File/Shift / Sequencer / **Program Control** / For/Break / Sp

CHAPTER 6

Arithmetic and Move Instructions

6-1 GOALS AND OBJECTIVES

There are three principal goals of this chapter. The first goal is to provide the student with information on binary arithmetic—adding, subtracting, multiplying, and dividing binary numbers. The second goal is to introduce the arithmetic and move instructions for the Allen-Bradley PLC 5, SLC 500, and Logix systems. The third goal is to show how the arithmetic and move instructions are applied to specific PLCs that are used in industrial automation systems.

After completing this chapter you should be able to

- Explain the concept of binary arithmetic.
- Describe one's and two's complement binary notation.
- Describe the arithmetic instructions (addition, subtraction, multiplication, division, square root, and clear) for the Allen-Bradley PLC 5, SLC 500, and Logix systems.
- Describe the move instructions (move, move with mask, and negate) for the Allen-Bradley PLC 5, SLC 500, and Logix systems.
- Develop ladder logic solutions using arithmetic and move instructions for the Allen-Bradley PLC 5, SLC 500, and Logix systems.

- Include arithmetic and move instructions in the empirical design process.
- Describe troubleshooting techniques for ladder rungs with arithmetic and move instructions.

6-2 BINARY ARITHMETIC

Before we discuss arithmetic PLC instructions, let's briefly examine binary arithmetic operations. These arithmetic operations include addition, subtraction, multiplication, and division.

The addition of binary numbers includes the following four sum combinations:

$$
\begin{array}{cccc}
0 & 0 & 1 & 1 \\
+0 & +1 & +0 & +1 \\
\hline
0 & 1 & 1 & 0 \text{ carry } 1
\end{array}
$$

Note that the results of the first three additions are obvious, but the fourth result needs some explanation. In the decimal system, $1 + 1 = 2$, but in the binary system $1 + 1 = 0$ with a carry of 1 to the next most significant place value because only two digits are available—1 and 0. Example 6-1 illustrates addition operations in the binary system.

EXAMPLE 6-1

Add the following decimal numbers using the binary system:

   a. 10 plus 2

   b. 28 plus 11

SOLUTION

Study the carrying concept in the solutions until you are familiar with it.

   a.   1   carry
      1010
      <u>0010</u>
      1100, which is 12

   b.   11   carry
      11100
      <u>01011</u>
      100111, which is 39

The subtraction of binary numbers includes the following difference combinations:

1	1	0	0	
-0	-1	-0	-1	
1	0	0	1	borrow 1

Note that the results of the first three subtractions are obvious, but in the fourth subtraction condition, borrowing a 1 from the next most significant place value is required. The borrowing concept in subtraction operations in the binary system is illustrated in Example 6-2.

EXAMPLE 6-2

Subtract the following decimal numbers using the binary system:

   a. 12 minus 2

   b. 28 minus 7

SOLUTION

Study the borrowing concept in the solutions until you are familiar with it.

   a.   1   borrow
      1100
      <u>0010</u>
      1010, which is 10

   b.   11   borrow
      11100
      <u>00111</u>
      10101, which is 21

The multiplication of binary numbers includes the following four product combinations:

$$0 \times 0 = 0 \quad 0 \times 1 = 0 \quad 1 \times 0 = 0 \quad 1 \times 1 = 1$$

EXAMPLE 6-3

Multiply 4 times 5 using the binary system

SOLUTION

```
            100
            101
            100
            000
            100
          10100, which equals 20
```

EXAMPLE 6-4

Divide 28 by 4 using the binary system

SOLUTION

```
          111 , which is 7
     100)11100
          100
          110
          100
          100
          100
          000
```

Binary numbers are multiplied in the same method as decimal numbers—form partial products and add them together. Example 6-3 illustrates this method. Likewise, dividing binary numbers is also accomplished in the same manner as decimal numbers. Division is illustrated in Example 6-4.

The binary arithmetic operations that were demonstrated involved only positive numbers. How negative numbers are represented in the binary system and used in arithmetic operations is discussed in the next section.

6-3 SIGNED BINARY NUMBERS

In binary systems, the plus sign, indicating a positive number, and the minus sign, indicating a negative number, cannot be handled in arithmetic operations. One method of representing a binary number as positive or negative is to assign a *sign bit* to the number as the most significant bit. If the sign bit is a 0, then the number is positive; if the sign bit is a 1, then the number is negative. There are two other methods available for representing the sign of a binary number—the one's complement and the two's complement. To *complement* a binary number means to change it to a negative number. The one's complement is obtained by changing 1s to 0s and 0s to 1s. The two's complement is obtained by adding 1 to the one's complement. Table 6-1 shows a decimal number and its equivalent binary number with a sign bit as a one's complement and as a two's complement. Two's complement is typically the preferred method because you can perform subtraction using addition.

Two's complement is the way computers represent integers. To get the two's complement negative notation of an integer, you write out the number in binary. You then invert the digits, and add 1 to the result. Suppose we're working with 8-bit quantities and want to find how −28 would be expressed in two's complement notation. Use the following steps.

1. First write 28 in binary form, which is 00011100.
2. Set the 0s to 1s and the 1s to 0s, which is 11100011.
3. Add 1, which yields 11100100, which is −28 in two's complement.

TABLE 6-1 Binary representation of decimal numbers.

Decimal Number	Magnitude with Sign Bit	One's Complement	Two's Complement
+7	0111	0111	0111
+6	0110	0110	0110
+5	0101	0101	0101
+4	0100	0100	0100
+3	0011	0011	0011
+2	0010	0010	0010
+1	0001	0001	0001
0	0000	0000	0000
−1	1001	1110	1111
−2	1010	1101	1110
−3	1011	1100	1101
−4	1100	1011	1100
−5	1101	1010	1011
−6	1110	1001	1010
−7	1111	1000	1001

EXAMPLE 6-5

Subtract 12 from 69 in 8-bit binary using the two's complement.

SOLUTION

The solution is 69 − 12 = 57 or 69 + (−12) = 57. When the negative 2's complement of 12 is added to 69, the result is 57.

> 01000101 (69)
> 11110100 (−12 in two's complement)
> 00111001 (57)

EXAMPLE 6-6

Subtract 69 from 12 in 8-bit binary using the two's complement.

SOLUTION

The solution is 12 − 69 = −57 or 12 + (−69) = −57. Note that the answer starts with a 1 in the sign bit to indicate that the answer is negative.

> 00001100 (12)
> 10111011 (−69 in two's complement)
> 11000111 (−57)

6-4 ALLEN-BRADLEY ARITHMETIC INSTRUCTIONS

Arithmetic instructions, or *math instructions* as they're called in some literature, allow the PLC to perform arithmetic and trigonometric operations on the contents stored in memory or register locations. The mnemonic, name, and description of the numerous instructions available in the Allen-Bradley PLC systems are displayed in Figure 6-1(a). The description of each instruction indicates what values are entered along with the location where the result of the math or trig operation is stored. All of the instructions in the figure are output instructions that are active when the rung is true.

6-4-1 Structure for Arithmetic Instructions

The *addition (ADD), subtraction (SUB), division (DIV), multiplication (MUL), square root (SQR), and clear (CLR)* instructions are used most often. The rest of the arithmetic instructions are used less often and typically in special applications. The first five instructions listed in Figure 6-1(a)

FIGURE 6-1: Allen-Bradley math instruction groups and symbols.

Instruction		Descriptions
Mnemonic	**Name**	
ADD	Add	Adds source A to source B and stores the result in the destination.
SUB	Subtract	Subtracts source B from source A and stores the result in the destination.
MUL	Multiply	Multiplies source A by source B and stores the result in the destination.
DIV	Divide	Divides source A by source B and stores the result in the destination and the math register.
DDV	Double Divide	Divides the contents of the math register by the source and stores the result in the destination and the math register.
CLR	Clear	Sets all bits of a word to zero.
SQR	Square Root	Calculates the square root of the absolute value of the source and places the integer result in the destination.
SCP	Scale with Parameters	Produces a scaled output value that has a linear relationship between the input and scaled values.
SCL	Scale Data	Multiplies the source by a specified rate, adds to an offset value, and stores the result in the destination.
ABS	Absolute	Calculates the absolute value of the source and places the result in the destination.
CPT	Compute	Evaluates an expression and stores the result in the destination.
SWP	Swap	Swaps the low and high bytes of a specified number of words in a bit, integer, ASCII, or string file.
ASN	Arc Sine	Takes the arc sine of a number and stores the result (in radians) in the destination.
ACS	Arc Cosine	Takes the arc cosine of a number and stores the result (in radians) in the destination.
ATN	Arc Tangent	Takes the arc tangent of a number and stores the result (in radians) in the destination.
COS	Cosine	Takes the cosine of a number and stores the result in the destination.
LN	Natural Log	Takes the natural log of the value in the source and stores it in the destination.
LOG	Log to the Base 10	Takes the log base 10 of the value in the source and stores the result in the destination.
SIN	Sine	Takes the sine of a number and stores the result in the destination.
TAN	Tangent	Takes the tangent of a number and stores the result in the destination.
XPY	X to the Power of Y	Raise a value to a power and stores the result in the destination.

(a)

FIGURE 6-1: (Continued).

(b) Math instruction symbol with three parameters

(c) Math instruction symbol with one parameter

(d) Math instruction symbol with two parameters

use the ADD instruction format with three parameters illustrated in Figure 6-1(b). These arithmetic operations are performed using the two operands, *Source A* and *Source B*, and the result of the operation is stored in the destination (*Dest*).

The structure for the clear instruction, Figure 6-1(c), has a single destination register to indicate the register value that goes to zero when the instruction's rung is true. The remaining instructions in

Figure 6-1(a) use the SQR instruction format with two parameters illustrated in Figure 6-1(d).

Data types for arithmetic operations. Most arithmetic operations in a PLC require only *single-precision arithmetic*, meaning the value of the operands and the result can be stored in one 16-bit register (one word). If the operation involves larger numbers, *double-precision arithmetic* is required. Double precision means that the PLC uses double the number of locations (32-bit registers) for the operation—two words for each operand and two words for the result. Table 6-2 indicates the register size and the numerical limits placed on data values for a number of different data types used with the math and trig instructions in the Logix processors. The PLC 5 and SLC systems have the same values except that they do not support double integers. Real data registers typically are double integers but can use three words to hold the value.

6-5 OPERATION OF ALLEN-BRADLEY ARITHMETIC AND MOVE INSTRUCTIONS

In the following subsections, the most commonly used arithmetic instructions and the move instructions are discussed. The discussion starts with the parameter requirements for the instruction registers and the updates to the status bits and math register that result from an instruction execution.

TABLE 6-2 Data types and binary value range for ControlLogix system.

Data Type	Bits						
	31	16	15	8	7	1	0
Bool	not used						0 or 1
Sint	not used				−128 to +127		
Int	not used			−32,768 to +32,767			
Dint			−2,147,483,648 to +2,147,483,647				
Real			-3.40282347E^{38} to −1.17549435E^{-38} (negative values)				
			0				
			1.17549435E^{-38} to 3.40282347E^{38} (positive values)				

Entering parameters. The values entered into the math instructions should conform to the following rules.

- Source: The *source* is the address(es) of the value(s) on which the mathematical or move operation is to be performed. This can be a word address or program constant value. An instruction that has two source operands does not accept program constants in both operands.
- Destination: The *destination* is the address where the result of the operation is placed. Signed integers in both the source and destination locations are stored in two's complement form.

Updates to arithmetic status bits. The arithmetic status bits are found in word 0, bits 0 to 3 in the controller status file, and the overflow trap bit is in word 5, bit 0. After an arithmetic instruction is executed, the arithmetic status bits in the status file are updated for the conditions described in Table 6-3.

The status bits are used in ladder programs to turn on warning lights when process calculations produce out of range results that could indicate a problem in the process. They also indicate when the result from an arithmetic operation exceeds the size of the destination register listed in the instruction.

Updates to the math register. Status word S:13 contains the *least* significant word of the 32-bit value of the MUL instruction. It contains the remainder for DIV instruction. Status word S:14 contains the *most* significant word of the 32-bit value of the MUL instruction. It contains the unrounded quotient for DIV instruction. S:13 and S:14 are not used when the math parameters are in the floating point or real data format.

Addressing floating point data file. The floating point file, F8 in the Allen-Bradley PLC 5 and SLC 500 systems, is used whenever fractional numerical data or numerical data with values greater than $+32,767$ or less than $-32,768$ are needed. Floating point data has two parts: an *integer* and an *exponent*. Two words are used to store floating point files, one for the integer and the second for the exponent. The Allen-Bradley SLC 500 systems support for floating point data registers in the math instructions starts with a model 503.

Floating point data is used most often with process systems where the data is *analog* and not *discrete*, and where field devices are analog process sensors and proportional control devices. In that setting analog input and output modules are required to pass the analog data into the PLC and back out for process control. The addressing used for floating point registers in the PLC 5 and SLC 500 systems is described in Table 6-4.

Floating point data is defined in the Logix processors by declaring the tag name a *Real data type* when the tag is defined.

6-5-1 Addition Instruction

The *addition instruction* (ADD) performs the addition of two values or operands that are placed in memory locations or registers and stores

TABLE 6-3 Status bits for arithmetic instruction.

Status Bit	Name	Description
S:0/0	Carry (C)	Bit is set if a carry is generated; otherwise it is cleared.
S:0/1	Overflow (V)	Bit is set if the result or value of the math instruction does not fit into the designated destination.
S:0/2	Zero (Z)	Bit is set if the result or value after a math, move, or logic instruction is a zero.
S:0/3	Sign (S)	Bit is set if the result or value after a math, move, or logic instruction is a negative (less than zero) value.
S:5/0	Overflow trap	The overflow trap bit (S:5/0) is set upon detection of a mathematical overflow or division by zero.

TABLE 6-4 Floating point register addressing.

Format		Explanation
Ff:e	**F**	Floating point file
	f	File number. Number 8 is the default file number (i.e., F8). A user-defined file number from 9 to 255 can be used if additional storage is required (e.g., F9 or F25).
	:	Element delimiter
	e	Element number. The element values range from 0 to 255 with each element using two words. As a result they are non-extended 32-bit numbers.
Examples	**F8:4** **F9:42**	Element 4, floating point file 8, Element 42, floating point file 9 (file 9 is a user-defined floating point file with 256 elements).

FIGURE 6-2: Allen-Bradley PLC 5 and SLC 500 systems addition instruction with PLC 5 input logic addresses.

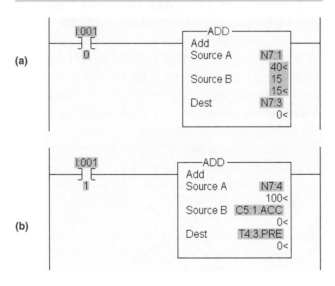

(a)

(b)

FIGURE 6-3: Allen-Bradley Logix system addition instruction.

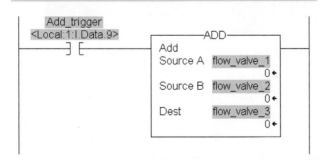

the result in another memory location or register. Figure 6-2 depicts the ADD instruction for the PLC 5 and SLC 500 systems. Figure 6-2(a) illustrates an ADD instruction where Source A points to an integer constant stored in N7:1, and Source B is set to a fixed value of 15.

Figure 6-2(b) illustrates a similar ADD instruction with two variables: an integer value in N7:4 and the value of the accumulator of counter C5:1. Note that the ADD instruction syntax is the same for PLC 5 and SLC 500, but the input address uses a PLC 5 format.

Note that in Figure 6-2(a) when I:001/0 is true, the value of Source A, N7:1 (40), is added to the fixed value (15) of Source B. The result of the addition is 55 and is stored in the destination, N7:3. In Figure 6-2(b), when I:001/1 is true, the value of Source A, N7:4 (100), is added to the value of Source B, C5:1.ACC, which is the accumulated value of counter number 1 in counter file 5. The result of the addition is stored in T4:3.PRE, which is the preset value of timer 3 in timer file 4.

In the ControlLogix system the operands in the ADD instruction are tag names as shown in Figure 6-3. Note that Source A is flow_valve_1, Source B is flow_valve_2, and the destination is flow_valve_3. The ControlLogix addition operation is the same as in the PLC 5 and SLC 500 systems.

6-5-2 Subtraction Instruction

The *subtraction instruction* (SUB) is shown in Figure 6-4. The value in Source B is subtracted from the value in Source A, and the result is stored in the destination. Note that when I:001/0 is true, the

value of Source B, N7:2 (25), is subtracted from the value of Source A, N7:1 (45). The result of the subtraction is 20, and it is stored in the destination, N7:3. As in the ADD instruction, the operands can be constants or variables for the PLC 5 and SLC 500 systems and are tag names for the Logix systems. On all arithmetic instructions, one constant can be entered directly into the arithmetic instruction without using an integer register to hold it.

6-5-3 Multiplication Instruction

The *multiplication instruction* (MUL) is shown in Figure 6-5. The value in Source A is multiplied by the value in Source B, and the result is stored in the destination. Note that when I:001/0 is true, the value of Source A, N7:1 (20), is multiplied by the value of Source B, N7:2 (3). The result of the multiplication is 60, and it is stored in the destination, N7:3. The operands can be constants or variables for the PLC 5 and SLC 500 systems and are tag names for the Logix system.

6-5-4 Division Instruction

The *division instruction* (DIV) is shown in Figure 6-6. The value in Source A is divided by the value in Source B, and the result is stored in the destination. Note that when I:001/0 is true, the value of Source A, N7:1 (40), is divided by the value of Source B, N7:2 (5). The result of the division is 8, and it is stored in the destination, N7:3. The operands can be constants or variables for the PLC 5 and SLC 500 systems and are tag names for the Logix system.

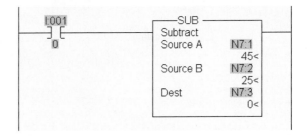

FIGURE 6-4: Allen-Bradley PLC 5 and SLC 500 systems subtraction instruction with PLC 5 input logic addresses.

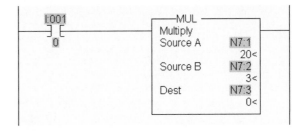

FIGURE 6-5: Allen-Bradley PLC 5 and SLC 500 systems multiplication instruction with PLC 5 input logic addresses.

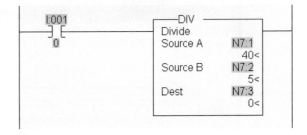

FIGURE 6-6: Allen-Bradley PLC 5 and SLC 500 systems division instruction with PLC 5 input logic addresses.

EXAMPLE 6-7

Design a ladder program with arithmetic blocks that converts degrees Fahrenheit to degrees Celsius.

SOLUTION

The formula that is implemented by the ladder program is

$$C = 5 \times (F - 32)/9$$

The solution is illustrated in Figure 6-7(a) using SLC PLC logic. The input and output values are shown in the data file view of integer registers N7:0 to N7:9 in Figure 6-7(b). The subtraction instruction subtracts Source B, N7:2 (32), from Source A, N7:1, which contains the value of the temperature 212 degrees Fahrenheit. The result of the subtraction operation (180) is stored in the destination, N7:3, which is also Source A of the multiply instruction. Source A is multiplied by Source B, N7:4 (5). The result of the multiplication operation (900) is stored in the destination, N7:5, which is also Source A of the division instruction. Source A is divided by Source B, N7:6 (9). The result, which is 100 degrees Celsius, is located in the destination, N7:7.

FIGURE 6-7: Solution for Example 6-7.

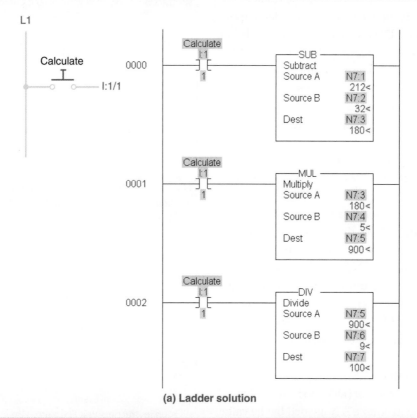

(a) Ladder solution

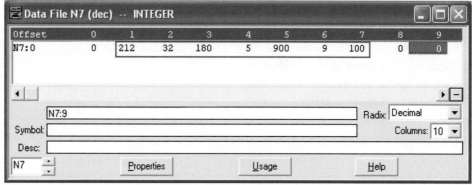

(b) Integer data register values

Field Device Power Rails. In previous chapters and problems, the input and output field device wiring was shown with all power sources and ground terminations illustrated. This was done so that the wiring of field devices to input and output modules could be learned. However, industry ladder documentation shows input contacts connected to a vertical power rail called L1 and all output field devices connected to a vertical power rail called L2. This simplified wiring convention will be used for the remainder of the ladder examples in the text. These power rails, L1 and L2, could be any positive DC voltage, an AC voltage, or a ground. It is assumed that the PLC input and output modules have been matched to the field device requirements for DC sinking/sourcing currents or an AC voltage level. A complete field wiring drawing is produced that indicates all power wiring and grounds. For input field devices, the only two things that must be known to analyze the ladder logic are the contact type (NO or NC) and the condition of the field device (activated or not activated). All output field devices are even simpler—if the OTE instruction is true the output field device is on, and if the OTE is false the field device is off.

EXAMPLE 6-8

Design a ladder program with arithmetic blocks that sets the upper and lower limits of a laboratory temperature chamber to plus and minus one-half percent of a manually set temperature.

SOLUTION

The solution is illustrated in Figure 6-8 using SLC 500 logic. The input and output values are shown in the data file view of floating point registers F8:0 to F8:9 in Figure 6-8(b). The multiplication instruction multiplies Source A, F8:1, which is the set temperature, by Source B, which is a constant value of 0.005. The result is stored in the destination, F8:3, which is also Source B of the subtraction and addition instructions. The results in F8:3 are subtracted from the set temperature, F8:1, and stored in the destination, F8:4, which is the lower temperature limit. Similarly, the results in F8:3 are added to the set temperature and stored in the destination, F8:5, which is the upper temperature limit.

FIGURE 6-8: Solution for Example 6-8.

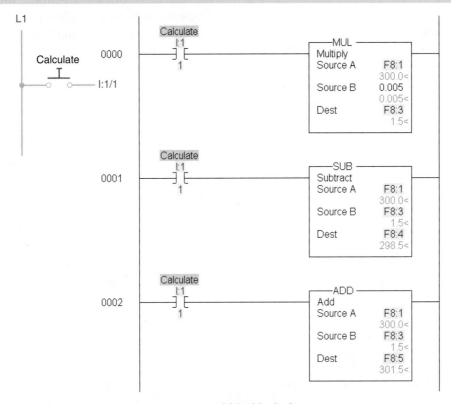

(a) Ladder logic

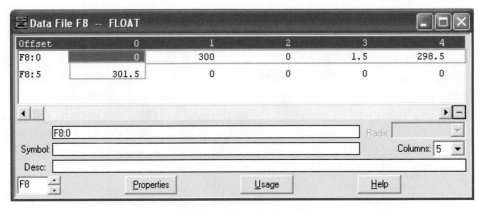

(b) Floating point data file

Changing register values. The integer and floating point registers shown in Figures 6-7(b) and 6-8(b) are the dialog boxes in the RSLogix 5 and RSLogix 500 computer-based software for the PLC 5 and the SLC 500, respectively. These boxes allow the user to view data results and to enter data into registers. Integer data is entered into an N7 register by first selecting the radix (lower-right drop-down menu) to be used for the value. Next, the data word in the register is selected by clicking on the current value. The new value is entered in the selected radix and then the Enter key is pressed. The new value appears in the register location and in the instruction field where that register is displayed. The changes can be made with the processor in program or run mode. If the radix is changed after a number is entered, then the display switches to the new radix value. This procedure works with the binary (B3) and floating point (F8) data files as well, except that the F8 registers can only be entered and displayed in the decimal radix. The Logix systems permit the same type of data value viewing in the program tags dialog box with the monitor tags tab selected. Data is entered and changed in the same dialog box but with the edit tags tab selected.

6-5-5 Square Root Instruction

The *square root* (SQR) instruction performs the mathematical operation of taking the square root of a constant or variable. As illustrated in Figure 6-9, the number whose square root is to

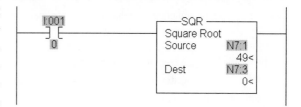

FIGURE 6-9: Allen-Bradley PLC 5 and SLC 500 systems square root instruction with PLC 5 input logic addresses.

be determined is in the source, and the result is placed in the destination. If the value of the source is negative, then the number in the destination is the square root of the absolute value of the source. Note that when I:001/0 is true, the square root of the value of the source, N7:1 (49), is taken. The result of the operation is 7 and is stored in the destination, N7:3. The operands can be constants or variables for the PLC 5 and SLC 500 systems and are tag names for the Logix system.

6-5-6 Move Instructions

The *move instructions* copy the contents of one memory location or register to another memory location or register. In this section, the following three move instructions are discussed:

- The *move* (MOV) instruction, which moves data from one location to another.
- The *move with a mask* (MVM) instruction, which moves only designated bits from one location to another.

EXAMPLE 6-9

Design a ladder program to calculate the hypotenuse of a right triangle whose side A is 6, side B is 8, and side C is the hypotenuse.

SOLUTION

The formula, which is the called the Pythagorean Theorem, is

$$C^2 = A^2 + B^2, \text{ or } C = (A^2 + B^2)^{1/2}$$

The solution is illustrated in Figure 6-10. The first MUL instruction multiplies Source A by Source B, which both are F8:1 (6), thus yielding side A squared that is stored in destination F8:3 (36). The second MUL instruction multiplies Source A by Source B, both of which are F8:2 (8). This operation yields side B squared, which is stored in destination F8:4 (64). The ADD instruction stores the sum of the squares (side A squared plus side B squared) in destination F8:5 (100). Note that F8:5 is also the source of the SQR instruction. The result of the SQR instruction is stored in destination F8:6, which is 10—the value of side C. The raise a number to a power (X to the power of Y) instruction, XPY, is another option where the MUL instructions are used.

FIGURE 6-10: Solution for Example 6-9.

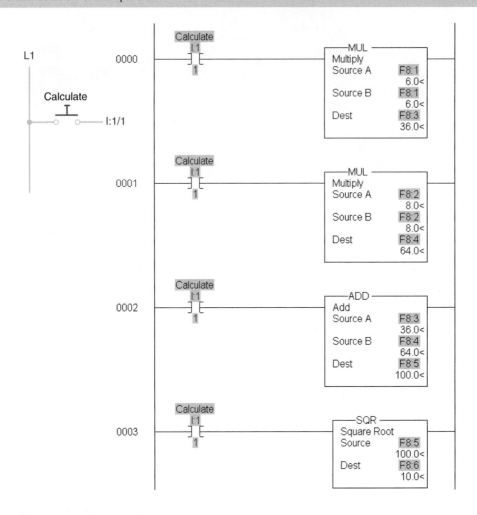

- The *negate* (NEG) instruction, which moves the negative representation of the data from one location to another.

Figure 6-11 illustrates all three move instructions for the SLC 500. Figure 6-11(a) illustrates the MOV instruction. When input contact I:1/1 is true, the contents of the source, N7:0, are moved to the location designated as the destination, N7:6. Figure 6-11(b) illustrates the MVM instruction. Now when I:1/1 is true, only the portion of the source, N7:1 (18998), that is aligned with the 1s in the mask, N7:2 (F0FFh), is moved to the destination, N7:3. Study the 1–0 bit pattern in Figure 6-11(b) until you are familiar with the move with a mask operation. The MVM instruction is effectively an AND operation between the source data and the mask data. When a 1 in the mask is ANDed with either a 0 or 1 in the source, the result in the destination is the value of the source bit.

When a 0 in the mask is ANDed with the source bit, the destination bit is always a 0. Finally, Figure 6-11(c) depicts the NEG instruction. The negative representation of the contents of the source, N7:4, is moved to the contents of the destination, N7:5. Positive numbers are stored in binary format; negative numbers in two's complement.

6-6 STANDARD LADDER LOGIC FOR ALLEN-BRADLEY MATH AND MOVE INSTRUCTIONS

Several standard ladder logic configurations are used in the design of rungs that include math and move instructions. Figure 6-12 illustrates four configurations with features that can be mixed and matched to solve most ladder logic requirements for math and move instructions. Note that the configurations show an addition (ADD) instruction as the output, but any of the other math (SUB, DIV,

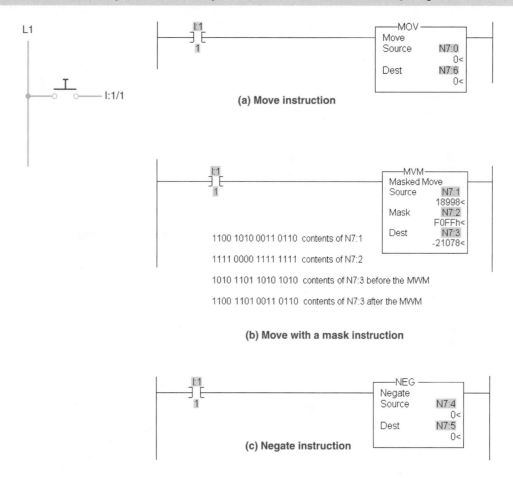

(a) Move instruction

1100 1010 0011 0110 contents of N7:1

1111 0000 1111 1111 contents of N7:2

1010 1101 1010 1010 contents of N7:3 before the MWM

1100 1101 0011 0110 contents of N7:3 after the MWM

(b) Move with a mask instruction

(c) Negate instruction

MUL, or SQR) instructions or the move (MOV) instruction could be substituted.

Math/Move standard A. The application addressed in Figure 6-12(a) features the use of an *unconditional rung* to activate an output instruction. In many applications the process requires that a mathematical manipulation or the transfer of data occur as often as possible. When no input logic is present the output instruction is true every scan. The sampling rate is equal to the scan rate because the output is true every scan. This configuration is used in applications that require continuous calculations or moves on real-time data to update the output register. For example, if a MOV output instruction is used and the source is the input address of an analog data channel from the output of a color sensor, then every scan of the color value is moved to a destination register.

Math/Move standard B. The configuration in Figure 6-12(b) uses one or more input logic instructions to determine when the math or move instruction is active. This is the more traditional implementation of the instructions. Output action occurs when the source register(s) is loaded and the input conditions make the rung true.

Math/Move standard C. The configuration in Figure 6-12(c) uses one or more input logic instructions to determine when the math or move instruction is active. In addition, a one-shot rising (OSR) instruction is placed just before the output instruction. This makes the math or move instruction active for only one scan. This configuration could be used, for example, to move data from a color sensor measuring the color of a part passing beneath it on

Application	Standard Ladder Logic Rungs for All Math and Move Instructions
Turn on an output math or move instruction as often as possible in the ladder logic. No input logic is present so the rung is always active. The result of this unconditional input condition is an addition instruction at the output that is executed with every scan. The sample rate for this active output is equal to the scan rate. While the addition instruction is used in the configuration example, any of the other math instructions (SUB, DIV, MUL, or SQR) or the move (MOV) instruction could be substituted. Also, this standard would be the same for the PLC 5 except for addresses and the same for ControlLogix except for the use of tags.	![diagram] ADD — Add; Source A N7:1 0<; Source B N7:3 0<; Dest N7:5 0< (a)
Schedule the activation of an output math or move instruction by the action of an input field device(s) and the true condition of the input ladder logic. The input field device(s) and the input ladder logic in the addition instruction rung determine when the output is active and the addition is performed. As a result, the addition operation is executed on a schedule and at a rate determined by the field devices. While the addition instruction is used in the configuration example, any of the other math instructions (SUB, DIV, MUL, or SQR) or the move (MOV) instruction could be substituted. Also, this standard would be the same for the PLC 5 except for addresses and the same for ControlLogix except for the use of tags.	I:1 0 ─] [─ ADD — Add; Source A N7:1 0<; Source B N7:3 0<; Dest N7:5 0< (b)
Turn on an output math or move instruction for only one scan after the action of an input field device(s) and the true condition of the input ladder logic. The input field device(s) and the input ladder logic in the addition instruction rung determine when the output is active and the one shot assures that the addition is performed for only one scan. While the addition instruction is used in the configuration example, any of the other math instructions (SUB, DIV, MUL, or SQR) or the move (MOV) instruction could be substituted. Also, this standard would be the same for the PLC 5 except for input addresses and the OSR instruction would change to ONS. It is the same for ControlLogix except for the use of tags and the change to the ONS instruction.	I:1 0 ─] [─ B3 3 ─[OSR]─ ADD — Add; Source A N7:1 0<; Source B N7:3 0<; Dest N7:5 0< (c)

EXAMPLE 6-10

Design the ladder logic that multiplies the accumulator of counter C5:3 with the first four bits of the input word I:2.0. Place the results in N7:4.

SOLUTION

Rung 0 in the solution, Figure 6-13, uses standard ladder logic A to continuously move the counter accumulator values into N7:3 from counter C5:3. Rung 1 (standard ladder logic B) moves values from the input image table, register I:2.0, to N7:2 through a mask (000F) that filters out all but the first four bits. The move occurs when input I:1/0 is true (NO push button pressed), and the multiply occurs when rung 2 is true, which requires that both push buttons be pressed. The results are placed in N7:4.

FIGURE 6-12: (Continued).

Application	Standard Ladder Logic Rungs for All Math and Move Instructions
Use an ADD or SUB instruction to build an incremental adder or subtractor in an X = X + A or Y = Y - B implementation. When an ADD instruction is used in this format, the value in an integer or floating point register (X) is added to a process variable or tag value (B) and the result or answer is placed back into the original register (X). The one shot assures that the instruction is executed one time for every false to true change in the input logic. The same format can be used with the subtraction instruction. Also, this standard would be the same for the PLC 5 except for input addresses and the OSR instruction would change to ONS. It is the same for ControlLogix except for the use of tags and the change to the ONS instruction.	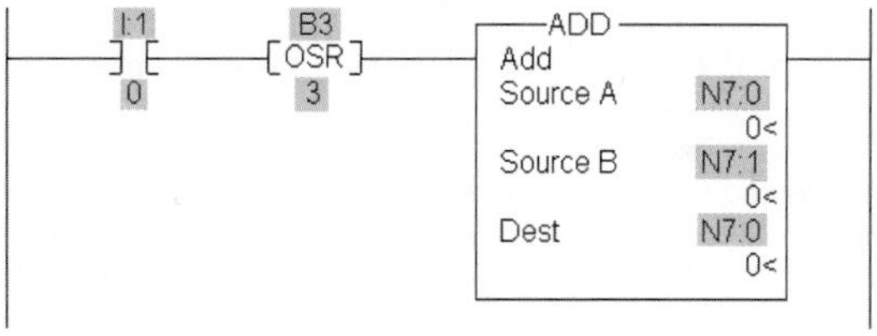 (d)

a conveyor. Figure 6-14 illustrates the timing diagram for the color sensor application. Note the following:

- The color values from the color sensor are only valid for a fixed time when the part is passing under the sensor. Values generated directly before and after the valid time are not usable.
- The trigger pulse produced by the sensor has a rising edge within the valid data region, but the falling edge of the pulse is outside the valid data region. The pulse width is not a valid

trigger since part of the pulse falls outside the valid data window.
- The narrow one-shot pulse produces one scan that falls within the valid data value.

The move instruction is active for only one scan time due to the one-shot instruction, even though the trigger signal is true much longer. The one-shot instruction moves the data in the narrow window of time when the data is valid. If the one-shot instruction was not present, then the trigger pulse from the sensor would produce multiple scans that included invalid color data. In that case, the last

---

EXAMPLE 6-11

Design a ladder program to move the part color value from a color sensor similar to that illustrated by the timing diagram in Figure 6-14. Two values should be moved to N7:0 and N7:1, and the average value should be calculated and placed in N7:2. The color data comes from I:2.0, and the color sensor trigger is connected to terminal 0 on the input module in slot 4 of the SLC 500. The color value is valid for 500 milliseconds; the trigger pulse starts 5 milliseconds after the color value is valid and is true for 700 milliseconds.

SOLUTION

The solution in Figure 6-15 uses the standard ladder logic from Figure 6-12(c) in rung 0 and Figure 6-12(b) in rung 2 for moving a color value at two different points in the sensor output into registers N7:0 and N7:1, respectively. The first sample requires OSR instruction in the rung because the trigger pulse is true for 700 milliseconds, but the second sample just uses an XIC instruction with the timer done bit since T4:0/DN is true for only one scan. This timer is used to delay the second sample and move until 400 milliseconds after the color value is valid. Therefore, one sample is taken at the beginning of the color reading and one is taken near the end. The final two rungs use math instructions to create an average value from the two readings.

FIGURE 6-13: Solution for Example 6-10.

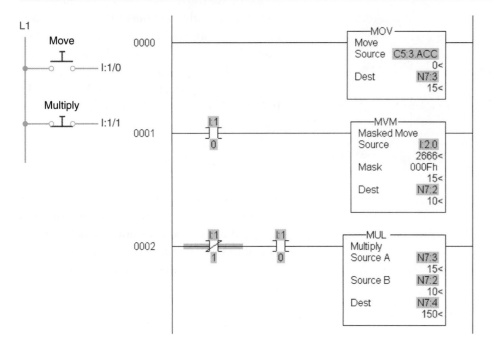

(a) Ladder logic

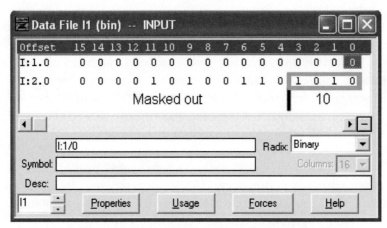

(b) Input image table and data file with masked out bits and passed
bits shown. Note passed bits have a value of 10

value moved before the trigger pulse returns from true to false would be the value stored in the destination register, and that value would be during invalid color data. This configuration is the opposite of the ladder in standard ladder logic A, which activated the output on every scan.

Math/Move standard D. The configuration in Figure 6-12(d) uses one or more input logic instructions and the OSR instruction to determine when this math instruction is active. This implementation is used with addition (ADD) and subtraction (SUB) instructions to perform cumulative addition or subtraction. The syntax for the ADD instruction in the rung in Figure 6-12(d) is N7:0 = N7:0 + N7:1, where (destination) = N7:0 (Source A) + N7:1 (Source B) or N7:0 = N7:0 + N7:1, where Source A can be any integer or floating point register (in SLC 503 and higher) and Source B is an integer or floating point

FIGURE 6-14: Color sensing timing diagram.

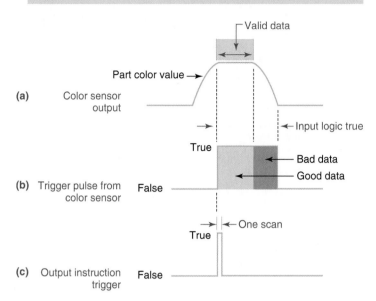

register that has changing values that must be added or subtracted. The value in Source A is added to the value in Source B and the sum is placed back into Source A as the destination register. This configuration is used when it is necessary to have a running total for the values in a register that is changing at regular intervals. If Source B is a fixed value then the register in Source A is incremented by that constant value with every execution.

When a math instruction rung is true, it will execute the instruction on every scan. Therefore, with this configuration it is important to have only one scan for each false to true transition of the input logic. The one-shot instruction takes care of this single scan requirement. This output action occurs when the Source B register is loaded and the input conditions make the rung true.

EXAMPLE 6-12

A vision camera scans the pallet bar codes as they pass, the number of parts on the pallet (not a constant value) is extracted from the bar code data, and that number is transferred to a PLC and placed in register N7:5. The B3:0/3 bit in the PLC is turned on by the vision system when the quantity data has transferred. The total number of pallets is stored in N7:4. Design a ladder program that keeps a running total for pallet parts in N7:6 and the number of pallets left in the batch in N7:4. Include logic for a normally open push button (PB) switch (I:1/4) that is used to clear register N7:6 at the end of a production run in preparation for the next batch.

SOLUTION

Rung 0 in Figure 6-16 totals the pallet parts, and rung 1 in the figure subtracts 1 from the total number of pallets in the batch. The standard ladder logic in Figure 6-12(d) is used for both rungs. The last rung uses the clear instruction to reset the parts counter at the end of the production run. This same PB input could be used with a move instruction to load the number of pallets for the next batch into N7:4.

This example illustrates how many PLC programs have numerous solution options. For example, rung 0 could be replaced by two rungs. The first rung would add N7:5 to the total in N7:6 and place the results in a third register, N7:8. Then the second rung would move the new total in N7:8 to the total register N7:6. Also, rung 1 could be built with a count down counter that keeps the total number of remaining pallets to be processed stored in the accumulator.

A second lesson learned is the value of instruction descriptions. Compare the solution in Figure 6-16 with the solution in Figure 6-15. Notice how the instruction descriptions in Figure 6-16 make it easier to understand and learn the operation of the ladder logic compared to an undocumented ladder.

EXAMPLE 6-13

A limit switch operates a counter, which counts rubber balls coming off a conveyer for loading into a shipping carton. Four different size balls use the same conveyer and the same size carton. The carton can hold 96 balls

---

for each math instruction, but often the same Boolean expression is used to trigger all calculations.

Step 3: (Determine the number of math instructions necessary to solve the stated equation): Often the equation as stated in the process description can be simplified to reduce the number of math instructions required. For example, the equation $Y = A \times B + A \times C$ would require three instructions: two multiplications for the two products and an addition to add the products together. However, if the equation is written $Y = A \times (B + C)$, then only two instructions are required: an addition for the sum in the parentheses and a multiplication for the final product. Therefore, Step 3 is to simplify the expression if possible and then determine the types of math instructions needed for the solution.

Step 4: (Determine the order or sequence of operation of the math instructions for the simplified equation): The examples in Step 3 illustrate this point. Note in the first equation $(A \times B + A \times C)$ that the sequence would be two rungs with MUL instructions followed by a rung with an ADD instruction. In the second case $[A \times (B + C)]$, the sequence would be an ADD instruction followed by an MUL instruction. A general rule is to make calculations in the following order: first, compu-

tations inside parentheses; next, multiplication and division; and finally, addition and subtraction.

Move instruction. The move instruction is often used to support the loading of parameters into other PLC instructions. For example, the preset values of counters and timers are often changed by a move instruction. In other cases the move instruction is used to shift data from one register to another. The complete empirical process is listed in Section 3-11-4; the modifications for move instructions follow.

Step 1: (Write the process description): Include a complete description of movement of data between registers and between registers and instruction parameter locations. Also, identify clearly the trigger used for the moves. The trigger, which includes input field devices and internal logic, falls into two categories: conditional using input logic and unconditional with a trigger initiated in every scan.

Step 2: (Write Boolean equations for all move instruction triggers): A Boolean expression is needed to describe the trigger for each move instruction.

Examples 6-14 and 6-15 demonstrate how math and move instructions are added into the design process.

EXAMPLE 6-14

Example 5-2 had the following problem statement.

Design the ladder logic for an industrial application that packages canned vegetables supplied by a conveyor. When 12 cans are detected by a current sourcing proximity sensor, a packaging operation is initiated. The production line must package 200 boxes of 12 cans per shift. When 200 packages have been completed, a red stack light is illuminated. While the system is packaging cans, a green stack light is illuminated. A total count of cans packaged per shift should also be recorded.

Modify the conveyor ladder solution in Figure 5-14 for Example 5-2 as follows:

- A label-checking sensor verifies that all cans have labels attached. All cans without labels are ejected before packaging station.

- The number of ejected cans is counted and the total number of cans currently on the conveyor is determined.

- The number of ejected cans and the total number of cans on the conveyor are transferred to integer registers every 60 minutes.

- Select registers as needed.

FIGURE 6-17: Solution for Example 6-13.

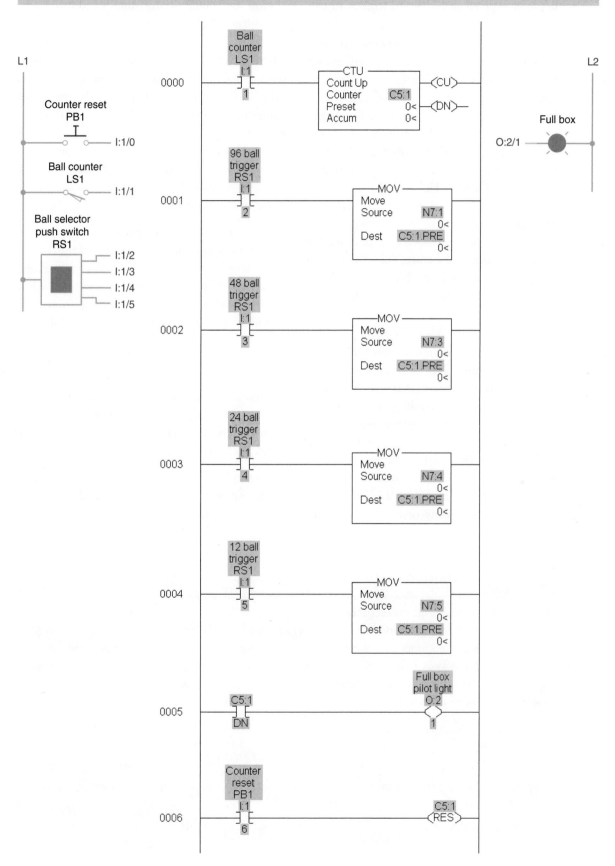

FIGURE 6-16: Solution for Example 6-12.

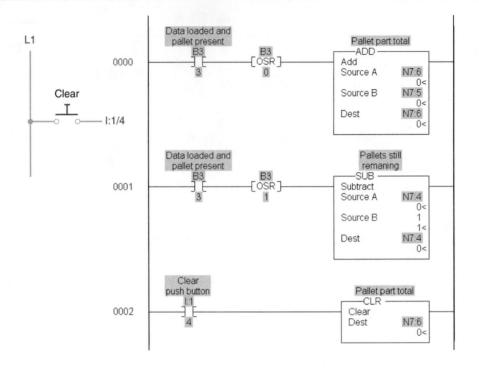

6-7 EMPIRICAL DESIGN PROCESS WITH MATH AND MOVE INSTRUCTIONS

The empirical design process, introduced in Section 3-11-4, is an organized approach to the design of PLC ladder logic programs. However, the term *empirical* implies that some degree of trial and error is present. As more instructions are added to the design, the process becomes more complex. However, the process used for new instructions is quite similar to that learned in the previous chapters.

6-7-1 Adding Math and Move Instructions to the Process

The first step in using mathematical and move instructions in PLC ladder designs is to know what parameter values are entered in the source and destination registers and all the standard math/move circuits illustrated in Figure 6-12. In addition, it is important to know when these output instructions should be true for only one scan, which dictates when a one-shot instruction is needed to trigger the outputs. Stop now and review these if necessary.

Math instructions. The use of math instructions implies a mathematical equation. Review

Examples 6-7 and 6-9 and notice that their problem statements listed an equation that required the math instructions to solve. The number of rungs required depends on the complexity of the equation. Every mathematical operation (ADD, SUB, MUL, DIV, and SQR) requires a separate output, which is usually on a separate ladder rung. The complete empirical process is listed in Section 3-11-4; the modifications for math instructions are as follows:

Step 1: (Write the process description): Include a complete description of the numerical solution necessary for the stated problem. Note especially the type of numeric data present, integer versus real numbers, since it dictates the data type for the tag names in ControlLogix or register types needed for PLC 5 and SLC 500. Also, identify clearly the trigger used for the calculations. The trigger, which includes input field devices and internal logic, falls into two categories: conditional using input logic and unconditional with a trigger initiated every scan. The required standard ladder logic configurations are often determined at this point as well.

Step 2: (Write Boolean equations for all math instructions): A Boolean expression is needed

FIGURE 6-15: Solution for Example 6-11.

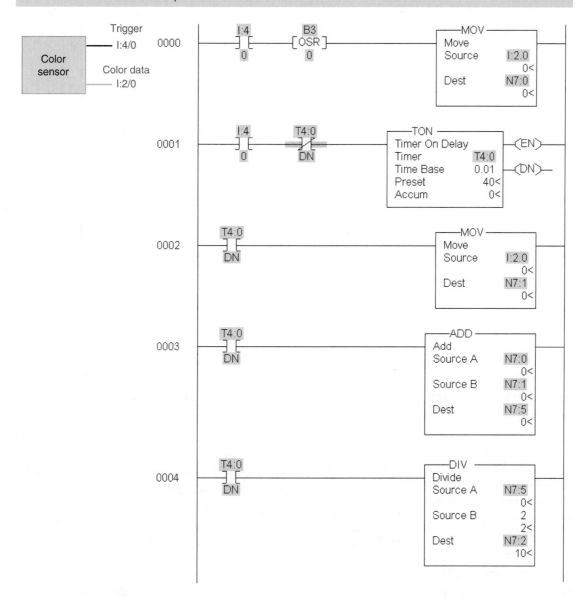

FIGURE 6-15: Solution for Example 6-11.

of type A, 48 balls of type B, 24 balls of type C, and 12 balls of type D. A pilot light is illuminated when the carton is full. Select the necessary input field devices and design a ladder logic program to satisfy this automation task.

SOLUTION

The solution is illustrated in Figure 6-17. The field devices selected for the design include a NO reset PB switch, the NO contacts on the limit switch ball counter, and a ball selector pushbutton to identify the types of balls on the conveyor. The destination for each move instruction is the counter's preset register, and the source for each counter is an integer register that holds the desired box ball count for each size of ball. When the ball selector pushswitch activates input I:1/2, source N7:1 (96) is moved to C5:1.PRE, which is the counter's preset. When the pushswitch activates input I:1/3, source N7:3 (48) is moved to the counter's preset. When the pushswitch activates input I:1/4, source N7:4 (24) is moved to the counter's preset. When the pushswitch activates input I:1/5, source N7:5 (12) is moved to the counter's preset. The done bit of C5:1 turns on the full box pilot light, and the push button PB1 resets the counter accumulator to 0.

FIGURE 6-17: Solution for Example 6-13.

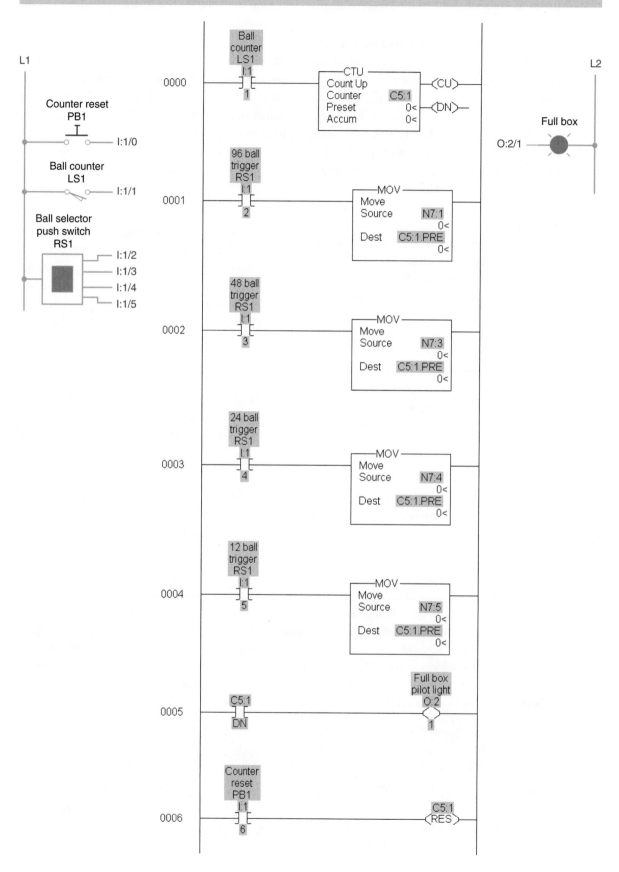

for each math instruction, but often the same Boolean expression is used to trigger all calculations.

Step 3: (Determine the number of math instructions necessary to solve the stated equation): Often the equation as stated in the process description can be simplified to reduce the number of math instructions required. For example, the equation $Y = A \times B + A \times C$ would require three instructions: two multiplications for the two products and an addition to add the products together. However, if the equation is written $Y = A \times (B + C)$, then only two instructions are required: an addition for the sum in the parentheses and a multiplication for the final product. Therefore, Step 3 is to simplify the expression if possible and then determine the types of math instructions needed for the solution.

Step 4: (Determine the order or sequence of operation of the math instructions for the simplified equation): The examples in Step 3 illustrate this point. Note in the first equation $(A \times B + A \times C)$ that the sequence would be two rungs with MUL instructions followed by a rung with an ADD instruction. In the second case $[A \times (B + C)]$, the sequence would be an ADD instruction followed by an MUL instruction. A general rule is to make calculations in the following order: first, compu-

tations inside parentheses; next, multiplication and division; and finally, addition and subtraction.

Move instruction. The move instruction is often used to support the loading of parameters into other PLC instructions. For example, the preset values of counters and timers are often changed by a move instruction. In other cases the move instruction is used to shift data from one register to another. The complete empirical process is listed in Section 3-11-4; the modifications for move instructions follow.

Step 1: (Write the process description): Include a complete description of movement of data between registers and between registers and instruction parameter locations. Also, identify clearly the trigger used for the moves. The trigger, which includes input field devices and internal logic, falls into two categories: conditional using input logic and unconditional with a trigger initiated in every scan.

Step 2: (Write Boolean equations for all move instruction triggers): A Boolean expression is needed to describe the trigger for each move instruction.

Examples 6-14 and 6-15 demonstrate how math and move instructions are added into the design process.

EXAMPLE 6-14

Example 5-2 had the following problem statement.

Design the ladder logic for an industrial application that packages canned vegetables supplied by a conveyor. When 12 cans are detected by a current sourcing proximity sensor, a packaging operation is initiated. The production line must package 200 boxes of 12 cans per shift. When 200 packages have been completed, a red stack light is illuminated. While the system is packaging cans, a green stack light is illuminated. A total count of cans packaged per shift should also be recorded.

Modify the conveyor ladder solution in Figure 5-14 for Example 5-2 as follows:

- A label-checking sensor verifies that all cans have labels attached. All cans without labels are ejected before packaging station.

- The number of ejected cans is counted and the total number of cans currently on the conveyor is determined.

- The number of ejected cans and the total number of cans on the conveyor are transferred to integer registers every 60 minutes.

- Select registers as needed.

Review the previous design and then design ControlLogix ladder rungs for the required modifications.

SOLUTION

The empirical design information includes:

- All data values present are integer data.
- The trigger for counting the cans without labels (bad_can_counter) can be either the missing label sensor input or the can ejector output.
- The trigger for the MOV and SUB instructions must be executed every 60 seconds, so an update timer with a preset value of 60,000 (60,000 units × 0.001 seconds per unit = 60 seconds) is required.

The standard ladder logic in Figure 6-12(b) is used since the SUB instruction must be triggered at regular intervals. The move instruction uses the same ladder configuration for the same reason. The following Boolean logic is used for the ladder rungs:

$$\text{Ejector} = \text{bad\_can\_sensor}$$
$$\text{Bad\_can\_counter} = \text{ejector}$$
$$\text{Move instruction} = \text{transfer\_timer/DN}$$
$$\text{SUB instruction} = \text{transfer\_timer/DN}$$

Based on this information the ladder solution in Figure 6-18 was developed for the Allen-Bradley ControlLogix PLC. Rung 0 uses a proximity sensor to detect cans that enter the conveyor system and to increment the accumulator of the counter Total_can_count. The can sensor is a diffused type photoelectric sensor used to reflect light from the bright metal can when the label is missing. The sensor does not detect cans with the paper label attached. Unlabeled cans are counted and ejected by rungs 1 and 2, respectively. Rung 3 is a regenerative timer used to generate a continuous stream of output pulses every 60 seconds. The done bit, used as a trigger for the move and subtraction instructions, is true for one scan. Rung 4 moves the bad_can_count to an integer register (Bad_can_total), and rung 5 calculates the total_cans_packaged from the total that entered the conveyor less the number of bad cans. Results are placed in tag Total_cans_packaged. Study the ladder logic solution and verify that the ladder satisfies the problem description in the example.

Notice how the Logix system's use of tag names for all variables and registers makes it easier to understand the ladder logic solution for the problem, even when instruction descriptions are not present.

EXAMPLE 6-15

Example 5-5 had the following problem statement.

A conveyor system, illustrated in Figure 5-26, sorts boxes so that each chute receives 10 boxes. The operation is as follows:

- *Gates 1 and 2 are up, sensor S1 counts 10 boxes for chute 1, and then gate 1 drops.*
- *Sensor S2 counts 10 boxes for chute 2 and then gate 2 drops.*
- *Sensor S3 counts 10 boxes for chute 3 and then gates 1 and 2 are raised and the process starts over.*
- *With average conveyor speed, it takes 4 seconds for the boxes to enter the chute after the sensor detects them.*

Modify the conveyor ladder solution in Figure 5-27 (Example 5-5) for the following operations.

- Determine the total box count for each chute.
- Determine the total box count for all three chutes.
- Move the counts to integer registers at the completion of each distribution cycle.
- Select registers as needed.

Review the previous design and then design SLC 500 ladder rungs for the required modifications. Note that the counter accumulator values generated in Figure 5-27 are used in the solution for this problem.

FIGURE 6-18: Solution for Example 6-14.

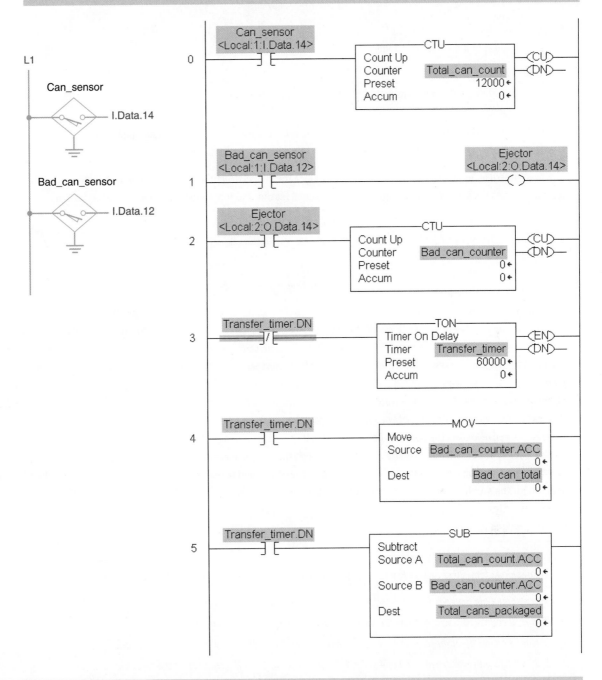

The empirical design information data types and event triggers includes (Note: the counter and timer instructions are from the ladder logic in Figure 5-27):

- All data values present are integer data.
- The chute 1 total trigger is the Chute 1 counter done (C5:0/DN).
- The chute 2 total trigger is the Chute 2 counter done (C5:1/DN).
- The chute 3 total trigger is the done bit of the last box delay timer (T4:0/DN).
- The data calculate and move trigger is the done bit of the last box delay timer (T4:0/DN).

The standard ladder logic in Figure 6-12(d) is used to add the new total to the previous total and place the answer back into the original register. The following Boolean logic is used to trigger the ADD instruction for the ladder rungs:

Chute 1 adder = C5:0/DN

Chute 2 adder = C5:1/DN

Chute 3 adder = C5:2/DN

Chute 1 and 2 subtotal = Last box delay timer (T4:0/DN)

Total box count = Last box delay timer (T4:0/DN)

Based on this information the ladder solution in Figure 6-19 was developed using an SLC 500 PLC. All three chute total adders (rungs 0, 1, and 2) are configured like the standard in Figure 6-12(d), so the total is continually updated. The OSR is used to make the ADD instructions true for only one scan. The last box delay signal timer (Figure 5-27) done bit is used to add the three chute totals together to determine the total box count. The solution could be simpler since all three chutes get 10 boxes, but the solution illustrated is valid if the box count per chute is changed. If the count would always remain the same, then the T4:0/DN bit could just add 30 (3 × 10) to the current box total. Study the ladder logic solution and verify that the ladder satisfies the problem description in the example.

6-8 TROUBLESHOOTING MATH AND MOVE LADDER LOGIC

The most difficult programs with math instructions to verify are those with multiple math instructions and that execute at a fast rate. An additional problem in troubleshooting math instruction rungs is to determine if the problem is in the program or if the data coming into the math instructions from the process is bad.

Move instructions offer few operational problems. If a section of the ladder that includes a move instruction is not operating properly, then you can use any of the following suggestions to troubleshoot it along with the math instructions present.

- If PLC rungs with math instructions do not produce the correct results, then first verify that the data from the process is correct by viewing the PLC 5 and SLC 500 dialog boxes for the input image table, integer image table, and floating point image table illustrated in Figure 6-20. If a ControlLogix processor is used the program and control tags are viewed in the dialog box displayed in Figure 6-21. Note that the register values can be displayed in binary, octal, hexadecimal, and decimal format, depending on the type of data present.
- Check the arithmetic status bit S5:0 (see the Section 6-5 subsection *Updates to Arithmetic Status Bits*) to determine if an overflow or divide by zero has occurred.

- Test the sequence of math rungs one rung at a time to verify that each rung is performing properly. Use the temporary end instruction, TND, described in Chapter 4 to halt the ladder execution after each rung.
- Use the suspend instruction, SUS, to verify status values for all registers and bits at critical points in the ladder. The SUS instruction is described in Section 5-8-1.
- Be aware of situations where computed math values are used to update internal PLC memory bits *and* cause the execution of process actions. Since the scan time and internal update time of registers is much faster than most process events, the event may not be able to complete the action before the drive signal for the event is removed. This type of problem is described well in the counter problem described in Section 5-8-2.
- Use the test options on some of the Allen-Bradley SLC 500 models in the single-step, single-scan, or continuous-scan test modes to isolate and run portions of the ladder logic. These tests are described in the next section.

6-8-1 SLC 500 Test Modes

Most of the test modes operate much like the program run mode with the exception of energizing the output field devices. The processor will read input field devices, execute the ladder program, and update the output image table; however, the output field devices are not turned on. The following

FIGURE 6-19: Solution for Example 6-15.

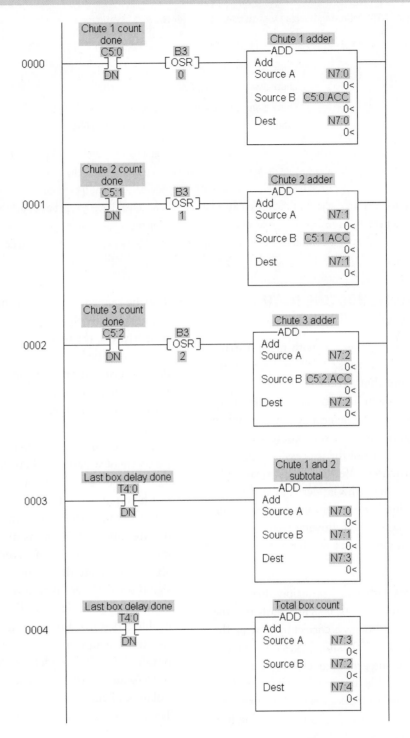

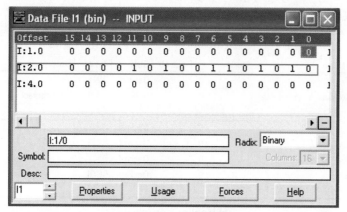

(a) Input image table data files

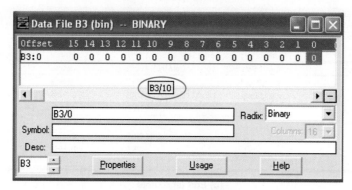

(b) Virtual relay data files

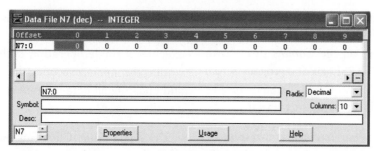

(c) Integer word data files

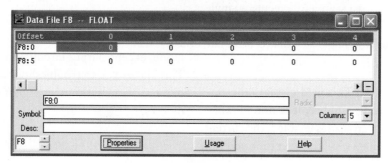

(d) Floating point word data files

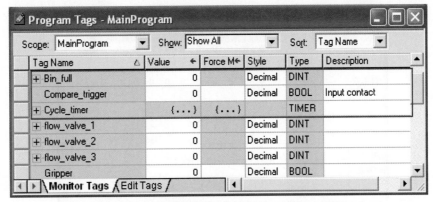

(a) Monitor tags table

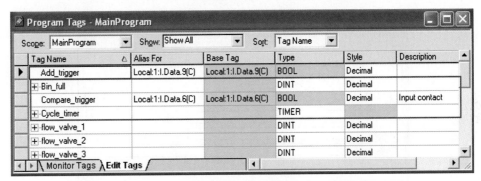

(b) Edit tags table

test modes can be used to test any PLC ladder program in the SLC 500 systems. The modes are selected by clicking on the *Comms* drop-down menu at the top of the RSLogix 500 program screen and then selecting *Mode*. The PLC system must be in the run mode for the options to be active.

Single-Step test mode. The *single-step test mode*, available on SLC 5/02 and higher controllers, initiates the processor to scan and execute a single rung or group of rungs. The mode is set up with parameters in the Test Single Step dialog box. The parameters include:

Current Location: This field displays the current file and rung number; it is not editable. When a single-step scan is enabled, the current location is retained until the next time you call up the dialog box.

Go Breakpoint: A *breakpoint* is established by entering a file and rung number from which the single-step scanning should begin. The scan is started by clicking *Go Single Step*.

Go Single Step: Initiates single-step scanning.

Single-Scan test mode. The *single-scan test mode*, available with all Allen-Bradley controllers, executes a single operating cycle that includes reading the inputs, executing the ladder program, and updating all data without energizing output circuits.

Go Single Scan: Click this button to start a single scan of the ladder program.

Continuous-Scan test mode. The *continuous-scan test mode* is the same as the REM run mode, except output circuits are not energized. This allows you to troubleshoot or test your ladder program without energizing output field devices.

6-9 LOCATION OF THE INSTRUCTIONS

The location of instructions from this chapter in the Allen-Bradley programming software is indicated in Figure 6-22.

FIGURE 6-22: Location of instructions described in this chapter.

Systems	Instructions	Location
PLC 5, SLC 500	ADD, SUB, MUL, DIV, SQR, NEG	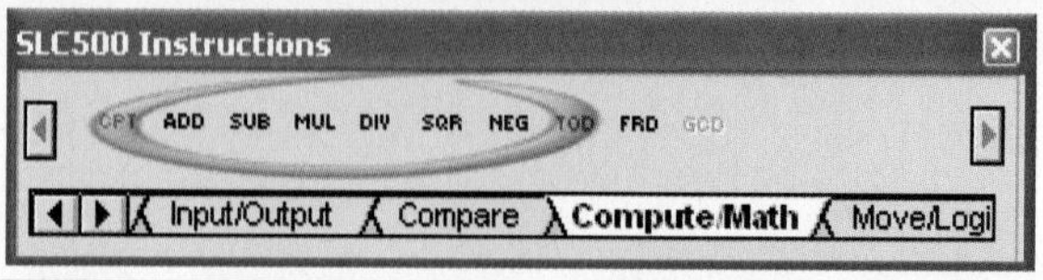
LOGIX	ADD, SUB, MUL, DIV, SQR, NEG	
PLC 5, SLC 500	MOV, MVM, CLR	
LOGIX	MOV, MVM, CLR	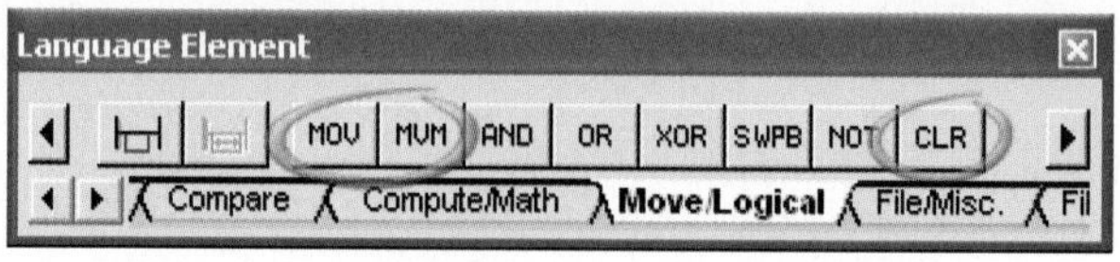

Conversion and Comparison Instructions

7-1 GOALS AND OBJECTIVES

There are two principal goals of this chapter. The first goal is to provide the student with information on the binary coded decimal and hexadecimal numbering systems and conversion instructions. The second goal is to show how the PLC's comparison and BCD conversion instructions are used in programs for industrial automation systems.

After completing this chapter you should be able to:

- Explain the binary coded decimal (BCD) and hexadecimal numbering systems.
- Use the convert to BCD (TOD) instruction and the convert from BCD (FRD) instruction.
- Convert numbers between the decimal, binary coded decimal, and hexadecimal systems.
- Describe the operation of the equal to, not equal to, less than, greater than, less than and equal to, greater than and equal to, and limit test instructions in Allen-Bradley PLCs.
- Design and analyze ladder logic programs, which use comparison and BCD conversion instructions.
- Develop automation solutions given an industrial control problem using the comparison and BCD conversion instructions for

Allen-Bradley (AB) PLC 5, SLC 500, and ControlLogix PLCs.
- Include comparison instructions in the empirical design process.
- Describe troubleshooting techniques for ladder rungs with comparison instructions.

7-2 BINARY CODED DECIMAL SYSTEM

The *binary coded decimal* (BCD) system is a binary number system with a relatively easy conversion process between the decimal (system used by humans) and binary coded decimal (system used for automation data) number representation. The BCD system uses four binary bits to represent the decimal numbers 0 through 9. The BCD representation of a decimal number is obtained by replacing each decimal digit by its equivalent four-bit binary number. Table 7-1 illustrates the relationship between the decimal, binary, and BCD numbering systems, and Figure 7-1 presents a decimal to BCD conversion example. The BCD number in Figure 7-1 is just the binary equivalent for each decimal digit. Use the data in Table 7-1 to verify the BCD answer in the figure.

A push switch, also called a pushwheel or thumbwheel switch, is often used to input numerical values and set points into a machine

TABLE 7-1 Decimal, binary, and BCD counting comparison.

Decimal	Binary	BCD		
0	0000			0000
1	0001			0001
2	0010			0010
3	0011			0011
4	0100			0100
5	0101			0101
6	0110			0110
7	0111			0111
8	1000			1000
9	1001			1001
10	1010		0001	0000
11	1011		0001	0001
12	1100		0001	0010
13	1101		0001	0011
18	10010		0001	1000
19	10011		0001	1001
20	10100		0010	0000
98	1100010		1001	1000
99	1100011		1001	1001
100	1100100	0001	0000	0000
498	111110010	0100	1001	1000
499	111110011	0100	1001	1001
500	111110100	0101	0000	0000

or process controlled by a PLC. A four-digit push switch is shown in Figure 7-2 with the + button and − button labeled. The push switch is a new version of the older thumbwheel switch where the digits were changed by rotating a geared thumbwheel. The push switch in Figure 7-2 can have 4 (BCD output), 8 (octal output), or 10 (decimal output) SPST (single pole single throw) switches with one terminal from each switch connected to a common terminal. Figure 7-2(b) shows the four SPST switches for a BCD version of the push switch with two BDC digits. The push switch has the decimal number 63 entered, with 6 representing the most significant digit. Note that the four switches for this most significant digit are wired to the four most significant bits of the eight point input module. The switches for the digit 3 connect to the least significant bits of the PLC input.

The push switch output tables in Figure 7-3(a and b) illustrate a 10-position 10 switch decimal and 10-position 4 switch BCD, respectively. The 10-position decimal push switch has 10 SPST switches corresponding to switch values 0 to 9. For example, when the switch has a value of 3, the third SPST switch connecting the common terminal to the output terminal of the switch is closed. The 10-position BCD push switch creates a BCD code for the value dialed into the push switch.

The new push and older thumbwheel switches are examples of a device that converts decimal numbers to BCD numbers and is used as an interface to PLC inputs. Likewise, the PLC output of a BCD number can be interfaced to a sevensegment display, which converts it to a decimal number. PLCs have instructions to convert BCD to binary because push switches produce BCD numbers, but the PLC instructions operate on the

FIGURE 7-1: Decimal to BCD conversion.

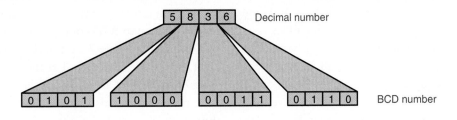

binary value of decimal numbers. Also, the binary to BCD instruction is necessary because seven-segment displays require a BCD output from the PLC. Figure 7-4(a) depicts a four-digit push switch as an input device connected to a PLC and a four-digit, seven-segment display as an output device connected to a PLC. The switch output lines are labeled 8, 4, 2, and 1 for each of the BCD number digits 9234_{BCD}. The BCD bit pattern of 1001 0010 0011 0100 is indicated by the blue and black signal wires (blue closed switch and black open switch). Note that the PLC output wiring, Figure 7-4(b), and seven-segment display input lines are similarly labeled. The Allen-Bradley BCD conversion instructions are covered in the following sections.

7-2-1 Allen-Bradley BCD Instructions and Standard Ladder Logic

The Allen-Bradley BCD conversion instructions are *convert to BCD* (TOD) and *convert from BCD* (FRD). Figure 7-5 illustrates these two instructions. The TOD instruction converts 16-bit integers to a BCD equivalent, and the FRD instruction converts a BCD number to its 16-bit integer equivalent.

Because the BCD number, before and after the conversion, is stored in a 16-bit integer register, the size of the register presents a problem. Note that status bit S:2/1 in Tables 7-2 and 7-3 indicates when this problem is present in the PLC 5 and SLC 500 PLCs. The problem arises because the number of bits required to store a number in BCD is larger than the bit total for the same number value stored in binary. An example illustrates this point. A 16-bit integer register with the maximum permitted value of $+32.767_{10}$ would have a bit pattern of 0111111111111111_2 or the first 15 bits for the number and a sign bit. When the same decimal number, $+32.767_{10}$ is converted to BCD, the representation is 0011 0010 0111 0110 0111_{BCD}. As you can see, it takes 20 bits to store the equivalent BCD number. The largest BCD number that a 16-bit integer register (four groups of four bits) can store is 9999. Each of the Allen-Bradley processors handles this problem differently.

PLC 5 BCD Instructions and Standard Logic. The BCD conversion instructions for the PLC 5 are limited to BCD values in the 0 to 9999

FIGURE 7-2: BCD push switch.

(a) BCD push switch

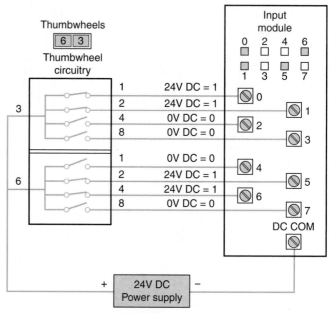

(b) Input wiring for BCD push switch

Courtesy of Cherry Electrical Products.

FIGURE 7-3: Input/Output truth table for 10-position decimal and BCD push witches or thumbwheel switches.

Ten-position decimal

Dial position	Common to:									
	0	1	2	3	4	5	6	7	8	9
0	●									
1		●								
2			●							
3				●						
4					●					
5						●				
6							●			
7								●		
8									●	
9										●

(a)

Ten-position BCD

Dial position	Common to:			
	1	2	4	8
0				
1	●			
2		●		
3	●	●		
4			●	
5	●		●	
6		●	●	
7	●	●	●	
8				●
9	●			●

(b)

Rehg and Sartori, Industrial Electronics, *1st Edition, © 2006, Reprinted by permission of Pearson Education, Inc., Upper Saddle River, NJ.*

FIGURE 7-4: Push switch input and seven-segment output.

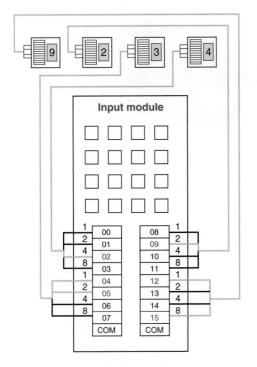

(a) Push switch input with SLC
PLC module in slot 2

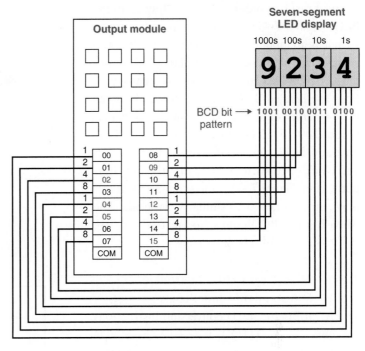

(b) Seven-segment output with SLC
PLC module in slot 3

FIGURE 7-5: TOD and FRD instructions.

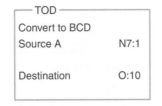

(a) Convert to BCD instruction (TOD)

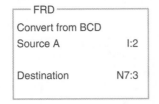

(b) Convert from BCD instruction (FRD)

range. As a result, the integer file bit length is adequate to handle all conversions with both instructions, TOD and FRD. However, the largest binary integer that can be converted to BCD is 10001111101111_2 or the decimal equivalent of 9999. The range of BCD values restricts negative number conversion into BCD as well.

Standard ladder logic rungs for the TOD and FRD instructions are illustrated in Figure 7-6. Read the implementation in the figure.

The status bits for the PLC 5 are listed and described in Table 7-2. A study of the table indicates that BCD values outside the accepted range cause the overflow bit to be set and a minor error to be generated. Zero results cause the S:2/2 status bit to be set to true.

SLC 500 BCD Instructions and Standard Logic. Model 502 and higher SLC processors execute the BCD instructions in the following modes:

Mode 1: If the BCD source address values are not over 9999 decimal or BCD, then the destination address can be the word address of any integer data file.

Mode 2: If the BCD source address values could reach the integer maximum value of 32,767, then the math register S:13 must be used for the destination address.

In executing the two modes, the SLC processor uses status bits to indicate the conditions

TABLE 7-2 PLC 5 status bits.

Status bit	Name	Description
S:2/1	Overflow (V)	Bit is set if the BCD result is outside the range of 0 to 9999 and a minor error is generated, but is reset otherwise.
S:2/2	Zero (Z)	Bit is set if the result or value after a conversion is negative or zero.

(a) Status bit table for TOD instruction

Status bit	Name	Description
S:2/2	Zero (Z)	Bit is set if the result or value after a conversion is a zero, but is reset otherwise.

(b) Status bit table for FRD instruction

TABLE 7-3 SLC 500 status bits.

Status bit	Name	Description
S:0/1	Overflow (V)	Bit is set if the BCD result is larger than 9999 and minor error bit S:5/0 is also set.
S:0/2	Zero (Z)	Bit is set if the result or value after a conversion is a zero, but is reset otherwise.
S:0/3	Sign (S)	Bit is set if the source word is a negative value, but is reset if the source word is a positive value.

(a) Status bit table for TOD instruction

Status bit	Name	Description
S:0/1	Overflow (V)	Bit is set if the source word is a non-BCD value or if the value is greater than 32,767, but is reset otherwise. If the bit is set the minor error bit S:5/0 is also set.
S:0/2	Zero (Z)	Bit is set if the result or value after a conversion is a zero, but is reset otherwise.

(b) Status bit table for FRD instruction

present in the BCD conversion. Study the status bits in Table 7-3 regarding the operational status of the two SLC 500 BCD conversion instructions.

In mode 1 the SLC operation is similar to the PLC 5 logic described in the standard ladder logic rungs in Figure 7-6. Integer registers are used for source and destination addresses. However, if a negative number is entered into the source address, then the absolute value of the number is generated before the conversion and the sign status bit, S:0/3, is set.

In mode 2 the SLC operation handles BCD numbers over 9999 but not greater than the integer maximum value of +32,767. The conversion of decimal numbers this large into their BCD equivalent requires 20 binary bits (five groups of 4 bits each), so the 16-bit data registers will not

work. To facilitate conversions of numbers of this size, the math registers S:13 and S:14 must be used. Also, since the number is larger than 9999, the overflow status bit, S:0/1, is set, and the fault condition must be reset. The standard ladder logic rungs used for the SLC 500 for this type of conversion are illustrated in Figure 7-7.

Some comments on the standard ladder rungs and examples in Figure 7-7 follow:

- When math register S:13 is placed in the source or destination address, both S:13 and S:14 data are used in the conversion.
- The S:5/0 minor error bit is reset in the ladder in Figure 7-7(a) before the end of the scan, so no major error occurs.
- In the TOD instruction in Figure 7-7(a), the converted decimal value is stored as a BCD

Application	Standard Ladder Logic Rungs for PLC 5 and SLC 500 BCD Instructions
Convert the binary value of a decimal number to its equivalent BCD value when a trigger is generated by the action of an input field device(s) and the true condition of the input ladder logic. The binary to BCD conversion instruction (TOD) in the PLC 5 system is used to convert a positive binary number with a decimal value of 9999 or less into the equivalent BCD value. The SLC 502 and higher processors use the same standard ladder logic for the TOD instruction to convert a positive or negative binary number with a decimal value of 9999 or less into the equivalent BCD value. Study the example solution illustrated below the ladder rung to understand how the TOD instruction performs when the source decimal values are not greater than 9999_{10}.	I:1 ⊣ ⊢ 1 — TOD — To BCD — Source N7:3 9760< — Dest N10:0 9760h< 9 7 6 0 N7:3 Decimal 0010 0110 0010 0000 ↓ ↓ ↓ ↓ 9 7 6 0 N10:0 4-digit BCD 1001 0111 0110 0000 (a)
Convert a BCD value to its binary equivalent value when a trigger is generated by the action of an input field device(s) and the true condition of the input ladder logic. The BCD to binary conversion instruction (FRD) in the PLC 5 system is used to convert a positive BCD value of 9999 or less into the binary number equivalent. The SLC 502 and higher processors use the same standard ladder logic for the FRD instruction to convert a positive BCD value of 9999 or less into the binary number equivalent. Study the example solution illustrated below the ladder rung to understand how the FRD instruction performs when the source BCD values are not greater than 9999_{BCD}.	I:1 ⊣ ⊢ 1 — FRD — From BCD — Source N7:3 9760h< — Dest N10:0 9760< 9 7 6 0 N7:3 4-digit BCD 1001 0111 0110 0000 ↓ ↓ ↓ ↓ 9 7 6 0 N10:0 Decimal 0010 0110 0010 0000 (b)

number (00032760) in math registers S:14 (most significant digits 0003) and S:13 (the least significant digits 2760).

- In Figure 7-7(a), the BCD number is moved from the math registers to two outputs: O:3.0, the least significant four digits (2760_{BCD} which is equal to 10080_2), and O:4.0, the most significant digit (3_{BCD} which is equal to 3_2). The output address uses the dot (.) 0 notation indicating that the 16-bit words 3 and 4 are the target of the BCD number move. Also, a masked move (MVM) instruction is used because only the four least significant bits of the S:14 16-bit word are critical (they hold the value 3).
- The math register (S:13 and S:14) is used as the source for the FRD instruction and holds

the BCD value of 32,760 in Figure 7-7(d). The 5-digit BCD number $32,760_{BCD}$ has a BCD bit pattern of

S:14	S:13			
3	2	7	6	0
0000 0000 0000 0011	0010	0111	0110	0000

The FRD instruction converts the $32,760_{BCD}$ to $32,760_{10}$, where the decimal value has a binary representation of

0111 1111 1111 1000

Note that when $32,760_{10}$ is converted to BCD the BCD value is $32,760_{BCD}$ but the bit pattern of the BCD number is not the same as the

Application	Standard Ladder Logic Rungs SLC 500 for BCD instructions Over 9999
Convert the binary value of a decimal number over 9999 to its equivalent BCD value when a trigger is generated by the action of an input field device(s) and the true condition of the input ladder logic. The TOD instruction in the SLC 502 and higher processors use the math registers S:13 and S:14 for the destination address for conversion of numbers over 9999. The larger number causes the overflow status bit S:0/1 and the minor error bit S:5/0 to be set. The ladder resets the minor error bit before the ladder completes the scan so no error flag is set. The results are then placed into math registers S:13 and S:14. Review the example solution illustrated below the ladder rung to understand how the TOD instruction performs when the source decimal values are greater than 9999_{10}.	

binary representation or bit pattern for the equivalent decimal value. This is a point of confusion when discussing binary coded decimal numbers and regular decimal numbers.

ControlLogix BCD Instructions and Standard Logic. The TOD instruction takes the decimal value between 0 and 99,999,999 stored in the source register and converts it to a BCD value that is stored in the destination register. The allowed source and destination date types are single integer (SINT), integer (INT), and double integer (DINT). The parameters placed into the source include variables in the form of tag names and positive integer values, called *immediate values* by Allen-Bradley. The parameter placed in

FIGURE 7-7: (Continued).

Application	Standard Ladder Logic Rungs SLC 500 for BCD instructions Over 9999
Convert a BCD value over 9999 to its binary equivalent value when a trigger is generated by the action of an input field device(s) and the true condition of the input ladder logic. The FRD instruction in the SLC 502 and higher processors used the math registers S:13 and S:14 for the source address for conversion of numbers over 9999. The overflow bit is only set if a non-BCD number is present in the source address or if the number is greater than 36,767. The S:14 bit is cleared in case the BCD value has only 4 bits (S:14 is not used) and current data in S:14 would make the conversion incorrect. Note that the N7:2 value of 4660_{10} is the decimal equivalent of the BCD number 1234_{BCD}. The FRD instruction registers always display the numbers in BCD. Study the example solution illustrated below the ladder rung to understand how the FRD instruction performs when the source BCD values are greater than 9999_{BCD}.	

the destination is a tag name. Placement of a negative value in the source creates a minor fault and clears the destination.

The standard ladder rung for the ControlLogix BCD TOD instruction is illustrated in Figure 7-8(a). Note that the rung looks like the PLC 5 and SLC 500 rungs except that tags are used in place of memory-specific registers found in the earlier PLCs.

The FRD instruction converts a BCD value in the source register to a decimal value and stores the result in the destination register. The allowed data types and parameters are the same as the TOD instruction, and no fault conditions are present. The standard ladder rung for the ControlLogix BCD FRD instruction is illustrated in Figure 7-8(b).

Standard Logic for BCD with One-Shot (OSR) Instruction. Output field devices used to display process parameters often require that their input

data or the output from the PLC be in a BCD format. The FRD instruction is used to convert the internal PLC integer file to a BCD format. The ladder rungs in Figure 7-8(a and b) convert input BCD values to binary and then convert binary results to BCD output values. The conversions are controlled by the input signal *Compare_trigger*. One problem must be addressed, however. If the input instruction in Figure 7-6(a) is true for several seconds, then the conversion instruction will execute on every scan while the instruction is true. Now, if the input data in N7:3 is changing rapidly, then those changes will be passed to the destination, N7:10, and eventually to an output display after every scan, which could make an output display flicker as numbers change.

This situation is solved by placing a one-shot rising (OSR) instruction in the TOD instruction rung. The solution is illustrated in Figure 7-9 in the

FIGURE 7-8: Standard ladder logic for ControlLogix BCD instructions.

Application	Standard Ladder Logic Rungs for ControlLogix BCD instructions
Convert the binary value of a decimal number from 0 to 99,999,999 to its equivalent BCD value when a trigger is generated by the action of an input field device(s) and the true condition of the input ladder logic. The TOD instruction in the ControlLogix processors converts the decimal tag value from the source into an equivalent BCD value and stores as the destination tag name. The negative number causes a minor error bit to be set.	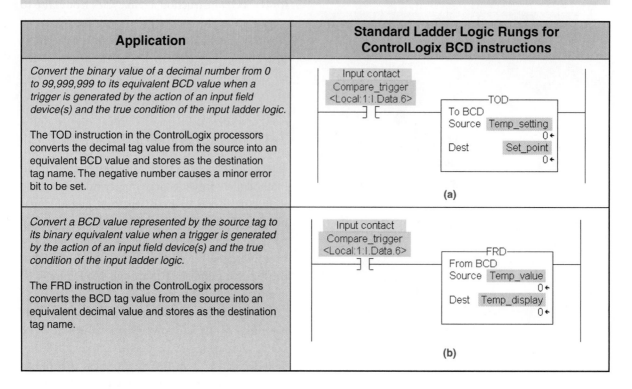
Convert a BCD value represented by the source tag to its binary equivalent value when a trigger is generated by the action of an input field device(s) and the true condition of the input ladder logic. The FRD instruction in the ControlLogix processors converts the BCD tag value from the source into an equivalent decimal value and stores as the destination tag name.	

FIGURE 7-9: Standard ladder logic for SLC 500 BCD instructions for BCD values sampled with a one-shot instruction.

Application	Standard Ladder Logic Rungs for SLC 500 BCD instructions
Convert the binary value of a decimal number coming from a rapidly changing source register or tag and convert it to BCD for display in any type of digital field device display. The input logic triggers the conversion of the integer decimal value from the counter accumulator to the BCD equivalent using the TOD instruction. The one-shot assures that the conversion is performed only one time during the first scan when the trigger logic changed from false to true, so the timer accumulator value present at that scan is converted to BCD. The BCD value in binary form is visible in the output register image data file. The binary representation of 375 in the counter data file would be different since it is the binary value before conversion to a BCD equivalent. Note: The standard ladder logic is for the SLC 500 PLC but would be the same for the PLC 5 and ControlLogix PLCs.	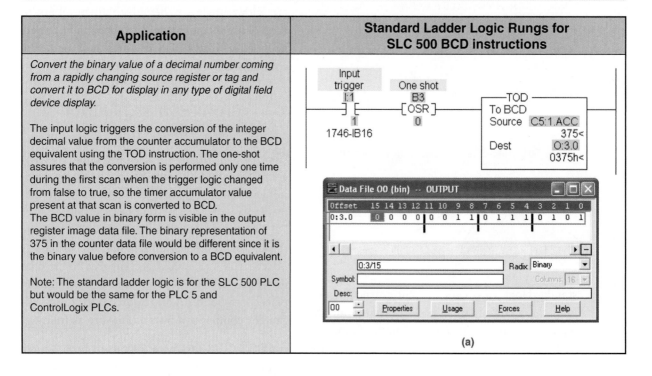

TABLE 7-4 Counting in binary and hexadecimal number systems.

Binary			Hexadecimal
		0000	0
		0001	1
		0010	2
		0011	3
		0100	4
		0101	5
		1010	6
		0111	7
		1000	8
		1001	9
		1010	A
		1011	B
		1100	C
		1101	D
		1110	E
		1111	F
	0001	0000	10
	1001	1110	9E
	1001	1111	9F
	1010	0000	A0
	1111	1110	FE
	1111	1111	FF
1	0000	0000	100

FIGURE 7-10: Hexadecimal to binary number conversion.

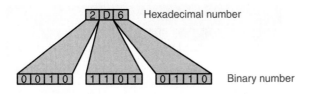

standard logic rung with the OSR instruction used with the TOD instruction. Note that while the input logic can be true for any length of time, the BCD instruction converts the counter accumulator to BCD only once on the rising edge of the input logic. The destination register is an output, O:3.0, that drives a seven-segment display. The next change in the readout occurs when the input logic for the TOD instruction again cycles from false to true.

Study the standard ladder logic for the BCD instruction, Figures 7-6, 7-7, 7-8, and 7-9, for all three Allen-Bradley PLCs until the operation of the TOD and FRD instructions is understood.

7-3 HEXADECIMAL SYSTEM

The *hexadecimal system* is another shorthand method of expressing large binary numbers using four binary bits to represent one hexadecimal number. Table 7-4 illustrates the relationship between binary numbers and hexadecimal numbers. Note that the letters A through F represent the decimal numbers 10 through 15. Figure 7-10 illustrates this relationship.

Whereas the decimal numbering system has multiples of 10 as its weighted values and the octal numbering system has multiples of 8, the hexadecimal system (using numbers 0 through 9 and letters A through F) has multiples of 16. Figure 7-11 illustrates the method to translate a hexadecimal number to a decimal number. Note that the decimal number is the sum of the products. Study the figure until you are familiar with translating hexadecimal numbers to their decimal equivalent. Hexadecimal numbers are used in many PLC instructions, including comparison instructions that are discussed next.

7-4 COMPARISON INSTRUCTION STRUCTURE

Comparison instructions, as the name implies, compare two sets of data—the contents of a memory location or register to the contents of another memory register or a fixed numerical value. Figure 7-12 illustrates the instruction structure used by the six basic comparison instructions. In the figure the data in Source A is compared to the data in Source B. The requirements for parameters placed into Source A and Source B for the Allen-Bradley comparison instructions are as follows:

PLC 5: The parameter placed in both Source A and B can be a numerical value or program constant, an integer data type, or a floating point data type.

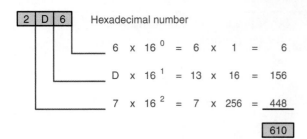

$6 \times 16^{0} = 6 \times 1 = 6$

$D \times 16^{1} = 13 \times 16 = 156$

$7 \times 16^{2} = 7 \times 256 = \underline{448}$

610 Decimal number

Comparison Criteria

Source A   -----

Source B   -----

SLC 500: Source A must be a bit or word address and Source B can be either a program constant or a bit/word address. Negative integers are stored in 2's complement.

ControlLogix: The parameter placed in both Source A and B can be any of the following data types: SINT (single integer), INT (integer), DINT (double integer), REAL (real), or string. The parameter can be either an immediately entered program constant or a tag name.

Care must be used when real data types are used in comparison instructions because the decimal component in real variables often causes problems when comparisons like EQU and NEQ are made. All comparison instructions are inputs for the ladder logic and make the rung true or false based on the evaluation of Source A and B parameters using the comparison condition.

Comparison instructions are widely used in industry and have many applications, such as initiating a process when an input is at a proper value, halting a process when an output has reached a prescribed value, and indicating when a process parameter is outside of a tolerance range.

7-5 ALLEN-BRADLEY COMPARISON INSTRUCTIONS

The Allen-Bradley PLCs have a set of comparison instructions available in all three processors. The following comparison instructions, common to all three PLC systems, are described in this section.

- Equal (EQU): evaluates whether two values are equal
- Not equal (NEQ): evaluates whether two values are not equal

- Less than (LES): evaluates whether one value is less than another
- Greater than (GRT): evaluates whether one value is greater than another
- Less than or equal (LEQ): evaluates whether one value is less than or equal to another
- Greater than or equal (GEQ): evaluates whether one value is greater than or equal to another
- Masked equal to (MEQ): evaluates whether one masked value is equal to the same masked area of another value
- Limit test (LIM): tests for values inside of or outside of a specific range

7-5-1 Standard Ladder Logic for EQU, NEQ, LES, and GRT Comparison Instructions

The ladder logic structure used for comparison instructions with Allen-Bradley PLCs is the same. All instructions are part of the input ladder logic and are used individually or in combination with other comparison or input instructions. The PLC 5 and SLC 500 use memory address registers for data, whereas Logix PLCs use tag names. The equal to (EQU), not equal to (NEQ), less than (LES), and greater than (GRT) instructions, illustrated in Figure 7-13, check for a simple comparison between two values. These examples use a variety of data types, Allen-Bradley PLC models, and register/tag examples to show how each would be used with a comparison instruction. Study the standard ladder logic for these comparison instructions in Figure 7-13 before reading the explanations that follow.

Allen-Bradley EQU Instruction and Standard Logic. The Allen-Bradley *equal to* (EQU) instruction compares two sources of data. If the two

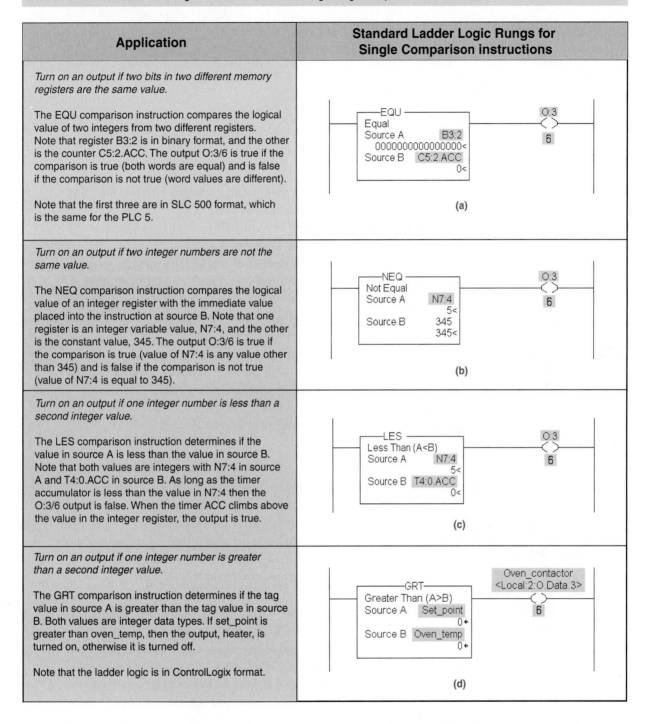

Application	Standard Ladder Logic Rungs for Single Comparison instructions
Turn on an output if two bits in two different memory registers are the same value. The EQU comparison instruction compares the logical value of two integers from two different registers. Note that register B3:2 is in binary format, and the other is the counter C5:2.ACC. The output O:3/6 is true if the comparison is true (both words are equal) and is false if the comparison is not true (word values are different). Note that the first three are in SLC 500 format, which is the same for the PLC 5.	(a)
Turn on an output if two integer numbers are not the same value. The NEQ comparison instruction compares the logical value of an integer register with the immediate value placed into the instruction at source B. Note that one register is an integer variable value, N7:4, and the other is the constant value, 345. The output O:3/6 is true if the comparison is true (value of N7:4 is any value other than 345) and is false if the comparison is not true (value of N7:4 is equal to 345).	(b)
Turn on an output if one integer number is less than a second integer value. The LES comparison instruction determines if the value in source A is less than the value in source B. Note that both values are integers with N7:4 in source A and T4:0.ACC in source B. As long as the timer accumulator is less than the value in N7:4 then the O:3/6 output is false. When the timer ACC climbs above the value in the integer register, the output is true.	(c)
Turn on an output if one integer number is greater than a second integer value. The GRT comparison instruction determines if the tag value in source A is greater than the tag value in source B. Both values are integer data types. If set_point is greater than oven_temp, then the output, heater, is turned on, otherwise it is turned off. Note that the ladder logic is in ControlLogix format.	(d)

sources of data are equal, then the instruction is true. Figure 7-13(a) illustrates the standard ladder logic for the EQU instruction. Note that bits are used and that the comparator is true if the bits are the same. If the value of the data in Source A and Source B are not equal, then the output of the instruction is false.

Allen-Bradley NEQ Instruction and Standard Logic. The Allen-Bradley *not equal to* (NEQ) instruction compares two sources of data. If the two sources of data are not equal, then the instruction is true. Figure 7-13(b) illustrates the standard ladder logic for the NEQ instruction. Note that an integer register is compared to a fixed value; if the value

the temperature is set to 300 by a BCD switch. An FRD instruction (rung 0) converts the BCD temperature value to binary and stores the value in N7:0, an integer register. The setpoint range is determined in the second rung and the upper and lower limits are established in rung 2 and 3. Floating point register are necessary because the temperature limits are set to tenths of a degree. The temperature is measured with an RTD and the value scaled to engineering units of degrees ° F. To reduce the complexity of the solution, the RTD input instruction and scaling instruction are not shown. The amended RTD reading is placed in F8:2. An LES instruction compares the RTD reading, Source A (F8:2), to the lower limit set point, Source B (F8:5). Note that Source B of the LES instruction is the same as the destination of the SUB instruction. If the temperature input is less than the lower limit, the heater contactor 0:4/3 is turned on and the lower-limit lamp 0:4/0 is illuminated. The 0:4/3 instruction seals around the 0:4/0 instruction so that the heater remains on after the oven temperature rises above the lower limit and the LES instruction returns to a false state. Also, note that a GRT instruction compares the temperature reading in F8:2, to the upper limit in Source B (F8:6). If the input is greater than the upper limit, the heater solenoid is turned off and upper limit lamp 0:4/1 is illuminated. Study the solution for the oven temperature controller until the use of the BCD and comparison instructions is clear.

7-6 EMPIRICAL DESIGN PROCESS WITH BCD CONVERSION AND COMPARISON INSTRUCTIONS

The empirical design process, introduced in Section 3-11-4, is an organized approach to the design of PLC ladder logic programs. However, the term *empirical* implies that some degree of trial and error is present. As more instructions are added to the design and the process becomes more complex, the empirical design requires more fixes and adjustments. However, the process used for these new instructions is quite similar to that learned in previous chapters.

7-6-1 Adding BCD Conversion Instructions to the Process

The first step in using BCD conversion instructions in PLC ladder designs is to know what parameters are entered for the source and the destination registers and to understand the standard BCD conversion logic circuits illustrated in Figures 7-6, 7-7, 7-8, and 7-9. The size of the BCD number dictates what types of ladder logic are required. In addition, it is important to know when a one-shot instruction is needed to trigger the conversions. Stop now and review all of these if necessary.

BCD Conversion Instructions. The use of BCD instructions implies that process values are required in both the decimal and binary coded decimal (BCD) formats. Review Example 7-1 and notice that the problem statement indicates that the temperature value for the oven is entered from a push switch. Since the push switch has a BCD output a conversion is necessary because

the PLC must perform the math in binary. The complete empirical process is listed in Section 3-11-4; the modifications for BCD instructions are as follows:

Step 1: (Write the process description): Include a description of the conversions that must be included; for example, BCD numbers in and BCD values out. Note especially the update rate of the source data in the BCD instructions and the length of time that the BCD rung input logic is true.

Step 2: (Determine the type of BCD instruction to use): Use a TOD instruction for conversion from binary to BCD and a FRD instruction for conversion from BCD to binary. Therefore, FRD is used to input data and TOD is used to output data.

Step 3: (Determine if a one-shot instruction is required): The update time for the data at Source A and the duration of the input logic that triggers the conversion are used to determine if a one-shot instruction is necessary. If the BCD data changes while the input logic in the BCD rung is true, then the value in the destination file will change with every scan. This is often not desired, so a one-shot instruction must be used to make sure that only one conversion occurs at the false to true transition of the input logic.

Step 4: (Determine what type of registers are needed for the size of BCD number present): Use the standard ladder logic in Figures 7-6 and 7-7 to select the correct register for BCD numbers from 0 to 9999 and to select registers for BCD numbers greater than 9999.

FIGURE 7-16: Solution for Example 7-1.

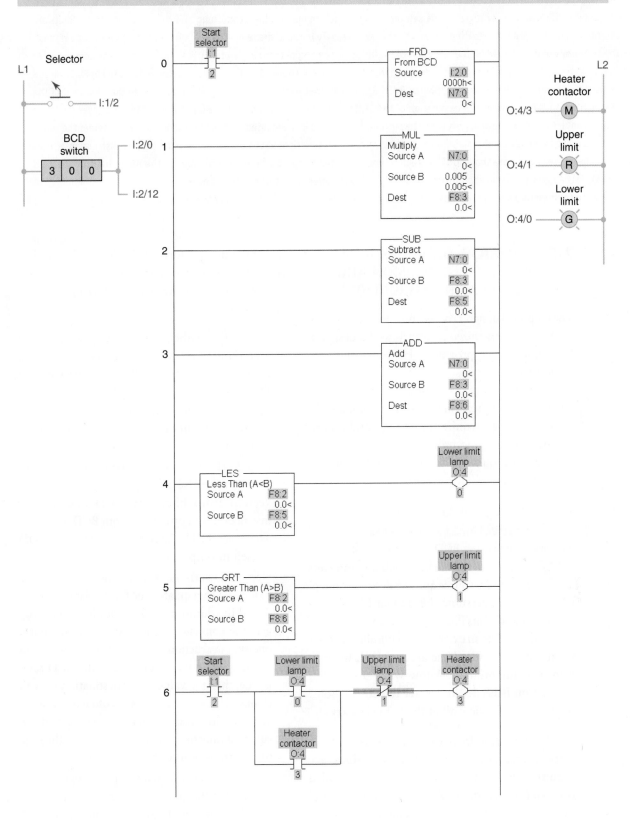

Application	Standard Ladder Logic Rungs for Multiple Comparison Instructions and Hysteresis
Turn on an output if one integer number is in a range that is less than or equal to the first reference integer but greater than a second reference integer when the trigger input is received. The LEQ and GRT comparison instructions are used in an OR configuration with an XIC contact to start the comparison evaluation ANDed to the OR circuit. Either of the ORed comparisons AND the trigger contact must be true for the output to be true. Any of the comparisons can be used in this configuration, and the trigger contact is optional.	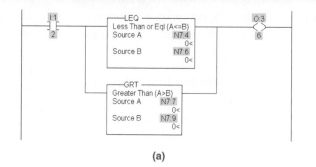 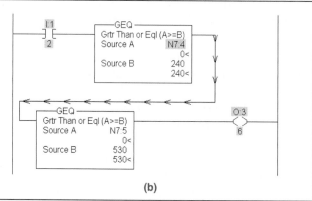 (a)
Turn on an output if one integer number is in a range that is greater than or equal to the first reference integer but less than a second reference integer when the trigger input is received. The GEQ and LES comparison instructions are used in an AND configuration with an XIC contact to start the comparison evaluation. All of the ANDed instructions must be true for the output to be true. Any of the comparisons can be used in this configuration, and the trigger contact is optional. Note the wider ladder rung used a wrap function to display the wider figure.	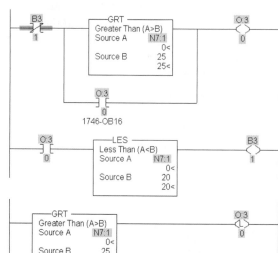 (b)
Turn on an output when an integer register reaches a specific value and reset the output when the integer register falls to a value below the higher trigger point. The logic circuit to perform this action includes a GRT and LES comparator along with a B3:0/1 contact to lock the O:3/0 bit on at values above 25. The output bit remains on until the register value drops below 20. The hysteresis band width is set by the values of the upper and lower trigger points in source B. The second ladder logic configuration uses latching and unlatching OTL and OTU instructions to achieve the same results. There are often safety issues when latching outputs are used so use of the second ladder would have to be checked for safety concerns before implementation. Note that the solutions use the SLC 500 format, but the solution would be similar for the PLC 5 and ControlLogix except for the addressing.	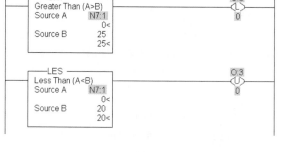 (c)

The three parameters shown in Figure 7-14(d), Low Lim(it), Test, and High Lim(it), can all be word addresses or tag names. However, if the test is a program constant, then both limits must be word addresses or tag names. If the test is a word address or tag name, then the two other parameters can be word addresses, tag names, or program constants.

7-5-3 Standard Ladder Logic for Multiple Instructions and Hysteresis

Combinations of comparison instructions are often necessary for some automation problems. In addition, it is often useful to have input triggers that include a controlled amount of hysteresis. The standard ladder logic rungs in Figure 7-15 illustrate how comparison instructions are combined and hysteresis is added. Read the description in the standard ladder logic in Figure 7-15 before reading the explanations that follow.

Standard Logic Multiple Compare Instruction. Combinations of comparison instructions are used when multiple input conditions must be tested. Any of the comparison instructions can be used in logical combinations of AND, OR, AND/OR, and OR/AND input logic. The problem description and the logic equation generation will dictate the comparison instructions, the parameters used, and the logic combinations. A trigger instruction to initiate the comparison process is illustrated in OR configuration in Figure 7-15(a) and in the AND configuration in Figure 7-15(b).

Standard Logic Comparison Instructions with Hysteresis. Process applications often require that the comparison process have hysteresis. For example, if a GRT instruction is used for the control of a valve, then the valve action will occur when one parameter exceeds another. However, if the measured parameter has some variation or noise, the valve will be cycled on and off when the input passes the trigger point and the input moves above and below the GRT value. Hysteresis fixes this problem by having the turn on value slightly higher than the turn off value. This means that after the GRT instruction is true, the process parameter must fall to some value below the original trigger point before the valve turns off.

Figure 7-15(c) shows two configurations of comparison with hysteresis. The first uses standard OTE output instructions and the second uses OTL and OTU latched outputs. The latch solution is simpler, but latches are not used for many types of outputs for safety reasons. Analysis of the first solution indicates that both output bits initially are off. This enables the GRT instruction (the B3:0/1 XIO instruction is true and has power flow) and disables the LES instruction because the O:3/0 XIC input instruction is false or has no power flow. When the process parameter is greater than 25, the O:3/0 output is true and the LES instruction is enabled (XIC input instruction has power flow). The O:3/0 sealing instruction assures that this output remains on even when the process parameter is less than 25. When the process parameter falls below 20 the B3:0/1 bit is true, which makes the top rung false and the rung output, B3:0/0, false as well. If the process parameter is an integer, then the hysteresis range is 19–26: 26 to turn on and 19 to turn off.

Review all of the standard logic circuits for the comparison instructions in Figures 7-13, 7-14, and 7-15.

EXAMPLE 7-1

Design a ladder program that sets the upper and lower limits of a laboratory temperature chamber to +/−1/2 percent of the temperature set point. The allowable temperature for the chamber is ambient temperature up to 500° F. The temperature set point is set manually using a thumbwheel or push switch. The push switch is set to 300° F in this example. Include comparison instructions to:

- Turn on a heater and turn on a lamp when the chamber temperature is below the lower limit, and
- Turn off the heater and turn on a lamp when the chamber temperature is above the upper limit.

SOLUTION

The ladder program is illustrated in Figure 7-16. The first through third rungs in the solution set the upper and lower limits by multiplying the temperature set point, N7:0, by the upper and lower limit percent variation. Note that

Application	Standard Ladder Logic Rungs for the SLC 500 Double Test Comparison instructions

Turn on an output if one integer number is less than or equal to a second integer value.
 	
The LEQ comparison instruction determines if the value in source A is less than or equal to the valuein source B. Note that both values are integers with N7:4 in source A and N7:6 in source B. As long as N7:4 is less than or equal to the value in N7:6 then theO:3/6 output is true, otherwise it is false.
	
	─┤LEQ├─────────────────────────────(O:3)
	  Less Than or Eql (A<=B) 6
	  Source A N7:4
	                        0<
	  Source B N7:6
	                        0<
	
	(a)

Turn on an output if one integer number is greater than or equal to a second integer value.
 	
The GEQ comparison instruction determines if the tag value in source A is greater than or equal to thetag value in source B. Both values are integer datatypes. If Bin_full is greater than or equal to Set_point. ACC, then the output, unload, is turned on, otherwise it is turned off. Note this is a ControlLogix ladder for the compare instruction.
	Oven_contactor
	<Local:2:O.Data.3>
	─┤GEQ├──────────────────────────────( )──
	  Grtr Than or Eql (A>=B)
	  Source A Bin_full
	                    0◆
	  Source B Set_point.ACC
	                    0◆
	
	(b)

Turn on an output if specific bits from one integer number are equal to that same bit area of a second integer value.
 	
The MEQ comparison instruction determines if the masked value in source A is equal to the same masked area of the value in source B. Note that thesource is the value you want to compare, and the compare value is an integer constant or a integer register address. The mask, which can be a hexadecimal number, indicates what bits are compared (mask bit values of 1) and what will be ignored (mask bit values of 0) when the comparison between the source value and compare value is performed.
 	
Note: 000F0 = 0000000011110000
	─┤MEQ├─────────────────────────────(O:3)
	  Masked Equal 6
	  Source N7:4
	                      0<
	  Mask 00F0h
	                     240<
	  Compare C5:0.ACC
	                      0<
	
	(c)

Turn on an output if an integer number falls between two limits or values.
 	
The LIM instruction has three parameters: LowLim(it), Test, and High Lim(it). If the low limit is less than the upper limit then the output is true if the test value is equal to or between the limits, otherwise it is false. If the low limit is greater than the upper limit then the output is false if the test value is between the limits, otherwise it is true. The format is for the SLC 500 but would be the same for the PLC 5 and similar for the ControlLogix PLCs.
	─┤LIM├──────────────────────────────(O:3)
	  Limit Test 6
	  Low Lim 100
	                  100<
	  Test T4:0.ACC
	                   0<
	  High Lim 125
	                  125<
	
	(d)

in Source A is less than the value in Source B the comparator makes the rung true. If the value of the data in Source A and Source B are equal, then the output of the instruction is false.

Allen-Bradley LES Instruction and Standard Logic. The Allen-Bradley *less than* (LES) instruction compares two sources of data. If the first listed source is less than the second listed source, then the instruction is true. Figure 7-13(c) illustrates the standard ladder logic for the LES instruction. Note that an integer register is compared to a timer accumulator value; if the value of Source A is less than the value of Source B, the comparator makes the rung true. Registers from counters and timers are often used in comparator instructions. If the value of the data in Source A is greater than or equal to the value of the data in Source B, then the output of the instruction is false.

Allen-Bradley GRT and Standard Logic. The Allen-Bradley *greater than* (GRT) instruction compares two sources of data. If the first listed source is greater than the second listed source, then the instruction is true. Figure 7-13(d) illustrates standard ladder logic for the GRT instruction. Note that tag values are compared in this application to demonstrate how a ControlLogix PLC program would look. If the tag name in Source A is less than or equal to the value of the tag in Source B, then the output of the instruction is false.

7-5-2 Standard Ladder Logic for LEQ, GEQ, MEQ, and LIM Comparison Instructions

The less than or equal to (LEQ), greater than or equal to (GEQ), equal to with mask (MEQ), and limit test (LIM) instructions check for two comparison parameters between two values. Read the standard ladder logic for these comparison instructions in Figure 7-14 before reading the explanations that follow.

Allen-Bradley LEQ Instruction and Standard Logic. The Allen-Bradley *less than or equal to* (LEQ) instruction compares two sources of data. If the first listed source is less than or equal to the second listed source, then the instruction is true. Figure 7-14(a) illustrates the standard ladder logic for the LEQ instruction. In this standard circuit example the two integer registers are compared.

If the value in Source A is greater than the value of the data in Source B, then the output of the instruction is false.

Allen-Bradley GEQ Instruction and Standard Logic. The Allen-Bradley *greater than or equal to* (GEQ) instruction compares two sources of data. If the first listed source is greater than or equal to the second listed source, then the instruction is true. Figure 7-14(b) illustrates the standard ladder logic for the GEQ instruction. Note that tag values are compared in this application to emphasize the similarity between the Logix implementations of comparison instructions and the older Allen-Bradley PLCs. If the value in Source A is less than the value of the data in Source B, then the output of the instruction is false.

Allen-Bradley MEQ Instruction and Standard Logic. The Allen-Bradley *masked equal to* (MEQ) instruction compares two sources of data that are masked over some of the bits. If those masked areas are equal, then the instruction is true. Figure 7-14(c) illustrates the standard ladder logic for the MEQ instruction. Source A and Source B are replaced with Source and Compare respectively. Therefore, the value in the Source is compared with the value of the Compare parameter. The mask is a hexadecimal number where a 1 in the mask indicates that the corresponding bits from each value are compared, and a 0 indicates that the bits are ignored. If the bits in the Source identified by the mask are equal to the value of the corresponding bits in the Compare parameter, then the output of the instruction is true. If they are not, then the instruction is false.

Allen-Bradley LIM Instruction and Standard Logic. The *limit test* (LIM) instruction is used to set an output when a test value is either inside or outside a lower and higher limit range. The instruction evaluates as follows:

- *The instruction is true if*: The lower limit is equal to or less than the higher limit, and the test parameter value is equal to or inside the limits. Otherwise the instruction is false.
- *The instruction is true if*: The lower limit has a value greater than the higher limit, and the instruction is equal to or outside the limits. Otherwise the instruction is false.

Application	Standard Ladder Logic Rungs for Multiple Comparison Instructions and Hysteresis
Turn on an output if one integer number is in a range that is less than or equal to the first reference integer but greater than a second reference integer when the trigger input is received. The LEQ and GRT comparison instructions are used in an OR configuration with an XIC contact to start the comparison evaluation ANDed to the OR circuit. Either of the ORed comparisons AND the trigger contact must be true for the output to be true. Any of the comparisons can be used in this configuration, and the trigger contact is optional.	(a)
Turn on an output if one integer number is in a range that is greater than or equal to the first reference integer but less than a second reference integer when the trigger input is received. The GEQ and LES comparison instructions are used in an AND configuration with an XIC contact to start the comparison evaluation. All of the ANDed instructions must be true for the output to be true. Any of the comparisons can be used in this configuration, and the trigger contact is optional. Note the wider ladder rung used a wrap function to display the wider figure.	(b)
Turn on an output when an integer register reaches a specific value and reset the output when the integer register falls to a value below the higher trigger point. The logic circuit to perform this action includes a GRT and LES comparator along with a B3:0/1 contact to lock the O:3/0 bit on at values above 25. The output bit remains on until the register value drops below 20. The hysteresis band width is set by the values of the upper and lower trigger points in source B. The second ladder logic configuration uses latching and unlatching OTL and OTU instructions to achieve the same results. There are often safety issues when latching outputs are used so use of the second ladder would have to be checked for safety concerns before implementation. Note that the solutions use the SLC 500 format, but the solution would be similar for the PLC 5 and ControlLogix except for the addressing.	(c)

FIGURE 7-16: Solution for Example 7-1.

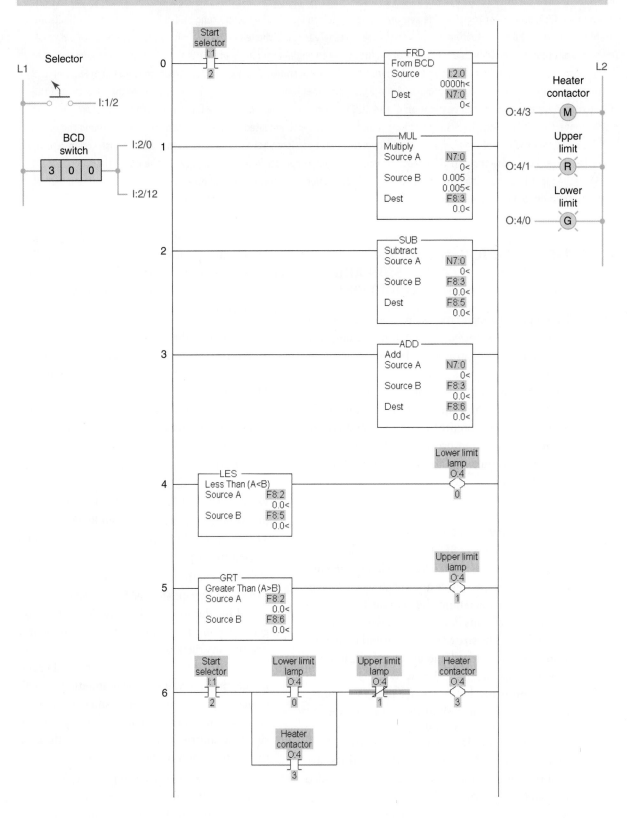

the temperature is set to 300 by a BCD switch. An FRD instruction (rung 0) converts the BCD temperature value to binary and stores the value in N7:0, an integer register. The setpoint range is determined in the second rung and the upper and lower limits are established in rung 2 and 3. Floating point register are necessary because the temperature limits are set to tenths of a degree. The temperature is measured with an RTD and the value scaled to engineering units of degrees ° F. To reduce the complexity of the solution, the RTD input instruction and scaling instruction are not shown. The amended RTD reading is placed in F8:2. An LES instruction compares the RTD reading, Source A (F8:2), to the lower limit set point, Source B (F8:5). Note that Source B of the LES instruction is the same as the destination of the SUB instruction. If the temperature input is less than the lower limit, the heater contactor 0:4/3 is turned on and the lower-limit lamp 0:4/0 is illuminated. The 0:4/3 instruction seals around the 0:4/0 instruction so that the heater remains on after the oven temperature rises above the lower limit and the LES instruction returns to a false state. Also, note that a GRT instruction compares the temperature reading in F8:2, to the upper limit in Source B (F8:6). If the input is greater than the upper limit, the heater solenoid is turned off and upper limit lamp 0:4/1 is illuminated. Study the solution for the oven temperature controller until the use of the BCD and comparison instructions is clear.

7-6 EMPIRICAL DESIGN PROCESS WITH BCD CONVERSION AND COMPARISON INSTRUCTIONS

The empirical design process, introduced in Section 3-11-4, is an organized approach to the design of PLC ladder logic programs. However, the term *empirical* implies that some degree of trial and error is present. As more instructions are added to the design and the process becomes more complex, the empirical design requires more fixes and adjustments. However, the process used for these new instructions is quite similar to that learned in previous chapters.

7-6-1 Adding BCD Conversion Instructions to the Process

The first step in using BCD conversion instructions in PLC ladder designs is to know what parameters are entered for the source and the destination registers and to understand the standard BCD conversion logic circuits illustrated in Figures 7-6, 7-7, 7-8, and 7-9. The size of the BCD number dictates what types of ladder logic are required. In addition, it is important to know when a one-shot instruction is needed to trigger the conversions. Stop now and review all of these if necessary.

BCD Conversion Instructions. The use of BCD instructions implies that process values are required in both the decimal and binary coded decimal (BCD) formats. Review Example 7-1 and notice that the problem statement indicates that the temperature value for the oven is entered from a push switch. Since the push switch has a BCD output a conversion is necessary because the PLC must perform the math in binary. The complete empirical process is listed in Section 3-11-4; the modifications for BCD instructions are as follows:

Step 1: (Write the process description): Include a description of the conversions that must be included; for example, BCD numbers in and BCD values out. Note especially the update rate of the source data in the BCD instructions and the length of time that the BCD rung input logic is true.

Step 2: (Determine the type of BCD instruction to use): Use a TOD instruction for conversion from binary to BCD and a FRD instruction for conversion from BCD to binary. Therefore, FRD is used to input data and TOD is used to output data.

Step 3: (Determine if a one-shot instruction is required): The update time for the data at Source A and the duration of the input logic that triggers the conversion are used to determine if a one-shot instruction is necessary. If the BCD data changes while the input logic in the BCD rung is true, then the value in the destination file will change with every scan. This is often not desired, so a one-shot instruction must be used to make sure that only one conversion occurs at the false to true transition of the input logic.

Step 4: (Determine what type of registers are needed for the size of BCD number present): Use the standard ladder logic in Figures 7-6 and 7-7 to select the correct register for BCD numbers from 0 to 9999 and to select registers for BCD numbers greater than 9999.

7-6-2 Adding Comparison Instructions to the Process

The first step in using comparison instructions in PLC ladder designs is to know what parameters are entered for Source A and Source B registers and to understand the standard comparison logic circuits illustrated in Figures 7-13, 7-14, and 7-15. In addition, identify the type of comparison, for example, simple tests like less than, greater than, or the limit test (Figures 7-13 and 7-14), or more complex checks like less than one value but greater than another [Figure 7-15(a) and (b)]. Also, the need for hysteresis should be determined [Figure 7-15(c)]. Stop now and review all of these if necessary. The complete empirical process is listed in Section 3-11-4; the modifications for comparison instructions are as follows:

Step 1: (Write the process description): Include a complete description of the types of comparisons required for the process, including all the values and registers associated with the process. Identify the outputs controlled by comparison instructions, applications that require hysteresis, and those that have more complex comparison requirements.

Step 2: (Write Boolean equations for all comparison instruction rungs): A Boolean expression is needed to describe each comparison instruction.

7-6-3 Process Tank Design

The following examples demonstrate how to design the control ladder logic using the empirical design process for a relatively complex process control problem. Study the process tank shown in Figure 7-17 and the operator control panel shown in Figure 7-18. After a complete review of the tank layout and operator panel, read the following process description. This is an example of how a process description should be written for the empirical design process.

FIGURE 7-17: Process tank.

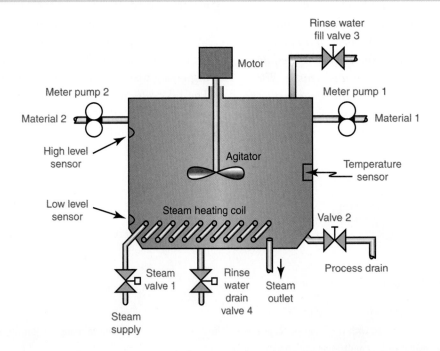

FIGURE 7-18: Process tank operator panel.

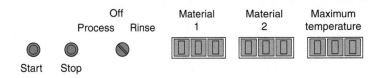

The volume in gallons of two liquid ingredients (material 1 and material 2 in the figure) and the maximum soak temperature are entered on three-digit push switches. The system has a start and stop push button and a two-position (center position off) normally open selector switch to select the rinse and process modes. One seven-segment readout with a three-digit display shows the current process temperature. Indicator lights display the following conditions: fill cycle, drain cycle, water fill valve open, water drain valve open, process drain valve open, steam valve open, and over temperature warning. The two process metering pumps pass 8 ounces of liquid per revolution. The tank has low and high level liquid sensors, and a temperature sensor and transmitter. A mixer, driven by a motor, is used to agitate the process.

When the process selector switch is moved to the process position, process rungs are selected. The process is started with the start push button, which sets a system start bit. Each pump rotates through the correct number of revolutions to put the desired volume of liquid into the tank. The mixer is on whenever the liquid is over the low level liquid sensor. When all liquids are loaded, the steam valve is opened and the process is heated to the temperature set point. When the set point is reached the heater is turned off and the process liquid is drained through the process drain valve. When the low level liquid sensor is not active the system start bit is turned off.

After the process liquid is drained, the system waits for the selector to be placed in the rinse position and the start switch to again be pressed. The tank fills with water and the mixer is on whenever the water is over the low level liquid sensor. When the water reaches the high level liquid sensor, the water is drained through the water drain valve. When the rinse cycle is completed the system returns to the stopped condition.

Complex process problems should be broken into logical solution groups. In this example the solution groups would be fill cycle, process heating and drain cycle, tank rinse cycle, and displays. There may be some overlap between these solutions when outputs are shared in two solution areas. For example, the mixer is used in the fill and rinse cycles, but that problem is addressed as it is uncovered. Working on the solution in these smaller chunks makes it easier to see the total solution. The problems at the end of the chapter include the design of the ladder logic program for displaying process status on the operator panel. The fill cycle, process heating and drain cycle, and tank rinse cycle solutions are addressed in Examples 7-2 and 7-3.

EXAMPLE 7-2—FILL CYCLE

Design the ladder logic used to start the system and complete the fill cycle for the process described above.

SOLUTION

The empirical design information includes:

- All data values present are integer data.
- Gallons data entered with the push switches and FRD instructions are converted to pump revolutions (1/2 gallon per revolution) by multiplying the gallons by 2.
- Outputs are FRD conversion instructions for the volume of each liquid, math instructions, counters for each pump, and motor contactors for each pump.

The following Boolean logic is used for the ladder rungs (logic is the same for both pumps):

- Start bit = start switch (with the start bit used as a sealing instruction) AND NOT stop AND [low level float switch OR start timer timing bit]

    After the start switch is pressed and the tank level is above the low level float switch, the float switch bit determines how long the process cycle and start bit (B3:0/0) are true. However, the low level float switch is initially off and does not come on until some liquid fills the tank, which takes about 80 seconds. Therefore, the start timer (timer timing bit) is used to seal around the low level sensor instruction until the liquid activates the low level sensor. The timer is preset to 120 seconds, so an additional 40 seconds is available to get the tank liquid above the low level point.

- TON timer = start switch (with a sealing instruction of timer timing)

    Note that the start switch is also needed to trigger the start timer input to get the timer active. The timer timing sealing instruction makes sure that the timer continues to increment when the momentary start switch is released.

- Volume FRD instructions = process selected AND start bit AND one shot [Standard logic Figure 7-9(a)]
- MUL instructions (gallons required × 2) = unconditional input [Standard logic Figure 6-12(a)]

    Each pump revolution supplies 0.5 gallons of material; therefore, the multiplication of gallons required times 2 produces the number of pump revolutions necessary to reach the required material amount. This result is placed in an integer register for comparison with the pump revolution counter.

- C5:0 = material pump contactor AND process selected AND pump revolution limit switch

    Every revolution of the pumps increment the pump counters. As a result, the counter ACC tracks the number of half-gallon increments of material placed in the tank.

- Pump contractor = Comparison of C5:0.ACC (pump revolutions) *less than* total number of required pump revolutions AND start bit

    Each pump revolution is 0.5 gallons of material and the total number of revolutions is required gallons times 2.

- Mixed contactor = low level sensor

Based on this information the ladder solution in Figure 7-19 was developed for the Allen-Bradley SLC 500 PLC. The input and output interface is shown for the inputs and output used in this portion of the solution. The sequence for the ladder solution is to:

1. Read in the volume for each liquid in gallons.
2. Calculate the number of pump rotations (0.5 gallons per revolution) to equal the desired material volume (number of half gallon revolutions is equal to the gallons required times 2).
3. Count the pump revolutions.
4. Compare the accumulated pump revolutions with the total required and keep the pump contactors true while the counter ACC value is less than the required value.
5. Start the mixer when the liquid is above the low level float switch.

Compare the solution with the problem statement. Can you identify any rungs or operations that need to be added?

The missing operation is a reset at the start of the process of the Pump 1 volume and Pump 2 volume counter accumulators. They must be zero for a correct comparison. Process statements rarely state control requirements for the instructions used because they may not be known when the process is being defined. The reset of the counters is an operational issue when counters are used, and the designer must recognize when they are necessary. A rung input with the start switch address and counter reset instructions at the output would fix this omission.

FIGURE 7-19: Process tank control ladder logic—fill cycle.

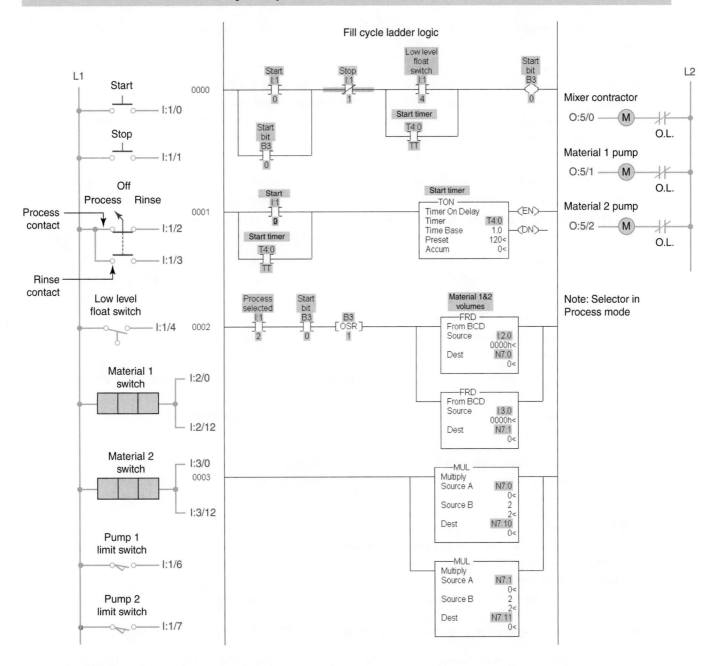

Fill cycle ladder logic

EXAMPLE 7-3—TEMPERATURE/DRAIN CYCLE

Design the ladder logic used to heat the liquid and the ladder logic for the system drain cycle described in the process statement.

SOLUTION

The empirical design information includes:

- All data values present are integer data.
- The steam valve must open when all liquid has been loaded.

FIGURE 7-19: (Continued).

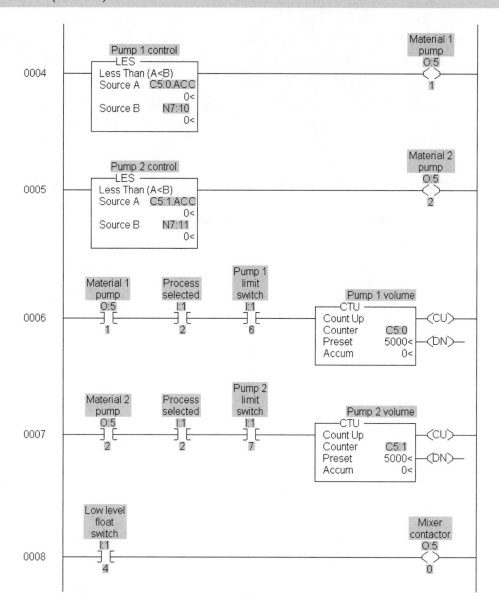

- Outputs are FRD conversion instructions for the heating temperature set point, process drain valve, steam valve, and temperature comparison bit.

  The following Boolean logic is used for the ladder rungs:

- Temperature FRD instructions = process selected AND start bit AND one shot [Figure 7-9(a)]
- Maximum temperature bit = GEQ (temp sensor > temp set point) [Figure 7-14(a) and (b)]

  The maximum temperature bit is on when the measured temperature (N7:4) is greater than the temperature set point (N7:3).

- Steam valve = start bit AND process selected AND NOT material 1 pump 1 AND NOT material 2 pump AND NOT process drain valve AND NOT maximum temperature bit

The steam valve is opened when both pumps are off, the process temperature is not at the set point value, the process drain valve is closed, and the start and selected bits are true. The start bit ensures that the steam valve does not turn back on when the drain valve returns to the closed state after the system drains.

- Process drain = process selected AND maximum temperature bit (sealed with XIC instruction using the process drain address) AND low level sensor

The maximum temperature bit opens the process drain valve, but a sealing contact from the output is necessary because the maximum temperature bit will not be true for the entire drain cycle. The low level sensor false condition closes the process drain valve.

Based on this information the ladder solution in Figure 7-20 was developed for the Allen-Bradley SLC 500 PLC. The input and output interface is shown for the inputs and output used in this portion of the solution. The sequence for this part of the ladder solution is to turn on the heater when both pumps are stopped, turn the heater off and the process drain valve on when the liquid reaches the set point temperature, and turn the process cycle and all outputs off when the tank is drained.

FIGURE 7-20: Process tank control ladder logic—temperature/drain cycle.

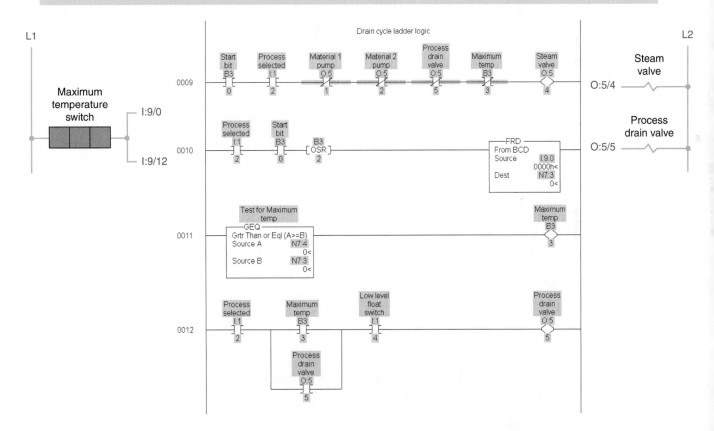

A review of the solution for Examples 7-2 and 7-3 indicates that instructions are often used in rungs to prevent the rung from changing state after the process controlled by the rung is complete. A good example of that is the start bit in the steam valve in rung 9 in Figure 7-20. The steam valve would turn back on when the drain valve closed at the end of the process because all the other instructions would be true at that time. However, the start bit is placed into the rung, B3:0/0, and it opens at the end of the process and keeps the steam valve off or closed.

EXAMPLE 7-4—RINSE CYCLE

Design the ladder logic used to rinse the process tank after each process reaction with the water fill, mix, and flush described in the process statement.

SOLUTION

The empirical design information includes:

- All data values present are integer data.
- The selector switch is in the rinse position and the tank is filled with water and then drained. The mixer is used throughout the cycle.
- Outputs are mixer contactor, water drain valve, and water fill valve.

The following Boolean logic is used for the ladder rungs:

- Mixer contactor = rinse selected AND low level float switch

    The same output in ladder logic should never be referenced or used in two different rungs. The mixer contactor already appears in rung 8 in Figure 7-19; therefore, this rung should be combined with rung 8.

- Rinse water fill valve = start bit AND rinse selected AND NOT high level float switch AND NOT rinse water drain valve

    The false XIO instruction for the high level float switch turns the rinse water fill valve off when the liquid closes the high level float switch contacts. The false XIO instruction for the rinse water drain valve holds the fill valve off until all the liquid is drained and the cycle is terminated with a false start bit.

- Rinse water drain = start bit AND rinse selected AND high level float switch (sealed with rinse water drain valve XIC instruction) AND low level float switch

    The true condition for the high level float switch opens the rinse water drain valve and makes the sealing instruction, O:5/7, true. The seal is needed since the high level float switch is false after the liquid starts to drain. The low level sensor terminates the water drain cycle when the tank is empty and the sensor is not active.

    Based on this information, the ladder solution in Figure 7-21 was developed for the Allen-Bradley SLC 500 PLC. The input and output interface is shown for the inputs and output used in this portion of the solution. The sequence for the ladder solution is to turn on the rinse water fill valve, turn on the mixer when liquid is over the low level float switch, turn off the rinse water fill valve and open the rinse water drain valve when the liquid is over the high level float switch, and end the cycle when the water drops below the low level float switch.

Review the solutions for all three parts of the process, Figures 7-19, 7-20, and 7-21. Lessons learned in this solution include:

- The use of a selector switch to select the process under control isolates each solution so that there is no rung interaction between two solutions. This is a good practice if the process permits this type of control.
- Dividing the process into logical sections—a fill cycle, temperature/drain cycle, and rinse cycle—creates three smaller problems instead of one big problem. This makes the problem easier to program and easier to troubleshoot.

7-6-4 Pneumatic Robot Design

The following example is a modification of the ladder logic, Figure 3-44, for the robot control problem in Example 3-14. Study the robot configuration and ladder logic solution in Figure 3-44. After a complete review of the example solution in Chapter 3, read the following modification to the earlier robot operational description.

The two-axis robot for this example does not have end-of-travel sensors to indicate when the axes have reached their limits as did the robot in the Chapter 3 example. To make sure that the robot has finished its

FIGURE 7-21: Process tank control ladder logic—rinse cycle.

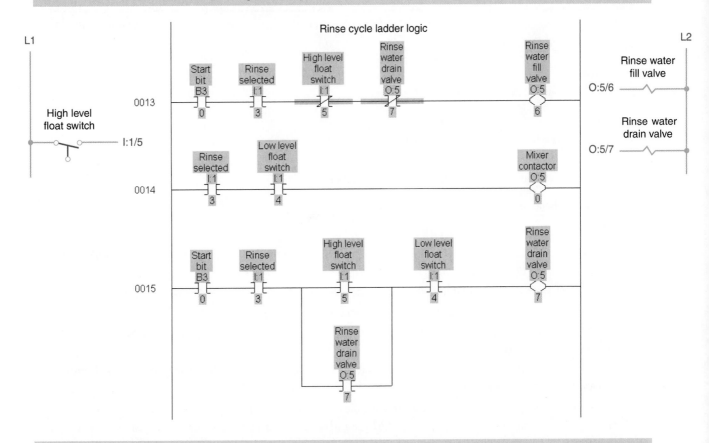

EXAMPLE 7-5—PNEUMATIC ROBOT

Design the ladder logic with ControlLogix ladder logic to control the pneumatic robot described at the start of this section.

SOLUTION

The empirical design information includes:

- A regenerative timer is used to establish the cycle time for the process.
- The timer and comparators are used for control since end-of-travel sensors on the pneumatic actuators are not present.
- The time for each axis move is provided, so the total cycle time for the robot is the sum of each axis move. The moves in Figure 7-22(a) include down, close gripper, up, out, open gripper, in, which results in a total cycle time of 13 seconds.
- Outputs are X-axis valve, Y-axis valve, and gripper valve.

Note that the two-axis pneumatic robot is driven by a set cycle time for all axes, so the optimum speed is not attained. A part is present before the start_selector is active.

The following Boolean logic is used for the ladder rungs:

- Timer = Start selector AND NOT timer done
- X-axis down = Start selector AND part sensor AND timer ACC less than or equal to 4 seconds
- Gripper close = Start selector AND timer greater than 2 seconds but less than or equal to 9 seconds
- Y-axis out = Start selector AND timer equal to 7 seconds but less than or equal to 11 seconds

Based on this information the ladder solution in Figure 7-22(b) was developed for the Allen-Bradley ControlLogix PLC. The input and output interface is shown for the inputs and output used in the solution. The sequence for the ladder solution follows the timing diagram for the robot in Figure 7-22(a).

FIGURE 7-22: Pneumatic robot control ladder logic.

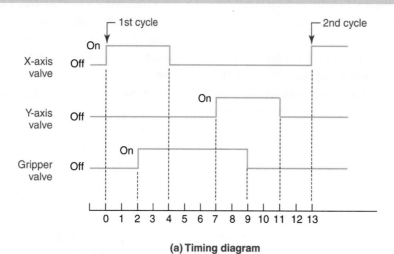

(a) Timing diagram

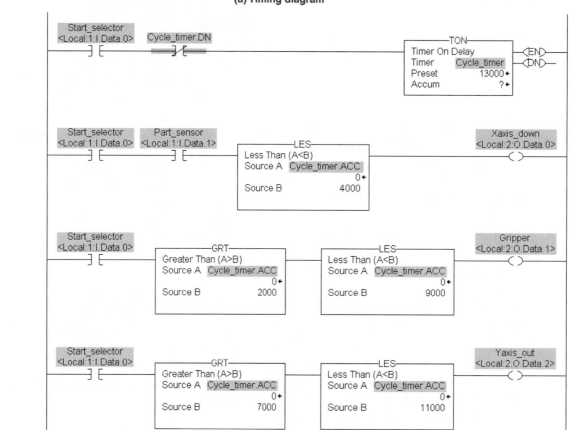

(b) Ladder logic

travel, each axis has a specified time for the travel. A cycle is started when the start selector switch is on AND when the pickup sensor indicates that a part is in the pickup location. Use the following list of actuator times to control the actuator and gripper sequences.

Vertical down – 2 seconds

Vertical up – 3 seconds

Horizontal out – 2 seconds

Horizontal in – 2 seconds

Gripper close – 2 seconds

Gripper open – 2 seconds

The timing diagram for the robot and program is illustrated in Figure 7-22(a).

Compare the solutions for the robot control in Figure 3-14, Figure 4-22, and Figure 7-22. Automation solutions can take numerous forms and still be correct. Some solutions are more efficient than others and some are simpler than others. PLC programmers make the best instruction choice for the application when they have a full understanding of all of the instructions. For example, the solution in Figure 3-14 was the only one possible until timers were learned. Similarly, the solution in Figure 4-22 was the only timer solution possible until comparators were covered. As your knowledge grows, your choice of solutions expands.

7-7 TROUBLESHOOTING BCD CONVERSION AND COMPARISON LADDER LOGIC

The conversion and comparison instructions offer few operational problems. If a section of the ladder that includes these instructions is not operating properly, then you can use any of the following suggestions to troubleshoot.

- If PLC rungs with BCD and comparison instructions do not produce the correct results, then first verify that the data from the process is correct by viewing the PLC 5 and SLC 500 dialog boxes for the input image table, integer image table, and floating point image table illustrated in Figure 6-20. If a ControlLogix processor is used the program and control tags are viewed in the dialog box displayed in Figure 6-21. Note that the register values can be displayed in binary, octal, hexadecimal, and decimal format depending on the type of data present.
- Test the sequence of BCD and comparison rungs one rung at a time to verify that each rung is performing properly. Use the temporary end (TND) instruction described in Chapter 4 to halt the ladder execution after each rung.
- Use the suspend (SUS) instruction to verify status values for all registers and bits at critical points in the ladder. The SUS instruction is described in Section 5-8-1.

- Be aware of situations where comparison instructions are used to make execution decisions and execute process actions since the scan time and internal update time for the instruction is much faster than most process events. This problem is similar to that described in the counter problem discussed in Section 5-8-2.
- Use the test options on some of the Allen-Bradley SLC 500 models in the single-step, single-scan, or continuous-scan modes to isolate and run portions of the ladder logic. These tests are described in Section 6-8-1.

7-7-1 Troubleshooting with the Module Indicators

Review the signal flow diagram in Figure 3-47 and notice that a fault could occur anywhere along the single path from input field device to output actuator. The faults could occur in any of the following locations:

- Input and output wiring between field devices and modules
- Field device/module power supplies
- Input mechanical switch devices
- Input sensors
- Output actuators
- PLC I/O modules
- PLC processor

The fault locations are listed in the order of most frequent to less frequent sources of problems. In the middle of the signal flow you have several indicators that are ideal troubleshooting tools. Locating the fault quickly requires observations and measurements at these input and output modules.

Input Module Troubleshooting Analysis. Earlier we discussd using the status lights on the input module for troubleshooting problems with input signals. Now we take a closer look at the information they provide. The input module falls near the center of the signal flow, Figure 3-47, so it is an ideal place to start troubleshooting. Starting in the center supports the "divide and conquer" rule introduced in the troubleshooting procedures in Chapter 1. Study the troubleshooting guide in Figure 7-23(a)

FIGURE 7-23: Troubleshooting discrete input modules.

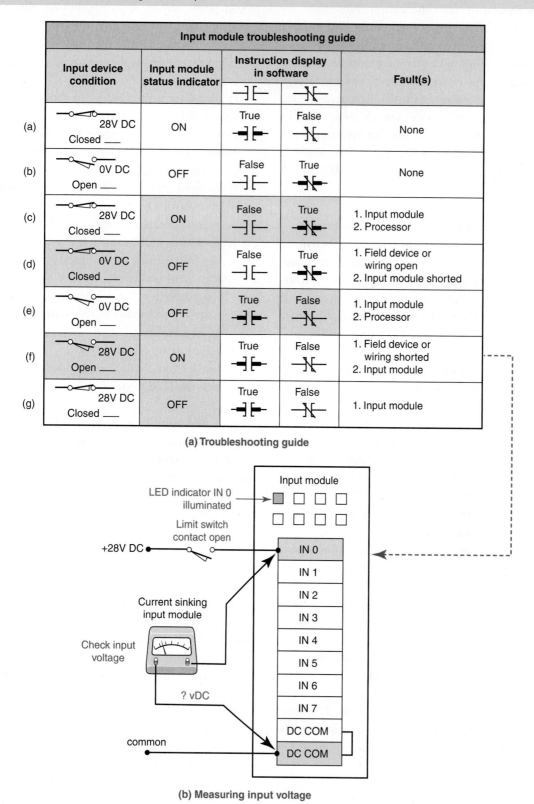

(a) Troubleshooting guide

(b) Measuring input voltage

for discrete input modules before reading a description of each indication. Note that the condition of the input field device and module status light is provided. In addition, the condition (highlighted or true and not highlighted or false) of the instruction displayed by the programming software is shown. The areas where the fault could occur are shaded. Finally, the most likely faults are stated in priority order. Refer to Figure 7-23(a) as you read the following descriptions of each possible fault condition.

a. Correct indications – no fault present.
b. Correct indications – no fault present.
c. Sensor condition, input voltage, and module indicator are correct, but the XIC and XIO ladder instructions have an incorrect indication. The problem is most likely in the input module I/O point, but the fault could be caused by the processor. Since the input module is the most likely cause, replace the module or move the input to another I/O point.
d. The module indicator and the XIC and XIO ladder instructions agree, but not with the state of the field device. The best check is to measure the input voltage at the I/O point as shown in Figure 7-23(b). If the voltage is 0 VDC, then it is either a broken field wire or a bad sensor.
e. The field device status, input voltage, and module indicator all agree, but the XIC and XIO ladder instructions do not. The problem is most likely the input module I/O point. The processor could cause it, but that is less likely.
f. The input voltage, module indicator, and the XIC and XIO ladder instructions agree, but the condition of the field device does not. The fault is most likely a short in the field device or the input wiring. The input module could cause the fault, but that is less likely.
g. The input voltage (28 VDC), the field device, and the XIC and XIO ladder instructions agree, but the module indicator does not. Check for a bad indicator in the input module.

In general, the following items should be remembered during troubleshooting discrete input modules:

- If inputs are fused, then verify that the fuse is not blown.
- If inputs are turned on when the electronic sensor field device driving the input is off, then verify that the sensor off leakage current is not greater than the turn on current for the current sinking input module.
- If the input module is suspected, then replacing it or moving the faulty input to another I/O point is a good test to verify a bad channel.
- If the module indicator and the XIC and XIO ladder instructions are in agreement, then a voltage measurement indicates:
  - The problem is in the input in the module if the input voltage agrees with the field device condition.
  - The problem is in the field wiring or field device if the input voltage does not agree with the field device condition.

Output Module Troubleshooting Analysis. The output module falls near the center of the signal flow, Figure 3-47, so it is another ideal place to start troubleshooting. Study the troubleshooting guide in Figure 7-24(a) for discrete output modules before reading a description of each indication. Note that the condition of the output field device and module status light is provided. In addition, the condition (highlighted or true and not highlighted or false) of the output coil displayed by the programming software is shown. The areas where the fault could occur are shaded. Finally, the most likely faults are stated in priority order. Refer to Figure 7-24(a) as you read the following descriptions of each possible fault condition.

a. Correct indications – no fault present.
b. Correct indications – no fault present.
c. Output instruction and output indicator agree but the field device does not. The problem is most likely that the field wiring is open or the module output circuit is bad. If outputs have individual fuses, then the fuse should be checked.

FIGURE 7-24: Troubleshooting discrete output modules.

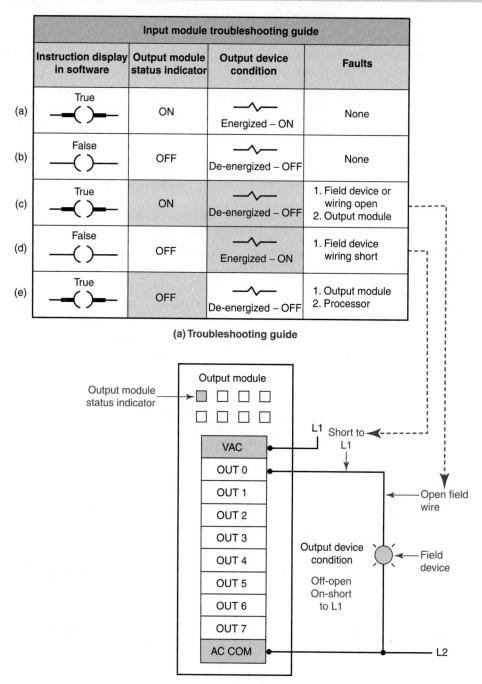

Input module troubleshooting guide			
Instruction display in software	Output module status indicator	Output device condition	Faults
(a) True —( )—	ON	Energized – ON	None
(b) False —( )—	OFF	De-energized – OFF	None
(c) True —( )—	ON	De-energized – OFF	1. Field device or wiring open 2. Output module
(d) False —( )—	OFF	Energized – ON	1. Field device wiring short
(e) True —( )—	OFF	De-energized – OFF	1. Output module 2. Processor

(a) Troubleshooting guide

(b) Measuring input voltage

d. Output instruction and output indicator agree but the field device does not. The problem is most likely that the field wiring is shorted to the power line.

e. The field device status and module indicator agree, but the output instruction condition does not. The problem is most likely the output module I/O point. The processor could cause it, but that is less likely.

In general, the following items should be remembered during troubleshooting discrete output modules:

• Many output modules have each I/O or channel fused. In most cases there is a blown fuse indicator that illuminates if the fuse is open when you turn on the output. If an output fails to turn on when the output indicator signals that the output is active, then check the fuse first. Next check for open field wiring using a voltmeter or ohm meter.

• You can use the bit forcing function to make a rung active without running the ladder logic program so that an output fault can be fixed.

7-8 LOCATION OF THE INSTRUCTIONS

The location of instructions from this chapter in the Allen-Bradley programming software is indicated in Figure 7-25.

FIGURE 7-25: Location of instructions described in this chapter.

Systems	Instructions	Location
PLC 5, SLC 500	TOD, FRD	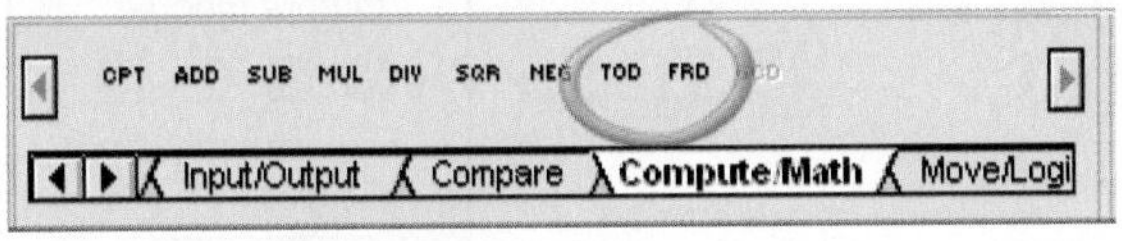
LOGIX	TOD, FRD	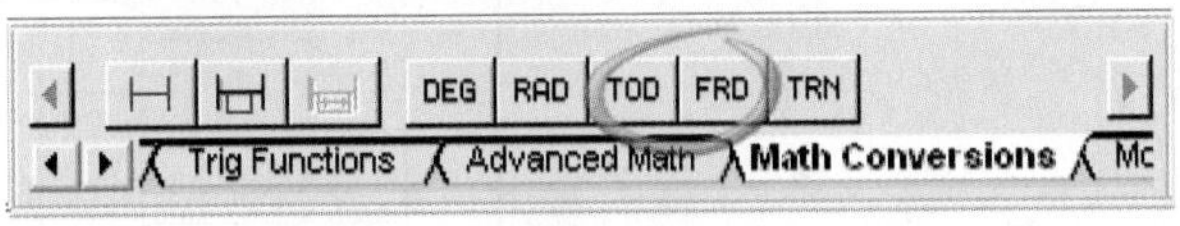
PLC 5, SLC 500	LIM, MEQ, EQU, NEQ, LES, GRT, LEQ, GEQ	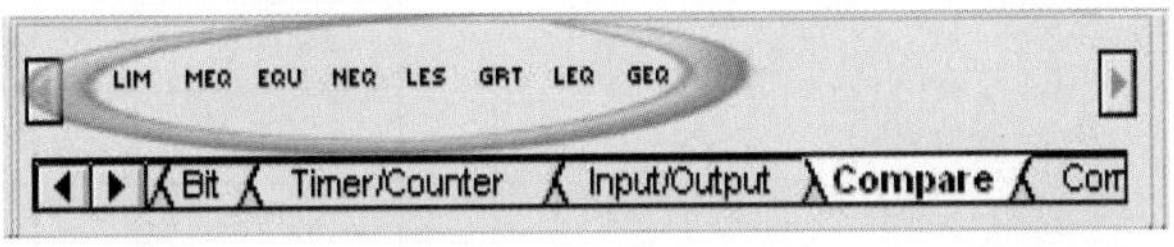
LOGIX	LIM, MEQ, EQU, NEQ, LES, GRT, LEQ, GEQ	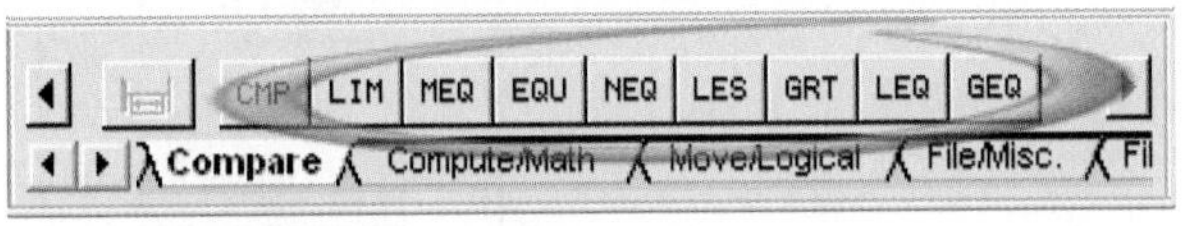

CHAPTER **8**

Program Control Instructions

8-1 GOALS AND OBJECTIVES

There are three principal goals of this chapter. The first goal is to provide the student with an overall picture of various program control instructions relative to subroutines and program scan. The second goal is to introduce the Allen-Bradley PLC 5, SLC 500, and Logix systems program control instructions that perform operations such as master control reset, jump, jump to subroutine, and immediate input and output functions. The third goal is to show how the program control instructions are applied to specific PLCs that are used in industrial automation systems.

After completing this chapter you should be able to:

- Explain the function of the program control instructions such as the master control and zone control reset instructions and jump and label instructions.
- Describe the operation of subroutines.
- Explain the function of immediate input and output instructions.
- Describe the operation of the clear instruction.
- Draw and describe ladder logic representing applications that use the program control instructions.

- Develop ladder diagram solutions using the program control instructions for the Allen-Bradley PLC 5, SLC 500, and ControlLogix systems.
- Use program control instructions and immediate input and output instructions in the empirical design process.
- Troubleshoot ladder rungs with program control instructions and immediate input and output instructions.

8-2 PROGRAM CONTROL INSTRUCTIONS

Program control instructions direct the flow of operation, as well as the execution of instructions, within a PLC ladder program. When programmed conditions are satisfied, portions of the program can be jumped over or their rungs not scanned so the outputs in these specific program groups or zones remain unchanged. In other words, the program control instructions allow the PLC to efficiently perform user-programmed routines that are executed only when specific automation conditions dictate. The program control instructions alter the program scan time, thereby optimizing total system response.

8-3 ALLEN-BRADLEY PROGRAM CONTROL INSTRUCTIONS

The Allen-Bradley program control instructions that are discussed in this section are as follows:

- The master control reset (MCR) instruction, which is used in pairs, fences in a group of instructions that can be executed or disabled.
- The jump (JMP) and the label (LBL) instructions are used together. When a JMP is enabled, the program jumps to the ladder rung with the LBL instruction and continues the execution of the subsequent instructions. Jumps can be either forward (skip ladder rungs) or backward (rescan ladder rungs).
- The jump to subroutine (JSR), the subroutine (SBR), and the return (RET) instructions are used together in the program. When a JSR instruction is enabled, the program jumps from the main program to the ladder rung in the subroutine program with the SBR instruction. The subroutine is executed until an RET instruction occurs. The RET instruc-

tion returns the program to the ladder rung in the main program that follows the JSR instruction rung.

8-3-1 Master Control Reset Instructions

Some output instructions, often called *override instructions*, provide a means of scanning a section of the control ladder when specific input conditions are present. Their use increases program flexibility and efficiency plus offers a reduction in scan time by jumping over portions of the ladder that are not utilized for specific process control situations. In relay logic these instructions are called *master control relays*; in the PLC they are called *master control reset*.

Electromechanical Master Control Relays. A hardwired master control relay (MCR) is used with relay ladder logic to shut down all or a portion of the relay ladder logic by turning on a master control relay with input relay logic. A hardwired master control relay ladder is illustrated in Figure 8-1. Note that rungs 1 and 2 always operate but rungs 4 through 31 operate only if the MCR contactor in rung 1 is active. An active MCR closes the MCR contacts and

FIGURE 8-1: Electromechanical master control relay ladder.

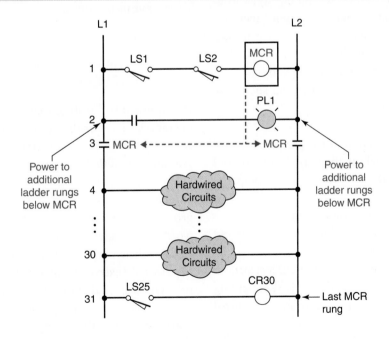

applies power to rungs 4 through 31. There could be additional relay ladder rungs that are not a part of the MCR circuit. These rungs do not rely on the MCR rungs for their power, so they are not controlled by the MCR contacts.

PLC Master Control Reset Instruction and Standard Ladder Logic. The PLC *master control reset* (MCR) output instruction is used in pairs and enables or inhibits the execution of a group or zone of ladder rungs, or it can be used to control the entire ladder logic program. The standard ladder logic for the MCR instruction is provided in Figure 8-2.

The PLC MCR works like its electromechanical counterpart. Two MCR instructions form a fence or zone in a program. Execution or scanning of the PLC instructions within the fence is controlled by the input logic in the rung of the first MCR instruction. The second MCR instruction, which signifies the end of the fence, does not have input logic, so its execution is unconditional. Read the description of the MCR instruction set provided in Figure 8-2. When the MCR instruction is false or de-energized, all non-retentive (non-latched) output instructions within the fence are false, even if their rung inputs are true. All non-retentive rungs are turned off simultaneously, and all retentive rungs remain in their last state. Conversely, when the MCR instruction is true or energized, the rungs within the fence operate as if no fence existed.

The operation of the MCR instruction is demonstrated in the example ladder logic in Figure 8-3. The first rung is labeled *fence start*, which is a rung with a conditional MCR instruction, and the last rung is labeled *fence end*, which is a rung with an unconditional MCR instruction. Note that the MCR instructions do not have an address. The operation of the zone is as follows:

Input I:1/1 is true (On/off switch closed): This causes the MCR instruction to be true, and the rungs within the fence act in accordance with their respective input logic conditions as if no

FIGURE 8-2: Standard ladder logic rungs for master control reset instructions.

Application	Standard Ladder Logic Rungs for Master Control Reset instructions
Control the scanning of all or part of a ladder logic program, disable output instructions, and force all non-retentive outputs to the off state with a single input logic instruction or a combination of instructions. Pairs of MCR output instructions are placed in a ladder logic program to control when the rungs between the instructions are scanned and executed. The MCR instructions are said to "fence" the ladder rungs that they bracket. The logic state (false or true) of the first MCR instructions dictates if the fenced rungs are scanned (true state) or passed over (false state). When the MCR is false, all non-retentive outputs in the fenced rungs are turned off and all retentive outputs retain their last condition. When the MCR is true, the rungs are scanned like the remainder of the ladder logic. The rung with the first MCR instruction is conditional and the second is unconditional as shown in the ladder rungs here.	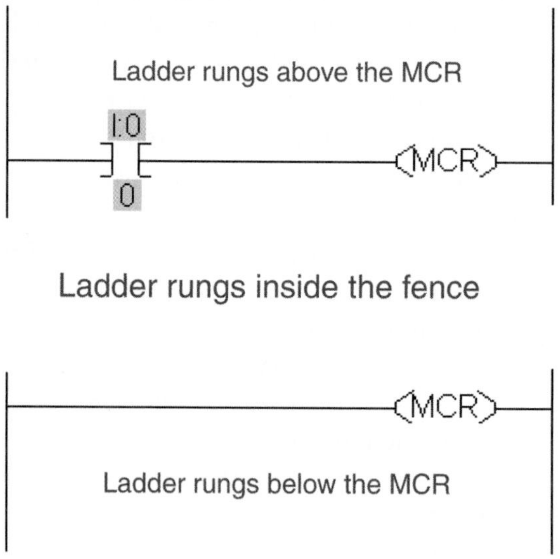 Ladder rungs above the MCR I:0] [⟨MCR⟩ 0 Ladder rungs inside the fence ⟨MCR⟩ Ladder rungs below the MCR MCR ladder rungs

FIGURE 8-3: Ladder logic example with MCR instruction.

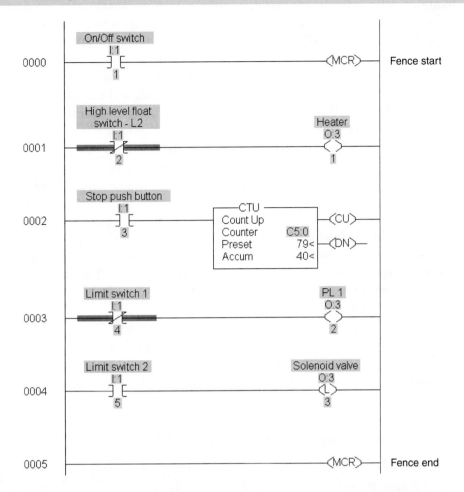

zone exists. With the zone active, input field devices for the ladder in Figure 8-3 turn on the *heater, pilot light,* and *solenoid valve.* The push button drives the *counter ACC* to 40, for example, and at this point, input I:1/1 goes false, and the rungs inside the fence respond as follows.

Input I:1/1 is false (On/off switch open): This causes the MCR instruction to be false, and all rungs within the zone are forced to a false state independent of the condition of the input logic. With the zone inactive, the non-retentive output instructions are false so the *heater* and *pilot light are off* even though their controlling input instructions are true. The *solenoid valve* remains *on* because it is a retentive output instruction and it was on when I:1/1 changed to a false condition. The *counter ACC* remains at 40, even though I:1/3 continues to cycle on and off.

The following comments apply to the MCR operation when the MCR is false:

- The input rung logic does not control the rung output.
- Non-retentive outputs are all false and retentive outputs hold the state they had when the MCR went from true to false.
- The counter accumulator stops incrementing even though the input logic changes state. The current count in the counter accumulator remains. When the MCR becomes active the counter starts from the previous value in the ACC.
- Note that the figure depicts only one MCR zone that includes the entire program. Multiple MCR zones can be constructed within a program that control only parts of the ladder logic program. However, MCR zones are never overlapped or nested.

The examination of PLC fault bits is another application of the MCR instruction. When used in this manner, the application places inputs addressed by fault bits in the first MCR rung and disables rungs with outputs that are creating the fault conditions with an MCR fence. The MCR instruction operates the same in the PLC 5, SLC 500, and Logix PLCs, that is, you create an MCR zone using pairs of MCR instructions.

8-3-2 Jump and Label Zone Control Instructions

The *jump* (JMP) output instruction and the input *label* (LBL) instruction are used together and allow the program scan sequence to be changed based on automation system conditions. Some manufacturers use the terms *skip* or *go-to* for their jump instruction. The jump instruction reduces the PLC scan time by jumping over (branching around) instructions that are not relevant to the program's operation at a particular time because of process or operator requirements. The jump instruction steps the program over a group of rungs to the label rung, as illustrated in Figure 8-5.

The *label* (LBL) instruction identifies the destination rung of the *jump* (JMP) instruction. The label instruction reference number must match that of the jump instruction with which it is used. The reference number can be assigned a three-digit address between 000 and 255. The PLC 5 and SLC 500 automatically place Q2: in front of the reference number. The label instruction, which is always true, is the first input instruction in the des-

FIGURE 8-4: Ladder solution for Example 8-1.

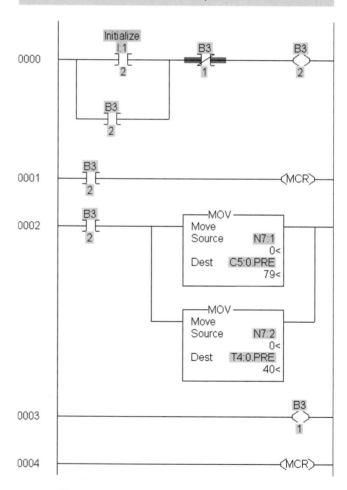

tination rung. The label is assigned the jump instruction's unique number. Ladder programs are permitted multiple jump instructions with the same number, but that number can be used only

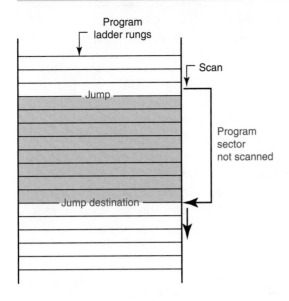

FIGURE 8-5: Jump instruction illustration.

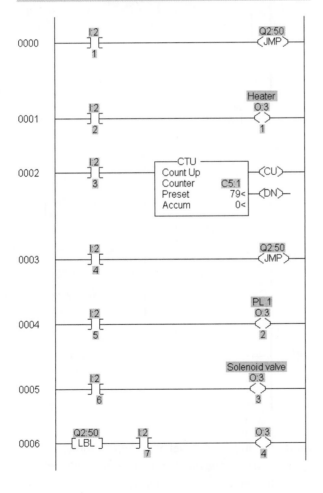

FIGURE 8-6: Ladder logic example with JMP and LBL instructions.

once on a label instruction. Jump instructions located on different rungs can use the same label instruction with the same reference number, as illustrated in Figure 8-6. The operation of the ladder program in the figure is as follows:

- If input I:2/1 is active, then the program jumps to rung 6 and continues the program sequence. Note that the counter in rung 2 will not increment because that rung is not scanned due to the jump. For this reason, the use of timers and counters inside the jump zone should be studied carefully.
- If input I:2/1 is false, then the program executes rungs 1 and 2.
- In rung 3, if input I:2/4 is false, then the program executes rungs 4, 5, and so forth.
- In rung 3, if input I:2/4 is true, then the program jumps over rungs 4 and 5 to rung 6 and continues the program sequence.

Finally, when using jump instructions, the following precautions should be observed.

1. Programming a jump instruction to go backward in the program should only be done with great care. Excessive backward jumps could cause the program to remain in a loop for too long and trigger a watchdog timer fault. The watchdog timer checks to see if the program scan time has exceeded a specific value.
2. Make sure that the LBL instruction is the first input instruction on the rung.
3. Programming a jump instruction into an MCR zone should never be done because the execution of the rungs between the rung with the label instruction and the last rung with the MCR instruction is dictated by the jump instruction and not by the initial MCR instruction.

In the ControlLogix PLC, text labels are used in place of the numeric code required in the PLC 5 and SLC 500 systems. The requirements for the text labels include a unique label name used only once for each jump, and label text with 40 or less characters that can be letters, numbers, and underscores (_).

Standard Ladder Logic for Jump and Label Instructions. There are three configurations of standard ladder logic for the jump and label instructions in the Allen-Bradley PLC systems. Read the description that accompanies each of the three configurations in Figure 8-7.

Figure 8-7(a) illustrates the standard forward jump instruction for the PLC 5 and SLC 500, and Figure 8-7(b) illustrates this for the ControlLogix PLC. Note that a reference number (preceded by Q2:) is used for the PLC 5 and SLC 500, but the jump and label are linked with a jump and label name for the ControlLogix PLC. The forward jump occurs when the input logic in the jump rung is true. The label instruction is placed in the extreme left location in the first rung to be scanned after the bypassed rungs.

Figure 8-7(c) illustrates the backward jump. Note that the label instruction is above (lower rung number) the jump instruction. As the ladder

FIGURE 8-7: Standard ladder logic rungs for jump and label instructions.

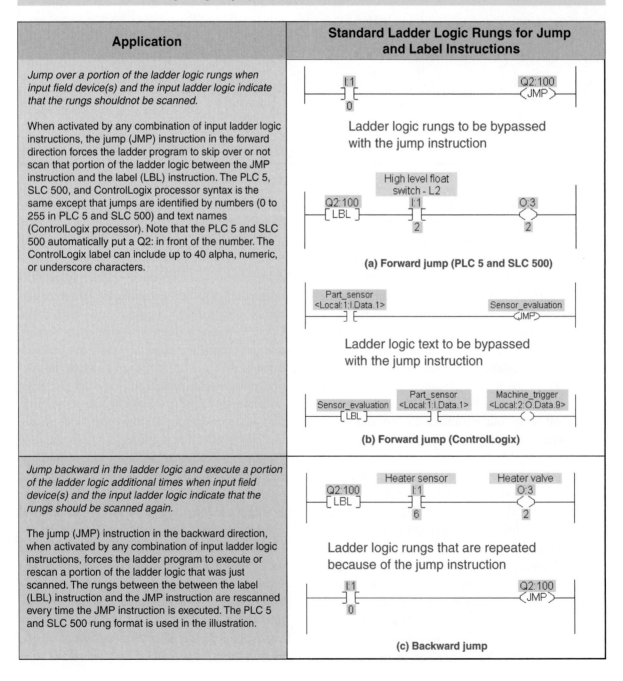

Application	Standard Ladder Logic Rungs for Jump and Label Instructions
Jump over a portion of the ladder logic rungs when input field device(s) and the input ladder logic indicate that the rungs should not be scanned. When activated by any combination of input ladder logic instructions, the jump (JMP) instruction in the forward direction forces the ladder program to skip over or not scan that portion of the ladder logic between the JMP instruction and the label (LBL) instruction. The PLC 5, SLC 500, and ControlLogix processor syntax is the same except that jumps are identified by numbers (0 to 255 in PLC 5 and SLC 500) and text names (ControlLogix processor). Note that the PLC 5 and SLC 500 automatically put a Q2: in front of the number. The ControlLogix label can include up to 40 alpha, numeric, or underscore characters.	**(a) Forward jump (PLC 5 and SLC 500)** **(b) Forward jump (ControlLogix)**
Jump backward in the ladder logic and execute a portion of the ladder logic additional times when input field device(s) and the input ladder logic indicate that the rungs should be scanned again. The jump (JMP) instruction in the backward direction, when activated by any combination of input ladder logic instructions, forces the ladder program to execute or rescan a portion of the ladder logic that was just scanned. The rungs between the between the label (LBL) instruction and the JMP instruction are rescanned every time the JMP instruction is executed. The PLC 5 and SLC 500 rung format is used in the illustration.	**(c) Backward jump**

FIGURE 8-7: (Continued).

Application	Standard Ladder Logic Rungs for Jump and Label Instructions
Jump over a portion of the ladder logic rungs from multiple locations in a ladder logic program to the same destination rung when input field device(s) and the input ladder logic indicate that the blocks of rungs should not be scanned and/or should be scanned again. The illustration shows two JMP instructions for a SLC 500. One is a forward jump to skip ladder rungs and the second is a backward jump to rescan a section of the ladder logic. Other options would be multiple forward jumps and multiple backward jumps or any combination of the two types.	Jump rungs sensor I:1 / 3 — Q2:100 〈JMP〉 Ladder rungs skipped Q2:100 [LBL] — Heater sensor I:1 / 6 — Heater valve O:3 / 2 Ladder rungs repeated Repeat rungs bit B3 / 4 — Q2:100 〈JMP〉 **(d) Multiple jump instructions to a single label**

scans from top to bottom the label instruction does not create any problems when the rung is scanned since it is always evaluated as true. The backward jump occurs when the input logic in the jump rung is true. The backward jump is used to rescan a block of ladder logic repeated times. The ControlLogix logic implementation is the same except for the difference in the jump and label identification.

The standard configuration for multiple jump instructions to a single label instruction is illustrated in Figure 8-7(d). The figure shows a forward jump and a backward jump, but multiple forward and backward jumps are also permitted.

Jump versus MCR Instructions. A study of the forward jump and MCR instructions indicates a good deal of similarity. Both permit an input logic condition to force the PLC scanner to skip over a block of PLC ladder logic. The primary difference, however, is in how the outputs are handled when the instructions are executed. The MCR sets all non-retentive outputs to the false state (the output image table bits are set to zero) and keeps the retentive outputs in their last state or condition. The jump leaves all outputs in their

last condition because the output image table bits are not changed.

8-3-3 Subroutine Instructions

A *subroutine* is a group of ladder logic PLC instructions outside the main ladder program that can be executed with the subroutine instruction. Thus, by using a single subroutine instruction repeated program routines do not have to be duplicated in the main ladder program when the routines must execute repeatedly. For example, when an automated machine has a sequence of rungs that must be repeated numerous times in the machine's cycle, that sequence of rungs could be programmed one time into a subroutine and just called when needed. Variable data can be *passed* to a subroutine when it is called, permitting the subroutine ladder logic to perform mathematical or logical operations on the data. Variable data or results produced in the subroutine can be passed back to the main program in a similar fashion. The subroutine concept is common in all PLCs, but the instruction that moves the program to the subroutine may differ between PLCs. The subroutine instructions in the Allen-Bradley PLCs are the *jump to subroutine* (JSR) output instruction, the

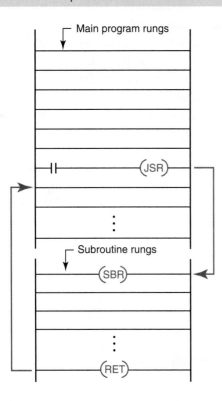

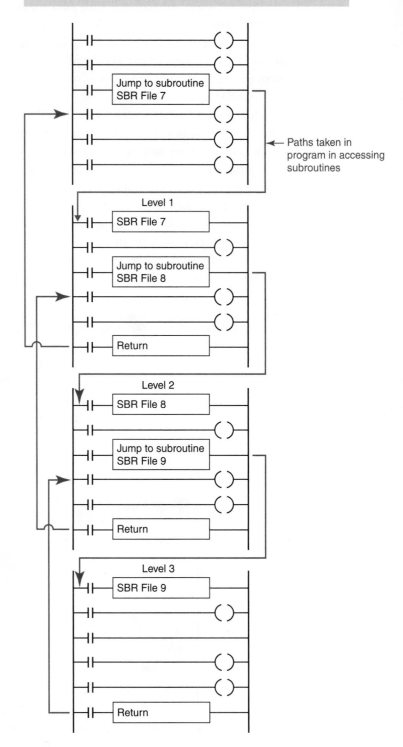

subroutine (SBR) input instruction, and the *return* (RET) output instruction.

Figure 8-8 illustrates the subroutine operation. Observe that the subroutine rungs with the SBR and RET instructions are a separate ladder logic program from the main program. Note that an RET instruction marks the end of the subroutine, similar to the last MCR instruction in an MCR zone. The return instruction is typically in an unconditional rung and returns the ladder program to the rung immediately after the rung containing the JSR instruction. However, if you want to end the subroutine before it completes all the rungs in the subroutine program, then a second conditional RET instruction may be inserted in a rung. Note in Figure 8-8 that the first rung of the subroutine contains the unconditional subroutine instruction SBR, which serves as a marker identifying that subroutine rungs follow.

Subroutines may be *nested*, which allows the programmer to direct the program flow to a subroutine, then to another and to another without returning to the main program each time. For example, sequential mathematical calculations that are needed by an industrial process can be implemented in nested subroutines for use by the main program whenever it's required. Figure 8-9 illustrates the nesting concept. Note that each subroutine return instruction routes the program flow to the previous subroutine, then finally back to the main program. The lines with arrows show the paths taken by the program in accessing the

subroutines. Also note that each subroutine is labeled with a level number and a file number. In the Allen-Bradley PLC 5 and SLC 500 systems the subroutines are numbered U:3, U:4, and so on, up to U:255. The ControlLogix system permits the programmer to name the subroutines so that they are identified by the application.

When nesting subroutines, care should be taken because scan time and the scanning rate of the main program may be impacted since the main program is not being scanned while the subroutine is executing. As a result, excessive delays in scanning the main program may cause inputs and outputs not to be assessed at the required time. These delays can be mitigated with the immediate input and output instructions covered later in this chapter.

8-3-4 PLC 5 and SLC 500 Subroutine Instructions

The Allen-Bradley subroutine instructions for the PLC 5 and SLC 500 PLCs are quite similar; however, the PLC 5 has parameter passing options like the ControlLogix PLC. Parameter passing is covered later in this section. The naming procedures used for the PLC 5 and SLC 500 subroutines are the starting point.

PLC 5 and SLC 500 Subroutine Setup. The procedure for selecting and naming the subroutine files in the PLC 5 and SLC 500 systems is illustrated in Figure 8-10. The process starts by right-clicking the Program Files folder in the left file menu, and then selecting New . . . to create a new ladder file [Figure 8-10(a)]. Note that

FIGURE 8-10: PLC 5 and SLC 500 subroutine setup.

(a) Left file menu – right-click program files so that New... can be selected

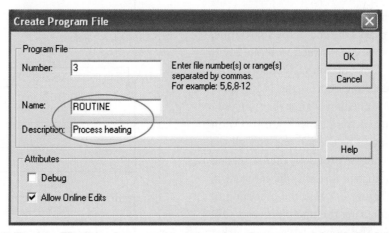

(b) Create Program File dialog box – used to enter subroutine name and description information

(c) Updated Left file menu with new subroutine program file, LAD 3 - ROUTINE

Application	Standard Ladder Logic Rungs for Subroutine Instructions
Identify the start and end of a block of rungs in a subroutine (these instructions are optional but recommended). The SBR instruction is used to mark the start of a subroutine and is always ANDed with the input logic instruction in the first rung of the subroutine. This instruction is always evaluated as true. While not required, the instruction is recommended so the start of the subroutine is identified. The RET instruction marks the end of subroutine execution or the end of the subroutine file. It causes the processor to resume execution in the main program file at the instruction following the JSR instruction where it exited the program. An RET instruction is not required, but is recommended for clarity. If it is omitted, the END statement (always present at the end of the subroutine ladder logic) automatically returns program execution back to the rung after the JSR instruction in the calling ladder program. Note: SLC 500 rungs are shown, but the operation would be the same for PLC 5 and ControlLogix. Schedule the execution of a subroutine block of ladder logic with multiple returns from the subroutine. The subroutine instructions are the same as in previous standard ladder logic, but the subroutine has multiple return instructions. This permits a return to the calling ladder logic at multiple ladder rungs before the entire subroutine ladder rungs are scanned. Note: SLC 500 rungs are shown, but the operation would be the same for PLC 5 and ControlLogix.	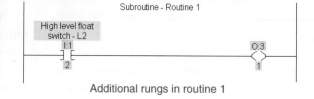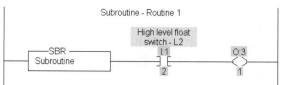
Schedule the execution of a subroutine block of ladder logic with multiple returns from the subroutine. The subroutine instructions are the same as in previous standard ladder logic, but the subroutine has multiple return instructions. This permits a return to the calling ladder logic at multiple ladder rungs before the entire subroutine ladder rungs are scanned. Note: SLC 500 rungs are shown, but the operation would be the same for PLC 5 and ControlLogix.	

illustrated in Figure 8-11(c). With the one-shot instruction included in this configuration, the subroutine will execute for only one scan after the input logic transitions from false to true. Although used less often, this configuration would be useful for situations where the trigger logic instruction does not return to the false state immediately.

Standard Ladder Logic for Subroutine and Return Instructions. The standard ladder logic for two configurations using the subroutine (SBR) and return (RET) instructions is illustrated in Figure 8-14. Read the description that accompanies each of the configurations in the figure.

Both of the SLC 500 subroutines in Figure 8-14(a) and (b) perform the same, but the subroutine in (b) uses the subroutine (SBR) and return (RET) instructions. When a subroutine is called by a JSR instruction, the program named in the JSR instruction will execute even without the SBR present. However, with the SBR instruction present it is clear that the ladder logic is a subroutine. The END rung present after the last rung of all programs serves the same function as the RET instruction. Although the SBR and RET instructions are recommended for clarity, they are required when parameters are passed using the PLC 5 and ControlLogix subroutine instructions covered later in this section.

The standard ladder logic for a solution with multiple subroutine return rungs is illustrated in Figure 8-14(c). There is no limit on the number of returns that are present in the subroutine. The subroutine in the figure shows two returns. Note that the last return is an unconditional rung, and all returns in the body of the subroutine ladder logic have conditional input logic to trigger the rung.

EXAMPLE 8-4

Modify Example 8-3 as follows:

There are two levels of faults in the production system that trigger the enunciator: level one faults do not require immediate attention; level two faults must be acted upon immediately. The enunciator for level one is the flashing lights only; the enunciator for level two includes both the lights and the horn with no delay for the horn. The trigger for a level one fault is latch bit, B3:0/2, while level two faults are triggered by B3:0/3. Redesign the subroutine so that it handles both types of faults. Reset of both types of faults is required.

SOLUTION

The two-level operator alert ladder logic program is shown in Figure 8-15. The modified JSR instruction rung from the machine control ladder logic is shown in Figure 8-15(a) and the modified subroutine is shown in Figure 8-15(b). Study the ladder solution.

The only change in the jump to subroutine rungs is the addition of the B3:0/3 bit for triggering the subroutine and resetting the operation. The subroutine has the following changes: The 60-second timer is removed, the horn is triggered only by the timer pulse output, and a return (RET) instruction is added between the flashing light and pulsing horn rungs. As a result, a level 1 fault executes only the upper half of the subroutine ladder, and a level 2 fault executes the entire subroutine ladder logic.

8-3-5 PLC 5 and ControlLogix Options for Subroutine Instructions

The Allen-Bradley subroutine instructions for the three PLCs are quite similar; however, the ControlLogix PLC uses a unique naming process plus some additional options. The naming procedure used for a ControlLogix PLC subroutine is illustrated in Figure 8-16.

ControlLogix Subroutine Setup. Study the procedure for selecting and naming ControlLogix subroutine files in the Figure 8-16. The process starts by right-clicking the MainProgram folder in the left file menu, and then selecting New Routine . . . to create a new program file [Figure 8-16(a)]. Note that MainRoutine is the default main program ladder logic file that is always present in this menu.

FIGURE 8-13: Ladder solution for Example 8-3.

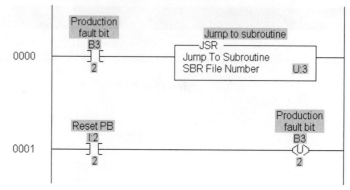

(a) Main routine – LAD 2

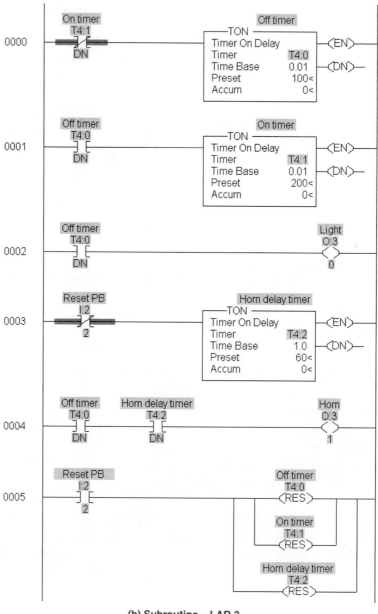

(b) Subroutine – LAD 3

FIGURE 8-12: Solution for Example 8-2.

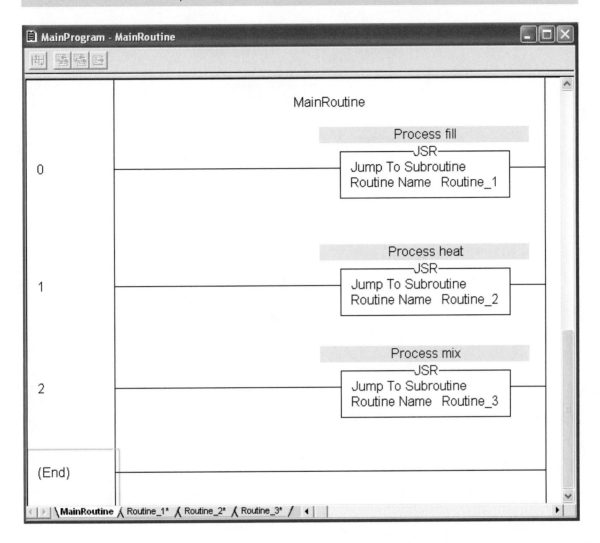

The operator alert ladder logic program is shown in Figure 8-13. The JSR instruction rung from the machine control ladder logic is shown in Figure 8-13(a) and the subroutine is shown in Figure 8-13(b). Study the ladder solution.

When any production fault is detected the system program [Figure 8-13(a)] latches the retentive bit B3:0/2. That bit is used to call the operator alert subroutine and is reset with the reset push button switch and the unlatch instruction for the B3:0/2 bit in rung 1 of the main program.

The light flashing logic in the subroutine [Figure 8-13(b)] is located in rungs 0 through 2, and the three remaining rungs provide the horn control. The flashing light is produced by two timers with cross-coupled done bits. T4:0 sets the off light time and T4:1 sets the on light time. The done output of T4:0 triggers the light. After T4:0 reaches 1 second, the light comes on (T4:0/DN) and remains on while T4:1 increments for 2 seconds. The output, T4:1/DN, resets the T4:0 timer and the light.

The horn enunciator is cycled on and off by the light timer done bit, T4:0/DN, after the 60-second timer has timed out. The reset for the operator alert also resets all three timers. Verify that the ladder solution satisfies the automation system requirements.

Application	Standard Ladder Logic Rungs for Subroutine Instructions
Execute all the ladder logic on every scan but isolate blocks of the rungs for better design management and easier editing. The use of subroutines permits a program solution in PLC 5, SLC 500, and ControlLogix to be divided into logical segments. No input logic is present in this standard ladder logic example, so the rung is always active. The result of this unconditional input condition is the execution of the subroutine instruction every scan. As a result, it is like pasting the block of rungs from the subroutine into the main program where the jump to subroutine instruction is located. However, the rungs in the subroutine are isolated for easy editing and maintenance. The tabs at the bottom of the page permit selection of the main program or any of the subroutine ladders. Note: SLC 500 rungs are shown, but the operation would be the same for PLC 5 and ControlLogix.	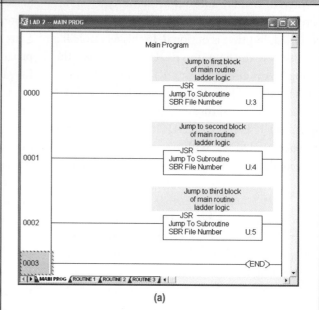 (a)
Schedule the execution of a portion of the ladder logic when one or a combination of input logic instructions make the rung with the subroutine jump instruction active. The input field device(s) and a combination of their input ladder logic instructions in the SLC 500 make the jump to subroutine rung active. As a result, the ladder logic rungs in the subroutine are executed on a schedule and at a rate determined by the field devices, input instructions, or internal virtual memory bits. The tabs at the bottom of the page permit selection of the main program or ladder logic for the subroutine, ROUTINE 1. Note: SLC 500 rungs are shown, but the operation would be the same for PLC 5 and ControlLogix.	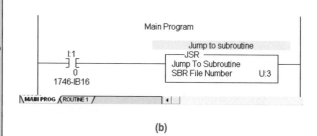 (b)
Execute a portion of the ladder logic for only one scan when an input instruction or a combination of input logic instructions makes the rung with the subroutine jump instruction active. The input field device(s) and the input ladder logic in the jump to subroutine instruction rung determine when the jump rung is active. The one shot assures that the jump to subroutine is performed for only one scan. Note: SLC 500 rungs are shown, but the operation would be the same for PLC 5 and ControlLogix.	Main Program Jump to subroutine JSR Jump To Subroutine SBR File Number U:3 I:1 B3 0 [OSR] 1746-IB16 0 MAIN PROG / ROUTINE 1 (c)

LAD 2 is the default main program ladder file that is always present in this menu.

In the Create Program File dialog box [Figure 8-10(b)], the number (3 to 255) of the desired file is entered. Usually subroutine files are just numbered consecutively. A name and description can be added, but that is optional. In this example file 3 is used with the name ROUTINE. When the dialog box is closed (click OK) the new file is visible in the left file menu [Figure 8-10(c)]. If LAD 2 is double-clicked the main program ladder will open, but if LAD 3 - ROUTINE is selected the subroutine ladder will open. Once they are opened, they can be quickly selected from the tabs at the bottom of the window.

Standard Ladder Logic for the PLC 5, SLC 500, and ControlLogix Jump to Subroutine Instruction. The standard ladder logic for the three configurations of the jump to subroutine (JSR) instruction is illustrated in Figure 8-11. Read the description that accompanies each of the configurations.

Figure 8-11(a) illustrates the standard unconditional subroutine instruction. Note that the subroutine ladders are called U:3, U:4, and U:5. The U: is the required preface and the number indicates the LAD number in the left file menu. Thus, when the first subroutine instruction (rung 0) in Figure 8-11(a) is executed, the ladder LAD 3 is scanned. Since each of the subroutine instructions is unconditional, the ladders in LAD 3, LAD 4, and LAD 5 are executed in that order. This allows a large program to be divided into three logical segments for easier development and maintenance. The naming procedures for the PLC 5 and SLC 500 systems are the same, but the ControlLogix PLC uses a tag to identify the subroutine. The PLC 5 and SLC 500 subroutine numbers are entered by first double-clicking the file number box. Clicking outside the instruction box after entering the number adds the subroutine number to the instruction.

The standard subroutine instruction with controlling input logic is illustrated in Figure 8-11(b). Note that the subroutine ladders are identified in the same fashion, but in this configuration the execution of the subroutines is controlled by the input logic on each subroutine rung. This is the most frequently used configuration for subroutines.

The standard subroutine instruction with controlling input logic and a one-shot instruction is

---

EXAMPLE 8-2

Implement the process control tank solution in Figures 7-19, 7-20, and 7-21 using the subroutine standard ladder logic configuration in Figure 8-11(a). Review the solution for the tank problem in Chapter 7, and then use unconditional subroutines for execution of the solution.

SOLUTION

The solution to the process tank problem, illustrated in Figure 8-12, is divided into three process solution areas: tank fill and mix (Figure 7-19), material heat and drain (Figure 7-20), and tank rinse (Figure 7-21). Three subroutines are created: Routine_1 (tank fill and mix), Routine_2 (material heat and drain), and Routine_3 (tank rinse). The ladder logic in the main program calls the three unconditional subroutines and the original 15-rung single ladder solution is executed by scanning the three process control ladder sections one after the other.

EXAMPLE 8-3

The PLC program for a production system has 15 fault conditions that stop the production system by latching a bit. Design an operator attention program that will flash a red fault light on the system with a 2-second on, 1-second off duty cycle when these faults occur. If the alert is not acknowledged in 60 seconds by pressing a normally open reset push button, a horn with the same duty cycle is added to the fault warning system. The ladder logic should be placed in a subroutine so it can be called from any one of the 15 locations in the machine control ladder logic where the faults are detected. The system reset should reset the fault indicator as well.

illustrated in Figure 8-11(c). With the one-shot instruction included in this configuration, the subroutine will execute for only one scan after the input logic transitions from false to true. Although used less often, this configuration would be useful for situations where the trigger logic instruction does not return to the false state immediately.

Standard Ladder Logic for Subroutine and Return Instructions. The standard ladder logic for two configurations using the subroutine (SBR) and return (RET) instructions is illustrated in Figure 8-14. Read the description that accompanies each of the configurations in the figure.

Both of the SLC 500 subroutines in Figure 8-14(a) and (b) perform the same, but the subroutine in (b) uses the subroutine (SBR) and return (RET) instructions. When a subroutine is called by a JSR instruction, the program named in the JSR instruction will execute even without the SBR present. However, with the SBR instruction present it is clear that the ladder logic is a subroutine. The END rung present after the last rung of all programs serves the same function as the RET instruction. Although the SBR and RET instructions are recommended for clarity, they are required when parameters are passed using the PLC 5 and ControlLogix subroutine instructions covered later in this section.

The standard ladder logic for a solution with multiple subroutine return rungs is illustrated in Figure 8-14(c). There is no limit on the number of returns that are present in the subroutine. The subroutine in the figure shows two returns. Note that the last return is an unconditional rung, and all returns in the body of the subroutine ladder logic have conditional input logic to trigger the rung.

EXAMPLE 8-4

Modify Example 8-3 as follows:

There are two levels of faults in the production system that trigger the enunciator: level one faults do not require immediate attention; level two faults must be acted upon immediately. The enunciator for level one is the flashing lights only; the enunciator for level two includes both the lights and the horn with no delay for the horn. The trigger for a level one fault is latch bit, B3:0/2, while level two faults are triggered by B3:0/3. Redesign the subroutine so that it handles both types of faults. Reset of both types of faults is required.

SOLUTION

The two-level operator alert ladder logic program is shown in Figure 8-15. The modified JSR instruction rung from the machine control ladder logic is shown in Figure 8-15(a) and the modified subroutine is shown in Figure 8-15(b). Study the ladder solution.

The only change in the jump to subroutine rungs is the addition of the B3:0/3 bit for triggering the subroutine and resetting the operation. The subroutine has the following changes: The 60-second timer is removed, the horn is triggered only by the timer pulse output, and a return (RET) instruction is added between the flashing light and pulsing horn rungs. As a result, a level 1 fault executes only the upper half of the subroutine ladder, and a level 2 fault executes the entire subroutine ladder logic.

8-3-5 PLC 5 and ControlLogix Options for Subroutine Instructions

The Allen-Bradley subroutine instructions for the three PLCs are quite similar; however, the ControlLogix PLC uses a unique naming process plus some additional options. The naming procedure used for a ControlLogix PLC subroutine is illustrated in Figure 8-16.

ControlLogix Subroutine Setup. Study the procedure for selecting and naming ControlLogix subroutine files in the Figure 8-16. The process starts by right-clicking the MainProgram folder in the left file menu, and then selecting New Routine . . . to create a new program file [Figure 8-16(a)]. Note that MainRoutine is the default main program ladder logic file that is always present in this menu.

FIGURE 8-14: Standard ladder logic rungs for SLC 500 subroutine instructions.

Application	Standard Ladder Logic Rungs for Subroutine Instructions
Identify the start and end of a block of rungs in a subroutine (these instructions are optional but recommended). The SBR instruction is used to mark the start of a subroutine and is always ANDed with the input logic instruction in the first rung of the subroutine. This instruction is always evaluated as true. While not required, the instruction is recommended so the start of the subroutine is identified. The RET instruction marks the end of subroutine execution or the end of the subroutine file. It causes the processor to resume execution in the main program file at the instruction following the JSR instruction where it exited the program. An RET instruction is not required, but is recommended for clarity. If it is omitted, the END statement (always present at the end of the subroutine ladder logic) automatically returns program execution back to the rung after the JSR instruction in the calling ladder program. Note: SLC 500 rungs are shown, but the operation would be the same for PLC 5 and ControlLogix. Schedule the execution of a subroutine block of ladder logic with multiple returns from the subroutine. The subroutine instructions are same as in previous standard ladder logic, but the subroutine has multiple return instructions. This permits a return to the calling ladder logic at multiple ladder rungs before the entire subroutine ladder rungs are scanned. Note: SLC 500 rungs are shown, but the operation would be the same for PLC 5 and ControlLogix.	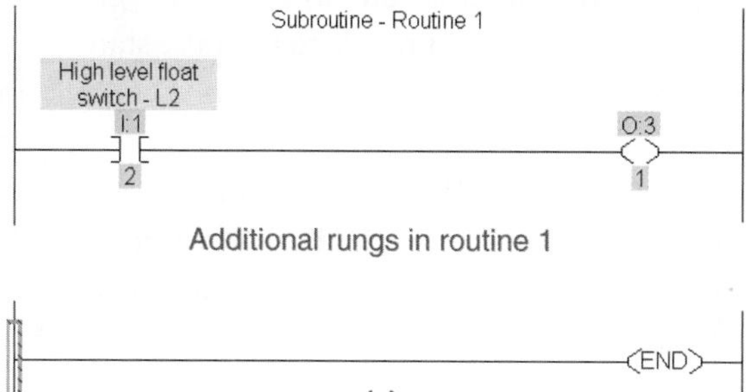 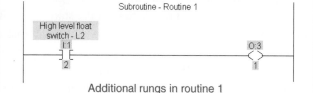 (a) 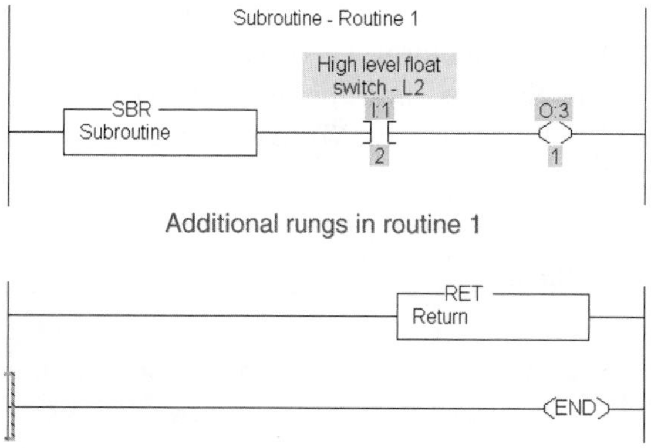 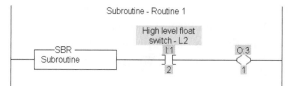 (b)
Schedule the execution of a subroutine block of ladder logic with multiple returns from the subroutine. The subroutine instructions are the same as in previous standard ladder logic, but the subroutine has multiple return instructions. This permits a return to the calling ladder logic at multiple ladder rungs before the entire subroutine ladder rungs are scanned. Note: SLC 500 rungs are shown, but the operation would be the same for PLC 5 and ControlLogix.	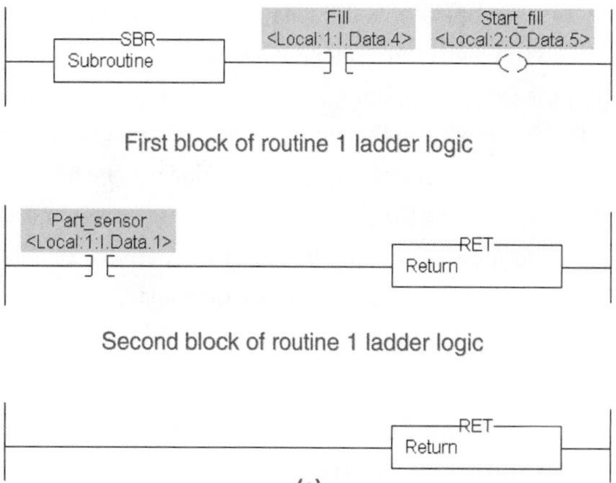  (c)

FIGURE 8-15: Ladder solution for Example 8-4.

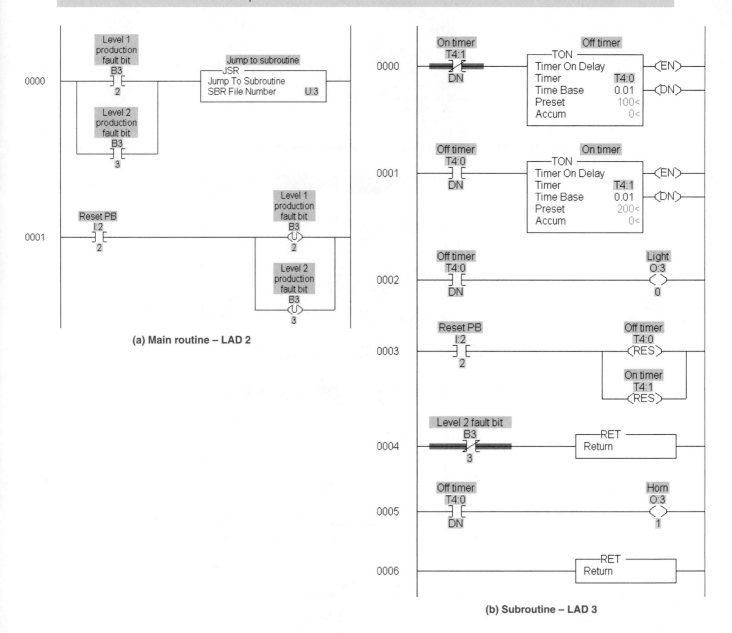

(a) Main routine – LAD 2

(b) Subroutine – LAD 3

In the New Routine dialog box [Figure 8-16(b)], the routine name (Routine_1) is entered (note spaces are not allowed and underlines are used). A description can be added, and the type of program must be selected [Figure 8-16(c)]. Ladder Diagram is selected in this example. When the dialog box is closed (click OK), the new file is visible in the left file menu [Figure 8-16(d)]. If MainRoutine is double-clicked the main program ladder is opened, but if Routine_1 is selected then that subroutine ladder is opened. Once they are opened, they can be quickly selected from the tabs at the bottom of the window.

PLC 5 and ControlLogix JSR, SBR, and RET Instruction Options. The PLC 5 and ControlLogix instructions for jump to subroutine (JSR), subroutine (SBR), and return (RET) have a parameter passing option. Parameter passing describes a process that moves one or more data values from the main routine to the subroutine at the time that the subroutine is called. Data can

FIGURE 8-16: Selecting and naming ControlLogix subroutines.

(a) Left file menu – right-click MainProgram so that New Routine... can be selected

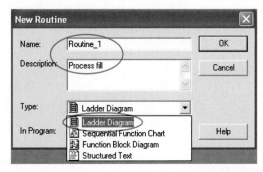

(b) New Routine dialog box – used to enter subroutine name and description
information plus to indicate the software language to be used

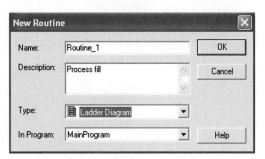

(c) New Routine dialog box with all data present

(d) Left file menu with MainProgram elements. Note MainRoutine and three
additional ladder files Routine_1, Routine_2, and Routine_3.

also be passed from the subroutine back to the main program. It is important to understand the concept of global and program data values before parameter passing is covered.

Global and Program Data Values. The terms *global* and *program* define where the data values represented by tag names or files can be used and how they are identified. For example, all the data or memory addresses in the PLC 5 and SLC 500 PLCs are global. This means that an input address, such as I:1/0, can be used in LAD 2 and in a subroutine ladder like LAD 3 – ROUTINE, shown in Figure 8-10(c). LAD 2 is the main ladder logic program and LAD 3 – ROUTINE is a separate set of ladder logic rungs

used as a subroutine. The value of address I:1/0 is the same whether an input uses this address in the main ladder logic or in any subroutine rung. As a result, if data addresses for bits or words change in one ladder rung they change at every other program location (LAD 2, LAD 3, etc.) where the address is used. Therefore, if you want to use the accumulator value of a counter located in LAD 2 in a comparator in subroutine LAD 3, you just use the counter ACC address.

The ControlLogix PLC, on the other hand, has both global data (controller scoped) and local data (program scoped). The term used by Allen-Bradley for global data is *controller-scoped data*. The controller-scoped tag can be used in all controller programs and it brings the tag value with it. Program-scoped tags, called local variables in computer programming, are restricted to a single program. For example, a program-scoped tag name such as liquid_temp could not be used in a rung in Routine_1. If the value from tag liquid_temp was required in Routine_1, then you could change to a controller-scoped (global) tag or use *parameter passing*.

Parameter Passing in ControlLogix and PLC 5 JSR, SBR, and RET Instructions. The ControlLogix JSR instruction is illustrated in Figure 8-17(a). Note that in addition to the Routine Name parameter there are locations for an input parameter (Input Par) and a return parameter (Return Par). Each parameter is defined as follows:

Routine Name: The routine name parameter is the name of the routine file to be executed. The steps in Figure 8-16 describe how this file is created.

Input Par (JSR and SBR): The input parameter value in the main routine represents process data that must be passed to the subroutine program identified in Routine Name. The data goes into the Input Par tag in the SBR instruction. Main routine input parameters can be fixed values or tag names with Boolean, integer, or floating point data types.

Return Par (JSR and RET): The return parameter value in the return instruction in the sub-

```
   ┌─JSR──────────────────────┐
   │ Jump To Subroutine        │
   │ Routine Name          ?   │
   │ Input Par             ?   │
   │ Return Par            ?   │
   └───────────────────────────┘
```

(a) ControlLogix jump to subroutine instruction

```
   ┌─SBR──────────────────────┐
   │ Subroutine                │
   │ Input Par        ?        │
   └───────────────────────────┘
```

(b) ControlLogix subroutine instruction

```
   ┌─RET──────────────────────┐
   │ Return                    │
   │ Return Par       ?        │
   └───────────────────────────┘
```

(c) ControlLogix return instruction

routine represents process data or subroutine calculations that must be passed back to the main routine program that called the subroutine. The data goes into the Return Par tag in the JSR instruction. The return parameter in the return instruction is a tag name with Boolean, integer, or floating point data types.

The subroutine (SBR) and return (RET) instructions are illustrated in Figure 8-17(b) and (c). Note that the SBR instruction has an input parameter, Input Par, and RET has a return instruction, Return Par. Multiple input and return parameters are allowed. The data passing and operation of the three instructions are illustrated in Figure 8-18.

The following data flow occurs in the figure.

1. The centigrade temperature value in Temp1 (tag in main routine) is transferred to TempC (tag in subroutine).
2. The subroutine ladder calculates the temperature value in Fahrenheit.
3. The temperature value in Fahrenheit in TempF (tag in subroutine) is transferred to Temp2 (tag in main routine).

FIGURE 8-18: Parameter passing for ControlLogix PLC.

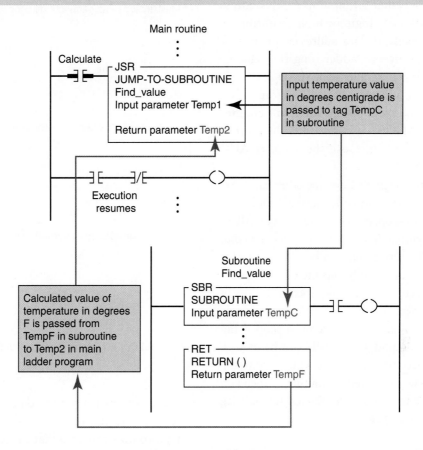

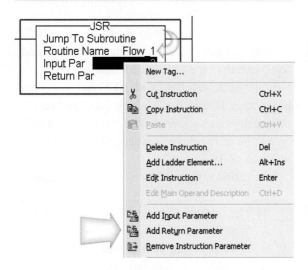

The JSR, SBR, and RET instructions in ControlLogix are used with and without passing parameters. Additional input and return parameters are added or parameters are removed by selecting a parameter location and right-clicking the mouse. Figure 8-19 shows the drop-down menu that appears. Note the add and remove commands and the program name that is present.

If no parameters are present, then the instruction operates like the subroutine instructions in the SLC 500. However, if input and return parameter tag locations are present, then they must have a tag entered. The number of parameters in the JSR instruction must agree with the number in the SBR and RET instructions.

Selection of PLC 5 Parameters. The parameter passing syntax is the same for the PLC 5 as that used in the ControlLogix PLC, but the technique for creating the input and return param-

eters is different. The first input parameter in the JSR instruction appears when the Enter key is used to input the subroutine number. A new input parameter is generated when the previous parameter is completed and the Enter key pressed. Pressing the Enter key with a blank input parameter box creates a return parameter entry box. Finally, pressing the Enter key with a blank return field cancels the entry mode. Input and return parameters are placed in the SBR and RET instructions by double-clicking the instruction.

Standard Ladder Logic for Parameter Passing in PLC 5 and ControlLogix Subroutine Instructions. The standard ladder logic for the ControlLogix JSR, SBR, and RET instructions

using parameter passing is illustrated in Figure 8-20. Read the description of the process in the figure. Note that the subroutine would function correctly for any JSR instruction with any input and return parameter tags located anywhere in the main routine. The ability to have different tags for the data in the main routine and in the subroutine is a major advantage to using parameter passing.

The ControlLogix standard ladder logic for no parameter would require removal of all parameters in the JSR, SBR, and RET instructions. With that accomplished, the ControlLogix instructions have the same form as the SLC 500 instructions. In addition, the variations on the standard ladders presented for the SLC 500 apply to the ControlLogix PLC as well.

FIGURE 8-20: Standard ladder logic rungs for parameter passing in the PLC 5 and ControlLogix subroutine instructions.

Application	Standard Ladder Logic Rungs for Parameter Passing in the ControlLogic Subroutine Instructions
Pass a variety of register values to reusable subroutine code using ControlLogix subroutine instructions. The JSR instruction has the following parameters: tag name of subroutine ladder logic (routine name), input parameter values (Chem1_vol and Chem1_den) to pass, and the return parameter (Chem1_weight) from the subroutine. The SBR instruction in the first rung of the subroutine has the tag that receives the passed parameter value for use in the subroutine. Note that the values from Chem1_vol and Chem1_den are placed in the tags volume and density. Finally, the RET instruction stores the calculated weight value in a tag named Tank_weight. When the return instruction is executed, the value in Tank_weight is transferred to the tag Chem1_weight in the JSR instruction for use in the main routine. The PLC 5 JSR instruction uses the same syntax except a number (U:3 to 255) is used to identify the subroutine in place of the tag name. Also, the input and return parameters can be fixed value Boolean, integers, and floating point numbers, logic element addresses such as N7:2, or logic structure addresses such as C5:0.ACC.	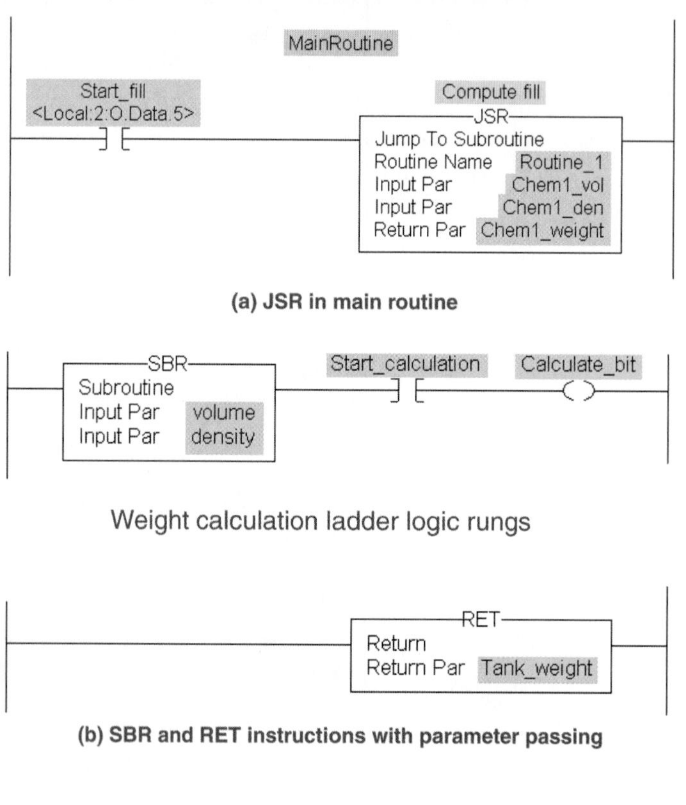

EXAMPLE 8-5

A stack light indicator system for a production area has three lights: green for normal operation, yellow for minor fault, and red for major fault. For each condition the respective light has an on and off duty cycle that is different. Design a ControlLogix PLC ladder logic program using a subroutine that will handle this requirement for stack light control.

SOLUTION

The ControlLogix stack light control ladder logic program is shown in Figure 8-21. Note that five parameters are passed to the subroutine as follows: three Boolean bits to indicate which of the lights should be turned on

FIGURE 8-21: Ladder logic for Example 8-5.

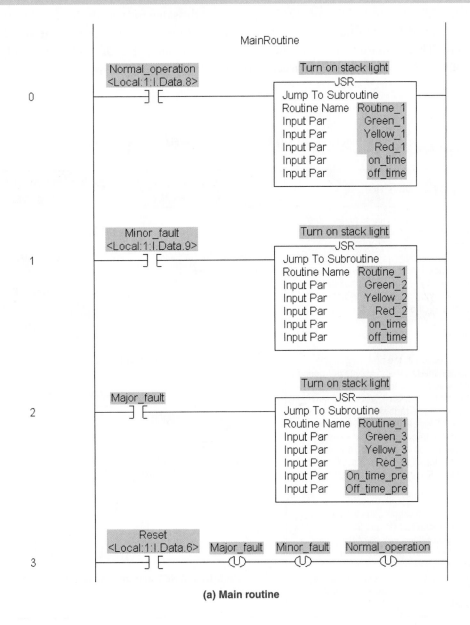

(a) Main routine

and two integers to pass the on and off times for the light. The Input Par bits have different values for each of the conditions. For example, Green_1, Yellow_1, and Red_1 have bits 1, 0, 0 loaded, respectively. So when the *normal_operation* input is true, the bits passed make the green stack light active and the yellow and red inactive. The bit patterns for the minor fault are 0, 1, 0; and for the major fault they are 0, 0, 1. Inside the subroutine, the light indicator bits are received in three tags, Green, Yellow, and Red. They are then used to enable rungs 2, 3, or 4, depending on what light should be on. The timer values for the on and off duty cycle are passed directly into the respective timer preset locations. A manual reset returns all system status bits to false and the system is restarted.

FIGURE 8-21: (Continued).

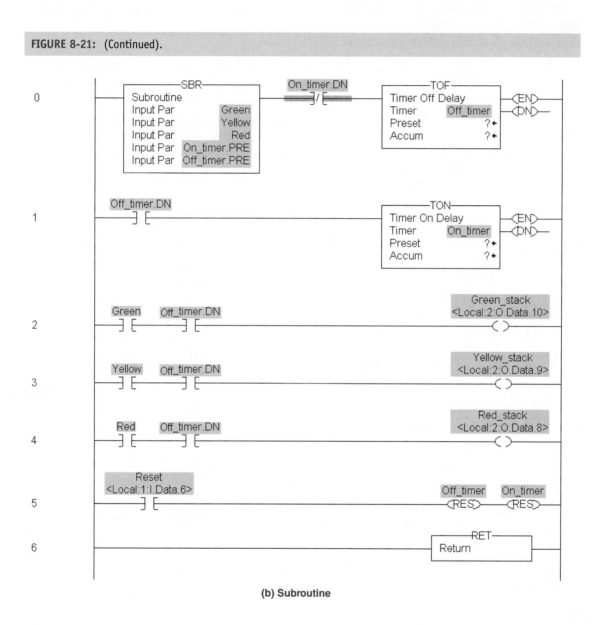

(b) Subroutine

8-4 ALLEN-BRADLEY IMMEDIATE INPUT AND OUTPUT INSTRUCTIONS

When the PLC program scan reaches an immediate input or immediate output instruction, the program flow is interrupted and the input or output data is updated. After the input or output data has been serviced, the program flow is returned to the point of interruption. These instructions are generally used for time-critical I/O data. In the following subsections the format and capability of these instructions are discussed for the PLC 5, SLC 500, and ControlLogix PLCs.

8-4-1 PLC 5 Immediate Input and Output Instructions

The *immediate input* (IIN) and *immediate output* (IOT) instructions are illustrated in Figure 8-22. They can have conditional and unconditional input logic. Note that the IIN and IOT instructions are located in the program scan after the program inputs and outputs have been serviced, noted as housekeeping in the figure. The (y) next to IIN in the figure is the address of the instruction, which is the rack number (two digits) and module group (one digit) of the input device. For example, IIN 014 represents rack 01 and module group 4. For the IIN instruction, the input image table is updated in accordance with the status of the input module, which reads the input field

device. Likewise, the (x) next to IOT in the figure is the address of the instruction, which is the rack number (two digits) and module group (one digit) of the output device. For the IOT instruction the output image table is updated immediately without completing the scan in accordance with the status of the output module, which drives the output field device.

The ladder diagrams for the PLC 5 IIN and the IOT instructions are illustrated in Figure 8-23(b) and (d). Note that the number above the IIN and IOT is the address of the instruction and represents the rack number and module group. In Figure 8-23(b), when the program scan reaches the IIN instruction the scan is interrupted and all bits of word 012 in the input image table are updated. In Figure 8-23(d), when the program scan reaches the IOT instruction the scan is interrupted and all bits of word 014 in the output image table are updated.

8-4-2 SLC 500 Immediate Input and Output Instructions

In the SLC 500 PLC these I/O instructions are called the *immediate input with mask* (IIM) and the *immediate output with mask* (IOM) instructions. These instructions provide the same function in the program scan as the IIN and the IOT instructions, which were described in Section 8-4-1. However, the mask provides an improvement in capability over the IIN and IOT instructions. The mask specifies the portion of the input or output data to be updated. This allows the programmer to specify which bits of the word are copied from an input module to the input image table or from the output image table to an output module. Figure 8-23(a) illustrates the IIM instruction, and Figure 8-23(c) illustrates the IOM instruction. The IIM instruction operates on the inputs assigned to a specific word of a rack slot, and the IOM instruction operates on the outputs assigned to a specific word of a rack slot. The function of the parameters of the instructions is as follows:

- Slot: The slot parameter represents the address of the input or output word and includes the slot and word within the slot that contains the data to update the input or output image tables. In Figure 8-23(a), I:1.0 indicates slot

FIGURE 8-22: Program scan with immediate input and output instructions.

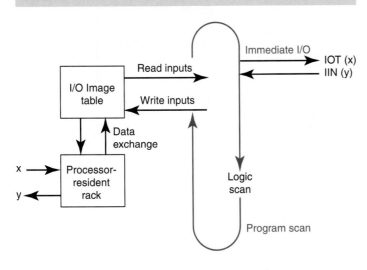

Application	Standard Ladder Logic Rungs for Immediate Input and Output Instructions
Input a word of data from a field device to a register or tag name without waiting for the completion of the scan cycle. The immediate input instruction in the PLC 5 and the immediate input with mask instruction in the SLC 500 can be implemented with conditional and unconditional input logic. In addition, a one shot can be added to limit the immediate data transfer to just one sample taken in a single scan. The masked version allows the programmer to designate which bits in the sampled input data are transferred to the input register. *Note: The SLC 500 is shown with all three input logic options. The PLC 5 is shown with only one but could have all three as well.*	 **(a) Immediate input with mask (SLC 500)** **(b) Immediate input (PLC 5)**
Output a word of data stored in a PLC register or tag to an output field device without waiting for the completion of the scan cycle. The immediate output instructions in the PLC 5 and ControlLogix plus the immediate output with mask instruction in the SLC 500 can be implemented with conditional and unconditional input logic. In addition, a one shot can be added to limit the immediate data transfer to just one sample taken in a single scan. The masked version allows the programmer to designate which bits in the sampled output register or tag are transferred to the output field device. *Note: All PLCs are shown with one input logic option; all could use any of the three shown on the SLC IIM instruction.*	 **(c) Immediate output with mask (SLC 500)** **(d) Immediate output (PLC 5)** MainRoutine **(e) Immediate output (ControlLogix)**

1 and word 0. Likewise, in Figure 8-23(c), O:3.0 indicates slot 3 and word 0. Up to 32 words can be associated with the slot depending on PLC capability.

- Mask: The mask parameter is typically a hexadecimal number that specifies what bits in the word are 1s and what bits are 0s. Every mask bit location with a 1 will pass that data bit and every 0 in a bit location inhibits the data transfer. Note that the mask in Figure 8-23(a) passes all bits except the four least significant bits and the four most significant bits.
- Length: The length parameter specifies the number of words (0 to 32 in some SLC processors) per slot that are transferred.

Use of immediate instruction increases the execution time significantly, so conditional rungs are recommended so that the input instructions control when the immediate instructions are executed. The standard ladder logic for the IOM instruction shows three control possibilities: unconditional, conditional, and conditional with a one-shot. The one-shot would provide the fastest execution time since the IOM instruction would be executed only one time.

8-4-3 ControlLogix Immediate Output Instruction

The immediate output instruction (IOT) for the ControlLogix PLC operates the same as the immediate output instructions for the PLC 5 and SLC 500 PLCs. Figure 8-23(e) illustrates the IOT instruction, which updates the specified output data. Note that when the IOT instruction executes, it immediately transfers the value of the Local:2:0 tag to the output module.

EXAMPLE 8-6

A production assembly system has three robots and numerous other automated assembly machines to produce a variety of products. The PLC program controlling the system has a large number of rungs. Each of the robots has a light curtain to indicate (closure of an NO contact) that an employee has entered the work envelope of the robot while it is running. Design a PLC program that inputs the intrusion data as fast as possible and performs three tasks equally fast:

1. Turn off the invaded robot's servo power (turn on a relay in the robot's control cabinet).
2. Sound a horn in the production area.
3. Light a red warning light over the robot whose light curtain was broken.

SOLUTION

The SLC 500 robot safety system ladder logic program and field device interface is shown in Figure 8-24. Each of the light curtain contacts triggers an immediate input instruction, which moves the word from the input module in slot 4 into the input image table. A mask (0000 0000 0000 0111) is used to block 1's in all bits except the first three locations. Note that the input word decimal value changes due to the terminal to which the curtain contact is attached. Based on input connections, robot 1 is 1_{10} (0000 0000 0000 0001), robot 2 is 2_{10} (0000 0000 0000 0010), and robot 3 is 4_{10} (0000 0000 0000 0100). Three equal to comparison instructions check for the values of 1, 2, and 4, and then cause the appropriate robot action and alarms. The operational sequence includes:

1. Load the following constant mask values in the IOM instruction in rungs 2, 3, and 4. Put 43 hex (0000 0000 0100 0011) into IOM in rung 2, 4C hex (0000 0000 0100 1100) in rung 3, and 70 hex (0000 0000 0111 0000) into IOM in rung 4.
2. Use an unconditional MOV instruction to put all 1's into the output image table for O:3.0.
3. The output (O:3.0) with all 1's present is moved through a mask with desired output bit patterns for each robot. The image table for O:3.0 has all 1's present, but the outputs are only true where there is a 1 in the mask. So the masks control what outputs are turned on (0043 for robot 1, 004C for robot 2, 0070 for robot 3).

Mask bits 0, 2, and 4 control the servo stop relays for robots 1, 2, and 3 because the relays are connected to terminals 0, 2, and 4, respectively. Similarly, mask bits 1, 3, and 5 control the red intrusion indicator light because terminals 1, 3, and 5 are used for the lights for robots 1, 2, and 3, respectively. Since the warning horn field device is wired to terminal 6 (bit 03.0/6) for all three robots, each mask has a 1 in that bit location.

FIGURE 8-24: Ladder logic for Example 8-6.

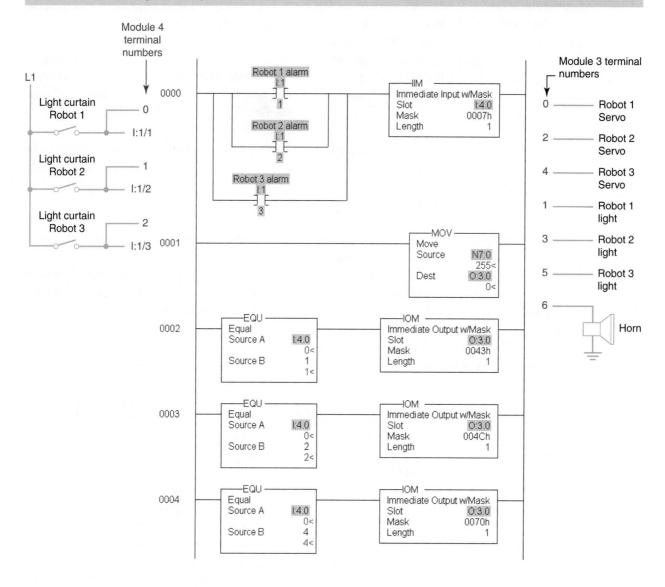

8-5 EMPIRICAL DESIGN PROCESS WITH PROGRAM CONTROL INSTRUCTIONS

The empirical design process, introduced in Section 3-11-4, is an organized approach to the design of PLC ladder logic programs. However, the term *empirical* implies that some degree of trial and error is present. As more instructions are added to the design and the process becomes more complex, the empirical design requires more fixes and adjustments. However, the process used for these new instructions is quite similar to that learned in previous chapters.

8-5-1 Adding Program Control Instructions to the Process

The first step in using program control instructions in PLC ladder designs is to know when to use master control reset (MCR); jump (JMP) and label (LBL); jump to subroutine, subroutine, and return (JSR, SBR, and RET); and immediate inputs (IIN and IIM) and immediate outputs (IOT and IOM). In addition, there are a number of standard logic configurations for each, so selecting the proper configuration adds another degree of challenge to the empirical design. The following discussion addresses some of the issues associated with these instructions.

MCR Instruction. The master control reset instruction offers numerous advantages and features for a control solution. The MCR instruction sets up a fence, called the MCR zone, around an entire ladder logic program or around a block of ladder rungs. The MCR zone is either scanned and executed or bypassed. Use this instruction when you want to:

- Control how frequently an entire program or a set of rungs in a program is scanned.
- Force a group of non-retentive outputs to the false state and freeze the state of retentive outputs in their current state.
- Force a group of outputs to the false state and ignore the condition of the input ladder logic.
- Pause the operation of a counter so that the accumulator stops incrementing even though the input logic changes state. The current count in the counter accumulator remains. When the MCR becomes active the counter starts from the previous value in the ACC.

JMP and LBL Instructions. The jump and label instructions offer advantages and features for a control solution similar to that found in the MRC instruction. The JMP and LBL instructions identify blocks of ladder rungs, called JMP zones, that are passed over and not scanned when the input logic for the JMP instruction is true. The JMP zone is either scanned and executed or bypassed. Use this instruction when you want to:

- Control how frequently an entire program or a set of rungs in a program is scanned.
- Retain the state of all outputs in the JMP zone when the ladder block is not scanned.
- Jump from multiple points in a ladder program to a common label rung.
- Jump either forward or backward in a ladder program.
- Pause the operation of counters and timers so the accumulator stops incrementing even though the input logic changes state. The current value in the accumulators remains.

When the JMP zone becomes active the counters and timers start from the previous value in the ACC.

JSR, SBR, and RET Instructions. The jump to subroutine, subroutine, and return program control instructions are used most often to change the flow of the ladder logic. There are numerous configurations and many benefits from using these instructions that allow the program to be directed to other ladder logic programs called subroutines. Use these instructions when you want to:

- Organize a program into smaller blocks of ladder logic.
- Isolate frequently used ladder logic blocks in a subroutine and execute them from numerous locations in the main ladder logic.
- Pass data to another program and execute algorithms containing that data.
- Return results from another program that can be used in the main routine.
- Reduce scan time and ladder rung count by separating the control logic into blocks that can be called from the main routine only when necessary.

IIN, IOT, IIM, and IOM Instructions. The immediate instructions change the program flow normally associated with traditional input and output instructions. The immediate instructions permit faster data measurement since the movement of the data value does not have to wait until the usual input or output update point in the scan cycle. Use these instructions when you want to:

- Move field device data to the input image table without waiting for the scan cycle to reach the image table update point.
- Interrupt the scan process and input a data word immediately after the logic rung with the IIN or IIM instruction is scanned.
- Interrupt the scan process and move a data word immediately after the logic rung with the IOT or IOM instruction is scanned.

- Interrupt the scan process and move only the masked portion of a data word immediately after the logic rung with the IIM instruction is scanned.

8-6 TROUBLESHOOTING PROGRAM CONTROL INSTRUCTIONS IN LADDER LOGIC

The program control instructions offer few operational problems. If a section of the ladder that includes these instructions is not operating properly, then you can use any of the following suggestions to troubleshoot.

- Use the always false (AFI) instruction in the input logic of MCR and JMP rungs to eliminate the MCR zone and JMP zone ladder rungs until the proper operation of the main part of the routine can be verified. The AFI sets its rung-condition-out to false; in other words, the AFI disables all the instructions on its rung.
- Use the temporary end (TND) instruction, described in Chapter 4, or the suspend (SUS) instruction, described in Section 5-8-1, to terminate an MCR, JMP, or JSR instruction immediately after the branch to examine the input logic conditions that caused the branch to occur. This is useful when branches occur under the wrong process conditions.
- Troubleshoot portions of a ladder not functioning properly by using the single-step mode. Put the SLC 500 PLC into the single-step mode (select the test mode instead of the run mode after a program is downloaded) and select Execute Step once to run one scan and then a second time to execute the first rung.

Subsequent clicks on Execute Step runs the next rung in the ladder.
- Use breakpoints in the single-step mode to execute the ladder down to a breakpoint inserted into the ladder logic. After selecting test mode and single step, select set end rung. The file number and rung number are entered to indicate where the breakpoint should be established. Every time the Enter key is pressed, one scan is executed with the processor stopping at the breakpoint.

In addition, verify that:

- MCR zones are never overlapped or nested.
- MCR zones and JMP zones do not overlap.
- Backward jumps do not cause a scan time greater than the watchdog timer. Backward jumps increase scan time when rungs are rescanned. If excessive backward jumps are performed and the watchdog timer is exceeded (maximum value is about 2.5 seconds), then the processor has a major fault condition.
- JSR and SBR instructions have the same number of input parameters.
- JSR and RET instructions have the same number of return parameters.
- The LBL and the SBR instructions are the first input instructions on the rung.
- The scope and data types of the tags are consistent with scope and data present in their use.

8-7 LOCATION OF THE INSTRUCTIONS

The location of instructions from this chapter in the Allen-Bradley programming software is indicated in Figure 8-25.

FIGURE 8-25: Location of instructions described in this chapter.

Systems	Instructions	Location
PLC 5, SLC 500	MCR, JMP, LBL, JSR, SBR, RET	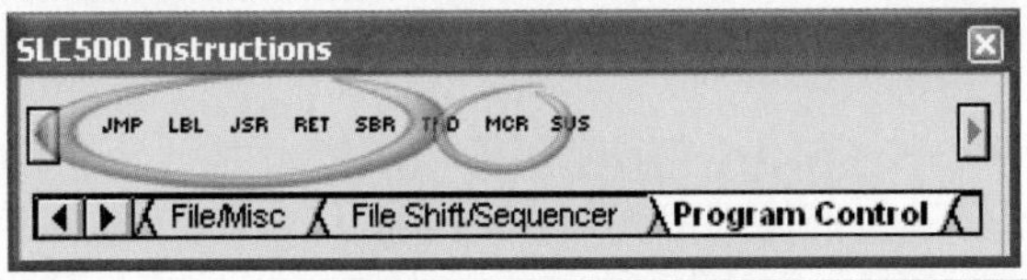
LOGIX	MCR, JMP, LBL, JSR, SBR, RET	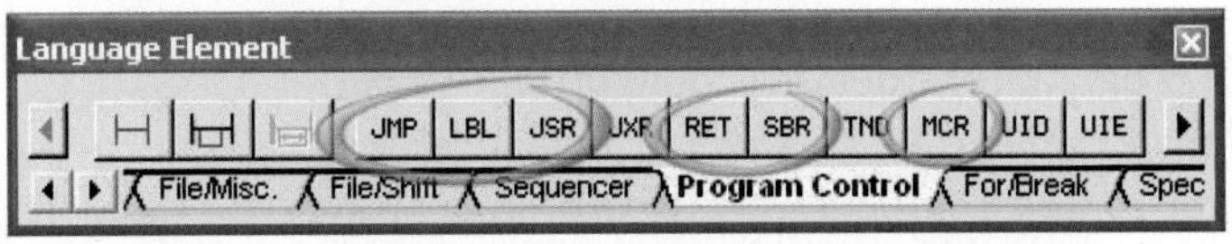
PLC 5	IIN, IOT	
SLC 500	IIM, IOM	
LOGIX	IOT	

Indirect and Indexed Addressing

9-1 GOALS AND OBJECTIVES

There are two principal goals of this chapter. The first goal is to provide the student with the overall concept of addressing. The second goal is to show how the addressing modes are applied to specific Allen-Bradley PLCs that are used in industrial automation systems.

After completing this chapter you should be able to:

- Explain the concept of direct, indirect, and indexed addressing.
- Describe how to combine addressing modes.
- Apply the indirect and indexed addressing modes to Allen-Bradley PLC 5 and SLC 500 PLCs.
- Create a multidimensional array for the ControlLogix PLC.
- Apply the indirect addressing mode to the ControlLogix PLC using arrays.
- Troubleshoot the indirect and indexed addressing modes.

9-2 ALLEN-BRADLEY ADDRESSING MODES

This chapter explores the addressing modes—direct, indirect, and indexed—used in the Allen-Bradley PLCs. An *addressing mode* is the means

by which the PLC selects the *data* that is used in an instruction. The addressing mode is determined by how you specify the instruction's *operand*. The terms data, operand, and addressing mode are defined as follows:

- *Data* are numerical values that are used in computations. For example, if the PLC has the value 3 in a memory location and the value 4 in another location, and there is an instruction to add the values in these two locations, then there are two data values involved: 3 and 4.
- *Operands* are the symbols in an instruction. Again, if the instruction were to add the two memory locations, then the data would be the same, but the operands would be the symbols for the locations.
- *Addressing mode* describes the relationship between the operands and the data, that is, how we use the operands to get the correct data.

9-2-1 Direct Addressing

In *direct addressing*, the memory address of the data is supplied with the instruction. Figure 9-1 illustrates this addressing mode. Note that the address (2112) in the instruction points directly to the address that contains the data (345).

FIGURE 9-1: Direct addressing mode.

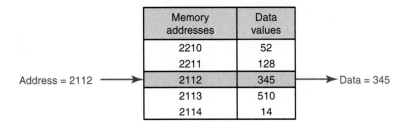

FIGURE 9-2: Indirect addressing mode.

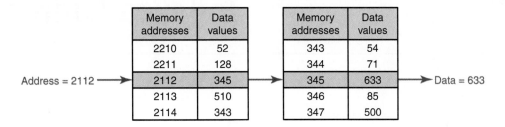

9-2-2 Indirect Addressing

In *indirect addressing,* the address in the instruction serves as a reference point and does not point directly to the data location. In other words, the instruction's memory address contains the address of a memory location, which either contains the address of the operand or specifies another location that contains the effective address of the data. This is confusing, so the example in Figure 9-2 helps to illustrate this addressing mode. Note that the address of the instruction points to a memory location that contains another address, 345, which contains the data. Memory data is a general term because it could be the value used for a timer preset value, the setpoint for a temperature comparator, or in this case the address for the location of the actual data.

An everyday example of indirect addressing is Internet domain names. When you point to an address, such as www.jimandglenn.com, you are really pointing to an entry in a Domain Name Service (DNS) table, which maps the domain name to a specific numeric address representing a physical server on the network. This is a simple two-stage indirection that allows people and documents to use more or less meaningful names instead of meaningless Internet address numeric strings. The cost of this indirection is that the DNS table entries must be maintained as servers' addresses change and as new servers and domain names come online. This cost is more than offset by the value of meaningful names and by eliminating the need for the documents that point to a given server to have to be updated every time the server's numeric address changes.

9-2-3 Indexed Addressing

Indexed addressing is an addressing mode for referencing a memory location that is the original memory address plus the value stored in an index register. In other words, the content of the index register is added to the original address of the instruction. Indexed addressing is useful to access elements in an array or list for the purpose of averaging a set of values in the array. The address in the instruction does not change, but the value in the index register is incremented, thus sequentially accessing array locations one by one. Figure 9-3 illustrates indexed addressing. Note that the address of the instruction (2112) is added to the index (23), thus forming the effective address of 2135 (2112 + 23), which contains the data.

Indirect addressing is preferred over indexed addressing because indirect addressing allows for a different pointer for each location where you want to use this "variable" addressing method.

FIGURE 9-3: Indexed addressing mode.

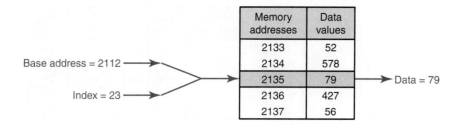

Since indexed addressing requires you to take your pointer and load it into a fixed "offset" location of S:24, there is one location for the pointer of all indexed addresses. Indexing also requires one more instruction than indirect since the pointer needs to be moved to S:24.

9-2-4   Indexed Indirect Addressing

Indexed and indirect addressing modes can be combined. One technique is called *pre-indexed addressing*, which is a combination addressing method that incorporates indexed addressing prior to the use of indirect addressing. Another technique is called *post-indexed addressing,* which is a combination addressing method that incorporates indexed addressing after the use of indirect addressing. Figure 9-4 illustrates the two combination addressing modes. In Figure 9-4(a) the result of the pre-indexed addressing mode supplies the address 3000 for the indirect addressing mode, which yields the data value of 77. Figure 9-4(b) shows the results when the index in Figure 9-4(a) is incremented by 1. In Figure 9-4(c) the result of the post-indexed addressing mode supplies the address 1533 for the indexed addressing mode, which yields the data value of 25. Figure 9-4(d) shows the results when the index in Figure 9-4(c) is incremented by 1. Now, before you continue, review the concepts of the indirect and indexed addressing modes until you are completely familiar with them because the next subsections discuss the addressing mode syntax for various Allen-Bradley PLCs.

9-2-5   PLC 5, SLC 500, and
Logix Systems Syntax

The syntax for the addressing modes in the AB PLCs is slightly different, but the addressing concept is the same. First of all, direct addressing mode is the mode that has been used in the exam-

ples of the PLC instructions in the first eight chapters. That is, when N7:1 is used as the address in an instruction, it is a direct address. The data located in address N7:1 is the data used in the instruction.

PLC 5 and SLC 500 Indirect Addressing. Allen-Bradley indirect addresses use brackets, [ ], to hold an address where the data is located. The brackets indicate that the logical address is being used in an indirect addressing mode. Figure 9-5 illustrates this addressing mode. Source A in the equal to comparison instruction uses indirect addressing for the location of the data file. The integer register has the indirect address, N7:2, enclosed in brackets. The actual data address is built by using the data value (5) at the indirect location, N7:2, to form the indirect address N7:5, which holds the actual data value of 13. Note that 5 is not the value of the data but rather an offset or the value placed in the address N7:[5]. This offset forces the file to point to address N7:5, which contains the data. Since the value in N7:[N7:2] or N7:5 is equal to 13, the output of the comparison instruction is true.

Figure 9-6 illustrates an indirect address similar to Figure 9-5, but in this case the indirect address is T4:0.ACC. The indirect address, T4:0.ACC, contains a 7. This offset of 7 points to the address that contains the data, which is N7:7. In other words, the value in N7:7, 10, is the number that is used in the comparison instruction, and thus the output of the comparison instruction is false. In this example, the address changes as the timer accumulator increments toward the preset value.

The indirect address can be used for a file number, word number (element + *subelement*), and

FIGURE 9-4: Indexed indirect addressing mode.

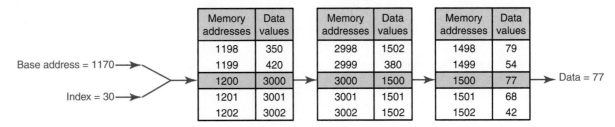

(a) Pre-indexed addressing method with an index of 30

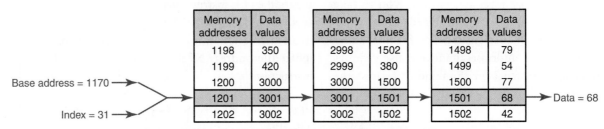

(b) Pre-indexed addressing method with an index of 31

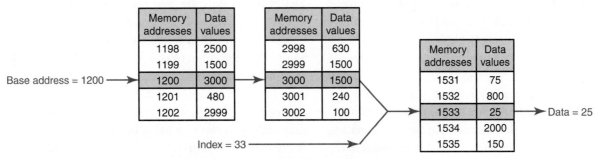

(c) Post-indexed addressing method with an index of 33

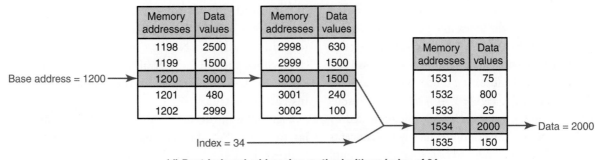

(d) Post-indexed addressing method with an index of 34

bit number. The indirect address(es) can be in one or all of these fields since the address is specified to the word or bit level. The indirect address is always enclosed in square brackets ([ ]). Any part of a bit or word address can use indirect addressing notation to point to the actual location of the data. Table 9-1 lists a number of examples of indirect addressing for the SLC 500 system.

PLC 5 and SLC 500 Indexed Addressing. The indexed address in an instruction consists of a prefix, the pound symbol (#), and the logical address referred to as the base address. The index value to be added to the base address is stored in the status file, word S:24. A move instruction is used to place either a positive or negative index value in S:24. However, when specifying indexed addresses make

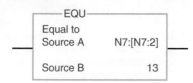

FIGURE 9-5: Indirect addressing in a comparison instruction where the instruction is true.

```
      EQU
Equal to
Source A        N7:[N7:2]

Source B              13
```

Data file

Addresses	Values
N7:0	1
N7:1	400
N7:2	5
N7:3	32
N7:4	250
N7:5	13
N7:6	42

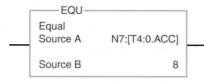

FIGURE 9-6: Indirect addressing mode in a comparison instruction where the instruction is false.

```
      EQU
Equal
Source A      N7:[T4:0.ACC]

Source B              8
```

T4:0.ACC = 7

Data file

Addresses	Values
N7:0	100
N7:1	250
N7:2	6
N7:3	5
N7:4	0
N7:5	0
N7:6	0
N7:7	10
N7:8	8

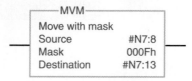

FIGURE 9-7: Move with mask instruction using indexed addressing.

```
      MVM
Move with mask
Source          #N7:8
Mask            000Fh
Destination     #N7:13
```

If S:24 has a value of 6, then the addresses are:

Location	Base addresses	Indexed addresses
Source	N7:8	N7:14
Destination	N7:13	N7:19

sure the value in S:24 does not cause the indexed address to exceed the file boundary. For example, if N7 contains 20 elements and S:24 contains a value of 10, then #N7:15 refers to (N7:15 + 10) which is outside the file boundary. This is referred to as *crossing a file boundary* and causes a fault. Figure 9-7 illustrates a move with mask instruction using indexed addresses. Note that when S:24 has a value of 6, the indexed Source base address, #N7:8, would actually reference location N7:14(8 + 6 = 14) for the source and #N7:13 would reference N7:19(13 + 6 = 19) for the destination.

ControlLogix Arrays. An array is a data structure that allocates a contiguous block of memory to store a specific data type as a table of values. The term *contiguous block* means memory locations that are adjacent to each other. Tag arrays in the Logix systems can have one, two, or three dimensions. Figure 9-8 illustrates and describes these three types of arrays. Read the description in the figure before continuing.

A one-dimensional array is used to store a series of values for use in a process problem. For

TABLE 9-1 Indexed Addressing Examples

Valid Address	Variable	Explanation
N7:[C5:8.ACC]	Word number	The word number is the accumulated value of counter 8 in file 5.
B3/[I:0.6]	Bit number	The bit number is stored in input word 6.
N[N7:4]:[N9:3]	File and word number	The file number is stored in integer address N7:4 and the word number in integer address N9:3.
S10:[N7:5].1	Element number	The element number is stored in N7:5.
I:[N7:0].1/4	Slot number	The slot number is stored in N7:0.

FIGURE 9-8: One-, two- and three-dimensional arrays.

Array types	Stores data in this structure	Description
One dimension		Single or one-dimensional arrays are called flat arrays since there is a single column of data just one layer deep. The data is stored in one long list of consecutive or contiguous memory locations. This is the most commonly used type of array structure.
Two dimension	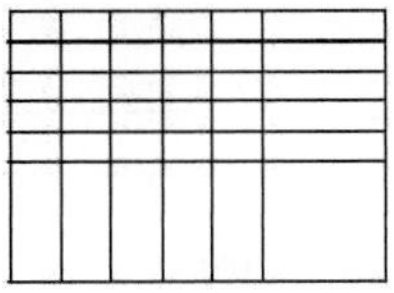	Double or two-dimensional arrays are also called flat arrays for files because there is just one layer. The data is stored in multiple long columns, which are placed next to each other. This is the next most commonly used type of array structure.
Three dimension	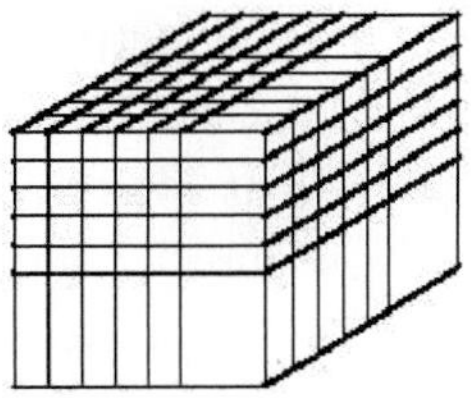	Three-dimensional arrays are not flat files since there are a number of two-dimensional arrays stacked on top of each other.

example, if a process had five different temperatures for a heating operation, then each of the five values would be saved in an element of a one-dimensional array with five elements. The ladder logic could recall any of the five temperatures by referencing the array element with the desired value. In another application, the process recipe values could be stored in a tag array and then recalled during the execution of the process control program.

A two-dimensional array is often just an extension of the one-dimensional array. If the one-dimensional array column is used to hold the numerical quantities for each ingredient of a recipe, then multiple columns in a two-dimensional array could hold ingredient quantities for other recipes. For example, if a process has four recipes with 10 ingredient values in each, then a 10 by 4 two-dimensional array would hold the data.

The previous two-dimensional array analog can be applied to a three-dimensional array. Assume that the 10 ingredients and four recipes are used for process A, but the automation area has two processes, A and B. The first two-dimensional array holds the quantities for process A, the second holds the quantities for process B. Therefore, the first dimension is for ingredient quantities, the second dimension has the quantities for different recipes, and the third dimension is the quantities for the two processes. The result is a 10 by 4 by 2 array where element 1,1,1 is the quantity of ingredient 1, for recipe 1, and process A, and element 6, 3, 2 is the quantity of ingredient 6, recipe 3, and process B.

Figure 9-9 illustrates an array tag (Tag name column), the double integer with dimensions (Data type column), and the value of each dimension (Dimension columns). The valid subscript ranges for the examples in Figure 9-9 are as follows:

- One-dimensional array with 7 elements and a valid subscript range: DINT[x], where x = 0 to 6
- Two-dimensional array with 4 and 5 elements in each dimension and a valid subscript range: DINT[x,y], where x = 0 to 3, y = 0 to 4
- Three-dimensional array with 2, 3, and 4 elements in each dimension and a valid subscript range: DINT[x,y,z], where x = 0 to 1; yx = 0 to 2, z = 0 to 3

FIGURE 9-9: One-, two-, and three-dimensional array parameters.

Tag name	Data type	Dimension 0	Dimension 1	Dimension 2	Total elements
one_d_array	DINT[7]	7	0	0	7
two_d_array	DINT[4,5]	4	5	0	20
three_d_array	DINT[2,3,4]	2	3	4	24

FIGURE 9-10: Setting up ControlLogix arrays.

(a) New tag dialog box

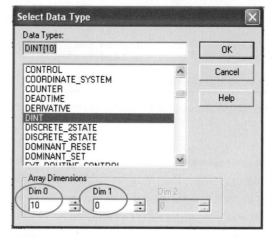

(b) Select data type dialog box with DINT selected

(c) Final data type displayed

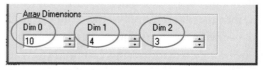

(d) Three array dimensions added

Note that the maximum range value is always one less than the dimension since subscript values start with zero.

Setting Up ControlLogix Arrays. Arrays are set up in ControlLogix by first creating a tag name and then defining or declaring the data type. Figure 9-10(a) shows the New Tag dialog box with the new tag and its description displayed.

Note that the default value of Boolean is present, but arrays in ControlLogix should be either DINT or REAL data types. DINT is selected in Figure 9-10(b), and the array dimension boxes appear at the bottom. Each higher dimension is grayed out until you enter values into the lower dimension. The illustrations in Figure 9-10(c) and (d) show the results of entering the three-dimensional array.

FIGURE 9-11: Indirect addressing example for ControlLogix PLC.

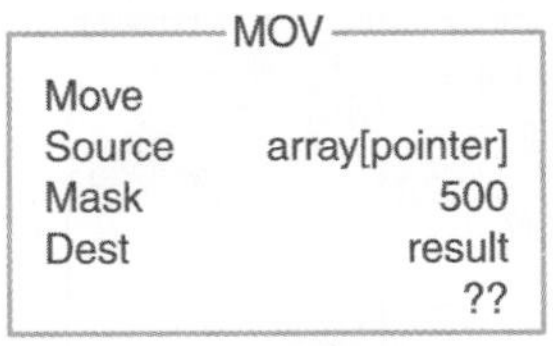

(a) Move instruction with indirect addressing using a one-dimensional array

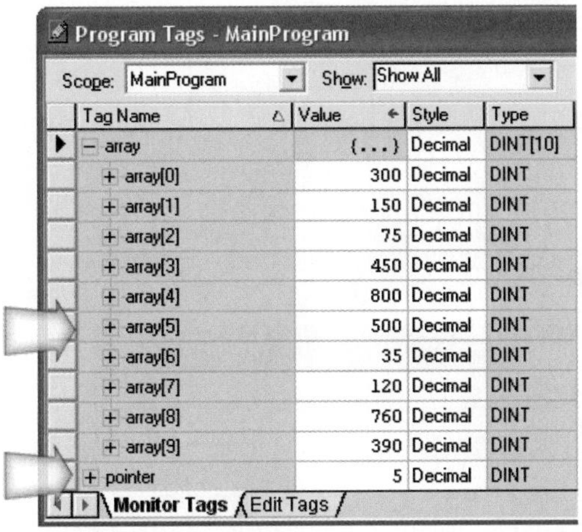

(b) Array values displayed in Program Tags Window

ControlLogix PLC Indirect and Indexed Addressing. The indirect addressing mode is illustrated in Figure 9-11, which includes a move instruction and a nine-element, one-dimensional array. Note that in the move instruction the indirect address is enclosed in brackets with the tag name pointer. By inserting a number between 0 and 9 in the pointer, data is moved from the array to the result. For example, if the pointer is set at 5, then the 500 is moved to the result tag in accordance with the array shown in the figure.

For indexed addressing you need to create an indexing mechanism because there is no index register in the ControlLogix processor. Many of the instructions that are used for functions requiring indexing use a control tag and are discussed in Chapter 10. A control tag is a unique tag that is created for each instruction instance. The control tag has both length and position fields for control of indexing and is used in place of the S:24 register in the PLC 5 and SLC 500 PLCs. The ControlLogix PLC cannot perform all the indexing maneuvers that the PLC 5 and SLC 500 PLCs can, but its advantages are not

having all index instructions using the same address to store the offset, and the ability to use user-defined arrays.

9-3 EMPIRICAL DESIGN PROCESS WITH INDIRECT AND INDEXED ADDRESSSING

The empirical design process, introduced in Section 3-11-4, is an organized approach to the design of PLC ladder logic programs. However, the term *empirical* implies that some degree of trial and error is present. As more instructions are added to the design and the process becomes more complex, the empirical design requires more fixes and adjustments.

9-3-1 Adding Indirect and Indexed Addressing to the Process

The most difficult aspect of indirect and indexed addressing is determining which to use and when to use them. A direct answer to these questions is difficult to compose, but some comments about each and some example problems should help remove some of the confusion. In many problems both could be used to solve the automation problem, but one is usually more efficient. Let's start with the indexed addressing used in the PLC 5 and SLC 500 systems.

Indexed Addressing Used in PLC 5 and SLC 500. The indexed addressing has a fixed offset stored in the status bit S:24. That address is added to the base address to determine the new address location. The problem is that the same offset value must be used with every indexed base address. Example 9-1 illustrates this point.

Indirect Addressing Used in ControlLogix PLC. The indirect addressing places an address within an address to indicate the location of that address parameter. In the PLC 5 and SLC 500 systems, the imbedded address changes an address parameter of the base address to determine the new address location. In the ControlLogix PLC, indirect addressing is linked to the use of DINT arrays. Example 9-2 illustrates this point.

EXAMPLE 9-1

The process tank design problem in Section 7-6-3 (Figures 7-17 through 7-21) has been modified as follows:

The material 1 and 2 quantity inputs by BCD push switches have been removed and receipts have been stored in memory for the needed quantities. The number of the receipt to run is entered with a BCD push switch and stored in N7:15 when an NO load push button is pressed. The material values are transferred by the same push button. The first three of the process receipts are listed in Table 9-2. Note that the offset listed in the table is located in S:24. Design an indexed addressing solution for this problem.

Solution

Review the process tank problem statement and the solution to tank problem in Chapter 7 before reading the solution to this modification.

The modified system ladder logic is presented in Figure 9-12(a) and the integer register values are illustrated in Figure 9-12(b). In the Chapter 7 solution, the material 1 and 2 quantities are placed into N7:0 and N7:1 and then multiplied by 2 with the results going into N7:10 and N7:11.

In this modification, the process starts with the load push button that loads the receipt number from the BCD switch into N7:15. The same load push button makes three comparison instructions active and the receipt number makes a EQU comparison instruction true, which loads the correct index offset into the S:24 register. Next, the indexed values from the receipt locations in N7:30 through N7:35 are multiplied by 2 and then placed into N7:10 and N7:11. From this rung forward the solution is unchanged from that illustrated in Figures 7-20 and 7-21.

TABLE 9-2 Receipt parameters for Example 9-1

Parameters	Receipt 1		Receipt 2		Receipt 3		
	Values	Address location	Values	Address location	Values	Address location	Base address
Material 1 (gallons)	50	N7:30	75	N7:32	60	N7:34	N7:0
Material 2 (gallons)	15	N7:31	25	N7:33	45	N7:35	N7:1
Offset		30		32		34	

EXAMPLE 9-2

A color sensor is used to check the color of products moving down a conveyor. The sensor returns two types of signals: a discrete signal to indicate that a part has been detected and a color value signal, which is an analog value based on the color sensed. In order to get a more reliable color value, the sensing ladder logic should sample the color 10 times and find the average value. Design a ladder logic program for collecting the color data.

Solution

The ladder logic solution and array for storing the data is presented in Figure 9-13. The solution has four rungs to sample the 10 color values. The rungs for averaging the values are not shown. The ladder action starts when the color_switch is true, indicating that a part is present. The data is stored in a one-dimensional array, Color_sample[Array_index.ACC]. The tag is found in the move instruction in rung 2, Figure 9-13(a), and in the Monitor

FIGURE 9-12: Solution for Example 9-1.

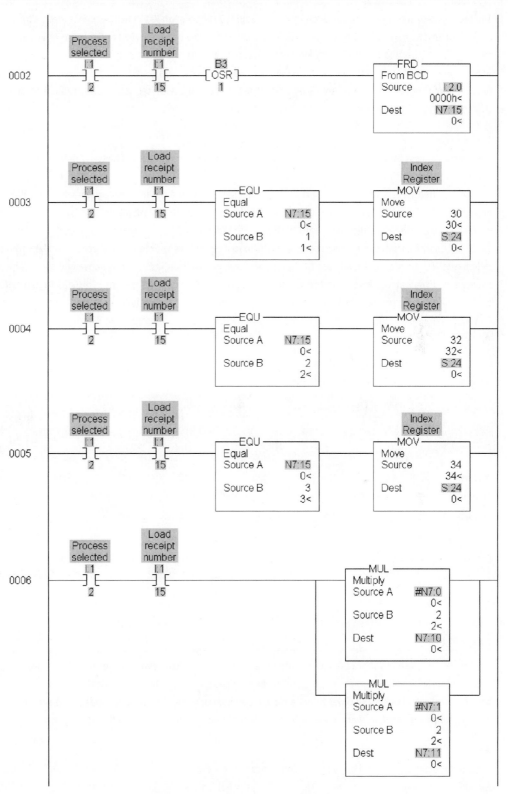

(a) Ladder logic for indexed addressing

FIGURE 9-12: (Continued).

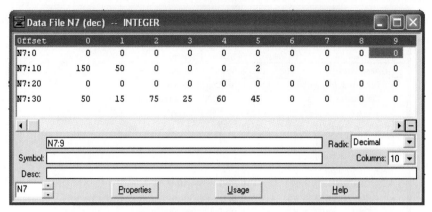

(b) Integer files with stored data values for indexed addressing

Tags tab of the Program Tags window, Figure 9-13(b). Note in the window that the database has the first three values stored and the fourth value is visible in the sensor tag, Color_data, for the color sensor.

A move instruction moves the value from the input image table, Color_data, every time the half-second timer's done bit becomes true. The timer triggers the counter, which acts as the index for the data array. The array is indexed by the tag Array_index.ACC, which is the accumulator of the counter. When the counter reaches 10 the counter done bit inhibits the timer and counter and the logic waits for the Color_switch to cycle off and reset the system.

FIGURE 9-13: Solution for Example 9-2.

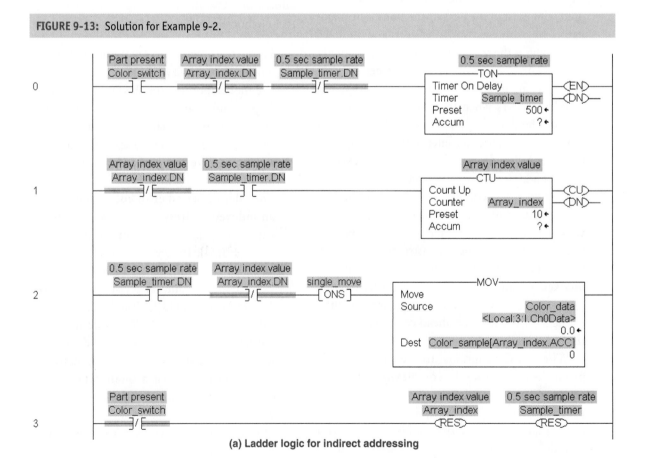

(a) Ladder logic for indirect addressing

FIGURE 9-13: (Continued).

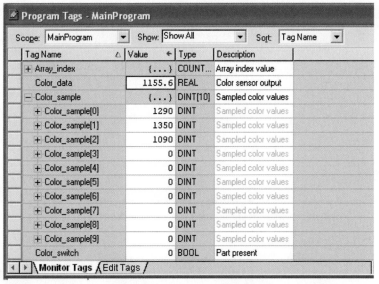

(b) Integer files with stored data values for indirect addressing of an array

9-4 TROUBLESHOOTING INDIRECT AND INDEXED ADDRESSING IN LADDER LOGIC

Addressing modes are not instructions but can be used with most of the PLC instructions. The major cause of problems with indirect and indexed addressing is the selection of the offset or pointer values. The pointers redirect the integer or floating point file to a new location in memory. The problem occurs when the redirected location is outside the data file boundary. In Allen-Bradley PLCs the boundaries for integer and floating point files are declared or set by the user. Indexed or indirect addresses that fall outside the file boundaries cause a fault condition. Problems in the PLC 5 and SLC 500 occur in indexed addressing, which uses the S:24 register to store the pointer index value. Some program instructions store values in this S:24 register and will overwrite the indexed pointer number placed there. A good practice is to move the index value for the pointer to the S:24 register just ahead of the rung where the indexing is performed.

When PLC programs are developed, some problems result from the complexity of the process problem to be solved, and others result from programming techniques that produce ladder rungs that are not a correct solution. If indirect or indexed addressing modes are present in the rungs where the process control solution is not working, then troubleshooting those rungs is far more difficult. Troubleshooting indirect addressing is more difficult than troubleshooting indexed addressing. Use the following guidelines when troubleshooting indirect and indexed addressing.

- Verify that pointers do not point to addresses outside the memory boundaries.
- Use the temporary end (TND) instruction to stop scanning at points in the ladder where addressing indexes can be verified.
- Use single-step options to scan one rung at a time to analyze how the pointers are changing the addressing flow.
- The value displayed in an instruction beneath an indexed address, such as #N7:5, is the value in N7:5, not the indexed value in N7:[5 + S:24]. To view the indexed value, add an unconditional rung to move the indexed value to another integer register for display.
- This guideline could be listed in the empirical design area as well. When designing an indexed or indirect addressing mode solution with a large database containing many elements, start with just a small data set. For example, if you can make the ladder operate with just a few receipts and a small number of ingredients, then you can easily expand it for the larger data set.

PART 2

Advanced PLC Instructions and Applications

GOALS

The goal for the second half of the text, Chapters 10 through 17, is to expand your knowledge of PLCs into the use of the more sophisticated PLC instructions and introduce some of the new programming and networking technology. In Part 1 a subset of the PLC instructions was covered, but that subset is used to write a majority of the ladder logic used in manufacturing automation. However, PLCs are being used for an increasing number of control requirements, and as they move into these new areas additional advanced instructions are required. Using these more complex instructions correctly is a goal of this section.

The PLC is a participant in the trend toward distributed control and use of information networks in factory automation. Therefore, another goal of Part 2 is to introduce the networks and subnetworks that permit PLC control to be distributed across the factory and across the Internet.

The final goal for Part 2 is to introduce the programming standard IEC 61131-3 with multiple programming language styles. As PLCs take on more complex control tasks, standard ladder logic is not sufficient for the task. The languages defined by the standard take PLC programming to the information system level. As PLCs move into this new territory, so must the men and women who install, program, and maintain them. Therefore, the general goal of Part 2 is to prepare you for the future of PLC control.

OBJECTIVES

After completing Part 2 you should be able to:

- Write a program using the four language formats supported by Allen-Bradley that are defined in the IEC 61131-3 programmable logic controller standard.

- Describe a control solution using sequential function charts techniques.
- Apply PLC instructions for data handling, shift register, and sequencer functions to the solution of control problems.
- Apply analog input and output hardware and the PID function to the solution of process control problems.
- Develop a PLC solution using network technology at three information technology levels.
- Apply sound troubleshooting and documentation techniques to systems under PLC control.
- Select industrial networks for factory floor applications.

CAREER INSIGHTS

The following insight provides some information on the jobs available to students who master the contents of Part 2 of the text. Some of the terms used in this description may not be familiar to you at this time but will be when the material in Part 2 is covered. Read the following paragraphs now to get a general feel for the additional opportunities in PLCs, then read it again after completing Part 2 to see where you could work in the PLC and automation control area. If you enjoy the technology and problems covered in this text, then there are numerous paths that you can follow in PLCs and manufacturing automation.

In Part 1 a number of paths were identified for students who enjoy PLCs and factory automation hardware and software responsibilities. The concepts learned in the second half of this text open up similar paths, but at a higher technical level. Although standard ladder

logic is still the primary programming tool used in North America, the more structured languages defined in IEC 61131-3 will work their way into PLC solutions. The new standard has languages that are graphical and text based. Learning the graphical is not a stretch for current ladder logic programmers; however, the development of PLC programs in the text-based languages requires skills learned in computer science. Some of the more advanced PLC instructions for motion control, process control, and data manipulation require greater understanding of related technologies such as servo and stepper motor control, closed loop feedback concepts, and databases. These advanced instructions require a broader educational preparation. As a result, the path for students interested in PLC program development diverges into several interesting directions.

PLC technology has embraced the movement toward distributed control through the use of vendor-specific networks and international network standards such as Ethernet/IP, DeviceNet, and ControlNet. Ethernet/IP (Ethernet Industrial Protocol) is a high-level network for linking industrial systems, whereas DeviceNet and ControlNet are subnetworks for linking devices and controllers. Knowledge in these communication technologies opens additional career doors for students who wish to work in distributed control using PLC systems. If you enjoy this technology, it is a wonderful career area.

Data Handling Instructions and Shift Registers

10-1 GOALS AND OBJECTIVES

There are three principal goals of this chapter. The first goal is to provide the student with the overall concept of how bits, words, and files are handled in a PLC. The second goal is to discuss the data transfer and manipulation by logical instructions, the file-arithmetic-logic instruction, and shift registers, including first in, first out and last in, first out operations. Also, the copy and fill instructions are included. The third goal is to show how data handling and shifting instructions are applied to Allen-Bradley PLC 5, SLC 500, and Logix PLCs.

After completing this chapter you should be able to:

- Explain the concept of how data is handled by bits, words, and files.
- Describe the logical instructions of and, or, and exclusive or.
- Describe the arithmetic-file-logic function.
- Explain the concept of shift registers.
- Describe the operation of first in, first out and last in, first out shifting functions.
- Describe the operation of copy and fill instructions.
- Describe the data handling and manipulation instructions for the Allen-Bradley PLC 5, SLC 500, and Logix systems.

- Develop ladder logic solutions using data handling and manipulation instructions for the Allen-Bradley PLC 5, SLC 500, and Logix systems.
- Include data handling and manipulation instructions in the empirical design process.
- Describe troubleshooting techniques for ladder rungs with data handling and manipulation instructions.

10-2 DATA HANDLING

Data handling includes the movement and manipulation of data by arithmetic and logical operations. This data handling is accomplished on *bits, words,* and *files,* where words are also referred to as registers and files as tables, blocks, or arrays. The relationship between bits, words, and files is illustrated in Figure 10-1. Note that bits are represented as 1s or 0s, a word is a group of bits, and a file is a group of words. Bit patterns in words and word patterns in files are discussed in the following subsections.

10-2-1 Bit Patterns in Words

The bit pattern in one word or register can be transferred to another word or register as shown in Figure 10-2. Note that in Figure 10-2(a), word 40 contains all 0s and word 43 contains a bit

FIGURE 10-1: Bits, words, and files.

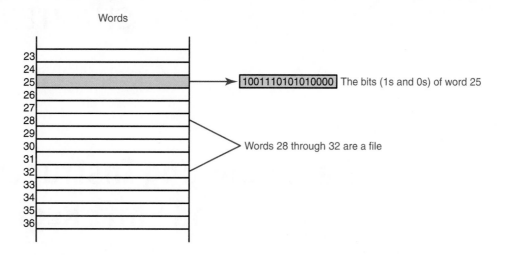

FIGURE 10-2: Bit patterns in words.

0000	0000	0000	0000	Word 40
–	–	–	–	Word 41
–	–	–	–	Word 42
1010	0011	0001	1011	Word 43

(a) Initial contents of words 40 and 43

1010	0011	0001	1011	Word 40
–	–	–	–	Word 41
–	–	–	–	Word 42
1010	0011	0001	1011	Word 43

(b) Contents of words 40 and 43 after the transfer

pattern of 1s and 0s. In Figure 10-2(b), the contents of words 40 and 43 are the same because the contents of word 40 were replaced or written over with the contents of word 43. Words 41 and 42 were unchanged. Even if the contents of word 40 were a pattern of 1s and 0s, its contents would still be replaced with the contents of word 43. Recall that an individual bit(s) within a word or register can be changed with the use of a mask, as discussed in Section 6-5-6.

10-2-2 Word Patterns in Files

The pattern of words that comprises a file has distinct *starting* and *ending* locations. In some PLC applications the entire sequence of words is transferred from one location to another. This *file-to-file transfer* is used when the words in one file represent a set of data that is used many times within a process, but must remain unchanged after each operation in the process. Because the data within the file is manipulated in a process, a second file is needed to handle the data changes. In addition to file-to-file transfers, *word-to-file* and *file-to-word* transfers are used in processes driven by a PLC. Figure 10-3 illustrates these three types of transfers. The *file-arithmetic-logic* (FAL) instruction is used to accomplish these transfers.

10-3 ALLEN-BRADLEY DATA TRANSFER AND MANIPULATION INSTRUCTIONS

The Allen-Bradley data transfer and manipulation instructions allow the user to operate on data with *logical*, *arithmetic*, and *shifting functions*, which handle single- or multiple-word data. The Allen-Bradley PLCs have data transfer and manipulation instructions available in all three processors. The following instructions, common to all three PLC systems, are described in this section.

- Bitwise and (AND): performs a bit-by-bit logical *AND* operation.
- Bitwise or (OR): performs a bit-by-bit logical *OR* operation.
- Bitwise exclusive or (XOR): performs a bit-by-bit logical *EXCLUSIVE OR* operation.

FIGURE 10-3: Word and file transfers.

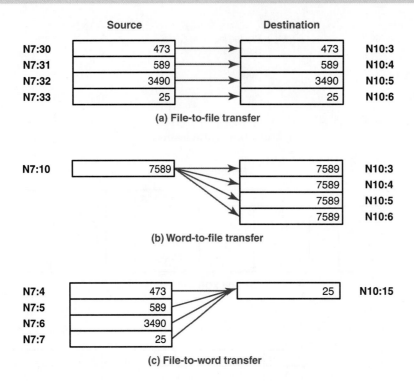

(a) File-to-file transfer

(b) Word-to-file transfer

(c) File-to-word transfer

- File-arithmetic-logic (FAL): performs copy, arithmetic, logic, and function operations on the data stored in files or arrays.
- Bit shift left (BSL) and Bit shift right (BSR): shifts the bits within a word or specified bits in an array one position to the left or right, respectively.
- FIFO load (FFL) and FIFO unload (FFU): loads data into a file and unloads data from a file, respectively. When used in pairs, they perform the FIFO function—first in, first out.
- LIFO load (LFL) and LIFO unload (LFU): loads data into a file and unloads data from a file, respectively. When used in pairs, they perform the LIFO function—last in, first out.
- Copy (COP): copies data files from one register location to another, maintaining the sequential sequence of the data.
- Fill (FLL): copies the contents of one register location to a specified number of other register locations.

10-3-1 AND, OR, and XOR Instructions

The *AND, OR,* and *XOR* instructions are logical instructions. They are illustrated in Figure 10-4(a)

for the SLC 500 system, but these instructions are also available in the PLC 5 and ControlLogix systems. These logical instructions perform a bit-by-bit logical operation using the values in Sources A and B and storing the result of the operation in the destination. Figure 10-4(b) illustrates the truth table for each of these logical operations. Figure 10-4(c) illustrates an AND, OR, and XOR operation on two identical words. The AB requirements for parameters placed into Sources A and B are:

PLC 5 and SLC 500: The parameter placed in both Source A and Source B can be a program constant or a bit/word address.

ControlLogix Systems: The parameter placed in both Source A and Source B can be any of the following data types: SINT (single integer), INT (integer), or DINT (double integer). The parameter used can be either an immediately entered program constant or a tag name.

Standard Ladder Logic for AND, OR, and XOR Instructions. The standard ladder logic illustrating how the AND, OR, and XOR instructions are

FIGURE 10-4: AND, OR, and XOR instructions.

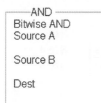

```
┌─ AND ──────────────┐   ┌─ OR ───────────────┐   ┌─ XOR ──────────────┐
│ Bitwise AND        │   │ Bitwise Inclusive OR│   │ Bitwise Exclusive OR│
│ Source A           │   │ Source A            │   │ Source A           │
│                    │   │                     │   │                    │
│ Source B           │   │ Source B            │   │ Source B           │
│                    │   │                     │   │                    │
│ Dest               │   │ Dest                │   │ Dest               │
└────────────────────┘   └─────────────────────┘   └────────────────────┘
```

(a) AND, OR, and XOR instructions

AND Instruction

Source A	Source B	Destination
0	0	0
1	0	0
0	1	0
1	1	1

OR Instruction

Source A	Source B	Destination
0	0	0
1	0	1
0	1	1
1	1	1

XOR Instruction

Source A	Source B	Destination
0	0	0
1	0	1
0	1	1
1	1	0

(b) AND, OR, and XOR truth tables

AND Instruction

Source A	1	0	1	0	1	0	1	0
Source B	1	1	1	0	0	0	1	1
Destination	1	0	1	0	0	0	1	0

OR Instruction

Source A	1	0	1	0	1	0	1	0
Source B	1	1	1	0	0	0	1	1
Destination	1	1	1	0	1	0	1	1

XOR Instruction

Source A	1	0	1	0	1	0	1	0
Source B	1	1	1	0	0	0	1	1
Destination	0	1	0	0	1	0	0	1

(c) AND, OR, and XOR operations

used in a ladder rung appears in Figure 10-5. Compare the ladder implementations with the descriptions and truth tables in Figure 10-4. Note that the AND instruction can be used for a masked move requirement because the destination bit pattern is the same as Source A for every bit that is a 1 in Source B. Also, 0's in Source B produces 0's in the destination. The XOR instruction works like a compare instruction, comparing each pair of bits and placing a 1 in the destination bit location when the bits are not the same, such as a 1 and 0 or 0 and 1. The OR instruction performs the logical OR between corresponding bits.

The use of the AND for a masked move instruction is illustrated in Figure 10-5(a). The mask is 0FF0h, so the middle eight bits are all ones ($0000\ 1111\ 1111\ 0000_2$). Source A has 3D49h and the mask eliminates the 3 and 9, but passes the D4. That passes the middle hex values ($D4h$ or $1101\ 0100_2$) from Source A to the destination.

The OR instruction produces a 1 in the destination register for every pair of bits with a 1 in either or both of the pair bits. The XOR instruc-

tion is a comparator that produces a 0 in the destination if the pairs of compared bits are equal (both ones or both zeros). Use the truth tables in Figure 10-4 to verify the destination values in Figure 10-5 for each instruction.

10-3-2 File-Arithmetic-Logic (FAL) Instruction

The *file-arithmetic-logic* (FAL) instruction is used to transfer data from one file to another and perform arithmetic and logic operations on files. The Allen-Bradley FAL instruction, available on the PLC 5 and ControlLogix PLCs, is illustrated in Figure 10-6.

The terms within the FAL instruction of Figure 10-6 are as follows:

* Control: the address of the control word, which provides the information necessary to execute the instruction.
* PLC 5: the address is in the control area R of processor memory and the default file 6. The operation and format for the control data file is described in the next section.

Application	Standard Ladder Logic Rungs AND, OR, and XOR Instructions

Perform a bit by bit AND operation between two registers or perform a masking operation while moving a value from one register to another.
 	
The bitwise AND instruction in PLC 5, SLC 500, and ControlLogix ANDs each bit of the Source A and Source B words and places the ANDed bit operation into the Destination register. The instruction can also be used as a masked move operation, which in not available in the PLC 5 and ControlLogix PLCs, by placing the data value to be masked and moved in Source A and placing the mask into Source B. The result is placed in the Destination.
 	
Note: SLC 500 rungs are shown, but the operation would be the same for PLC 5 and ControlLogix.
	Start
	I:1
	0
	
	—AND—
	Bitwise AND
	Source A N7:2
	      3D49h<
	Source B N7:5
	      0FF0h<
	Dest T4:2.PRE
	      0D40h<
	
	Note: middle 8 bits are passed so the destination has 0D40h after the AND
	(a)

Perform a bit by bit OR operation between two registers.
 	
The bitwise OR instruction in PLC 5, SLC 500, and ControlLogix logically ORs each bit of the Source A and Source B words and places the result of that OR operation into the correspond bit in the Destination register.
 	
Note: SLC 500 rungs are shown, but the operation would be the same for PLC 5 and ControlLogix.
	I:1
	5
	
	—OR—
	Bitwise Inclusive OR
	Source A N7:4
	      00C8h<
	Source B N7:8
	      0050h<
	Dest N7:1
	      00D8<
	
	(b)

Perform a bit by bit exclusive OR (XOR) operation between two registers to identify the bits in the two words that are not equal.
 	
The bitwise XOR instruction in PLC 5, SLC 500, and ControlLogix determines if the respective data bits in two registers are the same. If the two words are equal the result is zero for all bits. All bit patterns that are not equal will result in a 1 placed in that bit location in the Destination register.
 	
Note: SLC 500 rungs are shown, but the operation would be the same for PLC 5 and ControlLogix.
	C5:2
	DN
	
	—XOR—
	Bitwise Exclusive OR
	Source A T4:0.ACC
	      0082h<
	Source B N7:3
	      01C2h<
	Dest N7:11
	      0140h<
	
	(c)

- ControlLogix: the control address would be a tag such as control_1 with a data type of control.
- Length: the number that represents the length of the file.
  PLC 5 – a number from 1 to 1000
  ControlLogix – DINT (double integer)
- Position: the number that specifies the word location within the file. It typically starts at zero and indexes to one less than the file

FIGURE 10-6: FAL instruction.

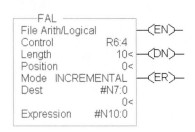

—FAL—
File Arith/Logical   —(EN)—
Control   R6:4
Length   10<   —(DN)—
Position   0<
Mode   INCREMENTAL   —(ER)—
Dest   #N7:0
      0<
Expression   #N10:0

length, although you can start at a number other than zero.

- **Mode:** there are three modes: In the *all* mode a complete file is transferred in one scan, in the *incremental* mode one element of data is operated upon for each time the FAL ladder rung instruction goes from false to true, and in the *numeric* mode a decimal number (1 to 1000) indicates the number of elements operated on per scan. The instruction remains true until all words are transferred in block size indicated.
- **Destination:** the address of the location for the result of the operation.
- **Expression:** the address that specifies the source of the file and the type of arithmetic or logical operation to be performed.

Control Word Addressing. This instruction marks the first use of *control words* or the *control data file* to provide the information necessary to execute instructions. The control data file, illus-

trated in Table 10-1(a), has three-word elements where word 0 is the status word, word 1 indicates the length of stored data, and word 2 indicates position. The control register is used with the following instructions: bit shift, FIFO shift register, LIFO shift register, and sequencer instructions in all Allen-Bradley PLC models. In addition, it is used in the file-arithmetic-logic (FAL) instruction in the PLC 5 and ControlLogix PLCs.

The addressable bits and words from the control data file are listed in Table 10-1(b) and the control elements or bits are in Table 10-1(c).

The addressing used for control data files in the PLC 5 and SLC 500 is described in Table 10-2.

Control data words in ControlLogix PLCs are tags with a data type of control. The control structure in ControlLogix is the same three-word sequence used in PLC 5 and SLC 500 and illustrated in Table 10-1. The addressing of bits and words from the three-word structure is similar as well, but tags are used with element and bit identifiers.

TABLE 10-1 Control word bit and word structure.

15	14	13	12	11	10	09	08	07	06	05	04	03	02	01	00	Word
EN	EU	DN	EM	ER	UL	IN	FD				Error Code					0
Length of Bit Array or File (LEN)																1
Bit Pointer or Position (POS)																2

(a) Control data file words

Addressable Bits	Addressable Words
EN = Enable	LEN = Length
EU = Update Enable	POS = Position

(b) Addressable bits and words

DN = Done

EM = Stack Empty

ER = Error

UL = Unload

IN = Inhibit

FD = Found

(c) Control bits

TABLE 10-2 Control data file addressing format.

Format	Explanation		
	R	Control file	
	f	File number	
	:	Element delimiter	Number 6 is the default file. A file number between 9 and 255 can be used if additional storage is required.
	e	Element number	Ranges from 0 to 255. These are three-word elements. See Table 10-1.
Rf:e.s/b	Rf:e	Explained above.	
	.	Word delimiter	
	s	Indicates word	
	/	Bit delimiter	
	b	Bit	

Examples:

R6:2	Element 2, control file 6. Address bits and words by using the format Rf:e.s/b
R6:2/15 or R6:2/EN	Enable bit
R6:2/14 or R6:2/EU	Unload Enable bit
R6:2/13 or R6:2/DN	Done bit
R6:2/12 or R6:2/EM	Stack Empty bit
R6:2/11 or R6:2/ER	Error bit
R6:2/10 or R6:2/UL	Unload bit
R6:2/9 or R6:2/IN	Inhibit bit
R6:2/8 or R6:2/FD	Found bit
R6:2.1 or R6:2.LEN	Length value
R6:2.2 or R6:2.POS	Position value
R6:2.1/0	**Bit 0 of length value**
R6:2.2/0	**Bit 0 of position value**

Standard Ladder Logic for the FAL Instruction. The standard ladder logic in Figure 10-7 describes how the FAL instruction copies a single element to an array, copies an array to an array, or copies an array to a single element. These three file transfers were introduced in Figure 10-3. The instruction in Figure 10-7 uses the ControlLogix PLC format, which includes arrays and array operations. You may want to review the array material in Chapter 9 if you are not familiar with their operation.

First, the *word-to-file transfer* using the FAL instruction is illustrated in Figure 10-7(a). Note that the mode is *incremental*, that is, with each enabling of the instruction, the contents of the expression are moved into the destination. The first time Color_switch is true, the position value is 0 and the contents of tag value_1 are moved into the first element of a two-dimensional tag, array_2[0,Control_4.pos]. On the second transition of the input instruction, the contents of value_1 are moved into the second element of the

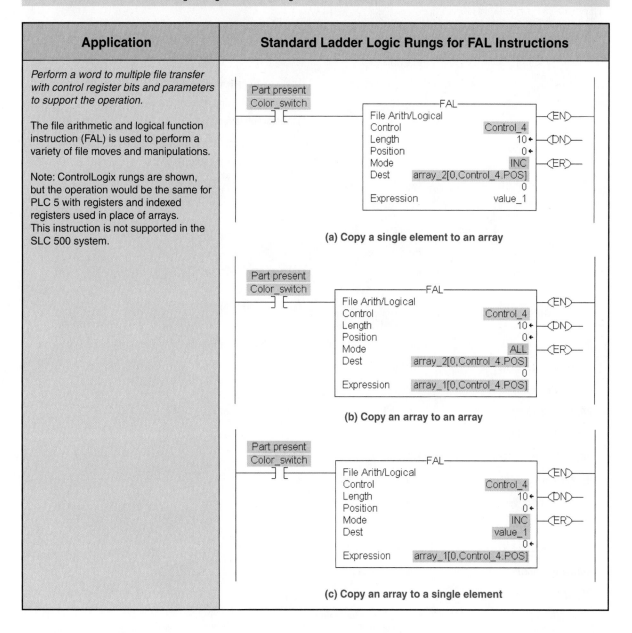

Application	Standard Ladder Logic Rungs for FAL Instructions
Perform a word to multiple file transfer with control register bits and parameters to support the operation. The file arithmetic and logical function instruction (FAL) is used to perform a variety of file moves and manipulations. Note: ControlLogix rungs are shown, but the operation would be the same for PLC 5 with registers and indexed registers used in place of arrays. This instruction is not supported in the SLC 500 system.	**(a) Copy a single element to an array** **(b) Copy an array to an array** **(c) Copy an array to a single element**

two dimensional array. After these two transitions, values are in array locations Array_2[0,0] and Array_2[0,1]. Eventually, the FAL instruction copies value_1 into the first 10 elements or positions of the two dimensional array. Therefore, the values are copied to the ten positions from Array_2[0,0] to Array_2[0,9].

Next, the *file-to-file transfer* using the FAL instruction is illustrated in Figure 10-7(b). Note that the FAL instruction is in the ALL mode, which means that all data are transferred in the first program scan when the FAL instruction is

enabled. The data moves all of the elements from Array_1 into the same position within Array_2. In this case Array_1[0,0] to Array_1[0,9] are moved to Array_2[0,0] to Array_2[0,9]. After this transfer, for example, Array_1[0,5] has the same value as Array_2[0,5].

The third transfer, the *file-to-word transfer*, is illustrated in Figure 10-7(c). It is similar to the word-to-file transfer except that the FAL instruction transfers the data from a sequence of array elements into a single tag. Each time the FAL instruction is enabled, it copies the current value

of array_1 to value_1. The FAL instruction uses the incremental mode, so only one array value is copied each time the Color_switch instruction is enabled. The next time the instruction is enabled, the instruction overwrites value_1 with the next value in array_1.

The FAL instruction has a control data register; therefore, in the ControlLogix system the tag used to identify the control data register must be a control data type. Figure 10-7(d) illustrates how the Control_4 tag is assigned a control data type.

PLC 5 FAL Instruction. Figure 10-8 illustrates an arithmetic operation using the FAL instruction in the PLC 5 system. When the input instruction I:001/0 is true, the FAL instruction is enabled, and the FAL instruction adds the

FIGURE 10-7: (Continued).

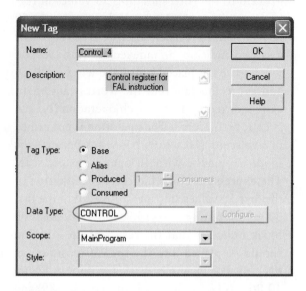

FIGURE 10-8: FAL operation in a PLC 5 processor.

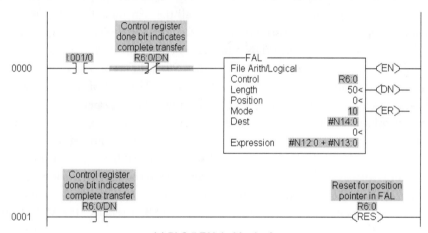

(a) PLC 5 FAL ladder logic

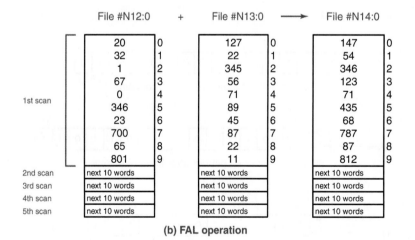

(b) FAL operation

50 integer values from registers starting at #N12:0 to the corresponding 50 values in registers starting at #N13:0 and then copies the 50 integer sums to registers starting at #N14:0. The # symbol indicates an indexed address. (Section 9-2-5). The # is placed before the word (#NR:D) address to indicate that the word is automatically indexed by 1 after each operation (N12:0, N12:1, N12:2, etc.). The operation is performed in five scans (10 words per scan) because the mode is numeric with 10 operations per scan. The expression block indicates the addition of the first 50 values starting at #N12:0 to the first 50 values starting at #N13:0, and the destination block indicates that the result of the addition should be placed into the first 50 positions in #N14:0. For example, using the data in Figure 10-8(b), N12:5 (346) is added to N13:5 (89) and the result is stored in N14:5 (435). After the transfer starts, input I:001/0 cannot stop the data transfer. Note that the control register done bit, R6.0/DN, is used to reset the pointer in the control register using the standard reset instruction. The example also illustrates that the R6.0/DN bit can be used with an XIO instruction (rung 0) to make the FAL instruction false after the 50 operations. Applications would use either the reset instruction or this inhibit bit for control of the FAL, but not both.

10-3-3   Shift Registers

The *shift register* is a logical operator that permits a register to move its contents to the right or to the left. The shift register, or *bit shift register* as it is often called, serially shifts a bit to the adjacent bit location through a register or group of registers. The concept of bit shifting to the right is illustrated in Figure 10-9. Note that at the most significant bit (MSB) end of the register there are two inputs—data and clock. Figure 10-9(a) shows the register before any shifting has taken place. Figure 10-9(b) shows the register after a data bit equal to 1 has been clocked into the register. Note that each bit within the register has been moved to the right, and the bit at the far right of the register has been lost. Figure 10-9(c) shows the register after a data bit equal to 0 has been clocked into the register and all bits have shifted to the right. Finally, shifting left is the same concept as shifting right but with the data and clock at the least significant bit (LSB) end of the register.

When a group of registers is involved in the shifting operation, they are connected as shown in Figure 10-10. Note that the clock is connected to all the registers. The data line is at the MSB end of the first register, the LSB of the first register is connected to the MSB of the second, and the LSB of the second is connected to the MSB of the third. The LSB of the third register is lost in this right-shifting operation.

Another shifting operation is rotate. *Rotate* is an operation of a shift register where the LSB connects to the MSB for a right rotate and the MSB connects to the LSB for a left rotate. Figure 10-11 illustrates the right rotate. Note that instead of losing the LSB, it replaces the MSB. Figure 10-11(a)

FIGURE 10-9: Shift registers.

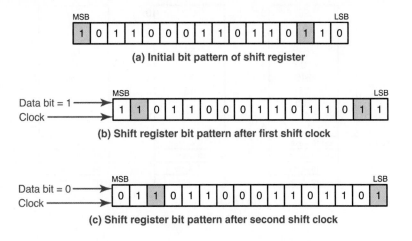

(a) Initial bit pattern of shift register

Data bit = 1 ⟶
Clock ⟶
(b) Shift register bit pattern after first shift clock

Data bit = 0 ⟶
Clock ⟶
(c) Shift register bit pattern after second shift clock

FIGURE 10-10: Multiple register shift registers.

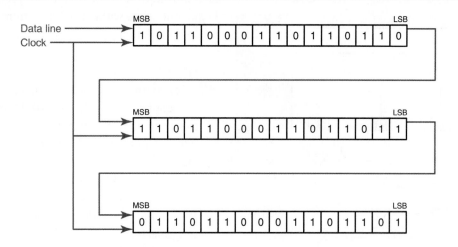

FIGURE 10-11: Right rotate shift registers.

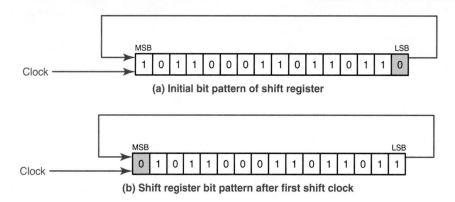

shows the register before the shift, and Figure 10-11(b) shows the register after the shift.

The following example illustrates how the shift register is used in an automated ice-cream cone conveyor system. In the process a PLC controls the following four actions:

1. Verify that the cone is not broken.
2. Put ice cream inside the cone.
3. Add sprinkles on the ice cream.
4. Add peanuts on the top.

If the cone is broken, we obviously don't want to add ice cream and the other items. Therefore, we have to track the bad cone down our process line so that we can tell the machine not to add each item. A sensor monitors cone quality, and if the sensor is on, then the cone is good; if it's off, then the cone is broken. Figure 10-12(a) depicts the automated process, and Figure 10-12(b)

depicts the operation of the PLC shift register that drives the process. Refer to the figure as you read the process functional description.

The automated process in Figure 10-12 depicts only the first four steps of the entire operation. These four steps function as follows:

Step 1: Sensor S1 monitors the first cone. Since it's a good cone, a 1 is shifted into register bit 00.

Step 2: S1 senses the second cone, which is broken, and a 0 is shifted into bit 00. Note that the 1 from bit 00 is shifted into bit 01, thus turning on M1, which puts ice cream in the first cone.

Step 3: S1 senses the third cone, which is good, and a 1 is shifted into bit 00. Note that the 0 from bit 00 is shifted into bit 01, which inhibits M1 from putting ice cream into the broken

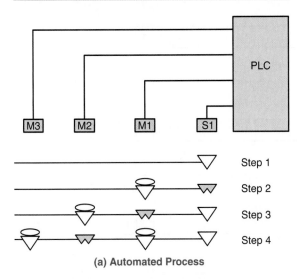

FIGURE 10-12: Shift register application.

(a) Automated Process

03	02	01	00	Bits
0	0	0	1	Step 1
0	0	1	0	Step 2
0	1	0	1	Step 3
1	0	1	1	Step 4

(b) Shift register contents for steps 1 through 4

cone. Also, the 1 in bit 01 is shifted into bit 02, thus turning on M2, which adds sprinkles on the first cone.

Step 4: S1 senses the fourth cone, which is good, and a 1 is shifted into bit 00. Note that the 0 from bit 01 is shifted into bit 02, which inhibits M2 from adding sprinkles. Also, the 1 in bit 00 is shifted into bit 01, thus turning on M1, which puts ice cream into the third cone. Also, the 1 in bit 02 is shifted into bit 03, thus turning on M3, which adds peanuts to the first cone.

Review Figure 10-12 and reread the description until you are familiar with shift register operation in an automated process. Shift registers are most commonly used in processes that involve conveyor systems, labeling, or bottling applications.

Bit Shift Left (BSL) and Bit Shift Right (BSR) Instructions. These two shift register instructions (BSL and BSR) allow you to shift a specific number of bits either to the left or right. The positions of shifted bits in the shift register are identified by a word/bit address or a tag for a one-dimensional array. The BSL and the BSR instruc-

tions are shown in Figure 10-13(a) for PLC 5 and SLC 500 and in Figure 10-13(b) for Control-Logix. The terms within the instructions have the following meaning:

- **File** (PLC 5 and SLC 500): the address of the bit array that is to be shifted. The bit array is a contiguous collection of 16-bit words from one word to the file maximum.
- **Array** (ControlLogix): an array tag specifying the array to be shifted.
- **Control:** the address of the operational structure, which consists of the following:
  PLC 5 and SLC 500: the operational structure is as follows:

Word	Contents
Control	Bit 15 (EN) is a 1 when the instruction is enabled
	Bit 13 (DN) is a 1 when the bits have shifted
	Bit 11 (ER) is a 1 when the length is negative
	Bit 10 (UL) stores the state of the bit that was shifted out of the range of bits
Length	The bit length of the file
Position	The current position of the bit pointed to by the instruction

ControlLogix: the operational structure is as follows:

Mnemonic	Data Type	Description
.EN	BOOL	Indicates the instruction is enabled
.DN	BOOL	Indicates the bits have shifted
.UL	BOOL	Stores the state of the bit that was shifted out of the range of bits
.ER	BOOL	Indicates the length is negative
.LEN	DINT	Indicates the number of array bits to shift

FIGURE 10-13: BSL and BSR shift register instructions.

(a) BSL and BSR instructions for the Allen Bradley PLC 5 and SLC 500m

(b) BSL and BSR instructions for the Allen Bradley ControlLogix

- **Bit address** (PLC 5 and SLC 500): the address of the data that is to be shifted.
- **Source bit** (ControlLogix): a tag identifying the bit to be shifted.
- **Length:** the number of bits in the register or array to shift.

The operation of the BSL instruction is illustrated in Figure 10-14(a). When the rung goes from a false to true transition, the EN bit is set and one left shift is generated. Note that the input bit address is I:1/5, which is typically a discrete input field device, such as a sensor, and the input status, which is 0, is shifted into bit position B3:12/0. All bits of the file are shifted one position to the left. Note that B3:13/10 (also called address B3:12/26) is the last bit of the 27-bit file and is shifted into the unload bit R6:0/UL. The state of the UL bit prior to the left shift is lost.

The operation of the BSR instruction is illustrated in Figure 10-14(b). When the rung goes from a false to true transition, the EN bit is set and one right shift is generated. In this second example, the input bit address is I:1/6, and the status of the field device, which is 1, is shifted into bit position B3:31/4 (or B3:30/20), which is the first bit in the 21-bit file. All bits of the file are shifted one position to the right. Note that the last bit is B3:30/0, which is the last bit of the file, and it is shifted into the unload bit R6:1/UL. Likewise, the state of the UL bit prior to the right shift is lost.

Bit shift registers often are used to track parts moving on a conveyor or transfer system. In some applications the locations on the conveyor are associated with bits in the shift register. The locations on the conveyor that hold parts have a 1 in the shift register and those that are empty contain a 0. Operations on the parts as they move along the conveyor are triggered by the 1s present in the shift register.

Standard Ladder Logic for BSL and BSR Instructions. The standard ladder logic for shift register operation is illustrated in Figure 10-15. Note that in Figure 10-15(a) the BSL instruction has input logic that is used to make the rung active. Therefore, the input logic must transition from false to true for every shift required in the BSL instruction.

Figure 10-15(b) illustrates the ControlLogix version of the BSR instruction. Tags are used for all parameters and an array is used for the shift register. The BSR and BSL instructions have similar formats to those demonstrated in the standard ladder logic in Figure 10-15.

The standard ladder logic in Figure 10-15(c) illustrates one of the most common applications for the bit shift register instructions, the tracking of parts on a synchronous conveyor. The conveyor layout and ladder logic are illustrated, and a complete description is provided. Study the two illustrations as you read the description of the operation. Example 10-1 applies these concepts to an industrial automation problem.

FIGURE 10-14: Shift register operation.

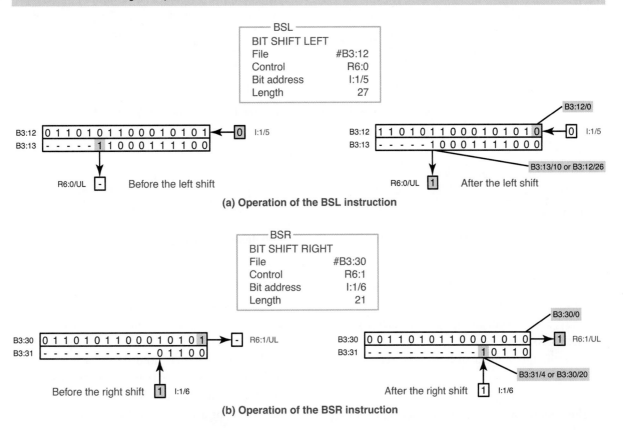

(a) Operation of the BSL instruction

(b) Operation of the BSR instruction

FIGURE 10-15: Standard ladder logic rungs for SLC 500 BSL and BSR instructions.

Application	Standard Ladder Logic Rungs for BSL and BSR Instructions
Shift the bits of a register from left to right while inputting bit values on the left and outputting bit values on the right. The operation of the bit shift left instruction is described in Figure 10-14. Note that bits are shifted in at the 0 bit location of register and shifted out at any bit location in that register or higher registers. The standard ladder indicates that each shift operation is triggered by a false to true transition of the input logic. The BSL is shown but the BSR operation would be similar. The ControlLogix BSR instruction is also displayed. The Control and Length are the same but Source Bit is used in place of Bit Address and Array is used in place of File. Note: SLC 500 and ControlLogix rungs are shown, but operation would be the same for PLC 5.	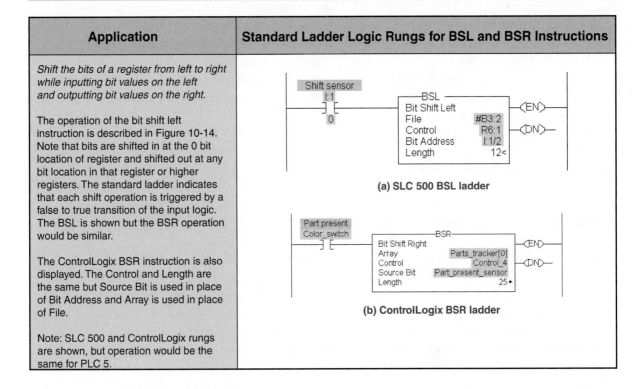

FIGURE 10-15: (Continued).

Application	Standard Ladder Logic Rungs for BSL and BSR Instructions

Track parts on a synchronous conveyor so that specific parts can be selected for a quality check or corrective action.

This standard ladder logic is used frequently to track parts that are equally spaced on a synchronous conveyor system. Every part over a portion of the conveyor is assigned a bit from the shift register. The conveyor and bits corresponding to conveyor positions are illustrated at the right. In this example the shift register length is 11 so 11 parts could be followed as they pass through this product window. For example, part quality could be checked by a sensor and passed to the shift register by input I:1/2. If that input is high (bad part) when the part is at position 0, then a 1 is entered into the shift register at the zero bit location. A second sensor at input I:1/12 shifts all register data left one bit as the parts move to the next location. When the bad part's bit is shifted 11 times, its bit value of 1 is in the 10th bit location in the register and the part is in the rejection location on the conveyor (one shift to bring it into the shift register from I:1/2 and 10 to move to location 10). The logic in the second rung on the right is used to eject the bad part that was detected at position 0. The part ejector can be located at any position along the conveyor that corresponds with a bit in the shift register. A second alternative is to place the ejector at location length plus one (11 + 1 = 12 for this ladder) and use the unload control bit (UL) to trigger the ejector. Several examples are provided so you can learn this important application for shift registers.

The BSL is shown but the BSR could be used in this standard logic as well. Also, the SLC 500 rungs are shown, but the operation would be the same for PLC 5 and ControlLogix.

(c)

EXAMPLE 10-1

The packing testing system in Figure 10-16(a) uses a proximity sensor (S2) to look through a box of material and determine if a metal part has been packaged. Design a ladder program using a shift register instruction to eject any box from the line at the ejector station that does not have the part present. A photoelectric thru-beam sensor (S1) detects every passing box.

SOLUTION

The solution for the problem, shown in Figure 10-16(b), follows the standard ladder logic concept from Figure 10-15(c) but with a 0 indicating that the location has a problem. The proximity sensor, S2, detects if the metal part is in the box through the box

FIGURE 10-16: Quality system for packaging testing system.

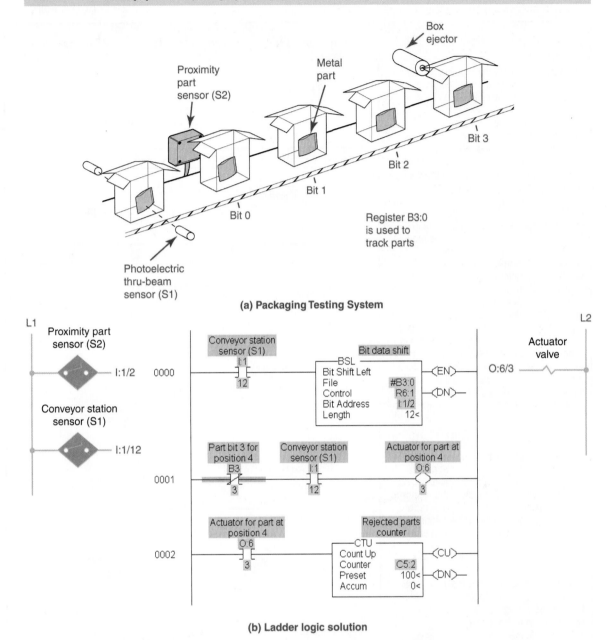

(a) Packaging Testing System

(b) Ladder logic solution

material. If it is present it places a 1 in the corresponding register bit; if it is absent it places a 0 in that register bit. All boxes without a part inside are ejected at position 4 based on the shift register bit 3 value. Good boxes have a 1 in their shift register location and bad boxes have a 0. Therefore, rung 1 uses an XIO instruction with the bit 3 address and an XIC instruction with the conveyor station sensor (S1) address. When a part is in the ejection position, sensor S1 is true and rung 1's logic state is controlled by the XIO (-] / [-) instruction and the value of bit 3 (B3:0/3 address). So if bit 3 has a 1 (good box) the rung is false and the actuator is off, but if bit 3 has a 0 (bad box) the rung is true and the actuator ejects the box. Rung 2 has a counter that counts the number of bad boxes. Figure 10-17(b) shows the register after one shift with a bad box detected and Figure 10-17(c) shows the register after four shifts with bit 3 holding the 0 for the bad box. Figure 10-17 shows the shift registers for four consecutive shifts after a bad box is detected.

10-3-4 First In, First Out (FIFO) Function

The *first in, first out (FIFO)* function is a word shift operation, which is similar to the bit shift operation that was discussed in Section 10-3-3. Word shifting provides a simple method of loading data into a file, usually called the stack. As in the bit shift register, two inputs are used in the FIFO or word shift operation—load and unload, which operate independently of each other. Figure 10-18 illustrates this operation. Note that the *load input* enters the data word into the next available word at the bottom of the stack from a source location, and the *unload input* removes the data word from the top of the stack into a destination location. Figure 10-18(a) and (b) shows the status of the stack before and after the load; Figure 10-18(c) and (d) shows the status of the stack before and after the unload. The data is shifted into the stack in the order in which it is received. Therefore, the first word shifted in will be the first word shifted out. For a practical example, think of a queue at a grocery store checkout or at a movie theater ticket window.

FIGURE 10-17: Bit movement in B3:0 register for good and bad boxes.

Part tracking bits with 4 good parts shown

Empty box in position 1 on the conveyor after first shift pulse

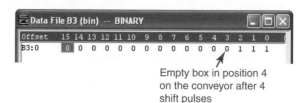

Empty box in position 4 on the conveyor after 4 shift pulses

FIGURE 10-18: Word stacks FIFO load and unload operations.

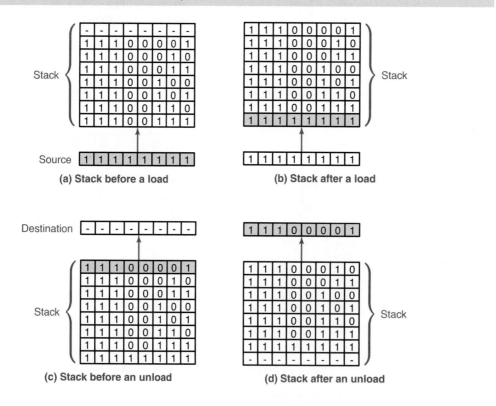

The first person in line is serviced first and leaves, then the next person, and so forth. The people enter and leave the queue at different times, but the first one in line is the first one out.

The FIFO function has many applications. One application of the FIFO function is a process where different parts are pulled from inventory to be used in production. Each part is assigned a unique code, which is loaded into a FIFO stack, and parts are pulled in the order prescribed by the stack. This type of inventory control ensures that oldest part in the inventory is used first. Another use of the FIFO function is the storage and retrieval of data that is synchronized to an external movement of parts on a conveyor or transfer machine. The FIFO function is also useful when keeping values that are obtained from a process in a *moving window* situation such as the process shown in Figure 10-19. Figure 10-19(a) illustrates the temperature profile as a function of time, and Figure 10-19(b) shows that the desired window from time t_0 to t_1 is kept in a FIFO stack. In this application the temperature values are sampled at regular time intervals and the stack load sample values are listed from the top to the bottom, with the first value in at the top of the stack. The data is unloaded from the top registers, so the first in is the first out. The stack has sufficient words to hold the samples over the specified time period t_1 to t_0 Thus, the stack always contains the most recent t_0 through t_1 temperature values.

FIFO Instructions. To program the FIFO function a pair of instructions is used—*FIFO load* (FFL) and *FIFO unload* (FFU). The FFL instruction loads data into a file from a source, and the FFU instruction unloads data from a file to a destination. The FFL and the FFU instructions are shown in Figure 10-20(a). Note that for the FFL and the FFU instructions, the FIFO addresses the same file, the control address is the same, and the length and position are the same. These common addresses/numbers are required so that the instructions operate on the same FIFO file. The terms within these instructions have the following meaning:

- **Source:** the address location of the data word that is the next value loaded onto the FIFO stack by the FFL instruction at the location contained in the pointer.
- **Destination:** the address location of the next data word that is unloaded from the FIFO stack by the FFU instruction.
- **FIFO:** the *indexed* address of the stack or an array tag. The same FIFO address is used for the FFL and FFU instructions.

FIGURE 10-19: Temperature monitoring process using a FIFO stack.

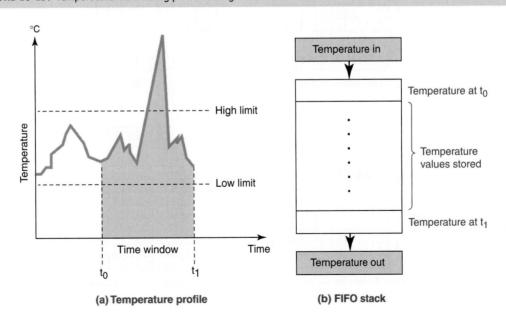

(a) Temperature profile

(b) FIFO stack

FIGURE 10-20: FIFO load and unload example.

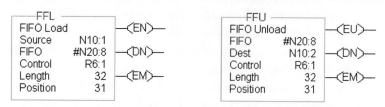

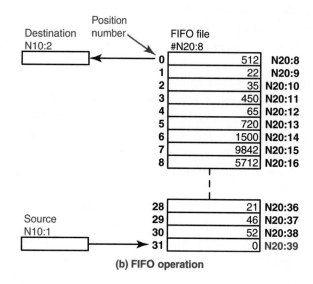

(a) FFL and FFU instructions for the Allen Bradley PLC 5 and SLC 500

(b) FIFO operation

- **Control:** the address of the command structure for the operation.

PLC 5 and SLC 500 have the following control structure:

Bit	Function	Description
15	EN load enable	Indicates if the FFL instruction is enabled
14	EU unload enable	Indicates if the FFU instruction is enabled
13	DN done bit	Indicates the FIFO stack is full. Note that when the DN bit is set, the transfer of data from the source to the stack is inhibited.
12	EM empty bit	Indicates the FIFO stack is empty, that is, all the data has been transferred to the destination. Note that if the FFU instruction is activated after the EM bit is set, then zeros are transferred to the destination.

Logix systems have the following operational structure:

Mnemonic	Data Type	Description
.EN	BOOL	Indicates if the FFL instruction is enabled
.EU	BOOL	Indicates if the FFU instruction is enabled
.DN	BOOL	Indicates the bits have shifted
.EM	BOOL	Indicates that the FIFO stack is empty
.ER	BOOL	Indicates length is negative
.LEN	DINT	Indicates number of elements to shift
.POS	DINT	Identifies where the next load/unload will occur

- **Length:** the number of words/elements in the stack.
- **Position:** the stack pointer, which is the stack address where the next source word/element will be loaded.

FIFO Load (FFL) Instruction. The PLC 5 and SLC 500 FIFO operation is depicted in Figure 10-20(b). Note that the length of the stack is 32 from N20:8 through N20:39. With each activation of the FFL instruction, the data from source N10:1 is loaded into the FIFO stack at the position indicated by the position parameter in the instruction. The position indicator is normally set to 0 for the start of the FIFO instruction, and the indicator value increases by 1 with every entry of data (false to true transition of FFL instruction) until it advances to the last file dictated by the length parameter. In this example, on the first activation of the FFL instruction the source data is loaded into N20:8, on the next activation it is loaded into N20:9, and so forth. When the stack is full, the DN (done) bit is set to 1. Note in Figure 10-20 that the position parameter is 31, so the stack has just one open element. If that element is loaded the done bit is set.

FIFO Unload (FFU) Instruction. When rung conditions change from false to true, the FFU enable bit (EU) is set. This unloads the contents of the element at stack position 0 into the destination, N10:2 in Figure 10-20. All data in the stack is shifted one element toward the position zero, and the stack element that contained the last data value is zeroed. The position value then decrements to point at this recently zero stack element. The FFU instruction unloads an element at each false to true transition of the rung, until the stack is empty. Applying this to the example in Figure 10-20, with each activation of the FFU instruction, the data from the starting address (N7:8) is loaded into destination N10:2, and all data are shifted one position toward the starting address. When all the data have been shifted out of the stack the EM (empty) bit is set to 1.

10-3-5 Last In, First Out (LIFO) Function

The *LIFO* function shifts words as does the FIFO function, but reverses the order of the data, outputting the last word received first and the first word received last. As a result, words can be added to the LIFO stack without disturbing the words already loaded on the stack. The load and unload of the LIFO stack operates similarly to that of the load and unload of the FIFO stack, only the last word in the LIFO stack is the first word that is unloaded from the stack. Figure 10-21(a) and (b) shows the status of the stack before and after

FIGURE 10-21: Word stacks LIFO load and unload operations.

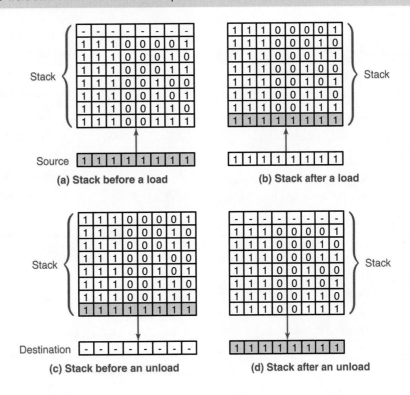

(a) Stack before a load

(b) Stack after a load

(c) Stack before an unload

(d) Stack after an unload

the load. Figure 10-21(c) and (d) shows the status of the stack before and after an unload. Typically the words are loaded onto the stack, then unloaded at a different time. For a practical example, picture a magazine parts feeder used in an automated process that works as follows. The first part placed into the feeder compresses the spring that is attached to the bottom of the feeder. When the second part is placed on top of the first, it further compresses the spring as the first part is pushed deeper into the magazine's case. This continues until the magazine is full. The first part in is at the bottom of the magazine and the last part in is at the top. This is just like the bullet magazines used on automatic pistols and rifles. In this situation the last part in is the first part removed. As in a FIFO operation, the load and unload of the stack occurs at different times in the LIFO operation.

LIFO Instructions. The LIFO operation is depicted in Figure 10-22 has two instructions: *LIFO load* (LFL) and *LIFO unload* (LFU). Note that the length of the stack is 32 from N20:8 through N20:39, with position numbers 0 through 31. With each activation of the LFL instruction, the data from source N10:1 is loaded into the LIFO stack, and the position is advanced by 1 toward the highest stack element position. With the stack empty and the LFL instruction activated, the position pointer is at 0 and the first entry goes into the stack at position 0. The position pointer is incremented in preparation for the next LFL instruction activation. At any point, an LFU instruction could become active. If this occurs the last data entered is pulled from the stack (position pointer = position pointer − 1). After the data is removed the position pointer is de-cremented by 1 to be ready for the next LFL or LFU instruction. When the stack is full, the DN bit is set to 1. With each activation of the LFU instruction, the last data entered is pulled and placed into destination file N10:2. When all the data have been shifted out of the stack the EM bit is set to 1.

The LIFO example in Figure 10-22 shows the stack with one open element. If an LFL instruction is executed, then position location 31 will be filled with the data from the source register,

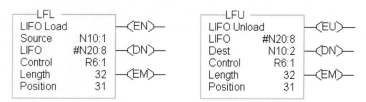

FIGURE 10-22: LIFO load and unload example.

(a) LFL and LFU instructions for the Allen Bradley PLC 5 and SLC 500

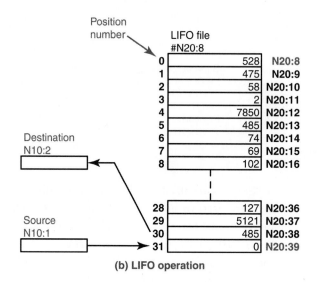

(b) LIFO operation

N10:1. However, if an LFU instruction is executed next, then the position pointer is changed to 30 (31-1) to point to last data entered so it can be moved to the destination register, N10:2.

To program the LIFO function LFL and LFU instructions are used. The LFL loads data into a stack file from a source, and the LFU unloads data from a stack file to a destination. The LFL and the LFU instructions are shown in Figure 10-22(a). Note that for the LFL and the LFU instructions, the LIFO addresses the same file, the control address is the same, and the length and position are the same. These common addresses/numbers are required so that the instructions operate on the same LIFO file. The terms within these instructions have the same meaning as the FIFO instructions described in Section 10-3-4.

ControlLogix FIFO and LIFO Instructions. The ControlLogix PLC operation with FIFO and LIFO functions like the corresponding instructions in the PLC 5 and SLC 500 except

FIGURE 10-23: FIFO and LIFO instruction illustration.

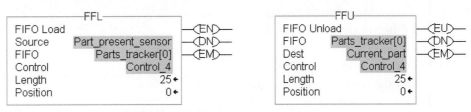

(a) ControlLogix FFL and FFU instructions

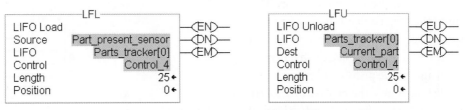

(b) ControlLogix FLF and LFU instructions

that arrays are used for the sequential files and tags are used to hold the parameter data. The instructions for ControlLogix are shown in Figure 10-23. Note that the instructions have the same parameters as the PLC 5 and SLC 500, but that you must use tags and arrays in the parameter definitions.

10-3-6 Copy and Fill Instructions

The copy (COP) and fill (FLL) instructions are word transfer instructions without any control bits. Therefore, bits are not available to indicate that the transfer has occurred and parameters, like length, are not present to indicate how many files to transfer. They are, however, useful for moving a number of data files (COP instruction) from one location to another or moving a single data file (FLL instruction) to a specified number of other data files.

COP Instruction. In the *copy instruction* the destination file type determines the number of words that are transferred from the source to destination. For example, if the destination file type is a counter and the source file type is an integer, three integer words are transferred for the counter file type since the counter is a three-word instruction. This provision is necessary because a control register is not present to specify the length for the transfer. However, if you

need an enable bit, program an output instruction (OTE) in parallel with the COP instruction using an internal bit as the enable bit indicator. The PLC 5 and SLC 500 instruction format is illustrated in Figure 10-24(a) and the process for the transfer is illustrated in Figure 10-24(b).

Enter the following parameters when programming this instruction:

- *Source* is the address of the file you want to copy. You must use the file indicator (#) in the address so that indexing of the address occurs.
- *Destination* is the starting address where the instruction stores the copy. You must use the file indicator (#) in the address so that indexing of the address occurs.
- *Length* is the number of elements in the file you want to copy where maximum length is based on the destination file type. If the destination file type is three words per element (timer or counter), you can specify a maximum length of 42. If the destination file type is one word per element, you can specify a maximum length of 128 words.

All elements are copied from the source file into the destination file each time the instruction is executed. Elements are copied in ascending order.

FIGURE 10-24: Copy instruction illustration.

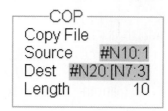

(a) PLC 5 and SLC 500 copy instruction

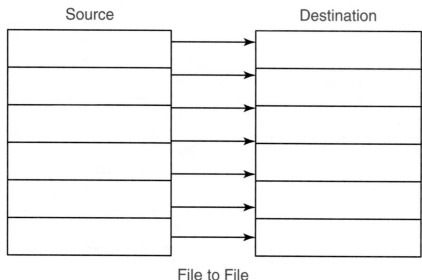

File to File

(b) Copy instruction data transfer

Fill Instruction. The fill (FLL) instruction loads a sequence of file elements or registers with either a program constant or a value from another file register address. The PLC 5 and SLC 500 instruction format is shown in Figure 10-25(a) and the process for the transfer is illustrated in Figure 10-25(b).

The following parameters are required for programming this instruction:

- *Source* is the program constant or element address and does not need a pound sign (#) file indicator because it is not indexed.
- Floating point and string values are supported for higher versions of the SLC systems.
- *Destination* is the destination starting address of the file to be filled and must be indexed, so the indicator (#) in the address is required.

- *Length* is the number of elements in the destination file that will be filled.
- The source value, typically a constant, fills the specified destination file each scan the rung is true. Elements are filled in ascending order.

ControlLogix Copy and Fill Instructions. The ControlLogix PLC operation with copy and fill instructions is like the PLC 5 and SLC 500 except that arrays are used for the sequential files and tags are used to hold the parameter data. In addition, the FLL instruction will not write past the end of an array. If the length is greater than the total number of elements in the destination array, the FLL instruction stops at the end of the array, but no major fault is generated.

For best results, the source and destination should be the same data type. If you mix data types for the source and destination, the data type

FIGURE 10-25: Fill instruction illustration.

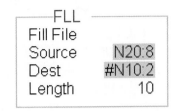

(a) PLC 5 and SLC 500 fill instruction

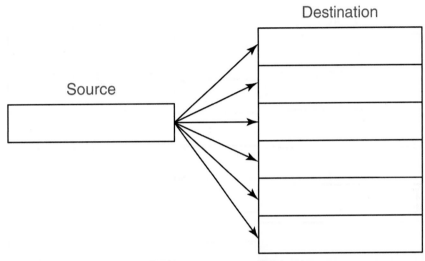

(b) Fill instruction data transfer

of the destination elements are used and they are filled with converted source values.

Standard Ladder Logic Rungs for PLC 5 and SLC 500 COP and FLL Instructions. The standard ladder logic used for COP and FLL are illustrated in Figure 10-26. The input logic is not unique but the addressing of the source and destination need some explanation. The source is a standard indexed address with the number symbol (#) placed before the starting address location. The source address starts at location N10:1 and increments to N10:10 due to the value 10 in the length parameter.

The destination is an addressing mode not discussed previously; it is called *indexed indirect addressing*. A combination of indexed and indirect, it permits the starting register location for the indexed address (#N20:) to be defined by the value in another address (N7:3). First the indirect address is resolved, and then the indexed final address is implemented. For example, if N7:3 has a value of 15, then the indexed address is #N20:15.

This addressing scheme is ideal for data lookup tables. Assume that three sets of five operational parameters needed for a process are saved in address locations starting at address N10:0. The three sets of data would look like that displayed in Table 10-3.

The starting register for each set is 0, 5, and 10 for sets 1, 2, and 3, respectively. Assume that the source address is #N10:[N7:3] and the destination is #N20:5. If 0, 5, or 10 is placed into N7:3, then the needed block of parameters is moved to the process locations starting at #N20:5. After an operator enters the set number into N7:3, the COP instruction picks the corresponding data and copies it to the process program file locations.

FIGURE 11-3: Sequencer parameters for SLC 500.

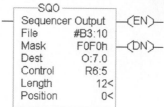

- Source: is the address of the input word or file for an SQC from which the instruction obtains data for comparison to its sequencer file.
- Destination: is the address of the output word or file for an SQO to which the instruction moves data from its sequencer file.
- Control: is the address that contains parameters with control information for the instruction and discrete outputs to indicate sequencer instruction results and status. The general control register file is described in Chapter 10 in Table 10-1 and 10-2. Review that information if necessary.

  The control file address is in the control area R of processor memory and the default file is 6. The first of three control words have status bits including:

- Bit 8: the *found bit* (FD) is only used for the SQC instruction. When the status of all non-masked bits in the source address match those of the corresponding reference file word, the FD bit is set. This bit is assessed each scan of the SQC instruction while the rung is true.
- Bit 11: the *error bit* (ER) indicates a negative position value or a negative or zero length value.
- Bit 13: the *done bit* (DN) is set by the SQO or SQC instruction after it has operated on the last word in the sequencer file. It is reset on the next false to true rung transition after the rung goes false.
- Bit 15: *the enable bit* (EN) is true when the rung goes from false to true and is used to indicate that the SQO or SQC instruction is enabled or active.
- Note in Figure 11-3 that the control bits present for each sequencer instruction are shown on the right side of the instruction

box. If they are true the bit initials are highlighted.
- Length: is the number of steps of the sequencer file starting at position 1. Since the file parameter starts at position 0, the number of words in the file is length plus one.
- Position: is the word location or step in the sequencer file from/to which the instruction moves data. The position pointer is incremented by 1 before action is taken by the sequencer instructions. Therefore, if the pointer is at 0, then after the first false to true transition of the sequencer rung the pointer is a 1 and points at the first word in the sequencer file. A position value that points past the end of the programmed file causes a runtime major error.

11-4-2 PLC 5 and SLC 500 SQO Instruction Operation

The *SQO instruction* is available in all Allen-Bradley PLCs, and the operation in the PLC 5 and SLC 500 processors is the same. The operation of the SQO during the first scan is different from the operation for all subsequent scans.

SQO Instruction Operation during the First Scan. When the processor is first changed from the program to the run mode, the operation of the SQO instruction is dependent upon the condition of the rung (true or false) at the time of the first scan. The two conditions are:

- If the rung is *true* at the time of the first scan and the position parameter is 0, then the data in the memory location at position 0 is transferred through the mask to the destination register and the position pointer is incremented by 1.

TABLE 11-1 Lighting sequence for theater illumination.

Step	Brightness level				
	Bank 1	Bank 2	Bank 3	Bank 4	Bank 5
1	H	H	H	H	H
2	M	M	M	M	M
3	L	L	L	L	L
4	Off	Off	Off	Off	Off

TABLE 11-2 Sequencer with seven steps and four outputs.

Step	01	02	03	04
1	0	1	0	0
2	0	0	0	1
3	1	1	0	0
4	1	1	0	1
5	0	1	1	1
6	1	0	1	1
7	1	0	0	0

11-3 BASIC PLC SEQUENCER FUNCTION

The basic *PLC sequencer function* provides the capability to program many steps and provide multiple outputs. Table 11-2 illustrates an output sequencer function that has seven steps and four outputs. Note that the steps are labeled 1 through 7, with each step having a specific pattern. For example, step 3's pattern is 1100. The outputs are labeled O1, O2, O3, and O4, and an output is on when a 1 is in its column and off when a 0 is in its column. The sequencer steps through the seven patterns, turning on the outputs as dictated by the pattern. Other sequencers change the output sequence bit pattern after comparing an input word with bit patterns stored in sequencer registers. Several types of sequencer instructions are discussed in the following sections.

11-4 ALLEN-BRADLEY SEQUENCER INSTRUCTIONS

The Allen-Bradley PLCs provide a group of sequencer instructions that can be used individually or in pairs. The operation of these instructions and specific PLC applications are addressed in the subsequent subsections. The instructions are as follows:

- Sequencer output (SQO): an output instruction that uses a file or an array to control various output devices (PLC 5, SLC 500, and ControlLogix).
- Sequencer input (SQI): an input instruction that compares bits from an input file or array to corresponding bits from a source address.

The instruction is true if all pairs of bits are the same (PLC 5 and ControlLogix).

- Sequencer compare (SQC): an output instruction that compares bits from an input source file to corresponding bits from data words in a sequence file. If all pairs of bits are the same, then a bit in the control register is set to 1 (PLC 5 and SLC 500).
- Sequencer load (SQL): an output instruction that functions like a word-to-file or file-to-file transfer (PLC 5, SLC 500, and ControlLogix).

11-4-1 PLC 5 and SLC 500 SQO and SQC Sequencer Instruction Structure

The SQO and SQC instructions are shown in Figure 11-3; the terms *file*, *mask*, *control*, *length*, and *position* are used in all instructions. The terms *destination* and *source* are used in SQO and SQC sequencers, respectively. These parameters used in sequencer instructions are defined as follows:

- File: is the starting address for the registers in the sequencer file, and you must use the indexed file indicator (#) for this address.
- Mask: is the code or bit pattern through which the sequencer instruction moves source data to the destination address. In the mask bit pattern, a 1 bit passes values (1 or 0) from source to destination and a 0 mask bit inhibits the data flow and puts a 0 in the bit location in the destination. Use a mask register or file name if you want to change the mask pattern under program control. Place an *h* behind the parameter to indicate that the mask is *hexadecimal* number notation or a *B* to indicate *binary* notation. *Decimal* notation is entered without any indicator.

FIGURE 11-1: Drum switch and contacts.

	Handle end		
	Reverse	Off	Forward
	1 o——o 2	1 o o 2	1 o o 2
	3 o——o 4	3 o o 4	3 o o 4
	5 o——o 6	5 o o 6	5 o——o 6

Internal switching

(a)   (b)

Courtesy of Square D/Schneider Electric.

FIGURE 11-2: Drum switch switching three-phase voltage to a motor.

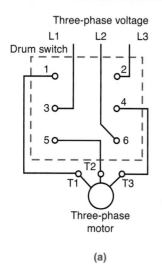

(a)

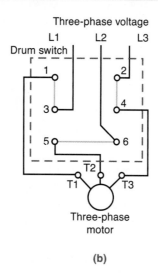

(b)

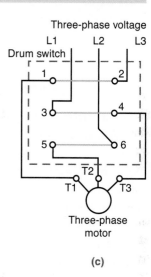

(c)

Rehg and Sartori, Industrial Electronics, 1st edition. © 2006, reprinted by permission of Pearson Education, Inc., Upper Saddle River, NJ.

how a drum switch can be used to operate a three-phase motor in a rotational switching application. Note that a three-phase motor must have any two of the three-phase input lines switched to reverse the direction of rotation of the motor. The three-phase motor and input voltages are wired to the switch, as illustrated in Figure 11-2(a). When the switch handle is in the forward position, the switch makes the connections illustrated in Figure 11-2(b) as follows: L1 is connected to T1, L2 to T2, and L3 to T3. When the switch is in the reverse position [Figure 11-2(c)] lines L1 and L3 are reversed, so L1 is connected to T3 and L3 is connected to T1.

Another electromechanical sequencing operation is the lighting in a movie theater, where a

motor-driven timing cam typically controls switches that set the theater illumination. This cam-operated sequencer is commonly known as a timer. The lighting sequence is shown in Table 11-1. Note that the four steps in the lighting sequence are as follows:

1. The five banks of lights are on high brightness, H, for the cleaning crew.
2. The five banks of lights are on medium brightness, M, during the pre-show time, allowing patrons to find seats.
3. The five banks of lights are on low brightness, L, for the showing of the previews.
4. The five banks of lights are off for the showing of the movie.

CHAPTER 11

PLC Sequencer Functions

11-1 GOALS AND OBJECTIVES

There are three principal goals of this chapter. The first goal is to provide the student with an introduction to the operation and function of electromechanical sequencing devices. The second goal is to introduce the basic PLC sequencer function and timing. The third goal is to show how the programmable sequencer instructions are applied to specific PLCs that are used in industrial automation systems.

After completing this chapter you should be able to:

- Identity and describe the operation and function of electromechanical sequencing devices.
- Describe the basic PLC sequencer function.
- Develop and describe the ladder diagram for the operation of a PLC sequencer with timing.
- Describe the technique of cascading sequencers.
- Develop ladder logic solutions using sequencer instructions for Allen-Bradley PLC 5, SLC 500, and ControlLogix PLCs.
- Troubleshoot ladder rungs with sequencer instructions.

11-2 ELECTROMECHANICAL SEQUENCING

Sequencing refers to a predetermined step-by-step process that accomplishes a specific task. A familiar application of sequencing events to achieve a specific task is the operation of a dishwasher or a clothes washer. Each washer sequences through multiple steps that perform a fixed routine of actions to complete its specific task. Simple sequencing is performed by electromechanical *drum switches*. A three-position, six-electrical-terminal drum switch is shown in Figure 11-1. The operator handle on the switch shown in Figure 11-1(a) is in the off position. Rotating the handle to the left creates the reverse contact condition, and moving it to the right creates the forward contact condition. These contact conditions are depicted in Figure 11-1(b).

Drum switches are frequently used for reversing the direction of AC and DC motors, or for controlling multispeed motors with two to four speed settings. Applications include directional control of motors for overhead hoists and doors, and speed control of motors used in blowers, mixers, pumps, and special machine tools. Figure 11-2 illustrates

FIGURE 10-30: Location of instructions described in this chapter.

Systems	Instructions	Location
PLC 5, SLC 500	AND, OR, XOR	
PLC 5, SLC 500	BSL, BSR, FFL, FFU, LFL, LFU	
PLC 5, SLC 500	FAL, COP, FLL	
LOGIX	AND, OR, XOR	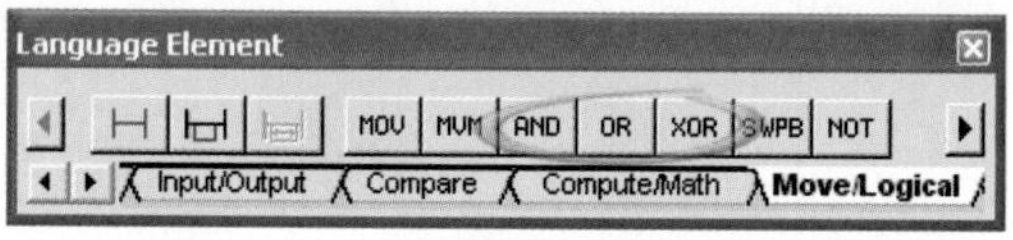
LOGIX	BSL, BSR, FFL, FFU, LFL, LFU	
LOGIX	FAL, COP, FLL	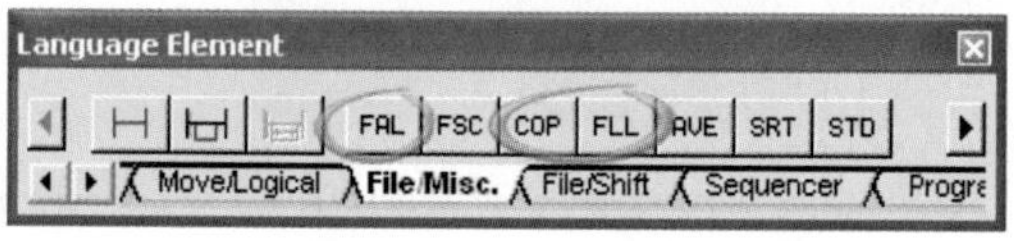

FIGURE 10-29: Solution for Example 10-4.

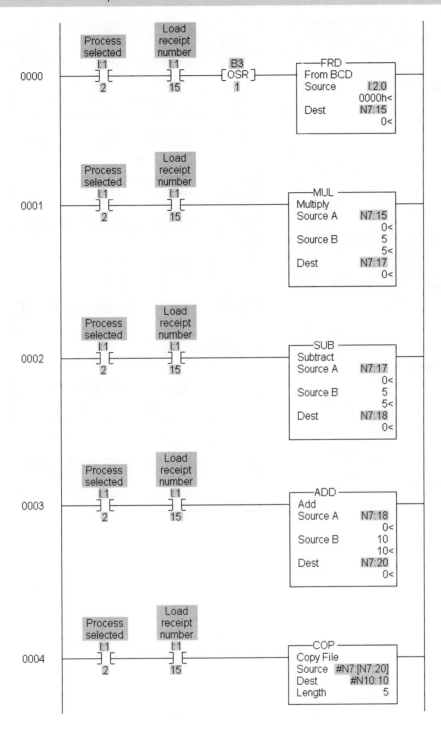

large data blocks or arrays, start with just a small data set. For example, if you can make the ladder operate with a FIFO instruction with a length of 3 you can make it work with a length of 100. So start with a small set and work up to the larger value.

10-6 LOCATION OF THE INSTRUCTIONS

The location of instructions from this chapter in the Allen-Bradley programming software is indicated in Figure 10-30.

EXAMPLE 10-4

Example 9-1 modified the process tank design problem in Section 7-6-3 (Figures 7-17 through 7-21) so that a receipt number could be entered by an operator to move the receipt values using indexed addressing. Review that solution in Figure 9-12.

Modify the process tank design again using an algorithm to calculate the indirect address offset from the receipt number, and use the COP instruction with indexed indirect addressing to load the number of half-gallon quantities of materials 1 and 2 into the process ladder logic.

Solution

The five-rung solution is illustrated in Figure 10-29.

Rung 0 loads the receipt number from a thumbwheel switch using the BCD to decimal conversion instruction to put the receipt number into N7:15.

Rungs 1 through 3 convert the receipt number into an offset that points to the starting address for each set of receipt parameters. The algorithm is:

$$\text{Starting register number} = [(RN \times NOI) - NOI] + SA$$

where RN is the receipt number, NOI is the number of ingredients, and SA is the starting address register number for the ingredients block of memory. In this example the starting address for the ingredients is N7:10, and there are three receipts with two ingredients in each. For example, if receipt 2 is desired, then:

$$\text{Starting register number} = [(2 \times 2) - 2] + 10 = 12$$

Note that the offset value of 12 is stored in N7:20, which indicates that receipt 2 data starts at N7:12.

Rung 4 copies the indexed receipt data from #N7:[N7:20] where #N7:[N7:20] is #N7:12 since N7:20 holds the value 12. The receipt data is copied to #N10:10 for use by the process.

This approach has many advantages. Most important is that the number of rungs of ladder logic does not increase as the number of receipts and ingredients gets larger

10-5 TROUBLESHOOTING DATA HANDLING INSTRUCTIONS AND SHIFT REGISTERS IN LADDER LOGIC

The data handling and shift register instructions use indexed, indirect, and indexed indirect addressing modes plus arrays to perform the data movement required in the instructions. As a result, all of the major causes of problems with addressing modes and array operations described in the last chapter would apply here as well.

If problems occur in rungs with data handling and shift register instructions using indirect or indexed addressing modes, use the following guidelines when troubleshooting these rungs.

- Verify that pointers do not point to addresses outside the memory boundaries.
- Use the temporary end (TND) instruction to stop scanning at points in the ladder where addressing indexes can be verified and data transferred checked.
- Use single-step options when available to scan one rung at a time to analyze how the data is changing and where the flow is incorrect.

These guidelines could be listed in the empirical design areas as well. When designs include data handling and shift register instructions with

FIGURE 10-27: Solution for Example 10-2.

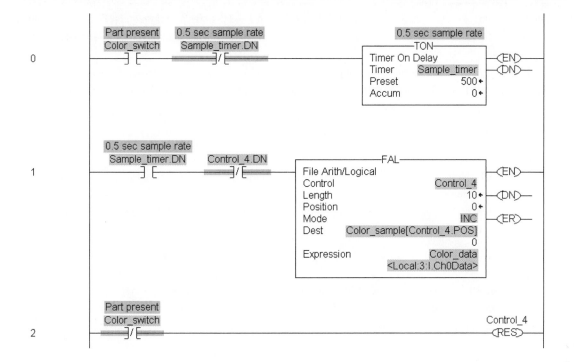

FIGURE 10-28: Solution for Example 10-3.

EXAMPLE 10-3

A machine makes 12 bits of data available at an output one bit at a time and provides a contact closure to indicate when each data bit is present. Design a ladder that captures the serial data in a register starting at B3:10 and transfers all bit values to a register at N10:0 when all 12 bits are captured.

SOLUTION

The three-rung solution is illustrated in Figure 10-28.

- Rung 0 uses a BSR instruction to move each bit into register B3:10. The data valid instruction, I:1/2, makes the BSR output true when the machine indicates that the data at I:1/3 is valid.

- Rung 1 has a COP instruction to copy the data from register B3:10 to N10:0. The input is true when the control data word's done bit is true. This indicates that all 12 bits have been stored.

- Rung 2 has a reset instruction activated by the same control done bit to reset the control data registers for another cycle.

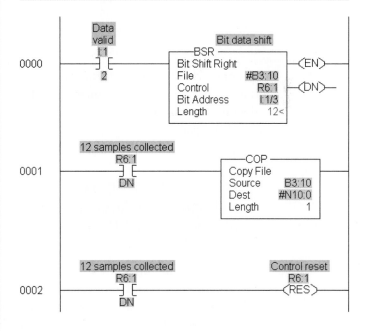

- Specific bits in a word to be changed to 1s while the rest of the word remains the same. An OR instruction with 1s for the mask bits is used for this type of masking.
- A comparison of two register values to identify the bits that are the same in both registers. XOR is used for this type of comparison.

BSL and BSR Instructions: Used in applications that require:

- A sequence of bits in a word to be sequentially shifted to a new location within the word.
- Tracking of a condition or part from one location on a conveyor to another location. In most cases, the parts and conveyor movement must be synchronous.

FAL, FFL, FFU, LFL, and LFU Instructions: Used in applications that require the movement of data words between registers and arrays with the support of a control data file to indicate the status of the operation.

- Use FAL for applications where movement of data must be completed in one scan or in successive scans. Note that this instruction is not available on the SLC 500 PLC.
- Use FFL and FFU for applications where movement of data is performed one data word at a time when the first data entered is the first data that must be pulled out.
- Use LFL and LFU for applications where movement of data is performed one data word at a time when the last data entered is the first data that must be pulled out.

COP and FLL Instructions: Used in applications that require the movement of data words between registers and arrays without the support of a control data file to indicate the status of the operation.

- Use COP to copy blocks of data from one set of registers to another in one PLC scan.
- Use FLL to copy a program constant or register contents from a single register or tag address to multiple register addresses or an array.

EXAMPLE 10-2

Example 6-11 had the following design statement.

Design a ladder program to move the part color value from a color sensor similar to that illustrated by the timing diagram in Figure 6-14. Two values should be moved to N7:0 and N7:1, and the average value should be calculated and placed in N7:2. The color data comes from I:2.0, and the color sensor trigger is connected to terminal 0 on the input module in slot 4 of the SLC 500. The color value is valid for 6 seconds; the trigger pulse starts 5 milliseconds after the color value is valid and is true for 7 seconds.

Review that problem statement and the solution in Figure 6-15.

Modify the color sensor sampling design by using an FAL instruction and ControlLogix software to copy 10 values of color data into an array when the color_switch is active.

SOLUTION

The three-rung solution is illustrated in Figure 10-27.

- Rung 0 is a 0.5-second regenerative timer activated by the color_switch tag. The timer done bit is true for one scan and false for 0.5 seconds. The timer starts when the color_switch tag is true.
- Rung 1 is triggered for one scan every half second. When the FAL is true it copies the data from Color_data to the array Color_sample[Control_4.POS]. Since the FAL mode parameter is set for incremental (INC), one data value is copied every time the FAL is true. The copies will occur until 10 array elements are full (length equals 10). The XIO instruction, with a Control_4.DN address, makes the input logic false after the tenth sample is copied (FAL is done). Note that the array Color_sample[Control_4.POS] is a tag with an indirect addressing mode. With every true transition of the FAL the position value is incremented, which gives the array an indirect operation.
- Rung 2 resets the FAL instruction (position is reset to 0) when the color_switch tag is false.

Compare the solution in Figure 6-15 with that in Figure 10-27. Note how much more efficient the FAL solution is.

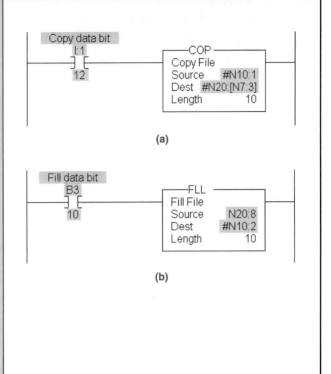

Application	Standard Ladder Logic Rungs for COP and FLL Instructions
Used in applications that require the movement of data words between registers and arrays without the support of a control data file to indicate the status of the operation. *Use COP to copy blocks of data from one set of registers to a second set in one PLC scan. Use FLL to copy a program constant or register contents from a single register or tag address to multiple register addresses or an array.* The copy instruction transfers blocks of data words from the indexed source address to the indexed destination address using the length parameter to indicate how many words to copy. Note that the destination address is an indexed indirect addressing mode. In this mode, the indirect address is solved first (the value in N7:3 is to identify the file number). For example, if N7:3 holds a value of 20, then the indirect address is N20:20. That value is indexed by one for ten locations, so N20:20 through N20:29 for the indexed part of the address. This is an an example where indexed addressing with an offset is often used. The fill instruction fills a block of words with the value from a single word. Indexed addressing is used in the example. Note: SLC 500 rungs are shown, but the operation would be the same for PLC 5 and ControlLogix PLCs. Also, the ControlLogix processors have a synchronous copy instruction, CPS.	

TABLE 10-3 Data for indexed indirect address.

Set	Address	Data
1	N10:0	1030
1	N10:1	58
1	N10:2	24526
1	N10:3	2345
1	N10:4	1450
2	N10:5	2030
2	N10:6	75
2	N10:7	31526
2	N10:8	2300
2	N10:9	2000
3	N10:10	3030
3	N10:11	158
3	N10:12	33526
3	N10:13	2745
3	N10:14	3450

10-4 EMPIRICAL DESIGN PROCESS WITH BIT AND WORD OPERATION INSTRUCTIONS

The empirical design process, introduced in Section 3-11-4, is an organized approach to the design of PLC ladder logic programs. However, the term *empirical* implies that some degree of trial and error is present. The instructions introduced in this chapter are used for special problem applications. Therefore, the use of these instructions in the design of ladder logic focuses on recognizing the types of problems where these instructions are required. Suggested application areas for the bit and word manipulation instructions follow.

AND, OR, and XOR Instructions: Used in applications that require:

- Specific bits in a word to be masked or changed to 0 while the rest of the word remains the same. An AND instruction with 1s for the mask or pass bits is used for this type of masking.

FIGURE 11-1: Drum switch and contacts.

Handle end

	Reverse	Off	Forward
	1 o——o 2	1 o o 2	1 o o 2
	3 o——o 4	3 o o 4	3 o o 4
	5 o——o 6	5 o o 6	5 o——o 6

Internal switching

(a)   (b)

Courtesy of Square D/Schneider Electric.

FIGURE 11-2: Drum switch switching three-phase voltage to a motor.

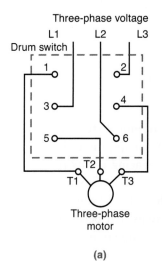

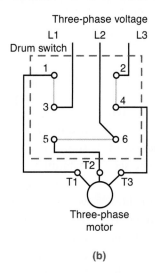

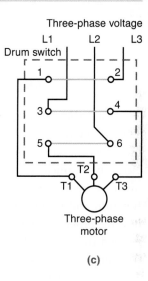

(a)   (b)   (c)

Rehg and Sartori, Industrial Electronics, 1st edition. © 2006, reprinted by permission of Pearson Education, Inc., Upper Saddle River, NJ.

how a drum switch can be used to operate a three-phase motor in a rotational switching application. Note that a three-phase motor must have any two of the three-phase input lines switched to reverse the direction of rotation of the motor. The three-phase motor and input voltages are wired to the switch, as illustrated in Figure 11-2(a). When the switch handle is in the forward position, the switch makes the connections illustrated in Figure 11-2(b) as follows: L1 is connected to T1, L2 to T2, and L3 to T3. When the switch is in the reverse position [Figure 11-2(c)] lines L1 and L3 are reversed, so L1 is connected to T3 and L3 is connected to T1.

Another electromechanical sequencing operation is the lighting in a movie theater, where a

motor-driven timing cam typically controls switches that set the theater illumination. This cam-operated sequencer is commonly known as a timer. The lighting sequence is shown in Table 11-1. Note that the four steps in the lighting sequence are as follows:

1. The five banks of lights are on high brightness, H, for the cleaning crew.
2. The five banks of lights are on medium brightness, M, during the pre-show time, allowing patrons to find seats.
3. The five banks of lights are on low brightness, L, for the showing of the previews.
4. The five banks of lights are off for the showing of the movie.

Chapter 11 PLC Sequencer Functions

TABLE 11-1 Lighting sequence for theater illumination.

	Brightness level				
Step	Bank 1	Bank 2	Bank 3	Bank 4	Bank 5
1	H	H	H	H	H
2	M	M	M	M	M
3	L	L	L	L	L
4	Off	Off	Off	Off	Off

TABLE 11-2 Sequencer with seven steps and four outputs.

Step	01	02	03	04
1	0	1	0	0
2	0	0	0	1
3	1	1	0	0
4	1	1	0	1
5	0	1	1	1
6	1	0	1	1
7	1	0	0	0

11-3 BASIC PLC SEQUENCER FUNCTION

The basic *PLC sequencer function* provides the capability to program many steps and provide multiple outputs. Table 11-2 illustrates an output sequencer function that has seven steps and four outputs. Note that the steps are labeled 1 through 7, with each step having a specific pattern. For example, step 3's pattern is 1100. The outputs are labeled O1, O2, O3, and O4, and an output is on when a 1 is in its column and off when a 0 is in its column. The sequencer steps through the seven patterns, turning on the outputs as dictated by the pattern. Other sequencers change the output sequence bit pattern after comparing an input word with bit patterns stored in sequencer registers. Several types of sequencer instructions are discussed in the following sections.

11-4 ALLEN-BRADLEY SEQUENCER INSTRUCTIONS

The Allen-Bradley PLCs provide a group of sequencer instructions that can be used individually or in pairs. The operation of these instructions and specific PLC applications are addressed in the subsequent subsections. The instructions are as follows:

- Sequencer output (SQO): an output instruction that uses a file or an array to control various output devices (PLC 5, SLC 500, and ControlLogix).
- Sequencer input (SQI): an input instruction that compares bits from an input file or array to corresponding bits from a source address.

The instruction is true if all pairs of bits are the same (PLC 5 and ControlLogix).

- Sequencer compare (SQC): an output instruction that compares bits from an input source file to corresponding bits from data words in a sequence file. If all pairs of bits are the same, then a bit in the control register is set to 1 (PLC 5 and SLC 500).
- Sequencer load (SQL): an output instruction that functions like a word-to-file or file-to-file transfer (PLC 5, SLC 500, and ControlLogix).

11-4-1 PLC 5 and SLC 500 SQO and SQC Sequencer Instruction Structure

The SQO and SQC instructions are shown in Figure 11-3; the terms *file*, *mask*, *control*, *length*, and *position* are used in all instructions. The terms *destination* and *source* are used in SQO and SQC sequencers, respectively. These parameters used in sequencer instructions are defined as follows:

- File: is the starting address for the registers in the sequencer file, and you must use the indexed file indicator (#) for this address.
- Mask: is the code or bit pattern through which the sequencer instruction moves source data to the destination address. In the mask bit pattern, a 1 bit passes values (1 or 0) from source to destination and a 0 mask bit inhibits the data flow and puts a 0 in the bit location in the destination. Use a mask register or file name if you want to change the mask pattern under program control. Place an *h* behind the parameter to indicate that the mask is *hexadecimal* number notation or a *B* to indicate *binary* notation. *Decimal* notation is entered without any indicator.

FIGURE 11-3: Sequencer parameters for SLC 500.

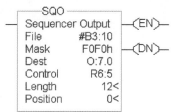

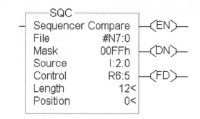

- Source: is the address of the input word or file for an SQC from which the instruction obtains data for comparison to its sequencer file.
- Destination: is the address of the output word or file for an SQO to which the instruction moves data from its sequencer file.
- Control: is the address that contains parameters with control information for the instruction and discrete outputs to indicate sequencer instruction results and status. The general control register file is described in Chapter 10 in Table 10-1 and 10-2. Review that information if necessary.

The control file address is in the control area R of processor memory and the default file is 6. The first of three control words have status bits including:

- Bit 8: the *found bit* (FD) is only used for the SQC instruction. When the status of all non-masked bits in the source address match those of the corresponding reference file word, the FD bit is set. This bit is assessed each scan of the SQC instruction while the rung is true.
- Bit 11: the *error bit* (ER) indicates a negative position value or a negative or zero length value.
- Bit 13: the *done bit* (DN) is set by the SQO or SQC instruction after it has operated on the last word in the sequencer file. It is reset on the next false to true rung transition after the rung goes false.
- Bit 15: *the enable bit* (EN) is true when the rung goes from false to true and is used to indicate that the SQO or SQC instruction is enabled or active.
- Note in Figure 11-3 that the control bits present for each sequencer instruction are shown on the right side of the instruction

box. If they are true the bit initials are highlighted.
- Length: is the number of steps of the sequencer file starting at position 1. Since the file parameter starts at position 0, the number of words in the file is length plus one.
- Position: is the word location or step in the sequencer file from/to which the instruction moves data. The position pointer is incremented by 1 before action is taken by the sequencer instructions. Therefore, if the pointer is at 0, then after the first false to true transition of the sequencer rung the pointer is a 1 and points at the first word in the sequencer file. A position value that points past the end of the programmed file causes a runtime major error.

11-4-2   PLC 5 and SLC 500 SQO Instruction Operation

The *SQO instruction* is available in all Allen-Bradley PLCs, and the operation in the PLC 5 and SLC 500 processors is the same. The operation of the SQO during the first scan is different from the operation for all subsequent scans.

SQO Instruction Operation during the First Scan. When the processor is first changed from the program to the run mode, the operation of the SQO instruction is dependent upon the condition of the rung (true or false) at the time of the first scan. The two conditions are:

- If the rung is *true* at the time of the first scan and the position parameter is 0, then the data in the memory location at position 0 is transferred through the mask to the destination register and the position pointer is incremented by 1.

- If the rung is *false* at the time of the first scan and the position parameter is 0, then the data in the memory location at position 0 is NOT transferred to the destination register and the position pointer is NOT incremented.

SQO Instruction Operation after the First Scan. After completion of the first scan, the SQO instruction operates as follows:

- When the rung has a false to true transition the position pointer is incremented by 1 and the data in the memory location at the new position is moved through the mask to the destination file.
- If the position memory location data changes while the rung is true, the SQO continues to update the destination file on every scan.
- When the rung goes false the output is no longer updated, and the SQO instruction waits for the next false to true rung transition.

After the first scan, every time the SQO rung is true the instruction increments the position number by 1 and moves the sequencer file for that position number through a mask to the destination file. Bits passing through a 1 in the mask are placed in the destination register (these are the *unmasked* bits) and those encountering a 0 in the mask are blocked (these are the *masked* bits). For example, the first time the input logic is true after a false first scan, the SQO instruction increments the position pointer from 0 to 1 and moves the data word from the first position in the file through the mask to the destination. On each subsequent true logic condition, data is moved from the second position, from the third position, and so forth until all word locations of the file have been moved to the destination location. When the position parameter reaches the value in the length parameter (all words have been moved), the done bit in the control register is set. On the next false to true transition of the rung with the done bit set, the position pointer is reset to 1. A simple illustration of how the SQO moves data from the file to the destination is illustrated in Figure 11-4 for the SLC 500. Figure 11-4(a) depicts the sequencer

FIGURE 11-4: Sequencer moving data from a file to an output.

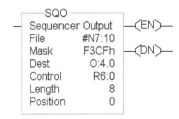

(a) Sequencer instruction for SLC 500

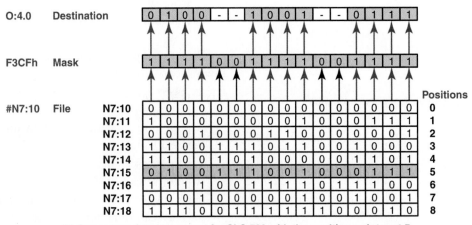

(b) Sequencer data movement for SLC 500 with the position pointer at 5

instruction where the file address is #N7:10, the mask is F3CFh, the destination is O:4.0, the length is 8, and the starting position is 0. Note that the length parameter indicates the file length starting with the data in position 1.

Figure 11-4(b) illustrates how the data flows when the sequencer file executes. Note that the data in position 5, which is file N7:15, moves through the mask to the destination location, O:4.0. The arrows in the figure indicate the unmasked bits that are passed through the mask and into the destination location. The dashes in the bits of the destination register indicate that those bits remain unchanged in the destination location during the sequencing. In many applications, timed pulses are used to automatically increment the sequencer through the positions in the file.

11-4-3 ControlLogix SQO Sequencer Instruction

The operation of the ControlLogix SQO instruction, shown in Figure 11-5, is similar to the PLC 5 and SLC 500 description. The operation dur-

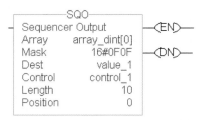

FIGURE 11-5: Sequencer SQO instruction for the ControlLogix PLC.

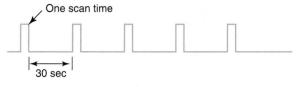

FIGURE 11-6: Pulses used to control SQO instruction.

One scan time

30 sec

(a) Constant duty cycle pulse sequence

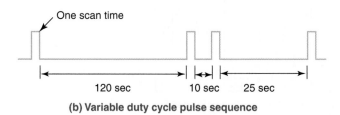

One scan time

120 sec   10 sec   25 sec

(b) Variable duty cycle pulse sequence

ing the first scan and for all subsequent scans is the same as that described in the previous section for the PLC 5 and SLC 500. Therefore, when this SQO instruction is enabled the first time after a false first scan, it first increments the position value from 0 to 1, passes the data from the File tag array_dint[1] through the mask 16#0F0F, and stores the result in the destination tag called value_1. Notice that the ControlLogix processor puts the radix and the # in front of the value to indicate the radix of the displayed number. The Control tag is control_1, the length is 10 (array_dint[1] to array_dint[10]), and the starting position value starts at 0. When the pointer reaches the value in the length parameter, the done bit in the control file is set. The first false to true transition of the rung after the done bit is set causes the position parameter to reset to 1 for the next sequence through the file array. Note that a tag is used for the destination location in place of the memory file parameter used in the PLC 5 and SLC 500 PLCs. Also, a one-dimensional array is used to hold the output word sequence in place of an integer memory file with the indexed mode (#) symbol. The array parameter tag is entered with a zero index, for example, array_dint[0]. The array index is set by the value in the position parameter.

Standard Ladder Logic for Time- and Event-Driven SQO Instructions. The SQO instructions are often used to force a sequential machine to move through a series of steps. The SQO instruction can be stepped to the next sequencer word by two types of triggers:

* A series of *timed pulses*
* A sequence of *external events*

When timed pulses are used, you have the following two options, which are illustrated in Figure 11-6:

* A pulse stream with a constant duty cycle, Figure 11-6(a); for example, pulses that are true for one scan time and false for 30 seconds.
* A pulse stream with a variable duty cycle, Figure 11-6(b); for example, each pulse is true for one scan time, but false for 120 seconds for the first pulse, false for 10 seconds for the

second pulse, and so forth with the off time dictated by the control requirements for the process machine.

The SQO instruction rung is false during the first scan for all timer-driven applications. Therefore, the data in the word in position 0 is not transferred and the position pointer remains at 0 until the first transition from the timer.

When external events are used to trigger the SQO instruction, each external event moves the next sequencer word to the destination file and a different set of outputs are turned on. If a robot is loading parts into a machine, then a sensor in the parts feeder indicating that a part is present would be the event that moves the robot to pick up the part. These events are called "transition conditions" because they indicate a transition from one machine state (certain outputs on) to a new machine state (other outputs on). Again, two options are available for the SQO solution when events are used to load words into the destination register. They are:

1. A machine that has less than four states or sequences with one or two transition conditions to indicate the next state.
2. A machine with numerous states or sequences and/or one with multiple transition conditions to indicate the next state.

The SQO instruction rung is usually false during the first scan for event-driven applications. Therefore, the data in the word in position 0 is not transferred and the position pointer remains at 0 until the first transition from the timer.

The standard ladder logic for the SQO instruction with a fixed duty cycle timer and an instruction with few machine states and transitions are illustrated in Figure 11-7. Standard ladder logic

FIGURE 11-7: Standard ladder logic rungs for SLC 500 SQO instructions.

Application	Standard Ladder Logic Rungs for SQO Instructions

A machine or process with a small number of machine or process states that are active for a fixed time period needs a PLC controller.

The SQO instruction is used with a pulse input pictured in Figure 11-6(a). The standard ladder logic has two rungs. The first has the timer done bit for the input logic and an SQO instruction for the output. The second rung has a regenerative timer with a preset time of 30 seconds and a 1 second time base. The timer is started by a field device with an address of I:1/1 and reset by its done bit. The done bit also increments the SQO instruction to the next output word. The process has three states: state one outputs are on for 90 seconds, state two outputs are on for 60 seconds, and state three outputs are on for 120 seconds. Since the sequencer is incremented every 30 seconds, it takes three words for state one, two words for state two, and four words for state three. This is a total of nine words. The outputs are the same for each group of words associated with a specific state. For example, the first three words are the same since they turn on state one outputs. The next two are the same and the final four are the same. The first word is in N7:21 and the last is in N7:29 so the length is nine and the starting position is 0. Three bits of O:3.0 are used for outputs, bits 0, 6, and 12. So the destination is O:3.0, control is R6:0, and the mask is 001000001000001B or 1041h. Outputs 0 and 12 are on for state 1, 6 for state 2, and all three for state 12. The word values are shown below the ladder logic.

Note: The operation would be the same for PLC 5 and ControlLogix PLCs.

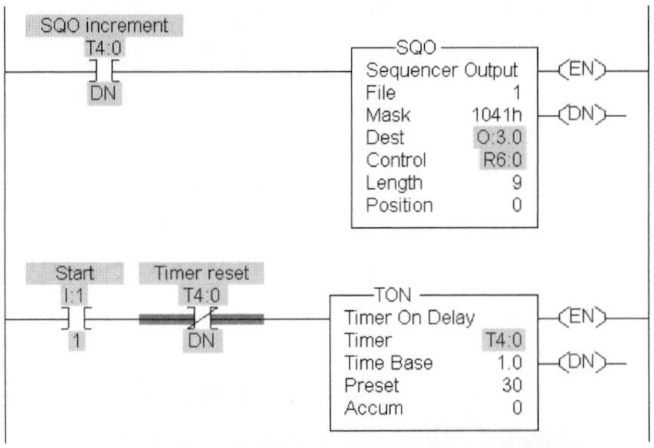

Offset	15	14	13	12	11	10	9	8	7	6	5	4	3	2	1	0
N7:20	0	0	0	0	0	0	0	0	0	0	0	0	0	0	0	0
N7:21	0	0	0	1	0	0	0	0	0	0	0	0	0	0	0	1
N7:22	0	0	0	1	0	0	0	0	0	0	0	0	0	0	0	1
N7:23	0	0	0	1	0	0	0	0	0	0	0	0	0	0	0	1
N7:24	0	0	0	0	0	0	0	0	0	1	0	0	0	0	0	0
N7:25	0	0	0	0	0	0	0	0	0	1	0	0	0	0	0	0
N7:26	0	0	0	1	0	0	0	0	0	1	0	0	0	0	0	1
N7:27	0	0	0	1	0	0	0	0	0	1	0	0	0	0	0	1
N7:28	0	0	0	1	0	0	0	0	0	1	0	0	0	0	0	1
N7:29	0	0	0	1	0	0	0	0	0	1	0	0	0	0	0	1

(a)

FIGURE 11-7: (Continued)

Application	Standard Ladder Logic Rungs for SQO Instructions
A machine or process with a small number of machine or process states and a limited number of unique external event signals needs a PLC controller. The machine has three states with an output word for each state starting at N7:1. The destination is O:3.0, the length is 3, and the starting position is 0. The output bits are 1, 3, 5, 8, and 12 for state one; 2, 3, 9, and 10 for state two; and 3, 4, 5, 8, and 12 for state three. That requires a mask of 0001011100111110B or 173Eh and uses control R6:0. The standard ladder logic has one rung, which consists of an SQO instruction with input ladder logic including the four input field device sensors. The input logic is [(S1 AND S2) OR S3 OR S4] where (S1 AND S2) triggers the state 1 outputs, S3 triggers state two outputs, and S4 triggers state 3 outputs. After state three outputs are moved, the position is equal to the length. When the state one outputs return to a true state, the position resets to 1 and the outputs in N7:1 are moved to the destination. The word values are shown below the ladder logic. Note: SLC 500 rungs are shown, but the operation would be the same for PLC 5 and ControlLogix.	

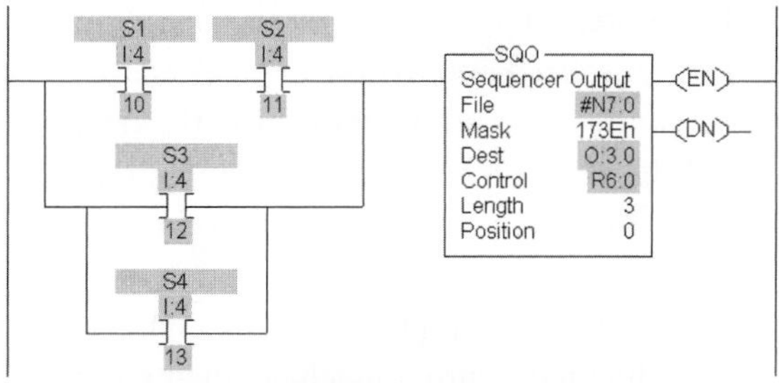

Offset	15	14	13	12	11	10	9	8	7	6	5	4	3	2	1	0
N7:0	0	0	0	0	0	0	0	0	0	0	0	0	0	0	0	0
N7:1	0	0	0	1	0	0	0	1	0	0	1	0	1	0	1	0
N7:2	0	0	0	0	0	1	1	0	0	0	0	0	1	1	0	0
N7:3	0	0	0	1	0	0	0	1	0	0	1	1	1	0	0	0

(b)

for the other two options is provided in the sections that follow. Study the standard ladders and read the descriptions in the figure.

The standard ladder logic for the SQO instructions demonstrates how a timer, Figure 11-7(a), or a set of input transitions conditions, Figure 11-7(b), are used to control a machine with data words stored in consecutive integer files. PLC sequencers are often used to control automatic industrial equipment that operates in a fixed and repeatable timed sequence. The PLC sequencer makes programming these applications much simpler. For example, the off/on operation of 12 lamps can be controlled using a PLC sequencer with one rung of a ladder diagram. By contrast, the equivalent PLC solution regular ladder logic would require 12 rungs (one for each lamp) in the ladder diagram.

When a fixed time base is used, data words are repeated to set the on time required for each output state. In the standard ladder logic example illustrated in Figure 11-7(a), the regenerative timer has a preset of 30 seconds so sequencer words are delivered every 30 seconds. The first, fourth, and sixth data words are repeated (3, 2, and 4 sets of identical words) in order to get the accumulated time required for the outputs in each state. The first state is on for 90 seconds (3 identical output words each on for 30 seconds), the second for 60 seconds, and the third for 120 seconds. Match the mask bits to the desired output bits and notice that every output bit has a 1 in the mask and all other bits are 0. This permits the programmer to use the other output bits for another output requirement without affecting this sequencer rung.

The event-driven sequencer in Figure 11-7(b) uses an *OR* configuration with four transition conditions in the three *OR* paths. Any one of the three paths can make the SQO rung true. So as each event occurs, that OR branch is true and the sequencer is stepped through the three output words to control the machine. S1 AND S2 trigger the word in position 1, S3 triggers the word in position 2, and S4 triggers the word in position 3.

Both of the standard circuits use SLC 500 logic rungs, but the operation would be the same for the PLC 5 and ControlLogix PLCs with the following modifications. The PLC 5 input addressing in Figure 11-7(b) would follow the rack/group/bit format, and the ControlLogix ladder would use arrays and tags in place of memory addresses.

EXAMPLE 11-1

Use a sequencer to control a dishwasher cycle that has the following timed steps in its operation sequence.

1. The pre-rinse timing cycle
2. The soap release
3. The wash timing cycle
4. The post-rinse timing cycle
5. The drying timing cycle

Table 11-3 shows the sequential steps for the dishwasher. Note that the sequence numbers are in the first column, the step numbers are in the second column, and the sequencing patterns are in columns 3 through 7. The sequencing pattern columns are labeled with the dishwasher actions, which are soap, fill, wash, drain, and dry. A 1 in these pattern columns indicates that the dishwasher action is on. Conversely, a 0 in these columns indicates that the dishwasher action is off. For example, in step 6, which is the second step in sequence 3, the wash cycle is on, and all other actions are off. Before continuing, study the table until you're familiar with all the sequences, steps, and patterns.

SOLUTION

The ladder diagram that implements the dishwasher steps is illustrated in Figure 11-8. Note that start and stop switches are located in rung 0, enabling or disabling the dishwasher operation. In the SQO sequencer, the length is 11. The mask is 001F hex (0000 0000 0001 1111 binary), which allows the first five bits from the sequencer file to be passed to the destination location. The timer T4:1 is an on-delay timer that is preset to 30 seconds. The description of the ladder diagram representing the dishwasher operation is as follows:

1. The momentary start switch input I:1/0 is turned on, which activates the start bit, output B3:0/0, thus energizing all the instructions that reference this virtual control relay.
2. The XIC instruction (B3:0/0) seals the start switch and activates the timer rung.

TABLE 11-3 Sequential steps for a dishwasher.

1	2	3	4	5	6	7	
Machine Sequence	Sequencer Step	Soap	Fill	Wash	Drain	Dry	
	0	0	0	0	0	0	N7:10
1	1	0	1	0	0	0	N7:11
1	2	0	0	1	0	0	N7:12
1	3	0	0	0	1	0	N7:13
2	4	1	0	0	0	0	N7:14
3	5	0	1	0	0	0	N7:15
3	6	0	0	1	0	0	N7:16
3	7	0	0	0	1	0	N7:17
4	8	0	1	0	0	0	N7:18
4	9	0	0	1	0	0	N7:19
4	10	0	0	0	1	0	N7:20
5	11	0	0	0	0	1	N7:21

FIGURE 11-8: Ladder diagram for dishwasher example.

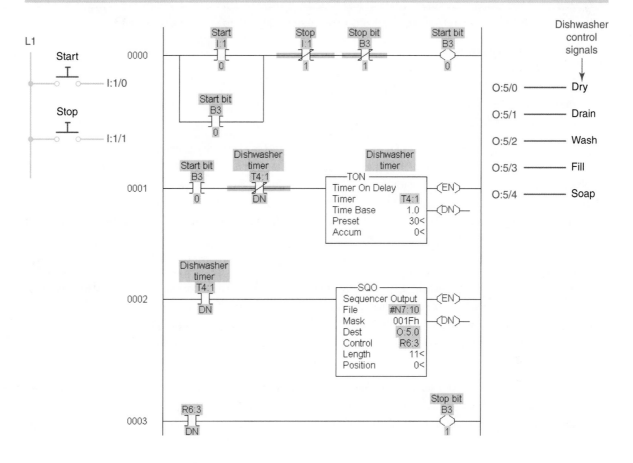

3. After 30 seconds the timer DN bit goes from false to true for one scan, which advances the sequencer from step 0 to step 1. Step 0 is the starting position pointing to file N7:10, step 1 is pointing to N7:11, and step 11 points to N7:21. The first five bits in these 11 files hold the 0 and 1 combinations from columns 3 to 7 in Table 11-3.

4. In step 1 the sequencer moves the word located in N7:11 to O:5.0, the output file to control dishwasher functions.

5. The timer DN bit deactivates the timer, which causes the DN bit to go from true to false, which reactivates the timer after one scan.

6. The previous three operational steps (3, 4, and 5) are repeated for sequencer steps 2 through 11. This moves files N7:12 through N7:21 to the output file (O:5.0) as each sequencer step is executed.

7. When the sequencer reaches step 11, the sequencer's control register (R6:3) done bit (DN) is activated, which activates the stop bit, output B3:0/1, and all instructions with that reference.

8. The binary bit (3:0/1) in rung 0 is true so the X10 instruction is false and the start bit is false, which makes the timer rung false.

9. The ladder is now ready for another activation of the start switch.

Each step in Table 11-3 is incremented every 30 seconds. The same time increment for every step is impractical because some steps in the dishwasher cycle require more than 30 seconds for the task. Assume that the fill and the drain cycles require 60 seconds each; the three wash cycles require 60 seconds, 180 seconds, and 120 seconds, respectively; and the dry cycle requires 240 seconds. Because all the cycle times are multiples of 30 seconds, they can be implemented by increasing the number of steps for each pattern to accommodate the required times. This implementation is shown in Table 11-4 and is loaded into registers N7:11 through N7:43.

TABLE 11-4 Dishwasher steps with non-uniform sequence times.

Machine Sequence	Sequencer Step	Soap	Fill	Wash	Drain	Dry	
	0	0	0	0	0	0	N7:10
1	1	0	1	0	0	0	N7:11
1	2	0	1	0	0	0	N7:12
1	3	0	0	1	0	0	N7:13
1	4	0	0	1	0	0	N7:14
1	5	0	0	0	1	0	N7:15
1	6	0	0	0	1	0	N7:16
2	7	1	0	0	0	0	N7:17
3	8	0	1	0	0	0	N7:18
3	9	0	1	0	0	0	N7:19
3	10	0	0	1	0	0	N7:20
3	11	0	0	1	0	0	N7:21
3	12	0	0	1	0	0	N7:22
3	13	0	0	1	0	0	N7:23
3	14	0	0	1	0	0	N7:24
3	15	0	0	1	0	0	N7:25
3	16	0	0	0	1	0	N7:26
3	17	0	0	0	1	0	N7:27
4	18	0	1	0	0	0	N7:28
4	19	0	1	0	0	0	N7:29
4	20	0	0	1	0	0	N7:30
4	21	0	0	1	0	0	N7:31
4	22	0	0	1	0	0	N7:32
4	23	0	0	1	0	0	N7:33
4	24	0	0	0	1	0	N7:34
4	25	0	0	0	1	0	N7:35
5	26	0	0	0	0	1	N7:36
5	27	0	0	0	0	1	N7:37
5	28	0	0	0	0	1	N7:38
5	29	0	0	0	0	1	N7:39
5	30	0	0	0	0	1	N7:40
5	31	0	0	0	0	1	N7:41
5	32	0	0	0	0	1	N7:42
5	33	0	0	0	0	1	N7:43

Sequence 1 encompasses six sequencer steps, which are two steps for the fill cycle, two steps for the wash cycle, and two steps for the drain cycle. Because each step is 30 seconds, the fill cycle, the wash cycle, and the drain cycle each take the required 60 seconds. The dry cycle encompasses eight steps in sequence 5, which is 240 seconds, the required drying time. Review all the steps in the table until you are confident that you understand the implementation of dishwasher operation with different cycle times.

The ladder logic in Figure 11-8 can be used for this more complete solution to the dishwasher problem by just changing the value of the length parameter in the SQO instruction from 11 to 33. With the data from Table 11-4 loaded into the files N7:11 through N7:43, the new dishwasher times are implemented.

EXAMPLE 11-2

A magazine parts feeder is shown in Figure 11-9. The feeder pushes a cylindrical part from the bottom of the stack to a pickup point for a robot. Three NO sensors are shown: S1 indicates when a part is in the pick up position, S2 indicates that there is a part in the feeder ready to be inserted, and S3 indicates that the push cylinder is retracted. When the start switch is closed, the system operates as follows:

1. The pusher cylinder valve (O:3/0) is turned on so that a part is pushed into the pickup point for the robot. The valve actuates only when the piston is fully retracted (S3 closed), when there is a part in the magazine (S2 closed), and no part is at the pickup point (S1 open). The feeder part pusher holds the part against the stop pins until the robot has acquired the part.
2. The robot input (O:3/1) is turned on when a part is at the pickup point to signal the robot program to acquire the part. The robot has two outputs: I:4/13 Part Acquired and I:4/8 Gripper Clear. The Part Acquired contacts close when the gripper closes on the part and remain closed until the Gripper Clear pulse returns to a false state, and the Gripper Clear pulse occurs when the part is above the pickup point.

Develop a SQO sequencer ladder program that meets this control description.

SOLUTION

The ladder diagram that implements the parts feeder is illustrated in Figure 11-10(a) and the data used in the sequencer is shown in Figure 11-10(b). Position 1 data (valve on) is present at the output when logic path Start AND NOT S1 AND S2 AND S3 is true. Position 2 data (robot pickup signal plus valve on) is present at the output when logic path S1 AND NOT Part Acquired is true. Position 3 data (all outputs off) is present when logic path Gripper Clear is true. The sequencer returns to position 1 when the part pusher returns to the retracted location and the logic path Start AND NOT S1 AND S2 AND S3 are true again.

FIGURE 11-9: Magazine round parts feeder.

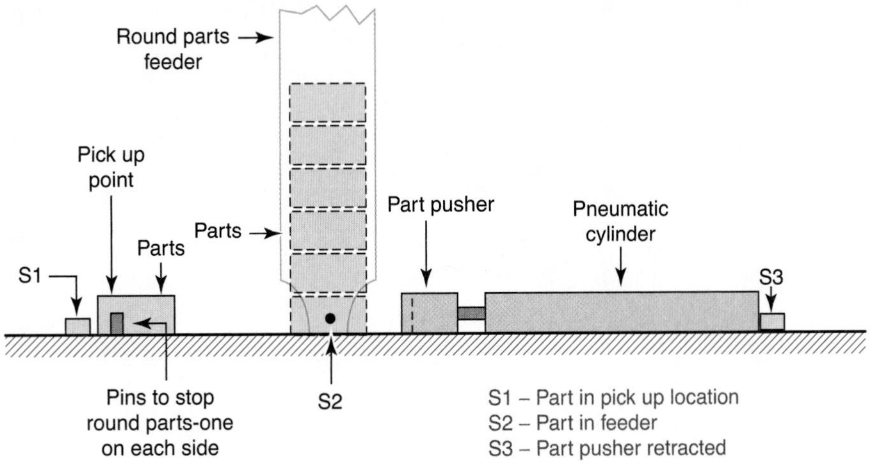

Round parts feeder

Pick up point

Parts

Parts

Part pusher

Pneumatic cylinder

S1

S3

Pins to stop round parts-one on each side

S2

S1 – Part in pick up location
S2 – Part in feeder
S3 – Part pusher retracted

FIGURE 11-10: Ladder diagram for magazine parts feeder.

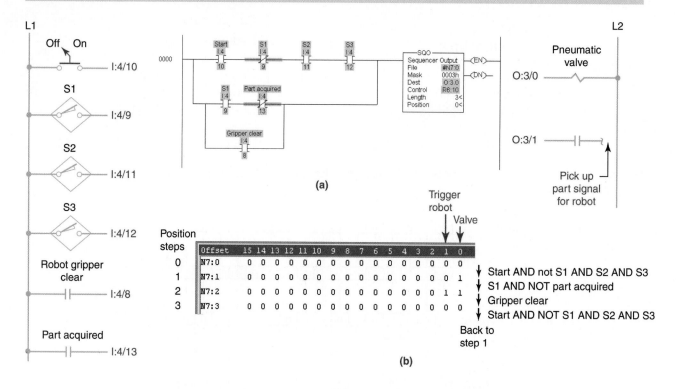

(a)

(b)

11-4-4 PLC 5 and ControlLogix Sequencer Input (SQI) Instruction

The *SQI instruction* is an *input* instruction available in PLC 5 and ControlLogix. The SQI is like an equal comparison instruction but a mask is added, and multiple word combinations can be compared using this instruction. Figure 11-11(a) illustrates this instruction for the PLC 5 and ControlLogix PLCs, and Figure 11-11(b) illustrates its operation using PLC 5 parameters. Note that the location of the *destination* parameter in the SQO instruction just studied (Figures 11-4 and 11-5) is replaced by the *source* parameter in the SQI instruction. The PLC 5 uses file registers and the ControlLogix uses tags and arrays. The source contains the address of the input data word to be compared against the sequencer file words. The initial position value is 0 and the length is the number of files used for the comparisons.

Figure 11-11(b) illustrates how the SQI instruction compares the input data in I:003 through the mask F3CFh with the data in the sequencer file N7:10 through N7:18. The specific data in the sequencer file used in the comparison is identified by the pointer in the position parameter. In Figure 11-11(b), the data at position 5 matches the unmasked input data, so the SQI instruction is true, thus making the rung true and also making any output instruction(s) on the rung true. When the unmasked source bits do not match the sequencer file word, the instruction is false and the rung is also false. In the SLC 500 the SQC performs a similar function that is covered in a later section.

The SQI Control Register. The SQI instruction has a control register like the SQO but eliminates the done bit. The SQI instruction does not automatically increment the position parameter on a false to true transition at its input like the SQO instruction. When the SQI is paired with an SQO instruction with identical control tags, the position pointer is incremented by the SQO instruction for both. If an SQI instruction is used alone, then the position pointer must be changed by other instructions such as an ADD and a MOV instruction in order to select another input. The logic required to use only an SQI instruction is illustrated in Figure 11-12. Note that the SQI instruction can be used to turn on an output when the input word tag, value_1, matches a word in the sequencer array, array_1[0]. The output instruction(s) can be placed in rung 0 with the

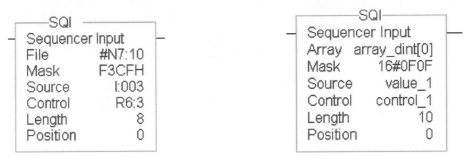

(a) Sequencer instruction for PLC 5 and ControlLogix

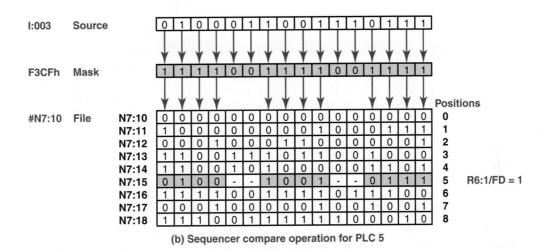

(b) Sequencer compare operation for PLC 5

FIGURE 11-12: Ladder logic for SQI instruction.

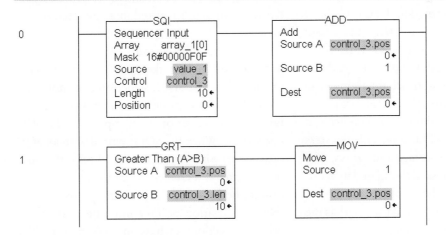

ADD instruction, which adds a 1 to the current pointer, control_3pos. In the next rung, a GRT instruction checks to see if the pointer, control_3pos, is greater than the length, control_3len. If it is, then the pointer is reset to 1 by the output MOV instruction.

Standard Ladder Logic for Paired SQI and SQO Instructions. In the PLC 5 and Control-Logix PLCs, the SQI and SQO instructions can be used in pairs as illustrated for the Control-Logix PLC in the standard ladder logic in Figure 11-13. Note that the control address, length, and

Application	Standard Ladder Logic Rungs for Paired ControlLogix SQI and SQO Instructions
A machine or process that operates in a sequential fashion must execute its operational sequence based on a changing set of discrete input field devices The paired SQI and SQO instruction ladder described in the text is illustrated in this standard ladder logic configuration. There are two versions shown, with the first being an unconditional execution and the second triggered by an external bit. In the unconditional configuration, the SQI tests the masked input word against the array value selected by the position pointer on every scan. The second ladder rung (b) only makes the test when the input instruction before the SQI is true. Parameter requirements include: • The control, length, and position parameters must be the same in both instructions. • The array tag in the array parameter must have the zero element of the array specified as shown in these ladders. • The source and destination parameter must be input and output tags, respectively. • The position parameter is set to zero and the length is the total number of values in the arrays, not counting position zero in the arrays. The instruction pair operates as follows: • The SQI source word, value_in, is passed through the mask and all 1's in the mask pass their respective bits and 0's block the transfer. • If the unmasked SQI source value, value_in, matches the array word, array_SQI, the SQI instruction is true and the rung is active. • If the rung is true, then the SQO increments the position pointer and moves the selected array word, array_SQO, through a mask to the destination location, value_out. • When the position pointer equals the length parameter, the last data file is moved to the output array and the control file done bit is set. • On the next false-to-true transition of the rung with the done bit set, the position pointer returns to position 1. • The control file error bit is set if the position value is negative. Sample array files are illustrated. Note: The operation would be the same for PLC 5.	

position parameters are the same. Also, the index on the sequencer array in the SQI instruction must be set to zero (array_SQI[0]). The array for the SQO must be set to a zero index as well. The inputs for the SQI instruction are in the source tag, value_in, and outputs for the SQO instruction are in the destination tag, value_out.

The operation of the SQO instruction during the first scan depends on the status of its rung during that scan. The standard ladder logic in Figure 11-13 assumes that the SQI instruction makes the rung false for the first scan, so the SQO instruction is false, which causes no action or change in the SQO during the first scan. If the standard ladder

in Figure 11-13(a) is used, then the SQI is forced to a false condition for the first scan by making the number in value_in different from the value of the number in array_SQI[0] when the first scan occurs. If the standard ladder in Figure 11-13(b) is used, then the SQI is forced to a false condition for the first scan by making the start input (XIC instruction) false when the first scan occurs. The start input could be a system start selector switch that is turned on after the PLC program is downloaded. Another option is to set the start input to the first scan status bit (true for first scan only) address and make the instruction an XIO type.

When used in pairs with the same control register parameter, the position pointer of both instructions is changed whenever the position in the SQO instruction is incremented. Restated, when the SQI instruction finds a match between the unmasked bits in the input tag and the SQI array value, the rung becomes true. This causes the SQO to increment the position parameter by 1 and move the value in the SQO array at this index or pointer location to the output tag. Because they share the same control tag name, the pointers of the SQI and SQO instructions are the same, so they work in unison as they step through their array values. This programming technique provides input and output sequencers that function in unison, resulting in the activation of a selected set of outputs when a set of specific inputs is present. The inputs used for control must all be connected to the same input word and the controlled outputs must be in the same output word. Read the description of the SQI and SQO pair in Figure 11-13.

The organization of the array data for the SQI and SQO instructions is illustrated in Figure 11-14(a) and described as follows:

- The input word that represents the input sensors and switches and the desired output words for each input are displayed in the first table in Figure 11-14(a). Note the input bit pattern and the desired output bit pattern.
- The output bit patterns are shown in the second table in Figure 11-14(a) in the order necessary to make the sequencer operate properly. Note that all zeros (0000) are loaded into the 0 element of the array, the last output (1101) is loaded in element 1, and the first output (0111) is loaded into element (2). All other output words are loaded in the array in their sequential order after the first output word.

With the arrays loaded, the operation of the standard ladder logic for the SQI and SQO pair, as shown in Figure 11-14, can be evaluated:

- **First scan:** The standard ladder in Figure 11-13(b) is used with the start input representing the system start selector switch. The switch is off for the download of the program, so during the first scan the SQO rung is false. This keeps the position value at 0 and no word is moved to the destination address.
- **Step 0:** When the start switch is turned on, the all zeros in value_in match the all zeros in the SQI array at position 0, so the rung goes true and the SQO increments the position parameter to 1 and moves the SQO array value of 1101 to the output file.
- **Step 1:** With the position parameter at 1, the value_in is changed to 0110, which matches the position 1 value in the SQI array. This forces the rung true and the SQO increments the position parameter to 2 and moves the SQO array value of 0111 to the output file.
- **Step 2:** With the position parameter at 2, the value_in is changed to 1100, which matches the position 2 value in the SQI array. This forces the rung true and the SQO increments the position parameter to 3 and moves the SQO array value of 1110 to the output file. Now the length

FIGURE 11-14: SQI/SQO array values and matches.

Process input value and desired output value

value_in	value_out
0000	0000
1001	1101
0110	0111
1100	1110

Sequencer array value organization

Position	SQI array array_SQI	value_in	SQO array array_SQO	value_out
0	1001	1001	0000	
1	0110	0110	1101	1101
2	1100	1100	0111	0111
3	1001	1001	1110	1110

(a)

FIGURE 11-14: (Continued).

First scan occurs with the rung false (start switch off). When the rung goes true (start switch on and Value_in equal to 1001) the pointer moves to 1 and moves 1101 into value_out.

Position	SQI array value	value_in	Rung condition	SQO array value	value_out	Operational steps
0	1001	1001	False to True	0000		
1	0110			1101	1101	1
2	1100			0111		
3	1001			1110		

Value_in is changed to 0110 and the sequencer increments to position 2 and moves 0111 to value_out.

Position	SQI array value	value_in	Rung condition	SQO array value	value_out	Operational steps
0	1001			0000		
1	0110	0110	False to True	1101		
2	1100			0111	0111	2
3	1001			1110		

Value_in is changed to 1100 and the sequencer increments to position 3 and moves 1110 to value_out.
With the position and length parameters equal, the done bit is set, and the sequencer position will reset back to 1 with the next false to true change in the rung.

Position	SQI array value	value_in	Rung condition	SQO array value	value_out	Operational steps
0	1001			0000		
1	0110			1101		
2	1100	1100	False to True	0111		
3	1001			1110	1110	3

Value_in is changed to 1001 and the sequencer increments to position 1 and moves 1101 to value_out.

Position	SQI array value	value_in	Rung condition	SQO array value	value_out	Operational steps
0	1001			0000		
1	0110			1101	1101	1
2	1100			0111		
3	1001	1001	False to True	1110		

(b)

and position value are the same, so the done bit in the control register is set to 1.

- Step 3: With the position parameter at 3, the done bit is set to 1 and the value_in is changed to 1001, which matches the position 3 value in the SQI array. This forces the rung true and the SQO does not increment the position parameter but resets it to 1, and the value of the SQO file at the 1 position is moved to the output file.

The sequencer continues to cycle through the outputs as the input values change. Note that the input word pattern that matches the output word pattern is not in the same element number in the SQI and SQO arrays. This is necessary because a match between an SQI input and an element in the SQI array cause the SQO to increment the position parameter *before* selecting the SQI array element to move to the output. As a result, the two arrays are off by one position for every move.

Standard Ladder Logic for Variably Timed SQO Instructions. The standard ladder logic described in Figure 11-7 illustrated how the SQO instructions are used for machines that have timed machine cycle elements. In the previous ladder logic standard and Example 11-1, variation in times among machine cycles was handled by having a constant timer pulse width and using multiple sequencer file words. Review this process and example before you continue.

The standard ladder logic in Figure 11-15 uses two SQO instructions and a TON timer. One is used to move the sequencer output files to the destination address for control of the process, and

FIGURE 11-15: Standard ladder logic rungs for SLC 500 timed SQO instructions.

Application

A machine or process that operates in a sequential fashion must execute its operational sequence based on a set of step times that are not the same.

The machine has three states with an output word for each state stored in memory. The true output bits for each state are 1, 3, 5, 8, and 12 for state one; 2, 3, 9, and 10 for state two; and 3, 4, 5, 8, and 12 for state three. The first state should be on for 100 seconds, the second for 50 seconds, and the third for 112 seconds.

The system requires two SQO instructions: one for the machine outputs (Output SQO) and one for the times at each state (State timer SQO). Both of the SQOs have R6:10 for control, 3 for length, and 0 for position. The other configuration for the SQOs includes:

The Output SQO (b) is:
- The three output words for states 1, 2, and 3 are stored in files N7:1, N7:2, and N7:3 so the file parameter is #N7:0.
- The mask is 0001011100111110B or 173Eh.
- The destination file is O:3.0.

The State timer SQO (c) is:
- The three output word values for the states are 100, 50, and 112 (seconds). They are stored in files N7:11, N7:12, and N7:13 so the file parameter is #N7:10.
- The mask is 00FFh.
- The destination file is T4:1.PRE.

The standard ladder logic (a) has two rungs and operates as follows:
- The regenerative timer cycles the two SQO instructions through their three states. The timer has an output waveform that looks like Figure 11-6(b) with the off time set by the values moved into the timer PRE parameter (T4:1.PRE) by the State timer SQO instruction.
- In position 1 the Output SQO moves the proper true bits through the mask to O:3.0. The timer has 100 seconds loaded into the timer PRE parameter, and state 1 is on for 100 seconds.
- In position 2 the outputs are on for 50 seconds. Output SQO moves the output bits and State timer SQO loads the correct on time to T4:1. Position 3 works in a similar fashion.

The output and timer data tables are shown below the ladder. SLC 500 rungs are shown, but the operation would be the same for PLC 5 and ControlLogix.

Standard Ladder Logic Rungs for SLC 500 Timed SQO Instructions

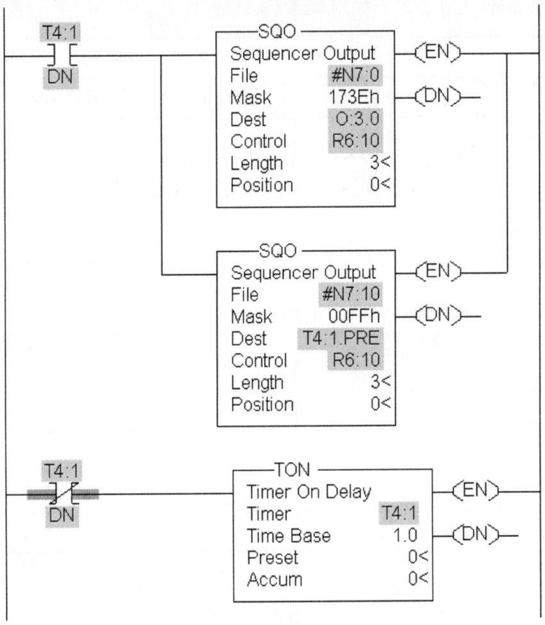

(a)

N7:0	0	0	0	0	0	0	0	0	0	0	0	0	0	0	0	0
N7:1	0	0	0	1	0	0	0	1	0	0	1	0	1	0	1	0
N7:2	0	0	0	0	0	1	1	0	0	0	0	0	1	1	0	0
N7:3	0	0	0	1	0	0	0	1	0	0	1	1	1	0	0	0

(b)

N7:10	0	100	50	112

(c)

the second is used to move the required time for that machine cycle to the timer preset location. The ladder logic in Figure 11-15 serves both as a standard and as an example of how this type of control is accomplished. Read the description for the application in Figure 11-15.

The timer is a regenerative TON instruction with a done bit that is true for one scan time and false for the time value placed into the preset parameter. Every time the timer done bit is true, the position pointers on both of the SQO instructions increment to the next location. The timer preset value SQO moves the next timer preset value to T4:0.PRE and output SQO moves the next combination of true output bits to the destination, O:3.0. The outputs remain active for the preset time moved into the timer. After the values for the three position steps are moved to the output, the position parameter is reset to 1 and the process repeats.

EXAMPLE 11-3

Develop ladder logic to control traffic lights for north/south and east/west lanes at an intersection using SQO instructions. The east/west red light time should be 25 seconds, the north/south red light time should be 35 seconds, and the yellow should be on for 5 seconds for all directions. The green plus yellow times must correspond to the red time values.

SOLUTION

The ladder and timing diagrams for the traffic light controller are illustrated in Figure 11-16(a), the sequencer output file is shown in Figure 11-16(b), and the timer preset file is shown in Figure 11-16(c). A start switch is added for control. Note that

FIGURE 11-16: Ladder solution for Example 11-3.

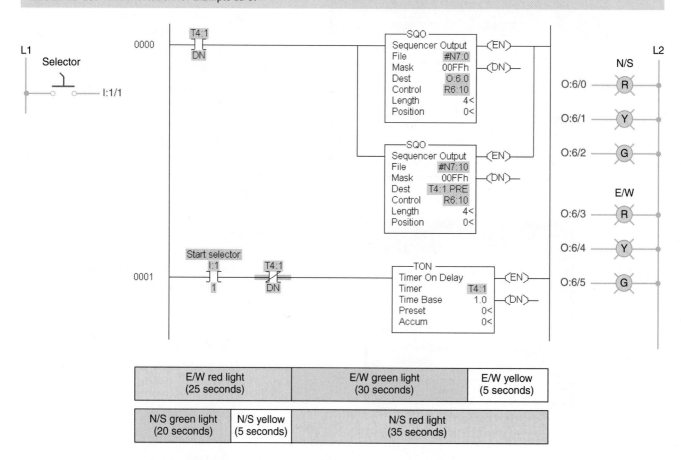

(a) Ladder and timing diagram for intersection traffic light

the position, length, and control on both SQO instructions are the same. The sequencer files and output destination files are different, so the SQOs operate in parallel but with different data and different target destinations.

Start with the position parameter at 0 and let the timer done bit become active for the first time. The position parameter is incremented to 1 and data at that location in both sequencer files is moved to the destination address. Output bits 0 and 5 are turned on for 0:6.0, and the 30-second value is moved to the timer preset, T4:1.PRE. The timer restarts with a 30-second delay, which keeps output bit 0 (N/S red) and bit 5 (E/W green) on for 30 seconds. When the done bit occurs after the 30 seconds, the sequencers move to position 2. The timer preset is changed to 5 seconds, and the data word here keeps the N/S red light on again (0:6.0 bit 0), while the E/W light changes to the yellow light (0:6.0 bit 4). Each time the timer done bit is true, the next data words (timer preset value and output bit on combination) are moved to the destination addresses. When the position parameter equals the length parameter, the position parameter returns to 1 on the next execution of the timer. This sequence continues until the start switch is false.

FIGURE 11-16: (Continued).

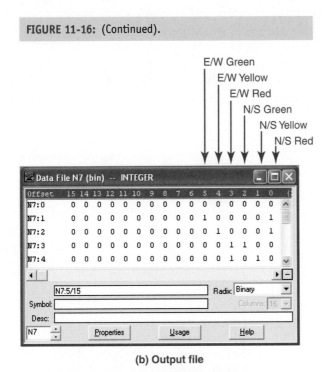

(b) Output file

(c) Timer preset file

11-4-5 Sequencer Compare (SQC) Instruction

Figure 11-17 illustrates the SLC 500 *SQC instruction*, which is similar to the PLC 5 and ControlLogix SQI instruction. The instruction parameters are the same as those used for the SQI instruction, but the differences between the two instructions include:

- The SQC is an output instruction in the SLC 500, whereas the SQI is an input instruction in the other two PLCs.
- Unlike the SQI instruction, the SQC instruction increments the position parameter when its input sees a false to true transition.
- The SQC instruction has an additional status bit—the *found bit* (FD). When the source pattern matches the sequencer file word pattern, the FD bit is a 1. It is a 0 under all other conditions.

The SQC instruction can be used as a diagnostic tool to determine if a machine has the correct switch/signal bit values in a register to start a production run. The control file found bit (FD) is

FIGURE 11-17: Sequencer SQC instruction for SLC 500.

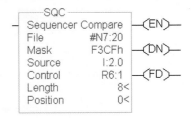

used to activate an indicator to let an operator know that the machine is ready for production.

The SQO and SQC instructions are also used as a pair, as illustrated in the standard ladder logic in Figure 11-18. This is similar to the SQO and the SQI pair for the PLC 5 and ControlLogix PLCs. In this case the FD bit in the control word is used to make sure that the pair of instructions increment in unison. In other words, if input I:2 matches the SQC file word, then the SQC instruction sets the FD bit, which in turn enables the SQO function. Read the description of the operation in Figure 11-18.

11-4-6   Sequencer Load (SQL) Instruction

The *SQL instruction* transfers data from a source address into a sequencer file on every false to true transition of the SQL instruction rung. It's a word-to-file transfer without a mask and is illustrated in Figure 11-19. With a length of 8, the 8 values or bit patterns of source I:4.0 are moved into file #N7:11 to #N7:18. In the figure, the SQL is at position 4 so the 4th value of the input bit pattern is being moved into file #N7:14 (see highlight). On each false to true transition at its input, the SQL instruction posi-

tion is incremented by 1. When the instruction has reached position 8, the length value, the DN bit is set. On the next false to true transition, the instruction recycles to position 1 and the value of input I:4.0 is moved into that location. The SQL instruction loads data into position 0 only if the instruction was true during the first PLC scan.

The most common application for the SQL instruction is for loading data registers for the SQC and SQI instructions. Loading a large number of input conditions for a large number of machine steps is tedious and prone to errors. The robot in Figure 11-20 is a good example. Note that each axis and the gripper have a sensor at the extremes of travel. Ladder logic using the SQL instruction could read the outputs of every sensor and move the sensor bit patterns into a contiguous set of sequencer word files. The procedure includes manually moving the robot to the home position and pressing a push button to make the SQL instruction true. With all the sensor outputs connected to the same input word, the SQL ladder logic moves the value of all sensors to an integer register. Next, the robot arm is moved to the first position and the sensor values are loaded. This

FIGURE 11-18: Standard ladder logic rungs for SLC 500 SQC and SQO instruction pairs.

Application	Standard Ladder Logic Rungs for SLC 500 SQC and SQO Instruction Pairs
A machine or process that operates in a sequential fashion must execute its operational sequence based on a set of discrete input conditions using an SLC 500 PLC. The SLC 500 does not have an SQI instruction like that found on the PLC 5 and ControlLogix. The sequencer compare, SQC, instruction performs the same function as the SQI but is an output instruction. The SQC can be paired with an SQO so that input words are used to send selected output words to the output destination address. Since both the SQC and SQI are output instructions, the SQC has a control bit, called Found (FD), that is used to link the two instructions. Ladder logic linking the two instructions using the found bit is illustrated on the right. Note that both instructions have the same control register, length, and position values. The input logic on both instructions is the NOT found bit. When the words in I:2.0 are the same as the 8 register words in N7:21 to N7:28, the found bit is true and the SQO instruction outputs the corresponding output words from N7:11 to N7:18 to the destination file.	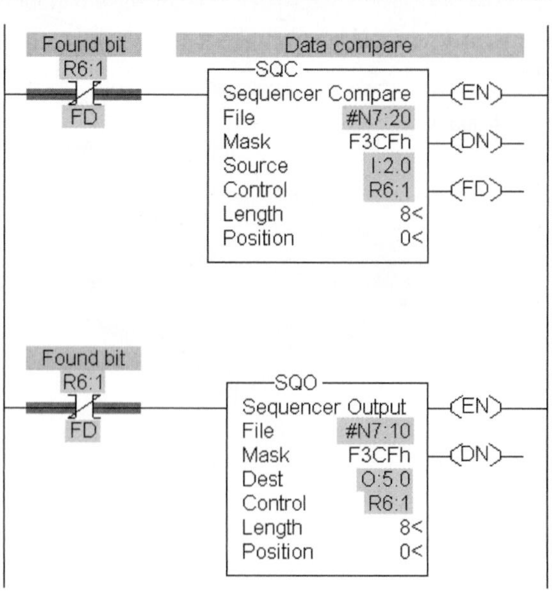

FIGURE 11-19: Sequencer load (SQL) instruction.

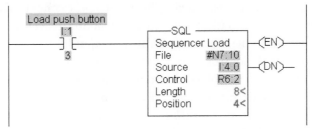

(a) Sequencer instruction

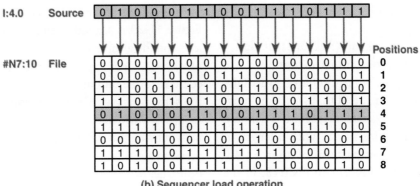

(b) Sequencer load operation

FIGURE 11-20: Two-axis robot part loader.

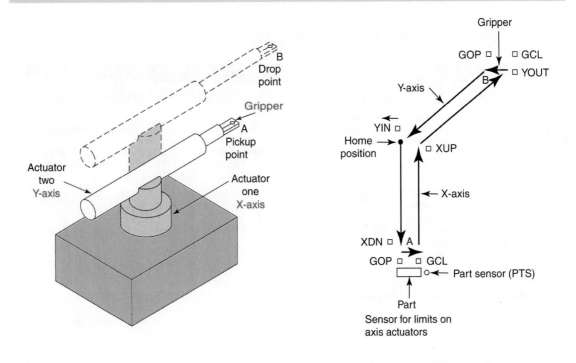

continues for every position in a complete robot motion cycle. The result is a complete sequencer file for use in an SQI/SQO pair or an SQC/SQO pair.

11-5 CASCADING SEQUENCERS

The technique of *cascading*, or *chaining* as it's called in some literature, provides a greater number of output bits than a single sequencer can provide with 16-bit words. Figure 11-21 depicts two 16-bit output sequencers, which are chained to achieve a 20-bit output. Figure 11-21(a) illustrates the pattern output for each step. Note that all 16 output bits of the top SQO are active and only 4 bits of the lower SQO are active, with the other 12 bits (bits 5 through 16) always zero. The active bits provide a 20-bit output. For example, the 20-bit output pattern for step 3 is 00110001001100001010. Figure 11-21(b) shows the ladder diagram of the two sequencers that

share the same control, length, and mask. Because the sequencers have common control, length, and mask parameters, they are always on the same step and sequence together through the 15 patterns. However, the destination files are chained by using consecutive output files O:5.0 and O:6.0. The mask in the second sequencer could be 000Fh since only the first four bits are used.

11-6 EMPIRICAL DESIGN PROCESS WITH SEQUENCER INSTRUCTIONS

The empirical design process, introduced in Section 3-11-4, is an organized approach to the design of PLC ladder logic programs. However, the term *empirical* implies that some degree of trial and error is present. In some chapters the instructions covered required numerous rungs. As a result of these more complex solutions more fixes and adjustments were necessary as the programs were

---

FIGURE 11-21: Cascaded sequencers.

Step	Lower SQO				Top SQO			
	Bits 16 - 13	Bits 12 - 9	Bits 8 - 5	Bits 4 - 1	Bits 16 - 13	Bits 12 - 9	Bits 8 - 5	Bits 4 - 1
1	0000	0000	0000	1101	0001	0010	1000	1000
2	0000	0000	0000	1000	0001	1000	0001	0011
3	0000	0000	0000	0011	0001	0011	0000	1010
4	0000	0000	0000	1010	1111	1010	0011	1000

Note: Only 4 of the 15 steps are shown.

(a) Cascaded sequencers pattern output

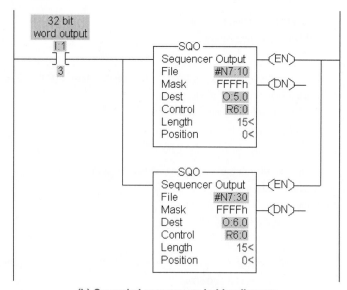

(b) Cascaded sequencers ladder diagram

debugged. However, the instructions added in this chapter use few rungs, so if the word data files are set up properly, the instruction parameters are selected properly, and the large amounts of data are entered correctly, then these rungs should require a minimum of change during initial tests.

11-6-1 Adding Sequential Instructions to the Process

The first step in using sequencer instructions is to know which instructions to use and in what combinations. The instructions available for the SLC 500 are SQO, SQC, and SQL; for the PLC 5 and ControlLogix they are SQO, SQI, and SQL. They operate the same in each PLC model except for the variable naming and memory iden-

tification differences mentioned frequently between the ControlLogix and the SLC 500 and PLC 5 processors. The guidelines in Table 11-5 can be used to identify the sequencer solution for a sequential process where the machine has a sequence of steps or states that are executed in order during every machine cycle.

In all the control requirements where an SQO instruction is used, the discrete control outputs are stored in a sequence of words. The PLC 5 and SLC 500 use integer or bit type memory registers and the ControlLogix uses arrays. Therefore, the deciding factor on which configuration to choose is based on the type of input used to trigger the move through the output data.

TABLE 11-5 Sequencer instructions for control requirements.

Processor/Sequencer Instructions	Control Requirements	Standard Ladder Logic Solution
All processors SQO	Each step or state in the sequence is active for a fixed time period.	(a) Standard logic in Figure 11-7(a) or in Figure 11-15 can be used for this requirement. If there are a small number of machine states and several have the same time, then the solution in Figure 11-7(a) can be used. If there are many machine states and the times for each vary widely, then the solution in Figure 11-15 is used. In general, the solution in Figure 11-15 is used for all timer-based sequencers.
All processors SQO	The sequencer input is driven by a small set of steps or states that are triggered from a set of external events.	(b) Use the standard logic in Figure 11-7(b).
SLC 500 SQC and SQO	Each sequencer output condition is triggered by a set of input bits from external field devices or other type of source register.	(c) Use the standard logic in Figure 11-18.
PLC 5 and ControlLogix SQI and SQO	Each sequencer output condition is triggered by a set of input bits from external field devices or other type of source register.	(d) Use the standard logic in Figure 11-12.
All processors SQL	Load a word date file with input field device bit patterns.	(e) Use the standard logic in Figure 11-19.

Determine the combination of sequencer instructions for all three processors that are required for programming the following automation situations.

1. The robot in Figure 11-20 when the robot does not have end-of-travel sensors on the actuators, and the times for each movement are 2 seconds for the gripper and 2 seconds for each linear actuator movement.
2. The robot in Figure 11-20 when sensors are present at the end of travel for each actuator and for the gripper.
3. The tank control problems in Figures 1-17 and 1-20(b).
4. The process rinse cycle in Figure 7-21.
5. A process that has seven states or steps with eight outputs per state. The states must be on or active for the following times in seconds: 33, 150, 3, 45, 67, 300, and 1 for states 1 through 7, respectively.
6. The robot in Figure 11-20 needs the SQC or SQI sequencer file or array loaded with input data for each machine state.

SOLUTION

The automation problems require the following solutions.

1. Use the solution in Table 11-5(a) with the standard solution from Figure 11-7(a).
2. Use the solution in Table 11-5(c) and (d), depending on the type of processor present.
3. Use the solution in Table 11-5(b) with the standard solution from Figure 11-7(b).
4. Use the solution in Table 11-5(c) and (d), depending on the type of processor present.
5. Use the solution in Table 11-5(a) with the standard solution from Figure 11-15.
6. Use the solution in Table 11-5(e).

11-7 TROUBLESHOOTING SEQUENCER INSTRUCTIONS

The major causes of problems with sequencer ladder rungs are incorrect data in the sequencer data files and arrays and improper entry of parameter values in the instructions. If a sequencer does not operate properly, use the following guidelines when troubleshooting the sequencer rungs.

- Verify all the data in the sequencer file(s).
- Verify the instruction parameters, especially the length value. In applications where the sequencer instruction is false during the first PLC scan, the 0 position is not included in the length value.
- If an SQO instruction is used with a timed input, then replace the timed input with a manual switch or forced input instruction to manually step through the sequencer file while all the sequencer outputs and machine actions are verified.

- If an SQC or SQI instruction is used to drive an SQO instruction, then add an input to force the SQO instruction to manually step through the sequencer file while all the machine inputs, sequencer outputs, and machine actions are verified.
- This guideline could be listed in the empirical design areas as well. When troubleshooting a sequencer problem with a large database having many elements, start with just a small data set. For example, if you can make the ladder operate with just a few machine inputs and sequencer outputs, then you can easily expand it for the larger data set.

11-8 LOCATION OF THE INSTRUCTIONS

The location of instructions from this chapter in the Allen-Bradley programming software is indicated in Figure 11-22.

FIGURE 11-22: Location of instructions described in this chapter.

Systems	Instructions	Location
PLC 5	SQI, SQO, SQL	
SLC 500	SQC, SQO, SQL	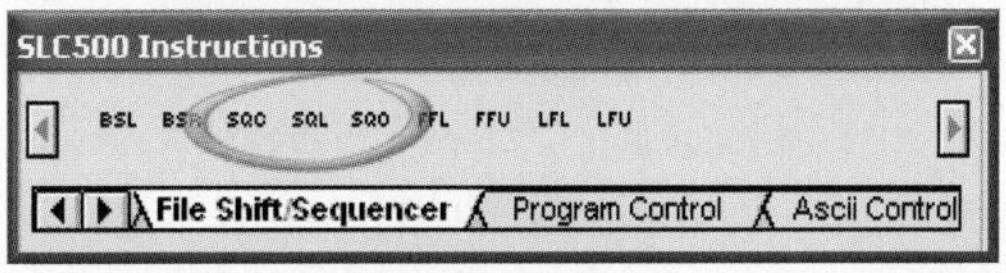
LOGIX	SQC, SQO, SQL	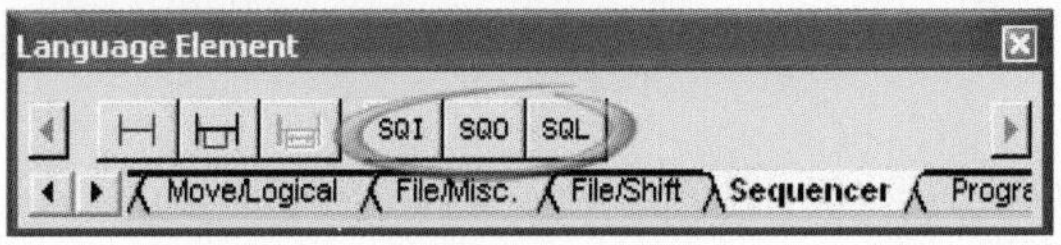

CHAPTER 12

Analog Sensors and Control Systems

12-1 GOALS AND OBJECTIVES

There are three principal goals of this chapter. The first goal is to provide the student with an introduction to the operation and function of analog sensors. The second goal is to describe the analog I/O modules and their operation for the Allen-Bradley PLC 5, SLC 500, and Logix systems. The third goal is to provide the basics of the closed-loop control system operation, including system attributes and PLC applications.

After completing this chapter you should be able to:

- Describe the operation and function of analog devices such as temperature, pressure, flow, and position sensors.
- Name and describe the components of a vision system and describe the operation.
- Select the appropriate type of vision and illumination system given the parameters for a sensing application.
- Describe the analog I/O modules for the Allen-Bradley PLC 5, SLC 500, and Logix systems.
- Explain the generalized closed-loop block diagram, and state the purpose of each of the blocks.

- State the characteristics that differentiate between an effective and an ineffective control system.
- List the general closed-loop control modes and explain how each acts to correct the system error.
- Describe PLC proportional closed-loop process control.

12-2 ANALOG SENSORS

Analog sensors, in contrast to discrete sensors, measure a range of input conditions and generate a range of output values. In analog temperature measurement, for example, the analog sensor typically produces an output that varies from 1 to 5 volts or 4 to 20 milliamperes when exposed to a temperature range of 08 to 1008 Celsius. Most sensors have a direct and linear relationship between the input condition and the output response. However, some sensors have inverse input and output relationships and others produce a nonlinear output from a linear change in the input. Analog sensors measure the common process parameters such as temperature, pressure, flow, level and position. These sensors and vision systems are discussed in the following subsections.

12-2-1 Temperature Sensors

Temperature sensors are classified based on their output as follows:

- **Resistance as a function of temperature:** resistance temperature detectors and thermistors
- **Voltage as a function of temperature:** thermocouples and solid-state temperature sensors

A *resistance temperature detector* (RTD) is a temperature-sensing device that detects a change in the resistance of a metal as a function of temperature. The most common metals used in RTDs are listed in Table 12-1 along with their temperature range and their resistance coefficient. Note that platinum has the widest temperature range and lowest coefficient of resistance. This large temperature range makes it the most popular metal for RTDs.

The resistance coefficient is the amount of resistance change for each degree of temperature change. The RTD's change in resistance must be converted to a change in voltage or current so it can be usable. Figure 12-1 depicts a two-terminal RTD in a bridge circuit and a differential amplifier connected to points X and Y of the bridge. Note that the RTD is represented as the variable resistor R_T. If the resistance of the RTD is at room temperature, the potential difference at the bridge output is zero volts, and the differential amplifier output is zero volts. If the temperature of the RTD changes, the resistance changes and the bridge is no longer balanced, producing a potential difference across the bridge at X and Y and causing an output voltage on the differential amplifier. In addition to the two-terminal RTD as depicted in the bridge circuit, three-terminal and four-terminal RTDs are available and used in applications that require high accuracy.

Thermistors are electronic components that exhibit a large change in resistance with a change in the device temperature. The symbol for a thermistor is the same as for an RTD, the variable resistor symbol. The word thermistor is a contraction of the words thermal resistor. Depending on the type selected, thermistors have either a negative temperature coefficient (NTC) or positive temperature coefficient (PTC) of resistance. NTC thermistors exhibit decreasing electrical resistance with increases in environmental temperature and

TABLE 12-1 Common materials used in RTDs.

RTD Material	Temperature Range In °C	Resistance Coefficient In Ohms/°C
Copper	−151 to +149	0.0042
Nickel	−73 to +149	0.0067
Platinum	−184 to +815	0.0039
Tungsten	−73 to +276	0.0045

FIGURE 12-1: Bridge circuit with two-terminal RTD.

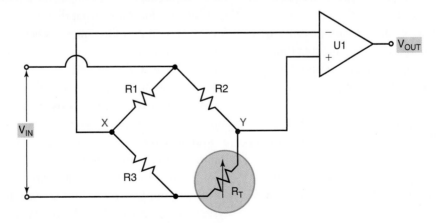

Rehg and Sartori, Industrial Electronics, 1st Edition, © 2006, Reprinted by permission of Pearson Education, Inc., Upper Saddle River, NJ.

increasing electrical resistance with decreases in environmental temperature, and PTC thermistors exhibit increasing electrical resistance with increases in environmental temperature and decreasing electrical resistance with decreases in environmental temperature. Figure 12-2 illustrates the resistance-temperature graph of both the NTC and PTC thermistors.

Thermocouples are temperature-sensing devices that produce a small voltage in the millivolt range as a function of temperature. Thermocouples are constructed using two dissimilar metal wires, which are listed in Table 12-2 along with the applicable temperature range and an assigned letter designating the thermocouple type.

The operation of the thermocouple can be traced to a discovery made by Thomas Seebeck in the early 1800s known as the Seebeck effect. The discovery was that if two wires made from dissimilar metals are connected at both ends, making two junctions, then when one end is heated a small amount of current will flow through the wires. Figure 12-3(a) illustrates the Seebeck effect. Figure 12-3(b) shows a voltmeter replacing one of the junctions where the millivolt level voltage is proportional to the amount of heat at the remaining junction.

With the hookup as in Figure 12-3(b), the connection between the thermocouple wire and the voltage lead forms another junction of dissimilar metals; thus a small voltage is produced, which is opposite to the voltage produced by the thermocouple junction, causing an erroneous

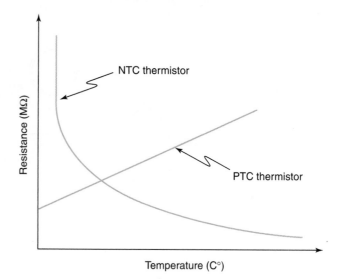

FIGURE 12-2: Resistance-temperature curves for thermistors.

Rehg and Sartori, Industrial Electronics, *1st Edition, © 2006, Reprinted by permission of Pearson Education, Inc, Upper Saddle River, NJ.*

voltage reading. However, if this newly created junction, called the *reference junction*, is at zero volts, then the voltmeter will read the correct voltage. In the late 1800s the reference junction was called the *cold junction* because it was immersed in an ice bath, which held the temperature to 0° Celsius, thereby holding the voltage to zero volts. Rather than the ice bath, a more convenient technique called a *reference* block, which is shown in Figure 12-4, uses junction temperature compensation to keep the block at a predetermined temperature. The extension wires in the

TABLE 12-2 Thermocouple materials.

Type	Thermocouple Materials	Temperature Range (°C)
B	Platinum & 6% or 30% Rhodium	0 to +1800
E	Chromel & Constantan	−190 to +1000
J	Iron & Constantan	−190 to +800
K	Chromel & Alumel	−190 to +1370
R	Platinum or Platinum & 13% Rhodium	0 to +1700
S	Platinum or Platinum & 10% Rhodium	0 to +1765
T	Copper & Constantan	−190 to +400

FIGURE 12-3: Thermocouple junction connections—Seebeck effect.

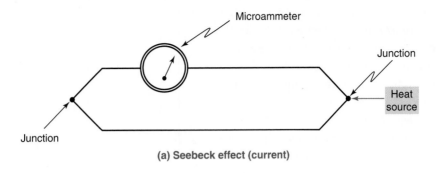

(a) Seebeck effect (current)

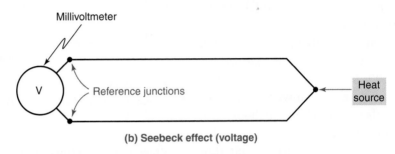

(b) Seebeck effect (voltage)

FIGURE 12-4: Thermocouple reference block.

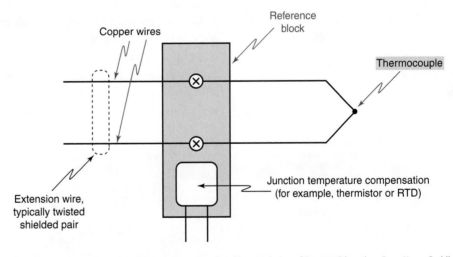

figure are standard copper conductors that are twisted, and sometimes shielded, and connected to an analog input of a PLC.

Solid-state temperature sensors are integrated circuits (ICs) whose output is linearly proportional to a temperature scale, typically Celsius.

Designers who have embedded these ICs in cellular phones usually include one or more sensors in the battery pack; notebook computers might have four or more sensors for checking temperatures in the CPU, battery, AC adapter, and heat-generating assemblies. Although they

TABLE 12-3 Temperature sensor comparisons.

Temperature Sensor	Advantages	Disadvantages
RTD	Very stable and very accurate	Expensive, requires external power supply and is self-heating
Thermistor	Fast reacting to temperature changes	Non-linear in parts of its response curve, limited temperature range and fragile
Thermocouple	Self-powered, rugged, operates over large temperature range	Non-linear in parts of its response curve, requires temperature compensation, least sensitive
IC Temperature Sensor	Most linear, most inexpensive	Limited temperature range, requires external power supply and is self-heating

cannot always replace the traditional temperature sensors—resistance temperature detectors, thermistors, and thermocouples—IC temperature sensors offer many advantages. For instance, they require no linearization or reference-junction compensation. In fact, they often provide reference-junction compensation for thermocouples. They generally provide better noise immunity through higher-level output signals, and some provide logic outputs that can interface directly to a PLC.

Finally, a *comparison of temperature sensors* is shown in Table 12-3, which lists the advantages and disadvantages of the RTD, the thermistor, the thermocouple, and the IC temperature sensor.

12-2-2 Pressure Sensors

Pressure sensors are devices that detect the force exerted by one object on another. Before we discuss the various pressure sensors, it's important to understand the terms that are used in the discussion. First, *pressure* is defined as the amount of force applied to an area, where pressure in expressed in pounds per square inch (psi). Pressure in liquids and gases is referred to as *hydraulic pressure*, but in the case of gases pressure may not be a constant, but a variable. The change in an object's shape when force is applied is called *stress* or *strain*. Force applies to many situations and is basically a push or a pull. Pressure sensors are typically classified based on their operational characteristics as follows:

- **Direct pressure sensors:** pressure is a function of the amount of deformation of an object.
- **Deflection pressure sensors:** pressure is a function of the amount of deflection of an object.
- **Differential pressure sensors:** pressure is a function of the difference in two measurements.
- **Piezoelectric and solid-state sensors:** pressure is a function of the deformation/deflection of a crystal or electronic component.

Direct pressure sensors measure *strain*, which is the amount of deformation of a body due to an applied pressure or force. More specifically, strain is defined as the fractional change in length—either positive (tensile) or negative (compression). It is measured by a *strain gage*, which consists of a very fine wire or metallic foil arranged in a grid pattern. When the grid pattern in Figure 12-5 is placed in parallel with the pressure it maximizes the amount of metallic wire or foil subjected to strain. The grid is bonded to a thin backing, called the carrier, which is attached directly to the test specimen. Therefore, the strain experienced by the test specimen is transferred directly to the strain gage, which responds with a small linear change in electrical resistance. This change in resistance is based on the principle that the thinner the wire the higher the resistance. So in a strain gage, the applied pressure elongates the wire, making it thinner, and thus increases its resistance.

FIGURE 12-5: Metal strain gage bonded to a carrier.

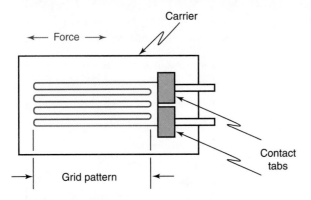

FIGURE 12-6: Active and dummy gages in a bridge circuit.

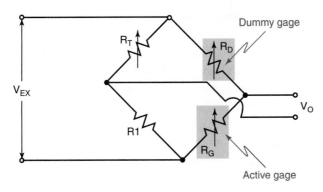

In order to make measurements of such small changes in resistance, strain gages are almost always used in a bridge circuit configuration, as depicted in Figure 12-6. Note that the figure shows two strain gages—an active gage and a dummy gage. The dummy strain gage is added to compensate for temperature changes, which impact the small resistance changes in strain gage. The dummy gage is attached perpendicular to the line of force, thus the force has no impact, but temperature changes occur in both gages and are canceled out since the gages are in opposite legs of the bridge. The balancing of the bridge by R_T compensates for resistor variations and for preload conditions.

Deflection pressure sensors such as the bourdon tube, diaphragm, and bellows consist of the following basic segments:

FIGURE 12-7: Primary segments of deflection-type pressure sensors.

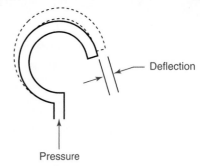

(a) Bourdon tube segment

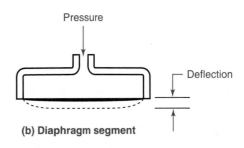

(b) Diaphragm segment

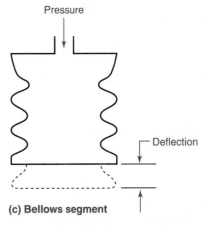

(c) Bellows segment

- A primary segment, which converts the applied pressure into a proportional displacement. (Figure 12-7 illustrates examples of the primary segments.)
- An intermediate segment, which converts the displacement into a change of an electrical component.
- A transmitter, which converts the change of the electrical element into a signal usable by a PLC.

The *bourdon tube* is a deformed hollow metal tube opened at one end and sealed at the other. The tube is available in various shapes, such as the shape of the letter C as illustrated in Figure 12-7(a), a spiral, or a helix. Bronze, steel, or stainless steel is typically used for the tube. The operation is as follows: The liquid whose pressure is being measured enters the tube at the mechanically constrained open end. As pressure increases, the tube tends to straighten, providing a displacement, which is proportional to the pressure.

The *diaphragm* illustrated in Figure 12-7(b) is a flexible membrane, which is made of rubber for low-pressure measurements and metal for high-pressure measurements. The diaphragm is mounted in a cylinder, creating a space on both of its sides. One space is open to the atmosphere and the other is connected to the pressure source to be measured. When pressure is applied, the diaphragm expands into the open space, and the amount of movement is proportional to the pressure being applied.

The *bellows* is a thin sealed metal cylinder with corrugated sides like the pleats of an accordion; it is illustrated in Figure 12-7(c). When pressure is applied to the bellows, the bellows expands and opens the pleats, producing a displacement that is proportional to the applied pressure.

Differential pressure sensors are modified diaphragm sensors where the diaphragm is located halfway between the ends of the cylinder. When pressure is applied to both ends the diaphragm will move toward the end with the lowest pressure. Figure 12-8 illustrates a differential pressure sensor, where P1 and P2 are the two pressure inlets of the sensor. A sensing device, whose output is sent to a PLC, detects the movement of the diaphragm, which is the difference between the two pressures.

Piezoelectric pressure sensors operate on the piezoelectric effect discovered in the late 1800s by Jacques and Pierre Curie. The piezoelectric effect occurs when pressure is applied to a crystal; the crystal deforms and produces a small voltage, which is proportional to the deformation.

Solid-state sensors derive measurements from pressure exerted on one side of a diaphragm. They differ from electromechanical sensors in that rather than consisting of several discrete components, these sensors have all their electrical and mechanical components built into a single piece of silicon. A small deflection of the diaphragm causes implanted resistors to exhibit a change in ohmic value. The sensor converts this change into a voltage that can be easily interpreted as a continuous and linear pressure reading. In addition, a laser-trimmed resistor network on the device provides temperature compensation and calibration.

FIGURE 12-8: Differential pressure sensor.

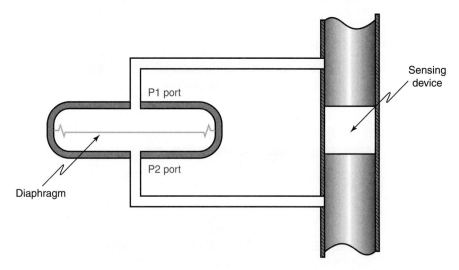

Rehg and Sartori, Industrial Electronics, *1st Edition, © 2006, Reprinted by permission of Pearson Education, Inc., Upper Saddle River, NJ.*

12-2-3 Flow Sensors

Sensing the flow of liquids and gases is an important measurement in industrial processes. The measurement of flow rate indicates how much fluid is used or distributed in a process and it is frequently used as control variable, which aids in maintaining the efficiency of a process. Flow rate is also used to indicate a fault such as improper flow of fluid through a pump or dysfunctional drain operation. Two broad categories of flow sensors are as follows:

- Intrusive: those sensors that disturb the flow of the fluid that they are measuring.
- Non-intrusive: those sensors that do not disturb the flow of the fluid that they are measuring.

However, before we discuss flow sensors, let's look at some of the terms and formulas that are used in industrial processes involving the measurement of flow. *Flow rate* is defined as the volume of material passing a fixed point per unit of time, whether the material is a solid, liquid, or gas—for example, lumber being conveyed into a sawmill or hydraulic fluid moving through a piping system. In this text, we'll be discussing the flow rate of fluids—liquids and gases. The flow rate of a fluid, flowing through a pipe, can be expressed in the following terms: $Q = V \times A$, where Q is the flow rate of the fluid through a pipe, V is the velocity of the fluid, and A is the cross-sectional area of the pipe.

Two more terms used to describe fluid flow are *laminar* and *turbulent*. They are depicted in Figure 12-9 and defined as follows:

- **Laminar flow**: fluid flows rather smoothly parallel to the walls of the pipe.
- **Turbulent flow**: fluid flows down the pipe, but swirls within the flow.

FIGURE 12-9: Laminar flow and turbulent flow.

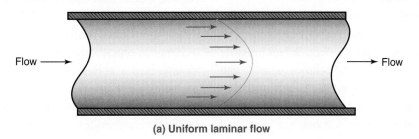

(a) Uniform laminar flow

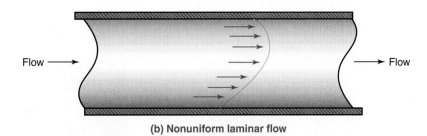

(b) Nonuniform laminar flow

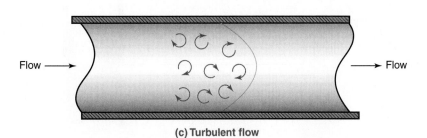

(c) Turbulent flow

Rehg and Sartori, Industrial Electronics, *1st Edition, © 2006, Reprinted by permission of Pearson Education, Inc., Upper Saddle River, NJ.*

The flows in Figure 12-9(a) and (b) depict laminar flow, but the shape of the flow in Figure 12-9(b) is non-uniform relative to the pipe walls, which indicates an imbalance in the frictional characteristics of the walls. Figure 12-9(c) depicts turbulent flow, illustrating the swirling action within the flow.

In the following subsections flow sensors are classified by their method of measurement because this is applicable to industrial applications. The *measurement methods* of flow sensors are classified as follows:

- Differential: the flow rate is determined by calculating the pressure difference (or pressure drop) as the fluid flows through an obstruction such as an orifice plate.
- Velocity: the flow rate is determined based on the velocity of the fluid as it passes through a turbine.
- Displacement: the flow rate is determined by measuring all the fluid used.
- Mass: the flow rate is determined based on the total volume of the fluid that passes through the sensor.
- Visual: the flow rate is determined by a visual reading of a graduated scale.

Differential Pressure Flow Sensors. Flow sensing from differential pressure (or pressure drop) is based on the fact that the difference in the pressure measurements on both sides of physical restriction in the flow of a fluid is proportional to the square of the flow rate. In other words, the *flow rate* is proportional to the square root of the pressure difference and is expressed as follows:

$$Q = k(P1 - P2)^{1/2}$$

Where Q is the flow rate

k is a constant specific to the type of restriction, in gallons per minute (gpm)

P1 is the pressure in front of the restriction in pounds per square inch (psi)

P2 is the pressure behind of the restriction in pounds per square inch (psi)

There are several types of devices that use this differential pressure relationship to flow rate. The method of generating a differential pressure differs in each of these devices, but all use the differential pressure sensor that was discussed in a previous section of this chapter to generate the output signal. The following is a brief overview of some of devices that are available in the marketplace.

- Orifice plate: An orifice plate is a washer-shaped device that is installed in a piping system, and the flow rate is determined from the measurements of pressure in front of and behind the plate. Figure 12-10 shows a diagram of an orifice plate installed in the pipe

FIGURE 12-10: Orifice plate flow sensor.

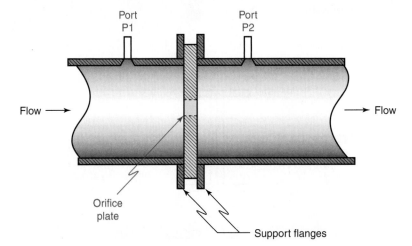

Port P1

Port P2

Flow

Flow

Orifice plate

Support flanges

with the hole shown as dashed lines. The hole in the orifice plate is accurately drilled to a specific size, which impacts the constant in the flow rate formula. The flange plates are part of the mounting assembly for the orifice plate and provide easy access to inspect or install the plate. Note that the pressure measurement ports are labeled P1 and P2 and are sampled by a differential pressure sensor for flow rate determination.

- **Venturi:** A venturi is a flow-measuring device that consists of a gradual contraction followed by a gradual expansion within a fluid-carrying pipe. Figure 12-11 illustrates a venturi. Where the pipe is narrowed, the flow is slightly restricted, creating a difference in pressure between the flow entering the narrow area and leaving the narrow area. The high-pressure port P1 is used to sample the pressure as the fluid enters the narrow area, and the low-pressure port P2 is used to sample the pressure as the fluid exits the narrow area. In larger venturies additional ports are used to provide a means to determine an average pressure. A venturi has no installed parts and causes much less disturbance in the fluid flow than an orifice plate.

- **Pitot tube:** A pitot tube is a flow-measuring device consisting of two tubes placed in the fluid flow that sense two pressures—impact pressure and static pressure. Note that pitot is pronounced *pea toe*. Figure 12-12 illustrates

FIGURE 12-11: Venturi flow sensor.

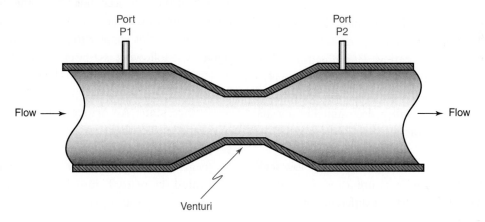

Rehg and Sartori, Industrial Electronics, *1st Edition, © 2006, Reprinted by permission of Pearson Education, Inc., Upper Saddle River, NJ.*

FIGURE 12-12: Pitot tube flow sensor.

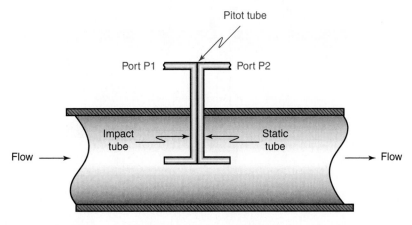

Rehg and Sartori, Industrial Electronics, *1st Edition, © 2006, Reprinted by permission of Pearson Education, Inc., Upper Saddle River, NJ.*

FIGURE 12-13: Flow nozzle flow sensor.

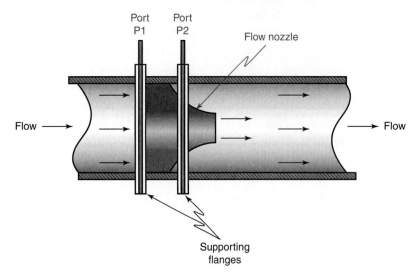

pitot tubes installed in a pipe. The pitot tubes are mounted inside of each other, with the inside tube, which faces the fluid flow, measuring the impact pressure. The second tube, which faces away from the fluid flow, measures the static pressure. The higher pressure is at the impact tube, whereas the lower pressure is at the static tube, and the difference between the two pressures are used to determine flow rate.

- **Flow nozzle:** A flow nozzle is a narrowing spout installed inside a piping system to obtain a pressure differential. It is illustrated in Figure 12-13. The nozzle is generally made of stainless steel, but it can also be made from other corrosion-resistant materials. A flow nozzle is typically installed between pipe flanges, but also is available with a machined ring on the outside diameter of the nozzle, allowing it to be welded between two sections of piping with the nozzle itself entirely within the pipe. Flow nozzles are often used as measuring elements for air and gas flow in industrial applications. Ports P1 and P2 are used to obtain the pressure differential measurements used in determining the flow rate.
- **Elbow:** An existing elbow in the piping system can be used to obtain a differential pressure; Figure 12-14 illustrates this technique. As the fluid flows through the elbow, it exhibits a slight pressure differential. The fluid that flows near

FIGURE 12-14: Elbow flow sensor.

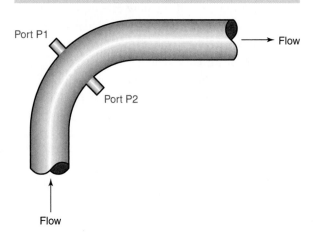

the outer radius of the elbow has a slightly higher pressure than the fluid flowing near the inside radius. The pressure ports are labeled P1 and P2; these are the higher-pressure port and lower-pressure port, respectively. Depending on the radius of the elbow, the distance traveled by the fluid could be relatively farther on the outer radius than on the inner. In that case, two ports on both sides of the elbow can be used to obtain an average of each pressure, resulting in a more accurate pressure reading. The pressure difference is used to determine the flow rate.

Velocity Flow Sensors. *Velocity flow sensors* are devices that measure the fluid flow rate based on changes in flow velocity. They include the paddlewheel, turbine, vortex, electromagnetic, and ultrasonic flow sensors.

- Paddlewheel flow sensor: This flow sensor is installed in a pipe so that the flowing fluid causes its paddlewheel to rotate. Figure 12-15 shows a paddlewheel flow sensor installation. The sensor is mounted in the pipe so that only a portion of the paddle extends into the flow. The paddlewheel flow sensor is mounted in a straight run of piping where the flow is laminar. The flow causes the paddlewheel to rotate, and its revolutions are converted to an electronic output. Generally a magnet is mounted to the paddles so that as they spin, a magnetic sensor converts the rotation of spin to electronic pulses. The sensor output is typically available as a square wave whose frequency is a function of the flow rate or as a variable voltage, but some sensors have a battery-powered electronic display mounted on the sensor for easy viewing.
- Turbine flow sensor: There are many different manufacturing designs of turbine flow sensors, but in general they are all based on

the same principle—if a fluid moves through a pipe and strikes the vanes of a turbine, the turbine will start to spin and rotate. Figure 12-16 illustrates the turbine flow sensor, whose operation is similar to the paddlewheel where the rate of spin is measured to calculate the flow. High-quality jewel bearings and nickel-tungsten carbine turbine that are used for long life and low friction. The flange fitting ensures correct depth placement of the turbine. The rotation of the rotor is typically detected by a magnetic field and converted to square wave pulses. The number of square wave pulses is proportional to the volume of liquid passing through the turbine, and the flow rate Q can be expressed as follows:

$$Q = V/T = (k \times N)/T$$

Where V is the volume of liquid
k is the turbine constant in cm^3
N is the number of pulses
T is the time interval when the pulses are counted

- Vortex flow sensor: The vortex flow sensor includes a non-streamlined object (a bluff body) placed in the fluid flow, which creates vortices (whirlpools or eddies) in a down-

FIGURE 12-15: Paddlewheel flow sensor.

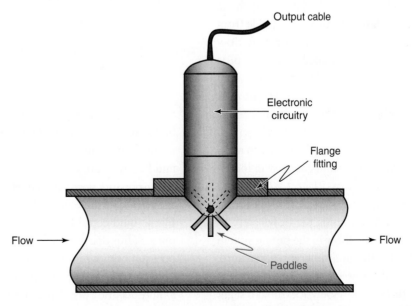

Rehg and Sartori, Industrial Electronics, *1st Edition, © 2006, Reprinted by permission of Pearson Education, Inc., Upper Saddle River, NJ.*

FIGURE 12-16: Turbine flow sensor.

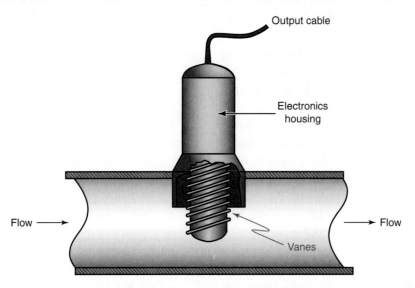

Rehg and Sartori, Industrial Electronics, 1st Edition, © 2006, Reprinted by permission of Pearson Education, Inc., Upper Saddle River, NJ.

FIGURE 12-17: Vortex flow sensor.

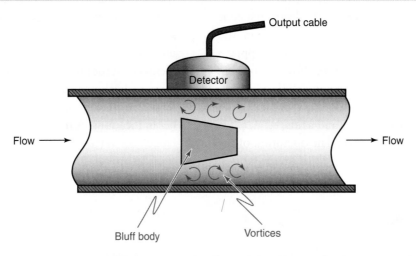

Rehg and Sartori, Industrial Electronics, 1st Edition, © 2006, Reprinted by permission of Pearson Education, Inc., Upper Saddle River, NJ.

stream flow. When fluid flow strikes the bluff body, a series of vortices are produced or *shedded*. Figure 12-17 illustrates the vortices around the bluff body in the fluid flow. Vortex shedding is the instance where alternating low-pressure zones are generated in the down-stream. On the side of the bluff body where the vortex is being formed, the fluid velocity is higher and the pressure is lower. As the vortex moves downstream, it grows in strength and size, and eventually detaches itself. This is followed by the forming of a vortex on the other side of the bluff body. The alternating vortices are spaced at equal distances. The bluff body is shown as a trapezoid, but other shapes also work as long as the bluff body has a width that is a large enough fraction of the pipe diameter so that the entire flow participates in the shedding. Vortex shedding frequency is directly proportional to the velocity of the fluid in the pipe, and therefore to volumetric flow rate. The shedding frequency

is independent of fluid properties such as density, viscosity, conductivity, etc., except that the flow must be turbulent for vortex shedding to occur.

- Electromagnetic flow sensor: The electromagnetic flow sensor measures the electrical charges in flowing fluid, which are proportional to the fluid velocity. Its operation is based on Faraday's Law, which states that the voltage induced in a conductor moving through a magnetic field is proportional to the velocity of that conductor. Figure 12-18 illustrates the electromagnetic flow sensor. The flow sensor has a small insertion depth (in the neighborhood of 0.2 inches), thus it creates no pressure drop. A set of coils creates a magnetic field, and as the fluid flows through the magnetic field it acts like an electrical conductor and becomes electrically charged. A set of electrodes detects and measures the electrical charge. The electrical charge is converted to velocity from which the flow rate can be determined. Electromagnetic flow sensors are used widely in urban and wastewater systems and in industrial applications where non-intrusive flow sensors are needed, such as measuring the flow rate of chemicals, heavy sludge, paper and pulp stock, mining slurries, and acids.

- Ultrasonic flow sensor: The operation of the ultrasonic flow sensor is based on the motion

of a sound source and its effect on the frequency of the sound. This phenomenon was observed and described in the mid-1800s by Christian Johann Doppler as *the frequency of the reflected signal is modified by the velocity and direction of the fluid flow*. If a fluid is moving towards a sensor, then the frequency of the returning signal increases, and if the fluid is moving away from a sensor, then the frequency of the returning signal decreases. The frequency difference is equal to the reflected frequency minus the originating frequency and is used to calculate the fluid flow rate. Figure 12-19 depicts an ultrasonic flow sensor that clamps onto a pipe and contains transmitting and receiving components. The bubbles or suspended solids in the fluid reflect the transmitted signal back to the receiver, which is a Doppler meter. The Doppler meter detects frequency differences between the transmitted frequency and the reflected frequency. This type of flow sensor does not insert an obstruction in the piping system, which makes it very portable. The ultrasonic flow sensor can be used as a troubleshooting tool for detecting improper flow rates, as backup to an already installed flow sensor, or to check existing meters in a number of locations. A handheld microprocessor-based converter is also available, which provides various functions such as local graph-

FIGURE 12-18: Electromagnetic flow sensor.

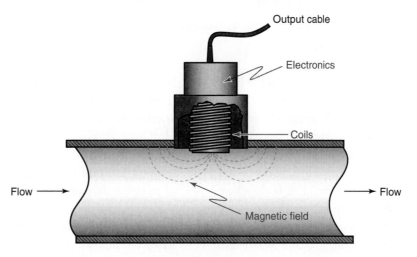

Rehg and Sartori, Industrial Electronics, *1st Edition, © 2006, Reprinted by permission of Pearson Education, Inc., Upper Saddle River, NJ.*

FIGURE 12-19: Ultrasonic flow sensor.

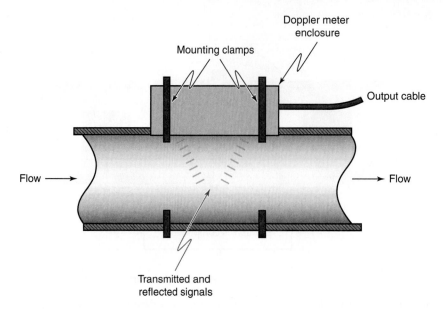

Doppler meter
enclosure

Mounting clamps

Output cable

Flow →

→ Flow

Transmitted and
reflected signals

ics display, an integral keypad for calling up menus for flow data, trend displays, and setting up site parameters.

Displacement Flow Sensors. The *displacement flow sensor* measures fluid flow by precision-fitted rotors as flow-measuring elements where known or fixed volumes are displaced between the rotors. The rotation of the rotors is proportional to the volume of the fluid being displaced. The number of rotations of the rotor is counted by an integral electronic pulse transmitter and converted to volume and flow rate. The displacement rotor construction is accomplished in several ways:

- Piston pumps: the fluid flowing through the piston is a known quantity, thus the flow rate is a function of the number of piston strokes.
- Oval gears: a fixed volume of fluid passes through two rotating, oval-shaped gears with synchronized close-fitting teeth for each revolution, thus shaft rotation can be counted to obtain specific flow rates.
- Nutating disks: these moveable disks are mounted on a concentric sphere located in a spherical chamber, and the pressure of the liquid passing through the chamber causes the disks to rotate in a circulating path without

rotating about its own axis. Each disk rotation traps a known amount of fluid and the number of disk revolutions is counted, thus the flow rate can be calculated.

- Rotary vanes: these vanes are equally divided, rotating impellers inside a casing. The impellers are in continuous contact with the casing, and a fixed volume of liquid is swept through as the impellers rotate. The revolutions of the impeller are counted and flow rate can be determined.

The displacement flow sensor may be used for all relatively nonabrasive fluids such as heating oils, lubrication oils, polymer additives, animal and vegetable fat, printing ink, and freon.

Mass Flow Sensors. *Mass flow sensors* directly measure the flow rate of fluids, especially gases, and tend to be highly accurate—they are off less than 0.1 percent. Two such sensors, the thermal mass flow sensor and the Coriolis mass flow sensor, are discussed in this section.

- Thermal mass flow sensor: The thermal mass flow sensor operates independently of density, pressure, and viscosity. This sensor uses a heated sensing element isolated from the fluid

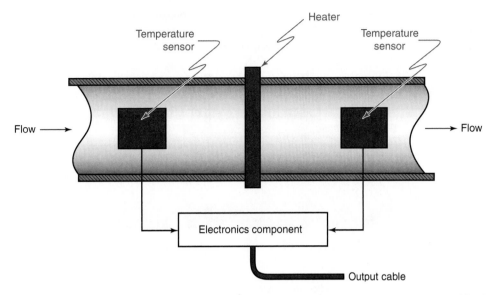

flow path where the flow stream conducts heat from the sensing element. The conducted heat is detected with thermal sensors, and the temperature difference between the sensors is directly proportional to the mass flow rate. Figure 12-20 illustrates a thermal mass flow sensor. Note that one temperature sensor is on the upstream side of the heater and the other sensor is on the downstream side. One type of temperature sensor used in thermal mass flow sensing is the *thermopile*, which consists of thousands of thermocouples gathered in a band of plastic or tape. The electronics component of the thermal mass flow sensor includes a flow analyzer, temperature compensation, and signal conditioner.

- Coriolis mass flow sensor: The Coriolis flow sensor uses a vibrating U-shaped tube to measure fluid flow rate based on an inertial force phenomenon as described in the mid-1800s by Gustave-Gaspard Coriolis and named the Coriolis effect. The fluid to be measured runs through a U-shaped tube, shown in Figure 12-21, that is caused to vibrate in an angular harmonic oscillation. The fluid flowing through the tube causes the tube to deform as in a twist, and the amount of twist is directly proportional to the fluid flow. Detection of the amount of twist is done by sensors, which are mounted near the tube and drive a signal conditioner whose output is typically a variable voltage. This voltage is used to determine the fluid flow rate. The Coriolis mass flow sensor does not require temperature compensation, which is an advantage over the thermal mass

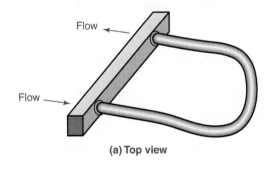

(a) Top view

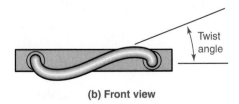

(b) Front view

flow sensor. In the dredging and other industries with slurries and highly corrosive and/or dirty liquids, using the inline Coriolis mass flow sensor is not practical at high velocities due to the wear on the tube.

Visual Flow Sensor. In some applications, a visual indication of flow rate rather than an electrical signal is more appropriate. The *visual flow sensor*, called a variable area flow meter or a rotameter, consists of a vertically oriented glass or plastic tube with a larger end at the top and a metering float, which is free to move within the tube. Figure 12-22 illustrates the visual flow sensor. Fluid flow causes the float to rise in the tube as the upward pressure of the fluid overcomes the effect of gravity. In other words, gravity pulls the float down and the fluid flow pushes it up. The float rises until the annular area between the float and tube increases sufficiently to allow a state of dynamic equilibrium between the upward pressure and the downward gravity factor. The tube is graduated in appropriate flow units, and the height of the float indicates the flow rate with a typical accuracy of 1 percent of full-scale. This type of flow indicator is used in industrial applications where water is used as a cooling agent in the process, and the flow is adjusted manually until the float is at the desired graduated mark on the sensor.

12-2-4 Position Sensors

Position sensors measure both linear and rotary motion and distance. In this section we will discuss three position sensors—the linear and rotary potentiometers and the linear variable differential transformer.

Linear and rotary potentiometers are sensors that produce a resistance output proportional to the displacement or position. *Linear potentiometers* are essentially variable resistors, which are either wire-wound or conductive plastic and either rectangular or cylindrically shaped. The resistance element is excited with a voltage, and the output voltage is ideally a linear function of the input displacement, thus providing a voltage as a position measurement. *Rotary potentiometers* are sensors that produce a resistance output proportional to a rotational position; they operate the same as a linear potentiometer.

FIGURE 12-22: Visual flow sensor.

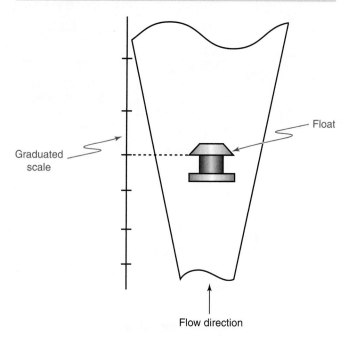

Graduated scale

Float

Flow direction

Rehg and Sartori, Industrial Electronics, *1st Edition, © 2006, Reprinted by permission of Pearson Education, Inc., Upper Saddle River, NJ.*

The *linear variable differential transformer* (LVDT) is a position sensor consisting of a transformer with a movable core, as shown in Figure 12-23. The transformer has a primary winding and two identical secondary windings that are wound around a hollow tube containing the movable core, and the movable core is attached to the item whose position is to be measured.

The output voltage of secondary A is greatest when the core is opposite it; conversely, secondary B's output is the greatest when the core is opposite it. If the core is equidistant between the two cores, the output voltage is zero, which is referred to as the null position of the sensor. This is shown in Figure 12-23(a). In between, the output voltage varies from zero volts to maximum volts. In the null position an equal voltage is induced into both secondary A and secondary B, but since they are wired so the voltages are opposed they cancel each other out, resulting in a zero output. When the core aligns with secondary A as shown in Figure 12-23(b), the output is in phase with the input voltage. Conversely, with the core aligned with secondary B, the output is out of phase with the input voltage, as depicted in Figure 12-23(c).

FIGURE 12-23: Linear variable differential transformer (LVDT).

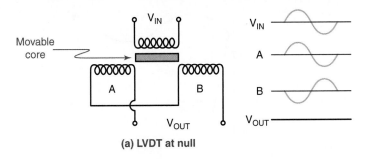

(a) LVDT at null

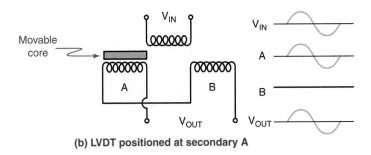

(b) LVDT positioned at secondary A

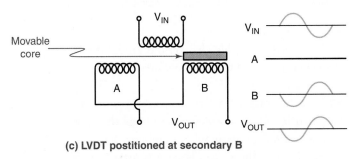

(c) LVDT postitioned at secondary B

Rehg and Sartori, Industrial Electronics, 1st Edition, © 2006, Reprinted by permission of Pearson Education, Inc., Upper Saddle River, NJ.

The electronics that interface with the LVDT sensor combine information on the phase of the output with information on the magnitude of the output, and provide a DC output voltage indicating where the core is relative to its electrical zero position.

12-2-5 Vision Systems

Vision systems are growing at a rapid rate in manufacturing automation because system cost has dropped, system capability and intelligence has significantly increased, and the size of the camera and camera controllers has plummeted. The applications fall into five general categories: part identification, part location, part orientation, part inspection, and range finding.

- **Part identification:** Vision systems store data for different parts in memory and use the data to distinguish between parts as they enter the work cell. The system can learn the characteristics of different parts and identify each part from its two-dimensional image. Based on the vision image and analysis, the system triggers actions on the part in the production system. Vision systems are also taking over many of the functions previously performed by bar code systems in reading bar codes and extracting product data from the production database.

- **Part location:** Vision technology allows the automation system to locate randomly placed parts entering the work cell. The vision system measures the X and Y distances from the center of the camera coordinate system to the center of the randomly placed part. This application is used most often by robot systems to direct the robot gripper to the location of the part to be moved.

- **Part orientation:** Part orientation and part location are linked because every part must be gripped in a specified manner by the robot gripper. The vision system supplies the orientation information and data that are used to drive the robot gripper into the correct orientation for part pickup. Many part orientation parameters, both measured and calculated from measured data, are provided by the vision system for use in automated part handling. Orientation is used when robots are not present to verify that parts or products are oriented properly for automated assembly.

- **Part inspection:** Vision systems are used to check parts for dimensional accuracy (for example, the diameter of a part) and geometrical integrity (for example, the number of holes). The parts are measured by the camera, and the dimensions are calculated; at the same time, the vision system checks the parts for any missing features or changes in the part geometry.

- **Range finding:** In some applications the system uses two or more cameras to measure the X, Y, Z location of the part. This technique is also used to measure and calculate the cross-sectional area of parts.

Vision Systems Operation and Applications. The block diagram of a vision system shown in Figure 12-24 illustrates the architecture used to implement vision technology. In this configuration the vision system is totally stand-alone; however, some robot manufacturers build the vision system directly into the robot controller. The basic vision system components shown include the following: one or more cameras, a camera controller, interface circuits and systems for the camera and work-cell equipment (PLC), discrete inputs for synchronizing sensors, power supply, a flat-screen LCD display, a programming console, and a lighting system for the parts.

Vision systems operate by processes images captured electronically on either CCD (charge-coupled device) or CMOS (complimentary metal oxide semiconductor) cameras. Both types of cameras use a solid-state array of light-sensitive cells, called pixels, deposited on an integrated circuit substrate. Each cell or pixel is a small light-sensitive transistor whose output is a function of the intensity of light striking its surface. The systems come in two basic configurations: *imaging* arrays and *linear* arrays. Figure 12-25 shows how each is organized. In Figure 12-25(a), a 1024 by 1280 image array camera with an LED light source attached is capturing numeric and bar code information on a moving conveyor. In Figure 12-25(b), a linear array of 6144 pixels is scanning in the data from a high-speed conveyor one line at a time. Higher scan rates are achieved with this type of

FIGURE 12-24: Vision system components.

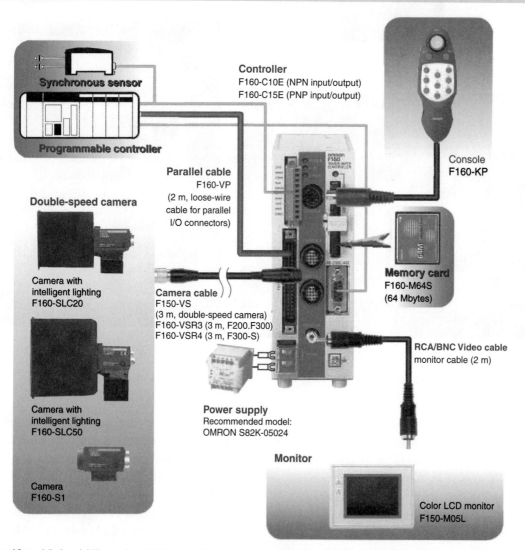

Rehg and Sartori, Industrial Electronics, *1st Edition, © 2006, Reprinted by permission of Pearson Education, Inc., Upper Saddle River, NJ.*

FIGURE 12-25: Image and linear array vision cameras.

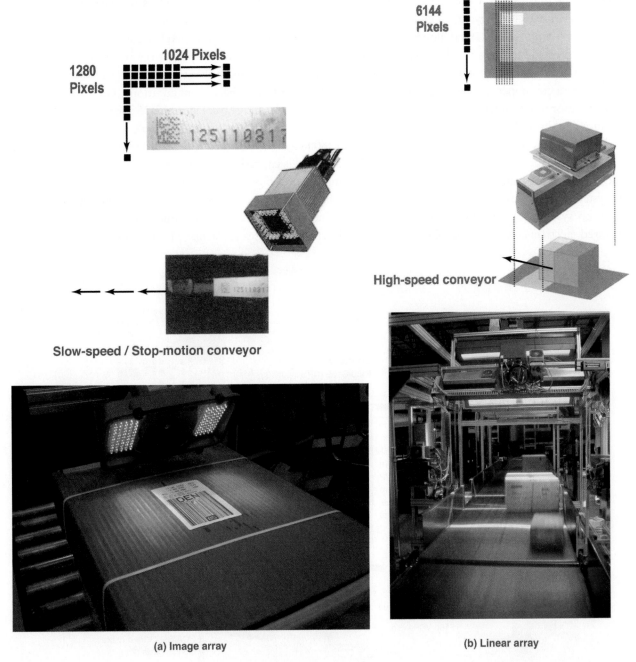

1280 Pixels **1024 Pixels**

6144 Pixels

125110817

High-speed conveyor

Slow-speed / Stop-motion conveyor

(a) Image array

(b) Linear array

Rehg and Sartori, Industrial Electronics, *1ˢᵗ Edition, © 2006, Reprinted by permission of Pearson Education, Inc., Upper Saddle River, NJ.*

system since the system processes only a small part of the image in each scan. The linear arrays perform a line scan, whereas the imaging arrays perform an area scan. Charge storage cameras are accurate, rugged, and have good linearity.

The unit of measurement in a vision system is the *gray scale,* the parameter measured is *light intensity,* and the measurement element is the *pixel.*

The vision system lens focuses light from the part onto the CCD or CMOS light-sensitive surface. The two-dimensional surface, Figure 12-25, is divided into small regions or picture cells called pixels. The resolution of the vision system is directly proportional to the number of pixels on the light-sensitive surface. For example, a CCD with a 1024 by 1280 array will have a higher resolution than a CCD

with a 128 by 128 array of pixels. Each pixel builds up charge proportional to the amount of light reaching the surface through the camera lens. This charge value is an analog signal that is digitized into a discrete binary value by the central vision processor. With no light present, the pixel is turned *off*, but when light reaches a *saturation level,* the pixel is full *on*. Between those two extremes are shades of gray that cause the pixel to be excited to a partially *on* condition. The number of excitation states between *off* and *on* is called the gray scale. Current systems have gray scales of 256. The gray scale of a pixel is the numerical representation of brightness for one small spot on the part. The cameras

in most vision systems conform to the RS-170 standard, which requires that images are acquired at a rate of 30 frames per second with even and odd line interlacing.

The vision system captures an image when a trigger signal from a sensor indicates that the part is in position for an image capture by the camera. When the image is captured, the system transfers the image to a central processing unit for analysis of the vision data. The type of analysis depends on the vision algorithms present and the requirements present in the vision application.

Four typical applications for a vision system are illustrated in Figure 12-26. In application

FIGURE 12-26: Vision system applications.

Product sorting
Sort boxed product by size labels and inspect seams

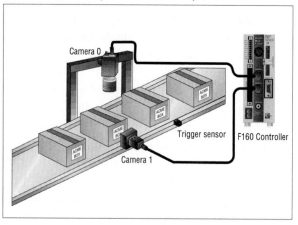

(a)

Optical character recognition
Pill presence/absence and Lot/Date code confirmation on blister pack

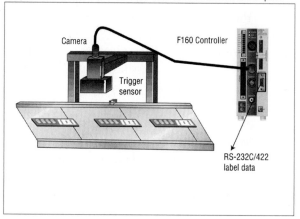

(b)

High speed bottle inspection
Inspect dimensions, conformance and date code

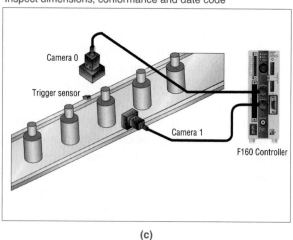

(c)

Position reference
Identify random, odd-shaped product positioning on a conveyor

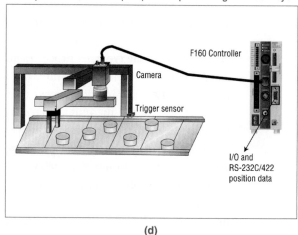

(d)

Rehg and Sartori, Industrial Electronics, *1st Edition, © 2006, Reprinted by permission of Pearson Education, Inc., Upper Saddle River, NJ.*

(a) a trigger sensor is used to synchronize the image capture with the time when a box is present. Note that the boxes are evenly spaced and the next box on the conveyor triggers the inspection. Camera 0 checks box size and a closed top seam, while camera 1 reads the label. In application (b), a vision system inspects blister packs to verify that pills are present and checks the lot and date code. Label data is sent from the vision system by serial transmission to a product data management system. Application (c) uses two cameras to check dimensions, conformance, and the date code on bottles moving by at high speed. Again, a trigger sensor synchronizes the image capture with a passing bottle. Application (d) uses a single camera to locate the X and Y position of randomly placed parts on a conveyor belt. The data is passed over a serial link to a robot controller that changes the robot arm's pickup point based on the data.

Vision Systems Classifications. Vision systems have three basic classifications—*binary systems, gray scale,* or *color processing.*

- *Binary systems,* the lowest in cost and easiest to use, do basic visual inspections. They operate on an image made up of black and white pixels and calculate results by counting the pixels to determine the shape or size of an object. Binary systems allow inspection of silhouettes, profiles, and outlines and are best suited for area measurement and sizing. On the other hand, this type of system performs poorly when light contrast is low or variable and cannot detect imperfections in product appearance.
- *Gray scale* imaging typically processes images using 256 levels of black and white. The most popular gray scale image-processing technique compares the incoming image with a template or model. The correlation between the image and template is used to decide acceptance or rejection of the part. Gray scale processing is more accurate than binary in dimensional measurements because of a technique called sub-pixel processing. Using this process, an edge is defined to an accuracy of

less than one pixel; as a result, surface imperfections, scratches, textures, and shadows can be detected. However, it is more expensive and in some applications has longer processing times.
- *Color processing* uses information from the red, blue, and green color spectra to detect and differentiate shades of color relevant in food industry and pharmaceutical applications. Finding blemishes in food and checking the color of pills in blister packs requires a color vision system. Color processing is more expensive than the two other types of visual systems, but it offers unique advantages for applications that justify the cost.

Vision System Configurations. Three vision system configurations are available: *stand-alone, PC-based, and VME-based.* While all three offer some degree of modularity for customization, *stand-alone systems,* like the system in Figure 12-24, have features that make them well suited for factory automation. These vision "black boxes" use Application Specific Integrated Circuit (ASIC) or Systems on a Chip (SoC) technology in the vision electronics that gives them accelerated processing power. As a result, they are the fastest systems available. In addition, stand-alone systems work seamlessly with other factory automation devices, such as programmable logic controllers, photoelectric and proximity sensors, and radio frequency identification systems, to enhance integration of the shop floor production and data tracking. Finally, they work over a wide range of temperatures, vibrations, and electrical interference.

A *PC-based system* generally consists of a microcomputer with a processing board that includes dedicated vision ASICs. Use of the computer's CPU lowers the system price and allows you to take advantage of advances in microprocessor technology. Although lower in cost, standard PC vision systems cannot operate in harsh factory environments. Industrial PCs are available, but the higher cost reduces the advantage offered by the PC-based vision approach.

VME-based systems, an IEEE bus standard used in reliability industrial inspection applications, combine a robust operating system with a

flexible user platform. Vision system and computer components are connected via a pin-and-socket connection to the bus, which improves signal transfer rates and is less affected by the industrial environment. However, these systems have a higher cost.

Each configuration offers performance at three levels, which are described as follows:

- **High performance, fixed position:** Applications at this level include scanning parcels using a single or multiple cameras with a 560 frames per minute capture rate. Package spacing is typically 8 inches with conveyors up to 75 inches across. Good field of view (FOV) is achieved with cameras set at 36 inches from the target objects.
- **Mid-range performance, fixed position:** Applications at this level are found in warehouse identification and bar code reading requirements, and also in general sorting of items on moving conveyors. Single or multiple cameras are used with a 350 frames per minute or less capture rate. The depth of field (DOF) coverage is typically 25 inches.
- **Low performance:** At the lowest level, the objects are stationary, indexed (move and then stopped), or moving at a slow speed. The applications are usually manufacturing lines and warehouse related. The frame rate is 250 frames per minute or less, the camera has a fixed focus lens, and FOV is small—usually in the 1- to 2-inch range.

Vision System Programming Methods. The programming options for vision systems range from no programming requirements for special-purpose turnkey systems for a single application to a highly flexible programming environment using Visual Basic or C++. In some systems a menu interface is used, which integrates an internal program with a point-and-click selection mechanism. This method is easy to use and offers a moderate degree of flexibility. In other systems a proprietary programming language must be used, which requires a high level of programming skills and knowledge of vision algorithms. The console in Figure 12-24 is used to program the stand-alone system for Omron.

Lighting for Vision Applications. Although lighting is an important consideration in every vision application, it is frequently overlooked. In many cases a greater effort on the lighting and optics problems would result in a less sophisticated and lower cost vision system. The objective of lighting is to create a high-contrast image that clearly distinguishes the features to be captured. Proper lighting can:

- Shorten the image analysis and recognition time.
- Increase the number of captured images in a fixed time.
- Improve the quality of the captured data.
- Reduce the shadows and glare that cause analysis problems.

Vision System Light Sources and Configurations. The light source chosen for the vision application is critical for a successful project. The major types of sources include *incandescent* and *quartz halogen, fluorescent, light-emitting diodes (LEDs), xenon flash,* and *lasers.* Each of the sources has unique properties such as the location of the source on the *electromagnetic radiation spectrum, operational life, heat generated, level of illumination energy, coherent structure,* and *compatibility* with human operators in the work cell. Significant characteristics of the frequently used sources include:

- **Incandescent and quartz halogen:** These commonly used light sources include devices ranging from standard household bulbs with reflectors to high-power quartz halogen lamps. The quartz halogen sources are often used with fiber-optic bundles to pipe the light onto specific locations on the part. Two major disadvantages are bulb life and high generated heat. However, they have an advantage of little decay of light intensity over time.
- **Fluorescent:** The reduced infrared energy (heat) produced by this type of illumination, plus the extended life of the tube, make it more efficient than the incandescent and quartz halogen source. The natural diffused light produced by a fluorescent source is preferred for vision applications with highly reflective parts.

- **LED:** Arrays of LEDs are arranged in a variety of configurations, including circular and linear sources to light objects. The LED has a long life and produces little heat.
- **Xenon flash:** When used as a *strobe light* source, the xenon flash tube is an important light source in vision applications. Xenon strobe light is used when the vision system must capture the image of a moving part. The 5- to 200-microsecond flash of light illuminates the part at one point in its motion. Since CCD vision cameras are temporary storage devices, the image of the part created by the flash is stored by the camera and the part features are scanned into the vision system memory. In addition, xenon tubes produce light with frequencies from a broad part of the spectrum and have high-intensity levels.
- **Lasers:** The laser is an important source because it produces coherent light that does not disperse as it travels from the source to the target. As a result, the diameter of the laser beam at the target is very close to the beam size leaving the laser. In *structured light* applications, lasers are used to place a thin line of light across the object. The light follows the contours of the part so the vision camera can capture the shape of the part.

Vision System Lighting Techniques. Two design decisions are associated with vision lighting:

1. What type of light source should be chosen?
2. How should the light be positioned with respect to the object?

In general, most lighting applications fall into two categories: front lighting and backlighting. In front lighting the object is lit from the top, and the angle of the lights is changed to achieve different desired effects. One problem in vision is specular reflection off of a specular surface. This is a surface that reflects a light ray in a single direction from any given point on the surface. If a specular surface is present, then the lighting system attempts to minimize the specular reflections. Backlighting provides an outline of the object because the light is placed behind or below the object. Figure 12-27 illustrates a number of lighting techniques and lists attributes and typical applications. Study it carefully until the many different lighting options are understood. The lighting schemes in Figure 12-27 would have to use a strobe source if the objects are moving rapidly past the camera.

Vision System Optics. Optics or lenses, like lighting, are crucial to obtaining effective operation of vision systems. A variety of lenses are available, from low-cost lenses designed for the surveillance industry to high-quality, high-resolution lenses necessary for precise measurement and for detecting defects on small parts. Identifying the required field of view is important in selecting a lens. It is a question of how much of the object needs to be in the image. The selection of a lens has the following steps.

1. Define the field of view (FOV) as illustrated in Figure 12-28(a). Note that the FOV does not have to include the entire object or product but only the area of interest.
2. Determine the distance from the camera to the viewed object, called the *setting distance*. Keep this distance flexible so that the lens choice is not restricted.
3. Find the approximate setting distance on the vertical axis of the graph in Figure 12-28(b), then find the FOV on the horizontal axis, and find the recommended lens where these coordinates intersect. The "t" value is the length of the lens extension tube, which is placed between the lens and the camera as shown in Figure 12-28(b). The extension is necessary to allow the lens to focus on the object at that setting distance.

12-2-6 Troubleshooting Analog Sensors

With the resistance temperature detectors (RTDs) and thermistors, an ohmmeter check is a simple way to validate that the device is operational, but the device must be removed or isolated from the circuitry. However, before isolating the device, make sure the leads are intact and not broken. With the ohmmeter connected to the device, heat the device and verify

EXAMPLE 12-2

Determine the steady-state output for the closed-loop cruise control system for a reference speed of 55 mph and grades of 0, 1, 10, and 20 percent.

SOLUTION

Evaluate for grade of 0 percent:

$$S = 0.999R - 0.007G_0$$

$$S = 0.999 \times 55 \text{ mph} - 0.007 \times 0$$

$$S = 54.945 \text{ mph}$$

Evaluate for grade of 1 percent:

$$S = 0.999 \times 55 - 0.007 \times 1$$

$$S = 54.938 \text{ mph}$$

Evaluate for grade of 10 percent:

$$S = 0.999 \times 55 - 0.007 \times 10$$

$$S = 54.875 \text{ mph}$$

Evaluate for grade of 20 percent:

$$S = 0.999 \times 55 - 0.007 \times 20$$

$$S = 54.805 \text{ mph}$$

As you can observe from the calculations, the error is very small as long as the controller gain is large (150). The following table compares errors for the open- and close-loop cruise control system for different grades and process gains.

The table illustrates the significant improvement that feedback provided. Consider the following observations.

- At grades starting at 1 percent, the open-loop system had an error of 4.55 percent; above that grade the errors increased dramatically.
- The largest error for the closed-loop system was 0.35 percent for a grade of 20 percent.

- Process gain is difficult to establish accurately and may not be constant, so the effect of process gain change is important to consider. Changes in the process gain had little effect on the closed-loop system, but significant impact on the open-loop implementation.
- The closed-loop system output error (0.10 percent) when all disturbances are zero is a part of the steady-state error inherent in all feedback systems.
- The insensitivity of output speed to disturbances and changes in process gain are due in part to the high controller gain (150). However, if the closed loop gain is too large the system could become unstable.

Control System	Grade	Process Gain	Output Speed	Percent Error
Open-Loop	0	5	55	0%
Closed-Loop	0	5	54.95	0.10%
Open-Loop	1	5	52.5	4.55%
Closed-Loop	1	5	54.94	0.11%
Open-Loop	2	5	50	9.09%
Closed-Loop	10	5	54.88	0.23%
Closed-Loop	20	5	54.81	0.35%
Open-Loop	0	4	44	20.00%
Closed-Loop	0	4	54.89	0.18%
Open-Loop	1	4	42	23.64%
Closed-Loop	1	4	54.90	0.20%

The control sequence for the tank in Figure 12-31(b) is as follows: The level in the tank falls (PV decreases) because the input flow decreases suddenly, the error value must decrease so that the controller output can decrease, and the drain valve is closed more to decrease the outlet flow. The controller is set to the *direct-acting* mode (Error = PV − SP) because the controller output needed to decrease when the PV decreased. Study the tank and control block diagram in Figure 12-31(b) until the direct-acting operation is clear.

12-4-2   Analysis of Closed-Loop Systems

Let us take a closer look at closed-loop operation by analyzing the cruise control system, which is illustrated in Figure 12-32.

The closed-loop system has the controller gain (G_2) set at 150 and a summing junction to compare the output, S, with the set point, R. This reverse-acting system will cause the output, S, to increase when the process variable (PV) decreases. The 150 value for the controller gain was not calculated for this model, but selected as a starting point. In industry the gain is some-times calculated theoretically, but most often it is determined experimentally on a functioning system. Determining optimum controller parameters is discussed later in this chapter.

The next step in the analysis is to develop the steady-state output equation.

Equation 1

$$S = 5 \times S_0$$
$$S = 5(R_0 - G_0)$$

Equation 2

$$R_0 = 150(R - S)$$
$$R_0 = 150R - 150S$$

Substitute equation 1 into equation 2 and solve for S.

$$S = 5(R_0 - G_0)$$
$$S = 5(150R - 150S - G_0)$$
$$S = 750R - 750S - 5G_0$$
$$S + 750S = 750R - 5G_0$$
$$751S = 750R - 5G_0$$
$$S = 0.999R - 0.007G_0$$

FIGURE 12-32: Closed-loop block diagram for the cruise control.

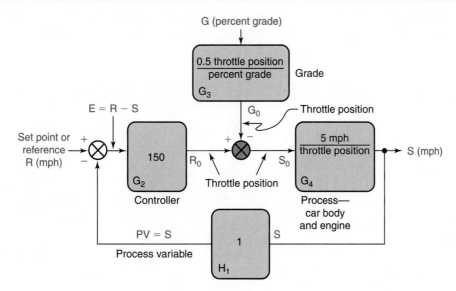

Rehg and Sartori, Industrial Electronics, *1st Edition*, © 2006, Reprinted by permission of Pearson Education, Inc., Upper Saddle River, NJ.

an example, two process tanks are illustrated in Figure 12-31. Figure 12-31(a) has a fill pipe controlled by a fill valve, and a drain pipe with back pressure from downstream processes that creates a non-uniform drain flow. Figure 12-31(b) shows the opposite situation. A drain valve controls outflow from the tank, and a fill pipe provides liquid at a non-uniform rate from upstream processes. The controller in each case must maintain the level in the tank for variations in the drain [Figure 12-31(a)] and for variations in the input flow rate [Figure 12-31(b)].

The control sequence for the tank in Figure 12-31(a) is as follows: The level in the tank falls (PV decreases) because the drain flow increases suddenly, the error value must increase so that the controller output can increase, and the input valve is opened more to increase the input flow. The controller is set to the *reverse-acting* mode (Error = SP − PV) because the controller output needed to rise when the PV decreased. Study the tank and control block diagram in Figure 12-31(a) until the reverse-acting operation is clear.

FIGURE 12-31: Direct and reverse error and process relationship.

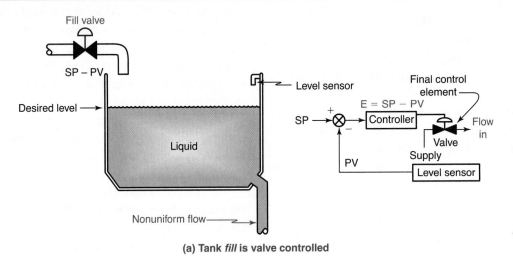

(a) Tank *fill* is valve controlled

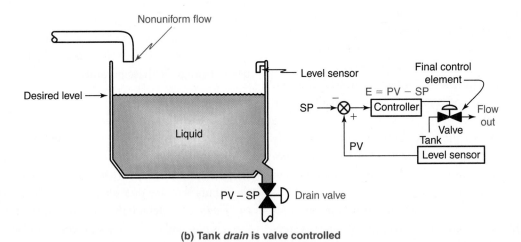

(b) Tank *drain* is valve controlled

Rehg and Sartori, Industrial Electronics, *1st Edition, © 2006, Reprinted by permission of Pearson Education, Inc., Upper Saddle River, NJ.*

Chapter 12 Analog Sensors and Control Systems

- **Backplane Current Load:** this value indicates the amount of current that the module requires from the PLC backplane. The backplane power supply supplies all the analog modules' current requirements.
- **Step Response:** this value specifies the time necessary for the signal to go to typically 95 percent of its final value.
- **Update Period:** this value specifies how often the I/O signal is updated by the PLC.
- **Resolution:** this number is expressed in bits and indicates how accurately the analog value can be represented digitally. The higher the number the more accurate is the analog value.

12-3-2   PLC 5, SLC 500, and Logix Options

The Allen-Bradley family of PLCs provides a collection of analog I/O modules to interface with various field devices. The I/O modules use a DAC or ADC to interface the analog signals to data-table values, giving the ladder logic direct access to I/O values. Analog modules also provide a high level of resolution for accurate control in a broad range of automated process applications. The analog modules for the PLCs provide the following options.

- **Input modules:** 2, 4, 8, or 16 channels per module with either differential, high-speed differential, or single-ended options and input ranges of +/−10 V or +/−20 mA.
- **Output modules:** 4, 6, or 8 channels per module with either differential, high-speed differential, or single-ended options.
- **Combination modules:** typically 2 input channels and 2 output channels available per module.
- **RTD and thermocouple modules:** uniquely designed modules for RTD inputs or thermocouple inputs with 4, 6, or 8 channels per module.
- **Special modules:** specific function modules that are used for a singular task such as stepper motor module, encoder module, high-speed counter module, and servo module. Additional specific modules continue to be developed as applications demand.

12-4   CLOSED-LOOP CONTROL SYSTEMS

Control systems, in which the PLC is a main component, can be classified as open-loop and closed-loop. *Closed-loop* control systems are self-regulating and eliminate many of the disadvantages present in open-loop control, such as sensitivity to disturbances and the inability to correct for these disturbances.

The major difference between open-loop and closed-loop systems is the addition of the feedback loop from the output back to the input in the closed-loop system. The insertion of this loop necessitates the addition of two other elements, an *output transducer* and a *summing junction* between the input transducer and controller. The output transducer is a device that is used to convert the measured value of the system output into a physical form that is consistent with the input requirements of the control system. The transducer is a combination *sensor* and *signal conditioner* that passes a sample of the *actual output* (controlled variable) back to the input to be compared with the *desired output* (set point). The gain of the transducer is often labeled with the letter H and has a value or gain of 1 in many feedback systems.

The signal conditioning function of the output transducer ensures that the feedback signal has the proper units for comparison with the output of the input transducer in the summing junction. The units of output and input transducers are dictated by the controller, which incorporates the *summing junction* function into its input circuits. Most controllers accept either 4 to 20 milliamps, 1 to 5 volts or −10 to +10 volts for the 0 to 100 percent range of these parameters.

12-4-1   Direct-Acting and Reverse-Acting Controllers

The summing junction that compares the process output with the set point has signs associated with the inputs that are *opposite*, since this is a *negative feedback* system. If the set point (SP) summing input is *plus* and the feedback process variable (PV) is *minus*, then the error (E) or actuating signal is SP − PV. If the signs are reversed, then the error changes to PV − SP. Process characteristics dictate which type of error equation should be used. As

FIGURE 12-30: Thermocouple connections to analog input module.

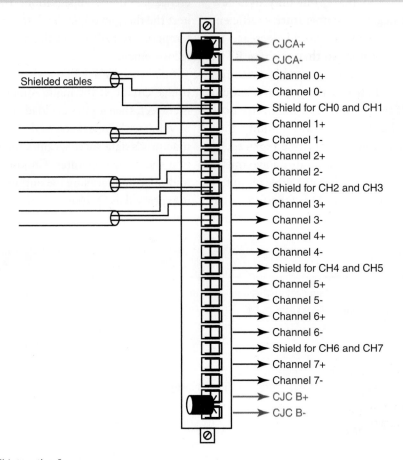

Courtesy of Rockwell Automation, Inc.

to protect the low-level voltage signal from outside electrical noise signals, which can cause errors in the reading of the millivolt signals.

12-3-1 Analog Input and Output Data

The two basic types of analog input modules are voltage sensing or current sensing. *Voltage-sensing* input modules accept either *unipolar* or *bipolar* data. If the field device outputs 0 V to +10 V then the unipolar modules would be used, whereas the bipolar analog module would be used if the field device outputs −10 V to +10 V. The bipolar module accepts both negative and positive input data. *Current-sensing* input modules typically accept analog data over the range of 4 mA to 20 mA, but can accommodate signal ranges of −20 mA to +20 mA. The analog input and output data are specified relative to operational parameters, which impose limitations on the PLC modules. The following is a list of typical I/O specification parameters, including a brief description.

- **Number of I/O:** this indicates the quantity of inputs or outputs that can be interfaced to the analog module. Some PLC types provide combination modules, which accept both inputs and outputs.
- **Data Format:** the representation of analog data that is used by the PLC. The data is represented in BCD, natural binary, or floating point.
- **Voltage Range:** the magnitude and type of voltage signal that is accepted.
- **Current Range:** the magnitude and type of current signal that is accepted.

that the resistance changes. With an RTD the resistance should increase, but only by a few ohms. With a negative temperature coefficient thermistor the resistance should decrease by many ohms, much more so than with an RTD. The manufacturer's data sheet, which specifies device characteristics over temperature, should be reviewed. If the resistance of the device does not change or if its value is always infinity, then the device is defective and must be replaced.

With thermocouples an accurate millivoltmeter is needed to measure the thermocouple output as a function of temperature. Most thermocouple manufacturers provide thermocouple testers, including a millivoltmeter, power supply, and reference junction compensation. You simply connect the thermocouple to the tester and select the temperature range, and the tester provides the measurement.

Strain gages act like resistance sensors in a bridge circuit. If the input voltage to the bridge is correct, then a physical load should be applied to validate the operation of the device. The manufacturer's data sheet specifies the range of loads that the device operates. Choose a value in the midrange and measure the output voltage, which is expressed as Output voltage = Maximum output voltage × test load/maximum load.

EXAMPLE 12-1

Validate the operation of a strain gage that can operate up to a maximum pressure of 600 pounds. Its output is 3 mv per volt of input voltage, which is set at 8 V.

SOLUTION
Recalling:

Output voltage = Max output voltage × test load/maximum load

Choose the test load at 300 pounds

Substituting   Output voltage = (3 mv/V × 8V) × 300 lb/600 lb

                     Output voltage = 12 mv

12-3 ANALOG MODULES AND FIELD DEVICES INTERFACING

Analog modules are used to interface with field devices so that the PLC can operate on digital values. Analog input modules convert analog inputs, typically from the sensors that were discussed in Section 12-2, to a digital value using an analog-to-digital (ADC) converter. Analog output modules convert digital data to analog outputs, typically to control elements such as valves and heating coils, using a digital-to-analog (DAC) converter. A typical analog I/O interface in an automated process is illustrated in a simple block diagram in Figure 12-29 where the PLC controls the heating of the liquid in a tank as a function of the temperature. The PLC controls a heating element via an analog output module and accepts the output of a temperature sensor via an analog input module.

Figure 12-30 depicts an 8-channel analog input module interfaced to thermocouples. Note that

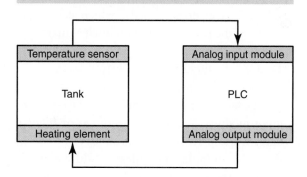

FIGURE 12-29: Analog I/O interface block diagram.

cold junction compensation (CJC) transducers are part of the module and are required to ensure accurate thermocouple readings. Each output of the thermocouples is a varying DC voltage in the millivolt range, which is proportional to the temperature. This voltage is digitized via an ADC and read by the processor on command from the PLC program. Note also that the wiring is shielded

FIGURE 12-27: (Continued).

Diffuse back lighting		• Provides the highest contrast and is easiest to set up • Object is between camera and diffused light source • Object appears as a black outline against a white background	Useful for emphasizing object edges for dimensional checks	Back light surfaces
Directional back lighting		• Like diffused back lighting but uses a collimator to make light waves parallel to each other	Used to produce shapely defined shadows of object details	Collimated light source
Dark field illumination lighting		• Cone of light is directed from behind transparent object • Object scatters light to camera to make transparent object visible • Edges of the transparent object are bright against a black background	Used to back light transparent objects that would not be visible with just diffused back lights	Dark field lights

FIGURE 12-28: Lens selection guide.

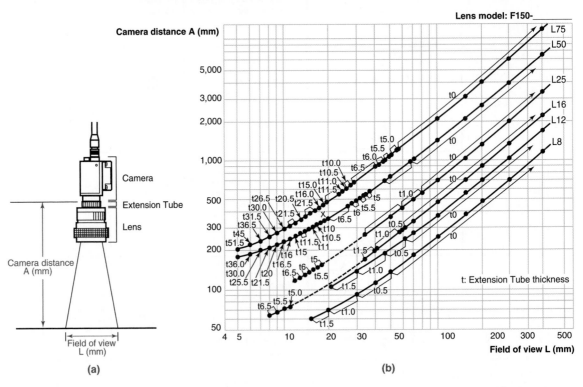

Rehg and Sartori, Industrial Electronics, 1st Edition, © 2006, Reprinted by permission of Pearson Education, Inc., Upper Saddle River, NJ.

FIGURE 12-27: Lighting options for vision systems.

Type of lighting	Lighting configuration	Description	Application	Light type
Directional front lighting		• Similar to oblique but light is at 30 degree or higher angle • The contrast between the object and the background is reduced	Extracts greater information from the flat surfaces of objects	Spot lights or ring lights
Diffuse front lighting		• Large area of uniform illumination • Eliminates shadows and specular reflections • De-emphasizes three-dimensional part characteristics	Applications where the shadow elimination is critical	Dome lights
Polarized lighting		• Polarized light is used and a polarizing filter, called an analyzer, is placed on the camera • Total elimination of specular reflections from any viewing angle are possible when light and camera polar filters are at right angles to each other	Applications where specular surfaces are present	Polarized lights
Fiber optic or LED ring lighting		• Ring lights provide intense shadow-free on axis lighting • Can be combined with polarizer and analyzers if specular reflections are a problem	Useful for images of highly reflective objects	Fiber optic and LED ring lights
Fiber optic near in-line lighting		• Light source is nearly aligned with viewing angle of camera • Difficult to use with shiny object having specular surfaces • Eliminates shadows from details on object surface	Useful for viewing raised details on the object without shadows to obscure the details	Spot light or fiber optic spot
Oblique lighting		• Called extreme directional lighting • Lighting has low angle of incidence to the surface being illuminated • For example, 20° angle is best for textured surface • Edges are illuminated and surfaces are black	Useful for showing surface texture or edge details on objects	Linear arrays or spots
Structured lighting		• A laser is often used to create structured light line or beam • A structured light line when falling onto an irregular surface shows all the contours of the surface in the capture image	Useful for surface feature and contour extraction	Fiber optic line light or laser

- **Backplane Current Load:** t[...]
  the amount of current [...]
  requires from the PLC bac[...]
  plane power supply suppl[...]
  modules' current requirem[...]
- **Step Response:** this value [...]
  necessary for the signal t[...]
  95 percent of its final valu[...]
- **Update Period:** this value s[...]
  the I/O signal is updated b[...]
- **Resolution:** this number is [...]
  and indicates how accura[...]
  value can be represente[...]
  higher the number the mo[...]
  analog value.

12-3-2 PLC 5, SLC 500, and [...]

The Allen-Bradley family of PL[...]
lection of analog I/O modules [...]
various field devices. The I/O m[...]
or ADC to interface the analog [...]
table values, giving the ladder l[...]
to I/O values. Analog modules a[...]
level of resolution for accurate c[...]
range of automated process a[...]
analog modules for the PLCs pr[...]
ing options.

- Input modules: 2, 4, 8, or [...]
  module with either differen[...]
  differential, or single-ended [...]
  ranges of +/−10 V or +/−2[...]
- Output modules: 4, 6, or 8 cl[...]
  ule with either differential, h[...]
  ential, or single-ended optio[...]
- Combination modules: ty[...]
  channels and 2 output chann[...]
  module.
- RTD and thermocouple mo[...]
  designed modules for RTD in[...]
  couple inputs with 4, 6, or [...]
  module.
- Special modules: specific fu[...]
  that are used for a singular t[...]
  per motor module, encoder[...]
  speed counter module, and [...]
  Additional specific modules[...]
  developed as applications de[...]

FIGURE 12-27: Lighting options for vision systems.

Type of lighting	Lighting configuration	Description	Application	Light type
Directional front lighting		• Similar to oblique but light is at 30 degree or higher angle • The contrast between the object and the background is reduced	Extracts greater information from the flat surfaces of objects	Spot lights or ring lights
Diffuse front lighting		• Large area of uniform illumination • Eliminates shadows and specular reflections • De-emphasizes three-dimensional part characteristics	Applications where the shadow elimination is critical	Dome lights
Polarized lighting		• Polarized light is used and a polarizing filter, called an analyzer, is placed on the camera • Total elimination of specular reflections from any viewing angle are possible when light and camera polar filters are at right angles to each other	Applications where specular surfaces are present	Polarized lights
Fiber optic or LED ring lighting		• Ring lights provide intense shadow-free on axis lighting • Can be combined with polarizer and analyzers if specular reflections are a problem	Useful for images of highly reflective objects	Fiber optic and LED ring lights
Fiber optic near in-line lighting		• Light source is nearly aligned with viewing angle of camera • Difficult to use with shiny object having specular surfaces • Eliminates shadows from details on object surface	Useful for viewing raised details on the object without shadows to obscure the details	Spot light or fiber optic spot
Oblique lighting		• Called extreme directional lighting • Lighting has low angle of incidence to the surface being illuminated • For example, 20° angle is best for textured surface • Edges are illuminated and surfaces are black	Useful for showing surface texture or edge details on objects	Linear arrays or spots
Structured lighting		• A laser is often used to create structured light line or beam • A structured light line when falling onto an irregular surface shows all the contours of the surface in the capture image	Useful for surface feature and contour extraction	Fiber optic line light or laser

Rehg and Sartori, Industrial Electronics, *1st Edition, © 2006, Reprinted by permission of Pearson Education, Inc., Upper Saddle River, NJ.*

FIGURE 12-30:

an example, two process tanks are illustrated in Figure 12-31. Figure 12-31(a) has a fill pipe controlled by a fill valve, and a drain pipe with back pressure from downstream processes that creates a non-uniform drain flow. Figure 12-31(b) shows the opposite situation. A drain valve controls outflow from the tank, and a fill pipe provides liquid at a non-uniform rate from upstream processes. The controller in each case must maintain the level in the tank for variations in the drain [Figure 12-31(a)] and for variations in the input flow rate [Figure 12-31(b)].

The control sequence for the tank in Figure 12-31(a) is as follows: The level in the tank falls (PV decreases) because the drain flow increases suddenly, the error value must increase so that the controller output can increase, and the input valve is opened more to increase the input flow. The controller is set to the *reverse-acting* mode (Error = SP − PV) because the controller output needed to rise when the PV decreased. Study the tank and control block diagram in Figure 12-31(a) until the reverse-acting operation is clear.

FIGURE 12-31: Direct and reverse error and process relationship.

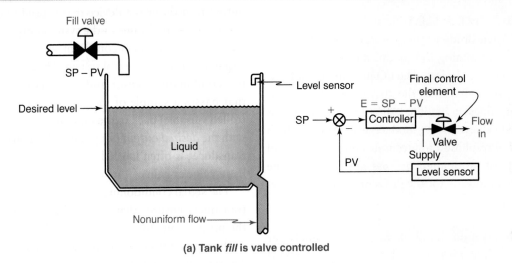

(a) Tank *fill* is valve controlled

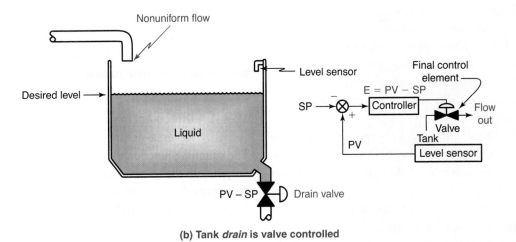

(b) Tank *drain* is valve controlled

Rehg and Sartori, Industrial Electronics, *1st Edition, © 2006, Reprinted by permission of Pearson Education, Inc., Upper Saddle River, NJ.*

to protect the l
side electrical
errors in the re

12-3-1 Anal
The two basic t
voltage sensing
input modules
data. If the fie
then the unip
whereas the b
used if the fiel
V. The bipolar
positive input
ules typically a
of 4 mA to 20
ranges of −20
and output dat

The control sequence for the tank in Figure 12-31(b) is as follows: The level in the tank falls (PV decreases) because the input flow decreases suddenly, the error value must decrease so that the controller output can decrease, and the drain valve is closed more to decrease the outlet flow. The controller is set to the *direct-acting* mode (Error = PV − SP) because the controller output needed to decrease when the PV decreased. Study the tank and control block diagram in Figure 12-31(b) until the direct-acting operation is clear.

12-4-2 Analysis of Closed-Loop Systems

Let us take a closer look at closed-loop operation by analyzing the cruise control system, which is illustrated in Figure 12-32.

The closed-loop system has the controller gain (G_2) set at 150 and a summing junction to compare the output, S, with the set point, R. This reverse-acting system will cause the output, S, to increase when the process variable (PV) decreases. The 150 value for the controller gain was not calculated for this model, but selected as a starting point. In industry the gain is some-times calculated theoretically, but most often it is determined experimentally on a functioning system. Determining optimum controller parameters is discussed later in this chapter.

The next step in the analysis is to develop the steady-state output equation.

Equation 1

$$S = 5 \times S_0$$
$$S = 5(R_0 - G_0)$$

Equation 2

$$R_0 = 150(R - S)$$
$$R_0 = 150R - 150S$$

Substitute equation 1 into equation 2 and solve for S.

$$S = 5(R_0 - G_0)$$
$$S = 5(150R - 150S - G_0)$$
$$S = 750R - 750S - 5G_0$$
$$S + 750S = 750R - 5G_0$$
$$751S = 750R - 5G_0$$
$$S = 0.999R - 0.007G_0$$

FIGURE 12-32: Closed-loop block diagram for the cruise control.

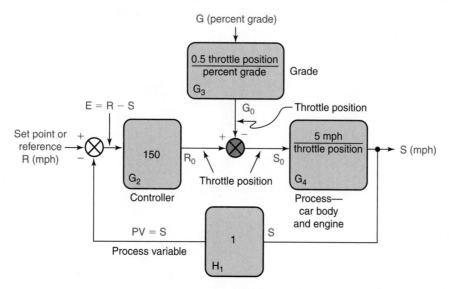

EXAMPLE 12-2

Determine the steady-state output for the closed-loop cruise control system for a reference speed of 55 mph and grades of 0, 1, 10, and 20 percent.

SOLUTION

Evaluate for grade of 0 percent:

$$S = 0.999R - 0.007G_0$$

$$S = 0.999 \times 55 \text{ mph} - 0.007 \times 0$$

$$S = 54.945 \text{ mph}$$

Evaluate for grade of 1 percent:

$$S = 0.999 \times 55 - 0.007 \times 1$$

$$S = 54.938 \text{ mph}$$

Evaluate for grade of 10 percent:

$$S = 0.999 \times 55 - 0.007 \times 10$$

$$S = 54.875 \text{ mph}$$

Evaluate for grade of 20 percent:

$$S = 0.999 \times 55 - 0.007 \times 20$$

$$S = 54.805 \text{ mph}$$

As you can observe from the calculations, the error is very small as long as the controller gain is large (150). The following table compares errors for the open- and close-loop cruise control system for different grades and process gains.

The table illustrates the significant improvement that feedback provided. Consider the following observations.

- At grades starting at 1 percent, the open-loop system had an error of 4.55 percent; above that grade the errors increased dramatically.
- The largest error for the closed-loop system was 0.35 percent for a grade of 20 percent.

- Process gain is difficult to establish accurately and may not be constant, so the effect of process gain change is important to consider. Changes in the process gain had little effect on the closed-loop system, but significant impact on the open-loop implementation.
- The closed-loop system output error (0.10 percent) when all disturbances are zero is a part of the steady-state error inherent in all feedback systems.
- The insensitivity of output speed to disturbances and changes in process gain are due in part to the high controller gain (150). However, if the closed loop gain is too large the system could become unstable.

Control System	Grade	Process Gain	Output Speed	Percent Error
Open-Loop	0	5	55	0%
Closed-Loop	0	5	54.95	0.10%
Open-Loop	1	5	52.5	4.55%
Closed-Loop	1	5	54.94	0.11%
Open-Loop	2	5	50	9.09%
Closed-Loop	10	5	54.88	0.23%
Closed-Loop	20	5	54.81	0.35%
Open-Loop	0	4	44	20.00%
Closed-Loop	0	4	54.89	0.18%
Open-Loop	1	4	42	23.64%
Closed-Loop	1	4	54.90	0.20%

In summary, closed-loop systems have the advantage of greater accuracy than open-loop systems, plus they are less sensitive to noise, disturbances, and changes in the environment. In addition, transient response and steady-state error are relatively easy to control with a gain adjustment in the loop or the addition of compensation to the controller. However, closed-loop systems are more complex and expensive than open-loop systems, and require some control system knowledge to efficiently implementation and maintain.

12-4-3   Load Change—Process Disturbance

The feedback system is called upon to bring the process output to the correct operational level when the input set point is changed or when a disturbance occurs. The term *disturbance* has been used frequently and appears on the block diagram in Figure 12-33. The two disturbances in the figure, Disturbance 1 and Disturbance 2, represent change imposed on one of the control elements and on the process, in that order. The type of change that is imposed most often is Disturbance 2, a forced change in the process's controlled variable, which includes a non-uniform input or output flow rate in a level control process or a non-uniform input fluid temperature in a tank temperature control process. The controlled variables, liquid level and process mixture temperature, have

a step-type change in the controlled parameter due to a disturbance. As a result, this type of forced change is called a *process load change*.

The *process load* is best described by a study of a home heating system. The loss of heat through the insulation in the walls, floor, and ceiling of a home is replaced by the heat generated by the furnace. The heat lost is changing continuously as the temperature and other climatic factors on the outside go through many step changes. The control system must balance the system load (heat lost) by regulating the rate at which energy is added back into the system through a change in the final control element (gas valve in the furnace) and eventually in the process variable (PV), which is the temperature in the home. The *load* is a disturbance that acts directly on the process, and the load on a process is always evident in the process variable. In feedback systems any change is evident in the process variable (PV) and system error. Controller action then causes a corresponding change in the setting of the final controlling element, which changes the process variable and corrects for the initial load change. In an ideal situation, the control action causes the manipulated variable to match the increased load placed on the process so that the controlled variable remains at the desired value.

FIGURE 12-33: Closed-loop system.

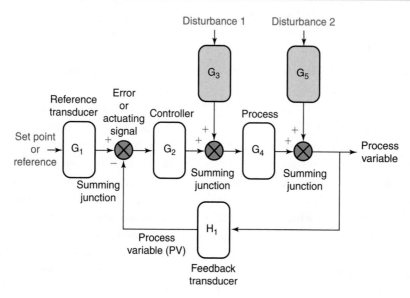

As a result, a good place to check for a system load is at the manipulated variable. Therefore, load is defined as follows:

The load on a control system is measured by the value of the manipulated variable required by the process to eliminate the effect of the load.

The load on a control system is never constant because disturbances that affect the controlled variable are all capable of causing a load change. When a process system must correct for load change, a self-correcting closed-loop system is necessary because it automatically makes the necessary change in the manipulated variable. Most often, uncontrolled system variables and parameters are the root cause of load changes. For example, changes in ambient conditions (temperature, humidity, pressure, power sources), the quality of the material used in the process, and flow rates for materials would require intervention by the control system.

12-5 ATTRIBUTES OF AN EFFECTIVE CONTROL SYSTEM

Control systems are *dynamic* because they respond to an input stimulus with a transient response before reaching a steady-state response that has an output level near the desired input set point. More dynamic input stimulus needs better control systems for the output to track changing input reference. To achieve this level of control, system analysis and design must address three major control objectives: producing the desired *transient response*, reducing *steady-state error*, and achieving *stability*. In addition, designers must also consider the trade-off between *performance and cost* and *system robustness*.

12-5-1 Transient Response
Transient response is an important control attribute because all physical systems have inertia that resists *change*, and change is the very thing that a control system tries to achieve. In some applications the rate at which the output responds to a change in the set point or to a load change is not as critical as others. For example, an aircraft autopilot system must react much faster to a change in direction due to a gust of wind than a process soup kettle must react to a

new temperature setting. In another example, the control system for a construction crane can be only as fast as the safe non-destructive movement of the large crane structure permits. Therefore, the application dictates the level of response, and the control system delivers an output that is most appropriate for the application. What is clear from our previous discussion of control systems is that the change in set point or the load change occurs and the control system's effort to conform to the new set point or to correct for the load change occurs some time later. The first objective of good control system is to respond to the demand for change as quickly as possible.

12-5-2 Response to Change
The waveforms illustrated in Figure 12-34 show a typical response from a temperature controller on a process mix tank. The tank mixes and heats several liquids in a continuous process. The load change occurs when one of the ingredients start to come in at a higher temperature than normal. The waveforms include the load change [Figure 12-34(a)], process variable (PV) [Figure 12-23(b)], and controller output (CO) [Figure 12-34(c)], which is the steam valve control signal. A study of the PV and CO curves indicates:

- The process change starts when the load change occurs, Figure 12-34(a).
- There is dead-time delay before the PV begins to react to the load change.
- The mix tank liquid increases in temperature, which forces the steam control valve to close and remove heat from the tank.
- The tank temperature then becomes too low and the steam valve opens to correct that problem.
- Oscillations continue until the steady-state condition is reached and the PV is constant again.
- The ideal PV response is indicated by the dashed line. To achieve this, MV would have to be at a closed position indicated by the dashed line on the MV graph.
- The steady-state response was not able to fully compensate for the increase in tank temperature, so a constant error, called the steady-state error or offset, is present.
- Study the figures and the analysis until the interaction between the curves is clear.

FIGURE 12-34: Response to a load charge.

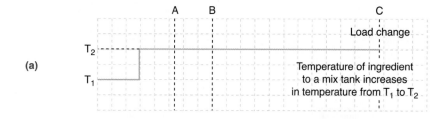

(a)

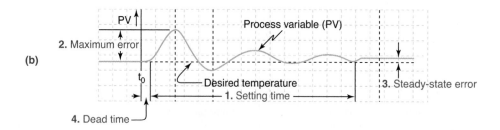

(b)

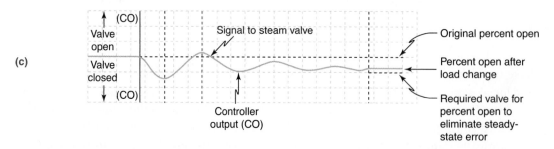

(c)

In order to achieve optimum performance, four attributes of the waveform must be reduced:

1. The length of the settling time
2. The maximum value of the response error
3. The residual or steady-state error
4. The dead time

The first two attributes are addressed in the transient analysis of the response, the third is addressed in the steady-state analysis, and the last, dead time, is the most difficult to correct and often cannot be fixed because it is inherent in the process. Some issues associated with dead time are addressed later in this section.

12-5-3 Controller Response and Damping

The first transient response objective of good control is to reduce the settling time required for the system to reach a steady-state value. The second is to reduce the maximum error. There are three distinct types of response curves: *overdamped, critically damped,* and *underdamped.* Figure 12-35 illustrates how a control system with each type would react to step set point change. In each graph the relative value of the rise time, the time required for the waveform to go from 10 to 90 percent of the final value, is reported. In addition, the relative value of the damping coefficient, a number between 0 and 1, is also listed. Some observations:

- The overdamped controller has a very large rise time and damping coefficient (0.8 or 0.9), whereas the rise time and damping coefficient (0.4 or 0.5) of the underdamped controller is very small.
- If fast response is required then a slightly underdamped response is necessary, but you

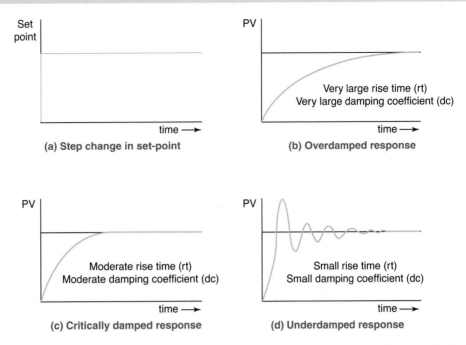

(a) Step change in set-point

(b) Overdamped response

(c) Critically damped response

(d) Underdamped response

Rehg and Sartori, Industrial Electronics, 1st Edition, © 2006, Reprinted by permission of Pearson Education, Inc., Upper Saddle River, NJ.

have to live with the larger maximum error and longer settling time. The oscillations present while the response settles to a final value are called *ringing*.

- The critically damped response is between the other two response extremes, with a moderately fast rise time produced by a damping coefficient in the 0.6 to 0.7 range but no overshoot.
- The damping and the controller response are directly related to controller gain. Therefore, increases in controller gain change the damping from overdamped to critically damped and finally to underdamped.

The optimum response is either critically damped or slightly underdamped with the optimum value dictated by the control requirements of the process. All design is a series of trade-offs, as the discussion on the three responses makes very clear. The optimum response for a given application requirement is a compromise.

12-5-4 Transient Response Options

The transient response form is dictated by the application requirements; however, for most applications a compromise between the *best* pos-sible *rise time*, *lowest* possible *overshoot* (another term for *maximum error*), and the *shortest* achievable *settling time* is a good choice. Design of controllers and feedback systems is a complex process. It is easy to find entire texts devoted to a discussion on one element in the process. However, as a starting point for an understanding of a good response consider the following four responses: *quarter amplitude decay, peak percentage overshoot, minimum integral of absolute error,* and *critical damping.* These are frequently used in industrial applications with less complex control requirements and are illustrated in Figure 12-36, along with the step change in set point used to test them. Each is described as follows:

- **Quarter amplitude decay** [shown in Figure 12-36(b)]: The level of ringing is specified such that each successive positive peak value is one-fourth of the value present in the previous positive peak. Control system parameters are adjusted until the desired results are obtained. Quarter amplitude decay is used frequently, easy to implement, and a good trade-off between rise time, overshoot, and settling time.

FIGURE 12-36: Workable transient response options.

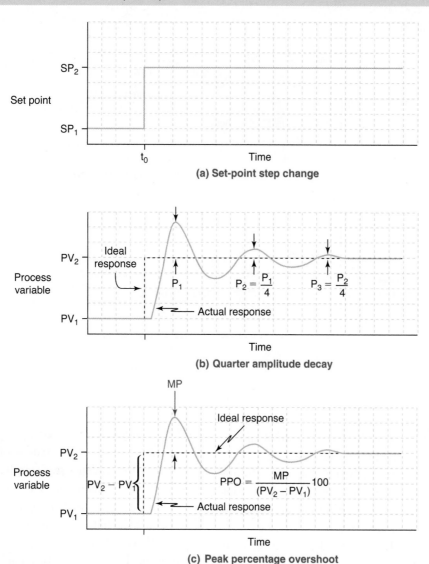

(a) Set-point step change

(b) Quarter amplitude decay

(c) Peak percentage overshoot

Rehg and Sartori, Industrial Electronics, *1st Edition, © 2006, Reprinted by permission of Pearson Education, Inc., Upper Saddle River, NJ.*

- Peak percentage overshoot [shown in Figure 12-36(c)]: Peak percentage overshoot (PPO) specifies the maximum peak (MP) overshoot as a percentage of the step change. The formula for MP is:

$$MP = \frac{PPO \times (PV_2 - PV_2)}{100}$$

where the peak percentage overshoot is selected for an anticipated change in PV and the MP is calculated. Control system parameters are adjusted until the desired results are obtained. Like the quarter amplitude decay,

this response form is easy to implement, and allows for rise time adjustments as a function of overshoot limits.

- Minimum integral of absolute error [shown in Figure 12-36(d)]: The basis for this response option is to keep the integral of the error (E) or the shaded area in the figure to a minimum. The shaded area represents the distance between the ideal response and the actual controlled variable. If that area is minimized, then the PV approaches the ideal response. This technique is used when the process has been modeled and a numerical

FIGURE 12-36: (Continued).

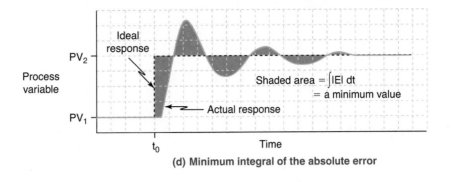

(d) Minimum integral of the absolute error

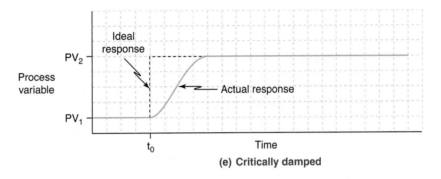

(e) Critically damped

representation of the control system can be used for the integration process.

- Critical damping [shown in Figure 12-36(e)]: Critical damping is selected when overshoot cannot be tolerated. Critical damping is the minimum damping that will bring the PV to the desired value with the best rise time with no ringing.

12-5-5   Steady-State Response

The second major control objective is to reduce the steady-state error that is often present in the steady-state response. Figure 12-34 illustrates the response element that remains after the transients have decayed to zero. If the steady-state response were always equal to the new set point value after a reference change or equal to the previous controlled variable output after a load change, then this discussion of steady-state response would end here. However, what often occurs is a steady-state error or offset in the PV after a change in the set point or load. First let's explore why steady-state error or offset is present, then we will look at corrections that are used.

12-5-6   Understanding Steady-State Error

The cause of steady-state error is often hard to understand for students studying feedback control for the first time. In the model section earlier, the closed-loop cruise control system analysis showed that the output of the cruise control was not exactly equal to the anticipated output as a result of steady-state error. Turn back and review those calculations.

From an analytical standpoint, steady-state error is present because some error or actuating signal is necessary to move the controlled variable closer to the desired output after a set point or load change. This concept is fairly abstract when described as text, so it is often easier to demonstrate the condition that produces steady-state error. Note the mechanical level control system and the results in Figure 12-37. Study the diagram.

The outlet flow from the vessel is 5 gallons per minute (gpm). The input valve is manually opened and the tank is allowed to fill to the 75 percent level [Figure 12-37(a)]. At that point the percent open value of the input valve is adjusted until it is also 5 gpm, so the level remains constant

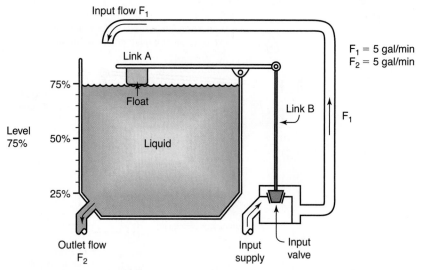

$F_1 = 5$ gal/min
$F_2 = 5$ gal/min

(a) Input flow is set equal to outlet flow by operator with level at 75 percent

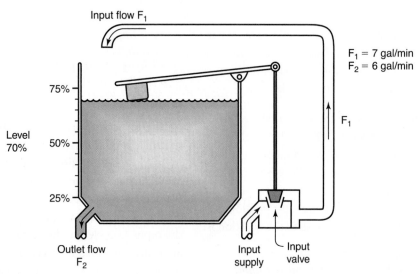

$F_1 = 7$ gal/min
$F_2 = 6$ gal/min

(b) Increased outlet flow to 6 gpm—level drops to 70 percent—input flow rises to 7 gpm

Rehg and Sartori, Industrial Electronics, 1ˢᵗ Edition, © 2006, Reprinted by permission of Pearson Education, Inc., Upper Saddle River, NJ.

at 75 percent. This may take some adjustment until the operator achieves this exact setting. At that point the length of link B is adjusted so that link A allows the float to rest on the liquid surface. The system is now in automatic control, and the mechanical control system keeps the liquid level constant. Let's explore a load change scenario.

1. Due to process problems the outlet flow is increased to 6 gpm in a step load change. The increased outflow causes the liquid level to fall to 70 percent [Figure 12-37(b)]. Link A at the float follows the float to the lower liquid level. This raises link B and increases the flow in the input valve to 7 gpm, which is an overcorrection.

2. The increased input (7 gpm) allows the level to recover from this load change response, and the liquid level rises and

FIGURE 12-37: (Continued).

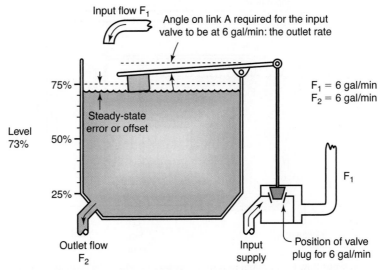

Input flow F_1

Angle on link A required for the input valve to be at 6 gal/min: the outlet rate

75%

Steady-state error or offset

Level 73%

50%

25%

F_1 = 6 gal/min
F_2 = 6 gal/min

F_1

Outlet flow F_2

Input supply

Position of valve plug for 6 gal/min

(c) Input flow and outlet flow are 6 gpm but level is at 73 percent

achieves a new equilibrium level of 73 percent [Figure 12-37(c)]. At this point the flow from the input valve is 6 gpm, which is the same as the new outlet flow.

After the load change the system only returned to the 73 percent level. Why is the level not at 75 percent, and why is link A at a slight angle compared to the initial system condition? The answer to these questions is the key to understanding why steady-state error is present and must be addressed by the controller. One response to the question is:

If the float was at the 75 percent level, then links A and B would put the input valve at a position for a 5 gpm flow as in the initial setup. Since this flow would not balance the new outlet flow of 6 gpm, the valve must be in the 6 gpm position. The 6 gpm input flow is only achieved when the liquid and float are at 73 percent, not 75 percent. That difference is the steady-state error.

The 2 percent difference between the desired level of 75 percent and the system response of 73 percent after a load change is the *steady-state error.* Another response is:

With this mechanical controller, the error is necessary to drive the final control ele-ment (input valve) into a 6 gpm position so that the system is balanced. If the error was 0, then the final control element flow would not match the new flow after the load change.

The response waveform for the load change that triggered the system response is illustrated in Figure 12-38(a). Following the disturbance of a 1 gpm increase in the outlet flow, the input flow rate, Figure 12-38(b), initially rises to 7 gpm and then reaches equilibrium at 6 gpm, the input rate. When the system comes into balance, distinguished by no change in the level, the input and output flow rates must be equal. The response of the controlled variable is illustrated in Figure 12-38(c). Note that the level drops rapidly at first due to the step increase in outlet flow to 6 gpm. The falls to 70 percent and starts to level off only when the input flow exceeds the new outlet flow of 6 gpm. As the input flow reaches the 7 gpm rate, the liquid level starts to climb toward the final value of 73 percent. The input flow falls to the 6 gpm flow necessary for a balance system when the level reaches 73 percent. Spend time studying Figures 12-37 and 12-38 and thinking about the two explanations just presented until the concept of steady-state response is clear.

FIGURE 12-38: Response curve for 1 gpm flow load change.

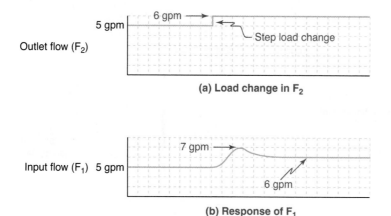

(a) Load change in F₂

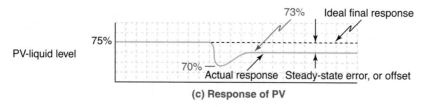

(b) Response of F₁

(c) Response of PV

Rehg and Sartori, Industrial Electronics, *1st Edition, © 2006, Reprinted by permission of Pearson Education, Inc., Upper Saddle River, NJ.*

EXAMPLE 12-3

The system outlet flow is at the 6 gpm rate as illustrated in Figure 12-37(c). The system outlet experiences 1 gpm decrease as a step load change. Determine the steady-state output for the system.

SOLUTION

The system change that results from the decrease in load is as follows:

1. The outlet now has a 5 gpm flow, whereas the input is still at the 6 gpm rate.
2. The greater input flow causes the liquid level to rise to 78 percent as the tank fills more rapidly than it drains.
3. The level increase raises the float and lowers link B, which closes the input valve, reducing the input flow to 4 gpm.
4. The decrease in input flow rate (4 gpm) allows the level to recover from this load change reaction, and the liquid level drops from 78 percent to an equilibrium level of 75 percent.
5. As the level falls to the 75 percent level, the input flow approaches 5 gpm, the same as the new outlet flow.
6. The system is back in balance and the steady-state error is zero.

No steady-state error occurs with the load change back to the initial system flows since the system was manually set up to control the level at 75 percent. No system error need be present to position the input valve for 5 gpm since that is the initial control condition.

12-5-7   Correction for Steady-State Error

A correction for the steady-state error is hidden in the load change analysis just completed. To help locate the solution, study the more detailed analysis of the system load change in Figure 12-39. The following important observations are made.

Figure 12-39(a) Observations (System setup – system balanced)

- The desired level is 75 percent and a liquid level at that percentage produces an outlet flow into the downstream process of 5 gpm.

FIGURE 12-39: Analysis of system steady-state error.

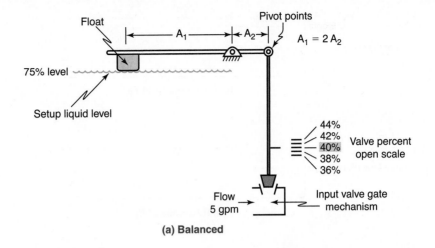

(a) Balanced

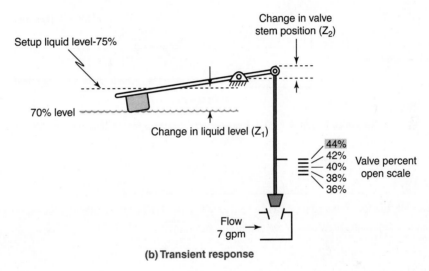

(b) Transient response

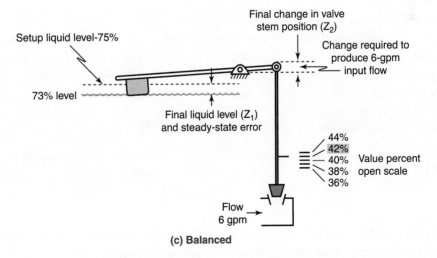

(c) Balanced

Rehg and Sartori, Industrial Electronics, *1st Edition, © 2006, Reprinted by permission of Pearson Education, Inc., Upper Saddle River, NJ.*

- To maintain a 75 percent level link B is adjusted so that the input valve is set at 40 percent open, which produces an input flow of 5 gpm.
- The system is now balanced.

Figure 12-39(b) Observations (Reaction to disturbance – transient response)

- The change in outlet flow from 5 gpm to 6 gpm causes the liquid level to drop initially to 70 percent.
- The change in the float and liquid level is indicated as Z_1. The fulcrum produces a corresponding change in the position of link B that is indicated as Z_2. Since A_2 is twice as long as A_1 (link A lengths on each side of the pivot), the Z_2 change is only half of the change present at Z_1.
- The rise in link B by the Z_2 value opens the input valve to 44 percent.
- The increased input flow of 7 gpm results from the valve opening of 44 percent and is a transient response to the increase in outlet flow.
- In this stage of the response the system is searching for a liquid level which will hold the input valve at a percent open value that will balance input flow with the new output flow of 6 gpm.
- The link B value, Z_2, is changing continuously as the system moves to a new balance condition.

Figure 12-39(c) Observations (New outlet and input flows – system balanced)

- The feedback system for the level control (links A and B) determines that a liquid level of 73 percent will produce a value of Z_2 that opens the input valve to 42 percent.
- A 42 percent valve opening produces an input flow of 6 gpm, which balances the new outlet flow of 6 gpm.
- The difference in the current level (73 percent) and the desired level (75 percent) is 2 percent; this represents the system steady-state error that results from the load change.
- The important insight at this point is that as long as the system is in balance, the valve *must stay at 42 percent* to produce the required flow of 6 gpm, so the *current value of Z_2 cannot change.*

It is not clear what must be held fixed for the system to reach a new balance after the load change. You might ask the question:

What could be changed in Figure 12-39(c) that would allow the liquid level to rise closer to 75 percent while keeping the value of Z_2 unchanged?

The answer to that question leads to one solution for steady-state error.

At this point it should be clear that steady-state error is present in control systems. There is more than one solution for steady-state error, but the one usually considered first is illustrated in Figure 12-40. The figure shows the level control problem after the load change disturbance [Figures 12-37(c) and 12-39(c)] when the system balance has returned with an input and outlet flow of 6 gpm. At this point the steady-state error is 2 percent (75% desired level − 73% actual level = 2% error).

The position of link B is fixed with the Z_2 value setting the input valve at 42 percent open and an input flow of 6 gpm. Link A is divided into two distances: the center of the float to the fulcrum location (A_1) and the fulcrum to the connection to link B (A_2). Since Z_2 cannot change the angle of link A is also fixed. Therefore, if the float was moved toward the fulcrum, then the liquid level could rise and the 6-gpm input valve position is not affected. So changing the position of the float from position P_1 (73 percent liquid level) to P_2 allows the tank level to increase to 73.6 percent, a reduction of 0.6 percent in the steady-state error. If the float was repositioned again to P_3, then the liquid could rise to the 74.3 percent level, which is only a 0.7 percent steady-state error. To understand what is changing in the control system to allow this improvement in steady-state error, the elements present in the tank process must be related to a block diagram.

The diagram in Figure 12-41 represents the tank control process. Compare the blocks and terms in the figure with the system in Figure 12-37 while you review the procedure used to set the initial level at 75 percent. Link B was adjusted to achieve the desired level; therefore, it is the set point. The float determines the current level, so it is the feedback position sensor. The controller is link A since it determines how much change should occur in the final control element when the set level and the actual level are not equal. The controller summing junction is the difference with a positive error for drops in tank level that would increase

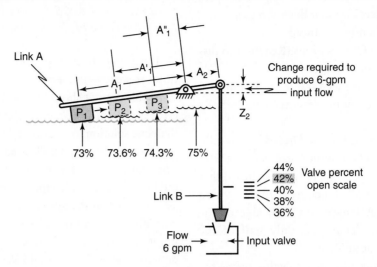

Rehg and Sartori, Industrial Electronics, *1st Edition, © 2006, Reprinted by permission of Pearson Education, Inc., Upper Saddle River, NJ.*

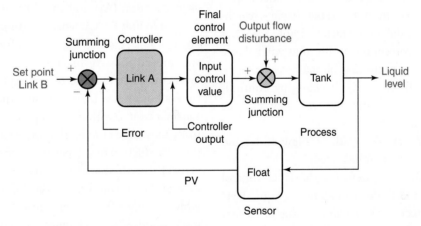

Rehg and Sartori, Industrial Electronics, *1st Edition, © 2006, Reprinted by permission of Pearson Education, Inc., Upper Saddle River, NJ.*

the opening on the input valve, the final control element. The disturbance summing junction is the sum of the balanced flow rate and the change in flow represented by a load change. Since it was a change in the location of the float along link A that improved the steady-state error, analysis of link A provides the reason for this reduction in error.

Link A is a lever with the requisite fulcrum. As the float moves from position P_1 to position P_2 the lengths of the link elements on the left side of the fulcrum changed. These changes are illustrated in Figure 12-42. Every lever has an input and out-

put end as illustrated in Figure 12-42(a). The change in input and output is the difference between the original position of the lever (horizontal) and the final position (some rotation about the fulcrum). In this case the input is on the left and the output is on the right. Using the relationship between sides of similar triangles, the mechanical advantage or gain is the ratio of y over x, as shown.

Apply the information from the lever analysis in Figure 12-42(a) to the position changes of the float in the tank level control problem. Note that as the float moved closer to the fulcrum the gain increased from 0.5 to 2. Earlier we determined

FIGURE 12-42: Controller analysis for gain.

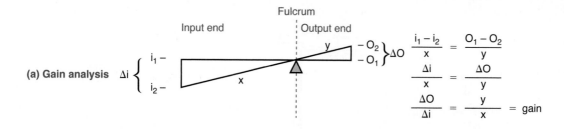

Rehg and Sartori, Industrial Electronics, 1st Edition, © 2006, Reprinted by permission of Pearson Education, Inc., Upper Saddle River, NJ.

that as the float moved closer to the fulcrum the steady-state error decreased. Therefore, we observe that control system steady-state error and gain have an inverse relationship.

An increase in the controller system gain decreases the steady-state error.

The control system gain includes the cumulative gain of all the control system functional blocks except the process block. For example, an increase in the final element gain reduces the steady-state error just as does an increase in the controller gain. However, the easiest place to change the gain is in the controller.

12-5-8 Controller Gain Side Effects

The decrease in the steady-state error as a result of an increase in controller gain causes problems in other parts of the system response. Analysis of the system during the transient phase of the response to a load change in Figure 12-39(b) illustrates the problem. Assume that the float is located at P_2, so the controller gain is changed from 0.5 to 1, and the system response is modified to incorporate the increase in gain by changing Figure 12-39(b) to the illustration in Figure 12-43. Compare the two figures until the effect on the valve position is understood.

FIGURE 12-43: Change in transient response for higher controller gain.

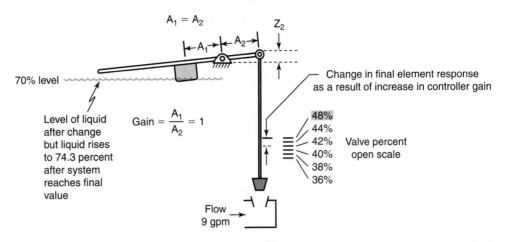

70% level

Level of liquid after change but liquid rises to 74.3 percent after system reaches final value

$$\text{Gain} = \frac{A_1}{A_2} = 1$$

$A_1 = A_2$

Z_2

Change in final element response as a result of increase in controller gain

48%
44%
42%   Valve percent
40%   open scale
38%
36%

Flow
9 gpm

Rehg and Sartori, Industrial Electronics, 1st Edition, © 2006, Reprinted by permission of Pearson Education, Inc., Upper Saddle River, NJ.

With gains of 0.5 and 1, the initial drop in the tank level after the load change is about equal at 70 percent. Also, the input and outlet flows balance at 6 gpm. However, two things are different. The steady-state level error drops from 2 to 1.4 percent with the higher gain, and the value of Z_2 the input valve transient change to correct for the disturbance, is twice as large when the gain is 1. The larger change in Z_2 causes the input value to open to 48 percent, which causes the input flow to jump to 9 gpm. This strong response reduces the amount that the level will fall, but it also causes the level to recover to over the 74 percent mark before settling down the steady-state value of 73.6 percent. Increased controller gain benefits steady-state response by reducing error and improving response rise time; however, the transient response becomes less optimum because of a higher maximum error and longer settling times. The ideal controller gain is a compromise built on the following criteria:

- The level of steady-state error that can be tolerated.
- The minimum rise time required.
- The maximum value of overshoot.
- The maximum allowed settling time.

If a compromise cannot be reached, then a priority for the criteria must be established for determining the controller gain.

12-5-9   Steady-State Error Correction with Bias

A second technique to reduce steady-state error is to use a *bias* or *offset* input to the controller. The functional block diagram for the tank level controller in Figure 12-41 has a bias or offset input added in Figure 12-44. Compare the two figures.

The function of the bias or offset input is to add enough signal to the final control element so that the steady-state error left in the system is removed. For example, in the tank control problem the bias input would replace the signal generated by the position of the float below the 75 percent fill level. If the bias increased the flow in the input valve, then the tank level would increase. Increased tank level would reduce the steady-state error and the amount of signal from the controller used to keep the input flow at 6 gpm. When the bias provides all the signal necessary for the input valve to deliver 6 gpm, then the error into the controller and its output can be zero. At this point the steady-error falls to zero.

The problem with this solution is that it is only good until another set point or load change occurs. At that point the bias may make the situation worse or at least must be changed every time a set point or load change happened.

12-5-10   Stability

Improving the transient response and reducing steady-state error is of little value if the system is

FIGURE 12-44: Controller bias for steady-state error reduction.

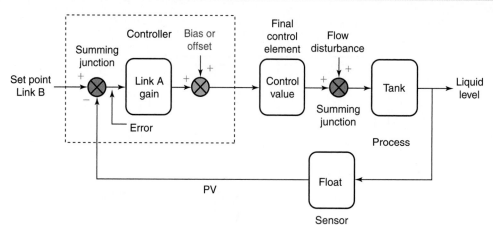

Rehg and Sartori, Industrial Electronics, 1st Edition, © 2006, Reprinted by permission of Pearson Education, Inc., Upper Saddle River, NJ.

FIGURE 12-45: Oscillatory system responses.

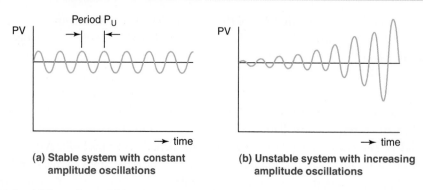

(a) Stable system with constant amplitude oscillations

(b) Unstable system with increasing amplitude oscillations

Rehg and Sartori, Industrial Electronics, 1st Edition, © 2006, Reprinted by permission of Pearson Education, Inc., Upper Saddle River, NJ.

not *stable*. *Stability* is linked to the *total* system response, which is the sum of the *natural* and *forced* system responses. The natural system response is what a system does after a disturbance or set point change; it must either die out to zero or oscillate for a stable system. In some systems, the natural response to a change is to initiate an oscillation with increasing larger peak values. The responses shown in Figure 12-45 illustrate two of these conditions. The first is called a stable system with a *constant amplitude oscillation response;* the second is called an unstable system with an *increasing amplitude oscillation response.* For many processes, the first condition causes no system damage and is used in tuning processes, but the second can be destructive for the process system. In each case the damping ratio is zero, so the system is not damped.

The total system response, as illustrated in Figure 12-46, includes the dead-time delay, transient portion, and steady-state portion. The total response is the sum of the natural system response and the forced response (the step change in Figure 12-46). In a stable system, the natural system response dies out after a disturbance or change in set point to leave only the forced response (the new step level). That is the case in Figure 12-46 but not in Figure 12-45. The natural response describes the way the system acquires and dissipates energy. The input to the system does not affect the form or nature of the natural response since it is dependent only on the system parameters. However, the system input directly affects the form or nature of the forced response. The total response illustrated in Figure 12-46 is what

FIGURE 12-46: System response curve.

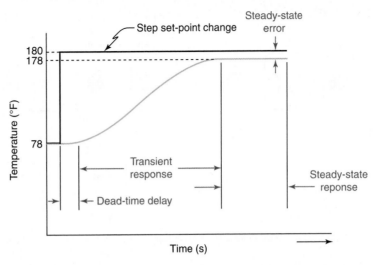

you actually see, and it is the combination of the natural and forced responses that has been divided into three components, dead-time delay, transient response, and steady-state response.

The natural response of a control system will approach zero or oscillate for a stable system. However, if the natural response oscillations grow without bound rather than diminishing to zero the system is *unstable*. In this case, the natural response is much greater than the forced response and control has been lost for the system. This condition is called *instability* and can cause the physical device to self-destruct if limit stops are not part of the design.

The goal is to design stable control systems. To achieve this goal the system's natural response must decay to zero or oscillate as time approaches infinity. The transient response is usually dominated by the system's natural response. Therefore, the system transient response will die out as time increases if the natural response decays to zero. What remains then is only the steady-state response, which is dominated by the forced response or input. The desired transient and steady-state response can be established during the design process for a stable system.

Two other important considerations must be considered in the design of a control system: cost constraints and robust design. Designers must consider the economic impact of control system design based on budget allocations and competitive pricing.

A second important consideration is robust design. Components that set system parameters and establish the transient response, steady-state errors, and stability can change over time after the actual system is built. As a result, the performance of the system changes and no longer fulfills the design goals. To solve this problem, designers try to design a robust system where the system is not sensitive to component and parameter changes.

Closed-Loop Process Control. The closed-loop control systems described in this chapter are used in every type of process and in every process industry. The development of a control system to drive these closed-loop requirements is the topic of Chapter 14. The following statements summarize the operation found in closed-loop systems.

- Disturbances to the controller or process are frequently present.
- Final control elements are continuous devices with outputs from 0 to 100 percent.
- Controller output values are the product of the controller gain (K) and the input error (SP − MV or MV − SP).

- The controller output changes the final control element so that the controlled variable moves closer to the desired set point.
- A continuous proportional control system has zero steady-state error only at the control variable and set point values established at system startup.
- If a disturbance or set point change occurs in a system with proportional control, then some steady-state error will result.
  - The steady state error and the proportional controller gain have an *inverse* relationship (increase gain and reduce steady-state error).
  - Transient response maximum peak and settling time have a *direct* relationship with controller gain (increase gain and increase overshoot and ringing).
  - Steady-state error cannot be completely eliminated with increases in controller gain.

12-6 TROUBLESHOOTING THE PROPORTIONAL GAIN CONTROLLER

Proportional gain controllers used in closed-loop processes involve many intricate machines and systems. As a result, it is difficult to provide a troubleshooting process for every conceivable process system. However, here are some general procedures and suggestions that can help in locating problems.

1. Know the process: before you can troubleshoot the proportional gain controller you must first understand the process inside and out—how it operates and how disturbances affect the process.
2. Know the control system: it is equally important to know the control system used in the process. It is important to separate controller issues from system component failure problems.
3. Process versus control problems: three situations may be present if the process product is defective:
   1. The process may be operating correctly, but the control system may be malfunctioning.
   2. The control system may be operating correctly, but the process may be malfunctioning.
   3. The control system and the process may be malfunctioning. This is generally ruled out because multiple failures are not as common as single failures.

CHAPTER 13

PLC Standard IEC 61131-3 Function Block Diagrams

13-1 GOALS AND OBJECTIVES

The goals for this chapter are to provide an overview of IEC 61131-3 graphic languages and to provide the Allen-Bradley implementation of the IEC 61131 Function Block Diagram language.

After completing this chapter you should be able to:

- Describe the difference between Ladder Logic, Function Block Diagram, and Sequential Function Chart graphic languages.
- Define the components of the Allen-Bradley Function Block Diagram (FBD) language.
- Describe the process used to build an FBD program.
- Create a function block diagram program for automation process problems using the Allen-Bradley implementation.

13-2 PLC STANDARDS

The first standard for PLCs was published in 1978 by the *National Electrical Manufacturers Association* (NEMA). However, the rapid growth in PLCs across national boundaries demanded a broader standard. In 1979 the *International Electrotechnical Commission* (IEC) established a working group to look at the complete standard-

ization of PLCs. The PLC standard, called IEC 1131 (changed later to IEC 61131), has the following parts.

- Part 1: General information establishes the definitions and identifies the principal characteristics relevant to the selection and application of programmable controllers (PLCs) and their associated peripherals.
- Part 2: Equipment requirements and tests specify equipment requirements and related tests for programmable controllers and their associated peripherals.
- Part 3: Programming languages define, as a minimum set, the basic programming elements; syntactic and semantic rules for the most commonly used programming languages, as well as major fields of application; and applicable tests and means by which manufacturers may expand or adapt those basic sets to their own programmable controller implementations. Five PLC languages are defined.
- Part 4: User guidelines is a technical report providing general overview information and application guidelines of the standard for the end user of programmable controllers.
- Part 5: Messaging service specification defines the data communication between programmable controllers and other electronic

systems using the Manufacturing Message Specification (MMS), according to International Standard ISO/IEC 9506.

- Part 6: Reserved for future use.
- Part 7: Fuzzy control programming defines basic programming elements for fuzzy logic control as used in programmable controllers.
- Part 8: Guidelines for the application and implementation of programming languages provides a software developers guide for the programming languages defined in Part 3.

Part 3 of the standard, *Programming Languages for Programmable Controllers*, was released in 1993 and specifies the standards for PLC software. The IEC 61131-3 standard provides a very specific and detailed definition of PLC configuration, programming, and data storage. The programming standard specifies five languages that PLC vendors should support if their controller is specified as IEC 61131 compatible. The languages are:

- Ladder Diagrams (LD)
- Sequential Function Chart (SFC)
- Function Block Diagram (FBD)
- Structured Text (ST)
- Instruction List (IL)

Ladder logic has been described in detail in the first 11 chapters of this text; the concepts learned there will make learning the other languages easier. This chapter covers the programming format for Function Block Diagrams, one of the three graphic languages. However, it is important to define all the languages in the standard.

13-2-1 IEC 61131-3 Standard Languages
A general description of each language follows.

- IL (Instruction List)—Textural: A low-level, text-based language that uses mnemonic instructions like those used in machine code in microprocessors. Consequently, IL is a powerful language but it has many disadvantages, such as a cryptic nature. In addition, Allen-Bradley does not support this language. It is not a good fit for most applications, and as a result it is used infrequently in the United States.

- ST (Structured Text)—Textural: A high-level, text-based language, such as BASIC, C, or PASCAL, with commands that support a highly structured program development and the ability to evaluate complex mathematical expressions. Structured text is covered in Chapter 15.

- LD (Ladder Diagram)—Graphical: The 61131-3 graphical language is based on traditional relay ladder logic. LD is used for logic operations involving only Boolean variables (e.g., True and False). The language elements include only input instructions (i.e., XIO and XIC) and outputs (i.e., OTE, OTL, and OUT) that are placed on a ladder rung to produce the required logic. If timers, counters, or other special functions are required, then function blocks with those functions are included. Most vendors do not support the LD part of the standard since they already have a fully functional ladder logic format for their PLC systems.

- FBD (Function Block Diagram)—Graphical: Another graphical language where the basic programming elements appear as blocks. They are linked together to form a final control circuit. The blocks manipulate or operate on the data that flows from input to output connections. Data can be Boolean, integer, real, or text with other types also supported. A large library of standard function blocks is available. Function block diagrams are covered in this chapter.

- SFC (Sequential Function Chart)—Graphical: Based on the French standard, GRAFCET, this is a graphical language used most often for sequential control problems. The basic language elements are steps or states that perform associated actions on the process and transitions used to move from the current step or state to next. The actions and transitions are defined in terms of the four other languages. As a result, the SFC language is often used for the basic sequential program flow with FBD, LD, and ST programs embedded into the SFC structure.

Two of the languages, Instruction List and Structured Text, are textural, so commands and their arguments are entered from a keyboard, one line at a time. Three, Ladder Diagram, Function Block Diagram, and Sequential Function Chart,

are graphical. A graphical editor is used to build the program on the computer screen of the programming device.

Compliance. Many PLC vendors support the 61131-3 standard; however, the degree of compliance with the standard varies greatly. Three levels of compliance are currently defined:

- **Base level compliance:** defines an essential core of the 61131 standard and the necessary features of each supported language. A product can be certified as base level compliant in one, several, or all of the languages. Base level compliance includes a small number of basic data types and a restricted set of standard functions.
- **Portability level compliance:** defines a larger set of required features and must incorporate an import/export tool to exchange 61131 software with other portability level compliant systems.
- **Full compliance:** full compliance indicates complete implementation of the 61131 standard and fully interchangeable programs.

Allen-Bradley implements the standard on their Logix family of PLCs, so all programming is performed with the RSLogix 5000 software. Achieving interchangeability of programs between different vendor PLCs is a long way off, but support for the standard has increased the programming options on PLCs. Since the standard is still relatively new and the task to achieve compliance is large, the majority of current vendors do not completely implement all the features specified in the standard.

13-3 FUNCTION BLOCK DIAGRAM (FBD)

The *Function Block Diagram (FBD)* language is used to program automation problems as a set of interconnected graphical function blocks. For example, to add two values you select an addition block. If you want a timer, then you select a timer block. Block inputs and outputs are connected by lines. This is very similar to the signal flows depicted in electronic circuit diagrams. A typical signal flow for an FBD is illustrated in Figure 13-1. Note that the function blocks are

---

FIGURE 13-1: Example FBD circuit.

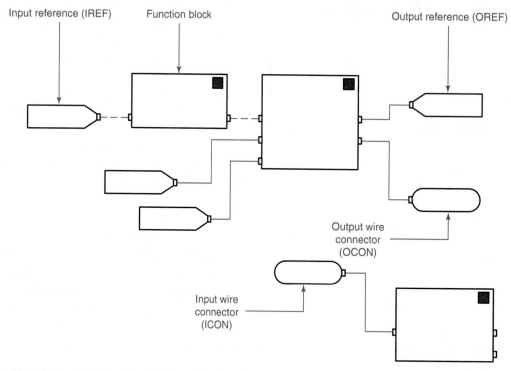

Rehg and Sartori, Industrial Electronics, *1st Edition, © 2006, Reprinted by permission of Pearson Education, Inc., Upper Saddle River, NJ.*

linked together to complete a circuit that satisfies a control requirement. The inputs, placed into an *input reference symbol*, are on the left and the outputs, placed into an *output reference symbol*, are on the right. The input and output tag names are placed inside the *IREF* and *OREF* symbols. A jump between segments of the FBD is represented by the *OCON* (output wire connector) and *ICON* (input wire connector) symbols.

The line type of the link between function blocks indicates what type of signal is present. A dashed line, as shown in Figure 13-2(a), indicates a Boolean signal path (e.g., 0 or 1) and a solid line indicates an integer or real value (e.g., 527 or 21.7) signal path. An FBD circuit is analogous to an electrical circuit diagram or system block diagram where links and wires depict electrical signal paths between components.

A function block is depicted as a rectangular block, as shown in Figure 13-2(a), with inputs entering from the left and outputs exiting on the right. The function block type is always shown within the block, a tag name for the block is placed above it, and the names of the FBD inputs (left side of the block) and outputs (right side of the block) are shown within the block. The default view of all boxes has some but not all of the input and output parameters visible when the box is placed into the program. The FBD properties box, used to set the visibility option of input and output parameters, is displayed by left clicking the selection button at the upper right of the FBD. The selection button, indicated in Figure 13-2(a), is clicked to produce the timer properties box displayed in Figure 13-2(b).

The properties box has two tabs: *Parameters* and *Tag*, in the upper left corner. The Parameter tab, which is displayed in the figure, shows a list of I/O functions that are available, the parameter value, the data type, and a description. The full description for a truncated listing is displayed by placing the cursor on the description in the box. Parameters with a check in the check box in front of the parameter are listed inside the FBD block when it is placed in the program. Parameter values can be entered directly into the dialog box. For example, the timer preset value could be entered into the dialog box in the Value cell after the PRE cell [see Figure 13-2(b)]. A second option would be to select the preset parameter so it appears in the FBD box and then use an IREF to hold the value [see Figure 13-2(a)]. All parameter values are

FIGURE 13-2: Example function block and standard displays.

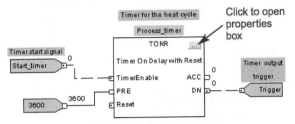

(a) TONR type timer default display

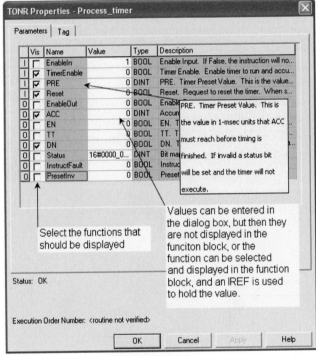

(b) Properties box

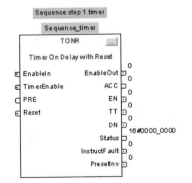

(c) TONR timer with all I/O functions displayed

displayed in the properties box and a select few are displayed in the FBD block in the program.

The Tag tab of the properties box permits the tag properties to be adjusted and descriptions to be entered. A timer function block with all input and output parameters displayed is illustrated in Figure 13-2(c). Note how much larger the block is when all input and outputs are displayed. The display for all function blocks is adjusted using this process. Study the block in Figure 13-2(a) to see a typical FBD with inputs and outputs. This is how a typical block appears in the FBD programming environment for the Allen-Bradley ControlLogix 5000 processor.

The table in Figure 13-3 describes how to choose FBD elements to build an FBD control circuit like that in Figure 13-1. Note that IREF and OREF symbols are used to define tags for the input and output values. The OCON and ICON symbols allow for breaks in the links between blocks to make the diagrams less cluttered and easier to read.

Each function block uses a *tag or variable* to store configuration information, status information, and parameter values for the function block instruction. When a function block instruction is added in the RSLogix 5000 software FBD language, a tag is automatically created for the block. This default tag name can be edited by double-clicking on it and changing it to a name that reflects the function of the block in the control program. In addition, the programmer must create a tag name or assign an existing tag for all IREFs and OREFs used with FBD inputs and outputs. The table in Figure 13-4 outlines the format for an FBD tag name, which is created like the tags in the ControlLogix ladder logic programs.

13-3-1   Signal Flow Types, Execution Order, and Data Latching

There are two types of signal data flows in an FBD: Boolean and real values. A dashed line indicates that the data is a discrete (1 or 0) or Boolean type. A solid line indicates that the data is an integer or real number.

Execution order is dictated by the signal flow and impacted by the *data latching* process covered next. *Signal flow* inside the FBD blocks is always from inputs on the left to the outputs on the right side. Outside the FBD blocks, signal flow moves from function block to function block in a left-to-right fashion, so it flows from a block output on the left to a second block input on the right.

If a feedback path is present, then the signal flows from the output of a block on the right back toward the left to the input of a block on

---

FIGURE 13-3: Choosing FBD elements.

If you want to:	Then use a(n):
Supply a value from an input device or tag	Input reference (IREF)
Send a value to an output device or tag	Output reference (OREF)
Perform an operation on an input value or values and produce an output value or values	Function block
Transfer data between function blocks when they are: • Far apart on the same sheet • On different sheets within the same routine	Output wire connector (OCON) and an input wire connector (ICON)
Disperse data to several points in the routine	Single output wire connector (OCON) and multiple input wire connectors (ICON)

Rehg and Sartori, Industrial Electronics, *1st Edition, © 2006, Reprinted by permission of Pearson Education, Inc., Upper Saddle River, NJ.*

FIGURE 13-4: Tag name generation for RSLogix 5000.

For a(n):	Specify:
Tag	*tag_name*
Bit number of a larger data type	*tag_name.bit_number*
Member of a structure	*tag_name.member_name*
Element of a one-dimension array	*tag_name[x]*
Element of a two-dimension array	*tag_name[x,y]*
Element of a three-dimension array	*tag_name[x,y,z]*
Element of an array within a structure	*tag_name.member_name[x]*
Member of an element of an array	*tag_name[x,y,z].member_name*

where:

x is the location of the element in the first dimension.

y is the location of the element in the second dimension.

z is the location of the element in the third dimension.

Rehg and Sartori, Industrial Electronics, *1st Edition, © 2006, Reprinted by permission of Pearson Education, Inc., Upper Saddle River, NJ.*

the left. Execution of each function block follows the signal flow path described in the graphic program and is generally from left to right. However, execution is affected by the data latching strategy utilized.

Data latching refers to how the PLC verifies that the data present at the input to an FBD is valid so that the algorithm within the function block can process the data and produce an output. When an IREF is used to specify input data for a function block instruction (see Figure 13-1), the data in that IREF is latched (held at the current value) for the scan of the function block routine. The controller updates all IREF data at the beginning of each scan. When the IREF tag is used at multiple inputs, each input latches the same data. The FBD is evaluated from left to right and top to bottom. Outputs are fixed at the value from the previous scan and not permitted to change until all inputs are latched.

13-3-2   Feedback Loops

When a wire from an output pin of the block is connected back to an input pin of the same block, a feedback loop around a block is created.

Figure 13-5(a) illustrates this concept. The loop contains only a single block, so execution order does not matter because the input pin uses an output that the block produced on the previous scan.

If a group of blocks are in a loop, as in Figure 13-5(b), then the controller cannot determine which block input to latch and execute first because it cannot resolve the loop. The question marks above the function blocks as shown in Figure 13-5(b) indicate that the order of execution is not clear. The problem is resolved by placing an Assume Data Available indicator mark, shown in Figure 13-5(c), at the input of the function block that should be executed first. In Figure 13-5(c), the input for block 1 uses data from block 3 that was produced in the previous scan. The problem is that the output from block 3 is dependent on the input to block 1. The Assume Data Available indicator defines the data flow within the loop and indicates what data should be latched and which block is executed first in the loop. To place the indicator, first select the interconnect wire by left-clicking on it, then right-click on it. The dialog box lets you place the indicator at the input where the selected wire is attached.

FIGURE 13-5: Feedback in function blocks.

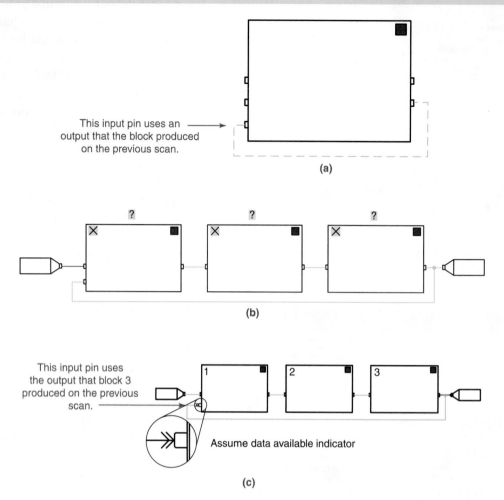

Rehg and Sartori, Industrial Electronics, *1st Edition, © 2006, Reprinted by permission of Pearson Education, Inc., Upper Saddle River, NJ.*

13-3-3 Function Block Diagram Program Development Sequence

The sequence used to develop an FBD routine for a control problem is as follows:

1. Develop the control strategy required for the problem. In ladder logic this meant to develop the Boolean logic for each output, considering the need for special instructions such as timers, counters, comparators, math functions, and one-shots; selecting the standard ladder logic for the application; and making a first cut at the automation solution. The FBD solution process is same, except that the solution must be visualized in function blocks instead of ladder rungs. The FBD standard block solutions, provided in Section 13-4, are useful because they illustrate how the ladder logic translates to FBD.

2. Choose the function block elements. A list of the blocks that are needed is generated. Be liberal here as you drag the blocks onto the solution window since it may be better to have a wider variety of blocks initially considered for the solution. Unused blocks can be deleted from the solution if they are not used.

3. Choose a tag name for each function block and a tag name or constant for each input (IREF) and output (OREF).

Setup for FBD program development.

(a) Open status of file menu

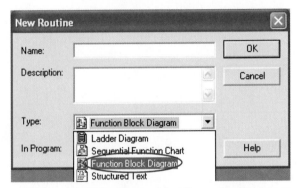

(b) Right-click MainProgram for selection of New Routine...

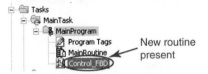

(c) New Routine dialog box to select the routine for the program

(d) New routine named Control_FBD is
now in the file list under MainProgram

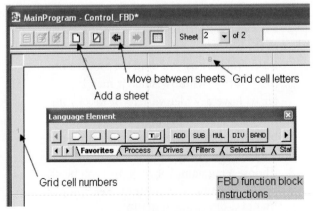

(e) Double clicking Control_FBD displays
the FBD graphic development window

4. Define the order of execution. Establish the order of the signal flow and group the blocks accordingly. Determine what calculation is performed first and how that result is used in the next set of blocks.
5. Identify any connectors and feedback loops.
6. Define program/operator control. Determine what field devices are required or available and how they will be used in the automation solution.
7. Add a function block element. Start with the blocks at the far left of the signal flow. These are the first blocks to interface with the input field devices. Configure the blocks by making the input and output parameters needed for the solution visible inside the block.
8. Build the signal flow from left to right.
9. Connect blocks with an OCON and ICON that are on different sheets.
10. Verify the routine.

An example problem later in the chapter will demonstrate how these steps are implemented. Another requirement is to open a programming session in RSLogix 5000 for use in programming an FBD solution.

The sequence used to open an FBD session is as follows:

1. Locate the MainProgam file list on the left of the screen [see Figure 13-6(a)].
2. Right-click on the MainProgram file to open the pop-up menu and then select the New Routine menu item [see Figure 13-6(b)].
3. The New Routine dialog box is opened and the drop-down selection list is expanded in the Type text window [see Figure 13-6(c)]. All four of the 61131-3 standard languages supported by Allen-Bradley are displayed. Select the Function Block Diagram entry and tag named for the program plus a description.
4. The new FBD program named Control_FBD is now listed under MainProgram [see Figure 13-6(d)].
5. Left-clicking Control_FBD twice opens the graphic development window for

FBD programs [see Figure 13-6(e)]. Note in the figure that the Language element window has been pulled onto the graphic development grid. FBD instructions are selected from this window, just as the ladder logic was earlier. The grid has cells identified by letters and numbers to help locate ICON and OCON jump links. Extra sheets can be added when the current sheet is full using the extra sheet icon. Movement between sheets is provided by the left and right arrows indicated.

The MainRoutine is always a ladder logic program in RSLogic 5000, and all other routines are called from the MainRoutine. So the MainRoutine will have one unconditional rung with a jump to subroutine (JSR) calling Control_FBD. The FBD program will execute from the JSR instruction. No subroutine or return from subroutine instruction in the FBD is necessary.

13-3-4   Allen-Bradley RSLogix 5000 FBD Programming

The Logix 5000 language FBD has a complete range of function blocks. The blocks are organized into 14 groups and the numerous instructions for each group are listed in Figure 13-7. Read through the instruction list to see the range of instructions available and to see which instructions are the same as those used in the ladder logic programming. The

FIGURE 13-7: Function blocks supported by RSLogix 5000.

Group Name	Function Block Name and Symbol
Advanced Math Instructions	Natural Log (LN) Log Base 10 (LOG) X to the Power of Y (XPY)
Bit Instructions	One Shot Rising with Input (OSRI) One Shot Falling with Input (OSFI)
Compare Instructions	Limit (LIM) Mask Equal To (MEQ) Equal To (EQU) Not Equal To (NEQ) Less Than (LES) Greater Than (GRT) Less Than or Equal To (LEQ) Greater Than or Equal To (GEQ)
Computer/Math Instructions	Add (ADD) Subtract (SUB) Multiply (MUL) Divide (DIV) Modulo (MOD) Square Root (SQR/SQRT) Negate (NEG) Absolute Value (ABS)
Drive Instructions	Pulse Multiplier (PMUL) S-Curve (SCRV) Proportional + Integral (PI) Integrator (INTG) Second-Order Controller (SOC) Up/Down Accumulator (UPDN)
Filter Instructions	High Pass Filter (HPF) Low Pass Filter (LPF) Notch Filter (NTCH) Second-Order Lead Lag (LDL2) Derivative (DERV)

(continued)

Rehg and Sartori, Industrial Electronics, *1st Edition, © 2006, Reprinted by permission of Pearson Education, Inc., Upper Saddle River, NJ.*

FIGURE 13-7: (Continued).

Math Conversion Instructions	Degrees (DEG) Radian (RAD) Convert to BCD (TOD) Convert to Integer (FRD) Truncate (TRN)
Move/Logical Instructions	Masked Move with Target (MVMT) Bitwise And (AND) Bitwise Or (OR) Bitwise Exclusive Or (XOR) Bitwise Not (NOT) Bit Field Distribute with Target (BTDT) Boolean AND (BAND) Boolean OR (BOR) Boolean Exclusive OR (BXOR) Boolean NOT (BNOT) D Flip-Flop (DFF) JK Flip-Flop (JKFF) Set Dominant (SETD) Reset Dominant (RESD)
Process Control Instructions	Alarm (ALM) Scale (SCL) Enhanced PID (PIDE) Ramp/Soak (RMPS) Position Proportional (POSP) Split Range Time Proportional (SRTP) Lead-Lag (LDLG) Function Generator (FGEN) Totalizer (TOT) Deadtime (DEDT) Discrete Two-State Device (D2SD) Discrete Three-State Device (D3SD)
Program Control Instruction	Jump to Subroutine (JSR) Subroutine (SBR) Return (RET)
Select/Limit Instructions	Select (SEL) Enhanced Select (ESEL) Selected Summer (SSUM) Selected Negate (SNEG) Multiplexer (MUX) High/Low Limit (HLL) Rate Limiter (RLIM)
Statistical Instructions	Moving Average (MAVE) Moving Standard Deviation (MSTD) Minimum Capture (MINC) Maximum Capture (MAXC)
Timer/Counter Instructions	Timer On Delay with Reset (TONR) Timer Off Delay with Reset (TOFR) Retentive Timer On with Reset (RTOR) Count Up/Down (CTUD)
Trigonometric Instructions	Sine (SIN) Cosine (COS) Tangent (TAN) Arc Sine (ASN) Arc Cosine (ACS) Arc Tangent (ATN)

instruction format for the RSLogix 5000 controller is documented in reference manuals available in Adobe Acrobat pdf file format from the CD accompanying the text or from the Allen-Bradley Web site. Access the 61131 programming manuals and review the operation for some instructions from the following groups: timers, counters, mathematic instructions, comparators, logical operations, flip flops, and one-shots.

13-4 EMPIRICAL DESIGN WITH FUNCTION BLOCK DIAGRAMS

The Function Block Diagram program development sequence is listed in the previous section. After you are familiar with the operation of the com-

monly used function blocks, following these design steps will yield good design results. However, to learn the program structure for an FBD solution it best to study FBD equivalents for the ladder logic rungs used in similar control problems.

13-4-1 Standard Function Block Control Solutions

The following standard function block programs indicate how function block solutions compare to common ladder logic rungs and standard ladder logic diagrams.

FBD Standard for Unconditional and Conditional Logic. The comparison between unconditional and conditional ladder logic and the FBD equivalent is illustrated in Figure 13-8(a)

FIGURE 13-8: FBDs for standard ladder logic with conditional XIC and XIO logic rungs and unconditional rungs.

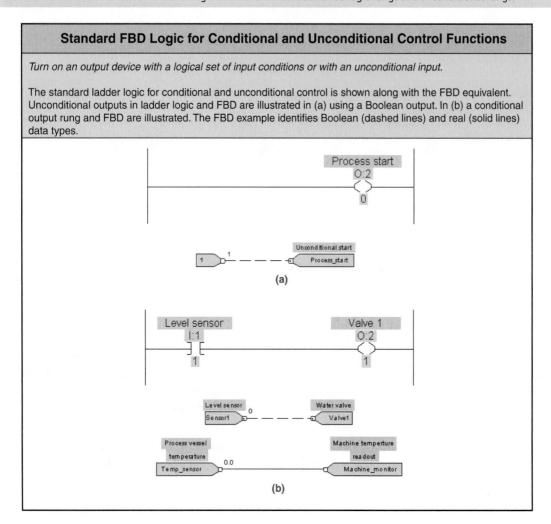

FIGURE 13-8: (Continued).

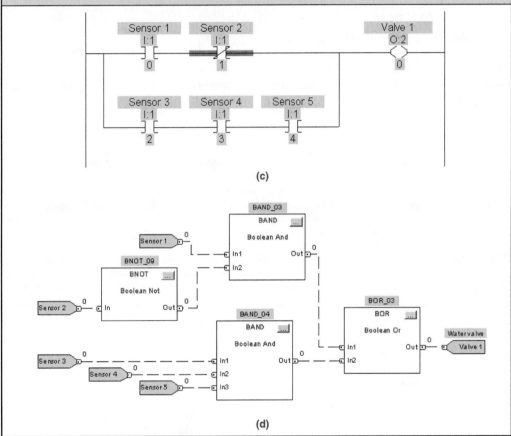

Standard FBD Logic for Combinational Logic

Turn on an output device for a logical combination of multiple input instructions.

The development of combinational logic in ladder rungs is simply AND/OR or OR/AND instructional groupings, Figure 13-8(c). When implementing the same logic in FBD, Figure 13-8(d), Boolean logic gates like BAND, BOR, BXOR, AND NOT are used to develop the combinational logic. The Boolean logic gates are used since the inputs and output are either on or off. Note that an XIO instruction in the ladder logic requires that a NOT function block is used in the FBD to produce the same logical output. The bitwise AND, OR, and XOR blocks (not shown here) are used with words and each bit in the word is compared with respective bits of other inputs using the logic of the function.

(c)

(d)

and (b). Read the description of the operation included in the figure. It is important to match the data types for the conditional logic. If the IREF tag is a Boolean, integer, or real data type, then the OREF tag must have the same data type.

FBD Standard for Combinational Conditional Logic. The comparison between combinational

logic for ladder logic inputs and their FBD equivalent is illustrated in Figure 13-8(c) and (d). Read the description of the operation included in the figure. Combinational logic is achieved in FBD through the use of Boolean logic functions such as Boolean ANDs, ORs, and NOTs.

FBD Standard for Timers. The comparison between timer instructions for standard ladder

FIGURE 13-9: Standard ladder logic for TONR timers in FBDs.

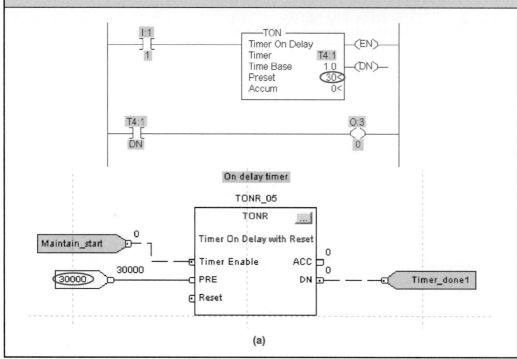

Standard FBD Logic for TONR Timers

Turn on an output device for a set time period when a maintain contact input device changes states.

The standard ladder logic for the TON timer in Figure 4-12(b) is shown below along with the FBD equivalent. The input for both is a NO maintain contact selector switch. If the switch is closed, then the FBD timer is enabled and the EN and TT bits (not shown) are true because tag Maintain_start is true. When the ACC equals the preset value of 30 seconds (30000 x 0.001) the done bit is set and output tag Timer_done1 is true. An output can also be taken from the TT bit (not shown) on the FBD timer block to get a timed pulse output.

(a)

logic inputs and their FBD equivalent is illustrated in Figures 13-9 and 13-10, respectively. The ladder logic uses the TON symbol and the FBD uses the TONR symbol for a *time on* timer. Read the description of the operation included in the figures. The timer instructions in FBD operate the same as the timers in the ladder logic. However, in FBD you can enter operational parameters, such as timer preset, into the properties box for the timer or as a fixed IREF value connected to the timer preset input.

FBD Standard for Counters. The comparison between counter instructions for standard lad-

der logic inputs and their FBD equivalent is illustrated in Figures 13-11 and 13-12, respectively. The ladder logic software has two instructions, CTU and CTD, to handle the count up and count down applications. In the function block software, there is just one instruction, which handles both functions. The function block, CTUD, has a CU enable for counting up and a CD enable for counting down. The operation of the FBD counter for counting up and counting down applications is illustrated in the standard circuits in Figure 13-11. The standard FBD in Figure 13-12 illustrates how an up/down counter is implemented with the function block counter

FIGURE 13-9: (Continued).

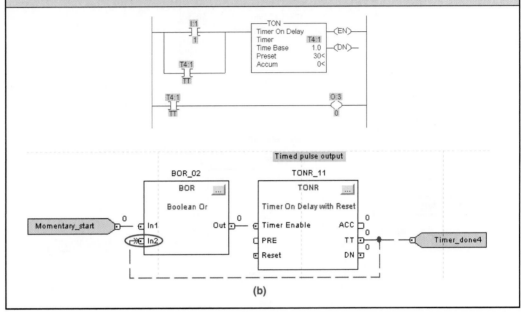

Standard FBD Logic for TONR Timers

Turn on an output device for a set time period when a momentary contact input device changes states.

The standard ladder logic for the TON timer in Figure 4-12(c) is shown along with the FBD equivalent. The input field device is a NO push button switch. If the switch is closed, then the tag Momentary_start is true and the TT bit is true. The active TONR_11.TT bit seals the input contacts and makes the output tag Timer_done4 true as well. The TT bit and output tag are true for the preset time value of 30 seconds. Note that the preset value is not visible since it was set in the properties box for the TONR timer. It can be viewed by double clicking the properties expansion button in the top right corner of the FBD instruction. An output can also be taken from the DN bit on the FBD timer block to get an on delayed timed output. Note that an assumed data available symbol is placed at the In2 terminal of the feedback loop.

(b)

instruction. Read the description of the operation included in the figures.

FBD Standard for Latch Outputs. The comparison between output latch instructions for standard ladder logic inputs and their FBD equivalent is illustrated in Figure 13-13. The ladder logic software has two instructions, OTL and OTU, to handle applications that require a retentive output. Function block software uses binary element (flip-flop) function blocks to create retentive outputs. There are four types of binary elements: D type flip-flop, JK type flip-flop, set dominant (SETD) flip-flop, and reset dominant (RESD) flip-flop. The set dominant and reset dominant types are used to create the retentive outputs. The operation of the FBD retentive outputs in control applications is illustrated in the standard circuits in Figure 13-13. Read the description of the operation included in the figure.

FBD Standard for One-Shots and Math Blocks. The comparison between one-shot and math instructions for standard ladder logic inputs and their FBD equivalent blocks is illustrated in

FIGURE 13-10: Standard FBD logic for TONR pulse generators.

Standard FBD Logic for TONR Pulse Generators

Turn on an output device with a pulse sequence where one half of the duty cycle has a variable time and the other has a time equal to the scan time of the ladder.

The standard ladder logic for the TON timer in Figure 4-12(e) is shown along with the FBD equivalent. The input field device is a NO maintain contact selector switch. If the switch is closed, then the tag Maintain_start is true along with the EN bit. As a result, the timer is incrementing the ACC and the TT bit is true. When the ACC equals the preset (5 seconds), the timer DN bit is true. This makes the In2 input to the BAND instruction false so the BAND output is false and the timer resets, which makes the DN bit true for only one scan, and the timer starts the timing process again.

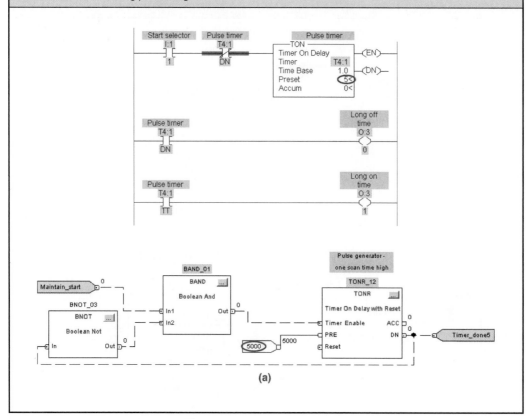

(a)

Figure 13-14. The one-shot is used in control programs to limit the execution of the output to one scan of the program. This is useful when an instruction or block executes every scan when the input is true, but the control requires just one execution. The one-shot output is true for one scan and the add block has its enable pin connected to the one-shot output. Therefore, the add block is enabled for only the first scan after the input goes high. This configuration is used most often with math and move blocks and could have a one-shot falling block used in place of the one-shot rising. Read the description of the operation included in the figure.

FIGURE 13-10: (Continued).

Standard FBD Logic for TONR Pulse Generators

Turn on an output device with a pulse sequence where both halves of the duty cycle have a variable time.

The standard ladder logic for the TON timer in Figure 4-12(f) is shown below along with the FBD equivalent. The input field device is a NO maintain contact selector switch. If the switch is closed, then the tag Maintain_start is true along with the EN bit of timer TONR_13. As a result, the timer is incrementing the ACC and the TT bit is true. When the ACC equals the preset (2 seconds), the timer DN bit is true. This enables the timer TONR_14 and it starts moving toward its 4-second preset value. When TONR_14's ACC equals 4 seconds its DN bit transitions to a 1, and this causes the first timer, TONR_13, to reset because the done bit is inverted. Note that the up time for the pulse is determined by the preset value of TONR_14 since it determines how long the done bit of TONR_13 is held on after its DN bit becomes true.

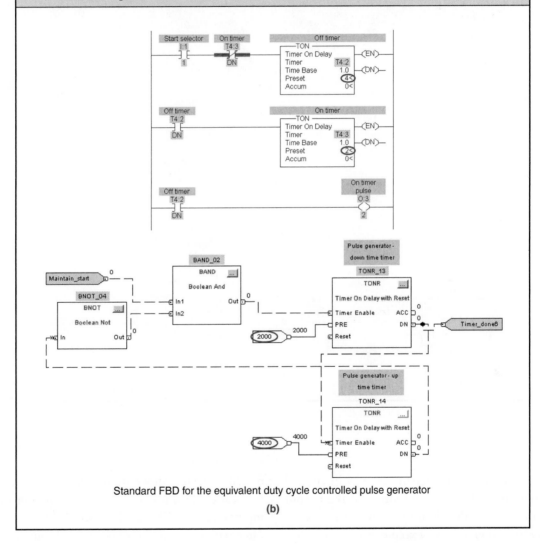

Standard FBD for the equivalent duty cycle controlled pulse generator

(b)

FIGURE 13-11: Standard ladder logic for counters in FBDs.

Standard FBD Logic for Counters

Turn on an output field device after a preset number of false to true transitions of the input logic or turn off an output field device after a preset number of counter inputs.

The standard ladder logic for the CTU counter in Figure 5-10(a) is shown along with the FBD equivalent. The function block software has a combination up and down counter, which can be used as an up counter, down counter, or as a combined up/down counter. If the CU enable input goes from false to true the accumulator increments up by one. If the CD enable input has that transition then the accumulator decrements down by one. So if both input are actively controlled, then the function moves the accumulator in response to both up and down active inputs. The preset value can be entered in the properties dialog box or by an IREF input as shown below. The reset input is used to reset the accumulator and the BNOT function block produces a NOT done output. If the CD enable is used then the FBD is a count down counter.

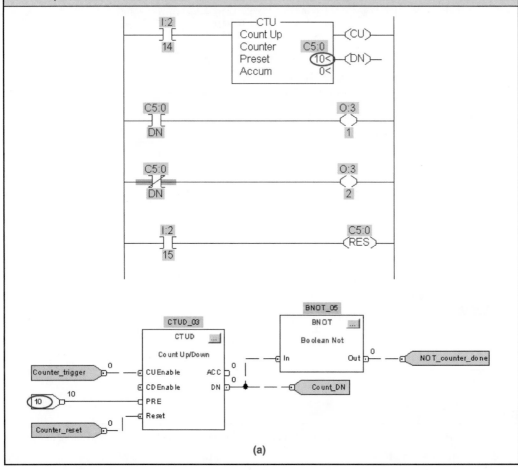

(a)

FIGURE 13-11: (Continued).

Standard FBD Logic for Counters

Turn on an output field device after a preset number of false to true transitions of the input logic or turn off an output field device after a preset number of counter inputs. Hold the ACC value at the PRE value when the ACC value equals the PRE value.

The standard ladder logic for the CTU counter in Figure 5-10(b) is shown below along with the FBD equivalent. The FBD implements this ladder standard by using a Boolean AND function block to combine the counter trigger with the counter NOT done bit. When the counter ACC is less than the preset value, the feedback bit is a 1 and counter trigger passes to the CU enable input, causing the counter ACC to increment with every input transition. When the done bit is true, the feedback is a 0 so all future input triggers are inhibited until the counter is reset. Note that an assumed data available symbol is added as shown. If the CD enable is used then the FBD is a count down counter.

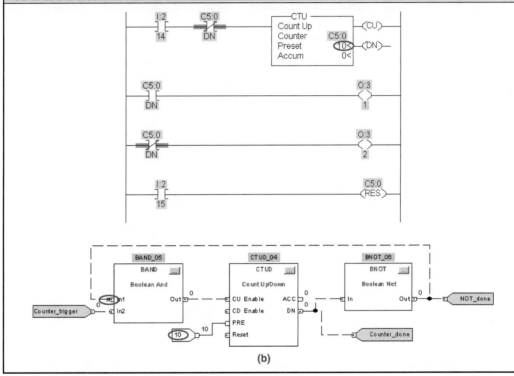

(b)

EXAMPLE 13-1

Design an FBD solution for the process tank problem illustrated in Figure 13-15. The tank should have 25 percent of one ingredient and 75 percent of a second by weight. It should be heated to 180 degrees and then mixed for 30 minutes. Mixing should continue until the tank has drained.

SOLUTION

Some other parameters need to be established. Total weight is 1000 pounds and the FBD solution steps are used to solve this process problem.

1. Develop the control strategy required for the problem.

    The control will use the following logic:

    Valve 1 = start switch AND tank liquid weight less than 250 pounds on fill cycle only
    Valve 2 = start switch AND tank liquid weight greater than 250 pounds but less than or equal to 1000 on fill cycle only
    Mixer on = tank liquid weight greater than 499 pounds

FIGURE 13-12: Standard ladder logic for an up/down counter in FBDs.

Standard FBD Logic for Up/Down Counters

Increment an accumulator tag for every false to true transition of an up count signal and decrement the same tag for every false to true transition of a down count signal. Turn on (or turn off) an output field device after the accumulator tag is equal to or greater than a preset value.

The standard ladder logic for the CTU plus CTD counters in Figure 5-10(d) is shown along with the FBD equivalent. The function block software has a combination up and down counter, which can be used as an up counter, down counter, or as a combined up/down counter. The standard FBD has a tag to signal count up, Up_count_trigger, and a tag to signal count down, Down_count_ trigger. The accumulator tag, CTUD_08.ACC, increments when the up trigger is active, and decrements when the down trigger is active. The done bit is true when the accumulator tag has a value of 10 or higher.

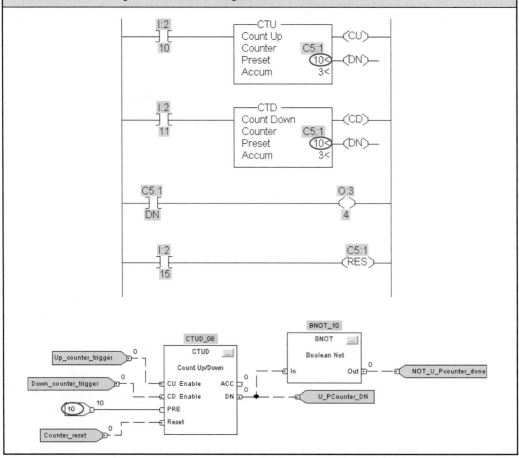

Mixer off = tank liquid weight equal to 0 pounds

Heater on = tank liquid weight equal to or greater than 750 pounds

Heater off = 30 minutes after tank full and temperature at 180 degrees

Valve 3 = tank liquid weight equal to 1000 pounds on drain cycle AND liquid temperature equal to 180 degrees for 30 minutes

2. Choose the function block elements.

Choosing FBD elements is an iterative process. You start with an initial set and then modify the list as you progress through the design. The list for this design includes the elements in the table in Figure 13-16.

3. Choose a tag name for an element and for each input and output.

FIGURE 13-13: Standard ladder logic for retentive outputs in FBDs.

Standard FBD Logic for Retentive Outputs

Latch and unlatch an output on with an input signal.

The standard ladder logic for the OTL and OTU instructions from Figure 3-32 is shown along with the FBD equivalent. The function block software uses a Set Dominant block, but a Reset Dominant could be used as well. The SETD block makes the output true when the set input is true regardless of the condition on the reset input. The block is reset by a true on the reset input, but only when the set input is false. The RESD block will reset the output when the reset input is true regardless of the condition on the set input. In RESD case the set input only sets the output when the reset input is false. The NOT output is also available.

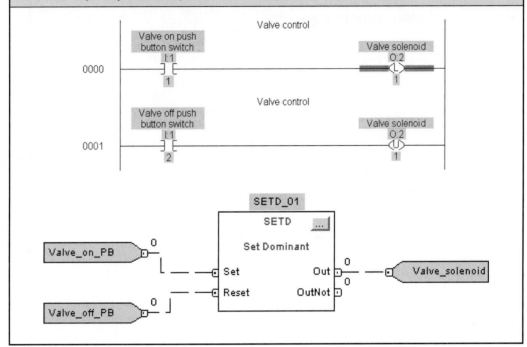

The tag names are variables that hold the data for the process. They should be as descriptive as possible using the fewest words. The tag names include the names of the data values (IREF and OREF) and names for the FBD blocks. Both are listed in Figure 13-17.

4. Define the order of execution.

5. Identify any connectors and feedback loops.

6. Define program/operator control.

7. Add a function block element.

8. Connect elements.

9. Verify that all tags and constant values for IREFs have been made and all outputs, OREFs are defined as well.

Connect blocks with an OCON and ICON that are on different sheets. Steps 4 through 7 are addressed as the function blocks are placed into the programming area in the software. Since it is a design, the development of the FBD program has much iteration, and there is more than one plausible solution. One possible solution is illustrated in Figures 13-18 and 13-19.

At first glance, the FBD solution seems complex and difficult to interpret, but with a little practice it is read more easily than a ladder diagram. The solid lines represent integers and real values, and the dashed lines Boolean or discrete on/off bit values. Input variable values are on the left and output values are on the right.

Standard FBD Logic for One Shots and Arithmetic Blocks

Turn on an output instruction or block like a math or move instruction for only one scan after an input field device(s) is active.

The standard ladder logic for the one shot and addition instruction in Figure 6-12(c) is shown along with the FBD equivalent. The input field device(s) determines when the output is active and the one shot assures that the addition is performed for only one scan. In applications that use blocks that are triggered every scan it often is important to execute those instructions for only one time. The one shot makes the instruction look like one that is triggered by a rising edge (false to true) on the input. While the addition instruction is used in this example, any of the other math instructions (SUB, DIV, MUL, OR SQR) or the move instruction (MOV) could be substituted. Also, the one shot rising block is used, but a one shot falling block could be used to trigger on a falling input edge (true to false input change).

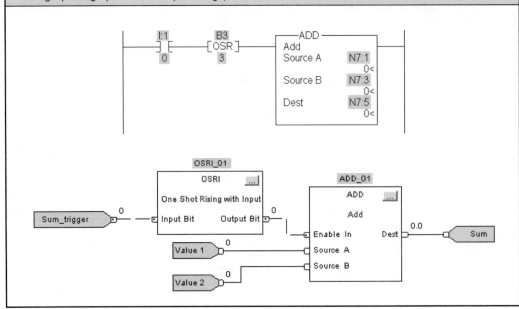

FIGURE 13-15: Process tank for Example 13-1.

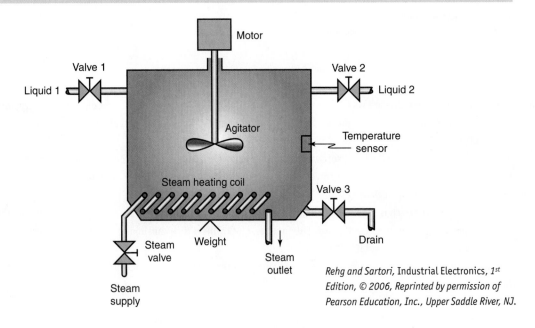

Rehg and Sartori, Industrial Electronics, *1st Edition, © 2006, Reprinted by permission of Pearson Education, Inc., Upper Saddle River, NJ.*

FIGURE 13-16: List of function block elements for Example 13-1.

FIGURE 13-17: Tag names, tad data types, and tag descriptions for Example 13-1.

Element	Description
IREF	Input variable or value
OREF	Output variable or value
ICON	Input connection point for a jumper
OCON	Output connection point for a jumper
OSRI	One Shot Rising with Input—one shot element that changes the output state from 0 to 1 and back to 0 when the input goes from 0 to 1
RESD	Reset Dominant—A set/reset latch that sets the Out pin high when set is high and sets the Out pin low when reset is high. If both inputs are high the reset determines the output
SETD	Set Dominant—A set/reset latch that sets the Out pin high when set is high and sets the Out pin low when reset is high. If both inputs are high the set determines the output
BAND	Boolean AND—An AND gate
BOR	Boolean OR—An OR gate
EQU	Equal To—Comparator that sets the output high when inputs are equal
LES	Less Than—Comparator that sets the set output high when A < B
GRT	Greater Than—Comparator that sets the set output high when A > B
GEQ	Greater Than or Equal To—Comparator that sets the set output high when A ≥ B
TONR	Timer On Delay with Reset—Timer that set the done bit high when the accumulator is equal to the preset values—accumulator increments when the enable input is high

Tag Name	Tag data type	Tag description
Heater	BOOL	Output variable
Mixer	BOOL	Output variable
Start	BOOL	Input variable
Stop	BOOL	Input variable
Valve_One	BOOL	Output variable
Valve_Three	BOOL	Output variable
Valve_Two	BOOL	Output variable
Liquid_weight	DINT	Input variable
Temperature	DINT	Input variable
Latch_Heater	DOMINANT_RESET	Function blocks
Latch_mixer	DOMINANT_RESET	Function blocks
Start_latch	DOMINANT_RESET	Function blocks
Heater_unlatch	DOMINANT_SET	Function blocks
Latch_tank_full	DOMINANT_SET	Function blocks
Timer_start_latch	DOMINANT_SET	Function blocks
Timer_start_AND	FBD_BOOLEAN_AND	Function blocks
Valve_one_AND	FBD_BOOLEAN_AND	Function blocks
Valve_three_AND	FBD_BOOLEAN_AND	Function blocks
Valve_two_AND	FBD_BOOLEAN_AND	Function blocks
Start_unlatch	FBD_BOOLEAN_OR	Function blocks
Temp_at_180	FBD_COMPARE	Function blocks
Weight_at_0	FBD_COMPARE	Function blocks
Weight_at_1000	FBD_COMPARE	Function blocks
Weight_over_249	FBD_COMPARE	Function blocks
Weight_over_500	FBD_COMPARE	Function blocks
Weight_over_750	FBD_COMPARE	Function blocks
Weight_under_249	FBD_COMPARE	Function blocks
Start_oneshot	FBD_ONESHOT	Function blocks
Timer_30min	FBD_TIMER	Function blocks

Rehg and Sartori, Industrial Electronics, *1st Edition, © 2006, Reprinted by permission of Pearson Education, Inc., Upper Saddle River, NJ.*

Rehg and Sartori, Industrial Electronics, *1st Edition, © 2006, Reprinted by permission of Pearson Education, Inc., Upper Saddle River, NJ.*

Wire interconnections are indicated with OCON (pointing right) and ICON (pointing left) symbols and the word *Jumper_x* inside. The numbers below each wire connector are the page coordinates for the other end of the connection.

10. Verify the routine.

   The routine is verified by the Rockwell software to uncover any format errors in the programming process, then it must be verified by the designer to ensure that it solves the design requirements for the process. The design verification requires the designer to go through the following steps:

   a. Assume that the start switch is off and the tank is empty for the first system scan—mark the input values before the scan and the output values after the scan for each FBD function block. This is time consuming but necessary to verify that the solution produces the correct results.

   b. Assume the start switch is pressed—mark the input values before the scan and the output values after the scan for each FBD function block.

c. Assume the liquid just passed the 250 point—mark the input values before the next scan and the output values after the next scan for each FBD function block.

d. Continue through the operational sequence, noting the change in inputs and outputs at each stage of the process operation.

e. Verify that the operation recorded conforms to the desired operation stated at the start of the design.

EXAMPLE 13-2

Study the mixer control routine in step 1 of Example 13-1 and verify that the system executes correctly using the FBD solution in Figure 13-18 (bottom two blocks in the figure).

FIGURE 13-18: Valve 1, valve 2, and mixer FBD for Example 13-1.

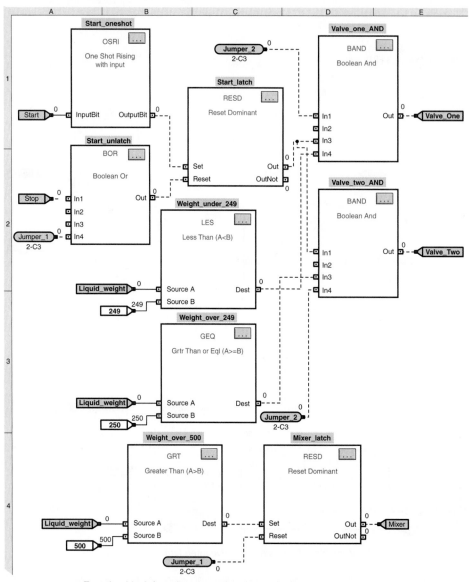

Function block for valve one, valve two, and mixer for Example 13-1

Rehg and Sartori, Industrial Electronics, *1st Edition, © 2006, Reprinted by permission of Pearson Education, Inc., Upper Saddle River, NJ.*

1. Liquid_weight is less than 500, so the comparator (Weight_over_500) output is not true or 0. The Reset Dominant latch (Mixer_latch) has 0 on the set input and the value generated from Jumper 1. The origin for Jumper 1 (Weight_at_0) is in Figure 13-19; study that routine. Initially Jumper 1 is true or 1 because Liquid_weight is equal to 0. Therefore, the Mixer_latch is 0 on the set and 1 on the reset, so the output is 0 and the mixer is off.

2. When the tank starts to fill, Jumper 1 changes to a 0 since the Liquid_weight is greater than 0. So the input to the Mixer_latch is set 0 and reset 0, the output remains 0, and the mixer is off. When the Liquid_weight exceeds 500, the Weight_over_500 comparator's output is true or 1, so the Mixer_latch set input changes to true or 1. This causes the output to change to true or 1 and the mixer to be energized.

3. The inputs to the Mixer_latch remain set 1 and reset 0 as the tank fills to 1000 and as the tank empties to 500. After the Liquid_weight drops below 500 the Mixer_latch inputs become set 0 and reset 0, the output remains true or 1, and the mixer remains energized. When the tank is empty, Liquid_weight equals 0 and Jumper 1 changes from 0 to true or 1. This causes the Mixer_latch reset input to be true and the output changes from 1 to 0. This turns the mixer off.

Use the technique in Example 13-2 to verify all the outputs in Figure 13-18 for this tank control solution.

FIGURE 13-19: Heat and valve 3 FBD for Example 13-1.

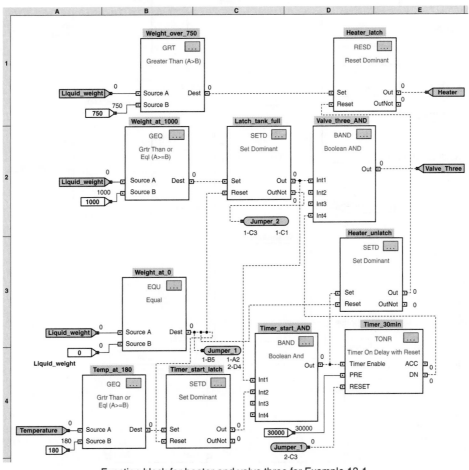

Function block for heater and valve three for Example 13-1

Rehg and Sartori, Industrial Electronics, *1ˢᵗ Edition, © 2006, Reprinted by permission of Pearson Education, Inc., Upper Saddle River, NJ.*

13-5 SITES FOR ALLEN-BRADLEY PRODUCTS AND DEMO SOFTWARE

RSLogix 5000 product information: *http://www.ab.com/catalogs/b113/controllogix/software.html*

RSLogix 5000 demo software ordering and download: *http://www.ab.com/logix/rslogix5000/*

RSLogix 500 demo software download (under Get Software): http://www.ab.com/plclogic/micrologix/

Rockwell Automation Logix product information: *http://www.ab.com/logix/*

Rockwell Automation manuals: *http://www.theautomationbookstore.com*; *http://www.ab.com/manuals/*

Intermittent and Continuous Process Control

14-1 GOALS AND OBJECTIVES

The goal of this chapter is to present closed-loop feedback control techniques for on/off and continuous processes using PLC as the control element.

After completing this chapter you should be able to:

- Cite the reasons why the on-off control mode is the most popular.
- Define the term *proportional band*.
- Discuss the problem of offset in proportional control, and show why it cannot be eliminated in a proportional controller.
- Explain why the proportional integral control mode overcomes the offset problem.
- Describe the effects of changing the integral time constant (reset rate) in a proportional integral controller.
- Explain the advantage of the proportional integral and derivative control mode over simpler control modes. State the process conditions that require the use of this mode.
- Describe the effects of changing the derivative time constant (rate time) in a proportional integral and derivative controller.
- Describe how digital controllers operate in the control of a process.

- Interpret a table that relates the characteristics of an industrial process to the proper control mode for use with a PLC implementation.

14-2 PROCESS CONTROL

Process control is classified into two categories, *intermittent* and *continuous*, that describe how it tracks the change in the process output. Intermittent control is a discrete or on-off control; therefore, its output usually has just two values—0 *or* 100 percent. In contrast, continuous control has output variability that ranges from 0 *to* 100 percent with an infinite number of values. The control modes for these two categories are as follows:

Intermittent
- On-off control
- Two-position control
- Floating control

Continuous
- Proportional control (P)
- Integral control (I)
- Derivative control (D)
- Proportional integral control (PI)

- Proportional derivative control (PD)
- Proportional integral and derivative control (PID)
- Fuzzy control

The types of controllers that are used to implement these control modes are the pneumatic, analog, and digital controllers. The first six continuous control modes are implemented using either analog or digital controllers, but fuzzy control is implemented only in a digital controller. A PID controller is a three-mode controller that has the characteristics of a proportional (P), integral (I), and derivative (D) mode. PID analog and digital controllers are the most versatile since they can be configured to operate in just proportional mode, proportional plus integral mode, proportional plus derivative mode, or with all three modes present. In general, controllers are not configured for pure integral or derivative mode control.

Process control started with pneumatic instrumentation, pneumatic controllers, and pneumatic final control elements. Today most pneumatic devices have been replaced with digital controllers. Digital controllers were initially developed as the computer implementation of an analog controller, but a modern digital controller is much more versatile than its analog counterpart. A digital controller can be configured to operate in all control modes plus some specialized and novel control algorithms.

Each control mode is addressed in the following sections. Following the sections on intermittent and continuous controllers, a section is presented on how digital control is used to implement the proportional, integral, and derivative modes.

14-3   INTERMITTENT CONTROLLERS

The basic intermittent controller is the *on-off* controller. The operation of the on-off controller is improved with the addition of hysteresis, which is typically called *two-position* control. An extension of two-position control is *floating* control, which provides three or more controller output levels for enhanced process control. These three types of control are discussed in the following subsections.

14-3-1   On-Off Control

On-off control is used in numerous applications such as home appliances, including oven heating, refrigerator cooling, and heating and cooling of all residential and commercial buildings.

In on-off control, the controller output instantly follows the change in the error (E) as shown in Figure 14-1 and where:

$$E = \text{set point} - \text{measured variable}$$

When the set point is less than the measured variable, the controller output is at 0 percent. When the set point is greater than the measured variable, the controller output is at 100 percent. This on-off control method is not as effective because, in the majority of applications, controller output is constantly switching between off and full on. The controller action for this type of control is illustrated in Figure 14-1. Note that negative error produces a 0 percent output response and positive error produces a 100 percent output response.

On-off control is not used as frequently as two-position control because of the frequent change in the control element due to a single trigger point at error equal to zero. The time constant or capacitance and inertia of the process dictate when on-off control can be considered. The time constant, capacitance, or inertia of the process is a measure of how fast the controlled variable will change in the process. For example, the capacitance for an average size house with good insulation would be relatively large, so it would take some time for the temperature to rise and drop. On the other hand, heat placed in a small un-insulated box would not remain at the set level for very long. The box would have a small time constant or low capacitance and inertia. If on-off control is used for processes with small time constants, then the

FIGURE 14-1: On-off control.

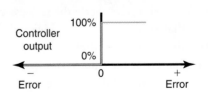

FIGURE 14-2: Digital control for on-off process.

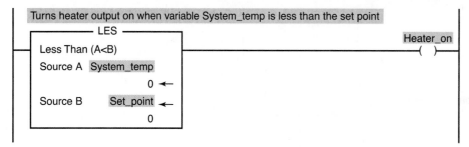

(a) Digital controller: PLC ladder logic

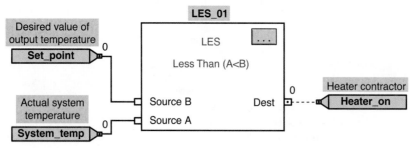

(b) Digital controller: PLC function block diagrams

Rehg and Sartori, Industrial Electronics, *1st Edition, © 2006, Reprinted by permission of Pearson Education, Inc., Upper Saddle River, NJ.*

control contactor is cycling on and off at a rapid rate. However, in processes where the process time constant or inertia is very large compared to the energy supply unit, such as when a large building is heated with a relatively small furnace, then on-off control is a good choice. If the measuring instruments have built-in hysteresis, they will compensate and permit on-off control to be used.

The ladder logic and Function Block Diagram (FBD) PLC solutions for on-off control are illustrated in Figure 14-2. The tag Set_point is the set point for the desired system temperature and System_temp the measured system temperature. The ladder rung compares the measured value to the set point variable and turns on the heater if the set point is above the measured value. The FBD solution performs the same function with one FBD block. Compare the two solutions and see how the ladder instruction is implemented in FBD.

14-3-2 Two-Position Control

Two-position control adds *hysteresis* or a *neutral zone* to the on-off controller operation. The addition of hysteresis causes the turn-on and turn-off error values to be shifted by the width of the neu-

tral zone to the left and right of the zero error value. Study Figure 14-3, which illustrates this concept.

The set point is in the center, so process variable (PV) movement to the right increases the PV and makes the error (SP − PV) value negative, thus the controller output should be *off*. To the left of center, the PV is decreasing and the error is positive and controller output should be *on*. However, the on-off action does not trigger immediately, but is delayed by the value of the error band. This hysteresis or neutral zone causes the controller to drive the *controlled variable (PV)* output value *above* the set point when the controller is *on* (100 percent output), and lets the *PV* fall *below* the set point when the controller is *off* (0 percent output). The addition of this neutral zone or hysteresis region in the control significantly reduces the on and off cycling of the output; however, it causes the PV to vary above and below the desired set point. The value selected for the neutral zone should be large enough to reduce the on-off cycling of the system but within the percentage change in PV allowed by the application. The neutral zone is called the *dead band* in some references. Example 14-1 illustrates this point.

FIGURE 14-3: Two-position controller.

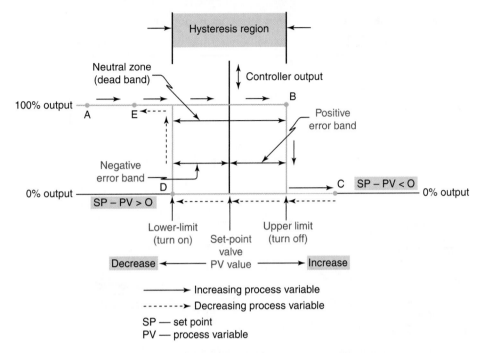

Rehg and Sartori, Industrial Electronics, *1st Edition, © 2006, Reprinted by permission of Pearson Education, Inc., Upper Saddle River, NJ.*

EXAMPLE 14-1

A home is heated with a gas furnace and controlled by a two-position thermostat. The PV is the house temperature and the measured variable (MV) is that temperature at the thermostat. The system specifications are as follows: temperature control range is 0° to 85° F, dead band is 2° F ($+/-1$° F), room temperature (MV) is 65° F, thermostat setting [set point (SP)] is 70° F, and error when the system is turned on (error = SP − MV = 70 − 65) is 5° F. Describe how the two-position controller will regulate the furnace on and off cycle.

SOLUTION

The control sequence for home heating system is as follows:

1. The two-position thermostat is turned to heat with the measured room temperature (MV) at 65° F and the set point (SP) at 70° F, which produces an error of 5° F that starts the control cycle at point A in Figure 14-3. The furnace turns on and maximum heat is distributed in every room by the furnace blower.

2. The value of MV at the thermostat starts to increase and follows the path marked by the solid arrows in Figure 14-3. As MV reaches and passes the set point (70° F) the furnace continues to generate heat and MV continues to increase.

3. When the MV reaches the upper limit (set point plus positive error band, or 72° F), point B in Figure 14-3, the furnace turns off. The MV moves higher than the upper limit or positive band because the thermostat is a temperature sensor and most have a first-order lag response, which delays turn off slightly. As a result of this delay and heat stored in the heating ducts, the MV continues to rise and reaches point C in Figure 14-3.

4. The MV starts to fall and follows a path marked by the dashed arrows from point C to point D, the lower limit (68° F) in Figure 14-3. Note that the MV is allowed to fall below the set point value of 70° F by a value of 2° F, the negative error band.

5. When the MV reaches the lower limit, point D, the furnace turns on (100 percent output). However, the MV continues to fall to point E because the blower is not turned on until the furnace has heated.

6. This cycle continues until the system set point is changed or the furnace is turned off.

FIGURE 14-4: Process variable output for two-position controller.

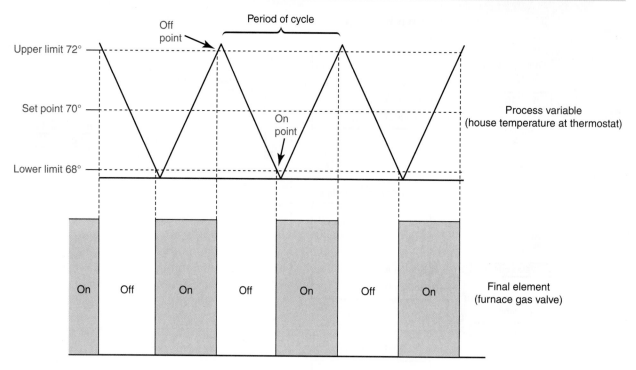

Figure 14-4 illustrates two-position control in a graphical presentation. Note that the process variable is the house temperature and the final element is the furnace gas valve, which is either on or off. The period of the cycle increases as the dead band increases and as the capacitance or inertia of the system increases. Any parameter that increases the heating or cooling part of the cycle will reduce the cycling of the controller. Two-position control can be implemented digitally and mechanically, and each of these implementations is covered in the following discussions.

Digital Two-Position Controller. A digital two-position controller implemented in Function Block Diagrams is illustrated in Figure 14-5. The primary control element is the Set/Reset binary element, SETD (set dominant binary element or flip-flop). SETD Out is true when the Set input is true. The Reset input can be either true or false for this action. SETD Out is false when the Reset input is true and the Set input is false. The digi-

tal controller uses the binary element to latch the output on (Set input true) when PV falls below the lower limit. The same latch element is reset as the PV rises above the upper limit (Reset input true and Set input false). In separate addition and subtraction blocks, the limits are calculated using the set point with the positive error band and negative error band constants. Study Figure 14-5 and the preceding description until the FBD program operation is clear.

Mechanical Two-Position Controller. A number of process switches were covered in Chapter 2, including pressure, temperature, and level. These switches and their associated controllers were implemented using mechanically closed electrical contacts. They represent the lowest cost and least complex solution. However, they are limited to some degree in the range of PV values that can be controlled. In addition, a single controller is only usable for a specific measurement span and differential value, which is the hysteresis value.

FIGURE 14-5: Digital two-position controller.

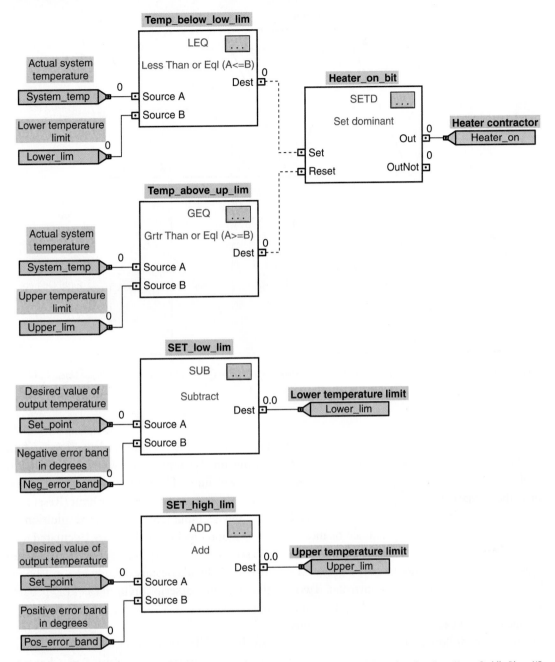

Rehg and Sartori, Industrial Electronics, *1st Edition, © 2006, Reprinted by permission of Pearson Education, Inc., Upper Saddle River, NJ.*

The two-position control pressure switch from Allen-Bradley, shown in Figure 14-6(a), has an adjustable span of 6 to 250 psi and a differential range within that span of 4 to 45 psi. The two-position temperature controller, shown in Figure 14-7, has an adjustable span of 200 to 360 degrees Fahrenheit and a differential range within that span of 8 to 72 degrees. The PV output for the pressure device is illustrated in Figure 14-6(b). Note that the output cycles between the differential values. Definitions of the terms used with the pressure switch and temperature controller are as follows:

Adjustable operating range: total span within which the contacts can be adjusted to trip and reset.

FIGURE 14-6: Two-position pressure controller.

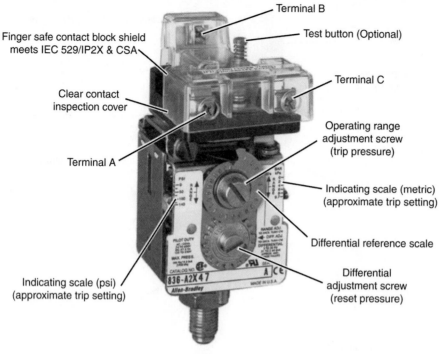

Terminal B

Test button (Optional)

Finger safe contact block shield
meets IEC 529/IP2X & CSA

Terminal C

Clear contact
inspection cover

Operating range
adjustment screw
(trip pressure)

Terminal A

Indicating scale (metric)
(approximate trip setting)

Differential reference scale

Differential
adjustment screw
(reset pressure)

Indicating scale (psi)
(approximate trip setting)

(a) Pressure controller

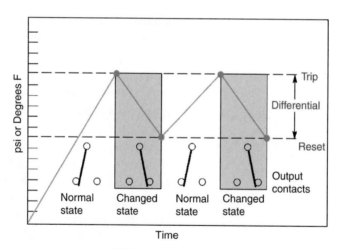

(b) Process variable output

Source: Courtesy of Rockwell Automation, Inc.

Trip setting: higher pressure or temperature setting at which the contacts transfer from their normal state to a changed state.

Reset setting: lower pressure or temperature setting at which the contacts return to their normal state.

Adjustable differential: difference between the trip and reset values.

14-3-3 Floating Control

Floating control is often called multiposition control. It is an extension of two-position control with three (0 percent, 50 percent, and 100 percent) or more controller output levels for control of the process. Figure 14-8 illustrates a multiposition controller with three operating states: 0, 50, and 100 percent, which is used to

FIGURE 14-7: Two-position temperature controller.

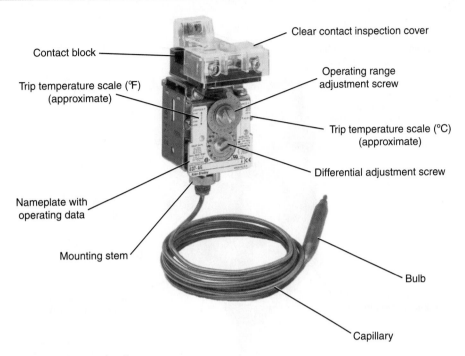

Clear contact inspection cover

Contact block

Operating range
adjustment screw

Trip temperature scale (°F)
(approximate)

Trip temperature scale (°C)
(approximate)

Differential adjustment screw

Nameplate with
operating data

Mounting stem

Bulb

Capillary

Source: Courtesy of Rockwell Automation, Inc.

FIGURE 14-8: Floating point controller.

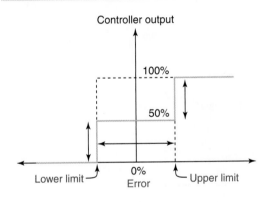

Controller output

100%

50%

0%
Error

Lower limit

Upper limit

*Rehg and Sartori, Industrial Electronics, 1st Edition, © 2006,
Reprinted by permission of Pearson Education, Inc., Upper Saddle
River, NJ.*

control a cooling system for a process. The controller has 100 percent output when the error value is over a high threshold (process temperature is too high), and the output is 0 percent when the error is less than a minimum threshold (process temperature is too low). If the error value is between the threshold values, then the controller output is 50 percent. Floating control reduces the

controller cycling rate compared with on-off and two-position control systems.

Multiposition control using Function Block Diagrams (FBDs) is illustrated in Figure 14-9. Note that three types of comparators (less than, greater than, and limit test) are used to determine where the error is relative to the upper and lower thresholds, and then a selective summer (SSUM) is used to pass the correct PV value. The LES comparator determines if the error is less than the lower limit and the GRT comparator checks for error over the upper limit. The LIM comparator determines if the error falls between the limits. The SSUM takes the integer or floating point values at each select input (In1, In2, etc.) and adds the values for those where the enable input (select1, select2, etc.) is true. The instruction then places the result in Out.

For example, if the error is less than the lower limit, then the select1 input is active and the value for minimum percent output (min_per_out) is applied to the final control element. The select2 and select3 inputs operate in a similar fashion. In this application, the SSUM block does not add the inputs but places one of the three at the out-

FIGURE 14-9: Digital floating point controller.

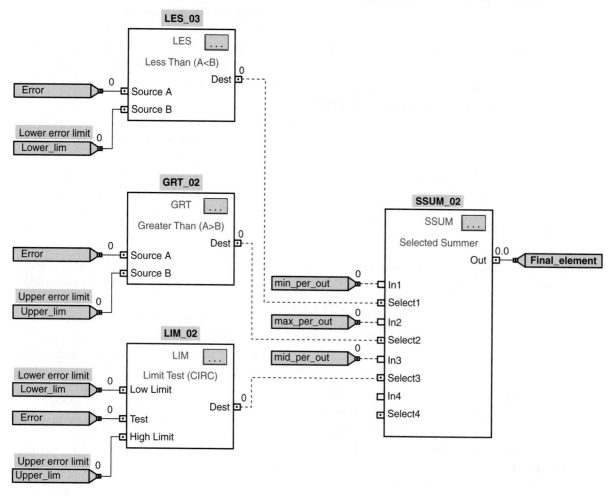

Rehg and Sartori, Industrial Electronics, *1st Edition, © 2006, Reprinted by permission of Pearson Education, Inc., Upper Saddle River, NJ.*

put since only one select input line is true at any one time. Note that not shown in the FBD are blocks to calculate the error (SP − MV) and the lower and upper limit error (Error − negative error band and Error + positive error band, respectively).

14-4   CONTINUOUS CONTROLLERS

Section 14-3 described the operation of intermittent controllers used in control applications where the system inertia or capacitance is large or where limited cycling of the process variable is acceptable. This section addresses continuous controllers. The classification of controllers and control modes is repeated so that you can see the number of continuous control options that are available. They are *proportional control* (P), *integral control* (I), *derivative control* (D), *proportional integral control* (PI), *proportional derivative control* (PD), *proportional integral and derivative control* (PID), and *fuzzy control*. There are few continuous controllers that use analog control in the process industry today. Most use some type of digital control implemented either as a bank of controllers, as a distributed control system (DCS), or with a programmable logic controller (PLC).

14-4-1   Proportional Control

On-off control requires a process PV that can swing between two limits and has sufficient inertia or

capacitance that the cycling will not be too severe. However, a proportional controller is necessary when:

- The process must be held at a specific set point value.
- The process has a small capacitance value.
- Disturbances to the controller or process could be present.

Proportional controllers have:

- Analog input and output values, expressed as integers or real numbers that vary over the range necessary for control of the process.
- Final control elements that are continuous devices with outputs from 0 to 100 percent.
- Output values that are the product of the controller gain (K) and the input error (SP − PV or PV − SP).
- An output value that changes the final control element so that the controlled variable moves closer to the desired set point.

The magnitude of the output of the controller has a direct relationship to the input error. If the error increases, then the magnitude of the controller output increases. If the error falls, then so does the output. There are two methods used to change the controller output in relation to the error: *pulse width modulation (PWM)* and *gain-error product*.

Pulse Width Modulation. Although PWM is not used often in process control it should be understood. In PWM the controller output is switched from full *off* to full *on* at a fixed frequency. The magnitude of the error determines the duty cycle of the square wave present at the output. For example, if a small error is present, then the on time for each cycle might be 5 percent of the period and the off time would be 95 percent. This is called a 5 percent duty cycle. The average value of such a square wave would be close to zero. This corresponds to a small error present at the input. Let's look at a larger error value. Such an error might produce a controller output with on time of 80 percent of one period and off time of 20 percent. This pulse train would have a larger average value corresponding to the larger error. Usually in PWM

systems the final control element is adjusted to produce a PV value equivalent to the set point when the output from the controller has a 50 percent duty cycle. Thus a zero error into the PWM controller produces a 50 percent duty cycle output. A change in the error from zero causes the duty cycle to increase or decrease based on direct-acting or reverse-acting requirements of the process.

Gain-Error Product. The most frequently used controller configuration is the gain-error product. In this configuration the controller output level is equal to the product of the controller gain (K_p) and the value of the error signal. The analog signal at the output of the controller is either a voltage or a current that is proportional to the size of the error signal. The value of the controller gain (K_p) is dictated by the control requirements of the process. The controller gain can be expressed in two ways: as *proportional gain* or as *proportional band*.

Proportional gain is the ratio of change in output to the change in input, as described mathematically by the following formula:

$$\text{Gain} = K_p = \frac{\text{Percentage output change}}{\text{Percentage input change}}$$

Review the tank level problem introduced in Figure 12-37 and developed further in Figures 12-39 through 12-43.

The system described in those figures and the text supporting them is a *continuous proportional controller*. The diagram in Figure 12-41 indicates that link A is the controller *gain element* for the system, and the gains for different link lengths are calculated in Figure 12-42. Conclusions reached from the analysis of the continuous proportional control system for tank liquid level are:

- A continuous proportional control system has zero steady-state error only at the control variable and set point values established at system startup.
- If a disturbance or set point change occurs in a system with proportional control, then some steady-state error will result.
- The steady-state error and the proportional controller gain have an *inverse* relationship (increase gain and reduce steady-state error).

- Transient response maximum peak and settling time have a *direct* relationship with controller gain (increase gain and increase overshoot and ringing).
- Steady-state error cannot be completely eliminated with increases in controller gain.

Figure 12-41 shows how all of the elements or blocks in the proportional control system are related. Figure 14-10 illustrates how each signal in the system reacts to a load change. Read the description of each process parameter in the figure. Notice how the controller output follows the error value.

FIGURE 14-10: Proportional controller action.

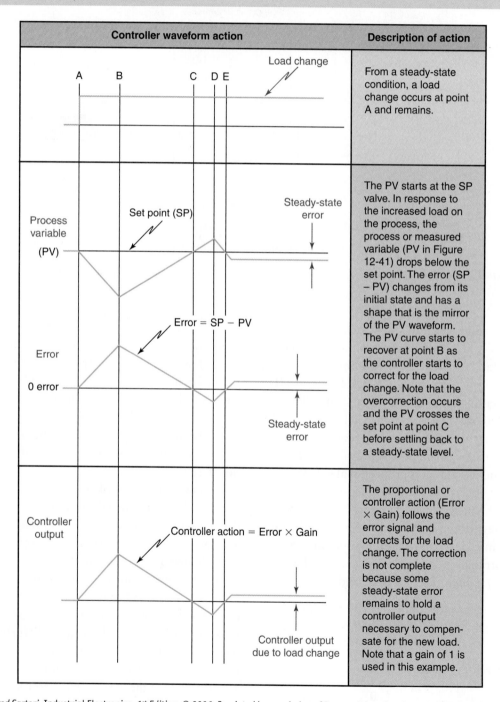

Controller waveform action	Description of action
	From a steady-state condition, a load change occurs at point A and remains.
	The PV starts at the SP valve. In response to the increased load on the process, the process or measured variable (PV in Figure 12-41) drops below the set point. The error (SP – PV) changes from its initial state and has a shape that is the mirror of the PV waveform. The PV curve starts to recover at point B as the controller starts to correct for the load change. Note that the overcorrection occurs and the PV crosses the set point at point C before settling back to a steady-state level.
	The proportional or controller action (Error × Gain) follows the error signal and corrects for the load change. The correction is not complete because some steady-state error remains to hold a controller output necessary to compensate for the new load. Note that a gain of 1 is used in this example.

Rehg and Sartori, Industrial Electronics, *1st Edition, © 2006, Reprinted by permission of Pearson Education, Inc., Upper Saddle River, NJ.*

FIGURE 14-11: Proportional controller.

(a) Block representation of a proportional controller

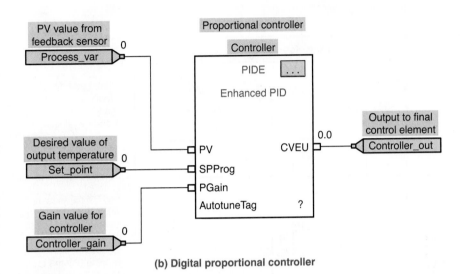

(b) Digital proportional controller

Rehg and Sartori, Industrial Electronics, *1st Edition, © 2006, Reprinted by permission of Pearson Education, Inc., Upper Saddle River, NJ.*

The representation used for a proportional controller in a block format is illustrated in Figure 14-11(a). Note that the proportional gain uses a K_p symbol. The Function Block Diagram PIDE instruction for a proportional controller in a ControlLogix PLC is illustrated in Figure 14-11(b). Note that the error summing junction is inside the controller, so inputs PV and SP are both present. The third input is proportional gain (K_p) and the only output is the controller output (CO) to drive the final control element. This is a simplified view of the PIDE instruction with the integral and derivative gain inputs not shown. Proportional gain can also be expressed as *proportional band* (PB). PB is defined as:

The percentage change in the error that causes the final control element to go through its full range.

Therefore, PB is:

$$PB = \frac{100}{\text{Controller gain}}$$

14-4-2 Proportional Integral (PI) Control

Proportional control is effective for many processes; however, when steady-state error must be reduced to near zero this controller needs another term. Steady-state error is eliminated when *integral action* is added to the proportional action. Integral action is never used alone but is always used in combination with some level of proportional gain.

Let's take another look at the tank level control problem introduced in Figure 12-37 and developed further in Figures 12-39 through 12-43. The load change produced a steady-state error. The change in proportional gain helped to reduce the steady-state error but introduced too much overshoot and ringing after a disturbance or set point change. The balanced output for the tank controller after the initial disturbance, which was shown in Figure 12-39(b), has been redrawn in Figure 14-12 in order to give a closer look at the steady-state error solution. Remember that link A with the fulcrum acts as

FIGURE 14-12: Integral action in tank level control problem.

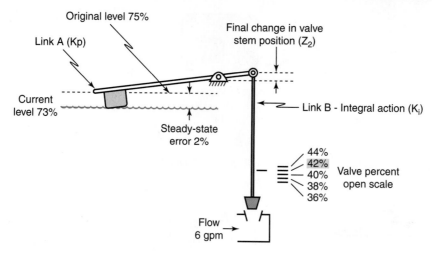

Rehg and Sartori, Industrial Electronics, *1st Edition*, © 2006, Reprinted by permission of Pearson Education, Inc., Upper Saddle River, NJ.

the proportional control element. To eliminate the steady-state error, the float and liquid in Figure 14-12 must be 2 percent higher; however, to correct for the load change the input valve must remain at an input flow of 6 gpm. To satisfy both of these requirements (tank level at 75 percent and the input value at 6 gpm) link B must shorten by the value Z_2 in the figure. Therefore, a link B that is automatically shortened by the value of the steady-state error is the integral controller element. Review this introduction to integral control so that the concept and requirements for the mechanical controller are clear.

The same integral action is implemented in digital controllers through program software. In each system the proportional gain corrects as much of the PV change from the set point or load change as possible, then the remaining steady-state error at the input to the integral controller is used to make the final correction.

The block format for an integral action element is illustrated in Figure 14-13(a). Notice that there are two distinct actions, the proportional and the integral, with the results added to get the final controller output. An FBD PIDE instruction representation for the ControlLogix PLC is illustrated in Figure 14-13(b). A comparison between Figure 14-11(b), the proportional controller, and Figure 14-13(b) indicates

that the only change is the addition of the integral gain input.

References to integral action often use the terms *reset, repeat,* and *integral time.* When steady-state error and an integral element are present, the controller output continues to rise after the proportional action has ceased. The rate at which the output increases is determined by the reset value or reset action. The following relationships describe these terms:

Reset = number of repeats per minute or second

Integral time = number of minutes or seconds per repeat

Integral action quickly becomes abstract when you start to use these terms. Reset defines the rate at which the output of the controller is changing relative to the change produced by the proportional control. If the proportional control produced a 10 percent change in the PV after a load change, then the integral element will produce an additional 10 percent change in 1 minute if the reset is 1/min. If the reset was 2/min, then the output adds the additional 10 percent in 30 seconds or adds an additional 20 percent in 1 minute. The higher the reset value is the greater the effect of the integral action. *Integral time* is just the reciprocal of reset action.

The integral waveform is added to the load change plots in Figure 14-10 and illustrated in

FIGURE 14-13: PI digital controller in FBD format.

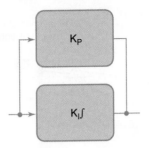

(a) Control system block diagram with an integral action element

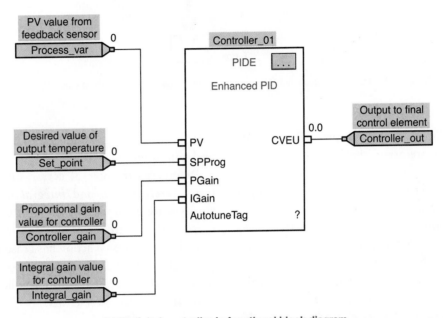

(b) PI digital controller in functional block diagram

Rehg and Sartori, Industrial Electronics, *1st Edition, © 2006, Reprinted by permission of Pearson Education, Inc., Upper Saddle River, NJ.*

the new Figure 14-14. Read the description of the actions in the figure before continuing.

Note the rate of change in the integral output and the effect it has on the steady-state error. The proportional output is superimposed on the integral response to show the effect of the reset action. Also, the integral response has a longer rise time, so the total response for PI usually is not as crisp as for the P response. As a result, integral action eliminates steady-state error but also reduces the quickness of the system response. The addition of derivative action adds quickness back into the system response.

14-4-3 Proportional Derivative (PD) Control

Sudden load or set point changes cause the process variable (PV) to deviate from the set point (SP),

and the faster the rate of change of the disturbance, the farther the controlled variable moves away from the set point. Increasing the proportional gain will compensate, but this is likely to cause the PV to overshoot more severely and produce excessive ringing. In some process applications, this situation is undesirable. If the proportional gain is increased to minimize this condition, the controlled variable will likely overshoot and oscillate. The third control mode, *derivative*, is used to correct for these rapidly changing disturbances. The derivative function produces a response whose magnitude is a function of the rate of change of the PV relative to the SP. Therefore, if the error is constant, then the derivative action is zero.

Like the integral, the derivative is not used without some proportional gain present. The

FIGURE 14-14: Proportional plus integral action.

Controller waveform action	Description of action
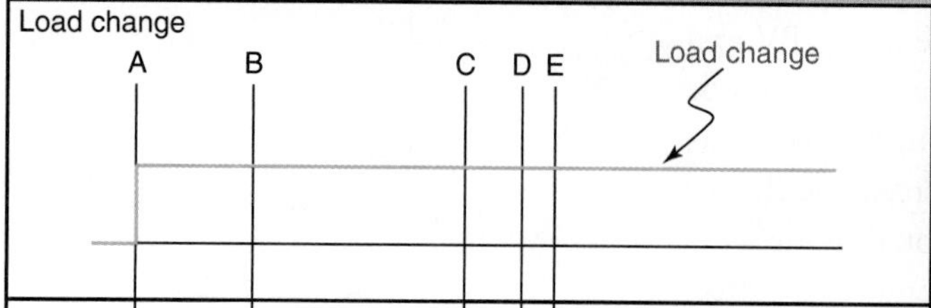 **Load change** (waveform showing Load change, points A, B, C, D, E)	From a steady-state condition, a load change occurs at point A and remains.
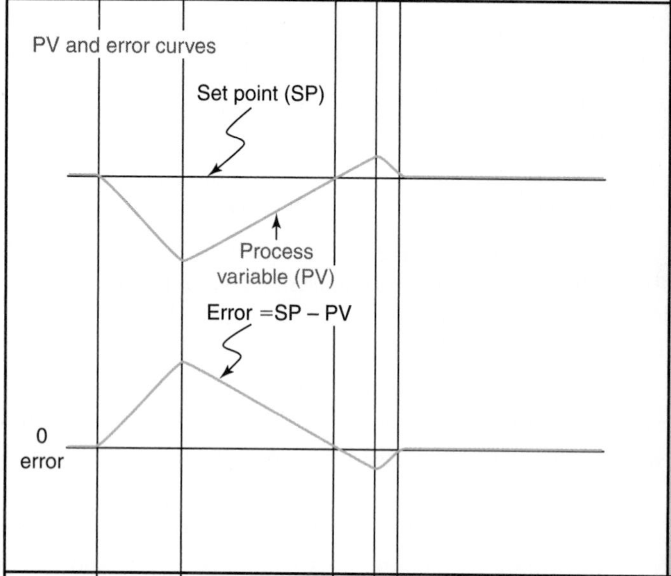 **PV and error curves** Set point (SP) Process variable (PV) Error =SP – PV 0 error	The PV starts at the SP value. In response to the increased load on the process, the process or measured variable (PV in Figure 12-41) drops below the set point. The error (SP – PV) changes from its initial state and has a shape that is the mirror of the PV waveform. The PV curve starts to recover at point B as the controller starts to correct for the load change. Note that the overcorrection occurs and the PV crosses the set point at point C before settling back to the original PV level.
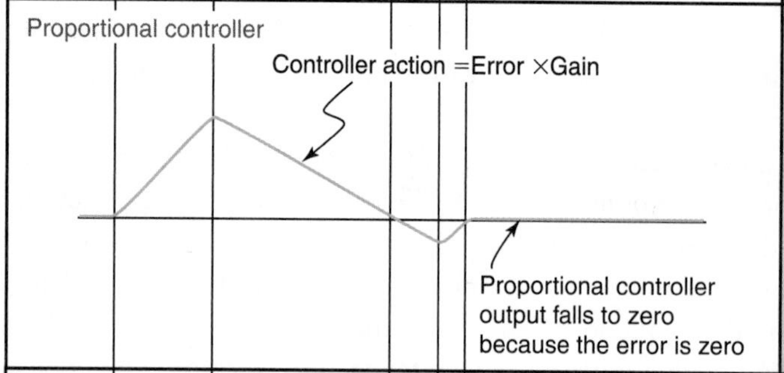 **Proportional controller** Controller action =Error ×Gain Proportional controller output falls to zero because the error is zero	The proportional or controller action follows the error signal to correct for the load change.
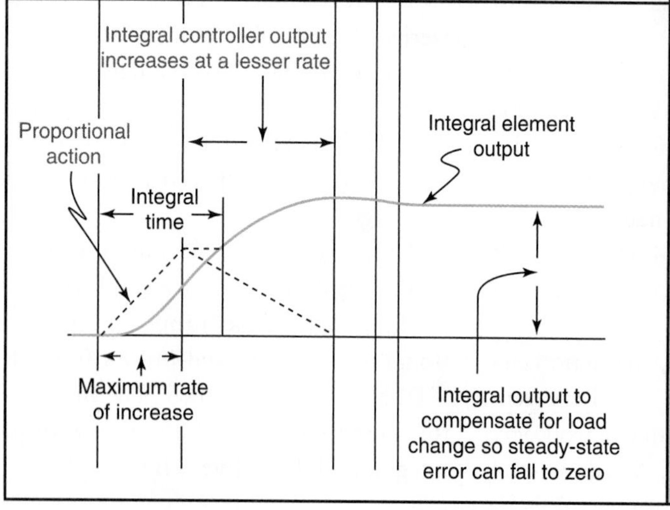 Integral controller output increases at a lesser rate Proportional action Integral time Maximum rate of increase Integral element output Integral output to compensate for load change so steady-state error can fall to zero	Note that steady-state error has been eliminated by the integral output. The rate of integral output is greatest between points A and B, when the error is increasing. It continues to rise between B and C but at a lesser rate because the error is decreasing due to the presence of the integral output. After point E, the integral level remains constant to compensate for the increased load on the system.

Rehg and Sartori, Industrial Electronics, *1st Edition, © 2006, Reprinted by permission of Pearson Education, Inc., Upper Saddle River, NJ.*

derivative element produces an output that combines with the proportional to move the final control element to a position to correct for the disturbance. For example, a large rapidly increasing load change causes a fast rise in the PV and subsequently in the error. The proportional mode element with a gain of 1 goes from 50 to 60 percent output, which matches the percentage change in the error. If only the proportional mode were present, the load change would significantly affect the PV because the proportional mode response is not sufficient to compensate. The derivative mode reacts to the rapid change in the PV by adding a derivative response of 30 additional percent to the controller output. The 90 percent controller output response quickly compensates for the large rapid load change.

The derivative mode parameter, called *rate time*, determines how much the derivative action changes the controller's output. Rate time compares the output duration for PD controllers versus P controllers. For example, a rate time setting of 1 minute will cause a response twice as fast as a setting at 2 minutes.

PD control is unsuitable for systems in noisy environments since noisy signals contain high-frequency components, which are amplified by the derivative action. These amplified signals will appear at the controller output and may cause unwanted changes by the final control element. Derivative control is beneficial for slow response systems that have large and rapid load changes. The derivative mode enables the controller to respond more rapidly and position the final control element more quickly than is possible with only proportional action.

A derivative element provides a short but large change in the magnitude of the controller output in response to a rapidly changing error signal. This prevents the PV from changing severely as the result of a large rapid change from a disturbance or the set point. Figure 14-15 shows that the maximum derivative effect occurs at the step change in the error value.

The block diagram for a derivative action element is illustrated in Figure 14-16(a). Representation using a PIDE instruction from ControlLogix is illustrated in Figure 14-16(b). A comparison

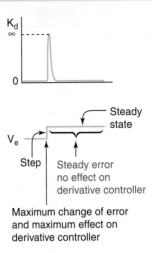

FIGURE 14-15: Derivative gain relationship to a step change in the error.

Rehg and Sartori, Industrial Electronics, *1st Edition, © 2006, Reprinted by permission of Pearson Education, Inc., Upper Saddle River, NJ.*

between Figure 14-11(b) and Figure 14-16(b) indicates that the only change is the addition of a derivative gain input to the pure proportional controller.

The derivative waveform is added to the load change plots in Figure 14-10 and illustrated in the new Figure 14-17. The magnitude of the derivative action is related to the slope of the error waveform. The slope or rate of change in the error from point A to B is twice the value from B to C. Therefore, the derivative action for A to B is twice that from B to C, as illustrated with the A and 2A notation in the figure. The response of the system is improved because the controller anticipates a large error and reacts to it. Derivative control cannot be used when a system has noise present since the derivative controller interprets the noise as rapid changes in the error. PD control is effective for changes in set point and load changes, especially those that are rapid and large.

The curves measured from the test system verify this result. In the last several sections control modes designated as proportional (P), proportional integral (PI), and proportional derivative (PD) have been described. The final and one of the most frequently used modes is proportional integral and derivative (PID).

FIGURE 14-16: PD digital controller in FBD format.

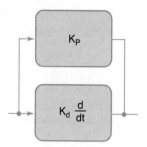

(a) Control system block diagram with a derivative action element

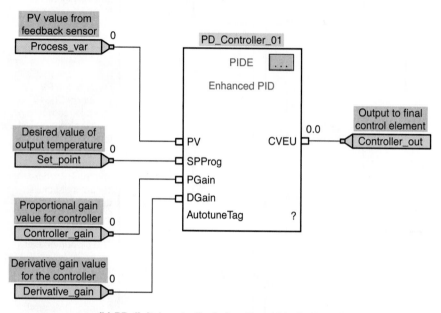

(b) PD digital controller in functional block diagram

Rehg and Sartori, Industrial Electronics, 1st Edition, © 2006, Reprinted by permission of Pearson Education, Inc., Upper Saddle River, NJ.

14-4-4 Proportional Integral and Derivative (PID) Control

Proportional integral and derivative control is the most common mode used in process control. The PID controller combines all the benefits of each control mode with few of the limitations. When combined into a single control loop the modes complement each other extremely well. Figure 14-18 indicates the parameters that dictate which mode of control would be best for an application. Each control mode in the left column is evaluated versus the process parameters across the top. Note that only one control mode,

PID, can tolerate any condition present in the process. Current digital controllers offer all the modes, so the cost to implement PID is no more than a proportional mode controller.

Digital controllers support the P, PI, PD, and PID modes, depending on what control parameters—proportional, integral, or derivative—have gain values greater than zero. A zero in a parameter removes it from the control algorithm. The digital controller implementation of the PID mode is illustrated in Figure 14-19, along with the block diagram symbols used when all three control modes are combined. The PIDE instruction has

FIGURE 14-17: Proportional plus integral action.

Controller waveform action	Description of action
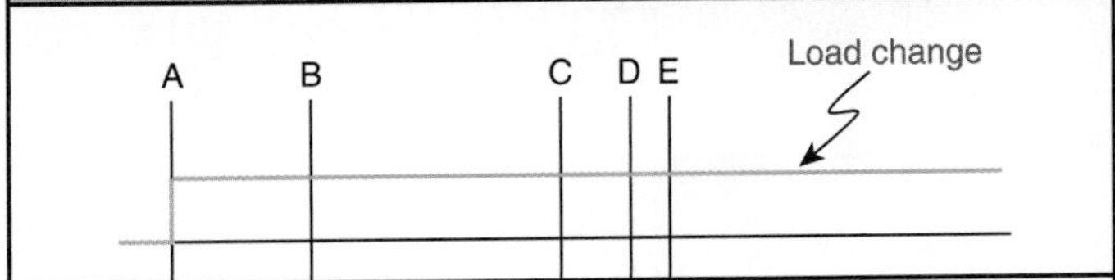 A B C D E Load change	From a steady-state condition, a load change occurs at point A and remains.
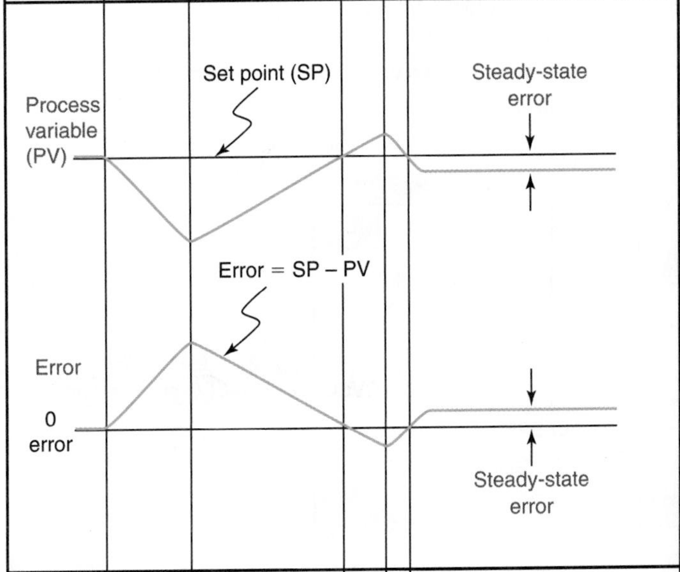 Process variable (PV) Set point (SP) Steady-state error Error = SP − PV Error 0 error Steady-state error	The PV starts at the SP value. In response to the increased load on the process, the process or measured variable (PV in Figure 12-41) drops below the set point. The error (SP − PV) changes from its initial state and has a shape that is the mirror of the PV waveform. The PV curve starts to recover at point B as the controller starts to correct for the load change. Note that the overcorrection occurs and the PV crosses the set point at point C before settling back to a steady-state level.
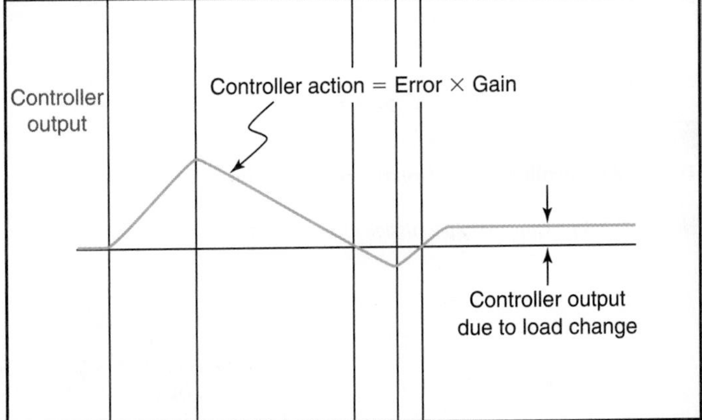 Controller output Controller action = Error × Gain Controller output due to load change	The proportional or controller action (Error × Gain) follows the error signal and corrects for the load change. The correction is not complete because some steady-state error remains to hold a controller output necessary to compensate for the new load. Note the gain is 1 for this example.
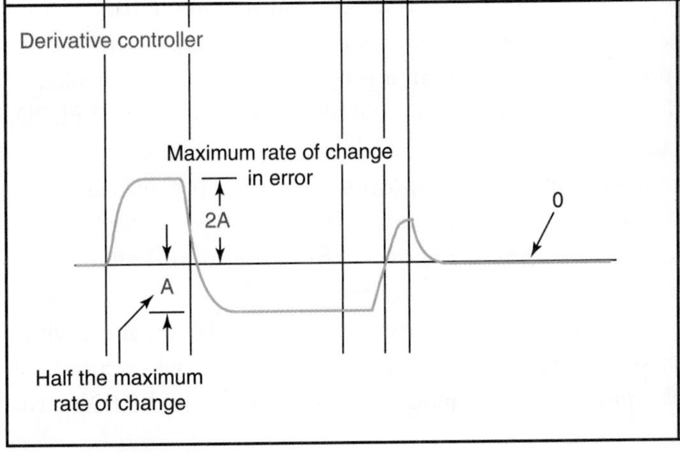 Derivative controller Maximum rate of change in error 2A A Half the maximum rate of change 0	The digital action responds only to the rate of change in the error signal. Note that the derivative starts at 0 and returns to 0 when the error is not changing. The amount of derivative action between points A and B is twice that between B and C. This results from the fact that the error is changing twice as fast before B than it is changing afterward.

Rehg and Sartori, Industrial Electronics, *1st Edition, © 2006, Reprinted by permission of Pearson Education, Inc., Upper Saddle River, NJ.*

FIGURE 14-18: Control mode selection versus process parameter conditions.

Control mode	Process reaction delay tolerated	Transfer lag tolerated	Dead time tolerated	Size of load disturbance tolerated	Speed of load disturbance tolerated
On-off	Only long never short	Almost none	Almost none	Small	Slow
Proportional (P) only	Moderate or long (cannot be too short)	Moderate	Moderate	Small	Slow
Proportional plus integral (PI)	Any	Moderate	Moderate	Any	Slow
Proportional plus derivative (PD)	Moderate or long	Moderate	Moderate	Small	Any
Proportional plus integral plus derivative (PID)	Any	Any	Any	Any	Any

Rehg and Sartori, Industrial Electronics, *1st Edition, © 2006, Reprinted by permission of Pearson Education, Inc., Upper Saddle River, NJ.*

gain input tags for all three parameters. The full complement of waveforms for a PID controller that has a load change disturbance is illustrated in Figure 14-20. The final waveform shows what the controller output looks like when the process has a set point change or a load change. Study the PID controller output and compare it with the outputs from each mode individually.

14-4-5 Fuzzy Control

Like many topics in this chapter, fuzzy control can fill an entire course. However, this subsection provides you with some basic concepts in fuzzy control and some situations when you may want to consider using it. This type of control uses artificial intelligence to readjust process parameters and is implemented with fuzzy logic algorithms on a digital controller. Rather than using a formula to calculate an output, fuzzy control evaluates rules by following three basic steps:

- First is *fuzzification*. In this step the process errors are changed from continuous variables to linguistic variables such as positive large or negative small.

- Next is *base rules/inference engine*. In this step simple if-then-else rules are evaluated and outputs are inferred, such as if the temperature is cold, then the output is very low.
- Last is *defuzzification*. In this step the output is changed from a linguistic variable to a continuous variable such as a solenoid valve position.

Fuzzy logic controllers (FLCs) implement these three basic steps. Typically, an FLC is placed in front of a PID controller to adjust the set points sent to the PID controller for elimination of overshoot and for improvement of process response to disturbances. In most implementations FLCs are used with conventional PIDs, they do not replace them. Fuzzy control is frequently used in supervisory control problems such as traffic control, quality control, and transportation systems, and is beneficial for the following types of control problems:

- Systems that are complex and difficult or impossible to model.
- Systems that must be controlled by human experts.

FIGURE 14-19: PID digital controller in FBD format.

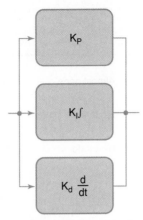

(a) Control system block diagram with all control elements

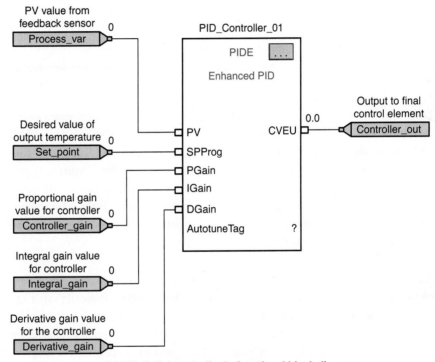

(b) PID digital controller in functional block diagram

Rehg and Sartori, Industrial Electronics, *1st Edition, © 2006, Reprinted by permission of Pearson Education, Inc., Upper Saddle River, NJ.*

- Systems driven by complex and continuous inputs and outputs.
- Systems where inputs or operational rules are based on human observation.
- Naturally vague systems such as in the behavioral and social sciences.

Advantages and Disadvantages of Fuzzy Control. Some of the advantages of fuzzy control include:

- A larger number of system variables can be evaluated.

FIGURE 14-20: PID action.

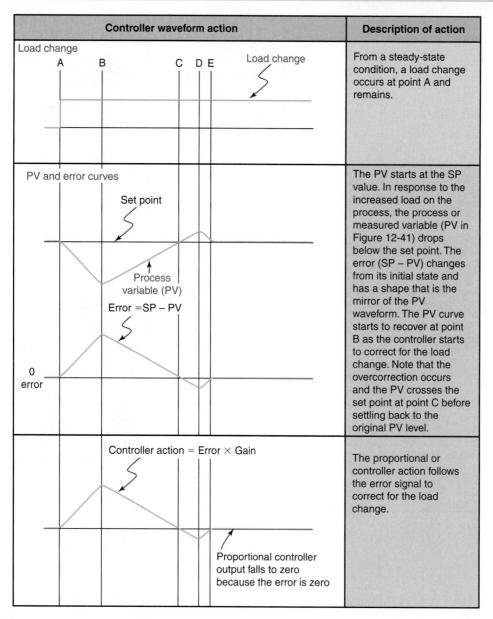

Controller waveform action	Description of action
Load change	From a steady-state condition, a load change occurs at point A and remains.
PV and error curves	The PV starts at the SP value. In response to the increased load on the process, the process or measured variable (PV in Figure 12-41) drops below the set point. The error (SP – PV) changes from its initial state and has a shape that is the mirror of the PV waveform. The PV curve starts to recover at point B as the controller starts to correct for the load change. Note that the overcorrection occurs and the PV crosses the set point at point C before settling back to the original PV level.
Controller action = Error × Gain	The proportional or controller action follows the error signal to correct for the load change.

Rehg and Sartori, Industrial Electronics, *1st Edition, © 2006, Reprinted by permission of Pearson Education, Inc., Upper Saddle River, NJ.*

- It is similar to the way humans think because linguistic variables are used.
- It permits a greater degree of uncertainty as the output is related to the input, thus better control is possible for some types of systems.
- It can be used for the solution of previously unsolved problems.
- Systems come together faster because a system designer doesn't have to know everything about the system before starting work.
- Knowledge acquisition and representation is simplified.

The disadvantages are:

- Extracting a model from a fuzzy system is difficult.
- Fuzzy systems require more fine tuning before they're operational.

The availability of low-cost microcomputers has fueled the recent strong gains in the adoption of fuzzy control. However, the cultural bias in the United States for mathematically precise linear models and PID control makes adoption of fuzzy control difficult.

FIGURE 14-20: (Continued).

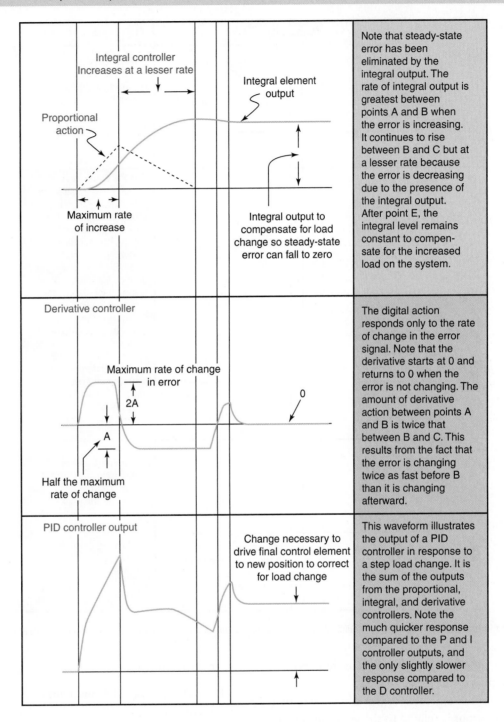

Note that steady-state error has been eliminated by the integral output. The rate of integral output is greatest between points A and B when the error is increasing. It continues to rise between B and C but at a lesser rate because the error is decreasing due to the presence of the integral output. After point E, the integral level remains constant to compensate for the increased load on the system.

The digital action responds only to the rate of change in the error signal. Note that the derivative starts at 0 and returns to 0 when the error is not changing. The amount of derivative action between points A and B is twice that between B and C. This results from the fact that the error is changing twice as fast before B than it is changing afterward.

This waveform illustrates the output of a PID controller in response to a step load change. It is the sum of the outputs from the proportional, integral, and derivative controllers. Note the much quicker response compared to the P and I controller outputs, and the only slightly slower response compared to the D controller.

14-5 DIGITAL CONTROL

Let's now take a look at how digital control is used to implement the proportional, integral, and derivative process control modes. Digital controllers have an operational mode that starts from the traditional differential equation for the controller output (CO) but is better expressed as a summation of incremental changes. Both of these expressions for the CO are described in this section. The PID algorithm for the analog controller was given as:

$$CO = K_p e + Ki \int edt + K_d \ de/dt$$

where CO is the controller output and the error value, e, is the set point minus the process variable ($e = SP - PV$). Analog controllers are implemented with operational amplifiers that are configured as proportional, integrators, and differentiators. The amplifiers change their output based on a change in the input at the speed or bandwidth of the amplifier. With the high speed present in operational amplifiers, the changes in the output appear to be instantaneous. The term *continuous* is often used to describe analog PID control because there appears to be no delay between the changes in the input and output. There is some very small delay, but the process component change is several magnitudes slower, so the delay is not an issue.

14-5-1 Digital Sample and Hold

A digital control system is not continuous in the sense of an analog amplifier since each action inside a digital system is paced by the speed of the system clock. The digital process control system also operates in this fashion. Figure 14-21 illustrates this concept by showing that the error at the input is read when S1 is closed and the controller output (CO) is changed some time later. The change in S1 and the calculation of the desired output that must occur are done in incre-

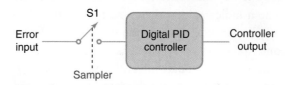

FIGURE 14-21: Sampling or system update for a digital controller.

mental time slices. The time for that process is called the *sampling* or *system update time*. The update or sampling interval, T, generates a series of error values that are available to the controller in the form of an error pulse train. The circuit inside the controller that holds the error values is called a sample and hold circuit. Once new error data is available, the controller calculates an output and makes that output value available until the next update time. The controller calculates and stores a new output only when new error data becomes available; hence, the controller output appears as a set of pulses that change at the same update rate.

Figure 14-22 illustrates a changing error wave form, the error generated at the system update

FIGURE 14-22: Error input and controller output by update interval.

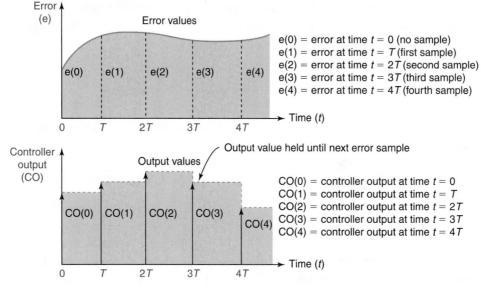

e(0) = error at time $t = 0$ (no sample)
e(1) = error at time $t = T$ (first sample)
e(2) = error at time $t = 2T$ (second sample)
e(3) = error at time $t = 3T$ (third sample)
e(4) = error at time $t = 4T$ (fourth sample)

CO(0) = controller output at time $t = 0$
CO(1) = controller output at time $t = T$
CO(2) = controller output at time $t = 2T$
CO(3) = controller output at time $t = 3T$
CO(4) = controller output at time $t = 4T$

interval, and the corresponding controller output levels. Conventionally, an error pulse train is represented by an e with an n in parentheses, e(n). The n indicates that there are a series of values for the variable e. When the value is specific for one update interval, the n is replaced with the number of the update interval. For example, e(2) represents the error for the second update interval. Study the figure and review this discussion of update intervals until the operation of the digital controller is clear.

14-5-2 Proportional Control Mode

Proportional output is simply the product of current error and the proportional gain coefficient. The expression for the output of an analog controller is:

$$CO = K_p e$$

The analog expression is differentiated to indicate that the error is changing at an interval rate set by the update time. The result is:

$$dCO/dt = K_p \, de/dt$$

The dCO/dt and de/dt terms represent the change in the variable with respect to time. The digital control proportional algorithm says that CO (controller output) changes by a value of K_p (controller gain) times the change in e (input error). Thus the general expression for the digital controller output can be written as:

$$CO(n) = CO(n-1) + K_p \, [e(n) - e(n-1)]$$

where n represents the update interval at which the controller output value is desired, and $n - 1$ represents values for the previous update interval. Note that the controller output for the previous update interval must be added since the calculation for the current interval is only the change from the previous interval. So at the end of the second update interval ($n = 1$) or time equal to T in Figure 14-22 the controller output is:

$$CO(1) = CO(0) + K_p \, [e(1) - e(0)]$$

So the new controller output is the previous controller output plus the proportional gain times the change in the error from interval 0 to interval 1.

EXAMPLE 14-2

Use the algorithm for a digital proportional controller and the value (percent of full scale) of the set point change and the corresponding changes in the process variable for 15 time intervals to complete a table showing how the algorithm generates the controller output.

SOLUTION

The results of the calculations are given in the table in Figure 14-23. The graphs showing set point, process variable, error, and controller output are illustrated as well. Note that the actual controller output cannot change more than 100 percent, so the change goes off of the graph. This means that the controller output is at the 100 percent level.

Example calculation: CO(5) = 210 = 280 + 7(30 − 40)

14-5-3 Integral Control Mode

In the integral mode any error present changes the controller output based on the area under the error curve. The algorithm for the integral mode controller is:

$$CO = K_1 \int e \, dt$$

In this analog expression the term $\int e \, dt$ is the area under the error curve in Figure 14-24.

Taking the derivative of the analog expressions results in:

$$dCO/dt = K_1 e \, dt$$

The dCO/dt term represents the change in the CO value with respect to time and the dt term on the right side is the incremental change in time. This change in time is the update time interval, T, set in the digital controller and shown in

FIGURE 14-23: Solution for Example 14-2.

n—update interval	Set point	Process variable	Controller output CO(n)	K_p	Error e(n)	Previous error e(n − 1)	Previous controller output CO(n − 1)
0	0	0	0	7	0	0	0
1	50	2	336	7	48	0	0
2	50	5	315	7	45	48	336
3	50	10	280	7	40	45	315
4	50	15	245	7	35	40	280
5	50	20	210	7	30	35	245
6	50	25	175	7	25	30	210
7	50	30	140	7	20	25	175
8	50	35	105	7	15	20	140
9	50	39	77	7	11	15	105
10	50	42	56	7	8	11	77
11	50	44	42	7	6	8	56
12	50	45	35	7	5	6	42
13	50	45	35	7	5	5	35
14	50	45	35	7	5	5	35

(a) Steady-state error = 5; final output = 35

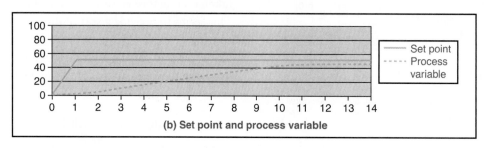

(b) Set point and process variable

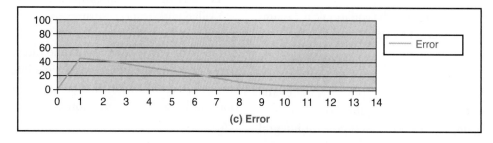

(c) Error

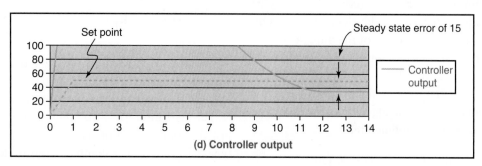

(d) Controller output

Rehg and Sartori, Industrial Electronics, *1st Edition, © 2006, Reprinted by permission of Pearson Education, Inc., Upper Saddle River, NJ.*

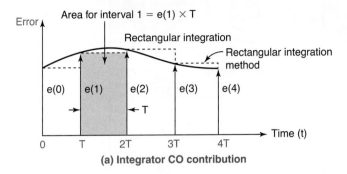

(a) Integrator CO contribution

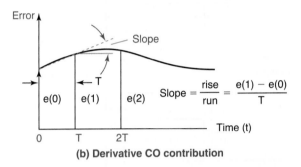

(b) Derivative CO contribution

Rehg and Sartori, Industrial Electronics, 1st Edition, © 2006, Reprinted by permission of Pearson Education, Inc., Upper Saddle River, NJ.

Figure 14-24. Therefore, the equation can be simplified and converted to single interval as:

$$CO(n) = K_1 e(n)\, T$$

The term on the right is the area under the error curve (e value × time duration) times the integral gain, K_1. So the digital control integral algorithm says that CO (controller output) changes by that term on the right as long as an error is present. The value of the integral contribution to the controller output changes at every update interval as indicated in Figure 14-24(a).

The algorithm for a PI digital controller is just the combination of the algorithms for each type individually. The combined terms yield:

$$CO(n) = CO(n - 1) + K_p[e(n) - e(n - 1)] + K_1 e(n)\, T$$

Using this expression, a PI controller can be constructed using any digital controller that has addition, subtraction, and multiplication functions available.

14-5-4 Derivative Control Mode

In the derivative mode any change in the error causes a change in the controller output based on the rate at which the error is changing. The algorithm for the derivative mode controller is:

$$CO = K_D\, de/dt$$

The de/dt term represents the instantaneous slope of the error curve at that point in time. Since it represents the slope it is an indication of the direction in which the error is moving and the rate at which it is changing. The derivative control gives some CO action based on the *tendency* of the error, so a corrective action can be taken even before error has reached a new level. This seems to provide a sort of intelligence to the controller—hence the name *anticipatory control*. The algorithm for the digital controller is found by taking the derivative of the analog CO expression, which results in:

$$dCO/dt = K_D\, d(de)/dt$$

The dCO/dt term represents the change in the CO value with respect to time, and the d(de)/dt term is the rate of change in the error or slope of the error curve over some time interval. The time interval is the PLC update time interval, T, shown in Figure 14-24(b). Therefore, the equation can be simplified and converted to a single interval as:

$$CO(n) = K_D \left[\frac{e(n) - e(n-1)}{T} \right]$$

The bracketed term on the right is the slope from the previous interval to the present and the K_D term is the gain for the derivative component.

The algorithm for a PID digital controller is just the combination of the algorithms for each type individually. The combined terms yield:

$$CO(n) = CO(n-1) + K_p[e(n) - e(n-1)] + K_1 e(n)\, T + K_D \left[\frac{e(n) - e(n-1)}{T} \right]$$

Using this expression, a PID controller can be constructed using any digital controller that has addition, subtraction, and multiplication functions available. However, a better delta e estimator is necessary to help smooth out the contribution of the derivative term to the controller output.

Improved Delta e Estimator. Estimator theory offers a number of choices, but a complete discussion is beyond the scope of this chapter. However, an improvement can be added by increasing the number of intervals over which the slope is calculated. A delta e estimator considered is:

$$\Delta e = [e(n) - e(n-1)] - [e(n-1) - e(n-2)]$$

Adding this estimator to the PID digital algorithms results in:

$$CO(n) = CO(n-1) + K_p[e(n) - e(n-1)] + K_1 e(n)T$$
$$+ \frac{K_D}{T}[e(n) - 2e(n-1) + e(n-2)]$$

where n is the number of the interval being evaluated, T is the sampling period or loop update time, K is the gain of the respective modes, CO is the controller output, and e is the error, or SP − PV. This form of the equation is often called the textbook PID. However, process engineers frequently make changes to get a better control result. The change made most often is the removal of the set point from the derivative term in the equation. Set point is removed because the derivative action is not necessary for a set point change. In the equation, e equals SP − PV and Δe equals SP − Δ PV. So in situations where the change in error is used it can be replaced with the change in PV since the SP is fixed and does not change. Making that change the PID algorithm becomes:

$$CO(n) = CO(n-1) + K_p[e(n) - e(n-1)] + K_1 e(n)T$$
$$+ \frac{K_D}{T}[PV(n) - 2PV(n-1) + PV(n-2)]$$

where PV is the process variable. This is the form of the equation used by many industrial controllers such as the Allen-Bradley ControlLogix System PLC. In some control problems the error

term for the proportional part of the equation is changed to PV because SP is removed there as well.

14-6 SCALING IN PROCESS CONTROL

In process control, process input variables typically need scaling, which is the resizing of a signal to meet the requirements of the using system component. Commonly, the input signal to be scaled is from an analog sensor and the scaled value is used by a PID controller as a process variable. The scale instruction (SCL) converts an unscaled input value to a floating point value and is illustrated in Figure 14-25. For example, let's say that the input source is a 12-bit analog input module, which is reading a liquid flow of 0 to 100 gallons per minute (gpm). You typically do not scale the module from 0 to 100 because that limits the resolution of the 12-bit input value (0 to 4095). Instead, you use the SCL instruction and configure the module to input an unscaled (0 to 4095) value, which the SCL instruction converts to 0 to 100 gpm (floating point) without loss of resolution.

The SCL instruction uses the following algorithm to convert unscaled input into a scaled value.

$$Out = (In - InMin) \times [(SclMax - SclMin)/ (InMax - InMin)] + SclMin$$

where: InMin and InMax are the minimum and maximum unscaled input values, respectively; and SclMin and SclMax are the minimum and maximum scaled values, respectively.

In simpler terms, the output of the SCL instruction is the input offset times the scaling rate (the terms within the brackets) plus the scaled minimum value.

FIGURE 14-25: Scale instruction.

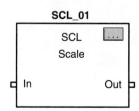

14-7 MANUAL CONTROL MODE AND BUMPLESS TRANSFER

Most industrial process controllers have a *manual control* mode. Operators can switch between automatic and manual mode as illustrated in Figure 14-26. In the manual mode the controller output is manually entered into the controller by the operator and the process final control element responds accordingly. Values for P, I, and D gains are entered, and the PV value is monitored. When the controlled variable reaches a value close to the set point, the process is switched to automatic by the operator. If the PV and SP are close in value the process switches to the automatic mode with

the controller taking over control with little or no disturbance in the controlled variable. If the controller has a *bumpless transfer* capability, then the switch can be made with the PV and SP separated by a greater value, and the controller will bring the PV and SP close before switching to automatic.

14-8 LOCATION OF THE INSTRUCTIONS

The location of instructions from this chapter in the Allen-Bradley programming software for Function Block Diagrams is indicated in Figure 14-27.

FIGURE 14-26: Manual control mode.

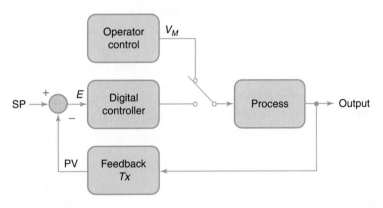

Rehg and Sartori, Industrial Electronics, *1st Edition, © 2006, Reprinted by permission of Pearson Education, Inc., Upper Saddle River, NJ.*

FIGURE 14-27: Location of instructions described in this chapter.

Systems	Instructions	Location
LOGIX	PIDE, SCL	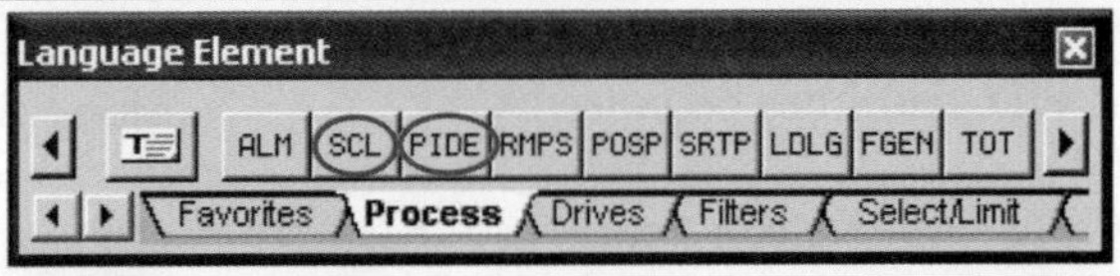 Language Element — ALM SCL PIDE RMPS POSP SRTP LDLG FGEN TOT — Favorites / **Process** / Drives / Filters / Select/Limit
LOGIX	SSUM	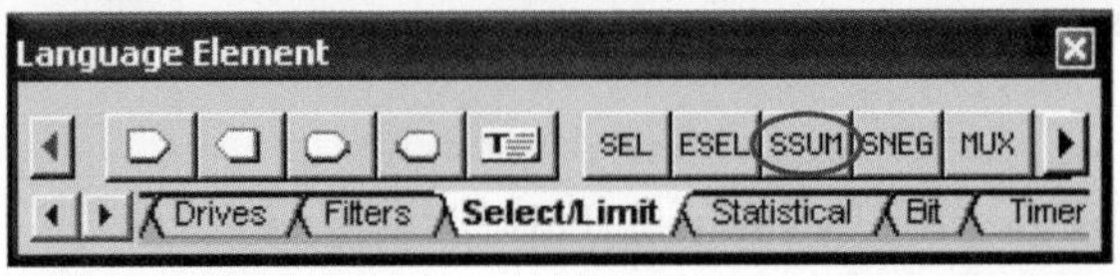 Language Element — SEL ESEL SSUM SNEG MUX — Drives / Filters / **Select/Limit** / Statistical / Bit / Timer

CHAPTER 15

PLC Standard IEC 61131-3— Structured Text Language

15-1 GOALS AND OBJECTIVES

The goals of this chapter are to provide an overview of IEC 61131-3 text languages and to provide the Allen-Bradley implementation of the IEC 61131 Structured Text language.

After completing this chapter you should be able to:

- Describe the difference between the Instruction List and Structured Text languages.
- Define the components of the Allen-Bradley Structured Text language.
- Describe the arithmetic, logical, and relational operators.
- Describe the various constructs of the Structured Text language.
- Create a Structured Text program for automation process problems using the Allen-Bradley implementation.

15-2 OVERVIEW OF IEC 61131-3 TEXT LANGUAGES

There are two text-based languages (Instruction List and Structured Text) that are used to solve automation process problems. Structured Text language is discussed in this chapter. However,

let's start with a general description of both languages.

- Instruction List (IL): A low-level, text-based language that uses mnemonic instructions like those used in machine code in microprocessors. Consequently, IL is a powerful language, but it has many disadvantages such as a cryptic nature. It is not a good fit for most applications, and as a result it is rarely used. IL should be used only as a last resort. Allen-Bradley does not support this language because of its marginal value in automated process applications.
- Structured Text (ST): A high-level, text-based language, such as BASIC, C, or PASCAL, with commands that support a highly structured program development and the ability to evaluate complex mathematical expressions.

15-3 ALLEN-BRADLEY IEC 61131 STRUCTURED TEXT IMPLEMENTATION

The Allen-Bradley version of ST is compliant with the 61131 standard. ST is not case sensitive and uses statements to define what to execute.

The Allen-Bradley ST implements the following components:

- **Assignment:** a statement that assigns values to tags
- **Expression:** part of an assignment or construct statement that evaluates a number or a true-false state
- **Instruction:** a stand-alone statement that contains operands
- **Construct:** a conditional statement used to trigger Structured Text code
- **Comment:** text that explains or clarifies what a section of Structured Text does

15-4 STRUCTURE TEXT PROGRAMMING

The Structured Text language in 61131 is similar to Pascal or other structured programming languages; however, ST has been specifically developed for industrial control applications. The program executes or is scanned on a line-by-line basis, starting at the first line in the program and continuing until the last line is executed. The statements or command syntax are sufficiently robust to avoid jump instructions (GOTO) that are used in some other languages, such as BASIC, to redirect the flow of execution.

ST language is rather straightforward to learn and use, and ST statements are written in a free style where tabs, returns, and comments can be inserted throughout the program. It is particularly useful for complex arithmetic calculations. The ST language is presented using the structure in Allen-Bradley's RSLogix 5000 software as an example.

15-4-1 Assignment Statements

Assignment statements are used to change the value stored within a variable or tag. An assignment has the following syntax:

Tag := expression ;

where:

Component	Description
tag	represents the tag that is getting the new value; the tag must be BOOL, SINT, INT, DINT, or REAL
:=	is the assignment symbol
expression	represents the new value to assign to the tag

If *tag* is this data type:	Use this type of expression:
BOOL	BOOL expression
SINT	
INT	
DINT	
REAL	numeric expression
;	ends the assignment

The **tag** retains the assigned value until another assignment changes the value.

The expression can be simple, such as an immediate value like an integer or another tag name, or the expression can be complex and include several mathematical operators and/or functions.

15-4-2 Expressions

Expressions are a part of every assignment statement and are a tag name, equation, or comparison. Expressions are written using the following:

- Tag names that store the value (variable)
- Numbers that you enter directly into the expression (immediate values)

- Functions, such as ABS, TRUNC
- Operators, such as +, −, <, >, AND, OR

The general rules for expressions include:

- Use any combination of uppercase and lowercase letters.
- For more complex requirements, use parentheses to group expressions within expressions. This makes the expression easier to read and ensures that the expression executes in the desired sequence.

In Structured Text, you use two types of expressions:

- BOOL expression: A Boolean expression produces either the Boolean value of 1 (true) or 0 (not true, or false).
  - A Boolean expression uses Boolean tags, relational operators, and logical operators to compare values or check whether conditions are true or false. The Boolean expression tag > 65 is an example.
  - A simple Boolean expression can be a single Boolean tag.
  - Typically, you use Boolean expressions to condition the execution of other logic.
- Numeric expression: A numeric expression calculates an integer or floating point value.
  - A numeric expression uses arithmetic operators, arithmetic functions, and bitwise operators. The numeric expression tag1 + 5 is an example.
  - Often, you nest a numeric expression within a Boolean expression. The expression (tag1 + 5) > 65 is an example.

15-4-3 Operators and Functions

Assignment statements also use operators and functions in the development of expressions. You can combine multiple operators and functions in arithmetic expressions to calculate new values. The following arithmetic operators are used in ST.

Arithmetic Operation	Operator	Optimal Data Type
Add	+	DINT, REAL
Subtract/negate	+	DINT, REAL
Multiply	*	DINT, REAL
Exponent (x to the power of y)	**	DINT, REAL
Divide	/	DINT, REAL
Modulo-divide	MOD	DINT, REAL

Arithmetic functions perform a specific mathematical operation on an integer or real constant, a non-Boolean tag, or an expression. The functions supported by ST include:

Function Names	Function Syntax	Optimal Data Type
absolute value	ABS (numeric_expression)	DINT, REAL
arc cosine	ACOS (numeric_expression)	REAL
arc sine	ASIN (numeric_expression)	REAL
arc tangent	ATAN (numeric_expression)	REAL
cosine	COS (numeric_expression)	REAL
radians to degrees	DEG (numeric_expression)	DINT, REAL
natural log	LN (numeric_expression)	REAL
log base 10	LOG (numeric_expression)	REAL

degrees to radians	RAD (numeric_expression)	DINT, REAL
sine	SIN (numeric_expression)	REAL
square root	SQRT (numeric_expression)	DINT, REAL
tangent	TAN (numeric_expression)	REAL
truncate	TRUNC (numeric_expression)	DINT, REAL

15-4-4 Relational Operators

Relational operators, used in expressions, compare two values or strings to provide a true or not true (false) result. The result of a relational operation is a Boolean value. If the result of the comparison is true, then the result is 1; if it is not true, or false, then the result is 0. Relational operators supported by ST include:

Comparison Name	Operator	Optimal Data Type
equal	=	DINT, REAL, string
less than	<	DINT, REAL, string
less than or equal	<=	DINT, REAL, string
greater than	>	DINT, REAL, string
greater than or equal	>=	DINT, REAL, string
not equal	<>	DINT, REAL, string

15-4-5 Logical Operators and Bitwise Operators

Logical operators are used in expressions to perform logical combinations on single bits or Boolean tags, whereas *bitwise operators* perform bitwise logical combinations on bits of DINT tags. If the result tag in the assignment statement is a Boolean data type, then logical operators are used, but if the data type is DINT, then bitwise operators are used. The result of a logical operation is a Boolean data type and the result of a bitwise operation is a DINT data type. Logical and bitwise operators are as follows:

Operator Name	Operator	Logical Operation Data Type	Bitwise Operation Data Type
Logical/bitwise AND	&, AND	BOOL	DINT
Logical/bitwise OR	OR	BOOL	DINT
Logical/bitwise exclusive OR	XOR	BOOL	DINT
Logical/bitwise complement	NOT	BOOL	DINT

The first six examples in the following table illustrate logical operations on Boolean data types and tags. The seventh example is a bitwise operation on DINT data types and tags with a DINT result.

Example	Problem Statement	Required Expression
1	If *fluid_temp* is a BOOL tag and your specification says: "If *fluid_temp_1* is on then . . ."	IF fluid_temp THEN . . .
2	If *fluid_temp* is a BOOL tag and your specification says: "If *fluid_temp* is off then . . ."	IF NOT fluid_temp THEN...
3	If *fluid_temp* is a BOOL tag, *temp* is a DINT tag, and your specification says: "If *fluid_temp* is on and temp is less than 100° then . . ."	IF fluid_temp & (temp <100) THEN...
4	If fluid_temp is a BOOL tag, temp is a DINT tag, and your specification says: "If fluid_temp is on or temp is less than 100° then . . ."	IF fluid_temp OR (temp<100) THEN . . .
5	If *fluid_temp1* and *fluid_temp2* are BOOL tags and your specification says: "If: • *fluid_temp1* is on while *fluid_temp2* is off or • fluid_temp1 is off while fluid_temp2 is on then . . ."	*IF fluid_temp1 XOR fluid_temp2 THEN . . .*
6	If fluid_temp1 and *fluid_temp2* are BOOL tags, *open* is a BOOL tag, and your specification says: "If *fluid_temp1* and *fluid_temp2* are both on, set *open* to true."	open := fluid_temp1 & fluid_temp2;
7	If *input1*, *input2*, and *result1* are DINT tags and your specification says: "Calculate the bitwise result of *input1* and *input2*. Store the result in *result1*."	result1 := input1 AND input2;

Note in examples 3 and 4 that a tag or variable was a DINT data type, but it was used in an expression that produced a Boolean result.

15-4-6 Constructs

Constructs are critical building blocks for program development. The structure provided by these elements permits linear program flow from top to bottom without the need for jump instructions. Constructs supported by ST include *IF . . . THEN, FOR . . . DO, WHILE . . . DO, REPEAT . . . UNTIL,* and *CASE . . . OF.* The following table indicates what programming conditions dictate the selection of a specific construct.

If You Want to	Use This Construct
Do something if or when specific conditions occur	IF . . . THEN
Do something a specific number of times before doing anything else	FOR . . . DO
Keep doing something as long as certain conditions are true	WHILE . . . DO
Keep doing something until a condition is true	REPEAT . . . UNTIL
Select what to do based on a numerical value	CASE . . . OF

There are usually a number of variations for the constructs and each has a required syntax that must be followed. Each is addressed in detail in the following sections.

IF . . . THEN. The syntax for the IF . . . THEN construct is:

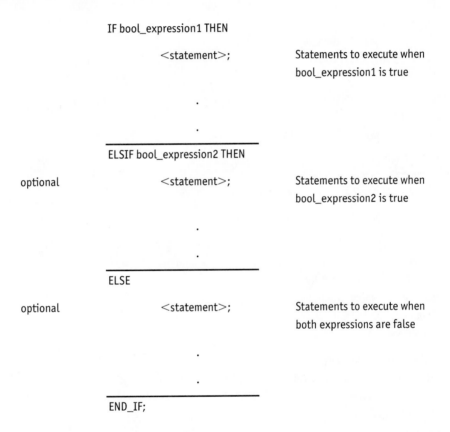

```
        IF bool_expression1 THEN

                <statement>;          Statements to execute when
                                      bool_expression1 is true

                      .

                      .

        ELSIF bool_expression2 THEN

optional        <statement>;          Statements to execute when
                                      bool_expression2 is true

                      .

                      .

        ELSE

optional        <statement>;          Statements to execute when
                                      both expressions are false

                      .

                      .

        END_IF;
```

To use ELSIF or ELSE, follow these guidelines:

1. If you have several possible conditions to be evaluated, add one or more ELSIF statements as follows:
   - Each ELSIF represents an alternative path.
   - Specify as many ELSIF paths as you need.

- The controller executes the first true IF or ELSIF and skips the rest of the ELSIFs and the ELSE.
2. To do something when the entire IF or ELSIF conditions are false, add an ELSE statement.

EXAMPLE 15-1

Turn off a conveyor direction light if the conveyor is moving in the forward direction. Keep the light on if it is not moving in the forward direction. Develop an ST program to solve this automation process problem.

SOLUTION

```
IF conveyor_direction THEN
    light := 0;
ELSE
    Light [:=] 1;
(* The [:=] tells the controller to clear light whenever the controller enters the RUN mode. *)
END_IF
```

Comments beyond a single line are indicated by bracketing them as follows (* comment *). Note the comment added in the previous code.

EXAMPLE 15-2

If the tank temperature is greater than 100 run the pump slow, but if the temperature is over 200 set the pump speed to high. Under all other conditions turn the pump off. Develop an ST program to solve this automation process problem.

SOLUTION

```
IF tank.temp > 200 THEN
    pump.fast :=1; pump.slow :=0; pump.off :=0;
ELSEIF tank.temp > 100 THEN
    pump.fast :=0; pump.slow :=1; pump.off :=0;
ELSE
    pump.fast :=0; pump.slow :=0; pump.off :=1;
END_IF
```

In both examples the ELSEIF and ELSE are optional and can be eliminated if the problem dictates.

FOR . . . DO. The FOR . . . DO construct performs an operation a specified number of times. The syntax is:

	FOR count := initial_value	
	TO final_value	
optional	BY increment	If you don't specify an increment, the loop increments by 1.
	DO	
	<statement>;	The statement you want to execute a number of times.

	IF bool_expression THEN	If there are conditions when
optional	EXIT;	you want to exit the loop early, use other statements, such as an IF . . . THEN construct, to
	END_IF;	condition an EXIT statement.

END_FOR;

The terms and elements used in the FOR . . . DO syntax are described in the following table.

Operand	Data Type	Format Options	Description
count	SINT	tag	Tag to store count position
	INT		as the FOR . . . DO
	DINT		executes
initial_ value	SINT	tag	Must evaluate to a number
	INT	expression	that specifies initial value
	DINT	immediate	for count
final_ value	SINT	tag	Specifies final value for
	INT	expression	count, which determines
	DINT	immediate	when to exit the loop
increment	SINT	tag	(optional) Amount to
	INT	expression	increment count each time
	DINT	immediate	through the loop; if you don't specify an increment, the count increments by 1

EXAMPLE 15-3

The required positions (open = 1 and closed = 0) for 10 valves are stored in an array called Pos [0 – 9]. The tags for the valves are also in an array called Valve starting at element 5. Write an ST routine to set the 10 valves from their database.

SOLUTION

```
FOR count := 0 to 9 BY 1 DO   //count is the index value
    Valve_num := count + 5
//Sets the valve number as 5 higher than the count
    Valve [valve_num] := Pos [count]
//On the first pass – sets the Valve [5] position to the values in Pos [0]
END_FOR
```

Note that single line comments are added to the program by using the // indicators.

WHILE . . . DO. The WHILE . . . DO loop executes for the full time that the Boolean expression is true or 1. The syntax is:

WHILE *bool_expression1* DO

	<statement> ;	Statements to execute while
		bool_expression1 is true.
	IF *bool_expression2* THEN	If there are conditions when
		you want to exit the loop
Optional	EXIT;	early, use other statements,
		such as an IF . . . THEN
		construct, to condition an
	END_IF;	EXIT statement.

END_WHILE;

EXAMPLE 15-4

The tank input valve, tag V23, should be open (valve on or power applied) as long as the level switch, tag LS_low, is not true or 0 and the drain valve, tag V10, is closed (valve off or no power applied). Develop an ST program to solve this automation process problem.

SOLUTION

```
WHILE NOT LS_low AND NOT V10 DO       //Low level switch and drain valve
                                      //are not true or 0
        V23 := 1;                     //Turn on input valve
        IF Emerg_stop THEN
               V23 := 0;
               EXIT;
END_WHILE;
```

REPEAT . . . UNTIL. The REPEAT . . . UNTIL loop executes until the Boolean expression is true or 1. This command has a syntax that is like the WHILE . . . DO construct but it operates with complementary logic. WHILE . . . DO executes as long as the condition is true, whereas REPEAT . . . UNTIL operates until the condition is true.

Another difference between WHILE . . . DO and REPEAT . . . UNTIL concerns how execution occurs. The REPEAT . . . UNTIL loop executes the statements in the construct and then determines if the conditions are true before executing the statements again. The statements in a REPEAT . . . UNTIL loop are always executed at least once. The statements in a WHILE . . . DO loop are not executed until the condition is true, and they continue to be executed until the condition is false.

CASE . . . OF. The CASE . . . OF construct uses a numeric value to determine what expression to execute. The CASE construct is similar to a switch statement in the C or C++ programming languages. However, with the CASE construct the controller executes *only* the statements that are associated with the *first matching* selector value. Execution *always breaks after the statements of that selector* and goes to the END_CASE statement. The syntax is:

```
CASE numeric_expression OF
```

selector1 : <statement>; ← Statements to execute when
       .   *numeric_expression = selector1*

Specify as many alternative selector values (paths) as you need

selector2 : <statement>; ← Statements to execute when
       .   *numeric_expression = selector2*

selector3 : <statement>; ← Statements to execute when
       .   *numeric_expression = selector3*

Optional

```
ELSE
```
    <statement>; ← Statements to execute when
      .   *numeric_expression is not equal to any selector*

```
END_CASE;
```

Switch position	Speed	Fans	Water pump
1	10 mph		
2	20 mph		
3	40 mph	1	
4 and 5	50 mph	2	
6 through 10	60 mph		1

EXAMPLE 15-5

Develop an ST program to set the speed of a vehicle and turn on fans and the water pump based on the following switch positions:

SOLUTION

```
CASE          speed_setting OF
1   :             speed := 10;
2   :             speed := 20;
3   :             speed := 40; fan1 := 1;
4,5 :             speed := 50; fan2 := 1;
6…10:             speed := 60; waterpump1 := 1;
ELSE

                  Speed := 0; speed fault := 1;

END_CASE
```

15-5 EMPIRICAL DESIGN WITH STRUCTURED TEXT

The structured text program development constructs are listed in the previous section. After you are familiar with the operation of the commonly used constructs, following these design steps will yield good design results. However, to learn the program structure for an ST solution it is best to study ST equivalents for the ladder logic rungs used in similar control problems.

15-5-1 Standard Structured Text Control Solutions

The following structured text programs indicate how structured text solutions compare to common ladder logic rungs and standard ladder logic diagrams.

ST Standard for Combinational Conditional Logic. The comparison between combinational logic for ladder logic inputs and their ST equivalent is illustrated in Figure 15-1(a) and (b). Read the description of the operation included in the figure. Combinational logic is achieved in ST through the use of Boolean logic functions such as Boolean ANDs, ORs, and NOTs.

ST Standard for Timers. The comparison between timer instructions for standard ladder logic inputs and their ST equivalent is illustrated in Figure 15-2(a) and (b). The ladder logic uses the TON symbol and the ST uses the TONR symbol for a time on timer. Read the description of the operation included in the figures. The timer instructions in ST operate the same as the timers in the ladder logic. However, in ST you can enter operational parameters such as timer preset.

ST Standard for Counters. The comparison between counter instructions for standard ladder logic inputs and their ST equivalent is illustrated in

FIGURE 15-1: ST for standard ladder logic with conditional XIC and XIO logic rungs.

Standard ST Logic for Conditional Control Functions

Turn on an output device for a logical combination of multiple input instructions.

The development of combinational logic in ladder rungs is simply AND/OR or OR/AND instructional groupings as shown in (a). When implementing the same logic in ST as shown in (b), IF...THEN...ELSE statements are used to develop the combinational logic. Note that an XIO instruction in the ladder logic requires that the NOT function is used in the ST to produce the same logical output.

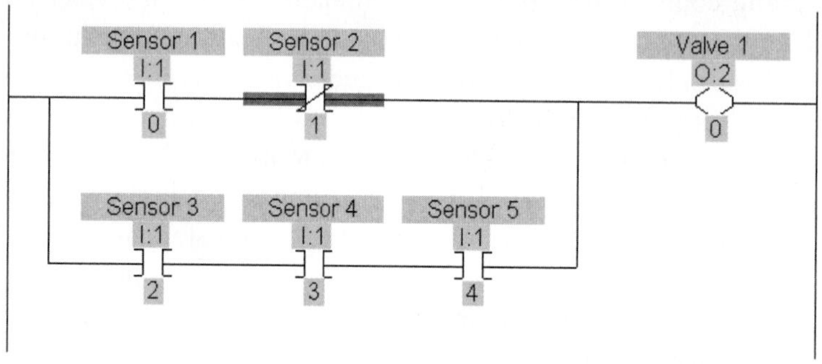

(a)

```
IF Sensor_1 AND NOT Sensor_2 THEN
        Valve_1 := 1;
ELSEIF Sensor_3 AND Sensor_4 AND Sensor_5 THEN
        Valve_1 := 1;
ELSE Valve_1 := 0;
END_IF;
```

(b)

FIGURE 15-2: ST for standard ladder logic for timers.

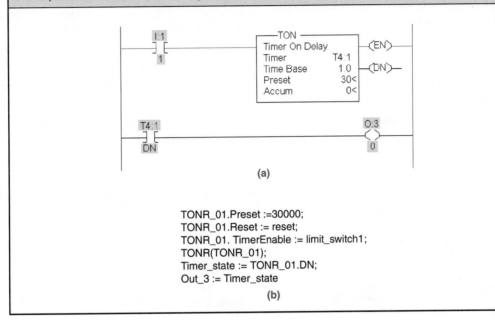

Standard ST Logic for TONR Timers

Turn on an output device after a set time period.

The standard ladder logic for the TON timer is shown in (a) and the ST equivalent in (b). The input for both is a NO maintain contact selector switch. If the switch is closed, then the ST timer (same notation as the FBD) is enabled. When the accumulator equals the preset value of 30 seconds (30000 x 0.001), the done bit is set and output is true. Note that the timer tag name is inside the parentheses.

(a)

```
TONR_01.Preset :=30000;
TONR_01.Reset := reset;
TONR_01. TimerEnable := limit_switch1;
TONR(TONR_01);
Timer_state := TONR_01.DN;
Out_3 := Timer_state
```

(b)

Figure 15-3(a) and (b). The ladder logic software has two instructions, CTU and CTD, to handle the count up and count down applications as does the ST implementation. Note that if you want an up counter only, then you eliminate the CU enable, and if you want a down counter only, then you eliminate the CD enable. Read the description of the operation included in the figures.

ST Standard for Latch Outputs. The comparison between output latch instructions for standard ladder logic inputs and their ST equivalent is illustrated in Figure 15-4(a) and (b). The ladder logic software has two instructions, OTL and OTU, to handle applications that require a retentive output. The ST implementation uses set dominant (SETD) and reset dominant (RESD) functions. Read the description of the operation included in the figure.

ST Standard for One-Shots and Math Blocks. The comparison between one-shot and math instructions for standard ladder logic inputs and their ST equivalent is illustrated in Figure 15-5(a) and (b). The one-shot is used in control programs to limit the execution of the output to one scan of the program. This is useful when an instruction executes every scan when the input is true, but the control requires just one execution. This

FIGURE 15-3: ST for standard ladder logic for an up/down counter.

Standard ST Logic for Up/Down Counters

Increment the tag for every false to true transition of an up count signal and decrement the same tag for every false to true transition of a down count signal. Turn on (or turn off) an output field device after the accumulator is equal to or greater than a preset value.

The standard ladder logic for the CTU counter is shown in (a) along with the ST equivalent in (b). The ST instructions have a combination up and down counter, which can be used as an up counter, a down counter, or as a combined up/down counter. Eliminate the CDEnable line for an up counter or eliminate the CUEnable line for a down counter. The output is turned on or off by the counter_state. ST does not have a reset function, but the operation can be handled with an IF...THEN structure. An assignment statement cannot be used since the reset input is a Boolean data type and the counter ACC is a DINT.

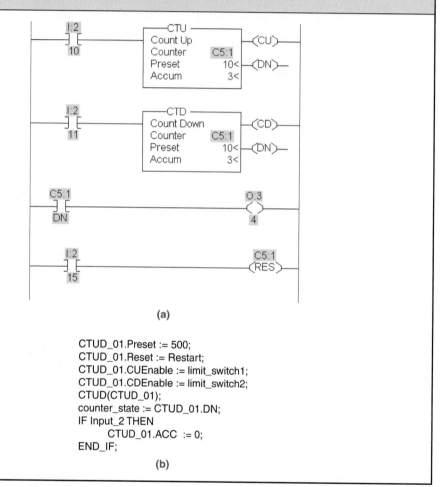

(a)

```
CTUD_01.Preset := 500;
CTUD_01.Reset := Restart;
CTUD_01.CUEnable := limit_switch1;
CTUD_01.CDEnable := limit_switch2;
CTUD(CTUD_01);
counter_state := CTUD_01.DN;
IF Input_2 THEN
        CTUD_01.ACC  := 0;
END_IF;
```
(b)

FIGURE 15-4: ST for standard ladder logic for retentive outputs.

Standard ST Logic for Retentive Outputs

Latch and unlatch an output on with an input signal.

The standard ladder logic for the OTL and OTU instructions is shown in (a) along with the ST equivalent in (b). The ST instructions use a Set Dominant (SETD) instruction, but a Reset Dominant (RESD) could be used as well. The SETD makes the output true when the set input is true regardless of the condition on the reset input.

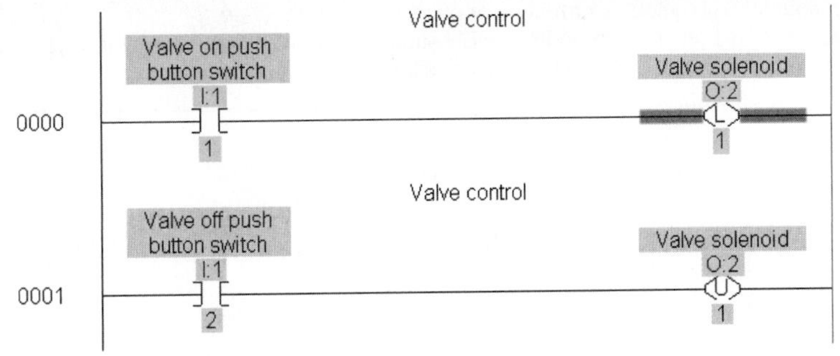

(a)

```
SETD_01.Set := set_input;
SETD_01.Reset := reset_input;
SETD(SETD_01);
output := SETD_01.Out;
not_output := SETD_01.OutNot;
```

(b)

configuration is used most often with math and move instructions and could have a one-shot falling instruction used in place of the one-shot rising. Read the description of the operation included in the figure.

15-5-2 Discrete and Process Implementation

Let's look at an ST implementation for the solution to an automated process example using the process tank as illustrated in Figure 15-6. The process is as follows:

- The tank should have 25 percent of Liquid 1 and 75 percent of Liquid 2 by weight.

- The liquid in the tank is heated when the liquid weight is greater than 750 pounds.
- The heating continues after the tank is full until the liquid temperature reaches 180 degrees.
- The drain cycle starts at 30 seconds after the heater turns off.
- Mixing should continue until the tank has drained.

The ST solution is illustrated in Figure 15-7. Note that the comments imbedded in the program aid the understanding of the solution. Study the ST program until you understand how the constructs and syntax are used for the solution.

Standard ST Logic for One Shots and Arithmetic Blocks

Turn on an output instruction like a math or move instruction for only one scan after an input field device is active.

The standard ladder logic for the one-shot and addition instruction is shown in (a) and the ST equivalent in (b). The input field device(s) determines when the output is active and the one-shot assures that the addition is performed for only one scan. The one-shot makes the instruction look like one that is triggered by a rising edge (false to true) on the input. The State tag enables the ADD function in the IF…THEN statement. While the addition instruction is used in this example, any of the other math instructions (SUB, DIV, MUL, or SQR) or the move instruction (MOV) could be substituted. Also, the one-shot rising is used, but a one-shot falling could be used to trigger on a falling input edge (true to false input change).

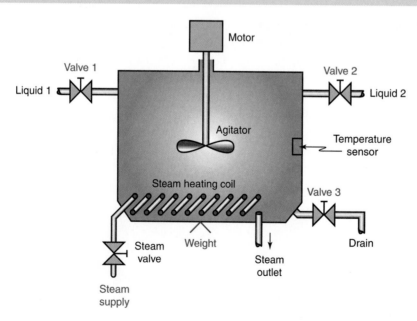

(a)

```
OSRI_01.InputBit := limit_switch1;
OSRI(OSRI_01);
State := OSRI_O1.OutputBit;
IF State THEN
        sum := value1 + value2;
END_IF
```

(b)

FIGURE 15-6: Process tank.

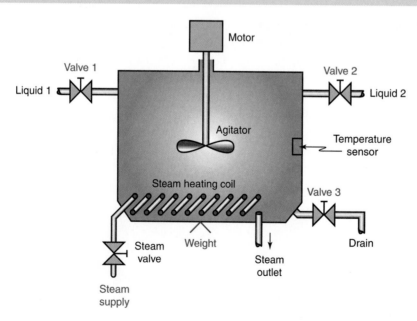

Rehg and Sartori, Industrial Electronics, *1st Edition, © 2006, Reprinted by permission of Pearson Education, Inc., Upper Saddle River, NJ.*

FIGURE 15-7: Structured Text program for the process tank example.

//Control for valve one and set control bits Tank_empty and system_reset to 0

IF Start & Liquid_weight < 249 & NOT Latch_tank_full THEN

```
            (* Note when Booleans, like Start and Tank_full are used in the condition,
            you should not put the relational operator (= 0 or = 1) into the condition.*)

            Valve_One [:=] 1;
            system_reset := 0;
ELSE
            Valve_One := 0;
END_IF;
```

//Control for valve two

```
IF Start & Liquid_weight >= 250 & NOT Latch_tank_full THEN
            Valve_Two [:=] 1;
END_IF;
```

//Control for the mixer

```
IF Liquid_weight > 500 THEN
            Mixer [:=] 1;
ELSE IF Liquid_weight < 500 & Latch_tank_full THEN
            Mixer := 1;
END_IF;
```

//Control for the heater

```
IF Liquid_weight > 750 & Temperature < 179 & NOT Valve_three & NOT Timer_start THEN
            Heater [:=] 1;
ELSE
            Heater := 0;
END_IF;
```

Rehg and Sartori, Industrial Electronics, *1st Edition, © 2006, Reprinted by permission of Pearson Education, Inc., Upper Saddle River, NJ.*

FIGURE 15-7: (Continued).

//Latch bit for tank full and turn off valve two

```
IF Liquid_weight >= 1000 THEN
        Latch_tank_full := 1;
        Valve_Two := 0;
END_IF;
```

//Full tank and temperature >= 180 timer control

```
IF Temperature >= 180 & Latch_tank_full THEN
        Timer_start [:=] 1;
END_IF;
```

//Function Block TONR timer with Preset at 30 min

```
Timer_30min.Pre := 30000;
Timer_30min.Reset := System_reset;
Timer_30min.TimerEnable := Timer_start;
TONR(Timer_30s);
Timer_done := Timer_30s.DN;
```

```
        (* These timer statements are the Structured Text (ST) equivalent for the
        FBD command TONR. Other options here include using a subroutine call to an
        FBD program with the TONR block present, or a subroutine call to a Ladder
        Diagram with a TON timer present.*)
```

//Tank empty cycle after 30 s time

```
IF timer_done THEN
        Valve_Three := 1;

END_IF;
```

//Establish starting condition for control bits

```
IF Liquid_weight = 0 THEN
        system_reset [:=] 1;
        Mixer := 0;
        Timer_start := 0;
        Valve_Three := 0;
        Latch_tank_full := 0;
END_IF;
```

CHAPTER 16

PLC Standard IEC 61131-3— Sequential Function Chart

16-1 GOALS AND OBJECTIVES

The goals for this chapter are to provide an overview of the Sequential Function Chart (SFC) graphic language and to provide an overview of the Allen-Bradley implementation of the SFC language.

After completing this chapter you should be able to:

* Describe the difference between Ladder Logic, Function Block Diagram, Structured Text, and Sequential Function Chart graphic languages.
* Define the components of the Allen-Bradley SFC language.
* Describe the process used to build an SFC program.
* Create an SFC program for automation process problems using the Allen-Bradley implementation.
* Given a problem statement, select the best SFC sequence with the most appropriate action qualifiers.

16-2 IEC 61131-3 STANDARD LANGUAGES

The first three Allen-Bradley 61131 language standards—Ladder Diagram (LD), Function Block Diagram (FBD), and Structured Text (ST)—have been discussed in previous chapters. The final language, Sequential Function Chart, is covered in this chapter. The Sequential Function Chart language is defined as follows:

> SFC (Sequential Function Chart): Based on the French standard, GRAFCET, this is a graphical language used most often for sequential control problems. The basic language elements are steps or states that have associated actions that produce the control and transitions with associated conditions used to move from the current state to the next. The actions and conditions can be defined in terms of the four other languages. As a result, the SFC language is often used for the basic sequential program flow with FBD, LD, and ST programs embedded into the SFC structure.

16-3 SEQUENTIAL FUNCTION CHART (SFC)

Sequential Function Chart (SFC) is a powerful graphical technique for describing the sequential behavior of a control program. The definition of the IEC Sequential Function Chart language has been derived from current techniques such as

GRAFCET, a graphical language based on a French national standard.

One of the most important aspects of SFC in the U.S. market is that it displays all the operational states of a system, all the possible *changes* of the states, and the *conditions* that cause those changes to occur. As a result, SFCs are often used to structure a control system solution, and then some combination of Ladder Diagrams, Function Block Diagrams, and Structured Text is used to program the solution. Structured list (SL), a fifth IEC standard language, could also be used with SFC programs, but not with Allen-Bradley SFC implementations since AB does not support the SL language.

16-3-1   Standard SFC Sequences

Because it is a graphical language, SFC is depicted as a series of steps, as illustrated in Figure 16-1. Each step in the SFC represents a *state* that the process exhibits where an *action* is performed. For example, consider Figure 11-9, where a pneumatic cylinder is used to push a part from a magazine parts feeder to a robot pickup point. The cylinder has two states: retracted and extended. The actuator is in each of these states for some period of time during its operational cycle. The signal to change these states, called the *transition condition*, comes from the automation system. In the extended state, the action would be to turn on the pneumatic valve. The transition to the next state, which is retracted, comes from a sensor that indicates a part is in the correct position or from a robot signal indicating that the part was acquired. The actions in an SFC can occur only while a step is active or can continue for more than one step. For example, the mixer in Figure 16-1 is only on during the Mix Solution step, but the action Open Valve 1 is started in the Fill Tank step and ended in the Mix Solution step.

The steps in Figure 16-1 are connected by vertical lines indicating the sequence or flow. The short horizontal line halfway between steps is the *transition condition*. The SFC remains in the current state executing the current action until the transition condition becomes true. At that point the current state becomes inactive and the next state becomes the active state. The flow of control follows the graphically linked rectangles. Study the simple control scheme illustrated in the figure. Each step in the process is listed and the transition between steps links the steps together.

The linear sequence in Figure 16-1 has an initial block outlined with double lines and all remaining blocks outlined with single lines. The steps indicate what action is occurring at the step and the action blocks display the program or a link to the program that produced the action. For example, in the second block the action is Fill tank, and the corresponding action block indicates that a program statement would be placed there, open valve 1. Step 3 indicates that there can be more than one action block and program segment associated with a step, and step 4 indicates that there can be more than one transition condition if a branch is necessary.

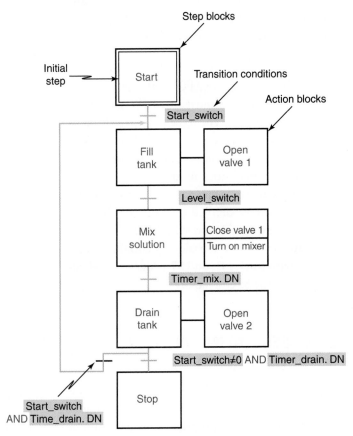

Transition conditions are Boolean expressions, which evaluate as either true (move on to the next step) or false (remain in the current step for one more scan). Also, the transition condition can be a logical combination of Boolean tags, as illustrated with the ANDed tags for the fourth step. A simple combination of steps, like that illustrated in Figure 16-1, is called a *sequence*. There are a number of sequence options permitted in SFCs.

16-3-2 SFC Sequences

There are four types of sequences into which all SFCs can be grouped: *single sequence, selection divergence, simultaneous divergence,* and *loop sequence.* Each of these options is illustrated and described in Figure 16-2. You are not limited to the number of steps shown or the number of parallel branches illustrated in the figure.

The single sequence is a linear set of machine states or steps. Single sequences are used to

FIGURE 16-2: SFC sequence options.

To:	Use this structure:	With these considerations:
Execute 1 or more steps in sequence: • One executes repeatedly. • Then the next executes repeatedly.	Single sequence 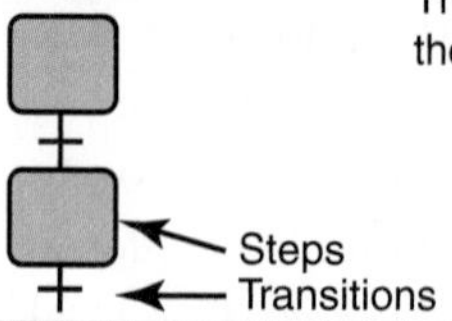 Steps Transitions	The SFC checks the transition at the end of the step: • If true, the SFC goes to the next step. • If false, the SFC repeats the step.
• Choose between alternative steps or groups of steps depending on logic conditions. • Execute a step or steps or skip the step or steps depending on logic conditions.	Selection sequence 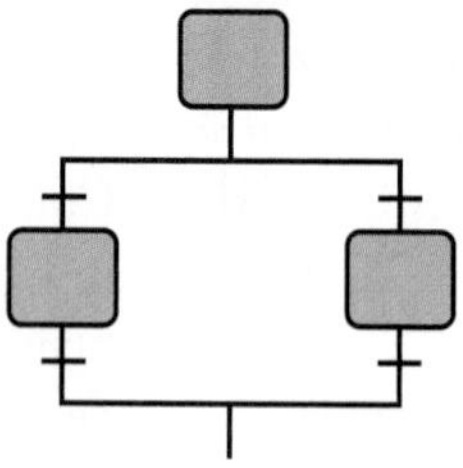 	• It is OK for a path to have no steps and only a transition. This lets the SFC skip the selection branch. • By default, the SFC checks from left to right the transitions that start each path. It takes the first true path. • If no transitions are true, the SFC repeats the previous step. • RSLogix 5000 software lets you change the order in which the SFC checks the transitions.
Execute 2 or more steps at the same time. All paths must finish before continuing the SFC.	Simultaneous sequence 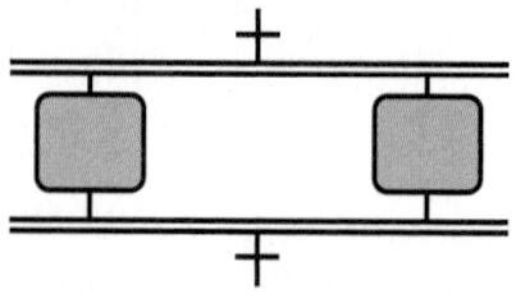 	• A single transition ends the branch. • The SFC checks the ending transition after the last step in each path has executed at least once. If the transition is false, the SFC repeats the previous step.
Loop back to a previous step.	Loop sequence 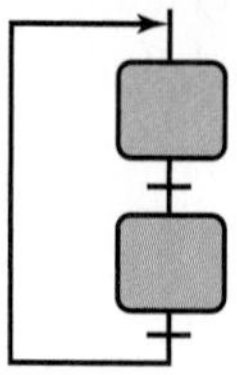 	• Connect the wire to the step or simultaneous branch to which you want to go. • *Do not* wire into, out of, or between a simultaneous branch.

Rehg and Sartori, Industrial Electronics, *1st Edition, © 2006, reprinted by permission of Pearson Education, Inc., Upper Saddle River, NJ.*

build the other types of SFC sequence options that follow.

The selection divergence sequence has a transition condition at the top of each of the linear branches. This transition condition is checked in an order specified by the programmer. The first entry transition condition in that order that is true indicates the linear path that is executed. The default condition is to check entry transitions from left to right, starting with the first one on the left. RSLogix 5000 permits the programmer to change the order in which paths are tested to see if their transition condition is true. As a result, you can think of the selection sequence as a priority OR type sequence flow, since the first true linear path out of the total number of linear paths in the order checked is executed.

The simultaneous divergence sequence has a single transition condition that must be true before the simultaneous divergence sequence can be executed. There is also one transition condition at the end of the simultaneous sequence where all the linear paths converge. This final or exit transition condition is not tested by the program until the action blocks for every linear path have finished executing and the action for all steps is satisfied. As a result, this SFC sequence option is an AND type because the exit transition condition cannot be tested until the last step in every parallel path has finished its action(s). The automation control requirements that dictate the use of each sequence are listed in front of each sequence in Figure 16-2, and the operation of each sequence is described in the right column. Review these descriptions if the operation of each sequence is not clear.

16-3-3 SFC Step Programming

After the SFC sequence is established each step must be configured for the solution to the problem. An example sequence from the Allen-Bradley RSLogix 5000 SFC is illustrated in Figure 16-3. Read all the descriptions in the figure before continuing.

A study of the figure indicates:

- Two steps are present.
- The Initialize step has one action block where the tag counter is set equal to zero using a line of program code from structured text (ST).

- The second step, with tag name ServosOn, has three action blocks. The first is an ST program to set the value of the tag counter, and the last two are function calls that turn on the axis 0 and axis 1 servos.
- The four action blocks have default tag names (Action_010, Action_009, Action_000, and Action_008). Action tag names can be changed to any accepted tag name. In addition, each action block has an action qualifier that dictates how that action will be carried out.
- Both the steps and the action blocks have links to their configuration dialog boxes.
- The action description can be just a simple ST assignment statement as in the first action block or a complex series of program statements as in Action_009.
- Transition conditions can be a logical expression or just a Boolean tag.
- A feedback loop enters this sequence between the two steps from another part of the program.
- Step 3 of the sequence is on another page of the program, and the branch to that continuation is shown at the bottom of this sequence.

Configuring the Step. Every step has a tag name to identify the step parameters. The step is configured using the dialog box illustrated in Figure 16-4, and the dialog box is activated from the link in the upper-left corner of the step box (Figure 16-3). Three tabs are visible at the top of the dialog box: *general, action order,* and *tag.* Under the general tab the step type and timers are configured. In addition, time and count data are displayed along with alarm parameters. Action order changes the priority for the actions attached, and tag support the tag name entry. Read the descriptions in Figure 16-4 for the parameters in the general dialog box. The step has a built-in timer that can be used to set the length of time that the step is active. The time value is entered in milliseconds in the preset text box, or an expression can be entered to calculate the desired time. When the preset value is reached, the step timer done bit is set and the step tag ServosOn.DN is true. ServosOn is the tag name for this step.

When more than one action block is attached to a step, the order of execution is set by select-

FIGURE 16-3: SFC example control application.

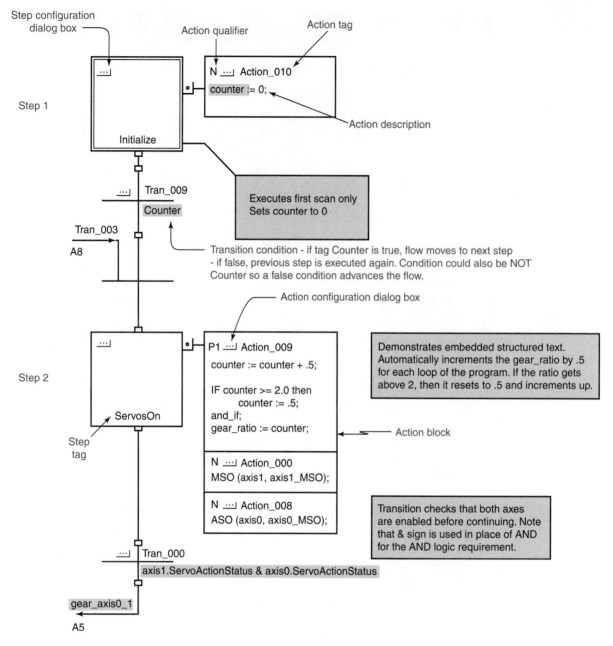

Step configuration dialog box

Action qualifier

Action tag

Step 1

N ⋯⌐ Action_010

counter := 0;

Action description

Initialize

Executes first scan only
Sets counter to 0

⋯⌐ Tran_009

Counter

Tran_003

A8

Transition condition - if tag Counter is true, flow moves to next step
- if false, previous step is executed again. Condition could also be NOT
Counter so a false condition advances the flow.

Action configuration dialog box

P1 ⋯⌐ Action_009

counter := counter + .5;

IF counter >= 2.0 then
        counter := .5;
and_if;
gear_ratio := counter;

Demonstrates embedded structured text.
Automatically increments the gear_ratio by .5
for each loop of the program. If the ratio gets
above 2, then it resets to .5 and increments up.

Step 2

ServosOn

Step
tag

Action block

N ⋯⌐ Action_000
MSO (axis1, axis1_MSO);

N ⋯⌐ Action_008
ASO (axis0, axis0_MSO);

Transition checks that both axes
are enabled before continuing. Note
that & sign is used in place of AND
for the AND logic requirement.

⋯⌐ Tran_000

axis1.ServoActionStatus & axis0.ServoActionStatus

gear_axis0_1

A5

Rehg and Sartori, Industrial Electronics, *1st Edition, © 2006, reprinted by permission of Pearson Education, Inc., Upper Saddle River, NJ.*

ing the action order tab at the top of the step dialog box. This dialog box, Figure 16-5, permits the order or the priority for the actions to be changed. The action at the top of the list has the highest priority. Study Figure 16-5 for the second step in Figure 16-3. The action blocks will execute in the order 009, 000, and finally 008.

Configuring the Action Block. Every step in an SFC is linked to one or more actions, which are described and executed in an *action block*. An action contains a description of one or more behaviors or actions that should occur when the step is active. Action blocks, attached to the step, have three elements that are required and one that is optional. The block (see Figure 16-6) must have an *action qualifier, action tag name,* and *action description* or *assignment statement.* The action description is an executable program that can be entered in any of the supported 61131 languages.

FIGURE 16-4: Step configuration dialog box.

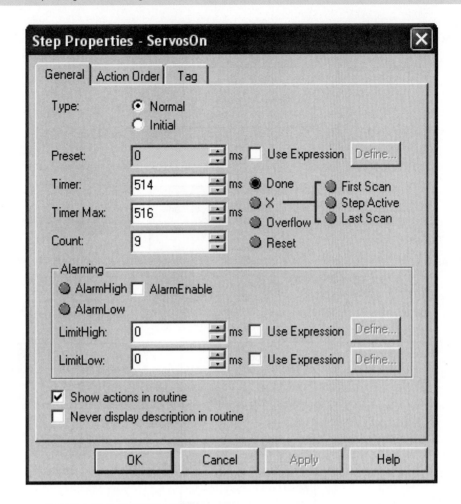

Step Configuration Information

Type: Use the *Type field* to make the first step the Initial step and all other steps Normal steps. Only one step can be an Initial step.

Preset: Each step has a built-in timer. Use the *Preset field* to enter the desired time or check the Expression checkbox and fill in an expression to calculate the timer time. When the accumulator equals the present time, the done bit is set and ServosOn.DN tag is true. ServosOn is the tag name for the step.

Timer: The *Timer field* displays the total time (in milliseconds) that the step is active during the last pass through the SFC sequence.

Time Max: In the *Timer Max field* the highest value ever reached by the Step Timer (T) is stored.

Count: The *Count field* stores the number of times the Step has been activated since the Step Count was reset by the last SFC reset.

Rehg and Sartori, Industrial Electronics, *1ˢᵗ Edition, © 2006, reprinted by permission of Pearson Education, Inc., Upper Saddle River, NJ.*

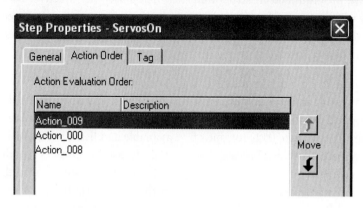

Rehg and Sartori, Industrial Electronics, *1st Edition, © 2006, reprinted by permission of Pearson Education, Inc., Upper Saddle River, NJ.*

FIGURE 16-6: SFC action block configuration.

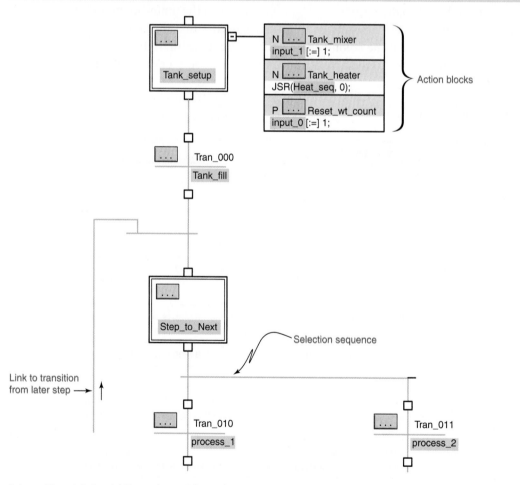

Rehg and Sartori, Industrial Electronics, *1st Edition, © 2006, Reprinted by permission of Pearson Education, Inc., Upper Saddle River, NJ.*

In most SFC programs in the Allen-Bradley system, the actions are programmed in structured text or ladder logic with less use of function block diagrams. Study the SFC in Figure 16-6 and observe the following:

- One step has three action blocks and one has none. The one without an action block is just there so the program can wait for a transition condition (Tran_010 or Tran_011) for one of the selection sequence branches (Process_1 or Process_2) to become active.
- The action qualifiers, described in the next section, are N and P.
- Two action descriptions have ST program assignment statements to turn Input_0 and Input_1 on, and the third has a subroutine call, JSR(Heat_seq,0), which causes the program Heat_seq to be executed with a zero value passed to the subroutine program.
- The two ST assignments use brackets (non-retentive condition) around the colon-equal assignment statement, [:=] to indicate that

the tag values should be set to zero when the step becomes inactive.
- The tag names for the three Action boxes are Tank_mixer, Tank_heater, and Reset_wt_count.

Action Qualifier. An action qualifier defines precisely how the action should be executed after the step becomes active. Eleven qualifiers are available and listed in Figure 16-7. The more frequently used qualifiers are described in detail in Figure 16-8. Note that in the timing diagram in the second figure, *Step* represents the state of the step (inactive = low and active = high). *T1 or TN* indicates when the transition condition becomes true relative to the time that the step is active, and *Action1* and *Action2* indicate when the program in the action block is executed relative to the time that the step is active. For example, the timing diagram for an N qualifier indicates that the action program executes the entire time that the step is active. That implies that the program will be scanned more

FIGURE 16-7: SFC action qualifiers.

Qualifier	Description
None	Non-stored, default, same as 'N'.
N	Non-stored, executes while associated step is active.
R	Resets a stored action.
S	Sets or stores an action activity that is later reset with an R qualifier.
L (See Note 1.)	Time-limited action, terminates after a given period.
D (See Note 1.)	Time-delayed action, starts after a given period.
P	A pulse action that only executes once when a step is activated (entered), and once when the step is deactivated (left).
P1	A pulse action that only executes once when a step is activated (entered).
P0	A pulse action that only executes once when a step is deactivated (left).
SD (See Note 1.)	Stored (executed) and time delayed. The action is set active (executed) after a given period, even if the associated step is deactivated before the delay period.
DS (See Note 1.)	Action is time delayed and stored (executed). If the associated step is deactivated (left) before the delay period, the action is not stored or executed.
SL (See Note 1.)	Stored and time limited. The action is started and executes for a given period.

Note: These qualifiers all require a time period.

Rehg and Sartori, Industrial Electronics, *1st Edition, © 2006, reprinted by permission of Pearson Education, Inc., Upper Saddle River, NJ.*

FIGURE 16-8: SFC action qualifiers with timing diagrams.

Qualifier	Description	Timing diagram
N	Normal—the output Action1 executes continuously while the step is active and one more time after the step is inactive.	Step / Action1 / T1 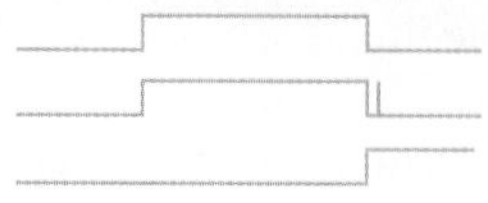
S	Set (S)—the output Action1 is started when the step becomes active and continues after the step is inactive.	Step / T1 / Action1 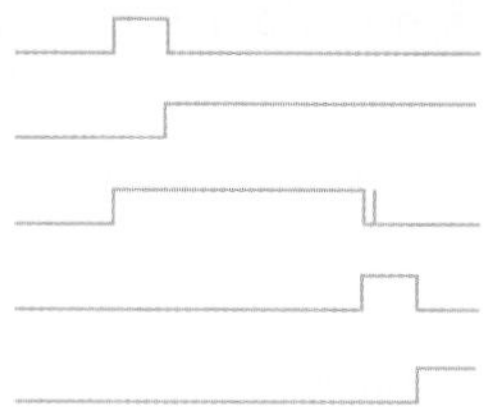
R	Reset (R)—the reset action occurs in a later step where the output Action1 is terminated at the start of the step when the step becomes active and then one more time.	StepN / TN
L	Time-Limited Action—the output Action1 is executed for a time duration set in the action configuration and then one time after that time. If the step becomes inactive before the timed duration for the output Action1, then the output Action1 terminates with step termination and then executes one more time.	Step / T1 / Action1 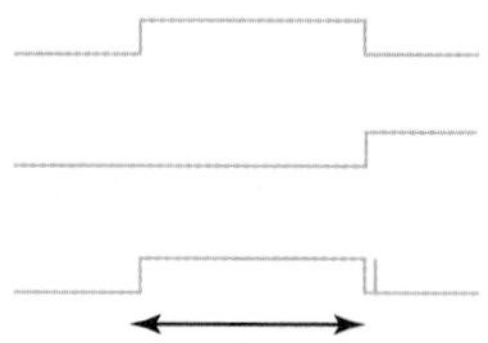 ←→ 4s
D	Timer-Delayed Action—the output Action1 execution is delayed for a time duration set in the action configuration and then terminates when the step becomes inactive. One more execution occurs after the step is inactive. If the step time is shorter than the delay timed duration no output Action1 occurs.	Step / T1 / Action1 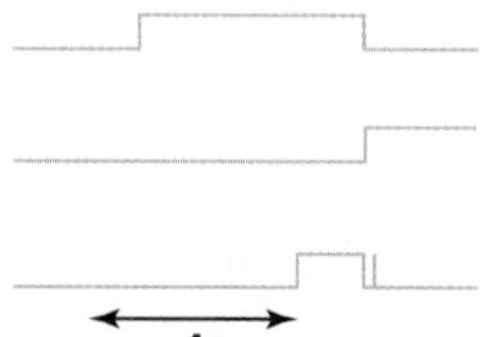 ←→ 4s
P	Pulse—the output Action1 executes once when the step is activated.	Step / T1 / Action1 
P1	Pulse On—the output Action1 executes once when the step is activated.	Step / T1 / Action1 / Action2 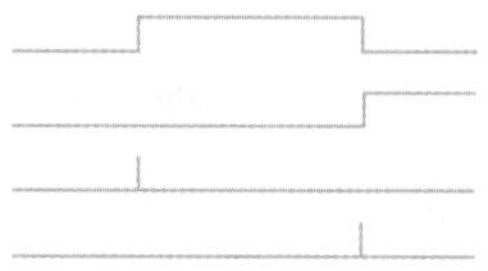
P0	Pulse Off—the output Action2 executes once when the step is deactivated.	

Rehg and Sartori, Industrial Electronics, *1st Edition, © 2006, reprinted by permission of Pearson Education, Inc., Upper Saddle River, NJ.*

than once while the step is active, but it will also be executed one more time when the transition condition becomes true and the step is inactive. Study the qualifiers until you understand the range of options available.

In general, the wide range of qualifier types makes the solution to any automation problem possible in an SFC. The N qualifier is used most frequently for actions. The S and R are used when the qualifier program must be scanned for a longer period of time that stretches over more than one step. The P limits the action program to one execution. It is like a single scan of a ladder rung output. Finally, P1 and P2 are used when

the action must start and stop during a single step. For example, if the step is timed, the P1 and P2 qualifier could be used in action blocks that turn on a pneumatic valve and then turn it off after a set time.

Transition Condition. The transition condition signals a change in steps or states. When the transition evaluates as true, the current active step becomes inactive and the following inactive step becomes active. It is often desired to have a step become active for specific times. In that case, the transition condition is triggered by the done bit on a timer. If the timer inside the step is used, then the transition condition will be step_tag.DN where step_tag is the tag or name attached to the step. Figure 16-9 shows how a

timer in a ladder rung can be called by a subroutine and used to time the end of a step. A study of the figure indicates the following:

- The JSR command in ST calls the LD program called LadderFile with 0 parameters from an action block in the step.
- The LD timer program executes and after 2 seconds sets the DN bit high for one scan.
- The timer.dn Boolean expression in the transition condition location is true after 2 seconds and the SFC transitions to the next step.

This is a good example of IEC program integration where the SFC program uses an ST jump to subroutine function to execute LD rungs to time the step in the SFC.

FIGURE 16-9: SFC transition conditions.

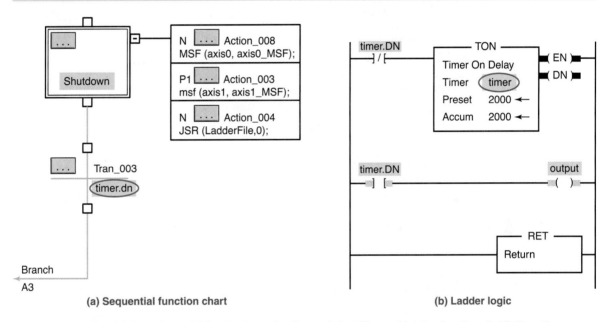

(a) Sequential function chart (b) Ladder logic

Rehg and Sartori, Industrial Electronics, *1st Edition, © 2006, reprinted by permission of Pearson Education, Inc., Upper Saddle River, NJ.*

EXAMPLE 16-1

Develop an SFC program for execution of the tank problem in Figure 16-10. The tank should have 25 percent of one ingredient and 75 percent of a second by weight. It should be heated to 180 degrees and then mixed for 30 minutes. Mixing should continue until the tank has drained. Total weight is 1000 pounds, and the control strategy required for the problem is as follows:

- Value 1 = start switch and tank liquid weight less than 250 pounds on fill cycle only
- Value 2 = start switch and tank liquid weight greater than 250 pounds but less than or equal to 1000 pounds on fill cycle only
- Mixer on = tank liquid weight greater than 499 pounds

- Mixer off = tank liquid weight equal to 0 pounds
- Heater on = tank liquid weight equal to or greater than 750 pounds
- Heater off = 30 minutes after tank full and temperature at 180 degrees
- NOT Valve 3 = tank liquid weight equal to 0 pounds on drain cycle only
- Valve 3 = 30 minutes after tank full AND temperature at 180 degrees

SOLUTION

Compare the SFC code for the tank solution in Figure 16-11 with the logic requirements given for the systems.

As you review the SFC solution for the Tank problem, first identify the actions that are produced at each step and compare those with the operation requirements for the process. Next, review the transition logic that takes the program from one step to the next. Note that the transitions are conditions given in the problem for when action should occur in the process. Finally notice that some actions start in one step (S qualifier) but do not end until a later step (R qualifier), so an action can occur during multiple steps. The controller was placed in the Automatic Reset mode, so the non-retentive reset type of equality ([:=]) was used for tags that needed to be reset when the program moved to the next step.

FIGURE 16-10: Process tank.

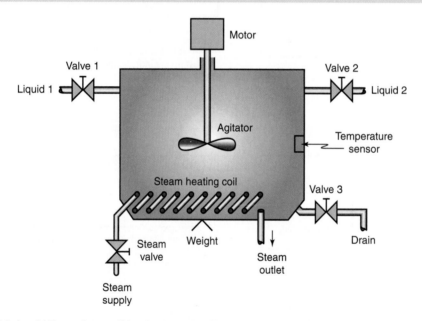

Rehg and Sartori, Industrial Electronics, *1st edition, ©2006, reprinted by permission of Pearson Education, Inc., Upper Saddle River, NJ.*

Note that Temperature_soak.dn in transition Tran_006 is a step timer that is set for 30 minutes.

SFC Program Design. The following design steps describe a process for developing a program for an event-driven sequential process.

1. Study the system operation until you become familiar with every detail of the process.

2. Make a numbered list of every step in the production sequence where an independent action must be executed. Draw SFC steps based on this analysis.

3. Identify and list all outputs for the system and the action required for the output. (These become the SFC action blocks, action descriptions, and output tags.) Group the actions with steps in the process

FIGURE 16-11: SFC solution for Example 16-1.

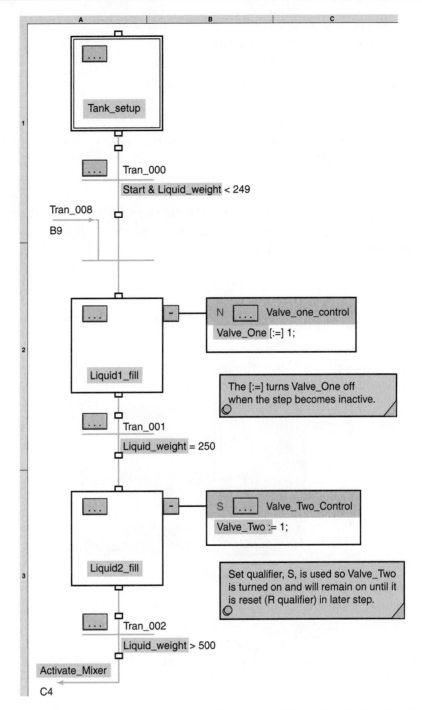

Tank_setup

Tran_000

Start & Liquid_weight < 249

Tran_008

B9

Liquid1_fill

N Valve_one_control

Valve_One [:=] 1;

The [:=] turns Valve_One off when the step becomes inactive.

Tran_001

Liquid_weight = 250

Liquid2_fill

S Valve_Two_Control

Valve_Two := 1;

Set qualifier, S, is used so Valve_Two is turned on and will remain on until it is reset (R qualifier) in later step.

Tran_002

Liquid_weight > 500

Activate_Mixer

C4

FIGURE 16-11: (Continued).

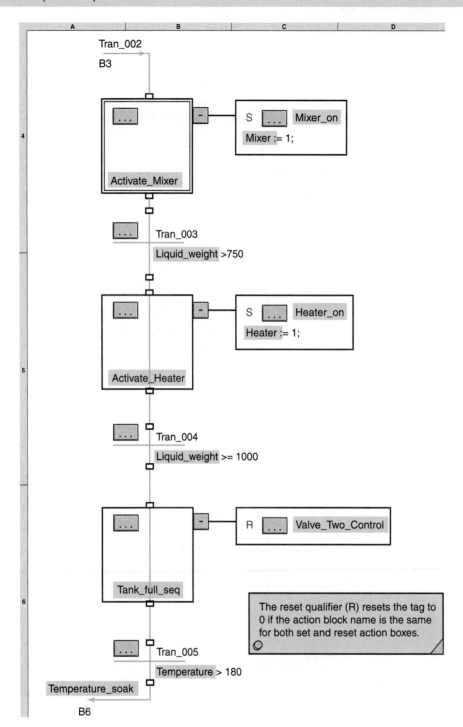

FIGURE 16-11: (Continued).

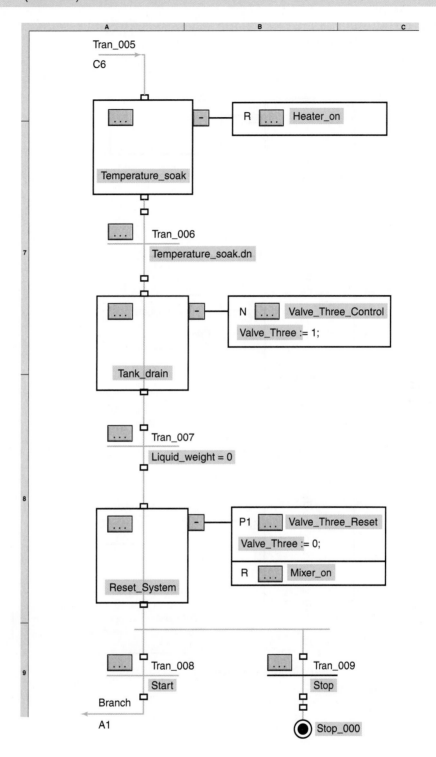

so that the number and type of action blocks for each step is identified. Using the type of action required, assign an action qualifier for each action block. Determine the program language to use for programming each action block. Perform the action programming in the action block or in a subroutine called from the action block.

4. Identify the transition conditions necessary to move from one production step to the next. These become the transition conditions in the SFC to move from one step block to the next. Determine the logic statement for the transition condition and program it in ST, use a function for the transition condition, or use a jump to subroutine for the transition condition. If a subroutine is used, then that program must be developed in one of the IEC languages.

5. Determine the duty cycle for the outputs or actions and determine if the actions must span more than one step, only one step, or just a part of a step. Draw the timing waveforms for the outputs on a process timing diagram if necessary. Verify that the action qualifiers selected earlier support the action timing requirements present in the timing diagrams.

6. List all the sensors in the system. Create input tags based on this analysis.

7. Use the data from steps 1 through 6 to create a Sequential Function Chart in the programming software for the PLC controller.

8. Verify the SFC design.

9. Test the system.

16-4 SITES FOR ALLEN-BRADLEY PRODUCTS AND DEMO SOFTWARE

- RSLogix 5000 Product Information: *http://www.ab.com/catalogs/b113/controllogix/software.html*
- RSLogix 5000 Demo Software Ordering and Download: *http://www.ab.com/logix/rslogix5000/*
- RSLogix 500 Demo Software Download—Under Get Software: http://www.ab.com/plclogic/micrologix/
- Rockwell Automation Logix Product Information: *http://www.ab.com/logix/*
- Rockwell Automation Manuals: *http://www.theautomationbookstore.com*, *http://www.ab.com/manuals/*

17

Industrial Networks and Distributive Control

17-1 GOALS AND OBJECTIVES

There are three goals of this chapter. The first goal is to provide a practical introduction to industrial networks such as Ethernet, ControlNet, and DeviceNet, as well as PLC vendor-unique networks. The second goal is to provide an overview of distributive control and distributed I/O. The third goal is to provide basic guidelines for the selection and design of networks.

After completing this chapter you should be able to:

- Describe the purpose and function of Ethernet, ControlNet, and DeviceNet.
- Describe special network interfaces such as SERCOS, smart I/O, remote I/O, serial-data interfaces, and wireless communication.
- Discuss PLC vendor network applications.
- Describe distributive control and distributed I/O.
- Recommend networks based on application requirements.
- Describe network design guidelines.

Note that this chapter provides an overview of networks and is not a substitute for a course in network theory. However, it does give an excellent practical introduction to networks that is essential to achieving a comprehensive study of PLCs.

17-2 PLC NETWORK ARCHITECTURE

The PLC and other intelligent machines are connected into the factory floor network architecture, as shown in Figure 17-1. Note that the network architecture is flattened into three layers—Ethernet, ControlNet, and DeviceNet/ FOUNDATION Fieldbus—and that PLCs are interfaced to all three layers. The function and operation of each layer is discussed in some detail in the subsequent sections.

- Ethernet: The highest level provides the information layer for data collection and program maintenance.
- ControlNet: The middle level supplies the automation and control layer for real-time input/output control, interlocking (coordinating update times between applications), and messaging.
- DeviceNet/FOUNDATION Fieldbus: The lowest level provides for cost-effective integration of individual devices—a primary

FIGURE 17-1: Factory floor network architecture with Ethernet, ControlNet, and DeviceNet/FOUNDATION Fieldbus layers.

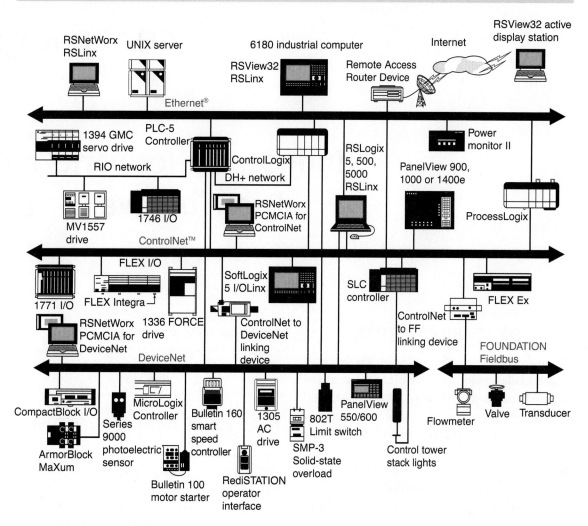

Courtesy of Rockwell Automation, Inc.

discrete interface with DeviceNet and analog control segment in process control with FOUNDATION Fieldbus. DeviceNet and FOUNDATION are two of the many fieldbuses available on the market today. Fieldbus is a term that basically means a network that is optimized to exchange data between small devices and a main larger device(s).

The PLCs and other intelligent machines on the network talk to each other via protocols, which are sets of communication rules. Each network type uses its own protocol. Network protocols handle problems and tasks such as communication line errors, data flow control, multiple device access, failure detection, data translation, and interpretation of messages.

17-3 ETHERNET

Dr. Robert M. Metcalfe invented Ethernet at the Xerox Palo Alto Research Center in the 1970s. It was designed to support research on the Office of the Future project, which included one of the world's first personal workstations, the Xerox Alto. The first Ethernet system ran at approxi-

mately 3 megabits per second (Mbps) and was known as experimental Ethernet. In 1980 a multi-vendor consortium turned the experimental Ethernet into an open, production-quality Ethernet system operating at 10 Mbps. A standards committee of the Institute of Electrical and Electronics Engineers (IEEE) then adopted Ethernet technology for standardization with the formal title of IEEE 802.3. Today, the Ethernet standard defines not only the 10-Mbps system, but also the 100-Mbps Fast Ethernet system, the Gigabit Ethernet, and the 10-Gigabit Ethernet. The Ethernet system consists of three basic elements:

1. The physical medium used to carry Ethernet signals between computers.
2. A set of medium access control rules embedded in each Ethernet interface that allows multiple computers to fairly arbitrate access to the shared Ethernet channel.
3. An Ethernet frame that consists of a standardized set of bits used to carry data over the system.

Ethernet and Ethernet Industry Protocol operation are covered in the following subsections.

17-3-1   Ethernet Operation
Each Ethernet-equipped intelligent machine, such as an industrial computer or PLC, operates independently of all other equipment on the network. All equipment or stations attached to an Ethernet are connected to a shared signaling system called the medium. Ethernet signals are transmitted serially, one bit at a time, over the shared signal channel to every attached station. The station listens to the channel and, when the channel is idle, transmits its data in the form of an Ethernet frame or packet. After each frame transmission, all stations on the network must contend equally for the next frame transmission opportunity—that is, when the channel is idle. This operation ensures that access to the network channel is fair, and that no single station can lock out the other stations. Access to the shared channel is determined by the medium access control (MAC) mechanism embedded in the Ethernet interface located in each station.

The Ethernet standard can be implemented in the following ways:

- 10Base5: standard thick coaxial cable
- 10Base2: thin coaxial cable
- 10BaseT: unshielded twisted-pair cable
- 100BaseT: unshielded twisted-pair cable
- 10BaseFL: fiber optic cable

This xBase$y$ nomenclature is interpreted as follows:

- x is the signaling rate in Mbps.
- Base is the term that means the signal uses the cable in a baseband scheme as opposed to a broadband, which is a multi-frequency, multi-channel modulating scheme.
- y is some indication of the media type.

17-3-2   Ethernet Industry Protocol
Ethernet Industry Protocol or *Ethernet/IP* is an open industrial networking standard that takes advantage of commercial off-the-shelf Ethernet communication devices and physical media. Unlike many options in industrial Ethernet systems, Ethernet/IP uses an open protocol and is backed by three networking organizations: ControlNet International (CI), the Industrial Ethernet Association (IEA), and the Open DeviceNet Vendor Association (ODVA). Ethernet/IP simplifies interoperability between different vendors' devices on the network by implementing a common DeviceNet application layer over commercial off-the-shelf Ethernet (IEEE 802.3) products. This open standard enables real-time deterministic communications between a wide variety of industrial automation products, including the PLC, robot controllers, input/output adapters, operator interfaces, and supervisory control stations. The term *deterministic* means that the speed of data transfers and the transmission and arrival times are predictable and not determined by conditions present on the network.

Ethernet/IP is constructed from the widely implemented standard used in ControlNet and DeviceNet, which is called Control and Information Protocol (CIP). This protocol organizes networked devices as a collection of

objects. It defines the access, object behavior, and extensions, which allow widely disparate devices to be accessed using a common mechanism. Hundreds of vendors currently support CIP with their Ethernet/IP products. Because Ethernet/IP is based on this widely understood and implemented standard, it does not require a new technology learning-curve period.

17-4   CONTROLNET

ControlNet is an open network, which means that any company can develop a ControlNet product without a license fee. It is positioned one level above DeviceNet in the control hierarchy. Its high-speed (5 Mbps) control and data capabilities significantly enhance input/output performance and user-to-user communications. ControlNet uses the producer/consumer network model to efficiently exchange time-critical application information for both processes and manufacturing automation. This model permits all nodes on the network to simultaneously access the same data from a single source. In addition, ControlNet's Media Access Method uses the producer/consumer model to allow multiple controllers to control I/O on the same network segment. This provides a significant advantage over other networks, which allow only one master controller on the network. ControlNet also allows simultaneous broadcast to multiple devices of both inputs and peer-to-peer data, thus reducing traffic on the media and increasing system performance. ControlNet operation and features are covered in the next subsections.

17-4-1   ControlNet Operation

Network access is controlled by a timing algorithm called Concurrent Time Domain Multiple Access (CTDMA), which regulates a node's opportunity to transmit in each network interval. The network is configured by how often the network interval repeats by selecting a network update interval (NUT). The fastest NUT you can specify is 2 milliseconds. Information that is time-critical is sent during the scheduled part of the NUT. Information that can be delivered without time constraints (such as configuration data) is sent during the unscheduled part of the NUT.

17-4-2   ControlNet Features

ControlNet is highly *deterministic* and *repeatable*. Determinism is the ability to reliably predict when data will be delivered, and repeatability ensures that transmitting times are constant and unaffected by devices connecting to or leaving the network. These two critical characteristics ensure dependable, synchronized, and coordinated real-time performance. As a result, ControlNet permits data transfers, such as program uploads/downloads and monitoring of real-time data, in flexible but predictable time segments. Management and configuration of the entire system can be performed from a single location on ControlNet or from one location on an information-level network, such as Ethernet. ControlNet can link a variety of devices, including motor drives, motion controllers, remote input/output modules, PLCs, and operator interfaces. In addition, ControlNet can provide a link to other networks such as DeviceNet and FOUNDATION Fieldbus. The following important features should be noted.

- In most applications, PLCs and industrial microcomputers use ControlNet scanner cards when adding a ControlNet network to an automation system.
- The devices attached to a ControlNet network include PLCs, industrial microcomputers, operator interface terminals, remote I/O modules, motor drives, and personal computers.
- Media used to transmit ControlNet data include both coaxial cable and fiber optic cable.
- ControlNet is a sub-network off of the Ethernet or Ethernet/IP.

ControlNet functions as the integrator of complex control systems such as coordinated motor- and servo-drive systems, weld control, motion control, vision systems, complex batch control systems, process control systems, and systems with multiple controllers and human-machine interfaces. It is ideal for systems with multiple PC-based controllers and PLC-to-PLC communication, allowing multiple controllers—each with their own input/output and shared inputs—to talk to each other with any possible interlocking combination.

17-5 DEVICENET

DeviceNet is an open network standard, which means that any company can develop a DeviceNet product without a license fee. It is based on the reliable Controller Area Networking (CAN) technology, which is used in virtually all industries, including automotive, manufacturing, agricultural, medical, building controls, marine, and aerospace. With many suppliers offering DeviceNet sensors and actuators, designers can select the best combination of devices from multiple suppliers to solve the control problem. As a result, DeviceNet is the fastest growing device network in the world, with over a half million installed devices. DeviceNet operation and features are covered in the next subsections.

17-5-1 DeviceNet Operation

DeviceNet operates on multiple messaging formats, which can be mixed and matched within a network to achieve the most information-rich and time-efficient information from the network at all times: The messaging types are as follows:

- Polling: Each device is requested to send or receive an update of its status. This requires an outgoing message and incoming message for each node on the network. This is the most precise but least time efficient way to request information from devices.
- Strobing: A request is broadcast to all devices for a status update. Each device responds in turn, with node 1 answering first, then node 2, 3, 4, etc. Node numbers can be assigned to prioritize messages. Polling and strobing are the most common messaging formats used.
- Cyclic: Devices are configured to automatically send messages on scheduled intervals. This is sometimes called a heartbeat and is often used in conjunction with change of state messaging to indicate that the device is still functional.
- Change of state: Devices only send messages when their status changes. This occupies an absolute minimum of time on the network, and a large network using this type can often outperform a polling network operating at several times the speed. This is the most time-efficient but sometimes least precise way to

obtain information from devices because throughput and response time becomes statistical instead of deterministic.

- Explicit messaging: The explicit-messaging protocol indicates how a device should interpret a message. It is commonly used on complex devices such as drives and controllers to download parameters that change from time to time but do not change as often as the process data itself. An explicit message supplies a generic, multipurpose communication path between two devices and provides a means for performing request/response functions such as device configuration.
- Fragmented messaging: For messages that require more than DeviceNet's maximum 8 bytes of data per node per scan, the data can be broken up into any number of 8-byte segments and re-assembled at the other end. This requires multiple messages to send or receive one complete message.
- Unconnected message manager: DeviceNet UCMM interfaces are capable of peer-to-peer communication. Unlike the plain-vanilla master/slave configuration (one device, the master, initiates communication; other devices, the slaves, respond), each UCMM-capable device can communicate with another directly, without having to go through a master. UCMM devices must accept all generic CAN messages, then perform filtering of irrelevant or undesired message types in the upper software layer. This requires more RAM and ROM than ordinary master/slave messaging.

17-5-2 DeviceNet Features

DeviceNet interconnects industrial devices such as limit switches, photoelectric sensors, valve manifolds, motor starters, process sensors, panel displays, and operator interfaces via a single network. Expensive wiring and failure due to the increase in the number of connections is eliminated. It also reduces the cost and time to install industrial automation devices while providing reliable interchangeability of components from multiple vendors. The direct connectivity provides improved communication between devices as well as important device-level diagnostics not easily accessible or available through hardwired

input/output interfaces. The following important features should be noted.

- DeviceNet supports individual devices designed with network communications electronics, such as sensors, operator stations, motor starters, motor controllers, pneumatic valves, and microcomputers.
- DeviceNet supports remote I/O ports with a variety of I/O card options. These remote network ports use standard discrete sensors and actuators.
- DeviceNet is generally a sub-network off of a PLC that is connected to a ControlNet, Ethernet, or Ethernet/IP.
- In most applications, PLCs and industrial microcomputers use DeviceNet scanner cards when adding a DeviceNet network to an automation system.
- A large body of sensors and actuators, such as limit switches, proximity and photoelectric sensors, valve blocks, and motor drives, are DeviceNet compatible. This means that these devices are connected directly to the DeviceNet network and no independent power and discrete I/O wiring is necessary.

DeviceNet is a connection-based protocol—all devices are required to establish a network connection prior to exchanging information. It adopts the object modeling approach, in which each information type is structured in different objects. Four basic objects are required to handle these information exchanges:

- **Identity object:** Identification information such as vendor ID, device profile, and revision of a device are stored in this object. Users can identify a particular object by remote access to this object.
- **Message router:** This object handles the explicit messages received by routing them to the proper destination objects.
- **DeviceNet object:** This object stores all DeviceNet-related information such as the device's MAC address and baud rate.
- **Connection object:** This object handles the connection of the messaging module, such as explicit messaging and input/output messaging.

17-6 SPECIAL NETWORK INTERFACES

PLCs connected into the factory floor network architecture often use special network interfaces such as *SERCOS, smart I/O, remote I/O, serial communications, wireless communications*, and the *human-machine interface* to further distribute data communications to remote control locations. These special network interfaces are described in the following subsections.

17-6-1 SERCOS Interfaces

This special communications module is a Serial Realtime Communications System, or SERCOS for short. SERCOS is a digital motion control network that interfaces the motion control module in the PLC with the servo motor drive through a fiber optic cable. The fiber permits serial motion data transmissions with improved noise immunity and fast update times. SERCOS allows motion control in velocity, torque, or position modes. Multiple servo drives can be daisy chained on a single SERCOS fiber network.

17-6-2 Smart I/O Interfaces

PLC vendors have proprietary network protocols to allow devices from the same vendor to communicate using that vendor's specific network interface. One common application for a proprietary network is the use of *smart I/O devices*. The term *smart* implies that the device or interface includes a microprocessor so that it can be programmed for network data exchange. PLC vendor-specific network interfaces are discussed in Section 17-7.

Let's look at an operator panel as an aid to understanding the concept of smart I/O interfaces. Operator panels have switches for control of process machines and devices, and the panels have lights to indicate the condition of process equipment. The operator panels are frequently located in a control room away from the process itself. The traditional approach in building an operator panel requires a minimum of one wire per switch and lamp plus several return wires between the operator panel and PLC input and output modules. As a result, the wire bundle between these two devices often has hundreds of wires that must be enclosed in conduit over distances of hundreds of feet. In contrast, the smart operator interface uses the same number of switches and lamps but

controls them with a small microcomputer located in the operator panel. This smart I/O interface between the operator panel and the PLC is just a single coaxial network cable that permits the operator panel's microcomputer to communicate with the PLC processor. A large number of smart external devices are available, including motor drives, process controllers, text readout devices, programmable CRT displays supporting full color and graphics, voice input and output devices, and discrete input and output devices.

17-6-3 Remote I/O Interfaces

In an effort to distribute the network control capability across a large automation system, PLC vendors provide *remote I/O or remote rack* capability. Figure 17-2 illustrates a remote I/O link. The rack uses the standard I/O modules for control of machines and processes; however, the processor module is replaced with a remote rack communications module. The processor in the main PLC rack sends control instructions over the single network cable to the communication

module in the remote rack and then to the I/O modules included in the remote rack. Use of this technology permits the I/O modules to be located close to the point of control, which eliminates the long wire runs required if the sensors are connected to I/O modules in the main PLC rack.

17-6-4 Serial Communication Interfaces

Serial communication interfaces are either built into the processor module or come as separate modules. In both cases, the interface permits serial data communication using several standard interfaces such as RS-232, RS-422, and RS-485, where RS stands for Recommended Standard, and Firewire, which is an IEEE 1394 implementation. The RS interfaces are used to connect devices such as the smart gages and bar code readers that must transfer quantities of data at a reasonably high rate between the remote device and the PLC. These serial communication interface standards use *data terminal equipment* (DTE) and *data communication equipment* (DCE) terminology. The DTE is the component that communicates

FIGURE 17-2: Remote I/O network.

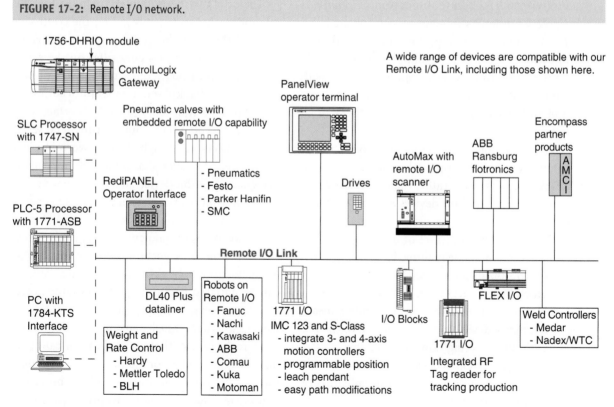

Courtesy of Rockwell Automation, Inc.

TABLE 17-1 Comparison of key characteristics of serial data interfaces

Specifications	RS232	RS422	RS485
Mode of operation	Single-Ended	Differential	Differential
Total number of drivers and receivers on one line (Note 1)	1 Driver 1 Receiver	1 Driver 10 Receiver	1 Driver 32 Receiver
Maximum cable length	50 ft.	4000 ft.	4000 ft.
Maximum data rate (Note 2)	20 Kbps	100 Kbps	100 Kbps

Note 1 – For the RS485, a maximum of 32 drivers can be connected together, providing that only one driver is on at any one time.
Note 2 – For the RS422 and RS485, the maximum data rate for a 40-ft. cable length is 10 Mbps.

with another component somewhere else, such as a PLC communicating with another PLC. The DCE is the component actually doing the communicating or performing the functions of the generator and receiver discussed in the standards, such as a modem. Table 17-1 provides a comparison of some of the key specifications for the RS interface standards.

Firewire Serial Communication. *Firewire* is Apple Computer's implementation of the IEEE 1394 standard high performance serial bus. Firewire is a single plug-and-socket connection on which up to 63 devices can be attached with data transfer speeds up to 400 megabits per second and provides:

- A simple common plug-in serial connector on many types of peripheral devices.
- A thin serial cable rather than the thicker parallel cable used on devices such as a printer or plotter.
- A very high-speed rate of data transfer that will accommodate multimedia applications of up to 400 megabits per second today with much higher rates later.
- *Hot-plug* or plug-and-play capability, meaning that a device can be connected to the bus without powering down the system.
- The ability to chain devices together in a number of different ways without terminators or complicated setup requirements.

Firewire and other IEEE 1394 implementations are expected to replace and consolidate today's serial and parallel interfaces such as the RS-232 and Small Computer System Interface (SCSI), pronounced scuzzy. Products with IEEE 1394 capability include digital cameras, digital video disks (DVDs) and tapes, digital recorders, and music systems. A brief description of the implementation of IEEE 1394 follows.

There are two levels of interface in IEEE 1394, one for the backplane bus within the controller and another for the point-to-point interface between the device and controller on the serial cable. A simple bridge connects the two environments. The backplane bus supports up to 50 Mbps data transfer. The cable interface supports up to 400 Mbps data transfer. The serial bus functions as though devices were in slots within the controller sharing a common memory space. A 64-bit device address allows a great deal of flexibility in configuring devices in chains and trees from a single socket. IEEE 1394 provides two types of data transfer: *asynchronous* and *isochronous*. Asynchronous is for traditional load-and-store applications where data transfer can be initiated and an application interrupted as a given length of data arrives in a buffer. Isochronous data transfer ensures that data flows at a pre-set rate so that an application can handle it in a timed way. For multimedia applications, the data transfer reduces the need for buffering and helps ensure a continuous presentation for

the viewer. The IEEE 1394 standard requires that a device be within 15 feet of the bus socket. Up to 16 devices can be connected in a single chain, each with the 15-foot maximum (before signal attenuation begins to occur), so theoretically you could have a device as far away as 325 feet from the computer.

Another approach to connecting devices is the Universal Serial Bus (USB), which provides the same hot-plug capability as the IEEE 1394 standard. It's a less expensive technology, but data transfer is limited to 12 Mbps. Small Computer System Interface (SCSI) offers a high data transfer rate (up to 40 Mbps) but requires address preassignment and a device terminator on the last device in a chain. Firewire can work with the latest internal computer bus standard, Peripheral Component Interconnect (PCI), but higher data transfer rates may require special design considerations to minimize undesired buffering for transfer rate mismatches.

17-6-5 Wireless Interfaces

Wireless communication uses radio frequencies or infrared waves to transmit data between machines or devices where the wireless local area network is located, referred to as WLAN or LAWN. A key component is the wireless hub, or access point, used for signal distribution. To receive the signals from the access point, a machine must have a wireless network interface. Wireless signals are electromagnetic waves that can travel through a medium such as air. Therefore, no physical medium such as cables is necessary in a wireless network. Wireless standards such as IEEE 802.11(WiFi), IEEE 802.16 (WiMAX), Bluetooth, and the European HiperLAN are used in network applications. In general, there are four types of wireless network applications. Each has its own benefit and purpose. Let's examine each:

- Peer to peer: This network is one in which each device communicates directly with another device. This is most common in a small and simple network.
- Point to multipoint: This is a network where one device talks to many devices at once. The master point broadcasts a message and all devices receive and react to it.

- Multipoint to point: In this configuration, remote devices communicate their data back to a central location. This is often used in data collection types of systems.
- Mesh network: This type of network is similar to a checkerboard. Each similar colored square on the checkerboard is connected to a neighbor. If we follow the colors we can get to any square on the checkerboard.

Wireless communication is set to invade the factory floor over the next 10 years in a big way. Even as many prepare for a factory floor future with Ethernet, forward thinkers are casting their gaze to a few years beyond. Some foresee a day when sensor-packed machines will talk to host controllers across hundreds of feet without a network cable. At an Intel Developer Forum, a Bluetooth solution was demonstrated. It took control-input commands from a Bluetooth-equipped notebook computer and remotely operated a robotic arm complete with gripper, wrist, elbow, and shoulder. However, many are leery of using Bluetooth protocols for large industrial applications, saying that Bluetooth lacks sufficient broadcasting range and costs too much.

Omron Electronics offers an alternative to the conventional network in its wireless DeviceNet, designed for radio transmission of input and output signals in a factory environment. Figure 17-3 illustrates Omron's WD-30 wireless DeviceNet. The product, based on industrial DeviceNet protocols, uses a unique technology and operates at

FIGURE 17-3: Omron WD-30 wireless DeviceNet network.

Courtesy of Omron Electronics, LLC.

2.4 gigahertz. The company foresees the technology being used to enable controllers to communicate with wireless pressure sensors, temperature sensors, and flow meters in the factory. In many cases, it will make more sense to do it wirelessly as opposed to running wires out to every sensor.

17-6-6 Human-Machine Interfaces

The *human-machine interface* (HMI) is where people and technology meet. This people-technology intercept can be as simple as the grip on an electromechanical hand tool or as complex as the flight deck controls on a commercial jet. Relative to industrial networks the *graphic terminal* is the HMI that is discussed in this section. Graphic terminals offer rugged electronic interface solutions in a variety of sizes and configurations. These robust devices are fully packaged (hardware, software, and communications) and provide HMI operation. You simply download your configured application file, set appropriate communication parameters, and connect the communication cable. Graphic terminals replace traditional wired panels as the input and output mechanism for operator interaction machines. These terminals are capable of providing process information over a variety of industrial networks such as DeviceNet, ControlNet, Ethernet/IP, and Remote I/O.

A popular graphic terminal is the Allen-Bradley PanelView shown in Figure 17-4. The PanelView has a high contrast ratio of 300:1, making this graphic terminal an excellent choice for bright ambient light applications such as environments using halogen or fluorescent lights. PanelView 1400e graphic terminals offer opti-

mum color pixel graphics and high-performance advantages, are available in touch screen or keypad, and are designed to satisfy the most demanding process control applications.

17-7 NETWORK APPLICATIONS

In this section three popular network applications are discussed—the European Profibus, the Allen-Bradley Data Highway, and the Group Schneider (Modicon) Modbus.

17-7-1 Profibus Network

Process Field Bus *(Profibus)* was created in 1989 in Germany by a consortium of factory automation suppliers. It is used primarily in Europe but is gaining worldwide acceptance. Originally developed to enable discrete manufacturing, it has expanded into process automation and enterprise-wide applications. Figure 17-5 shows the architecture of the Profibus, which encompasses several industrial bus standards including:

- *Profibus-DP*, which is a device-level bus that supports both analog and discrete signals.
- *Profibus-PA*, which is a full-function fieldbus that is generally used for process control and process-level instrumentation.
- Pro*fibus-FMS*, which is a control bus generally used for communications between DCS (Distributed Control Systems) and PLC systems.

Profibus-DP, where DP stands for Decentralized Periphery, uses a direct data link mapper, providing access to the user interface with application functions defined in the user interface. It is functionally comparable to DeviceNet. The physical media is defined via the RS-485 or fiber optic transmission technologies. Profibus-DP communicates at speeds up to 12 Mbps over distances up to 1,200 meters.

Profibus-PA, where PA stands for Process Automation, is called the Process Control Network and is an extension of the Profibus-DP for data transmission. It is functionally comparable to FOUNDATION Fieldbus. It uses IEC 1158-2, which provides intrinsic safety for process-level instrumentation, communicates at 30 Kbps, and has a maximum distance of 1,900 meters. These

FIGURE 17-4: Allen-Bradley PanelView graphic display.

Courtesy of Rockwell Automation, Inc.

FIGURE 17-5: Profibus network.

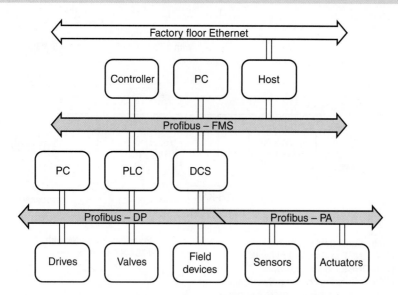

Rehg and Sartori, Industrial Electronics, *1ˢᵗ edition, ©2006, reprinted by permission of Pearson Education, Inc., Upper Saddle River, NJ.*

process control networks are the most advanced fieldbus networks in use today. They provide connectivity of sophisticated process measuring and control equipment and can be easily deployed for new or existing process equipment, and today's engineering tools allow for correct, efficient design. Devices typically connected to process control networks include control valves, temperature and pressure transmitters, level measurement equipment, flow meters, and process analytical instruments.

Profibus-FMS, where FMS stands for Fieldbus Message System, supplies the automation and control for real-time input/output control. It's functionally comparable to ControlNet. It is ideal for systems with multiple PC-based controllers and PLC-to-PLC communication, allowing multiple controllers—each with their own input/output and shared inputs—to talk to each other with any possible interlocking combination.

17-7-2   Data Highway Networks

The Allen-Bradley data highway networks, Data Highway Plus (DH+) and the DH-485, provide simple communication and simple implementation. Figure 17-6(a) illustrates the Data Highway Plus network. DH+ is a bus configuration, token-passing network. A bus configuration network is simply a network with one long cable, a trunk

line. To connect your PLCs and other intelligent machines to the network you simply tap into the trunk. In other words, we create a branch off of the trunk line and add our device. So, think of the network as a tree. Token-passing network means that only one intelligent machine on the network can communicate. No token equals no speak. After the device with the token transmits, it electronically passes the token to the next device in line. It's like at a large meeting where only the person with the microphone can speak, and when that person is finished the microphone is passed.

DH+ programming software is available to program the PLC controllers over the DH+ network, which means that a single industrial terminal connected to the network can be used to program all the PLC controllers on all links of the network. Benefits includes switches on each interface that make it easy to reconfigure the network as it changes and incorporate network diagnostics that help to avoid costly downtime and improve network efficiency.

Figure 17–6(b) illustrates the DH-485 network. Note that the DH+ is connected to the DH-485 via a PLC and that a PanelView is connected to the DH-485 network. DH-485 is a local area network designed for factory floor application and allows for the connection of devices such as SLC 500 and MicroLogix 1000 controllers,

FIGURE 17-6: Allen-Bradley Data Highway Plus and DH-485 networks.

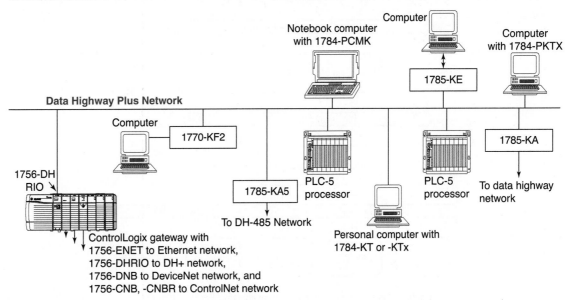

(a) Data highway plus network

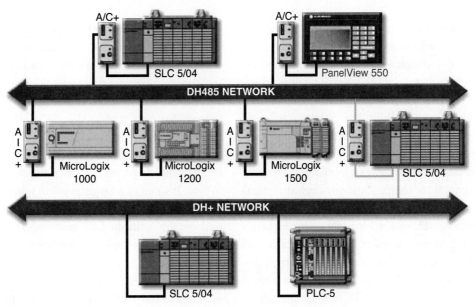

(b) Allen Bradley DH485 network

Courtesy of Rockwell Automation, Inc.

color graphics systems, and personal computers. The DH-485 network offers:

- intercommunication of up to 32 devices
- peer-to-peer capability
- the ability to add or remove nodes without disrupting the network
- a maximum network length of 4000 feet, which can be extended to 8000 feet with two Advanced Interface Converter (AIC+) units

The peer-to-peer network capability means that any controller on a DH-485 network can initiate or respond to communications with any other device on the network. With the ability to initiate communications, any controller can serve as a single initiator (also called a master or parent) on the network. The DH-485 peer-to-peer capability minimizes network traffic by allowing each controller to initiate unsolicited communications. This eliminates the need for a dedicated initiator controller,

which can tie up the network with constant polling of the responder (also referred to as slave or child) controllers. You can include other devices running DH-485 as well, for example, operator interface products such as PanelView, bar code products, and drives. Also, a single personal computer can program all the controller units on the network.

17-7-3 Modbus Network

The Group Schneider (Modicon) developed the Modbus network, which uses a master/slave communication technique. This means that only one device (i.e., the master) can initiate communication. The other devices (i.e., slaves) respond to the master's communication messages, sending back the requested data or performing the requested operation. The master communicates with individual slave units or all slave units at one time—a broadcast message. The Modbus protocol establishes the format of the master's query, including a function code defining the required action, any data to be sent, and an error-checking field. The master sends the message, the slave receives it, and replies back in the same format. It's important to note that all messages have a known starting and ending point. This allows the receiving devices to know that a message has arrived, figure out if it's for them or not, and know that the message has been completely received.

Figure 17-7 shows how devices might be interconnected in a hierarchy of networks where, in message transactions, the Modbus protocol is

FIGURE 17-7: Modbus network.

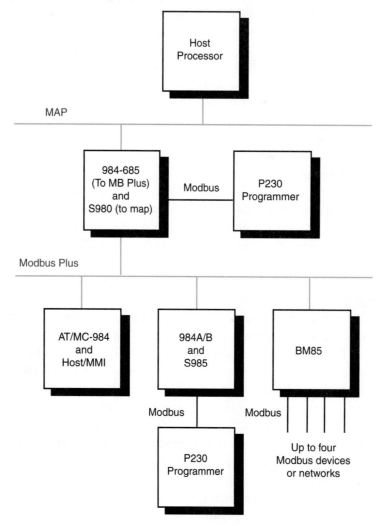

embedded into each network structure, providing a common language so that all devices can exchange data. Note that Map is a standard network similar to Ethernet and Modbus Plus; it functions similar to ControlNet.

17-8 TROUBLESHOOTING NETWORK SYSTEMS

Troubleshooting is the process of taking a general problem, narrowing it down to one specific component, and then fixing it. The initial step in troubleshooting a network system problem is to collect information from the users as to the nature of the problems that they're experiencing and to collect data from the network. Troubleshooting network systems is especially important because it is rarely done at your leisure—it is strictly reactive. Generally, if something is broken, it needs to be fixed right away because network downtime can cost the company an incredible amount of money.

The *cost of downtime* can be broken into components—repair expenses, business lost, and reduced productivity. The simplest factor of the cost of downtime is the expense of repairing the problem, which is made up of several components, including hardware replacement costs and the salaries of those performing the troubleshooting. Although this is the most tangible component of downtime cost, it is generally the least of the company's concerns. Productivity and revenue lost during periods of downtime can be so great that companies will spend almost unlimited funds to repair a failed network system. Companies that have spent money to build a network often rely on that network for business- and process-critical functions. This is especially true for companies such as Internet service providers, which rely on networking as their primary source of revenue. For these organizations, downtime may translate directly into lost revenue.

Network problems come in many different forms, but generally start with user or operator complaints. One needs an organized troubleshooting process to expeditiously fix the problem process. Start by investigating the network cabling system because many network failures are cable related.

- Make sure that the cable connections are tight. In newly installed networks that's a real problem, and in existing networks machine vibration can cause a loose connection.
- Make sure that the cables are grounded properly. Coaxial cables are troublesome and shielded twisted-pair cables should be grounded at one end of the cable only.
- Make sure that cables run properly. In other words, make sure that the communication cables are not next to power lines. That, of course, will lead to electrical noise issues that tend to give sporadic problems.

When the cabling system proves reliable, troubleshooting using network diagnostics tools such as network analyzers is the next step. Each network has its own unique set of tools, both hardware and software, to evaluate and resolve network problems. Discussion of these tools is beyond the scope of this text. A course on networks, which discusses the Open Systems Interconnect (OSI) model, is a good source. The OSI model systematically defines network architecture in seven layers and is an excellent troubleshooting tool.

17-9 DISTRIBUTIVE CONTROL

Distributive control is the mechanism to access data across a highly distributed network to manage control of field devices. It allows the flexibility to do process control while using the advanced capabilities of network-based process instrumentation. An example of distributive control is the FOUNDATION Fieldbus Linking Device (FFLD). The FFLD includes the unique ability to bridge the Ethernet/IP and the High Speed Ethernet (HSE) to the FOUNDATION Fieldbus network. Bridging these networks facilitates the information flow. This information flow includes device configuration, such as setup, operation, and diagnostic data, and factory floor process information such as temperature and flow data. The advantage of this type of distributive control is that complex control strategies can be developed to best fit an automated application. For complex control scenarios, regulatory loops, which include pumps, can be executed at the controller level and backed up

at the device level. For simple control scenarios, the regulatory loop can be run at the device level.

Figure 17-8 illustrates the FFLD networked into a ControlNet network. Note that each of the FFLDs is a ControlNet node that connects to two H1 networks. H1 networks are factory floor local area networks that provide connectivity to field devices. The H1 networks function as DeviceNet networks. The FFLD accesses data across the ControlNet network and distributes the data to the field devices on the H1 networks.

An application of distributive control is shown in Figure 17-9, which illustrates a storage tank system. In this application it is important to control the temperature of the tanks, which are located throughout the facility and where each tank temperature is controlled by a single loop PID controller. Management and maintenance of these distributed sensors and controllers are difficult and require an information technology to inspect them regularly. Through an FFLD, the highly distributed requirements can be maintained

FIGURE 17-8: Distributive control configuration.

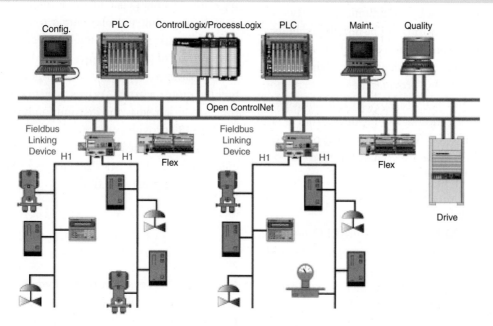

Courtesy of Rockwell Automation, Inc.

FIGURE 17-9: Tank storage system.

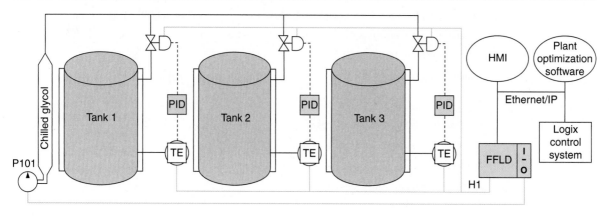

Courtesy of Rockwell Automation, Inc.

while providing remote configuration and monitoring of all loops and devices. Thus critical process or device information can be directly accessed by plant-level systems such as HMI or some plant optimization software.

17-10   DISTRIBUTED I/O

Input/output (I/O) interfaces can be located or distributed around the application or integrated with the PLC. The various PLCs, including the Allen-Bradley PLC-5, SLC 500, and Control-Logix PLCs, offer I/O that can be installed locally in the same chassis as the processor. Additionally, through the use of I/O communication networks, I/O for these platforms can be distributed in locations remote from the processor, closer to the sensors and actuators, which reduces wiring costs. Distributing the I/O provides the freedom to monitor and control I/O across an I/O link, which allows the selection of I/O products from a variety of platforms. There are two types of distributed I/O; these are commonly referred to as in-cabinet I/O and on-machine I/O.

17-10-1   In-cabinet I/O
In-cabinet I/O has the distributed I/O mounted in a central cabinet, thus not requiring an additional enclosure for environmental protection and allowing easier maintenance. In-cabinet I/O is offered in modular and block styles. *Modular I/O* is a system of interface cards and communications adapters that interface directly to the sensors and actuators of the machine/process and communicate their status to the controller via a communication network. It allows the designer to mix and match I/O interfaces and communications adapters. *Block I/O* is a complete assembly of sensor and actuator interface points including a network adapter. It may or may not include a power supply and is available in fixed configurations.

17-10-2   On-machine I/O
On-machine I/O is the placement of automation components directly on a machine rather than housing them in a central cabinet. This is possible with the emergence of more modular, compact devices; plug-and-play connectivity; flexible communication networks; intelligent devices; and a wide array of products with improved environmental ratings. On-machine components can include motor starters, drives, sensors, contactors, network media, and distribution boxes. On-machine I/O provides reduced wiring and system costs, improved mean time to repair (MTTR), enhanced control system reliability, increased productivity, and greater flexibility.

17-11   SELECTING AND DESIGNING NETWORKS

In general, the selection of a network is based on application requirements. Here are some typical application requirements and the network that would best serve the requirements.

If your application requires:	Choose this network
1. High-speed data transfer between information systems and/or a large quantity of controllers 2. Internet/Intranet connections 3. Program maintenance	Ethernet/IP
1. High-speed transfer of time-critical data between controllers and I/O devices 2. Deterministic and repeatable data delivery 3. Program maintenance 4. Media redundancy or intrinsic safety options	ControlNet

1. Connections of low-level devices directly to controllers without the need of I/O devices	DeviceNet
2. More diagnostics for improved data collection	
3. Less wiring and reduced startup time than traditional hard-wired systems	
1. Plant-wide and work cell-level data sharing	Data Highway Plus
2. Program maintenance	
1. Connections between controllers and I/O adapters	Remote I/O
2. Distributed controllers with each having its own I/O communication	
1. Connections to modems	Serial
2. Messages that send and receive ASCII characters to and from devices	

In discussing network design guidelines we will concentrate on the Ethernet, ControlNet, and DeviceNet networks because of their popularity. In designing an Ethernet network where many computers, controllers, and other devices communicate over vast distances, it's important to correctly specify the switches and interfaces that are responsible for the high-speed connectivity. Figure 17-10 illustrates an Ethernet network with the hub/switch block and the Ethernet interface (ENI) depicted. When specifying the switches in the hub/switch block in the figure, make sure that the switches have the following design features:

- Full duplex transmit and receive capability on all ports
- High-speed switching design
- Capability to control traffic flow from different systems

FIGURE 17-10: Ethernet network with Ethernet hub/switch block and Ethernet interface module.

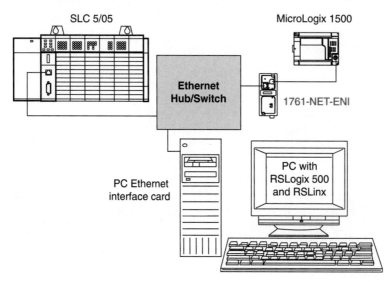

Courtesy of Rockwell Automation, Inc.

- Support redundancy for effective fault isolation
- Frame prioritization
- Address blocking to restrict traffic to a specific range
- Auto-restore of switch configuration capability for replacement
- Method to back up configuration information

Suppliers of switches that encompass these design features include Cisco, Hirshmann, and N-Tron.

In Figure 17-10 the Ethernet interface (ENI) module provides messaging connectivity for all full-duplex devices. The ENI allows network designers to connect controllers onto new or existing Ethernet networks and upload and download programs, communicate between controllers, and generate email messages. A variation of the ENI is the Web-enabled Ethernet interface (ENIW). The ENIW has the same features as the ENI plus the capability to enable the display of data Web pages with user configurable data. Both the ENI and the ENIW are available from the PLC manufacturer.

In designing the ControlNet network that transmits time-critical information and provides real-time messaging services, it's imperative that you consider the following design guidelines:

- Set your design for a maximum of 40 nodes per network, thus providing better perfor-

mance and having bandwidth available for other communications.
- Design for a minimum reserve of 400 Kbytes of available memory for unscheduled data transfer, thus improving message throughput and workstation response.
- Install serial communication modules in the local chassis, thus avoiding data to be scheduled over the network.
- Save each controller's project file when you change network settings.
- Place each processor and its respective I/O on isolated ControlNet networks, thus reducing the impact of changes.
- Place shared I/O on a common network available to each controller that needs the information.

Figure 17-11 illustrates a ControlNet network depicting two key design components—the scanner module and the adapter module. The scanner module provides scheduled network connections for the controllers, and with scheduled messaging, I/O events can be controlled. The adapter module can enable multiple chassis of I/O modules to produce/consume scheduled I/O on the network. Both the scanner module and the adapter module provide media redundancy and the ability to upgrade firmware. Both of these modules are available from the PLC manufacturer.

In designing the DeviceNet network as a low-level communication link between devices and

FIGURE 17-11: ControlNet network with scanner and adapter.

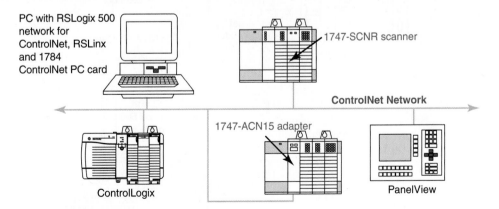

PC with RSLogix 500 network for ControlNet, RSLinx and 1784 ControlNet PC card

1747-SCNR scanner

ControlNet Network

1747-ACN15 adapter

ControlLogix

PanelView

Courtesy of Rockwell Automation, Inc.

controllers, it's imperative that you consider the following design guidelines:

- Verify that the total network data does not exceed the DeviceNet communication module's data table size.
- Place the DeviceNet communication scanner modules in the local chassis to maximize performance.
- Configure a device's parameters before adding the device to the scanner's device list.
- Keep the highest node address open, typically node 63, as a test node so that you can add a new device, then change the address of the new device when it checks out.
- Keep at least one node open, like node address 62, so that a computer can be attached for troubleshooting.

Figure 17-12 illustrates a DeviceNet network depicting two key design components—the scanner module and the DeviceNet Interface (DNI) module. The scanner module is needed to enable communication between the controller and the DeviceNet-compatible I/O devices. The scanner acts as the DeviceNet master, enabling data transfer between the DeviceNet devices—the slaves.

Most controllers support multiple scanners installed in a single-processor chassis. The DNI allows connection of compatible devices to the network where the DNI functions as the slave. In addition, the DNI enables the setup of a peer-to-peer communication network on the DeviceNet with other devices using DNIs. Both the scanner and the DNI modules are available from the PLC manufacturer.

In conclusion, the fact is that network design never stops. After the initial requirements analysis, which leads to a basic network design, you buy and deploy equipment. After the network is up and running, the organization discovers unforeseen uses for the network, which leads to design changes, new networking equipment, and new discoveries. The cycle goes on and on.

17-12 WEB SITES FOR INDUSTRIAL NETWORKS

The universal resource locators (URLs) for suppliers of network products and network technology that were discussed in this chapter follow. However, the URLs for supplier sites often change, so if any of the following are not active,

FIGURE 17-12: DeviceNet network with scanner and interface adapter.

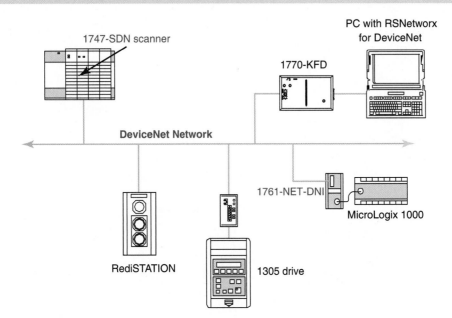

Courtesy of Rockwell Automation, Inc.

use the appropriate network term of interest in a search engine to find on-line material.

- LAN Technology Products at Cisco and Allen-Bradley: http://www.cisco.com, http://www.ab.com
- DeviceNet and Ethernet/IP Technology at ODVA: http://www.odva.org

- ControlNet, DeviceNet, and Ethernet/IP at Allen-Bradley: http://www.ab.com/networks
- Profibus Technology: http://www.profibus.com
- Modbus Technology: http://www.modbus.org
- Fieldbus Technology: http://www.fieldbus.com
- Protocol/Network Analyzers at Acterna: http://www.acterna.com

APPENDIX

Glossary

Absolute pressure	The difference between measured pressure and a perfect vacuum
Accelerometers	Transducers that measure acceleration
Accumulated value	An integer that indicates the number of increments that a timer or counter has accumulated and is generally set to zero
Addressing mode	The means by which a PLC selects the data that is to be used in an instruction
Algorithm	A set of equations or procedures that solve a problem
Alias tag	A tag that references another tag
Ambient temperature	The temperature of the air around a device
ANSI	American National Standards Institute; a government organization that sets electrical standards
Application	The combination of routines, programs, tasks, and I/O configuration used to define the operation of a single controller
ASCII	American Standard Code for Information Interchange; a 7-bit code (with an optional parity bit) that is used to represent alphanumeric characters, punctuation marks, and control-code characters
ASIC	Application-specific integrated circuit used in PLC processors
Assembly language	A low-level programming language that maps into machine language and uses the mnemonic instructions of the CPU
Assignment	A statement that assigns values to tags
Asynchronous	Actions that occur independently of each other and which lack a regular pattern

Backplane	A printed circuit board that delivers power to the plug-in modules and provides a data bus to exchange data between the modules and the CPU
Bandwidth	The frequency range in which a system is designed to operate, expressed in Hertz
Base tag	A tag that represents the memory address where the data is stored
Bellows	A thin, sealed metal cylinder with corrugated sides like the pleats of an accordion
Binary coded decimal (BCD)	Four binary bits that represent decimal numbers 0 through 9
Binary number	Integer values displayed and entered in base 2 where each digit represents a single bit
Bit	The smallest unit of data in the binary numbering system; short for binary digit
BOOL	A data type that stores the state of a single bit, where 0 equals off and 1 equals on
Bourdon tube	A deformed hollow metal tube opened at one end and sealed at the other
Branch	A parallel logic path within a program
Broadcast	A mechanism where an intelligent machine can send data on a network that is simultaneously received by more than one machine
Byte	A group of 8 adjacent bits
Calibration	The procedure of determining the accuracy of a measuring device and replacing or repairing the device if it does not meet a predetermined accuracy
CCD	Charge coupled device
Central processing unit (CPU)	The electronic circuitry that controls all the data activity of the PLC, performs calculations, and makes decisions with its operation controlled by a sequence of instructions
Closed loop	A control system using feedback from a process to maintain outputs at a specific level
CMOS	Complementary metal oxide semiconductor
Comment	Text that explains or clarifies what a section of structured text does
Connection	A communication link between two devices, such as between a controller and an I/O module, PanelView terminal, or another controller
Construct	A conditional statement used to trigger structured text code
Contactor	A relay designed to switch large currents from large voltage sources
Control system load	The value of the manipulated variable required by the process to eliminate the effect of the load

Control system response	The response of any control system to a given input stimulus; this is a measure of how well the control system was designed
Controlled variable (CV)	The actual output from the process system
ControlNet	An automation and control layer for real-time input/output control, interlocking, and messaging
Counter	A device that counts the number of events and controls other devices based on the number of counts recorded
Current sinking	The characteristic associated with an NPN transistor where it is saturated (turned full on) so that it provides a low resistance path to ground
Current sourcing	The characteristic associated with a PNP transistor where it is saturated (turned full on) so that it provides a low resistance path to the power source
Data handling	The movement of data and the manipulation of data by arithmetic and logical operations
Data latching	A technique used to read the value of the input data that will be operated on by the instructions with a function block
Dead time delay	The delay when the feedback sensor is incorrectly located with respect to the location where the process control is occurring
Debouncing	The technique of reducing intermediate noise from a mechanical switch
Debug	The process of locating and fixing software or hardware problems
Decimal number	Integer values displayed and entered in base 10
Decrement	A term indicating that the value of a counter has decreased
Defuzzification	The process that converts fuzzy logic output conclusions to real output data and sends the data to an output device
Determinism	The ability to reliably predict when data will be delivered
DeviceNet	A device layer for cost-effective integration of individual devices
Diagnostics	Software routines that aid in identifying the causes of faults
Diaphragm	A flexible membrane, which is rubber for low-pressure measurements and metal for high-pressure measurements
Differential distance	The difference between the resetting distance and the sensing distance
Differential pressure	The difference between measured pressure and a reference pressure
Dimension	The specification of the size of an array
DINT	A data type that stores a 32-bit (4-byte) signed integer value
Direct addressing	An addressing mode in which the memory address of the data is supplied with the instruction

Discrete inputs	Connections to the PLC that convert an electrical signal from a field device to a binary state (off or on), which is read by the CPU each PLC scan
Discrete outputs	Connections from the PLC that convert an internal ladder program result (0 or 1), which turns an output device off or on
Distributed control	The system organization in which machine control is divided into several subsystems, each managed by a separate PLC
Doppler effect	The frequency of the reflected signal is modified by the velocity and direction of the fluid flow
Double word	Thirty-two bits or four bytes
Down counter	A counter that starts a specific number and decrements to zero
Drum switch	An industrial control switch typically used for motor control
Duplex	Two-way communication
Dwell time	The length of time that a machine such as a PLC pauses between operations
EIA	Electronic Industries Association; an agency that sets electrical/electronic standards
Elapsed time	The total time required for the execution of all operations configured within a single task
Electromagnetic flow sensor	A sensor that measures the electrical charges in flowing fluid, which are proportional to the fluid velocity
Element	An addressable unit of data that is a sub-unit of a larger unit of data
Empirical design	A design approach that develops the ladder solution one rung at a time
Ethernet	An information layer for enterprise-wide data collection and program maintenance
Ethernet/IP	An open industrial networking standard that takes advantage of commercial off-the-shelf Ethernet communication devices and physical media; IP refers to industrial protocol
Examine if closed (XIC)	An instruction that is true if the addressed bit is on and false if the addressed bit is off; XIC refers to open contact instructions
Examine if open (XIO)	An instruction that is true if the addressed bit is off and false if the addressed bit is on; XIO refers to closed contact instructions
Expression	Part of an assignment or construct statement that evaluates a number or a true-false state
Faraday's law	The voltage induced in a conductor moving through a magnetic field is proportional to the velocity of that conductor
Fiber optic cable	Transmits information via light pulses down optical fibers
Fieldbus	A network that is optimized to exchange data between small devices and a main large device(s)

File	A group of words or block of data treated as one unit
Firewire	Serial communication accomplished over a single wire
Flow nozzle	A narrowing spout installed inside a piping system to obtain a pressure differential
Flow rate	The volume of material passing a fixed point per unit of time, where material is a solid, liquid, or gas
Force	A push or a pull
FOUNDATION Fieldbus	A data network capable of handling all the complexities of process management, including process variables, real-time deterministic process control, and diagnostics
FOV	Field of view
Frequency response	The maximum rate at which the output is caused to change states
Full duplex	Data communication in which data can be transmitted and received simultaneously
Function block	Rectangular block with inputs entering from the left and outputs exiting on the right
Functional Block Diagram (FBD)	Graphical language where the basic programming elements appear as blocks
Fuzzy control	The implementation of fuzzy logic algorithms on a digital controller
Gage factor	The ratio of fractional change in electrical resistance to the fractional change in length
Gage pressure	The difference between measured pressure and atmospheric pressure
Gray code	The binary numbering system in which any value can be changed to the next higher value by changing only one bit
Half duplex	Data communication in which data can be transmitted in two directions but in only one direction at a time
Hard wired	Electrical connectivity through physical wiring
Hexadecimal number	Integer values displayed and entered in base 16 where each digit represents four bits
High level language	A programming language tending toward English and mathematical instructions with no implementation details for the CPU operation
Hysteresis	An operational dead band that eliminates false indications such as in a sensor reading
IEC	International Electromechanical Commission; an agency that sets standards, which include PLC programming guidelines
Image table	An area of PLC memory reserved for I/O data where 1s represent an on condition and 0s represent an off condition
Increment	A term indicating that the value of a counter has increased
Index	A reference used to specify an element within an array

Indexed addressing	An addressing mode for referencing an address that is the original address plus the value stored in an index register
Indirect addressing	An addressing mode in which the address of the instruction serves as a reference point instead of the actual address
Instantaneous contacts	Normally open/normally closed contacts that operate independently of a timer's time-delay period
Instruction	The command that causes a PLC to perform one specific operation
Instructional List (IL)	Low-level, text-based language using mnemonic instructions like using machine code in microprocessors
Interrupt	An external request typically from a peripheral device requesting service
Keying	A technique to prevent the insertion of a module or connector into the wrong location or slot
Ladder Diagram (LD)	Graphical language based on traditional ladder logic
Ladder logic	A graphical programming technique that depicts the program control logic on horizontal rungs of a ladder
Laminar flow	Fluid flowing rather smoothly parallel to the walls of the pipe
LAN	Local area network; a group of computers and devices connected to serve a region
Latching relay	A relay that when commanded to a position remains in that position until it's commanded to another position
Least significant bit (LSB)	The bit that represents the minimum bit value of a byte or word
Light emitting diode (LED)	A semiconductor whose junction emits light when current flows through it in the forward direction
Limit switch	An electrical switch that is activated when the motion of a machine or equipment physically contacts the switch
Limit test	A test that determines if a value is inside or outside a specified range
Linear variable differential transformer (LVDT)	A position sensor, consisting of a transformer with a movable core
Load cell	A force transducer that employs a direct application of a bonded strain gage
Machine language	A programming language that consists of 1s and 0s and is used directly by the CPU in the microprocessor
Major fault	A fault condition that is severe enough for the controller to shut down, unless the condition is cleared
Manipulated variable (MV)	The variable regulated by the final control element to achieve the desired value in the controlled variable
Mask	A binary number used to pass and inhibit data, generally where a 1 allows data to pass and a 0 inhibits the data
MCR	Master control reset (PLCs) ; master control relay (relay logic)

Minor fault	A fault condition that is not severe enough for the controller to shut down
Modbus	A network that uses a master/slave communication technique
Most significant bit (MSB)	The bit that represents the greatest bit value of a byte or word
Mnemonic	A small group of letters that assist a person in remembering a word or a phase; e.g., SQR is the mnemonic for the square root instruction
NEMA	National Electrical Manufacturers Association; a standards organization for electrical equipment
Nested subroutine	A subroutine that begins and ends within another subroutine
Nibble	Four bits or one half of a byte
Node	A hardware connection point in a network
Normally closed (NC) contact	A relay contact that provides a conductive path when the relay is de-energized
Normally open (NO) contact	A relay contact that provides a conductive path when the relay is energized
Numeric expression	In structured text, an expression that calculates an integer or floating point
Object	A structure of data that stores status information
Octal number	Integer values displayed and entered in base 8 where each digit represents three bits
Off-delay timer	A timer that changes state some time after power has been removed
On-delay timer	A timer that changes state some time after power has been applied
One shot	A programming technique that sets a bit for only one program scan
One's complement	The inverse of a binary number obtained by changing the 1s to 0s and the 0s to 1s
Open loop	A system that has no feedback or autocorrection
Operands	Symbols in an instruction
Orifice plate	A washer-shaped device that is installed in a piping system; the flow rate is determined from the measurements of pressure in front of and behind the plate
OSHA	Occupational Safety and Health Administration; a government agency that sets and enforces work rules and safety practices
Overflow	An indication that a counter has incremented above its maximum positive number
Overload monitor	A device that typically opens contacts when the monitored object exceeds a specific temperature
Overdamped response	A system response in which the damping coefficient is greater than 1, which causes the response to overshoot the set point before settling to it

Parity bit	An additional bit added to a binary number that makes the sum of the quantity of 1s in the number even or odd
Perfect vacuum	A pressure of zero
Photoelectric device	A device that senses the presence of an object when it either breaks a light beam or reflects a beam of light to a receiver
Piezoelectric effect	When pressure is applied to a crystal, the crystal deforms and produces a small voltage, which is proportional to the deformation
Pilot switches	Various switch types that have a high current rating
Pitot tube	A flow-measuring device, consisting of two tubes placed in the fluid flow that sense two pressures—impact pressure and static pressure
PLC	Programmable Logic Controller; a special-purpose computer designed for single use or one of several controllers on an automation network for the control of a wide variety of manufacturing machines and systems using one of five programming languages
Pole	An internal conductor in the switch that is moved by the switching mechanism
Preset value (PRE)	An integer that indicates the number of increments that a timer or counter accumulates in order to provide some action
Pressure	The amount of force applied to an area, usually expressed in pounds per square inch (psi)
Pressure sensors	Services that detect the force exerted by one object on another
Process	A continuous manufacturing operation
Process variable (PV)	The value of the output that is present at the feedback input of the summing junction
Profibus	European communication standard that was developed to enable discrete manufacturing but has expanded into process automation and enterprise-wide applications
Program	A set of related routines and tags
Proportional band	The percentage change in the error that causes the final control element to go through its full range
Proportional derivative control (PD)	A control used to correct for rapidly changing disturbances in a control system
Proportional integral and derivative control (PID)	A control that combines the benefits of PI and PD controls in a control system
Proportional integral control (PI)	A control used to eliminate the steady-state error component in a control system
Proportional valves	Electromechanical devices, which adjust the flow of fluid over the range of 0 to 100 percent
Protocol	Rules used by machines to communicate with each other

Qualifier	In the action of a sequential function chart (SFC), a qualifier defines when an action starts and stops
Rails	The two uprights in a PLC ladder program
Real	A data type that stores a 32-bit (4-byte) IEEE floating point value
Relay	A remotely operated switch consisting of an electromagnet, a solenoid, and switch contacts
Repeatability	Ensures that transmitting times are constant and unaffected by devices connecting to or leaving the network
Resetting distance	The point at which the output of the sensor changes from on to off as an object is withdrawn from the sensor
Resistance temperature detector (RTD)	A temperature-sensing device that detects a change in resistance in a metal as a function of temperature
Resolution	Indicates how accurately an analog value can be expressed digitally and is specified in bits
Retentive timer	A timer that accumulates time whenever powered and retains the accumulated time when power is removed
Ringing	The oscillations present while the response settles to a final value
Routines	Blocks of code that perform one function such as calculating the sine of an angle or performing an initialization sequence
RS-232, RS-422, RS-423, RS-485	Communication standards that specify electrical, mechanical, and operational characteristics of interfaces for exchanging data between intelligent machines
Safety	The freedom from danger, risk, or injury
Scaling	The resizing of a signal to meet the requirements of the using component of a system
Scan time	The time required to read all inputs, update all outputs, and execute the control program; the scan time is not constant
Selection sequence	In a Sequential Function Chart (SFC), the selection sequence checks each entry transition in a specified order
Sensitivity	The measure of how closely a device can discriminate between levels
Sensors	Devices that are sensitive to a physical condition such as heat, pressure, motion, and light and output an electrical signal proportional to the physical input
Sequence table	A sequential list of operations of a sequencer
Sequencer	A device that is programmed so that a fixed set of actions occurs repeatedly
Sequencing	Predetermined step-by-step process that accomplishes a specific task
Sequential Function Chart (SFC)	Graphical language whose basic language elements are steps or states with associated actions and transitions with associated conditions used to move from the current state to the next

Serial real-time communication system (SERCOS)	An open controller-to-intelligent digital-drive interface specification
Set point (SP)	An integer or real value entered into the control system that indicates the desired value of the process output
Setting distance	The maximum sensing distance for a sensor and the object when worst-case ambient temperature and supply voltage variations are assumed
Shift register	A register that allows the movement of its contents to the right or to the left
Signal conditioning	The converting of a level or type of signal to another level or type of signal to be used by another stage of the system
Simultaneous sequence	In a Sequential Function Chart (SFC), the simultaneous sequence is the AND type—the exit transition cannot be checked until the last step
SINT	A data type that stores an 8-bit (1-byte) signed integer value
Solenoid	An electromechanical device that converts electrical energy into linear mechanical motion
Solenoid value	An electromechanical device that is used to control the flow of air or fluids such as water, inert gas, light oil, and refrigerants
Status indicators	LEDs that indicate the on-off status of an input or output point and are visible on the outside of the PLC
Step	In a Sequential Function Chart (SFC), a step represents a major function of a process
Step response	The time necessary for a signal to go to typically 95 percent of its final value
Strain	The amount of deformation of a body due to an applied pressure or force
Stress	The change in an object when force is applied
String	Group of data types that store ASCII characters
Structured Text (ST)	High-level, text-based language like BASIC, C, or PASCAL with commands that support a highly structured program development and the ability to evaluate complex mathematical expressions
Subroutine	A group of instructions that are outside the main program and executed only when accessed
Syntax	The rules that govern the structure of a language
Tag	A text-based name for an area of the controller's memory where data is stored
Task	It holds the information necessary to schedule the program's execution and sets the execution priority for one or more programs
Temperature	The degree of hotness or coldness of a body or environment

Terminal	An attachment point for field devices on a PLC module
Thermistors	Electronic components that exhibit a large change in resistance with a change in its body temperature
Thermocouples	Temperature-sensing devices that produce a small voltage in the millivolt range as a function of temperature and are constructed using two dissimilar metal wires
Thermopile	The serial connection of several thermocouples to enhance their resolution
Thumbwheel	A mechanical device used to manually enter a number
Timed contacts	Normally open/normally closed contacts that are activated at the end of a timer's time-delay period
Timer	A device that can be preset to a specific number and control the operation interval of other devices
Toggle switch	A small electrical switch with an extended lever
Token ring	A technique that provides an ordered transmission sequence between machines where a binary number or token is circulated among nodes and used by the nodes to gain access to the network
Topology	The shape of the network, in other words, the connection pattern of the network nodes
Transducer	A device that receives one type of energy and converts it to another type of energy and generally includes a sensor and a transmitter
Transistor	A three-terminal device in which the current through two terminals can be controlled by small changes in current or voltage at the third terminal
Transition	In a Sequential Function Chart (SFC), a transition signals a change in steps or states
Transmitters	Devices that convert small signals into larger, more usable signals
Triac	A solid-state device that switches AC current
Troubleshooter	A skilled person employed to locate trouble or make repairs on machinery or technical equipment
Troubleshooting	The intricate process used to solve problems, which is predominantly mental with the use of equipment and including electrical and mechanical manipulation of objects
Troubleshooting problem	A situation in which an answer, solution, or decision is not immediately apparent but may be found with a logical methodology that often has an intuitive component
Truth table	A listing of a set of inputs and the state of an output as a function of the inputs
Turbulent flow	Fluid is flowing down the pipe, but swirling within the flow
Twisted-pair cable	A pair of wires that form a circuit that can transmit data; the wires are twisted to provide protection against crosstalk

Two's complement	The inverse of a binary number obtained by changing the 1s to 0s and the 0s to 1s and then adding 1 to the result
UL	Underwriters Laboratory
Underdamped response	A system response in which the damping coefficient is less than 1, which causes the response to oscillate around the set point before settling to it
Underflow	An indication that a counter has incremented below its maximum negative number
Up counter	A counter that starts a specific number, typically 0, and increments up
Vacuum	A pressure less than atmospheric pressure
Velocity flow sensors	Devices that measure the fluid flow rate based on changes in flow velocity
Venturi	A flow-measuring device that consists of a gradual contraction followed by a gradual expansion within a fluid-carrying pipe
Vision system	A camera and lighting system that is used for part identification, part location, part orientation, part inspection, and range finding
Vortex flow sensor	A sensor that uses a non-streamlined object placed in the fluid flow, which creates vortices in a downstream flow
Word	A group of 16 bits or 2 bytes treated as one unit
Work cell	A group of machines, generally including a robot, working together to produce a particular product
Zero energy state	A system state where all sources of energy are removed to minimize the possibility of personal injury
Zone	The portion of a PLC ladder program that can be enabled or disabled by a control function

PLC Module Interface Circuits

B-1 PLC MODULE INTERFACES

There are numerous input and output modules because of the variety of input and output field devices and the voltage and current requirements present. DC modules often have either a current sinking or current sourcing feature, while AC modules are both current sinking and sourcing. This important concept is illustrated in Figures 1-13 and 1-14, and an input module example for current sinking and current sourcing is presented in Figure B-1. A study of this figure indicates that the sourcing sensor normally uses a PNP output transistor for the output circuit, and the sinking sensor uses an NPN transistor for the output. Note how the field device power supply is connected to provide the correct conventional current flow for the sinking and sourcing input modules. Read the description in the figure.

B-1-1 Input Interface Circuits

There are many different types of input circuits used for PLC input modules. Five of the most common (AC/DC, TTL, DC sinking, DC sourc-

ing, and AC) are illustrated and described in Figure B-2. Read the descriptions of the circuits in the figure as you study these Allen-Bradley SLC 500 circuits to find the common elements that are present.

All have opto-isolation between the field device power and the PLC power. Noise and operational problems are eliminated when the power and grounds of the PLC and other work cell systems are isolated and independent. The isolation (diode and transistor without a base at the far right of the circuit) is produced with a light emitting diode (LED) and photo-triggered transistor. Note that the current sinking and sourcing types have *one* diode in the opto-isolator, and the AC types have *two* LEDs in opposite directions to handle the AC current when it changes direction. Circuits (b), (c), and (d) in Figure B-2 have LEDs, which provide an indication on the front of the module when an input signal is present. The input resistor limits input current and the capacitor filters out input noise.

The inverting Schmidt trigger in the TTL interface in Figure B-2(b) produces some hysteresis, so the output will not switch on and off as the input

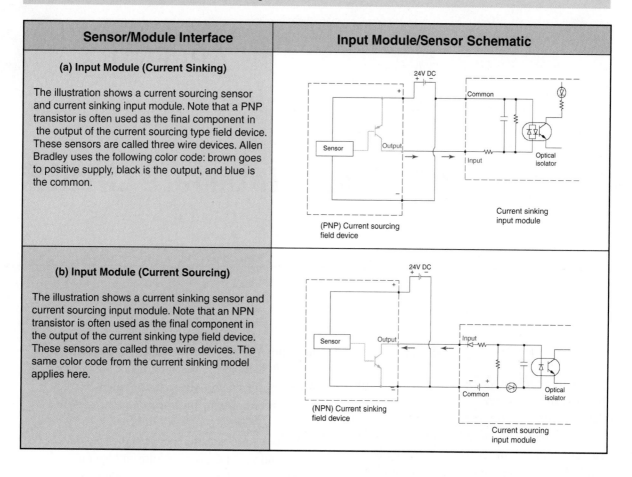

Sensor/Module Interface	Input Module/Sensor Schematic
(a) Input Module (Current Sinking) The illustration shows a current sourcing sensor and current sinking input module. Note that a PNP transistor is often used as the final component in the output of the current sourcing type field device. These sensors are called three wire devices. Allen Bradley uses the following color code: brown goes to positive supply, black is the output, and blue is the common.	
(b) Input Module (Current Sourcing) The illustration shows a current sinking sensor and current sourcing input module. Note that an NPN transistor is often used as the final component in the output of the current sinking type field device. These sensors are called three wire devices. The same color code from the current sinking model applies here.	

moves above and below the trigger point. In addition, it inverts the input signal so that a true input produces a 0 or false condition in the input image table. When this module is used the PLC input instruction type must be the opposite of that normally used. For example, if an XIC instruction would normally be used, an XIO instruction must be used when this input module is present. Read the descriptions of all the input circuits in Figure B-2 until you understand how the numerous types of input modules function.

B-1-2 Output Interface Circuits

There are many different types of output circuits used for PLC output modules. Four of the most common (DC, AC, TTL, and relay) are illustrated

and described in Figure B-3. Read the descriptions of the circuits in the figure as you study these Allen-Bradley SLC 500 circuits to find the common elements that are present.

Like the input modules just discussed, all have opto-isolation between the field device power and the PLC power. The isolation (diode and transistor at the far left of the circuit) is produced with a light emitting diode and photo-triggered transistor. The circuits operate the same as the input opto-isolators. Many modules also have an LED that indicates on the front of the module when an output signal is present.

The TTL inverter in the output interface in Figure B-3(c) produces the output voltage and drive necessary for the TTL field devices. In

Input Module Description	Input Module Schematic
(a) AC/DC Input Module The AC/DC input modules support both types of input signals. They can be used with all AC field device outputs with compatible voltage levels. In addition, they can be used with sinking or sourcing DC type field devices. Note that an opto-isolator has reversed parallel diodes to handle the AC input and to permit the DC current to flow in either direction for an active input.	
(b) TTL Input Module (Current Sinking) The TTL input modules are designed to handle the voltage levels and current drive limits of integrated circuit logic. The inputs are current sinking types so the field devices must be current sourcing models. The modules have a DC voltage source terminal common to all input points and a common also connected to all input ports. The inverting Schmidt trigger is used to add hysteresis to the input and make the switching point crisper. However, the inversion causes the module to place a logic 0 in the input image table when the field device and input are active. This is handled by using the opposite type of logic element in the input ladder.	

addition, the inverter inverts the output signal, so a true output or a 1 in the output image table produces a false output condition and an off field device. When this module is used the ladder logic must produce an output state that is the opposite of that normally used. For example, if the output field device must be on for a given condition of the input field devices, then the ladder rung logic must evaluate to a false so that the output is false. This will turn the field device on when the inverter changes the false output to the true state at the terminals of the output module.

The final circuit, a relay output module, uses mechanical contacts, either normally open or normally closed, to switch power on and off to the output field device. Read the descriptions of all the output circuits in Figure B-3 until you understand how the numerous types of output modules function.

Input Module Description	Input Module Schematic
(c) DC Input Module (Current Sinking) The sinking input modules have a current flow into the input terminal when the input is active. As a result the signal from the field device at the terminal must be a positive voltage for an active input. To achieve that, the field device must have a sourcing type of output. All of the commons for all input points on the module are connected to the DC common. Note that an opto-isolator is used to separate the power from the sensor from the power for the module.	
(d) DC Input Module (Current Sourcing) The sourcing input modules have a current flow out of the input terminal when the input is active. As a result the signal from the field device at the terminal must be a ground for an active input. To achieve that, the field device must have a sinking type of output. The other terminals for all input points on the module are connected to the DC power. Again an opto-isolator is used to isolate the two power sources.	
(e) AC Input Module The AC input modules have a current flow that changes direction every half cycle. So the AC modules require two diodes in the opto-isolator each pointing in the opposite direction so that the isolator is conducting on both half cycles. If the field device is a switch contact, then it is placed in series with an AC source. If it is a sensor with an AC ouput it is just connected to the AC module input with the commons aligned.	

Output Module Description	Output Module Schematic
(a) DC Output Module (Current Sinking) The sinking output modules have a current flow into the output terminal when the output is active. For compatibility, the field device must have a sourcing type of input. All of the commons for all output points on the module are connected to the DC common and a positive DC voltage is applied to each output port as well. Note that an opto-isolator is used to separate the power from the actuator from the PLC power. The sinking output circuit is shown with NPN type transistors for the opto-isolators and drive transistors. A sourcing version of this circuit is also available where the NPN is replaced with a PNP transistor and the power and common lines are reversed.	
(b) AC Output Module The AC/DC output modules use a Triac to turn on the output field device actuator. An AC source is connected to L1 and the actuator is placed in series with that AC source and connects to the output terminal. They can be used with all AC field device outputs with compatible voltage levels.	

Output Module Description	Output Module Schematic
(c) TTL Output Module (Current Sinking) The TTL output modules are designed to handle the voltage levels and current drive limits of integrated circuit logic. The outputs are current sinking types so the field devices must be current sourcing models. The modules have a DC voltage source terminal common to all output points and a common also connected to all output ports. The transistor in the opto-isolator would make the output a sourcing type but the inverting operational amplifier adds inversion to the output signal, making it a sinking output. As a result, the inversion causes the module to output to false or not active when the output image table is true and indicating that the field device should be turned on. This is handled by changing the rung logic so the rung coil is off for an on condition of the field device.	+5DC 74AC14 OUT 74AC14 OUT DC COM
(d) Relay Output Module The relay output modules have a normally open relay contact for each output port. This permits moderately larger load currents and the ability to switch either AC or DC field devices.	VAC/VDC OUT OUT

C

Programmable Logic Controller History

C-1   INTRODUCTION

Dick Morley conceived the concept of the first programmable controller in the United States on January 1, 1968. He later produced it under the company name Modicon, which is short for MOdular DIgital CONtroller. Morley is pictured with the first PLC in Figure C–1. The first installed Modicon in industry was the model 084. Although the first installation at the Oldsmobile Division of General Motors Corporation and the Landis Company in Landis, Pennsylvania, occurred in 1970, the fledgling company's growth was slowed because of industry concern for replacing relays with computer controlled logic. However, Modicon's growth increased as a result of engineer Michael Greenberg's development of the model 184, a more sophisticated version of the original model. Gradual industry acceptance and the success of this new technology created a global PLC industry in the 1970s. Over time the generic term programmable controller, or PC, became the device designation. The introduction of the personal computer, also shortened to PC, in the late 1970s caused confusion in the

technology reference, so the term programmable logic controller, or PLC, was adopted and is still used today.

C-1-1   Relay Replacers

The first PLCs were promoted as "simply relay replacers." This indirect approach concealed the computer nature of the PLC from users who were reluctant to embrace the complexities of computer systems. Reliability was then and continues to be a real concern in manufacturing automation, so early PLC adoptions would have been lost if they were portrayed merely as an industrial computer programmed in ladder logic. Instead the PLC was sold as a new form of mechanical relay, timer, and counter. The present difficulty of moving away from ladder logic programming in the United States is a result of this original promotion strategy.

As the applications for PLCs expanded to a broad range of manufacturing sectors, users demanded more features, including subroutines, complex math functions and data handling, interrupts, analog input/output, proportional integral and derivative process control, distributive control, and the ability to communicate between

Courtesy of Dick Morley and R. Morley, Inc.

PLCs over network cable. However, since each vendor developed its own network technology, the different networks were not compatible. Only systems from the same vendor could share data over the communications network because each was proprietary.

C-1-2 PLCs in the 1980s

A shift away from proprietary, dedicated, and expensive PLC programming terminals occurred when companies outside the PLC manufacturing group provided PLC programming software that would run on standard IBM PCs and compatibles. The PLC and PC became compatible technology, with the PC used for programming and the PLC used for control. Some vendors introduced software that would permit the PC to take over all the functions associated with the traditional PLC.

The 1980s also focused on the initial efforts at PLC standardization in communications with General Motor's standard called Manufacturing Automation Protocol (MAP). The industry also worked on reducing the size of the PLC; as a result, the world's smallest PLC today is about the size of a pack of cigarettes.

C-1-3 PLCs in the 1990s

The 1990s witnessed increased efforts toward standardization of PLC programming languages with the introduction of the International Electrical Commission standard IEC 1131-3 in 1993. This standard was later changed to IEC 61131.

A second major thrust in this decade was the introduction of sub-networks standards, such as ControlNet, DeviceNet, or FOUNDATION Fieldbus, that distribute system control by the PLC over an extended cable network. In addition, the standard assures that devices and controllers from different vendors can coexist on the same sub-network.

C-1-4 PLCs in the 2000s

It is difficult to predict the future in technology due to the current rate of change. However, the Internet is a technology that has had a significant impact in the past and will continue to impact the direction of automation control in the future. Internet/IP is a new technology standard that will open the door for using the Internet as a major network for exchanging automation information between PLCs and the input and output devices, called field devices, used in the processes. An increasing number of wireless networks will be used in automation control in the future. Automation designers in this decade will also witness increased standardization in the programming languages used for PLC automation applications.

Index

MEET CORPORAL KAMNITZER

Spiritual descendent of Gunner Asch, an ingenious cross between Asch, Sergeant Bilko and Milo Minderbinder, with a majestic talent of his own for Machiavellian intrigue and impudent defiance against army tyranny—in his one-man crusade against the lunatic injustice of the military's muttonheads . . .

WHAT BECAME OF GUNNER ASCH

"A marvelous spoof of the Wehrmacht's successor, the Bundeswahr. . . . Here is one German who is not going to let Germany forget the stupidity that twice has brought it to ruin"

—*Chicago Tribune*

"Author Kirst has a true feel for the barely perceptible pulse of illogic that throbs in the military wrist and he taps it like a surgeon"

—*Worcester Telegram*

"Brilliant

D1213349

What Became of

Gunner Asch

HANS HELLMUT KIRST

Translated from the German by
J. MAXWELL BROWNJOHN

 PYRAMID BOOKS • NEW YORK

WHAT BECAME OF GUNNER ASCH

A PYRAMID BOOK Published by arrangement with Harper & Row
Pyramid edition published March 1966

Copyright © 1963 by Verlag Kurt Desch, Munchen-Wein-Basel
Copyright © 1964 in the English translation by Wm. Collins
    Son & Co. Ltd.

Library of Congress Catalog Card: 64:25129

PYRAMID BOOKS are published by Pyramid Publications, Inc.
444 Madison Avenue, New York, N. Y. 10022, U.S.A.

RECENTLY—it might have been yesterday or the day before—a trial took place in a West German town. The defendant, a private soldier charged with having assaulted a superior officer, was convicted and sentenced.

While this was not a miscarriage of justice, it was a direct result of failings within the Bundeswehr. Some of its members had apparently mistaken illusion for idealism and blind obedience for discipline, an almost invariable characteristic of the Bundeswehr's predecessors. Once again, the consequences proved to be extremely dangerous.

Nevertheless, this story of two equally unfortunate men, Grenadier Recht and Captain Ahlers, is far from being the whole story of the Bundeswehr. It merely tells of men in uniform and of their private lives, which they tried to lead in as uncomplicated a fashion as possible. If their story is not without its more humorous aspects, the final outcome yet remains a catastrophe.

What Became of Gunner Asch

GRENADIER RECHT flung open the window and leaped into the night. He landed in a narrow back yard, knocking over a trash can in the process. The accumulated garbage spilled across the flagstones and lay there in a stinking heap. Martin Recht breathed heavily.

"Stop!" called a powerful, beery voice. It had a benevolent, almost wheedling tone, like that of a mother coaxing a reluctant child to eat.

Martin Recht had no intention of stopping. He blundered on until he came to a gate, which gave under his weight with a crash of splintering boards. Before him, like a long dark tunnel, lay a deserted street. From behind him, as though in the far distance, came the wail of a jukebox, whose languishing strains oozed through the open window like artificial honey. The sergeant major was still standing there, peering over the sill. "You there, stop!"

But Recht plunged on into the darkness, feeling as if he were diving off a springboard into a pool of unknown depth. Although he was stationed in the town, its topography was still a mystery to him. He only knew the location of his barracks, the main square and the espresso bar known as La Paloma—or, as his fellow recruits called it, "the passion parlor." It was from a first-floor window of the latter establishment that he had just made his escape.

"Stupid fool!" said the sergeant major in charge of the regimental military police, resentfully. "Who does he think he is, running off like that?"

"Let him go," said the sergeant who was acting as second-in-command. He had no wish to take part in a prolonged chase. In his experience such ventures resulted in nothing but sweat, and his thirst needed no added stimulation.

The sergeant major, however, was outraged. "He just wouldn't stop, the sneaky son-of-a-gun." An order—his order—had not been complied with. Besides, the man had directly flouted the military police instituted by the garrison commander himself.

"Get after him!" he called in rousing tones.

"It's pointless," the sergeant temporized. "He's got a good head start, and I'm no four-minute miler."

"Don't worry, he's running in just the right direction."

The sergeant major, who was well versed in police work, knew the small town like the back of his hand. He listened contentedly to the sound of pattering feet as their owner

9

sped due south, parallel to the Koenigstrasse. He was making for a district which could be easily combed, like a model on a table.

"We'll get him, don't you worry," he said confidently.

"Why all the fuss, for God's sake?" demanded the sergeant, snorting indignantly, but his snorting was in vain. By now the sergeant major was wrapped up in his role as M.P. commander and firmly resolved to catch the miscreant who had dared to evade his clutches.

"I'm going to have him by the short hairs, that's why," the sergeant major declared with something akin to solemnity. Then, hastily reflecting that expressions of this sort were now frowned upon in higher quarters, he corrected himself:

"We'll show him what discipline means."

And, so saying, he set off in pursuit.

Reaching the outskirts of a housing project, Grenadier Martin Recht paused for a moment. He strained his ears for sounds of nocturnal movement, but all he could hear at first was his own breathing.

He was in full uniform, which was as it should be. Recht was still a relatively new recruit and recruits were not allowed to wear civilian clothes on week nights—or not, at least, in his battalion, whose members were known locally as the Ironclads in deference to their C.O., a man of iron determination.

Recht felt his head. His cap was askew, his hair felt damp and he was sweating like a race horse. He tried to calm down, forcing himself to inhale and exhale slowly.

"Damn it all," he muttered, "how did I get into this mess?"

He was always getting into messes, or so it seemed to him —at least since he had donned uniform. Ever since that day he had been oppressed by a sense of having hitherto seen the world in a false light. Suddenly there were no more curves, only angles, and he had to conform to them. His locker was too small, his rifle too big, his boots too tight, his shirt too baggy and his handkerchief never clean enough. Quite a few of his superiors regarded him with suspicion, a sentiment which he reciprocated.

Guided by the dim light of the street lamps, Recht's gaze turned to a gleaming brass plate suspended from a gate post. On it, in bold capitals, was the name TURNER, and beneath it, smaller but no less bold, the word COLONEL. He shrank back, and as he did so his ears caught the

10

sound of an approaching car. It was the sort of harsh, grinding sound which only a carelessly driven military vehicle would emit. Simultaneously there came the noise of hurrying, clattering feet. Recht realized that the police had split up and were executing a pincers movement. He set off again down the dark, empty tunnel of the street. The beery voice of the sergeant major floated after him. It still sounded genial, though slightly labored. It was extremely unusual for the M.P. commander in this garrison to have to indulge in nocturnal sports of this kind. One word normally sufficed to bring the boys to heel.

Mindful of this, the sergeant major once more brought his most highly developed organ into play. Even at a considerable distance, his voice sounded as though it had been amplified by a loudspeaker. "You, there!" he called. "This is your last chance! Come back!"

The next sentence might have been: "Or I'll fire!"—but it was never uttered, or else Recht never heard it.

He boldly veered left and crossed the next sizable street —the Koenigstrasse, not that he realized it. Here, however, he was brought up short by a wall. It was smooth and plastered, and looked grayish white in the meager light of the moon—a wall of compressed cotton wool, but uninvitingly high.

Martin Recht could hear the raucous voice of the sergeant major again, bawling now, but largely drowned by the noise of the swiftly approaching engine. He was dominated by a panicky urge to run for his life. Panting like a wrestler in the closing round, he skirted the wall at a trot but suddenly slid to a halt when his eye was arrested by something out of the ordinary. Outlined against the smooth, forbidding surface of the wall were two bold vertical lines connected by a number of other horizontal lines. It might have been a mirage, but it proved to be a ladder—a rope ladder.

Recht found time to shake his head in astonishment before scrambling up the mirage with trembling knees and bursting lungs. Gasping like a steam locomotive at full throttle, he reached the top of the wall.

Beneath him, not very far away, he could see two figures. They swam before his eyes like fish in an aquarium, but he recognized them as the garrison police: the sergeant major, bulky as a footlocker, and the sergeant, round as an inflated balloon. They were both staring up at him like twin allegories of unbelief.

But Recht was already hauling up the ladder.

11

Recht pulled up the rope ladder and let it down the other side of the wall. Secure for the time being, he descended cautiously, step by step, until, to his relief, he felt solid ground beneath his feet once more. He had absolutely no idea where he was.

Then he heard a voice behind him say: "Who have we got here?"

The voice sounded entirely friendly—a veritable cello by comparison with the sergeant major's bass trombone. Recht turned hopefully to face his unexepected interlocutor, only to see a man in uniform, this time an officer.

"This is an unexpected pleasure," said the man in officer's uniform. "Welcome, my dear sir."

Martin Recht could muster no reply. He stood there like a rabbit who runs happily into a clover field and finds himself struggling in a snare. Now that his eyes had grown accustomed to the light he saw that the man was wearing the insignia of an air force captain.

"Follow me," said the captain, in a tone of invitation rather than command. He opened a nearby door, and blinding light pierced the gloom.

The captain entered, followed by Recht. By rights, he should have been feeling like a lamb led to the slaughter, but he had reached the stage where everything was of consummate indifference to him.

"Make yourself at home," said the captain with disconcerting bonhomie.

He dropped into a chair, waving Recht into the chair opposite him. His clear blue eyes scanned the young soldier's agitated face appraisingly. Then he began to smile.

The figure before him was that of a boy, smooth-skinned, mild-eyed, and awkward. He looked as nervous as a greyhound before the start—ready to spring, but painfully aware that he has no idea which way to turn.

"My name's Ahlers," said the captain. "I'm a squadron leader in the transport wing here. This is my office. As you can see, I'm doing some overtime."

The captain's voice sounded sympathetic, but his lean features were stern, gray and fine-drawn. Deep lines furrowed his brow and cheeks, and skirted the corners of his mouth. He looked as though he had spent many long and sleepless nights in the course of his career.

"And who are you?" he inquired gently.

"Grenadier Recht—Martin Recht." The youngster opened his breast pocket and fumbled for his pass with trembling but eager fingers. By now, he had reconciled himself to

12

the idea that his nocturnal adventure was at an end, though he dared not reflect on its possible consequences.

Captain Ahlers waved the pass away. "No need to rush things," he said easily. "You look as though you could do with a stiffener, Recht. How about a whisky? I brought some back from Scotland last week—duty free, of course."

Recht, who was buttoning up his breast pocket, managed a nod. He exuded mistrust from every pore as he incredulously watched the captain fill two glasses and push one across to him.

Ahlers raised his glass. "Visitors are always welcome here," he said with a smile. "The bonds between the army and the air force should be strengthened whenever possible —for the greater good, if you like. Let's drink to that."

They had hardly drained their glasses when the door was pushed open and a warrant officer appeared, a tall lean man with the craggy features of a Hollywood sheriff. He paused in the doorway, blinking at Captain Ahlers in the bright light.

Martin Recht waited for the customary ritual to unfold: the warrant officer, or subordinate, would come to attention, cap clasped to his chest and right hand raised in salute. Only when this performance had been completed, and not before, would the reason for his presence be voiced.

But nothing of the sort happened. Without preamble, the warrant officer burst into an indignant torrent of words. "What a lousy mess! I've gone and lost my bet."

Martin Recht regarded the strange apparition with dismay. He was breaking all the rules. Such a thing was quite impermissible, at any rate in a Grenadier battalion, which constituted Recht's only field of military experience. He stared at Captain Ahlers in bewilderment.

The latter's smile did not fade. He even seemed to be enjoying the situation. "May I introduce you two gentlemen? Warrant Officer Vossler of my squadron: Grenadier Recht, an unexpected guest."

"Sorry, didn't notice you sitting there," said the warrant officer, going over to Martin Recht and extending his hand. "At the moment all I can see is red. But if you knew what had happened you'd sympathize."

Vossler sat down uninvited and reached for the whisky bottle. He poured himself a glass and drained it.

Martin Recht's bewilderment grew with every passing minute. To one accustomed to the rigid discipline of the Ironclads, this warrant officer was behaving as though he

had never heard of the correct relationship to be maintained between a subordinate and his superior.

"Hell and damnation!" Vossler continued. "It's too bad I lost that bet. I'm half a dozen bottles of champagne lighter, though that's not what I'm annoyed about. It's the thought of that fat slug Langhorn beating me back to barracks. Some idiot hauled up my rope ladder. Was it you, Ahlers?"

"I'm afraid it was our young friend here," said the captain, indicating Recht. "Apparently his need was greater than yours."

The warrant officer looked searchingly at the disconcerted grenadier. "Since when do visitors climb in over walls?"

"Since people started leaving rope ladders around, I imagine," commented Ahlers.

"He must have had a pretty good reason," Vossler said, looking intrigued. "What was it?"

"Our young friend seems to need some enlightenment, too." The captain's tone was kindly. "I have a feeling that the world's tumbling about his ears tonight—to be exact, the world his superior officers in the Ironclads cultivate so carefully. Isn't that so, Recht?"

"I don't know," the grenadier said with an effort. His face seemed to indicate that he didn't know anything any more.

"He really does look as though he could do with an explanation," the warrant officer agreed.

Captain Ahlers nodded. "On one point in particular. Our guest is evidently puzzled by the way warrant officers treat captains in this establishment. Well, that's easily explained. Vossler and I served together in the war. We made a hundred sorties in the same crew."

"Successful ones, of course," supplemented Vossler.

"But it wasn't an unmixed pleasure. We've always been more interested in flying itself than in the possibility of being shot down while doing so. Anyway, here we are together again, and my old friend Vossler is the best pilot we've got."

"Come off it," said Vossler cheerfully. "You only say that so you can saddle me with tricky missions you ought to fly yourself. You're a better pilot than I ever was."

They both laughed, and even Martin Recht ventured a diffident smile. His spirits rose slightly. He hadn't deserted the frying pan for the fire, or so it seemed.

Their cheerful laughter was cut short by the buzz of the

telephone. Captain Ahlers picked up the receiver and listened in silence. Eventually he said: "Tell the gentlemen to wait."

He replaced the receiver on its cradle with a thoughtful expression. Then he picked up his glass and drained it.

"It's a funny business," remarked Vossler, refilling his squadron leader's glass with whisky, "your paying us a visit across the wall like that. Surely the gate would have been more convenient."

"More convenient," said Ahlers, "but not so appropriate in this case—am I right?" He regarded Recht quizzically.

Recht realized that he was expected—not required—to tell the truth. If only because of this slight but important difference in approach, he felt impelled to be completely honest.

"I was trying to get away from the regimental police," he said. "I don't know this town yet—I've only been out of barracks a few times before—so I had no idea the wall bordered air force property. When I saw the rope ladder I used it. I didn't know where it would lead."

"It led you to our whisky, among other things," the warrant officer remarked dryly. "What's more, you've done me out of half a dozen bottles of champagne. That rope ladder was mine. It was put there to help me win a bet."

"We'll talk about that later." Captain Ahlers sounded suddenly businesslike. "First, I'd be interested to know why you were running away from the patrol. Not just for fun, I imagine?"

"No," Recht conceded. "I'd been in a coffee bar called La Paloma, in the back room."

"The so-called passion parlor," Warrant Officer Vossler interjected knowledgeably. "It's off limits to army personnel."

"There were seven of us." Recht seemed to have lost all his inhibitions now. "Seven—a friend of mine, an air force corporal, an American soldier, three girls, and me."

"The usual thing, in fact," explained Vossler. "They sit around in rows, exchanging small—ah—tokens of mutual affection in a dimly lit room."

"Just that?" inquired the captain.

The warrant officer answered for Martin Recht, who only had to nod his assent. "You can't do much more in that dump. Hence the nickname."

"And that's all there is to it?"

"Yes. Too bad, isn't it?" Vossler gave Recht a sympathetic

15

grin. "Places like that are a positive threat to normal relations between the sexes. If things don't change radically, I foresee a dangerous decline in local morale."

"Anyway," Recht went on, "then the patrol turned up. They forced their way in and I—well, I ran for it."

"Why?"

"I can't say why, exactly. Perhaps because I remembered all the black marks I'd earned already and realized I mustn't get caught. Not that anything very terrible happened, but I'd have been embarrassed to get picked up in a place like that. Well, when the M.P.s arrived, I grabbed my cap and raced up the back stairs with them after me. I jumped out of the first-floor window into the yard."

"I'd probably have done the same myself," said Vossler, turning to Ahlers. "After all, why should the lad risk getting booked and reported? Not for the sake of the tarts who patronize the passion parlor, surely?"

"Anyway, sir, that's what happened," Recht concluded.

Captain Ahlers rose, paced up and down the office, and halted beside his desk. "That phone call I had just now was from the duty officer. He tells me there's a military police patrol at the barrack gates. They say that a soldier they were chasing climbed over our wall."

"Ridiculous!" Vossler said gaily. "Since when have the Ironclads been in the habit of sticking their noses into our business? Surely they're not thinking of trying to introduce their methods here? We ought to leave them standing there until they take root."

"Unfortunately," Captain Ahlers said with deliberation, "there's one thing that can't be dismissed: the existence of a rope ladder—your ladder, Vossler. It's a concrete fact, and I'm not sure that I can invent a plausible explanation for its presence."

"I didn't use it, though, did I?"

"No, but you put it there. That makes you a sort of accessory after the fact—and me too, for having sanctioned your little game with Langhorn. Of course, we couldn't reckon with complications of this kind."

"You'll think of something," Vossler said confidently. "Anyway, what if we do have a rope ladder, and what if it was hanging on the wall? We might have been planning a night exercise or something. The main thing is, any explanation you give must sound strictly official."

"And what shall we do with Recht here?"

"Quite simple—chuck him back over the wall." Vossler evidently saw not the slightest difficulty in this. "He can

16

vanish into the night and double back to barracks, conveniently forgetting everything that's happened here. Isn't that right, Recht?"

"I'm awfully sorry about it all," said the grenadier. "I'm ready to give myself up and take the blame."

"He suffers from noble impulses, this lad," said Vossler. "We'll have to do something about that, don't you agree, Klaus?"

OUTSIDE THE GATES of the air force barracks, which were adjacent to the air field with its four hangars and two runways, stood the regimental police patrol: the sergeant major in a commanding pose beneath the lamp over the gate, and behind him, yearning for his bed and surreptitiously yawning, the sergeant. The sergeant major presented a picture of adamantine fortitude, faithful to his battalion commander's ideal of dogged determination in the face of overwhelming odds.

As luck would have it, they had come up against a sentry of horrendous obstinacy, an air force corporal who was possessed by the simple conviction that an air force base existed for air force personnel only. It had nothing to do with the army, let alone those professional bullies the Ironclads, who sometimes referred to their air force colleagues as "the brilliantine brigade," "the slop merchants" or simply "the armchair warriors."

In short, the sentry showed not the least inclination to take orders from the Ironclads. He merely informed the guard commander, who informed the duty officer, who informed the squadron leader, Captain Ahlers, who always seemed to be on call at any hour of day or night.

"Tell the gentlemen to wait," Ahlers had said. "They're to wait," the duty officer told the guard commander, who told the sentry, who relayed the message to the picket. "You're to wait," he announced indifferently, like a butler shaking off a couple of importunate vacuum-cleaner salesmen at the servants' entrance.

"How long are we supposed to wait?" the sergeant major inquired resentfully.

"Don't ask me, pal," the sentry replied, grinning insolently. To him, the Ironclads were a lot of dim-witted louts. Two of them had tried to muscle in on his girl friend the Saturday before, a piece of impertinence which he was glad of a chance to repay.

17

"Listen here," the sergeant major said majestically. "I don't think you realize who you're talking to."

"What makes you so sure?" the sentry asked, unabashed.

Seeing the sergeant major draw in his breath and prepare to fire a salvo, the sergeant pulled him aside. With some difficulty, he managed to smooth his superior's ruffled plumage. "After all, this isn't the Grenadiers."

"Worse luck," growled the sergeant major.

"But," went on the sergeant, who was of a practical turn of mind, "that's got its advantages too. An outfit like this is always up to its ears in fresh coffee and cigarettes, straight from Greece and Turkey. What about seeing if these warriors can show a little fellow feeling from that point of view?"

"Haven't you any pride?" the sergeant major asked reprovingly.

"Of course I have, but I'm thirsty too." The sergeant gazed longingly at the electric percolator on the guardroom window sill. "It wouldn't hurt to get them to pour us a cup."

"Yes it would," snapped the sergeant major, who had never felt less thirsty in his life. "Do you want to let our side down in front of these half-civilized buffoons? That's all we need!"

Meanwhile, Captain Ahlers was trying to arrange matters. In the first place he believed Martin Recht's story; secondly, he had taken to the boy, who reminded him a little of his own dead son; and thirdly, he had to cover his own personal responsibilities. His friend Vossler's rope-ladder operations were not entirely above reproach, certainly as seen through the eyes of an iron-willed Ironclad. Awkward investigations would have to be avoided as far as possible.

"We must try to take the wind out of these supermen's sails," he said meditatively.

"Splendid!" cried Vossler, winking at Recht. "It's one of his favorite occupations, you know. He's got a secret passion for taming the mad military."

"I'm merely concerned with human relations," said Ahlers.

Vossler chuckled. "That's one way of putting it. You're a born cleaner-up of messes, anyway. What's the first move?"

"The first move," said Ahlers, "will be to put through a call to Colonel Turner."

Warrant Officer Vossler emitted an admiring whistle. Col-

18

onel Turner, the wing commander and area commandant, was a sort of demigod who sat enthroned behind his desk most of the time. Normal mortals—that is, men of junior rank—seldom if ever set eyes on him. His decisions had scarcity value, mainly because a great deal had to happen before he came to a firm conclusion about anything. In addition, Turner was a philosopher of a sort. Legend even had it that he was working on an original, and doubtless important, book. He had settled on a title—*Soldiers and Society*—five years ago.

The colonel answered the phone promptly in a voice at once sonorous and benevolent. Ahlers began by apologizing for making a late call.

"Please, please!" Turner replied cordially. "I'm always at the service of my colleagues. Besides, I was still working on my book. What can I do for you?"

Captain Ahlers reported the presence of a military police patrol outside the gates of the air force barracks, allegedly waiting to arrest a runaway soldier "on our territory, sir." It was a highly questionable and precipitate action undertaken with insufficient justification and absolutely no prospect of success—in short, an intrusion.

"I understand," said Colonel Turner in his best bedside manner. "From what you say, it appears to be a clear enough case. I have the fullest confidence in your judgment."

"Then I have your authority to take the appropriate steps, sir?"

"But of course, my dear chap—within regulation limits, which are familiar to you all, I trust. I also trust that you will show tact and discretion. You're aware of the slightly strained relations that exist between us and our army friends, I imagine?"

This was a question which demanded an affirmative answer, and Captain Ahlers supplied one. "So I can act on your behalf, sir—as deputy area commandant?"

"Of course you may, my dear Ahlers. I'm certain you won't disappoint me, just as I'm certain you won't let yourself be influenced by certain prevailing prejudices. After all, the methods employed by our army colleagues in achieving their training objectives don't concern us. Such things are their affair. We merely act according to the rules laid down by higher authority."

Such was Colonel Turner—invariably courteous, slippery as an eel, and the most agreeable commanding officer imaginable—as long as no one saddled him with any unpleasant-

nesses. He would have allowed his subordinates to get away with murder, provided that it was committed exactly in accordance with standing orders.

Captain Ahlers downed some strong coffee and made some more telephone calls.

First, he instructed the duty officer to inform the military police patrol, firmly, that air force territory was outside their jurisdiction—which was equivalent to telling them where they got off. Then he put through an urgent call to the C.O. of the Panzergrenadier battalion.

The latter, Major Bornekamp by name, was widely known as a fire eater and widely respected in consequence. Having been one of the heroes of the last war, he intended to give a repeat performance in the next. Hence it was one of his brass-bound principles to be ready for action at any moment, even in the depths of peace.

At present he was in the mess, coaching some of his younger officers in *savoir vivre* as he understood it. The Y.O.s called him "Old Leather Face," and his manner was correspondingly tough.

"So you're at it again, are you, Ahlers?" Bornekamp asked, chuckling harshly into the telephone. "Well, fire away."

Ahlers delivered his broadside and then rang Herbert Asch, the local burgomaster and most influential civilian for miles around, being not only the town's first citizen but president of its thriving sports club and proprietor of the Hotel Asch, a centrally located establishment with café, restaurant, and public house attached. Ahlers requested an interview with him as well.

"Certainly," was Asch's terse reply.

"Now for some infighting!" Vossler said expectantly.

Martin Recht was still standing there, confused and uncertain what to say. Ahlers gave him an encouraging nod. "Don't worry, we'll arrange things."

"It'll be a pleasure, what's more," Vossler assured him, adding confidentially: "There are some people we don't mind making trouble for."

Ahlers frowned slightly. "You can forget that remark, I'm merely concerned with a few fundamental issues, one of them being the simple recognition that a soldier is a human being and ought to be treated as such."

A few minutes later Captain Ahlers climbed into an official car. Warrant Officer Vossler acted as driver, and Grenadier Recht was enjoined to sit in the back and stay there.

The car turned out of the barrack gates, rolled smoothly along the Koenigstrasse, crossed the market place and headed for the Grenadier barracks. Here the gates were flung wide in deference to prior notification of arrival issued by the C.O. in person. No passes were demanded.

Grenadier Recht had—or so it seemed—been brought to safety.

Ahlers' INTERVIEW with Major Bornekamp, commander of the local Grenadier battalion, began satisfactorily and without formality. It took place in the mess. Bornekamp shooed a couple of lieutenants away from his table and invited Ahlers to drink a glass of champagne and beer, mixed.

"You would come disturbing me in the middle of the night, wouldn't you!" growled Bornekamp with apparent good humor, scrutinizing Ahlers like a man studying enemy dispositions. "I can think of better things to do at this hour. Would you like me to be more explicit?"

Captain Ahlers did not press for details—he could imagine them. Bornekamp set store on being known not only as a dashing warrior but as a lady killer—two roles which, in his estimation, went hand in hand. Ahlers surveyed the hero of many and varied battles with a certain amusement.

"The would-be soldier," Bornekamp declared stoutly, "must always be ready to test his mettle." He laughed raucously at his own remark, watching to see whether his visitor appreciated its enormous subtlety, and was gratified to see Ahlers smile.

"I'm here," Ahlers said, "in the role of deputy station commander, Major."

"We've always worked well together," Bornekamp said promptly, though with slightly less volume than before. There was no need for the young officers seated respectfully in the background to hear everything, to know that even he, the father figure of the battalion, was occasionally forced to make concessions. "Our cooperation has never been in doubt, has it?"

"Of course not, there's been no cause for complaint," Ahlers assured him. "Not until now, that it."

Bornekamp screwed up his eyes like a marksman focusing on a target. Then he broke into a booming laugh. "Well, let's have a drink first," he said, clinking glasses with Ah-

21

lers and draining his at a gulp. "You're not proposing to make difficulties, are you, my dear fellow?"

"I'm here to eliminate them," Ahlers hastened to explain, not unaware of the latent menace in the C.O.'s question.

"Good," said Bornekamp. His boisterous bonhomie had given way to an expression of alert watchfulness. "Well, what's the trouble?"

"A military police patrol tried to force its way into the air force barracks this evening."

Bornekamp's reaction was swift. "Damned fools!" he snapped. "What do they think they're up to? They must have been out of their minds. I hope you kicked them in the crutch."

"In a manner of speaking," said Ahlers. "I told them to get lost."

"Good for you," the major said approvingly, though his mien, even at this juncture, wholly befitted one who commanded the Ironclads: tough, resolute, and unyielding. "Well, do you expect a personal apology?"

Ahlers hastened to avoid a head-on collision. "There's no question of that, Major."

"What did you come for, then?"

"Partly to create a better climate of cooperation. Colonel Turner sets great store by that. I spoke to him on the phone just now, and he was most insistent on the point. Little misunderstandings will always occur, he said, but they mustn't be allowed to mar our team spirit."

"He said that, did he?" Bornekamp uttered the words with vague displeasure. He was determined not to be cajoled by these "tailor's dummies," as he termed a large proportion of the air force. It was sheer impertinence to provoke him like this. "I resent the implication."

"It was a misunderstanding," Ahlers interposed, slightly taken aback by the major's sudden indignation. He had intended to clear the air in the pleasantest possible manner, but Bornekamp seemed determined to have a smash-up. "In my opinion, the proper course is to take note of such misunderstandings and then forget them again as quickly as possible."

"That," said the major, inaccessible as a castle keep, "may be the air force attitude, but it's not one that prevails in the units under my command. I don't tolerate misunderstandings, let alone forget them—I investigate and eradicate them. Any other course is idle compromise, and if there's one thing I abhor it's that. Good night, Captain."

"**H**ERR ASCH," said Captain Ahlers, "I think you were an officer, weren't you?"

"Are you appealing to my esprit de corps?" Herbert Asch asked with a faintly ironical smile. "I wasn't an officer the whole time, you know. I spent a far greater proportion of my army career in the ranks, and I haven't forgotten the fact."

"All the better," Ahlers assured him. "You'll find it much easier to understand me."

"In what respect, Captain?"

"I need your support."

"As a hotel keeper, as a mayor—or as a man?" Herbert Asch laughed. "Or perhaps you mean as a soldier? Preferably not that, Captain. I've always been in favor of plain speaking, and I can afford to indulge in it these days."

Captain Ahlers had always felt free to speak his mind in the mayor's presence, but he phrased his next question with care. "You don't think much of the army, do you?"

"I learned to avoid generalizations very early in life, Captain. What soldiers are or aren't depends entirely on what's beneath their uniforms—and the uniforms of the men who lead them."

"Exactly." Ahlers sensed that he was expected to make a statement of principle at this stage, but Asch was opening a bottle of carefully cooled Franconian wine, a sure sign that there was no need to rush things.

Thus encouraged, Ahlers launched into a lengthy preamble, its gist being: anything which wants to exist must be prepared to defend its existence; consequently, soldiers are a fact of life. The world is not a perfect place, and soldiers of any nationality are anything but perfect beings. Every military organization has its shortcomings, the Bundeswehr included. The main thing is to strive to make the best of it: in other words, to effect improvements wherever possible, even when this involves—as it sometimes does—clashing head-on with incorrigible elements.

"Not badly put," commented Asch. "But I assume your remarks aren't intended merely as a theoretical exercise. Presumably you're about to draw some practical conclusions. Well, Captain, what do you expect of me?"

"This evening," said Ahlers, "a military police patrol raided a local place of entertainment—La Paloma—you probably know it."

"I know it," Herbert Asch said with some amusement, "and I know what goes on there."

"Disregarding that, Herr Asch, do you imagine the patrol marched in there purely by accident—that it was just a chance raid? It's quite possible that there may be an attempt to put other establishments under surveillance tomorrow—establishments belonging to you, for instance. What then?"

"They could try it," Asch said coolly, "but the results of such a step might well prove surprising—and not only for the patrol."

"Then you agree that one can't just let such a thing pass?"

"I'm beginning to understand you, Captain. In fact, I'm pretty sure I know what you want me to do." Herbert Asch lifted his glass and sipped it without removing his eyes from his visitor. "I assume you wouldn't take it amiss if a protest were lodged by so-called authoritative circles of the civilian population against such methods of control—an effective protest, preferably delivered by me in my capacity as mayor. Am I right?"

"Yes," said Ahlers. "I appreciate your having spared me the need to express myself too clearly. I should have found it embarrassing."

"All the same," Asch said thoughtfully, "I can't take the whole weight off your shoulders. I'm not saying I won't do it, but I've no intention of taking sides prematurely. What I mean is, I haven't the least desire to be played off against the army by the air force—or vice versa, for that matter."

"There's absolutely no question of that, Herr Asch."

"I hope not," Asch replied. "Your internal squabbles are nothing to me. Besides, I prefer to play my own game."

"Thank you, Herr Asch. I have a feeling you want to help. I hope you're satisfied that my motives are of the best."

Asch smiled. "We've known each other for some time now. I think we both know what to expect from each other."

"If I may say so," Ahlers ventured, "you're one of the few people I should like to count among my friends."

"Please do that, Captain." Asch toasted his guest with a look of genuine pleasure. "I've often wished you would come and see me as plain Klaus Ahlers, not Captain Ahlers, deputy station commander. How does the idea appeal to you?"

"You're very kind." Ahlers' face had changed. His eyes looked weary and the lines in his cheeks seemed to have deepened. He clasped his hands together as though they needed mutual support. "I know what you mean, Herr Asch. You're aware of my private circumstances, but let's not discuss them now. Don't worry, I'll manage."

Asch nodded. He knew what Ahlers meant by private circumstances: he knew that his son, the apple of his eye, had died in a frightful accident the year before, and he also knew the story of his daughter, who had suffered from a malformation of the spine since her birth during the closing months of the war, and had been forced to undergo several major operations which had cost, if not a fortune, sums which an ordinary air force captain must have found it hard to scrape together.

"All right, we'll leave the subject," Asch said. "But if the occasion ever arises, please remember that I'm your friend. Will you promise me that?"

"Of course," Ahlers said gratefully.

"And what else can I do for you, apart from pouring you another glass of wine?"

"May I send a young soldier to see you?"

"Why not?" Asch said. "What am I supposed to do with him?"

"He's a grenadier and his name is Martin Recht. He needs a little looking after—deserves it, I should say. I'm afraid he's got into bad company. Would you mind keeping an eye on him occasionally?"

"A relative of yours?" asked Asch, looking interested.

"No, no—I got to know him quite by chance." Ahlers hesitated before continuing, with a hint of embarrassment: "To be honest, he reminds me a little of my son."

"Then go ahead and send him to me. You've whetted my curiosity."

"ON YOUR FEET, gentlemen!" came the orderly sergeant's friendly bellow. Throwing the door wide and flinging open all the windows with an eye to the health-giving properties of fresh air, he proceeded to strip the recumbent inmates of Room 13 of their bedclothes, keeping up a stream of cheerful encouragement as he did so.

"Don't catch cold, men!" he shouted. "Up, up."

Room 13 demanded his special vigilance, being the home

of "Kamnitzer's Commandos," who had already driven more than one N.C.O. to the verge of a nervous breakdown. Corporal Kamnitzer, it should be explained, was the company's leader of fashion and made a habit of sleeping with a copy of Army Regulations under his pillow.

The orderly sergeant had more or less mastered the comparatively new-fangled rules of the military game. Grinning, he rattled the window frames, noisily shifted chairs around, and drummed cheerfully on a locker. Not even the deaf could have slept on in the face of such a carefully organized barrage of noise.

"Anything else I can do for you, men?"

"Yes," muttered Corporal Kamnitzer, heaving himself upright with a groan, "you can tell me why everyone looks so goddamn stupid at this unearthly hour of the morning."

"Everyone?" asked the orderly sergeant with sudden asperity. Six bleary faces regarded him with interest. Although he sensed the challenge behind Kamnitzer's remark, he quickly realized what was required of him. The only way to remain master of the situation was to refuse to be provoked.

"Always good for a laugh, aren't you, Kamnitzer?" he said, retiring hastily.

Corporal Streicher, who was the room senior and had a bed by the door, said: "You might be a bit more careful, Kamnitzer. Your behavior leaves something to be desired, and the rest of the room suffers for it."

"You most of all, I suppose," Kamnitzer said boldly. "Shut your trap or I'll shut it for you."

Corporal Streicher did not reply. He grinned scornfully, but not before turning his back. Kamnitzer was insufferable in the early morning, and the best thing was to ignore him.

The first inmate of Room 13 to make for the bathroom was Grenadier Martin Recht. Weary but willing, he trotted down the corridor with his wash roll clamped under his arm and a towel thrown over his shoulder.

"Wait up, chum!" Kamnitzer called after him. "Don't wear your legs out. It's not worth it."

Recht paused to let Kamnitzer catch up. He was a short, wiry youth with a thin, humorous face illumined by a pair of sharply observant eyes. He moved lithely, like a cross between a dancer and a wrestler. In addition, he was the owner of a powerful voice which could sink, when he chose, to a whisper as soft as a sea breeze.

"Well, how was it?" he whispered. "Did you give the M.P.s the slip yesterday?"

"By the skin of my teeth."

"How did you get back into barracks?"

"Professional secret, Karl."

Karl Kamnitzer, always a creature of boundless curiosity, pricked up his ears.

"What?" he asked with interest. "Do you mean to say there's a place where even a novice like you can climb over the wall safely? If there is, I'd like to know where."

"I came in through the barracks gates, Karl, I promise you." To whet Kamnitzer's curiosity still further, he changed the subject. "How about you? Did they catch you?"

"That'll be the day!"

They were in the washroom by now and had laid out their things on two adjoining basins. Kamnitzer lathered his face thoughtfully. "You did the right thing, clearing off like that when the patrol arrived. Me, I just sat there—moved away from the girls, stuck my paws on the table, and sat there looking like a village idiot. It comes easy to me. I know those M.P.s like the back of my hand. When they saw you run for it they went after you like a dose of salts and left us to carry on necking in peace."

"Bright and cheery this morning, aren't you?" came a voice from behind them. It had a companionable, slightly ingratiating note, and it belonged to Corporal Streicher.

Martin Recht hastened to disabuse him. "Not particularly."

"Push off," Karl Kamnitzer told Streicher with brutal relish, "I don't fancy you this morning."

"No harm in asking, is there?"

Kamnitzer turned the water full on and stuck his thumb in the tap, directing a knifelike jet into Streicher's face.

Streicher jumped back, wiping his eyes. "You've got a nerve," he said indignantly. "I warn you, I won't be treated like this. I'm in charge here."

"Not as far as I'm concerned," replied Kamnitzer. "I wouldn't put you in charge of a roll of toilet paper, even if I had two."

Corporal Streicher withdrew, watched belligerently by Karl Kamnitzer. Kamnitzer seemed to be fighting back an urge to kick him in the rear, but he was no stranger to the impulse. "That chap would report me if I told him what I really thought of him."

"You're exaggerating as usual. What have you got against Streicher? He always seems very friendly to me."

"Precisely," said Kamnitzer, reaching for the soap. "That's what makes me suspicious."

"Karl," Recht said at length, "if you were asked who you were with in La Paloma last night, would you mention my name?"

"Come off it," Kamnitzer expostulated. "You're not trying to appeal to my better nature, are you?" He grinned. "Still, you do sleep in the bunk above me, so I suppose that gives us some claim on each other."

"Then I can count on your keeping quiet?"

"A bit naïve, aren't you?" said Kamnitzer. "I'm not a welfare organization. I'm a faithful defender of the Fatherland, and I intend to be released in one piece." He patted Recht on the back. "But don't worry, you're in luck. Some of these animated uniforms get on my tits. I enjoy doing them down—just for the hell of it."

"**I**'M GOING to crucify those two." Major Bornekamp addressed these words with grim composure to his adjutant, who stood there like a block of stone. "I'll show those deadbeats what happens to people who overstep the mark."

"Yes, sir," the adjutant said deferentially. As the third officer to serve Bornekamp in this capacity within the past twelve months, he was resigned to anything. Even the choicest products of the Major's vocabulary had lost their power to irritate, although they were reserved mainly for him. When a third party was present the Major managed —if only for a limited period—to create an impression of breeding, not to say culture.

"Blithering idiots like that should be hanged, drawn, and quartered," Bornekamp went on. "Dunderheads who undermine the army's reputation deserve no mercy. I'll show them what's what."

At this juncture, shepherded by the adjutant, the regimental police patrol for the previous night marched in: the sergeant major with the footlocker physique and the sergeant who looked like a balloon on the point of bursting. Both men stared woodenly at the C.O., who stared back at them as though from a great height—no mean feat, in view of the fact that he was appreciably shorter than either of them.

"Well, gentlemen!" Bornekamp rasped. On the walls around him hung maps, plans, and directives, but no pictures—not even one of the Federal President or the Defense

28

Minister of the day—nothing but the symbols of a stern and purposeful devotion to duty. "Well, gentlemen!" Bornekamp repeated scathingly.

In Major Bornekamp's idiom, no more awesomely framed reprimand could have been conceived. It was one of his basic maxims that the man he did not call "friend" was not one, and the very air about him was expected to freeze to attention. After all, he commanded a battalion which was—in his eyes—destined to become an elite unit. The Americans had their Leathernecks: the Germans would, if he had anything to do with it, have their Ironclads.

"I am grieved, gentlemen," the Major continued sarcastically. "I would never have believed you capable of such a blunder, and I don't intend to let it pass." He refrained from uttering the other, riper version of this sentence which sprang to his mind.

The sergeant major attempted to defend himself.

"Sir, it was brought to our attention by a junior N.C.O. that certain nuisances were being committed in La Paloma espresso bar."

"Well, did you see them for yourself?"

"One man ran away, sir, and we tried to catch him. We chased him as far as the air force barracks."

"But you failed to arrest him," said Bornekamp, which, being interpreted, meant: so you couldn't even catch one idiotic runaway, you half-witted nincompoops. "That's what I call a really successful night's work," he commented.

The fat sergeant was oozing sweat at every pore, but the sergeant major stood his ground bleakly like a bare tree on a winter's night.

"There was this ladder, sir," he said finally. "A ladder hanging from the wall of the air force barracks."

"Balls!" exclaimed the C.O. "I mean," he amended quickly, "that's quite incredible. Since when do ladders grow on barracks walls?"

At this point the adjutant intervened. "Perhaps we ought to check the sergeant major's statement, sir," he suggested with due diffidence, "just as a matter of form. It may have been a piece of training equipment which someone left lying about by accident, or an optical illusion. There are any number of possibilities."

"Not in this case," the C.O. announced emphatically.

Bornekamp was a firm believer in the principle that what is impermissible is impossible, especially when the object in question happens to be a ladder allegedly suspended from a barracks wall. What could be more absurd!

"There's only one thing that carries weight with me, and that's success. Anything else is rank failure or wishy-washy theory. So you didn't catch this long-distance runner—you failed to arrest the man who tried to evade arrest. What about the other patrons of this sink of iniquity? Did you get any of them?"

"No, sir," stammered the sergeant major. He felt as if he were drifting away into the arctic night like a wounded seal on an ice floe.

The sergeant puffed and blew violently. He opened and closed his mouth twice before speaking. "We went after the man who ran away," he blurted out, "but there was another grenadier who stayed behind. I'd remember his face anywhere. Perhaps we can find him, sir."

"What's the use?" Bornekamp demanded balefully. "You ought to have caught him yesterday—on the spot, red-handed." The case was closed as far as he was concerned. All that remained was to put his two scapegoats through the hoop.

"All the same, sir," the adjutant remarked, discreetly curious, "it would be interesting to know what our men are up to in that place."

The sergeant major could supply the answer to that. "They sit side by side on benches, one man to each girl, listening to decadent music—jazz and so on. And they fumble with each other."

"How's that? How do you mean, 'fumble'?"

"They fumble with each other, sir."

"What the devil do you mean by that?"

Here the adjutant intervened once more. "I believe," he said, "that the technical term for this activity is petting—an American expression, sir, if I'm not much mistaken."

"Explain yourself, damn it!"

"I'm not particularly well informed on the subject," said the adjutant, "but I believe that the word 'petting' implies manual caresses—below the waist included. It does not, however"—he cleared his throat—"imply going the whole hog."

"That's right, sir," the sergeant major corroborated. "They just fumble with each other, like I said."

The C.O. was outraged, knowing from his long experience of army life that no true soldier would behave in such a fashion. "We'll soon put a stop to that. I won't tolerate pigsty behavior in my battalion. Find me the men who were there."

WHEN THE ORDER requiring the battalion to parade at full strength eventually reached No. 3 Company, the first man to lay hands on it was Company Sergeant Major Kirschke. This might have been described as an accident, since Kirschke had recently developed the habit of taking lengthy naps during working hours.

"What's all this?" he drawled.

"Orders from Battalion," the corporal clerk replied tersely.

"Well, what of it?" demanded Kirschke, yawning again. He emitted several more yawns—justifiably, in his opinion. What had lately been going on in No. 3 Company was more than could be readily endured by any normal modern man and soldier—and God knew he regarded himself as such. He had been quite prepared to enter wholeheartedly into the new army spirit, but the past few weeks had encouraged him in the belief that it was pointless. Extended spells of sleep appeared to be the just man's last resort.

Wearing an air of extreme weariness and indifference, Kirschke betook himself to the company commander's office, the order from Battalion fluttering sadly from his hand like a flag at half mast.

"Your salute," said Lieutenant Dieter von Strackmann, "could do with a little brushing up."

Kirschke considered it beneath his dignity to reply. In his eyes, Lieutenant von Strackmann was a complete novice who had still been wetting his diapers when he, Kirschke, was commanding a gun crew in a close support artillery unit—though his troop commander got the Iron Cross that should have gone to him.

"Deal with it," said Lieutenant Dieter von Strackmann, casting a cursory glance at the order. "Get the company there on time, Sergeant Major."

"It's not as simple as that," Kirschke said.

"Simple or not," snapped the lieutenant angrily, "an order's an order—and that goes for you too."

Kirschke's eyes closed, though not from weariness. He looked far more as if he were trying—if only for a brief instant—to blot out the sight of the uniformed dilettante at the desk.

Ever since young von Strackmann had assumed temporary command of the company in place of the regular company commander, a captain who had been in the hospital

for some weeks, suffering from jaundice, he had done his best to be the most ironbound Ironclad of all.

"Some of the men are out on firing practice," Kirschke explained patiently, "and some are in town collecting stores. The M.T. class is swanning around somewhere in the area, and No. 2 Platoon is doing field training."

"I couldn't care less," said Lieutenant von Strackmann with mounting annoyance.

"But I could," said Kirschke in the tones of an indulgent schoolmaster. "I'm not a miracle worker."

"Kindly do as I tell you, Kirschke!" von Strackmann yelped. His youthful features, coarse-grained, angular, and prematurely seamed by devotion to duty, tried to don an air of authority. To him, Kirschke was a clandestine saboteur, at least of the von Strackmann career. "If you wish to remain C.S.M. of this company, you will obey my orders."

These words seemed to afford Kirschke some amusement. He had difficulty in suppressing a broad grin. The fact was that he had been classified—on the strength of rigorous aptitude tests—as a senior N.C.O. of outstanding ability, whereas von Strackmann's record as an acting company commander was still a blank page. He was the one who had to prove himself, not Kirschke.

"How you organize it is your business," the lieutenant continued. He rose and walked to the door, unable to endure Kirschke's presumption any longer. "The main thing is that the company turns out at the stated time."

The company turned out on time. All C.S.M. Kirschke had to do was to mobilize a number of junior N.C.O.s, which he did, still yawning incessantly, with the easy assurance of a virtuoso who could manipulate the controls of the military machine in his sleep. Punctually to the minute, the members of No. 3 Company streamed in from all directions.

They thronged the parade ground docilely, not inquiring why they had been summoned because they were not interested in knowing. The only thing that still aroused interest in the company since von Strackmann had taken over was the prospect of an evening off.

Only Martin Recht, standing in the front rank next to Karl Kamnitzer, felt any nervousness.

"Look, there's the patrol!" he whispered excitedly. "They're making straight for us. I can guess what'll happen now."

They were still some distance away, being shepherded along by the battalion adjutant. Looking positively cheerful

32

in the absence of Bornekamp, the adjutant almost danced along, with the patrol trotting at his heels like a pair of bloodhounds. Von Strackmann strutted out to meet them with peacock strides.

"Get into the rear rank," Kamnitzer told Recht. "I'll give these lads something to chew on."

Martin Recht needed no second bidding. Corporal Streicher tried briefly to make difficulties, but a menacing look from Kamnitzer quelled him.

The adjutant and the acting company commander, both lieutenants, exchanged salutes, whereupon C.S.M. Kirschke negligently reported that the company was ready for inspection.

The next command was: "Open order, march!"

When this maneuver had been completed, von Strackmann nodded to the adjutant. "All right," said the latter, addressing the patrol in a slightly bored voice. "You can repeat the process, and let's hope we have more luck this time."

The sergeant major propelled himself forward, followed by the sergeant. Portentously, they started to pace along the front rank.

"I'll stake my life it wasn't a member of this company," von Strackmann assured the adjutant in an undertone.

"Steady, my friend," said the adjutant, a man of humane impulses when he was out of the C.O.'s reach, "you may be courting death."

Meanwhile the patrol strode onward, slowly, deliberately, and intent on doing a thorough job. Sergeant major and sergeant looked from one indifferent face to the next, from eyes which regarded them coolly or appraisingly to others which shone with humble devotion. Cows, bulls, and calves, thought the sergeant major, but cattle one and all.

Suddenly both men paused, rooted in astonishment. A grinning, expectant face had swum into view. It belonged to a corporal.

"Are you looking for me?" he inquired.

"That's the fellow!" the sergeant cried exultantly.

"Name?" asked the sergeant major.

"Kamnitzer," the corporal replied, "Christian name Karl. What can I do for you?"

"Were you in town last night?"

"Certainly I was." With satisfaction, Karl Kamnitzer sensed that every eye had turned in his direction. Even Lieutenant von Strackmann stared at him with his mouth

33

slightly open, possibly recalling his pledge of two minutes earlier.

"I was in La Paloma yesterday evening," Kamnitzer volunteered. "I was sitting there with a few friends of mine and some girls when you gentlemen walked in. I just went on sitting there."

"Right, follow me," commanded the sergeant major.

"With pleasure," replied Kamnitzer, sounding as if he meant it.

"We've got him, sir!" the sergeant major reported to the adjutant. So complete was his triumph that he loftily ignored the skepticism written on a couple of faces, among them those of the adjutant and Corporal Kamnitzer. "Perhaps we can get to the bottom of this now."

"Getting to the bottom of this" took the form of a semi-official interrogation. This was limited to the basic facts and took place in the battalion reading room.

"Well, out with it!" prompted the sergeant major.

"Out with what?" Karl Kamnitzer looked eager to oblige but slightly puzzled. "I don't know what you want me to say."

Lieutenant von Strackmann subjected Kamnitzer to a gaze of searching inquiry which was apparently lost on him. The adjutant, meanwhile, stared at the bookshelves, crammed almost to bursting point with an impressive array of books. The "Democracy" section contained various works by Heuss, memoirs by Churchill and de Gaulle, *Gedanken und Erinnerungen* by Bismarck, and the standard works *Great Germans*, *German Generals*, and *Soldiers of the German Nation*. All gleamed with cleanliness, fresh as the day they emerged from their wrappers, since hardly any of them had ever been read or taken off the shelves except for dusting.

"So you were in the bar in question yesterday evening?"

"Yes, I told you that already." Kamnitzer's tone was conversational, like that of a guest at a tea party. "You could have had a word with me last night if you'd wanted, but you didn't seem particularly interested. You steamed through the place so fast I hardly had time to salute."

The sergeant gave a suppressed snort and glanced warningly at the sergeant major, but the sergeant major pressed on regardless, the flames of his enthusiasm fanned by an encouraging nod from Lieutenant von Strackmann. Only the adjutant preserved an attitude of indifference.

"Who was the man who ran for it?" asked the sergeant major.

Kamnitzer's face betrayed utter astonishment. "You say someone ran for it?" He shook his head. "All I know is, someone made for the men's room in a hurry just as you came in. Quite a natural reaction, I thought."

"Who was this man?" pursued the sergeant major.

"How should I know? I didn't take any notice, but if you were so interested in him you could have asked him his name—or wouldn't he tell you?"

"Are you trying to make a fool of me?"

"I wouldn't dream of it, Sergeant Major."

"That's enough of that!" Lieutenant von Strackmann said incisively. He pushed the sergeant major to one side and stationed himself in front of Kamnitzer, who eyed him with a look of pleasurable anticipation. The adjutant had interrupted his inspection of the bookshelves and was now wearing a thoughtful expression.

"Well, come on!" von Strackmann demanded vigorously, convinced that the corporal had merely misconstrued the situation. "Let's have some names!"

"You want the girls' names, sir?" Corporal Kamnitzer smiled. "I'm sorry, I only know their Christian names, and I can't give you their addresses."

"Damnation!" shouted the lieutenant. "I want the name of this man!"

Kamnitzer inclined his head slightly as if to get a better view of von Strackmann, whom he appeared to consider worthy of close scrutiny. "Sir," he said with deliberation, "when I visit a place of that sort it's not because of the other men there. I'm not interested in them off duty— least of all on Saturday nights. I only go there for the sake of the girls."

"It's intolerable," declared the lieutenant.

"My attitude toward girls? Surely not, sir. It's quite natural, really."

"It's intolerable that you won't give a straight answer to my question."

"I don't see how I can make myself plainer, sir."

The adjutant considered it advisable to intervene at this stage. He drew his brother officer aside and presented him with a cogent résumé of the situation. The corporal either knew nothing or declined to say if he did. Coercion seemed inopportune, and the C.O. was waiting for results.

Major Bornekamp was indeed awaiting the outcome of the interrogation, and awaiting it with impatience. He was

35

standing beside his desk to receive the two officers. Propelled forward by the adjutant, Lieutenant von Strackmann summarized the results of the investigation, striving for well-disciplined brevity.

In conclusion, he reported: "The man who attempted to evade arrest was a member of the armed forces—of this battalion, what's more—but his name could not be elicited."

"You've exhausted all possibilities?"

"In regard to Corporal Kamnitzer, sir?"

Bornekamp answered von Strackman's query with a vigorous nod, and the lieutenant hastened to cover himself. "Well, sir, his attitude is rather mystifying. He's a hard nut to crack, if you'll pardon the expression. I just can't understand the man. He strikes me as secretive, obstinate, and downright difficult. It may take a little time to convince him where his duty lies."

"I want concrete results," Bornekamp cut in, "and I want them quickly. To achieve this, I suggest we issue a sort of appeal to the men's conscience—to their sense of honor."

The adjutant gazed at the office ceiling—whether in veneration or resignation it was hard to tell—but Lieutenant von Strackmann gave an emphatic nod of approval, effectively conveying that he understood the C.O. as well as, and probably better than, any officer under his command.

"A proclamation to the battalion!" Bornekamp dictated to the adjutant in sovereign tones. "One of my men has attempted to evade the regimental police patrol instituted by me. This may have been understandable in view of the circumstances, but the man in question has been identified. I therefore call upon him to come forward voluntarily, and I shall regard his voluntary surrender as a mark of confidence in myself."

Major Bornekamp nodded contentedly. "That ought to do the trick, don't you agree, gentlemen?"

A QUARTER OF AN HOUR later a two-tone Porsche 1600 drew up outside the gates of the Grenadier barracks. At the wheel sat Herbert Asch, who informed the sentry that, in his capacity as mayor, he wished to speak to the commanding officer.

This request was conveyed to the adjutant, who transmitted it to the C.O. without delay. "Any idea what the fellow wants?" Bornekamp asked thoughtfully.

"No, sir," said the adjutant. "It's never easy to tell what Herr Asch has in mind, but I imagine you'll have to see him."

"Of course I will," boomed the C.O. "You don't think he scares me, do you? I've had breakfast off better men than him before now. I even gave the Führer a piece of my mind once."

This episode was widely known, having been more than adequately publicized by Bornekamp himself. Apparently the Russian campaign would have turned out quite differently if Hitler had taken his advice—which he didn't, as events had since proved. The adjutant retired speedily.

Major Bornekamp advanced a few steps to meet his visitor, extending his arm to deliver the iron handshake which the occasion warranted. Herbert Asch endured it without blinking an eyelid.

The C.O. had a certain weakness for the local mayor, who had always proved helpful and generous. Quite apart from that, Asch had a pronounced feeling for the soldierly way of life, as he proved—yet again—by reporting the arrival of a new consignment of Chablis and Meursault from France.

"I'll send you round a selection," promised Asch.

"Please do," said the C.O.—an entirely official request, since Bornekamp, besides being commander of the Grenadier battalion, was also senior member of the mess and, as such, responsible for the welfare of his officers. Only the best was good enough for them, and Asch could be relied upon to produce it.

Even so, the C.O. could not entirely banish a sense of mistrust. There was virtually no one in his entourage whom he did not mistrust, and only concrete achievement could persuade him otherwise.

"But you're not going to tell me, Herr Asch," he said, with a mixture of geniality and wariness, "that the sole reason for your visit was to sell me some white Burgundy."

"Did I say it was?" Asch asked with a smile.

"Of course not." The C.O. laughed raucously. He was convinced that he knew Asch, and equally convinced that the man had only become mayor in order to feather his nest with greater facility. "You've got something on your mind, I can see."

Herbert Asch had come across a wide variety of officer types in the course of his not unduly long life, but the major appeared to be a new sub-species—a buzzard who sometimes endeavored to coo like a dove. The Bundeswehr's

37

preoccupation with democracy had made him something of a quick-change artist, though a comparatively primitive practitioner of the art.

"You see," Bornekamp went on, "it didn't escape me that you expressly announced yourself as Mayor Asch." His eyes narrowed. "Well, let's have it!"

"I had a long and not altogether agreeable telephone conversation with the proprietor of La Paloma this morning."

"Aha!" barked the C.O., lowering himself into his chair with an air of expectancy. "So that's the way the wind blows."

Herbert Asch had selected a turn of phrase which neatly sidestepped the awkward fact that he had contacted the proprietor of the coffee bar on his own initiative. The C.O. would infer that the owner of the "passion parlor" had contacted him, the mayor.

"It's simply ludicrous," Bornekamp continued loftily. "There's no point in wasting words on a man who owns a shop like that. The place sounds like an utter pigsty to me. You haven't come here to complain about my patrol, surely?"

"More than that, Major—I must request that you refrain from using such methods of surveillance in future."

"Come off it, Asch!" the C.O. exploded, contriving to mitigate the effect of his outburst with a confidential wink. "After all, it can't do you anything but good if I wipe out one of your competitors."

"It would be a very short-sighted policy, Major. Setting aside the fact that I'm not worried about competition from a pigsty, as you call it, where do you propose to draw the line? What goes for the passion parlor today may apply to my hotel tomorrow."

"I understand—you want to cover yourself."

"All I want to do is clarify the situation as far as possible. I've no wish to meddle in your affairs, I assure you. Why not return the favor? The barracks are your sphere of operations, places of entertainment in the town are ours —that is, unless you're prepared to see misunderstandings arise between the garrison and the civilian population, or between us personally?"

"Of course not," the C.O. assured him. "But I'm puzzled, to say the least. I never thought you'd try to hold a pistol to my head in this way. Have you studied the implications carefully?"

"I merely want to avoid unnecessary complications."

38

Bornekamp scrutinized Asch like a military map. The mayor was not the sort of obstacle to be taken by frontal assault. The best course for the moment was a tactical detour. "Don't worry, Herr Asch, we'll arrange something."

"I'm delighted to hear that."

"Well, let's get down to business. What are your precise requirements?"

"Not requirements, Major," said Asch, "just a polite request—a suggestion, if you like: Call off your dogs. Cease fire. Demonstrate your generosity and understanding. The civilian population will be grateful to you, I'll see to that."

"Agreed," Bornekamp said with well-simulated heartiness, but his slightly narrowed eyes remained cool as ice. "I'll get him yet," he told himself. "I'll get him yet."

CORPORAL STREICHER sat next to Grenadier Recht at lunch—purely by chance, or so it seemed. "I'm junior ranks' welfare representative for No. 3 Company, you know," he began. "I'm just reminding you so you'll know you can trust me."

"Fair enough," said Martin Recht. "You're welcome to the job as far as I'm concerned. It doesn't worry me."

Corporal Streicher thoughtfully dissected his veal cutlet. "Did you see the C.O.'s announcement, Martin?"

"I did," said Recht, chewing vigorously on his cutlet, which was as tough as old boots, and telling himself—as one who was always ready to look on the bright side—that it was good for his teeth.

"The C.O. expects the man to come forward voluntarily."

"I know," said Recht, ruefully reflecting that if there was one veal cutlet in the dining hall which was as tough as a rubber tire, it was inevitable that it should turn up on his plate.

Things like that were always happening to him. The sweatband in his helmet was made of corrugated iron, his denims let in water like a sieve and his boots might have been designed as instruments of torture, but he always did his best to be adaptable.

"You can talk freely to me," Corporal Streicher declared. His own cutlet spurted with juice and cut like butter.

The dining hall was crowded. Its long tables were packed with soldiers, most of whom ate silently and with mechanical fervor. Many of them had eaten worse in the course of

39

their short lives, but their main object was to fill their bellies, it didn't much matter what with.

"I'm not stupid, you know," said Corporal Streicher, pleasurably inhaling the scent of dessert, a vanilla pudding with raspberry syrup. "I make it my business to keep my ears open, so I know you were in La Paloma yesterday evening."

"In that case, either report me or shut up about it."

"I want to help you, that's all," Streicher explained in friendly tones. "I hope you appreciate that.

"Not much escapes me, you see," Corporal Streicher pursued. "I need hardly tell you that you can rely on me, and if you're wise you'll take advantage of the fact."

Martin Recht parried the remark. "Perhaps I will, if the occasion arises."

"You did go to La Paloma with Kamnitzer, didn't you?" Streicher insisted.

"It's possible," said Recht. He pushed the remains of his lunch away, his untouched pudding included.

Corporal Streicher pulled the plate over in front of him. Sweet things, he told himself, fortified his nerves and meant more to him than tobacco and alcohol. It was a matter of taste, of course, but he liked to subscribe to a set of definite principles.

"Martin," he went on, having devoured his second plate of pudding, "I appeal to your conscience. Be absolutely honest—you were in La Paloma when the patrol arrived, weren't you?"

"Mind your own business," Recht advised moodily.

But Streicher was not to be deterred. "When Kamnitzer pushed you into the rear rank just before the patrol came round—that's when it dawned on me."

"Then keep your trap shut."

"You don't appreciate the situation," the corporal said mildly. "You've put me in an awkward position. We all make mistakes, I know, but we ought to own up to them. Don't you agree?"

"Is that what you insist on my doing?"

"I'm not insisting on anything, Martin. I only want what's best for you. I'm your friend, after all. Also, as I told you, I'm the company welfare representative. Please remember that. You see, under certain circumstances I should have to report what I know—it would be my duty to."

"I can see you doing it, too."

Corporal Streicher looked aggrieved. "I'll tell you this much, Martin. That guy Kamnitzer is not the right sort of

40

company for you. He's always trying to involve you in his escapades, can't you see that? If you're not careful he'll get you into serious trouble one day—mutiny, even. Believe me, the only thing to do is own up voluntarily. The C.O. will take it into account."

"Are you trying to force me?"

"Who said anything about forcing? I'm just offering you some advice. If I were you I'd take it."

"Well," Martin Recht said resignedly, "it looks as though I haven't got any alternative."

Grenadier Martin Recht was in no hurry to lodge his report—voluntary or involuntary. He decided to speak to Kamnitzer first, in the hope that he could assuage the welfare representative's oversensitive conscience.

Karl Kamnitzer was nowhere to be found, however, having left barracks during the lunchtime break. He had been put on stores detail for the afternoon and had vanished into the town prematurely to avoid getting involved in duties of a more arduous nature. Ever since von Strackmann had been in charge of the company, training programs and duty rosters had been subject to lightning alteration, and Kamnitzer had no taste for surprises of that kind. Being on stores, he was not expected back before the end of working hours.

"Been to the C.S.M. yet?" Corporal Streicher demanded, when Recht returned to Room 13.

Recht shook his head and told him that Kirschke was not in the company office.

"Then you must go and look for him, Martin. I'll be happy to help you." Streicher seemed genuinely worried. "You must get this business over as quickly as possible. Don't wait too long—it'll make a bad impression."

Eventually, worn down by Streicher's tireless solicitude, Recht left the room and made reluctantly for the company office.

C.S.M. Kirschke, however, was enjoying his siesta. His usual custom before retiring to bed was to inform the office staff that he was going to change his trousers. In the normal way, this took about two hours.

After Martin Recht had waited patiently in the corridor for a considerable period, Kirschke actually emerged. He sauntered along to the office, yawning heartily, with Recht at his heels.

"You wanted to see me?"

"Yes, Sergeant Major."

"Couldn't it wait till tomorrow?"

Kirschke sensed that Recht wanted to lodge a report, and reports of any kind were distasteful to him. If they had to be lodged at all, the right time to lodge them—in his opinion—was the morning. And the next morning was tomorrow morning.

However, Grenadier Recht would not be put off. After listening wearily to everything that Recht deemed it necessary to tell, the C.S.M. closed his eyes as though urgently in need of further sleep. Then he said: "Not a bad yarn, Recht."

"It's the truth, Sergeant Major."

"It's a load of poppycock," said Kirschke, with an unabashed yawn which revealed his tonsils. "What's the matter with you—got a hero complex, or are you just feeling suicidal? Whatever it is, I'm not the man to help you. Besides, you're in luck. My hearing's pretty poor sometimes—like now. I didn't hear a word you said."

"But what about the C.O.'s announcement?"

"God Almighty!" exclaimed Kirschke. "You're beginning to bore me. You look overtired. Get a good night's sleep and come and see me tomorrow."

He was on the point of turning away when Lieutenant von Strackmann strode up, his rubber-soled boots thumping the ground like pile drivers. He stared past Kirschke, glad of an excuse to ignore his salute, which would have done credit to a cripple, and focused his attention on the young grenadier's agitated face.

"What's going on here?" he demanded imperiously.

"Nothing special," C.S.M. Kirschke replied in casual tones. "This man's got a bee in his bonnet about something. Push off, Recht, and stop wasting my time."

"Stay here!" called Lieutenant von Strackmann.

Kirschke's manner was provocative in the extreme, he told himself, but there was something of a challenge in having been selected to deputize for a company commander who seemed—with Kirschke's help—to have turned his unit into an undisciplined rabble. "Well, what does he want?"

The C.S.M. shrugged his shoulders and abandoned Recht to the ever-eager lieutenant, whose first step was to transfer the proceedings from the corridor to his office. Kirschke loped after him like an amiable St. Bernard, less from curiosity than as a safety measure.

Martin Recht repeated his voluntary statement from the beginning, watched by von Strackmann as a hawk watches

its prey. When he had finished, the lieutenant exhaled audibly and told him to wait in the outer office. Then he drew a deep breath and looked at C.S.M. Kirschke as though he were seeing him properly for the first time.

"This is absolutely outrageous!" he said at length.

"A piece of stupidity, that's all."

"I was referring to your behavior, Sergeant Major. It's incredible! Scandalous! Someone brings you information which the C.O. is urgently waiting for—and what do you do?"

"The only thing to do, sir, under the circumstances— wait and see. Never rush things, that's what the company commander always says."

"Your conduct is alarming in the extreme!" the lieutenant exclaimed furiously. "It's little short of sabotage."

The C.S.M. remained imperturbable. "Orders are hardly ever final. Even written orders often turn out to have been superseded by the time they reach this office. If I were you I'd start by asking Battalion whether the C.O.'s announcement still stands."

"But you're not me!"

Kirschke's face registered no sign of regret at this misfortune, but Lieutenant von Strackmann was already on the line to the C.O. "The man in question has been found, sir," he reported, not without pride. "His name is Recht, Martin. Rank: grenadier."

Von Strackmann heard Bornekamp growl like an infuriated dog. Then he barked: "For God's sake, man, don't bother me with all that nonsense!"

"But," von Strackmann stammered in bewilderment, "the announcement which you personally . . ."

The C.O. cut him short. "It's been countermanded, and I must request you not to trouble me with matters which have already been settled. Concentrate on bringing your company up to scratch instead. You seem to have an unusual number of deadbeats in your outfit. Do something about them, Strackmann, and don't take too long about it!"

"Yes, sir!" cried the acting company commander, still bewildered but eager to demonstrate his zeal. However, a short, sharp click on the line told him that Bornekamp was no longer listening. It was like a slap in the face.

Von Strackmann was painfully embarrassed. He refrained from looking at his company sergeant major, correctly gauging that the latter must be grinning like a Cheshire cat—and he could not have endured the sight.

43

"I'm surrounded by deadbeats!" he growled eventually, in a fair imitation of the C.O.'s voice. "Slackers, the lot of them—but things are going to change round here. We'll give 'em a field exercise, for a start."

FIELD EXERCISES could not be held often enough. Such, at least, was the view of Major Bornekamp, who would have preferred every form of training—drill parades, P.T., and educational classes included—to be transferred to open country. However, he told himself, things had not yet reached that stage in the Bundeswehr, which still labored under the regrettable influence of certain self-styled democratic elements.

Nevertheless, as an old wartime commander, he fundamentally approved of sudden practice alerts and unexpected field exercises. All that was required was a brief word to the adjutant, who merely reported that the company in question was moving off. Since Lieutenant von Strackmann had been deputizing for its jaundice-stricken commander, No. 3 Company's itinerant habits had earned it the name of The Hiking Club.

"What's the plan this time?" inquired Sergeant Major Rammler, a recognized expert in hand-to-hand combat training and one of No. 3 Company's N.C.O. platoon commanders. "How long is this little tea party likely to last?"

"How should I know?" Kirschke replied equably. "I'm only the C.S.M. here. Anyway, since when have you been interested in the duration of an exercise? I thought you were a glutton for that kind of punishment."

"I like stretching out somewhere else occasionally—not just in a slit trench." Rammler laughed coarsely. "I'm on the track of something really big. The hottest bit of stuff for miles around—you've never seen such a pair of beauties, not even in the movies. I tell you, if I'm back in barracks by retreat it'll be a wonder."

"You're otherwise engaged this evening. I take it," Kirschke said dryly.

"You're telling me! First the movies, then a couple of quick ones, and then the Municipal Gardens—or her room, with a bit of luck."

Kirschke looked dubious. "I don't know about the Municipal Gardens. You'll probably still be out on the moors. Don't forget you're wearing full marching order."

"That doesn't mean we'll be out half the night. It may just be ballast."

Ballast it certainly was. The men were loaded like pack mules with rifles, light machine guns, bazookas, shovels, field telephones, walkie-talkies, smoke bombs, practice ammunition, water bottles, iron rations, ground sheets, sleeping bags, semaphore flags, ropes, and snipers' rifles complete with telescopic sights. No motor transport had been laid on.

Lieutenant von Strackmann, too, turned out in battledress, but all he carried was a pistol, a map case, a whistle, and a packet of paper handkerchiefs. He naturally considered it a point of honor to conduct any field exercise in person.

Before giving the order to march off, von Strackmann went in search of C.S.M. Kirschke.

"You're coming too, of course!"

"I'm afraid not," Kirschke said stolidly.

"I'm afraid you are!" countered the lieutenant. "A little fresh air wouldn't do any harm."

"I wouldn't suffer, perhaps, but my work would."

"Tomorrow's another day, Sergeant Major."

"Precisely, tomorrow's the day when we've got to produce the clothing store inventory. It's due at Battalion first thing tomorrow morning and we've hardly started on it yet. All the same, if you say it can wait . . ."

"All right, get working on it," von Strackmann said furiously, "but catch up with us when you've finished."

"I may get there pretty late," Kirschke remarked amiably. "Very late, in fact—if at all."

Von Strackmann strode off, seething with rage, to rejoin his heavily laden company. The C.S.M. watched his superior's retreating form with a bland smile. Then, yawning heartily, he informed the company clerks that he was going to change his trousers again.

CORPORAL Karl Kamnitzer, meanwhile, was still in town on stores detail. The official object of his mission was a radio set priced at approximately two hundred marks and destined for the Junior Ranks' Canteen.

No one was better suited to such a task than Kamnitzer. He proposed to expend a mere half hour on buying the radio and divide the remaining four or five hours between the cinema and the Café Asch—an enjoyable afternoon

which he planned to follow up with a no less enjoyable evening.

The Café Asch was little frequented at this hour, a fact of which Kamnitzer could only approve. He stood in the entrance and surveyed the interior with a look of anticipation, but evidently failed to find what he was looking for.

Strutting up to the counter, he raised his hand to the peak of his cap in a salute of gaily exaggerated precision. "Good afternoon, ma'am," he said brightly. "May one inquire the state of your esteemed health?"

The woman behind the counter, who was sorting cash slips, looked up and smiled when she recognized Kamnitzer. It was Frau Elisabeth Asch, who normally supervised the café while her husband looked after the hotel side when he was not involved in his mayoral duties. Asch was universally respected, but his wife was venerated—even by Kamnitzer.

"Disappointed it's only me?" she asked with a smile.

"Madame!" Kamnitzer protested gallantly. "I can't imagine a lovelier sight. If you were still a free woman I wouldn't leave you alone for an instant."

Elisabeth Asch smiled, and Kamnitzer was struck yet again by her charm. No man was worthy of her, he reflected, not even her husband.

"Take a seat over there on the right, near the window," she suggested. "You're bound to get the best service there."

Kamnitzer did as he was bidden, pulling his chair round so that he could survey the entire establishment. He noted with grateful satisfaction that Frau Elisabeth had opened the door to the kitchen. "A customer for you, Fräulein Wieder!" she called.

After a moment or two the object of his visit appeared. Helen Wieder was probably the most efficient member of the Asch staff and certainly the most decorative. She sauntered up to Kamnitzer's table, swinging her sturdy but pneumatic hips.

"There you are at last!" he cried rapturously.

"I know, don't tell me," Helen Wieder said, unimpressed. "You lie awake every night thinking about me. Well, I'm on duty now. What can I get you?"

"I leave it to you."

"I wouldn't—you might get nothing at all."

Helen Wieder studied Kamnitzer as if he were a troublesome insect. "It'd serve you right if I simply ignored you. Where were you yesterday evening? I thought we had a date."

"I was officially detained," Kamnitzer said. "By a regimental police patrol. I realize how much I missed, believe me, but we can make up for it. What about this evening?"

"Sorry, I've already got a date this evening."

Kamnitzer looked outraged. "You must be joking! I don't think you understand what it means to be a forces' sweetheart. Are you trying to undermine our morale? I'm held up by a patrol for once, and you go making dates with other men. Do I know him?"

"Do you mind?" Helen Wieder said grimly. "We're not married—we're not even engaged—so I can make dates with anyone I choose. Come on, let's have your order."

"Are you trying to keep me on ice for a while, or is this the big brush-off?"

"One coffee, then," said Helen. "Anything else?"

"This evening, when you're finished here, I'll explain the whole thing to you. All right?"

"I'll be busy then," Helen said coldly, and flounced off.

"What do you mean, 'busy'?" Kamnitzer called after her. "Who's been poaching on my preserves, that's what I'd like to know!"

THE GRENADIERS field training area was comparatively easy to get to. It began a bare twenty minutes' march from the barracks gates and extended for some miles north of the town. It was an ideal mixture: bare scrub, dense woodland, and low-lying marshes—no place for tanks but a veritable paradise for iron-willed infantrymen.

"This afternoon," Lieutenant von Strackmann told the company when they had reached the edge of the woods, "we'll start with some basic procedures like digging-in and camouflage."

He radiated martial comradeship, convincing almost everyone that he would have liked nothing better than to set an example by attacking the ground himself, entrenching tool in hand.

First, however, he summoned the platoon commanders together. There were three of them: two downy-cheeked second lieutenants and Sergeant Major Fritz Rammler, the battle-scarred expert on hand-to-hand combat.

"Gentlemen," the lieutenant said, "a company is a unit. It's like a human body, each organ of which must function

47

efficiently. If they don't, the body is sick. Transferring the analogy to this company, we might possibly speak of soft, flabby, or destructive elements. I don't say there are any, but I say that, if there are, they must be spotted and dealt with! This exercise is part of the cure. Any questions, gentlemen?"

Although the inquiry was meant to be purely rhetorical, it evoked a response, surprisingly enough, from Sergeant Major Rammler.

The lieutenant nodded, not overgraciously, to indicate that Rammler had permission to speak. Rammler spoke: "Is the exercise likely to last very long, sir?"

Von Strackmann looked disagreeably surprised. He had not expected an undisciplined interjection of this sort from anyone, let alone Rammler. He was saddened by the thought that even a reliable instructor like the sergeant major was subject to human failings and symptoms of flabbiness. The unit certainly needed to be brought up to scratch—and quickly, too, as the C.O. had so rightly said.

"The exercise will last for as long as I deem it necessary," the lieutenant replied coldly. He might just as well have said "for an indefinite period," which effectively dashed Rammler's hopes of an enjoyable night in town.

Removing the members of his platoon from the gaze of Lieutenant von Strackmann, Rammler deployed them over a wide area and shooed them into the nearest patch of woods. From there he pushed on in the direction of a signalman's cabin on the railway line that skirted the heath.

A few hundred yards short of his destination, he stationed himself in the middle of his platoon, legs apart and hands on hips. His expression seemed genial and his voice gentle as that of a favorite uncle about to tell a fairy tale, but all he said was: "Nuclear attack."

He had no need to say more. These two words meant: "Dig in!" and thirty entrenching tools swung into action. Rammler's platoon would be fully occupied for the next half hour at least.

Rammler himself stalked past his human moles and plunged into the undergrowth as though he intended to check their progress from a hidden vantage point, but he emerged on the other side and made for the signalman's cabin. There was nothing for it but to telephone his new discovery, warn her that he might be late, and beg her to be patient.

H̲ELEN W̲IEDER served Karl Kamnitzer his coffee, slamming the crockery down in front of him as though he had already been convicted of evading payment.

"I'm the easiest person in the world to get on with," Kamnitzer ventured. "It's just that I'm always being misunderstood."

"Misunderstood? Seen through, you mean."

"I'm the soul of gallantry," Kamnitzer pursued. "I desert my platoon in broad daylight, just for you, and what thanks do I get?"

Helen Wieder retired, but not before emitting a scornful laugh. Kamnitzer eyed her rear view with rapture. He could have watched her for hours on end, but he was not permitted to.

"I trust you're not trying to keep my staff from their work," came an amused voice from behind him. He turned and saw Herbert Asch.

The two men had met some time before, the day Karl Kamnitzer had discovered Helen Wieder, in fact, though "discovered" was not quite the right word. He felt like a ship-wrecked mariner who had been cast ashore on some palm-fringed, silver-shored island of delight. One look, and he had known that she was the girl for him—and then Herbert Asch had materialized, just as he did now.

Asch sat down opposite him, as he had done before, and smiled. "Well, how's the market doing?" he asked, meaning the Grenadier barracks, which seemed to hold a certain degree of interest for him.

"Alarums and excursions over a regimental police patrol," Kamnitzer volunteered. "A false alarm, probably. You know what a fuss they make over things in our mob, but the M.P.s behaved like bulls in a china shop. It was 08.15 all over again, and even our revered C.O. gets worried about that sort of thing."

"It almost sounds as though you were there," Asch said intently.

"Of course I was. Trust me to be in the thick of it. I haven't seen a stupider bunch of faces for a long time."

"Tell me more," demanded Asch, but Kamnitzer's attention was distracted by the appearance of Frau Elisabeth.

"There's a phone call for Fräulein Wieder," she said. "Isn't she with you?"

49

"No, worse luck," said Kamnitzer. "She's avoiding me like the plague, and she won't let me explain."

"I'm sorry," Frau Elisabeth said sympathetically. "The phone call sounds urgent, though. It's a Herr Rammler."

Kamnitzer's eyebrows shot up. "Who?" he asked.

"Rammler—a sergeant major, so he says."

"Leave him to me!" said Kamnitzer cheerfully.

He hurried over to the counter, picked up the receiver and said briskly: "Yes, what can I do for you?"

He identified the answering voice readily enough, though it lacked its usual harshly imperious note of parade-ground superiority. "May I speak to Fräulein Wieder, please?" it cooed into Kamnitzer's ear.

"Sorry," said Kamnitzer, grinning, "completely out of the question at the moment. What do you want with her?"

Sergeant Major Rammler seemed to hesitate. He breathed heavily. Eventually he said: "I have an engagement with Fräulein Wieder this evening, but I probably won't be there at the time we agreed—I'll be on duty. Would you be kind enough to tell her?"

"I beg your pardon!" Kamnitzer exclaimed in a husky, assumed voice. "We're not a call-girl establishment here, you know. This is a reputable house, and we resent being used like a brothel."

"Who am I speaking to?" demanded Rammler, suddenly hoarse with rage. "Your voice sounds familiar. I know you, don't I? Who are you?"

"You know what you can do?" Kamnitzer inquired with relish. "You can take a running jump at yourself, with my compliments."

With that, he slammed the receiver back on its hook, confident that he had won a battle but forgetting that it takes more than one battle to win a war.

SERGEANT MAJOR RAMMLER reeled out of the signalman's cabin like a man who has just been hit over the head with a club. Feeling in need of moral support, he reached for his hip flask.

Almost mechanically, he elbowed his way back through the undergrowth to his platoon. The men were still digging, supervised by their section commanders.

Rammler stationed himself nearby and studied them like an animal trainer watching his charges go through their

paces. He felt embittered, and started to ask himself who was to blame.

The conclusion he reached was not devoid of a certain logic: the guilty party was the man responsible for this performance—some flabby individual who had landed the company, i.e., his pals, with this extra duty and robbed Rammler, i.e., his superior, of a promising evening.

But Rammler's logic did not stop there. If it weren't for this wet fish, this "destructive element," he reasoned shrewdly, they wouldn't be here now. If they weren't here, he would be in town, and if he were in town he would have been spared that embarrassing telephone call. Consequently, if someone had done his best to make mincemeat of him on the phone, only one person was to blame, and that was the man he was going to track down.

"Excuse me, Sergeant Major, but is it advisable to take the direction of the wind into account when siting a slit trench—even when there's no wind?"

Rammler turned on the questioner in surprise, certain that his leg was being pulled. Then he saw that it was Corporal Streicher, and the sight was as welcome as a glass of beer in a heat wave.

"Streicher," he said, not unkindly, "a rectangular slit trench should always be sited so that the short side faces the wind. That's the rule. But when there's no wind, like now, you can dig whichever way round you like, as far as I'm concerned."

"All I wanted to do," said the corporal, "was to take into account the direction of the wind normally prevailing in this area at this time of year. Even though there's no wind at the moment, one might spring up at any moment. Isn't that right, Sergeant Major?"

"Dead right," Rammler agreed, nodding approvingly.

"Right," said Streicher, addressing his section. "Short side facing east—northeast, to be more exact."

One or two of the men nearby stopped digging and seized the opportunity for a short breather. Fortunately for them, Rammler was not watching. He drew Streicher to one side and began to pace up and down with him.

"Streicher," he said, in what, for him, were honeyed tones, "you're the company welfare representative, and you're quite a useful soldier as well. If it was up to me, you'd have your third stripe by now. Tell me quite frankly: have you any idea why this jaunt was arranged?"

"It's possible, Sergeant Major." Streicher studiously hesitated for a moment before registering eagerness to respond

51

to the confidence reposed in him. "I can't say for certain, of course, but I've got a theory—only a theory, mind you."

"All right, all right, Streicher," Rammler said. "Let's have it."

Streicher launched into an account of the facts as he knew them: the raid by the patrol, the chase through the streets, the rope ladder, the investigation, and its possible consequences. "The man in question was ready to own up, but it was probably too late by that time."

"Who?" Rammler asked.

Corporal Streicher pointed to a towering molehill some yards away. The man behind it was throwing up earth like a machine, rhythmically, vigorously and with astonishing regularity—pile upon pile of it. It might have been the work of a mechanical excavator.

Rammler walked over and peered into the trench. Grenadier Martin Recht's grimy face peered back, glistening with sweat.

"You there!" called Rammler, after subjecting Recht to intense scrutiny. "You're reassigned to tree sniping."

Recht knew what that meant. Springing out of the weapon pit like a cork from a bottle he seized a rifle with telescopic sights and climbed the nearest large tree. He scrambled through the branches, monkeylike, until he reached the top, where he tried simultaneously to clear a field of fire and camouflage himself. Below, he could feel the sergeant major's searchlight gaze focused on him.

"That's the wrong tree," Rammler called mildly.

Martin Recht clambered down and doubled to the next tree, but no sooner had he reached the top than he again heard Sergeant Major Rammler's voice, still comparatively mild, calling: "Not enough field of fire."

Rammler's verdict on the next tree was "Not enough cover," and on the fourth "Too much cover and hardly any field of fire." His voice had taken on a slight edge.

It was not until he reached the summit of the fifth tree, gasping for breath and drenched with sweat, that Recht formed some idea of what the sergeant major was trying to do. He clung to the bough on which he was squatting with trembling hands. The branches swam before his eyes like a barbed-wire entanglement.

"What are you doing up there, having a nap?" Rammler called in tones of suppressed fury. "A lively lad like you! Come on, come on, don't tell me you're tired! Next tree!"

It struck Recht with staggering clarity that there must be dozens of trees in a wood of that size.

THE CAFE ASCH was full by this time, its tables crowded with chattering, cake-gorging, coffee-swilling customers.

"I think you said you were present when the patrol raided La Paloma, Herr Kamnitzer?" Herbert Asch put the question with the innocuous expression of a dentist approaching a patient.

Kamnitzer looked up from his gargantuan slice of cherry flan in some surprise. He had accepted the proprietor's invitation all the more readily because it meant that Helen Wieder had to serve him, but she continued to treat him like part of the furniture.

"I said I was there when the patrol arrived," Kamnitzer replied through a mouthful of flan, "but I didn't say anything about La Paloma. Who told you that, Herr Asch?"

"This Martin Recht—what sort of chap is he?"

Kamnitzer choked violently. "Who else knows?" he spluttered. "Just you, or is it all over town? If it is, I might as well pack my bags."

At this point a man in a shabby civilian suit came up. Asch greeted him warmly and introduced him to Kamnitzer as Herr Ahlers. Kamnitzer took him for a sales representative, possibly for washing machines.

"Herr Kamnitzer," Asch said, inclining his body slightly in Ahlers' direction, "seems to know your friend Martin Recht fairly well."

Kamnitzer nodded. "He sleeps in the bunk over mine."

"Are you a friend of his?" asked Ahlers.

"Friend's a big word. You might call him a pal of mine, but perhaps that doesn't go far enough."

"The choice of words doesn't matter," Ahlers said amiably. "You seem to like him, that's the main thing. May I ask why?"

Kamnitzer glanced discreetly at Asch, who nodded as if to imply that frankness was in order.

"Sometimes," said Kamnitzer, "Martin's like one of the Babes in the Wood—you know, always getting lost and whistling to keep his spirits up. I suppose there are a lot of people like him in the world—many more than you suspect, anyway."

"He's not just a sheep?"

"No, far from it, though he may look like one some-

times. That's why he's such a challenge to the sheep dogs —and there are plenty of them in the army."

Ahlers leaned forward a little. "You're not fond of soldiering, I gather?"

Karl Kamnitzer hesitated. Then, reflecting that the man was in civilian clothes and seemed to be a friend of Asch, he decided to treat him as a civilian. "Give people a chance to ride over other people roughshod or lead them up the garden path, and most of them will, if it's required or expected of them. If you go one better, and persuade them that they're doing it for the sake of an ideal—patriotism, liberty, it doesn't matter what—then they'll really put their backs into it. People ought to realize that—and that's just where Martin Recht falls down."

"I'd like you to introduce me to Martin Recht sometime, Herr Kamnitzer," said Asch. "Invite him here—this evening, if you like."

"You're up to something, aren't you?" Kamnitzer said, intrigued.

Asch smiled. "If I am, it's nothing that will hurt Recht."

"Then I'm all for it," Kamnitzer declared, and wolfed the rest of his flan.

M{AJOR} BORNEKAMP usually lingered in the battalion offices for a considerable time after the end of duty hours. He leafed through files, studied plans and directives, nosed through the contents of his underlings' desks and made surprise checks by telephone. The adjutant stood by, mute for the most part, like a well-trained sheep dog.

The major's appetite for work was generally construed as an unwearying love of efficiency. Those who knew him better, however, realized that he was prompted by quite another motive: a straightforward reluctance to go home, which was entirely comprehensible to anyone who knew the major's wife.

"Call my house," Bornekamp commanded the adjutant.

"Yes sir," said the latter. He needed no telling what to say—it was always the same: the major was still working and didn't know when he would be through.

Bornekamp moved on to the outer office. This was a favorite haunt of his because it was where the civilian typists worked, and he derived immense pleasure from teasing them in a robust, virile way.

"What—not gone home yet?" he boomed jovially. "You must have a crush on me!"

The object of his attentions, a maiden of forty, essayed a blush, but without success. She had already had ample opportunity to get to know the C.O. In her eyes, Bornekamp was a perfect cavalier in the old tradition, and it was almost a pleasure to do overtime for him.

"So you can't tear yourself away from me, eh, beloved?" bellowed the major, assuming what he imagined were the tones of a Lothario. "Go on like this, and I may yield to temptation!"

The adjutant smiled indulgently. He read Bornekamp like a book, every page of which was identical. As far as these women were concerned, the major might tease them heartily, but he would never do more than that—not, at any rate, in his official domain.

"I'm still waiting for a report from No. 3 Company," the secretary explained. "It's already completed, C.S.M. Kirschke says, but it's still got to be signed by the company commander."

Cocking an eye at the vast timetable which filled one wall of the office, Bornekamp saw that the blue card referring to No. 3 Company's activities that day had been criss-crossed with red diagonals. This signified that duties in camp had been replaced by external duties.

"That's news to me," Bornekamp said to the adjutant. "Why wasn't I informed?"

The C.O.'s genial, jocular tone had abruptly become cold and incisive. The adjutant did his utmost to avoid an internal collision by drawing attention to a standing rule which the C.O. himself had laid down. Its gist was that field exercises were to be welcomed, and that to alter the training schedule accordingly required no express approval from Battalion, only a routine report to the adjutant.

"But not in this case!" Bornekamp cried furiously. "I made it very clear that I regarded a certain matter as closed. I don't like arbitrary behavior. It encourages people to think that they can start special operations in my command without a by-your-leave."

"In that case, sir," the adjutant said humbly, "there must have been some misunderstanding on Lieutenant von Strackmann's part."

"Kindly ensure that he packs up his picnic immediately. He's to report to me in the mess as soon as he gets back."

The adjutant transmitted this order verbatim to Kirschke, who listened delightedly to the expressions "pack up," "pic-

nic," and "immediately." Then he mounted the company bicycle and pedaled off, at considerable speed, into the country.

He found Lieutenant von Strackmann in a small birch-wood, discoursing to a group of N.C.O.s on the methods to be adopted when bivouacking in trees in an emergency. He had just moved on to the problem of how to live off roots and weeds when cut off from supplies, when he caught sight of Kirschke's pedaling figure.

"Ah, there you are at last," he called. "You can join No. 3 Platoon."

"For the march back to the barracks?" Kirschke inquired, grinning.

"That may not be until tomorrow morning," the lieutenant said with authority.

"Within the next quarter of an hour, at most," Kirschke gently corrected him. "Orders from Battalion. You're to pack up this picnic immediately."

Not without an effort, Lieutenant von Strackmann gave a perfect display of self-control. For almost ten seconds he stood there, rigid and unspeaking. Then he drew a deep breath, stared past Kirschke, and ordered: "Cease operations!"

When this order reached No. 3 Platoon—by runner—Sergeant Major Rammler appeared to be standing by himself at the edge of the wood. His men were all up trees, and in the tallest of them cowered Grenadier Martin Recht, clinging precariously to a swaying branch.

A glance at his watch told Rammler that it was already too late for him to keep his date, but he had not yet taught Recht the lesson which, in his opinion, he so richly deserved.

"Close on me!" he yelled up at the trees.

While the platoon members were scrambling down and gathering round him in open formation, Rammler had been devising a brief final maneuver. Time was short, but the terrain was favorable and a small river flowed invitingly close at hand.

"Enemy has occupied edge of wood," Rammler announced. "Platoon will advance in nor'-nor'-westerly direction to relieve units at present engaged. Speed essential!"

There was nothing wrong with this move, tactically speaking, but it meant that the platoon had to advance, screened from the eyes of an imaginary enemy by trees and bushes, straight across the river—and the sweat-soaked

Martin Recht had been singled out for the special privilege of carrying a light machine gun.

Obediently, the platoon trotted through the water, knee deep at first, then up to their chests. Martin Recht gasped. He was a nonswimmer, and panic flickered in his eyes.

"Come on," Rammler exhorted him from the bank. "Not scared of a little water, are you?"

It was Rammler's last enjoyable moment of the day, however. A minute later Lieutenant von Strackmann appeared.

"You're holding us all up!" he yelled at Rammler. Unpleasant visions of the C.O. waiting for him in the mess flitted through his head. "The exercise is over—didn't you understand my order? No more detours, Sergeant Major!"

Rammler stood stiffly to attention until the lieutenant had departed. Then he glowered at Martin Recht, up to his neck in water but still on his feet. "The things I have to put up with!" he growled to himself. "And all because of a little sod like that!"

Back in barracks, Rammler went straight to C.S.M. Kirschke's room. "That chap Recht is a shit of the first order," he announced.

"Could be," said Kirschke. "There are plenty around."

"He needs a dose of extra guard duty—tonight, what's more."

"No reason why not," Kirschke said equably. "But tonight's guard is already detailed."

Rammler refused to give in. He demanded, he requested, he even pleaded. In the end he appealed to Kirschke as a brother sergeant major and Kirschke, whose prime concern was a quiet life, finally consented. "All right, if you're so set on it."

Grenadier Martin Recht, however, was not to be found. Apparently he had gone into town as soon as the field exercise was over.

"That's that, then," said Kirschke.

"He's got to be found at once!" Rammler insisted. "He can't just piss off like that!"

"Why not?" asked Kirschke in mild amusement. "You don't expect him to ask your permission every time he goes off duty, do you?"

Rammler, who felt as though he were floundering helplessly in a sea of mud, experienced a vague sense of betrayal. Even the warrant officers' trade union seemed to have stopped functioning.

57

"This lousy outfit!" he mumbled resentfully. "Just a lot of deadbeats, that's all they are."

So saying he retired to his room, where he changed his shirt, sprayed himself with eau de cologne and smeared his hair liberally with brilliantine. A glance in the mirror reassured him that he was a fine, upstanding figure of a man, which raised his spirits. To raise them still further, he treated himself to a small tot of schnapps (brand name: Strong Man's Milk) in his tooth mug.

Thus stimulated, he marched off into town at high speed and steered straight for the Café Asch. On arrival he asked in ringing tones for Helen Wieder, only to be informed politely by the woman behind the counter that Fräulein Wieder had already left—with a soldier.

Rammler gave a snort of indignation. "Who's in charge of this shop?" he inquired belligerently.

The woman behind the counter, who happened to be Elisabeth Asch, retained her good humor. She gestured invitingly toward a table near the window, where two men in civilian clothes were sitting, namely Herbert Asch and Klaus Ahlers. Their laughter sounded downright provocative to Rammler, who could not dismiss the possibility that they were laughing at him.

Resolutely, he marched across to them. He diagnosed them as two typically frivolous civilians, devoid of martial sternness, dignity, and poise. Not, of course, that he was fundamentally ill-disposed toward the civilian population, but his world was the barracks-room world—what was more, the barracks-room world of tomorrow, as he envisaged it, rooted in the traditions and experience of yesterday.

"What can we do for you?" asked one of the civilians.

"Who," Rammler demanded, "is in charge here?"

"In charge of what?" asked Herbert Asch.

"That telephone, for one thing." Rammler's expression was a blend of disdain and condescension, as befitted a soldier confronted by a lounge lizard.

The lounge lizard had the effrontery to smile. "What's the trouble exactly?" he asked.

"When I rang this place earlier, some objectionable bastard answered."

"It's quite possible," Asch agreed. "The telephone is a much-abused instrument."

"Don't try to dodge the issue!" Rammler thundered. The amused smile on the other man's face gave way to a hearty laugh, which rang provocatively in Rammler's ears. "Who

58

the hell are you, anyway?" he demanded rudely, as the café transformed itself under his irate gaze into an extension of the barracks square. It was his conviction that the town lived off the garrison, and it didn't live badly. A little gratitude was the least that could be expected. "I don't like your attitude," he pursued grimly.

"I can't say how my attitude strikes you," Asch said, still unruffled, "but I'll gladly tell you who I am. Among other things, I'm the owner of this establishment."

"There you are, then!" Rammler said triumphantly, determined not to be impressed by such a display of self-confidence on the part of a civilian. "That means you're responsible for the misuse of your telephone, blast you!"

"Perhaps you could do with a black coffee," Asch suggested. "Be my guest, if you're agreeable."

Rammler haughtily dismissed the suggestion. "What do you take me for—a sponger?"

"I don't know what you take me for," Klaus Ahlers mused, "but you're probably wrong. It's easy enough to make a mistake."

"You keep out of this. I wasn't talking to you."

"But I'm talking to you," said Ahlers. "It may interest you to know that I'm an air force captain."

Rammler was nonplused for a moment, but an expert of unarmed combat is always prepared for tricky countermoves on the part of an opponent. "Anyone can say that," he parried.

"Would you care to see my identity card?" Ahlers inquired affably.

Rammler hesitated again, this time for an appreciable span. After about five seconds he delivered what he conceived to be a short, sharp rabbit punch. "This has got nothing to do with you. I'm speaking to the owner of this dump, so there's no need for you to interfere. All I'm interested in is this telephone call. Besides, I'm here as a private individual."

"I'm glad to hear that," said Herbert Asch, "but I suggest you behave accordingly."

"I want to know who I was speaking to on the phone!" Rammler persisted. "I'll find that guy if it's the last thing I do."

"**S**IT DOWN," said Major Bornekamp. "It's about time I told you a few home truths."

This invitation was addressed to Lieutenant von Strackmann. The C.O. studied him closely, not without deriving mild satisfaction from his air of eager endeavor and willing deference.

"If I hadn't sent for you, Strackmann, what would you have been doing at this hour?"

"Working, sir."

"And when you had finished your work?"

"There's always something to do, sir."

Bornekamp imbibed some of the ruby-eyed contents of his glass. It was Turk's Blood, equal parts of native German champagne and French red wine. "Have you got a girl friend, von Strackmann?" he asked.

Von Strackmann repudiated the idea almost as if he were dismissing an unworthy suspicion. "No time for that sort of thing, sir. I hardly ever get out of barracks."

"My dear young friend," the C.O. said didactically, "there are some things one simply has to make time for, like shaving or personal hygiene. And there are certain young officers' activities which can be classified as part of personal hygiene."

Lieutenant von Strackmann tried to look amused. Everyone knew that when the C.O. indulged in turns of phrase like these it was advisable to humor him.

Having thus created what he felt to be a pleasant atmosphere of confidence, Bornekamp went so far as to pour the young officer a glass of Turk's Blood.

"I want to be able to rely on my officers," he continued, "especially those who work closely with me, like company commanders."

Von Strackmann nodded with alacrity. He was passionately eager to prove himself, and looked up to experienced superiors with quasi-religious fervor.

"Our world," said the C.O., "is a world apart. We must avoid letting outsiders exert an influence on our way of life. They must be given no occasion to do so."

This struck him as a peculiarly subtle piece of phrasing. What he really meant was: civilians, mayors included, have got no control over what we do here. Even so, they can't simply be slapped down when they dare to interfere with us. We just give them a friendly grin and leave it at that.

No other visible reaction of any kind—let alone a hastily organized field exercise.

"Do we understand each other, Strackmann?"

"Yes sir," the lieutenant assured him eagerly.

"Good," said Bornekamp. "Carry on like that, my dear boy, and you'll find yourself something more than an acting company commander in the near future."

Von Strackmann glowed, less with Turk's Blood than with pride. "Thank you, sir!"

"Would you do me a personal favor?" Bornekamp asked, almost confidentially.

"Name it, sir!"

"Go and see my wife—this evening if possible, and take a bottle of cognac with you. I promised her one. Give her my regards and tell her I shan't be home until very late, if at all. I have several things to check on and a stack of papers to look through. All right? Then I won't detain you any longer."

SERGEANT MAJOR RAMMLER crouched over his table in the Café Asch like an ornamental lion. He had commandeered a seat where he could watch the entrance and was lying in wait for Helen Wieder.

"You're probably wasting your time," Elisabeth Asch told him. "It's highly unlikely that Fraülein Wieder will be back tonight."

"But it's possible, isn't it?"

"It's not out of the question, certainly, but you may have to wait a very long time."

"I'll wait," Rammler said with dour determination. "I've got time, and I don't give up easily—anyone'll tell you that. Bring me a double, and make sure it's the brand I like."

"I'll pass your order on," said Frau Asch, gladly leaving her unwelcome guest to his own devices.

Rammler stared suspiciously at the fashionable café's smart décor until a waitress brought him his double dose of Strong Man's Milk. He inspected her carefully. She did not rate comparison with Helen Wieder in any respect, and was thus incapable of dispelling his mood of exasperation.

And then, in the doorway, he caught sight of a feminine apparition who seemed to be well worth a second look. The

girl, who had a lithe, athletic figure, stood there, taut as a steel spring, surveying the café like a sprinter about to perform on a cinder track.

She strode across the room, apparently making straight for Rammler, and sat down at the next table. She was a chic little thing, he noted expertly, with plenty of spirit and a smart get-up that would have done credit to a soldier.

Blithely ignoring the fact that the table next to him was the only free table in the café, Rammler construed her proximity as an invitation to dance.

"Well, what about it?" he asked, leaning forward confidentially.

Everything about the girl was cool and bright: her hair, her eyes, and her dress. Her voice was no exception. "Have we met?" she inquired.

"We have now," Rammler said adventurously. In the first place, the girl appealed to him, and, in the second place, that artful bitch Helen Wieder deserved a lesson. He'd show her she wasn't the only pebble on the beach!

"Will you come to my table, or shall I sit with you?"

"Neither," said a male voice over Rammler's shoulder. "Don't bother, friend—the lady already has a date."

Rammler looked round indignantly to see a slim man of medium height dressed in civilian clothes. "My name's Vossler," he said with a cheerful smile.

"It could be Adenauer, for all I care. I was speaking to this young lady, not you."

"My answer to that," said the girl in tones of relief, "is: get lost."

It was an unmistakable brush-off, and a man with less self-confidence would have accepted it as such—but not Rammler. He was slightly taken aback but far from discouraged.

Observing the couple at the next table with some resentment, he noted that she called him Viktor and he called her Gerty—presumably a shortening of Gertrud—and that they behaved like a couple of turtledoves. Wresting his exasperated gaze away from them he focused it on the counter, and what he saw there exasperated him still further.

Grenadier Martin Recht was standing there—Recht, the very person responsible for his disappointing day. He had already taught him a preliminary lesson, but the boy was looking cheerful enough. He chatted casually to the woman behind the counter until, almost as though he felt Rammler's gaze on him, he glanced in the sergeant major's

direction. Rammler drew himself up in his seat to ensure that Recht caught sight of him, and the grenadier, with a sudden start, saluted in a most irregular manner.

Rammler did not deign to return the compliment. Instead, he waggled the index finger of his right hand, and Recht moved obediently in his platoon commander's direction.

"What do you think you're doing here?" demanded Rammler.

Realizing that there was no satisfactory answer to this sort of question, Recht remained mutely at attention, his eyes pleading for at least a modicum of human decency.

"I'll tell you what you're doing," Rammler pursued ruthlessly. "Flirting, when you're supposed to be on guard duty."

"I had no idea . . ."

Rammler glowered at the grenadier, still casting around for the best course to adopt.

At this point the man in the civilian suit at the next table had the effrontery to intervene for a second time. He interrupted his billing and cooing, stood up and walked over to Recht. "Hello!" he exclaimed. "Who have we got here? It's last night's visitor, isn't it?"

"Hello, sir," said Recht, feeling immeasurably relieved. "How are you?"

"Fine," said Warrant Officer Vossler. "I'm enjoying an evening out. You ought to do the same—don't let anyone put you off."

Recht smiled gratefully at Vossler and clasped his outstretched hand like a drowning man clutching a lifeline.

"Won't you join us, Herr Recht?" Vossler asked cordially. "Fräulein Ballhaus and I would be delighted."

"Do you mind!" said Rammler with barely suppressed fury. "Who do you think you are, sticking your nose in like this? My conversation's got nothing to do with you."

"Keep your hair on, chum." Vossler regarded Rammler placidly. "You've got the wrong end of the stick: you're the one who's barging in. I wouldn't, unless you want to make an exhibition of yourself."

"What do you mean—'chum'!" shouted Rammler. "I'm talking to one of my men on an official matter. I won't tolerate any interference!"

Viktor Vossler placed one arm protectively round Martin Recht's shoulders, and his voice took on the quiet but incisive tones of a muted violin. "Calm down, my friend. Take a few deep breaths and count up to ten—and don't

forget the old soldier's motto: things are never as bad as they seem."

"Cut it out!" Rammler shouted irascibly, his blood pressure rising several points as he registered the impudent smile on Gerty's face. "I won't be talked to like that, do you hear!"

At this point, Herbert Asch bore down on the group, unerring as a hawk, and stationed himself between the adversaries like a referee. "Do you mind turning the volume down a bit, gentlemen?" he asked. "This is a café, not a barracks."

"Maybe," thundered Rammler, "but I'm dealing with an official matter. It's got nothing to do with anyone except Grenadier Recht and me."

"You're mistaken," Asch said calmly. "This is my sphere of jurisdiction, not yours."

Martin Recht stood there like a forlorn sheep in a deserted field. He could hear the wolves howling all round him, but somehow he felt safe.

"Listen, you!" Rammler hissed at Asch. "I'm warning you—don't stick your nose into army business."

"Better let me handle this," Vossler suggested. "It's far easier to settle these things if you talk the same language."

"Quite unnecessary," said Asch. "I'm in charge here, no one else. That being so, Herr Rammler, I must regretfully ask you to stop annoying my customers and leave at once."

"You're not serious!" Rammler eyed Asch incredulously. "You're not chucking me out?"

"Call it what you like."

"All right, I'm going," Rammler said menacingly. "But you'll regret this, I promise you!"

He departed without paying his bill; Asch ordered it to be debited to his personal account as running expenses, and then devoted himself to Martin Recht. He invited the slightly bemused grenadier to his private quarters, partly so that Recht could renew his acquaintanceship with Captain Ahlers, and partly so as to leave Vossler and his girl friend in peace.

Sergeant Rammler, meanwhile, strode through the swing doors determined to endure his heavy lot with dignity. He felt himself to be the victim of malicious and uncomprehending civilians, of fellow N.C.O.s without any sense of solidarity, and of women who lacked all appreciation of real values.

Smiling contemptuously, he started down the stairs that

64

led to the street, then stopped as though rooted to the spot. Helen Wieder was on her way up, accompanied by Karl Kamnitzer.

"Good evening, Sergeant Major!" called Kamnitzer. "Not leaving, are you?"

"You!" the sergeant croaked. "You're the one I spoke to on the phone!"

"Am I?" Kamnitzer asked, eyes twinkling. "When was that? And if it was did you enjoy it?"

Helen Wieder pushed past Rammler. "Fine behavior, I must say," she remarked in quiet but challenging tones, "shooting a big line with a girl and then standing her up. I'm not used to that sort of thing, I can tell you."

Rammler felt that he had been abruptly forced onto the defensive. Instead of venting his anger in a flood of accusations, as he had meant to, he was now being called upon to justify himself. Helen Wieder evidently doubted his good will, his tried and proven reputation for reliability.

"But I sent my apologies," he said. "I was held up by work—an unexpected field exercise."

Helen Wieder stared at him incredulously, and Rammler turned, with a mixture of reproach and entreaty, to Kamnitzer. "Didn't you tell Fräulein Wieder that?"

"Me? Why should I have?"

"We talked to each other on the phone, for God's sake!"

"Did we?" Kamnitzer looked mightily surprised. "Was that really you?"

"Of course! Who did you think it was?"

"That's funny," said Kamnitzer, "I could have sworn it was someone trying to pull my leg. He called himself Sergeant Major Rammler, but I've been had like that before."

"Who do you think you're fooling?" Rammler demanded furiously. "I know your type, don't worry."

"You're not being fair, Sergeant Major," Kamnitzer said with an ingenuous smile. "Put yourself in my place. Some guy rings up and gives your name, bellowing something about a field training exercise—to me, when I happen to know our training program backward and could have told him there was no field exercise scheduled for today."

"It was changed without warning, you fool!"

"Really? But how could I have known that? Besides, your voice sounded different from the way it does in barracks —quite charming, it was."

"This is too stupid!" said Helen Wieder. "I can't stand around here all night."

"But I'm only trying to explain, Fräulein."

65

"I've heard quite enough," she snapped, and made her way up the steps.

The sergeant major and the corporal stared after her, reduced to rapt silence by the sight of her undulating posterior, which might have fulfilled any soldier's dream of home and beauty.

"I hope you'll excuse me," said Kamnitzer, "but I'm a bit pushed for time. You see, Sergeant Major, I've offered to entertain Fräulein Wieder—as your deputy, so to speak. I couldn't let her just sit there, all dressed up and nowhere to go. I'm the persevering type, too. I'll do my best to go on entertaining her, if that's all right with you. It's the least I can do."

So saying, Kamnitzer deserted the sergeant major and started up the steps after Helen. Rammler stood there open-mouthed for some time, as though turned to stone. Then he clamped his jaw shut, shook his head ponderously and stamped away, telling himself that people couldn't treat him like that with impunity.

THE FOLLOWING morning opened with the daily but ever-enjoyable spectacle of Lieutenant von Strackmann personally cleaning his boots, a task which he performed in the corridor outside the door of his room, where his example could be observed by all.

At the same time, he summoned the duty N.C.O. and asked, still polishing busily, for his report. "Nothing special to report, sir," was the form it took, morning after morning, to which his invariable reply was: "I'd like it even better if there were."

After the duty N.C.O. had feasted his eyes sufficiently on the person of the acting company commander, it was the C.S.M.'s turn to appear.

Kirschke was late as usual, but he turned up in the end, looking comparatively rested at this early hour of the day. The two men eyed each other with mistrust.

"Well," said the lieutenant, "what's on today?"

"The usual," Kirschke replied laconically.

The lieutenant demanded details. He knew the day's program like the back of his hand, but he wanted to know if the C.S.M. was equally well informed. Kirschke drew a mimeographed sheet from his pocket and prepared to read its contents aloud.

"Don't bother with that!" Von Strackmann's contempt for

the refractory sergeant major was so intense that he forgot to polish his boots for a moment. "I want to know what you—you personally—intend to do today."

"The usual," Kirschke delivered himself of this remark with unremitting indifference. "Routine jobs, that's all."

"Company Sergeant Major Kirschke," the lieutenant said acidly, "I expect my senior N.C.O.s to produce at least one good idea a day."

Kirschke would have had no difficulty in producing the requisite good idea, but he sagely kept it to himself. Von Strackmann behaved as though he were in the Boy Scouts, he reflected. If von Strackmann had seen the light of German day twenty years earlier the Hitler Jugend could scarcely have gained a more promising recruit, but he had been born into a democracy, worse luck.

The indefatigable von Strackmann spent the first few hours of this particular day playing the sheep dog, as Kirschke termed it. He watched over his flock, circled it alertly and intently, shepherded stragglers back into the fold and generally kept things on the move. While he did so his thoughts returned repeatedly to the C.S.M., who seemed, quite apart from anything else, to be one of the stiffest hurdles in his path to professional success. There were, he told himself, ample reasons for removing the said hurdle. Its elimination was imperative not only in his own interests but in the interests of the company.

At last, when he could withstand the voice of decision no longer, the lieutenant went to the company office. The C.S.M. was not there, but von Strackmann's persistent inquiries as to his whereabouts elicited the information that he was "in his room, probably, changing his trousers."

Kirschke had actually announced his intention of changing his trousers two hours before, but no one thought to inform the lieutenant of this fact and he omitted to ask.

Borne along on wings of suspicion, he made for the C.S.M.'s room, which gave off a downstairs corridor. He did not get further than the door, however, because it was locked. His knocking, discreet at first, like that of a chambermaid, produced no response.

"Sergeant Major Kirschke!" he called imperiously. "Open up!"

The door remained shut.

"Open up, Sergeant Major!" he repeated, this time thundering on the panels like a detective armed with a warrant. "This is Lieutenant von Strackmann! I know you're in there!"

He beat a few more tattoos, but his only answer was continued and provocative silence.

Quick as a flash, the lieutenant raced along the corridor, out the door and around the block to the spot where he judged Kirschke's window to be.

The window was about ten feet above the ground, but von Strackmann was an athletic young man. Leaping up, he grasped the window sill and performed a textbook pull-up—much to the delight of several watching grenadiers.

Looking through the window with his chin on the sill, von Strackmann was rewarded by the sight of a plump posterior clad in underpants. While von Strackmann was peering through the window into the room, Kirschke was peering through the keyhole into the corridor.

This vision seemed to rob von Strackmann of his remaining reserves of strength. He dropped to the ground, panting slightly. Then he marched off at speed, round the block, along the corridor, and up to Kirschke's room. The door was now open, and the C.S.M. was looking out.

"You haven't heard the last of this," said von Strackmann, still breathing heavily.

"What's up?" Kirschke demanded. "Can't a man change his trousers these days?"

"Behind locked doors?" the lieutenant asked sternly.

"Certainly, sir. I always lock the door before changing my trousers. One of the lady cleaners might walk in."

"We'll see about that," von Strackmann said grimly. "I shall conduct the requisite investigations in person."

"By all means, sir." Kirschke appeared unimpressed. He was satisfied that he was more than a match for a pompous ignoramus like von Strackmann, but, on the other hand, the lieutenant was capable of making a nuisance of himself, so it might be advisable to distract his attention. "All the same, there are more urgent matters to attend to."

"Kindly allow me to decide that!"

"Of course, sir. But there was a call for you earlier from a Herr Asch, proprietor of the hotel of the same name. He wanted to know whether you could persuade members of your unit not to behave like animals in his establishment."

Von Strackmann drew himself up stiffly, like a wax effigy. "He said that—to you?"

"That's right, sir. He wanted to speak to you at first, but you were too far away to be reached."

"The man actually said that?"

Kirschke noted the lieutenant's expression of outrage with gratification. Herbert Asch had not employed such a harsh

turn of phrase, of course, but Kirschke's rendering was an accurate interpretation of his meaning, and von Strackmann was evidently prepared to accept it at its face value.

The lieutenant immediately recalled his momentous conversation with the C.O. on the previous evening, particularly the disguised injunction not to be pushed around by civilians.

"Who does he think he is?" he demanded unsuspectingly. He knew very little about conditions in town. His life was dedicated exclusively to the army, and he seldom looked beyond the confines of the barracks—except in the direction of the training area. Consequently, he had no idea who Herbert Asch was and cared less.

"Here's his telephone number," said Kirschke, proffering a slip of paper.

Von Strackmann snatched it as a pike snaps at a minnow. "I'll show him where he gets off!"

Five telephone calls ensued in the next few minutes. First, von Strackmann called the hotel and asked the switchboard to connect him with Herbert Asch. He told him, among other things, that indirect accusations were valueless and that any complaints should be communicated in writing through official channels.

Herbert Asch was slightly taken aback. "I hope you realize who you're speaking to," he said mildly.

"As long as you know who you're speaking to," von Strackmann replied, "that's good enough for me."

Herbert Asch did know, and it was he who conducted the second conversation in the series, this time with Captain Ahlers.

Asch told him of his precautionary telephone call to No. 3 Company. His sole intention had been to curb the high spirits of a sergeant major named Rammler and thereby protect Martin Recht. He had first spoken to a Sergeant Major Kirschke, who appeared to be a calm, congenial, and understanding person, but had later been telephoned by another man, Lieutenant von Strackmann by name.

"I know him slightly," Ahlers said. "He's a bit officious, but he probably means well."

"I'm glad to hear it. He dressed me down as though I was a pickpocket."

"Did he?" mused Ahlers. "We'll see about that."

The third phone call was made by Ahlers to Colonel Turner. "Deal with it, my dear chap," said the latter, after listening in attentive silence. "Deal with it for me—in the regulation manner, of course."

Captain Ahlers pointed out that the situation was not so straightforward this time. "You see, sir," he confessed, "I was the one who advised Herr Asch not to lodge an official complaint. I thought it better to settle the matter as unobtrusively as possible."

"Nothing wrong with that," Turner said approvingly. "I consider that your advice was most apt, under the circumstances."

"Except that it was addressed to the mayor of the town by the deputy area commandant, in a sense, so Herr Asch regarded my suggestion as semi-official. Lieutenant von Strackmann's brusque manner was extremely ill-judged, to say the least. I think a word to his commanding officer wouldn't be out of place, and it can only come from you, sir. Your experience of interservice diplomacy is infinitely greater than mine."

Although Colonel Turner found some difficulty in swallowing this, he saw no alternative but to make the suggested telephone call.

He picked up the receiver and asked to speak to Major Bornekamp. It was not his habit, he said, to offer unsolicited advice, and he did his best not to interfere in other spheres of command—"but a commanding officer is responsible for his officers, as I'm sure you'll agree."

"Are you speaking in general terms, Colonel, or have you a particular case in mind?"

"One of your officers, a Lieutenant von Strackmann, has made a serious blunder. He spoke to the mayor, Herr Asch, in a manner which I can only describe as inconsiderate in the extreme. I can't believe that you would have approved, Major. After all, Herr Asch is the local civilian leader—at least until the next elections. As area commandant, I'm rather concerned, but I'm sure you'll deal with the matter in the correct and befitting manner."

The major received this gentle but unmistakable reprimand with a grinding of teeth. He knew that the colonel would now compile a report giving the place, date, time, and exact details of their conversation. Apart from that, he felt that von Strackmann had let him down. He had credited the lieutenant with more intelligence, but he must have been deceived. At all events, it was von Strackmann who had called down this unpleasant rebuke upon his head.

Thus it was Major Bornekamp who made the fifth telephone call. Summoning Lieutenant von Strackmann to the

phone, he pulverized him—as Kirschke later described it—like a tank running over a frog.

"Sheer idiocy—that's what it was!" the C.O. bellowed. "Iron things out immediately, or you'll find yourself out on your neck!"

Lieutenant von Strackmann stood there like a block of stone while C.S.M. Kirschke, who had heard every word, grinned happily.

"Do you want me to put myself on a charge now," Kirschke inquired, "for sleeping during the hours of duty?" He might almost have added: "At least a sleeping man doesn't make idiotic phone calls," but this would have been superfluous. Von Strackmann could guess what the C.S.M. was thinking.

"YOU MUST excuse my husband's absence, Herr Recht. He seems to have been detained."

Frau Ahlers smiled at her guest as she spoke, and there was no hint of resentment in her voice.

"We live very simply," she continued, "but I don't need to tell you that—you can see for yourself."

Martin Recht could, but it didn't embarrass him. The furniture was simple and functional, the materials tasteful but obviously cheap, the carpet a plain, inexpensive broadloom. Recht knew a little about such things because his mother owned a shop which sold modern furnishings.

"I must get back to the kitchen," Frau Ahlers went on, "but my daughter will keep you company in the meanwhile."

Her thin, serene face appealed to Recht. She hesitated for a moment, then asked: "Did my husband tell you that our daughter is an invalid—I mean, that she has a disability which hasn't been cured yet?"

"Yes, he did mention it."

"Did he say what it was?"

"No."

"You're bound to notice," said Frau Ahlers, "but I'm sure you'll know how to treat it."

Carolin Ahlers appeared a moment or two later. Looking at her, Recht became aware that her eyes were bright and her skin the color of white roses bathed in evening sunlight. Her long sweeping hair was like a silken curtain and her smile, he noted blissfully, reminiscent of a princess

in a fairy tale. In short, Martin Recht experienced a brief moment of poetic rapture.

He couldn't help himself. There was a sort of enchantment about the girl which gently but irresistibly fired his imagination. Then he saw her walking, and was jolted back to reality. She walked carefully, uncertainly, as though not in full command of her limbs. It might have been said that she limped, but that was not an entirely apt description of her deliberate but somehow tentative movements. Although he registered all this objectively, Martin Recht knew at the same time that he would not have been unduly surprised if she had risen into the air and floated slowly toward him.

She noticed his expression and smiled—not a brave smile, but one which seemed to contain more sympathy for Recht than for herself. Watching her visitor closely, Frau Ahlers was happy to see that he quickly overcame his surprise.

"Can I help you?" he asked, hurrying forward to meet the girl.

"Oh no, thank you!" she replied with unexpected gaiety. "I can walk quite well by myself. You must just try to get used to it—or don't you like sick people?"

"What makes you think that?" he said, pulling a chair forward for her. "My sister had polio, and she did her best to exploit us all—had the family running around like slaves."

"What about you—did you let her exploit you?"

"Of course, I enjoyed it." Recht took Carolin's arm without undue hesitation. "Do let me. You mustn't discourage my chivalrous instincts."

Frau Ahlers smiled at her daughter and nodded at Martin Recht with a mixture of gratitude and encouragement before leaving the room.

Recht drew up a chair and placed it next to Carolin's. At first he found it slightly disconcerting to be gazing into that gentle, radiant, smiling face at such close quarters. This time it reminded him—borne away on another flight of fancy—of a spring morning, but he forced himself to concentrate on her disability.

"How do you come to walk like that?" he asked, frankly curious. "What's the trouble exactly?"

"Partial paralysis of the legs," Carolin replied. "There's something wrong with my spine."

"I'm so sorry," said Recht, trying to sound as matter-of-fact as possible. "How long have you had it?"

72

"Ever since I was born."

Martin Recht could not conceal his surprise. He looked at her inquiringly.

"I'm a sort of hangover from the last war," Carolin went on. "I was born in Lübeck in nineteen forty-five, during the trek from the East. The hospital was packed and the doctors were working round the clock. Anyway, they made a mess of me."

"What can I say?" Recht said gently.

"Nothing. There's nothing to be said. I'm like that— and that's all there is to it." Carolin leaned back in her chair looking resigned and a little tired. "It's not as bad as all that, is it? I'm quite used to it."

"What about the doctors? Can't they do anything?"

"They've done a lot already. I've had several operations, you know. It was much worse in the old days. I used to sit in a wheelchair the whole time, but now I can walk." She added, smiling: "A little, anyway. That's something."

"It's a lot!" Martin Recht broke in. "It's a great deal— and a good beginning. Do you ever go for walks?"

"Sometimes, with my mother. In the Municipal Gardens, usually."

"Does it tire you?"

"No, not if people are patient with me."

"Splendid," Martin Recht said firmly. "Then you can come for a walk with me sometime."

Carolin eyed him dubiously. "Do you mean it?"

"Why shouldn't I?"

The rosy flush on her cheeks seemed to deepen. "You're just saying that to be polite, or to cheer me up—or perhaps because you feel you owe something to my father. But you've no need to, really you haven't."

"Listen to me," said Recht, drawing a deep breath and searching for the bluntest way of expressing what he wanted to say. He had always found it the best way of handling his invalid sister. "You're talking nonsense. I like you—that's all that matters. Or doesn't the idea of my company appeal to you?"

"It's not that."

"Then it's settled."

"Maybe."

"When are we going for this walk, then?" he persisted.

"Sometime soon."

"Why not this evening, after supper?"

Carolin shook her head doubtfully. "I don't know—we oughtn't to rush things."

"There's no point in waiting. Is it a date? Please say yes."

Carolin Ahlers smiled. "Well, yes, of course," she said.

"You ought to install a waiting room," Corporal Kamnitzer suggested. "I feel as if I were visiting the dentist."

"What dentist," asked Asch, "would supply his patients with free drinks?"

"Am I a patient of yours?"

"Let's say I regard you as a sort of guinea pig."

"What's the experiment?"

"I'm interested in finding out whether common sense ever prevails in the army."

"You've come to the wrong man, Herr Asch. It doesn't need any common sense to do what I do occasionally—just instinct. I hope you don't think I'm hellbent on throwing a monkey wrench into the military works, because that's the last thing I want to do. It's an entertaining sight, army life—like a circus. I sit back watching it and waiting for the end of the performance."

Herbert Asch regarded Kamnitzer benevolently. There were moments when he saw the young man as a reincarnation of himself, but things had changed a good deal since he last wore uniform. Or had they?

Asch had invited Kamnitzer into his office so that he could wait there quietly, and without charge, for Helen Wieder.

"Go on like this," said Kamnitzer, "and you'll find yourself running a soldiers' canteen."

"Surely you don't regard everyone in uniform as a soldier?"

Kamnitzer grinned. "You want me to stick my neck out, don't you?"

"Don't you trust me?" Asch asked, amused.

"It's not that, exactly," Kamnitzer replied casually. "But I can put two and two together, and I know the garrison brings you in a fair amount of business."

"You mean I make money out of it?"

"Of course. Quite a bit, too—not that I grudge it to you."

"I'm happy to hear it."

This conversation, which Asch seemed to be enjoying, was rudely interrupted by the appearance of Viktor Vossler, who walked in without knocking, stalked over to Asch and

halted in front of him with an expression of mock severity on his face.

"Oh dear!" Asch chuckled. "Have you come to read the riot act? I've already had one lecture."

"The way you treat your employees," Vossler said pleasantly, "verges on slavery. Overtime seems to be the order of the day with you lately."

"I second that," said Kamnitzer. He regarded Vossler, whom he had not met before, with interest.

"Don't be too hasty, my friend." Herbert Asch rubbed his hands gleefully, and those who knew him well could have forecast that he was about to make one of his little jokes. "After all, you may both be waiting for the same girl— what then?"

Vossler and Kamnitzer, each in civilian clothes, eyed one another with mounting distrust. As men of similar caliber, it occurred to them that they might well appeal to the same girl, despite their difference in age.

"Don't you gentlemen know each other?" Asch asked amiably. "Allow me to introduce you: Warrant Officer Vossler—Corporal Kamnitzer."

"I won't say I'm delighted to meet you because I don't know whether I am yet," said Kamnitzer, without rising from his chair. "But I'd like to point out—just in passing —that I'm here as a private individual."

"So am I," said Vossler, extending his hand after a moment's hesitation.

Asch enjoyed watching the two men jockeying for position in ignorance of the fact that Kamnitzer was waiting for Helen Wieder, still on duty in the café, and Vossler for Gertrud Ballhaus, Asch's private secretary, who was finishing off some letters for him.

Kamnitzer took Vossler's hand and shook it casually. "Maybe you'd prefer me to salute?" he said.

"Forget it," said Vossler, dropping into an armchair.

"What do you mean—forget it?" Kamnitzer asked. "I'm here privately, I'm in civvies, and I'm a guest of Herr Asch, so you can't expect me to salute. I don't expect you to, either."

Vossler felt slightly worried. He was taken aback by Kamnitzer's cool effrontery because he knew it was what appealed to Gerty in himself. He smiled uneasily and made no reply.

Kamnitzer, however, pressed on regardless. "If you want to know, it doesn't matter to me whether a man's a warrant officer or a postman. I couldn't care less."

75

"That makes two of us," said Vossler.

"Then we're all agreed," Asch interposed, pushing a brimming wineglass toward each of his guests. Before they drank he enlightened them about his little joke, deriving as much amusement from their relief as he had from the mutual hostility that preceded it.

"All the same," Vossler confessed, "for a moment I really thought you'd been poaching on my preserves."

"I'm honored," Kamnitzer said. "The same goes for me."

Vossler smiled. "Glad to have met you, anyway."

Herbert Asch leaned back contentedly in his chair. It pleased him when his friends got on well with one another.

"Tell me something," Kamnitzer said after a pause. "For a warrant officer, you're almost human. Don't you feel a bit lonely in your mob, or are there more where you come from?"

"Plenty," Vossler assured him.

"And you're not regarded as undesirable types?"

"We're in the majority. It's the others who are the undesirables."

"That's terrific!" Kamnitzer exclaimed. "You're not pulling my leg, are you?"

"Pay us a visit sometime," Vossler suggested. "Any time —I'd be happy to show you round."

"I'll take you up on that," said Kamnitzer. "I always find it a bit hard to believe that all barracks aren't identical." A look of sudden distrust flitted across his face. "Or do you look on yourselves as a sort of feudal club?"

"We're flyers," Vossler said. "That's all we're interested in—flying."

"Ah!" said Kamnitzer. "And it doesn't matter to you whether you fly around carrying bombs, medicine, ammunition, or underpants?"

"The types you dig up!" Vossler said, turning to Asch. "Who does our friend think he is—a frustrated missionary or something?"

Asch smiled almost affectionately at Kamnitzer. "He suffers from attacks of conscience sometimes, only he won't admit it."

"Oh well," Kamnitzer shrugged, "let's not go into that. Whatever you do in the air, Herr Vossler, I've a feeling we mightn't get on badly on the ground."

"How nice of you to find time to drop in again," said Frau Bornekamp, opening the front door wide.

Before her stood Lieutenant von Strackmann, Christian name Dieter. Holding the upper part of his body rigid, like a sack stuffed with sawdust, he described a series of movements which might have been interpreted as something between a correct military salute and a deferential greeting. "I hope I'm not disturbing you, ma'am," he said courteously.

"What do you think!" Elfrieda Bornekamp cried with the spirited graciousness of one born to command. "No false modesty, now! You know you're very welcome."

Von Strackmann expressed his gratitude in what he deemed to be the regulation manner. Not for nothing had he passed the officer cadets' course entitled "Social Etiquette," a success which was recorded in his personal file.

Docilely, he followed the C.O.'s lady inside, circling her attentively in an effort to keep on her left side. Before he could unwrap his bottle of cognac—the second he had delivered (at the C.O.'s suggestion) within a week—he found himself in the drawing room, and not only in the drawing room but on the couch.

Elfrieda Bornekamp switched on a table lamp and extinguished the center light. "We can chat better like that. It's much cozier, don't you think?" Then she sat down beside him at a distance of approximately twelve inches.

"This is a great honor for me," the lieutenant declared manfully. "I'm most grateful for all your kindness and generosity."

Von Strackmann did indeed feel privileged. Not only had he, a young officer, been appointed to stand in for an ailing company commander, but the C.O. had made him a repository of his personal confidence. He had conversed with him privately and introduced him to his family circle.

To Frau Elfrieda, there was something endearing about the young officer's fresh, idealistic approach. She shifted four inches closer, conscious that the subdued glow of the table lamp behind her enhanced her charms.

"My husband," she said without resentment, "is so busy all the time."

"Duty comes first with him," the lieutenant declared. "He never spares himself. It's remarkable."

77

"Remarkable," Frau Elfrieda agreed. "But he never neglects me. Look at the way he sends you to see me."

"I regard it as a great honor," said von Strackmann. He was determined to prove himself worthy of the C.O.'s trust, and it occurred to him that the most effective way of doing so would be to reveal some of his personal plans. Frau Bornekamp would undoubtedly tell her husband about them. "I started a debit-and-credit book today."

"A what?" Frau Elfrieda had been on the point of sliding another four inches closer.

"A debit-and-credit book," repeated von Strackmann. "You know, an assessment of individual merit, based on a points system. The C.O.'s extremely receptive to new ideas, but he tries to combine them with traditional methods of training. I think it's a first-class principle."

Frau Elfrieda sank back as though slightly exhausted. As she did so, her left knee brushed Dieter's right. "I beg your pardon!" he said politely, withdrawing the offending limb in haste. Then he cleared his throat and went on: "I always do my utmost to follow the C.O.'s suggestions."

"Do you really?"

"In every respect," he assured her. "Hence my debit-and-credit book. By keeping it, I'm implementing one of the C.O.'s most stimulating suggestions. You see, traditional methods of character assessment ignore some of the finer psychological points."

"And you feel you're a good judge of character?"

"I try to be. Anyway, I shall do my best to observe the requisite gradations as accurately as possible in future. For instance, do you know the difference between an admonition and a reprimand?"

"No," said Frau Elfrieda, almost tartly.

Quite oblivious, von Strackmann plunged into greater detail. He spoke of the severe reprimand, which does not exclude the possibility of improvement, and expatiated at some length on the "warning," which was equivalent to disapproval and implied that the recipient might be reported to a superior. Finally—

"You're being a bore," Frau Elfrieda said bluntly.

Von Strackmann was dismayed. "I'm so sorry," he said, trying to master his embarrassment. "Please tell me what I can do. . . ."

"Open that bottle of cognac," commanded Frau Elfrieda, "and come here."

Major Bornekamp, meanwhile, was indulging in his favorite pastime: war. It was only a paper war, of course, but—in default of the real thing—it seemed to be claiming his fullest attention.

A reporter named Flammer from the local *Town and Country News* had been waiting outside for a considerable time, but Bornekamp let him wait. To the major, Flammer was just a cheap penny-a-liner who produced half a page of marketable padding for forty or fifty marks. A few years back he had probably been churning out articles entitled "Peace in Our Time," but now, no doubt, he was writing decent German again. Reflecting that he was not one to bear a grudge, Bornekamp waited a while longer and then asked Herr Flammer to come in.

"Well, fire away, my dear boy," the C.O. said indulgently, leaning back in his chair with the air of a *grand seigneur*. "What do you want to know?"

His sovereign sense of superiority was so complete that he omitted to ask another, equally important question: namely, what had inspired the journalist to come and see him in the first place. Flammer might, of course, have attributed the interview to general public interest, but he might also have answered, more truthfully, that he was following up a suggestion made by Mayor Asch.

In fact, Asch had done more than inspire Flammer to visit the major. He had even worked out the various questions to be put at the interview. The first of these sounded entirely innocuous.

"What is your opinion of the latest intake of recruits?"

Bornekamp gave a superior smile at this naïve inquiry. "I'd describe them as first-rate material," he said without hesitation. "Young men free from false, airy-fairy idealism. Down-to-earth, realistic, clear-thinking—and fundamentally reliable as a result. They've got their feet firmly planted on democratic soil."

The journalist did not look up from his notebook as he put the second question.

"How would you describe the relationship between your men and the civilian population?"

The major was secretly amused. Naïve wasn't the word for this hack, he told himself. The man was a blithering idiot. What was more, he doubted whether Flammer had

ever seen service. You could tell that just from the slovenly way he sat, hunched up like a sack of potatoes.

"Relations with civilian population . . ." Bornekamp knew all the appropriate clichés on this subject, and he reeled them off like a gramophone record. "Improving day by day, thanks to increased understanding on both sides. The men like it here. Occasional isolated and trivial incidents make no difference. We still have to overcome the after-effects of certain slanderous allegations leveled at the army in the past—but overcome them we shall!"

Flammer scribbled away busily. He had a whole string of similar questions in stock, and Bornekamp's answers bubbled forth like spring water. He quoted whole pages from army periodicals, interspersing them with choice extracts from his own lectures to officers' instructional classes.

Flammer's pencil continued to race across the paper. He gave no indication of whether he understood the finer points of the major's discourse, but simply wrote down whatever was said. Little by little, his questions coaxed the C.O., by now in full spate, out onto the thin ice of politics.

"Do you consider that traditional barracks-square methods, as generally understood, have been abolished?"

"There was no need to abolish them," Bornekamp asserted, "because they never existed—except in a few isolated cases which had no bearing on the army as a whole. It should be realized that the stories one heard about such things in the old days were often concocted by irresponsible idiots or deliberate liars. They were either exaggerated or based on rare and exceptional cases. Any allegations to the contrary are slanderous falsehoods put about by left-wing intellectuals for their own nefarious ends."

Major Bornekamp had got the bit firmly between his teeth by this time, but he was bolting in the desired direction. Flammer only needed to put one last question, and he did so with a well-simulated air of innocence.

"What is your opinion of conscientious objectors?"

This, as Herbert Asch knew, was one of the major's pet subjects. The red rag having been unfurled, the bull launched himself at it with predictable ferocity. "Conscientious objectors? Either Communists or cowards. Stick 'em into a striped suit and you'd soon see the last of 'em!"

"Thank you, Major," said Flammer, closing his notebook. "I'm sure your remarks will arouse great interest—very great interest indeed."

Sᴇʀɢᴇᴀɴᴛ Mᴀᴊᴏʀ Rᴀᴍᴍʟᴇʀ was paying another visit to the Café Asch. His objective, needless to say, was Helen Wieder, but he had not come alone this time. The privilege of accompanying him had fallen to Corporal Streicher.

"They don't make soldiers like they used to," Rammler declared, looking about him scornfully. "You're not up to standard either, Streicher, but you could be. You've got the makings. You know how to treat your superiors properly."

Although Streicher knew better than to attach too much importance to such figures of speech, he experienced a certain sense of gratification. Sergeant Major Rammler obviously had a weakness for him, and that could be useful, especially as he wanted to rise to the rank of sergeant.

"It won't be long before you get your third stripe," Rammler told him confidentially.

"Really, Sergeant Major?"

"If I say so." Rammler stared across the café to where Helen Wieder was standing. "Just between you and me, Streicher, you've already been recommended for promotion."

Streicher was not unaware of this, either, but he feigned pleased surprise. Discreetly, he asked if he might order a round.

"Two or three, if you like," said Rammler, raising his hand. Helen Wieder ignored the gesture. She publicized her refusal to serve him by sending over the stringy female who had incurred his displeasure once before.

"This world stinks," Rammler said darkly. "Take it from me, Streicher."

Streicher concurred, even though he was an optimistic person who brimmed with orthodox ideas. "All the same, Sergeant Major, there are constructive forces at work too."

Rammler gave a nod of agreement, but his excursion into philosophy was not over yet. "Artificial, that's what this world is," he brooded. "A lot of fairies, that's all they are these days, and the women fling themselves at them—God knows why."

Still meditating on this gloomy prospect, he tore his gaze away from Helen Wieder and looked toward the swing doors. Martin Recht, that milksop of a soldier with his typically civilian mannerisms, was just entering, accompanied by a girl who walked with a slight limp.

81

"Look what Recht's dug up!" exclaimed Rammler. "Just his type, I reckon."

Martin Recht's whole attention was chivalrously concentrated on Carolin Ahlers. He had eyes for her alone, and her slight air of helplessness only strengthened his tender feelings for her. He found a table near the entrance, oblivious of the fact that Rammler was sitting nearby.

He held Carolin's chair and sat down opposite her, with his back to the sergeant major. Then he reached for her hand, which was trembling slightly, and covered it with his own.

"You see," he said cheerfully, "it wasn't as bad as all that."

"You made it easy for me, Martin."

Recht looked a little shy. "Keep up the good work," he said hurriedly, "and we'll soon be able to take quite long walks together."

"That would be lovely," Carolin said, looking down at the table, where his hand lay on hers.

Rammler, who heard every word of this conversation, snorted contemptuously as he watched the neighboring table being subjected to a sort of invasion.

The first to appear was Helen Wieder, who gave the couple a cordial welcome and took their order—a bottle of mineral water for Carolin and a coffee for Martin. Rammler watched her retreating form in an agony of frustration.

A moment later Frau Asch arrived. She greeted the young couple like old friends—more than that, she sat down at their table and chatted with them for some minutes until Helen Wieder reappeared with their order. "I'll leave you to yourselves now," she said, rising. "I hope we'll be seeing a lot of you both in future."

No one paid any attention to Rammler, although he was a regular customer. Helen Wieder seemed to have a penchant for inferior forms of life, he reflected savagely. What was worse, she concentrated her attentions on the less admirable members of the species. He decided to make it a matter of principle.

Turning portentously in his chair, he tapped Recht on the shoulder and said, more parenthetically than severely: "Your eyesight bad, or something?"

Martin Recht gave a start of surprise and swung round to face the sergeant major. Flushing to the roots of his hair, he said: "I beg your pardon, Sergeant Major, I didn't see you." He rose, saluted, and sat down again.

"Too busy, I suppose?" asked Rammler, feigning amuse-

ment. "Your eyes really must be bad, though—mistaking me for a chair and a lame duck for a swan." He laughed as if he had just made a coarse but good-natured jest.

Martin Recht sprang to his feet again, this time as though he were about to throw himself at the sergeant major, who sat there with a gleam of anticipation in his eyes. Almost simultaneously, Corporal Streicher leaped into the breach, presumably in his capacity as roommate and welfare representative.

"Don't do anything foolish, Martin!" he said, gripping his arm.

Martin violently shrugged off the corporal's restraining grasp and bent over Rammler with clenched fists.

"Martin," said Carolin, and her voice, though soft, was clear and distinct, "you were just going to tell me about tomorrow evening. Where did you say we were going?"

Martin Recht straightened up. He relaxed, turned slowly to look at Carolin and resumed his seat. "Thanks, Carolin," he said with a half-hearted smile.

Now it was her turn to put her hand on his.

Sergeant Major Rammler exhibited grim amusement. "What was all that about?" he demanded of Streicher. "Wanted to wring my neck, did he? Well, that takes the cake! Never mind, we've got ways of dealing with his sort."

That evening, later known as Gloomy Thursday, appeared to end on a successful note as far as Sergeant Major Rammler was concerned. He was not a man who gave up easily, and he also knew the value of the strategic withdrawal.

His first move was to make an obtrusive exit from the Café Asch. He did not wait for Herbert Asch to put in an appearance, nor the delinquent Kamnitzer, nor the unsoldierly Vossler, his air force rival of the previous evening. He marched out, grandly ignoring both Helen Wieder and Martin Recht, who reluctantly saluted him for the second time.

"Types like that," he announced to Streicher, who retained the privilege of escorting him, "ought to be shot."

"It's not that I like playing the nursemaid, Sergeant Major," Streicher remarked cautiously, "but he doesn't find soldiering easy."

"Then he ought to pull his finger out!" snapped Rammler. "Though it doesn't matter what a guy like Recht does —he'll never amount to more than a pinch of chicken shit."

"Perhaps he feels at a disadvantage, Sergeant. They say he's half Jewish."

"So what?" Rammler had heard this before. "What am I supposed to do—give him preferential treatment? Lay off the subject, I'm sick of it."

Streicher did not regard Rammler as anti-Semitic, but it seemed unwise to pursue this theme further. All he wanted to do was register a small, discreet warning.

By this time they were standing in the middle of the market place. Rammler gazed about him like a boxer with victory in his grasp. "What is there to do in this God-forsaken dump?" he demanded.

The houses of the little town stared mutely back, their sturdy half-timbered façades softly illumined by the moon. It would not have seemed unduly surprising if a night watchman had materialized, complete with lantern and staff.

"There must be something to do here!"

"Maybe it would be better if we went home," Corporal Streicher suggested vaguely. By "home" he meant barracks.

"Balls," said Rammler. "I'm nowhere near ready for bed yet. What about paying a visit to La Paloma?"

Streicher tried to talk him out of the idea. "It's hardly the place for senior N.C.O.s, Sergeant Major."

"You poor fool," Rammler said, undeterred, "get this straight: as soon as we walk into a place, it belongs to us. We set the tone wherever we choose to park our asses, get it?"

Sweeping into the espresso bar with a proprietorial air, he made straight for the so-called passion parlor, taking the steps two at a time. Streicher followed him reluctantly.

All Rammler could see to begin with was a cloud of smoke, so thick that it might have been emitted by a smoke bomb. Then he made out a densely packed throng of figures, preponderantly male, ranged round the small tables and along the miniature bar counter. The juke box was churning out a sentimental ballad about the deep blue sea.

Rammler, who was wearing civilian clothes, cleared a path by pushing Streicher along in front of him like a battering ram. When he reached the bar counter he ordered his favorite drink—"Strong Man's Milk, and make it a large one!"—and proceeded to take stock of the situation.

"At least three men to every bird," he announced. "That means two-thirds of them are in the way."

"It's not always like this," a youth beside him remarked moodily. "The Italians got here first tonight."

"The who?" Rammler asked in astonishment. "I didn't know we were on the Adriatic."

The young man was happy to enlighten him. It seemed that there was a factory on the outskirts of the town where insulating materials were manufactured with the aid of imported Italian labor. The foreigners weren't badly paid, either, especially by comparison with the average soldier.

"Fair enough," Rammler said indulgently. "They can make as much insulating tape as they like, but what right have they got to muscle in on our women?"

The youngsters round him shrugged. "That's all very well, but what can we do about it? They were here first."

Rammler, who had realized at a glance that his bar companions were servicemen in civilian clothes, was outraged. "What can you do? What a bloody stupid question! You must be air force men, aren't you?"

They nodded.

"That explains it." Rammler ordered himself another double ration of Strong Man's Milk, turning his broad back on the airmen as he did so.

He then embarked on a stentorian conversation with Streicher, doing his best to fan the flames he had already kindled. When frequent use of the expression "macaroni merchants" failed to have any effect, Rammler resorted to wartime reminiscences.

The Italians gradually caught on. Three of them deserted their German dates and elbowed their way toward the men at the bar. Mildly, at first, they demanded an explanation.

"Sensitive, aren't they?" said Rammler. "But then, you air force boys let people get away with murder." So saying, he moved in the direction of the Gents, noting as he did so that Corporal Streicher had already beaten a retreat. On the way, he shoved two or three airmen aside with rough camaraderie. It apparently escaped him that one of them ricocheted into an Italian, just as it escaped him that the Italian took umbrage and shoved the airman in return.

A moment later Rammler was standing in the Gents, listening with satisfaction to the growing tumult outside. Judging by its intensity, the airmen were making a take-over bid.

When Rammler re-emerged some minutes later, the place looked emptier but considerably more comfortable. Two-thirds of the customers had disappeared, and there

now seemed no reason why he shouldn't bring his day to a successful conclusion.

"Do you mean to say our friends from Italy have deserted us already?" he asked with a wink.

The others laughed. They were enjoying the situation, and continued to do so until the air police patrol arrived.

GRENADIER MARTIN RECHT was still smiling happily when he got up next morning.

"What's the matter with you?" said Kamnitzer, watching him closely. "You look as if you'd won the pools or found your discharge papers in your pocket."

"That's just about how I feel, Karl."

Karl Kamnitzer went on making his bed, but he continued to observe Martin Recht. Apart from the fact that he could make his bed with his eyes shut, Recht seemed far more worthy of his attention. The boy's evident sense of well-being worried him.

"Yesterday evening," Recht went on blithely, "I got the urge to knock Rammler's teeth down his throat."

"I get it all the time," said Kamnitzer, "but I make sure I don't give way to it. I just grin at him—he knows what I think of him just the same."

"If Carolin hadn't stopped me," Recht continued, "I'd have clouted him."

"You must be dreaming. What did you have to eat last night?"

Martin Recht was not to be deterred. "It was a relief, believe me, Karl. Just for a few seconds, I felt like a different person."

"You'd better tell me all about it," Kamnitzer said, frowning. They sat down together on the lower bunk and Recht launched into an account of the scene in the Café Asch. The longer Kamnitzer listened, the fewer questions he asked. Eventually he lapsed into silence.

"Well, what do you think of that?" asked Recht.

"I think you're crazy," Kamnitzer said dryly.

"What did you expect me to do," Recht expostulated, "let him insult the girl?" His face darkened. "Lame duck! It was a lousy thing to say. Anyway, he's wrong—she's not a lame duck."

"Of course she isn't," said Kamnitzer, "but some remarks are best ignored." He appeared to be thinking deeply. "I reckon your best plan is to lodge a complaint."

"What's the point? I'd only be making a mountain out of a molehill."

"You've no choice, buddy! Rammler won't let anyone get away with that sort of thing, least of all you!"

"The matter's closed as far as I'm concerned. Maybe he thinks so too. He must have a conscience, after all."

"Yes, but not our sort. The way he looks at it, you've assaulted a superior officer—at least in spirit. That's why he'll have you on the ropes if you don't book him first. You stand a good chance, too, especially as the girl's a captain's daughter. You've got to report him—you've no alternative. I'll act as middleman, if you like, just to get things under way properly."

"Maybe you're right," Martin said reluctantly. "But Carolin may get dragged into it—for questioning, say—and I don't like that idea. I couldn't ask her to do it."

"You're not in love with the girl, are you?"

"Yes, I think so."

Karl Kamnitzer clicked his tongue. "That's bad—I mean to say, it may make it harder to deal with Rammler, but we'll have to try all the same. Let's leave it up to him: if he has a sudden attack of decency and apologizes, fair enough, but if he's still mad for the sight of blood we'll make sure it's his own."

LIEUTENANT VON STRACKMANN, once more engaged in polishing his boots to the delight of all, was gratified to receive what he took to be signal confirmation of the confidence reposed in him by his men: Sergeant Major Rammler appeared, gave an immaculate salute, and asked for permission to speak.

"I'm listening," von Strackmann said benignly. The more he saw of Rammler in recent days, the more favorably he compared him with Kirschke. Rammler knew the meaning of discipline and his platoon was regarded as one of the smartest in the battalion. Substitute Rammler for Kirschke, and No. 3 Company would soon be on its feet.

"Quite by chance," Rammler reported, "I entered La Paloma espresso bar yesterday evening."

"Not exactly the sort of place for you," von Strackmann commented with an indulgent smile.

"I was thirsty, sir, but my real object was to gain some information," Rammler stated with an unclouded brow. "I wanted to find out if any members of my platoon used the

place. For that reason, I took one of my most reliable men with me—Corporal Streicher."

Lieutenant von Strackmann nodded. Streicher was of the clay from which acceptable sergeants could be molded.

"While I was in the urinal, sir, a fight broke out between some foreign workers and air force personnel in civilian dress."

"Most regrettable." Von Strackmann reached for a duster and began to impart a final shine to his handiwork. "But I infer from your account that you had nothing to do with it."

"Nothing whatsoever, sir," stated Rammler. "Corporal Streicher can confirm that. In fact, when the air police arrived I did my best to assist them."

This was the literal truth. Rammler had at once placed himself at their disposal, brandishing his identity card.

"I'm sure your behavior was entirely above reproach. It's only what I should have expected of you."

"Anyway, sir, I thought I'd report the matter at once."

Von Strackmann nodded approvingly. "I appreciate your frankness, Sergeant Major."

He surveyed his boots—the best polished in the battalion —with satisfaction. "We must be able to trust one another," he went on. "Mutual trust is the only thing which can provide a sound basis for the restoration of esprit de corps which this company so urgently needs—and which I mean to give it. I'm relying on people like you, Sergeant Major. I'm confident you won't let me down."

CAPTAIN KLAUS AHLERS was having breakfast with his family. Very often it was the only half hour in the day which he was able to spend with his wife and daughter.

Ahlers always enjoyed this brief interlude, but today he found it particularly enjoyable. Carolin, looking unusually cheerful and relaxed, chattered away vivaciously about her outing of the previous evening. "We walked quite a long way," she said proudly. "It did me good."

Ahlers shot an inquiring glance at his wife, but she smiled reassuringly. "Carolin was well looked after, I'm sure. Martin Recht seems such a nice young man. I felt I was leaving her in safe hands."

Carolin launched into an account of her visit to the Café

88

Asch. "It was awfully funny," she said. "A soldier at the next table called me a lame duck."

"And that struck you as funny?"

"Very," she said gaily. "You see, when he said it, I thought: he should have seen me before, when I could hardly move. What would he have said then? And what will he say if he sees me when I can walk properly?"

Ahlers patted his daughter's arm delightedly. He was more than pleased at her reaction to such a tasteless remark. Far from detroying the fundamental serenity of her nature, her disability seemed to have enhanced it.

When the doorbell rang, Ahlers noted with surprise that it was Carolin who rose to answer it. As she went out, he got the impression that she moved more easily than usual. She merely walked like someone who was slightly stiff and tired after taking physical exercise.

Then Ahlers heard Vossler's voice. Not without satisfaction, he gathered that Vossler, too, had noticed the change in Carolin. "What's all this!" he exclaimed. "You'll be cross-country running next! Come here and give us a hug."

Viktor Vossler behaved like a member of the family. After greeting them affectionately he sat down at the breakfast table without waiting to be invited.

"We've got time," he declared. "At least fifteen minutes, and my car's outside. I wouldn't say no to a cup of coffee if someone asked me."

The car outside, a pale blue 4-door, was more than smart enough for the officers' married quarters. Not even Colonel Turner possessed a better car, but then Vossler could afford such extravagances. He owned mineral springs on an estate in Franconia and employed a reliable agent to handle his business affairs. All that interested Viktor Vossler was flying—and, lately, Mayor Asch's secretary, Gerty Ballhaus.

He sipped his cup of coffee, chatted with Frau Ahlers and made facetious remarks to amuse Carolin, offering to race her over a hundred yards in the near future and pretending to be worried about the result.

When Ahlers and he left the house and emerged into the street, the warrant officer suddenly turned into a subordinate. Vossler knew that there were probably onlookers in the married quarters—ladies who had nothing better to do than peer through their lace curtains—so he opened the car door for Ahlers and waited until he had taken his seat. No private chauffeur could have been more attentive.

"Your daughter's becoming more and more of a live

wire," he remarked as they drove through the married quarters toward the barracks.

"Yes, let's hope she keeps it up."

"Whether or not it's a permanent improvement, this seems to be a favorable opportunity"—Vossler slowed down slightly—"you know what I mean, Klaus. What about that final operation? The doctor said it would be worth doing when she was strong enough."

"Perhaps," said Ahlers, "but let's not talk about it now."

Viktor Vossler knew what lay behind Ashlers' silence. He was also familiar with a string of figures: 6,500 marks for Carolin's seven-month sojourn in the hospital, 2,100 marks for three operations performed by a leading surgeon, and more than 3,000 marks for routine checkups, drugs, and medical attention.

"Klaus," Vossler said, "I've offered to help more than once."

"Thank you, Viktor, but you know I can't accept."

"What nonsense! I'm not a poor man. Besides, it's beginning to annoy me, the way you always turn me down."

"Cut it out!" Ahlers said with forced cheerfulness. "You're my friend, not my moneylender. I'm afraid the two things don't mix, and if I have to choose one or the other I'd sooner have a friend."

No. 3 Company had assembled for Military Education. Everyone was in attendance except the officers, those on sick call, leave, and guard duty, and Company Sergeant Major Kirschke, who knew everything and therefore needed no further enlightenment.

Lieutenant von Strackmann was speaking—with the aid of *Collected Examples of Approved Lessons*—on the subject of loyalty, obedience, and courage. He was confident that the men were listening attentively, being unaware that Kamnitzer, for instance, had acquired the knack of sleeping with his eyes open.

"Loyalty," announced the lieutenant, quoting almost verbatim from his manual, "is an automatic prerequisite in any form of organization. What is meant here is loyalty toward one's employer—in this case"—and here he deviated slightly from the text—"the Fatherland."

The members of No. 3 Company received his remarks much as they would have if he had announced that river

90

water always flows downstream or hot air expands—that is, impassively.

"The soldier," von Strackmann continued, "has, in addition, to show unswerving obedience to the orders of his superiors, who are acting on behalf of the employer—that is to say, the Federal Republic."

This early-morning period, the first of the day, was regarded by the company as a welcome extension of its night's repose. Most of the men dozed in attitudes of profound concentration, while Streicher, alone among them all, busily took notes.

"Courage," von Strackmann recited, "should be regarded as a natural attribute in cases where the rights and liberties of the German people have to be defended."

This formula, which appeared on page 86 of the standard work called *The Officers' Manual*, seemed to hold particular appeal for the lieutenant. He raised his forefinger to stress the point.

The men below him, Kamnitzer excluded, were finding it difficult to keep their eyes open. The classroom was too small to accommodate the whole company in comfort, so the men sat packed toegther, almost in each other's laps, like sardines in a tin. A musty, sweetish-sour smell pervaded the air.

"Comradeship," von Strackmann continued, still quoting, "forms the basis of any community, especially when its members are obliged to live in close proximity."

At that moment C.S.M. Kirschke appeared. He murmured something into the lieutenant's ear, but not so softly that the men in the front rows, among them the sergeants and other N.C.O.s, could not catch it. "The C.O. wants you immediately."

"The C.O. wishes to speak to me," announced von Strackmann, his tone suggesting that the C.O. was in urgent need of his advice. "I shall be back as soon as possible. Sergeant Major Rammler will supervise you in the meantime."

Corporal Kamnitzer perked up at this announcement. "Now we can have some fun," he whispered, digging Recht, his next-door neighbor, in the ribs.

The others evidently seemed to share this view. A general sense of anticipation filled the air, for Rammler, who had only been asked to supervise, seemed bent on continuing the lesson himself. The manual lay open on the lectern, and he could read aloud as well as the next man.

"Take the following example," Rammler read. "Grenadier

91

X habitually turns up late for duty. He also manages to get out of unpleasant routine jobs such as room orderly, guard duty, fatigues, etc. How would you describe this man's conduct?"

Kamnitzer's hand shot up, but Rammler ignored it. "Let's hear what you've got to say, Grenadier Recht."

Recht rose obediently to his feet. He knew what answer was expected of him, having learned it by heart. "The soldier has committed a breach of faith. Loyalty is shown in the execution of all forms of duty. A soldier who commits a breach of faith in peacetime will not fight bravely in wartime."

Comparing Recht's exemplary answer with the text, Rammler found that it tallied word for word.

"That's all very well," he said peevishly. "Anyone can learn a thing by heart. It's whether you put it into practice that matters."

"Quite right, Sergeant Major!" Kamnitzer called with spurious approval. He got up without waiting to be asked. "For instance, I wonder why they call guard duty an unpleasant routine job—also, how Grenadier X manages to avoid it. I'd be interested to know that, Sergeant Major."

Rammler deemed it wise to give a general answer rather than examine Kamnitzer's question in detail. "It's like this," he explained in resounding tones. "You've got to obey— that's what loyalty means."

"Under any circumstances?" Kamnitzer inquired pensively. "Even someone like Hitler?"

"Stop splitting hairs!" Rammler bellowed in outrage. "What's this got to do with Hitler? You're talking about two completely different worlds."

Kamnitzer's voice was mild. "But some people manage to live and obey just as well in either sort of world, wouldn't you say, Sergeant Major?"

"That's enough of that!" shouted Rammler. "Class is suspended until the company commander gets back. Hands on the table, everyone! Sit to attention! We'll have a bit of singing. I suggest 'Westerwald.'"

Kamnitzer grinned. "As for you," Rammler said menacingly, "I'm going to report you. You're going to answer for those remarks!"

"By all means, Sergeant Major," Kamnitzer replied. "I'll be interested to see what happens."

CAPTAIN AHLERS shook hands with his office staff and wished them good morning, as he did every day. The only civilian employee in his office was a high-spirited brunette known to all and sundry as Monika. Vossler was convinced that she owed her dark beauty to some anonymous ancestor from the Middle East, and called her "Turkish Delight," but she was a highly efficient secretary.

"Anything special today?" Ahlers inquired.

"I don't think so," said Monika. "I'm sure Captain Treuberg will have other ideas, though."

Treuberg, equal in rank but junior to Ahlers, was one of the twelve captains on the station—which meant that there were eleven too many for his taste. He was, however, Ahlers's official deputy and a highly conscientious officer.

"He's waiting for you inside," Monika went on.

Treuberg waited for Ahlers every morning, but then he was always waiting for something, if only a chance to demonstrate his worth. Ahlers did not hurry. He had a final word with Viktor Vossler and the sergeant clerk before entering his own office.

"A most unfortunate business," Treuberg began, before they had even saluted each other. "Take a look at this report from the air police patrol."

Ahlers read the report through in silence, watched impatiently by Treuberg, who found it hard to endure his chief's untroubled composure.

"I wouldn't shoulder the responsibility for this, if I were you," insinuated Treuberg.

"You don't have to," Ahlers replied. "It's my job."

He sent for the patrol commander, a sergeant with an expressionless apple of a face, smooth, round, and gleaming.

"I gather from your report," Ahlers said, "that you were alerted by telephone yesterday evening, though the informant didn't give his name. You then proceeded to La Paloma. Am I right so far?"

"Yes sir," replied the sergeant.

"In this bar," Ahlers continued amiably, "you found several airmen in civilian dress together with a number of young women, presumably of medium price range. We are not, however, responsible for commercial transactions of this sort when they are conducted outside barracks. Are we agreed so far, Sergeant?"

"Yes sir." The sergeant's piscine eyes rested trustfully on Ahlers. He did not appear to notice Treuberg's presence, but then Treuberg did not count.

"I now ask you the following: who lodged the information? The proprietor? One of the airmen? One of the girls? One of the foreign workers?"

"No idea, sir," the sergeant replied truthfully.

"To resume: Was there any direct threat to the garrison's reputation? Did you enter the premises in order to prevent or put a stop to physical violence? Did you observe any definite act of immorality or indecency?"

"No sir," said the sergeant.

"In that case," said Ahlers, "I think we can regard the matter as closed." He glanced at the sergeant, who nodded. Ahlers tore up the report. "With your permission," he said to the sergeant, who nodded again.

"I don't know if I entirely agree with you there," said Treuberg, when the sergeant had departed.

"That's all right, Treuberg, your agreement's not essential."

The two men exchanged a brief look of mutual antipathy. To Treuberg, Ahlers was a man devoid of any well-developed sense of discipline and military exactitude—a practical man, perhaps, but not one who was willing and able to perform administrative duties in an irreproachable manner. To Ahlers, by contrast, Treuberg was merely a deputy who had every intention of stepping into his shoes.

"Without in any way trying to influence you, sir, I should like—with all due discretion, of course—to record my misgivings on this particular subject."

"No one's stopping you, with or without due discretion." Ahlers contemplated his deputy without malice. Treuberg had been assigned to him and was not his personal choice. "But it's part of our job to make decisions. You'll get used to the idea in time."

"Of course, sir, of course. It's just that I don't see why we should take responsibility—precipitately, in my view—for something which may lie outside our jurisdiction. It might have been advisable to notify Colonel Turner."

Captain Treuberg, as Ahlers knew only too well, always did his best to surround himself with an impregnable rampart of directives, regulations, decrees, orders of the day, and amendments to the same. He accepted the paper war which dominated the station as if it were a natural phenomenon.

"In doubtful cases," Treuberg concluded, "it's always wiser to cover oneself."

"For God's sake!" exclaimed Ahlers. He crumpled the torn remains of the sergeant's report into a ball and threw it into the wastepaper basket. "Everyone tries to hide behind everyone else in this place. Nobody seems to be willing to accept responsibility voluntarily. It's a second-rate attitude, Treuberg—a bureaucratic attitude."

"Aren't you oversimplifying things a little, sir?"

"Things are simple," Ahlers declared. "At least, they ought to be. The only point to remember is that a grain of humanity is worth a mountain of red tape."

COMPANY SERGEANT MAJOR KIRSCHKE sat in the company office, yawning.

"I'm putting that bastard Kamnitzer on a charge!" bawled Rammler. "He had the cheek to compare the Bundeswehr with Hitler during class."

Kirschke shook his head sleepily. "Even you can't believe that, Rammler. Kamnitzer's far too cunning to say such a thing in front of witnesses. He doesn't make bloopers like that."

"He did this time. I can swear to it if necessary."

"I hope it won't be." Kirschke slumped back in his chair and stretched out his legs, savoring a sense of superiority. The wild buffalo leaning over his desk might be a first-rate leader of cannon fodder but he hadn't got the makings of a company sergeant major.

"You mustn't underestimate Kamnitzer," he said mildly, mollified by this thought. "If I know him he'll swear he said the exact opposite, and find a pal to back him up. In the end, it'll be the same old story—either you misheard him, or he was misunderstood and meant something quite different."

"All right, send for him," said Rammler. "The little swine won't dare deny it to my face."

"Listen here," said Kirschke. "If you really want to hang something on him, my advice is as follows: get him to slap you round the chops—in the presence of at least two friendly witnesses. Then you may get somewhere."

Rammler, however, remained adamant. "I insist!" he bellowed.

"Very well," Kirschke said wearily. "If you're really set

on the idea I won't stop you." He turned to one of the company clerks. "Fetch Corporal Kamnitzer."

"You've been reported to me," said Kirschke, when Kamnitzer had been found.

"As far as that goes," replied Kamnitzer, "I've got a complaint to make myself."

"Against me?" Rammler demanded in amazement.

Kirschke's face broke into a delighted grin. He knew the ropes, and he knew Kamnitzer.

"In the case of this complaint," Kamnitzer explained obligingly, "I'm acting as a sort of intermediary. The actual complainant is Grenadier Recht. His young lady, who is slightly disabled, was described in his presence—and in a crowded restaurant—as a lame duck. I can produce witnesses if necessary."

"Is this true?" Kirschke asked Rammler.

"Well, you know how one says things sometimes," Rammler mumbled vaguely.

"The young lady in question," Kamnitzer went on, "happens to be the daughter of an officer—a captain, to be precise."

Kirschke closed his eyes in ecstasy. His judgment of human nature had scored yet another triumph. He had gauged both men—Kamnitzer and Rammler—correctly.

"How could I have known that?" Rammler expostulated. Kamnitzer's allusion to the captain's daughter had manifestly disturbed his equilibrium. "If I really did pass such a remark, it was only meant as a joke. Anyway, I don't remember. It may be a misunderstanding."

"It was a direct and unmistakable insult," Kamnitzer pursued, "and Grenadier Recht is entirely justified in lodging a complaint."

"But not with me!" protested Kirschke. He saw his well-earned afternoon nap threatened by two pieces of tedious paperwork instead of one, and both seemed equally superfluous. "I haven't the least wish to get involved in your troubles."

"If you mean," Kamnitzer said obligingly, "that someone's in trouble round here, Sergeant Major, you're dead right—and I don't think it's me, either."

"Do I have to put up with this?" Rammler demanded.

"In this case—yes." Kirschke winked at Kamnitzer as he spoke, and Kamnitzer winked back.

"Is it going into the wastepaper basket, then?" Kamnitzer asked.

The C.S.M. nodded. "You can go, Kamnitzer. You're back to square one again. Nought plus nought equals nought."

He dismissed Kamnitzer with a gracious wave of the hand.

"I never thought you'd side with a bastard like that," Rammler said bitterly. "Never!"

"There are two ways of looking at it, Rammler," said Kirschke. "I could ask you what choice I've got, when my senior N.C.O.s go around behaving like wild animals. Alternatively, I could ask you when you're going to realize that things have changed in the past few years."

Rammler looked suddenly exhausted. He deposited his massive haunches on Kirschke's desk and mopped his perspiring brow. "So the little s.o.b.'s trying to get me, is he?" he muttered. "Well, he's picked the wrong man."

"You can do what you like out in the country," Kirschke said, "—worse luck. But not here in barracks or in my presence. I'm more of a nursemaid than a boxing referee."

"I'll show those lads," Rammler said doggedly. "There's a map-reading exercise this afternoon."

Kirschke shrugged. "Just watch out you don't lose your own bearings, that's all."

"**W**OULD YOU like a quick trip to Athens?" Ahlers asked. "We've got to fly some equipment there."

"No thanks," said Vossler, who was sitting back comfortably in an armchair in Ahlers's office. "It's too hot for me—puts me off my whisky."

"In that case, I could assign you to a flight to Bordeaux." This, as Ahlers well knew, was an extremely tempting offer. Warrant Officer Vossler had a distinct penchant for the *grands vins de Bordeaux.* "You'd have three hours there," he added, implying that Vossler would have plenty of time to lay in a couple of dozen.

Vossler continued to display a marked lack of enthusiasm. "Anyone's welcome to go buzzing around Europe, as far as I'm concerned," he said. "Personally, I don't feel the slightest inclination to. I've lost the urge, somehow."

This was something new. Vossler normally jumped at any opportunity to fly. He was not only the keenest but the most reliable pilot in the squadron, and Ahlers tended to give him preference as a matter of course, when the choice was left to him.

"I'm sick of the whole business, Klaus," Vossler said. "I'm

97

thinking of handing in my papers. I've had enough offers from civilian airlines, God knows."

"But you're not the employee type," protested Ahlers. "It would bore you stiff to operate on a fixed schedule arranged weeks or months ahead. You like a bit of freedom, and you'll only get that here with us."

"But I'm only a warrant officer," Vossler grumbled. "To a lot of people, that means an underling—and I don't always like it."

"You could get a commission any time you wanted."

"I wouldn't dream of it," Vossler said stubbornly. "Can you see me sitting through a training course at my age? And where would it get me? I want to go on flying, that's all, and becoming an officer won't make me a better pilot."

Klaus Ahlers felt slightly at a loss. He failed to see what Vossler was getting at. All he had to do was issue the order "Flight 347 to Bordeaux, usual crew, take-off: 1300 hours" and Vossler would merely say, "Yes sir." But that was too simple.

"Have you had a row with someone, Viktor—Captain Treuberg, say?"

Vossler eyed his friend reproachfully. "I know better than to row with Treuberg. For one thing, a warrant officer is junior to a captain, and for another he belongs to a different class of society—even if he's called a friend in private."

"That's absolute poppycock," said Ahlers, "and you know it."

"Really? Then prove it sometime. It wouldn't be difficult. If you need money for Carolin's operation, I'll gladly let you have it. How many more times do I have to tell you?"

"Thanks, I know you mean it."

"Then for God's sake behave as if you did!"

Ahlers passed a hand across his brow. "All right, if I can't scrape it together any other way I'll call on you. But there's no getting round it, Viktor, military regulations contain very strict rulings on the subject."

"They don't apply to personal friends."

"Yes, they do—when the friends in question voluntarily submit to the existing military code."

"Come off it! I'm not trying to bribe you—I'm not even giving you a present. You can make it a loan if you like, and pay interest—at the highest prevailing rate, if it'll salve your conscience. Or don't you want Carolin to be cured completely?"

"All right," said Ahlers. "If the doctor thinks it's worth

doing the operation now and I don't manage to raise a loan elsewhere, I'll take you up on the offer."

"Done!" cried Vossler. "I'll put a couple of thousand marks at your disposal straight away. You can give me an I.O.U. and pay a steep rate of interest if you like. If it's against regulations for an officer to exploit his subordinates, we'll try it the other way round."

"ANYTHING SPECIAL?" demanded Lieutenant von Strackmann, expecting to hear the C.S.M. produce his usual stereotyped negative.

"Yes sir!" replied Kirschke.

Von Strackmann had just returned from an officers' conference in the C.O.'s office and was feeling rather exhausted. He had been obliged to take note of seventeen new additions to standing orders, of which fourteen superseded rulings of an earlier date.

"You must be joking, Sergeant Major. Did I hear you say yes?"

"Yes sir," the C.S.M. repeated. "I've just received a disturbing report from Sergeant Major Rammler."

Kirschke took care to say this in the presence of two witnesses: the corporal clerk and a civilian employee. He was determined to spoil von Strackmann's lunch hour before embarking on his own midday siesta.

"Sergeant Major Rammler," he continued, "is under the impression that he heard Hitler and the Bundeswehr mentioned in the same breath, so to speak, in front of the assembled company."

Lieutenant von Strackmann's brows contracted and his mouth opened in what was, for a man of iron, a slightly helpless expression. He felt like someone who has been lured onto thin ice and can only move with the utmost caution.

"I hope," he said eventually, "that there's been some mistake."

"It's possible that Sergeant Major Rammler misheard," Kirschke generously conceded, having laid his egg. The fact that his report had been parenthetical in tone did not make it any less official. What the lieutenant made of it was up to him, at least for the moment. Kirschke could always turn it to account later if he felt like it.

"Has anyone made a written deposition on the subject?" inquired von Strackmann.

"Not to me."

Von Strackmann heaved a sigh of relief. "So it could be just hot air." Then, covering himself in the time-honored manner, he went on: "Anyway, I can see you didn't take it seriously, Sergeant Major. I'm sure you handled the matter correctly."

"Begging your pardon, sir, I didn't handle it at all. I merely asked Sergeant Major Rammler if he had considered things carefully, and he didn't seem too sure. Whether there's anything in his story I'm not in a position to judge."

This sort of tug-of-war could have gone on for some time if von Strackmann had not decided to break off the engagement. He didn't want any complications. As one who found it hard enough to cope with the present, he felt that having to cope with hangovers from the past was asking too much of him.

"As far as I'm concerned, a report which hasn't been submitted doesn't exist." The lieutenant's voice betrayed his conviction that the case was closed, and Kirschke did not disabuse him.

HERBERT ASCH sat opposite his wife, looking at her tenderly and reveling in his hour of lunchtime privacy. The staff was forbidden to disturb him, and even the telephone had been disconnected.

"Have I told you that I love you?" he asked.

Elisabeth smiled. "Not recently, but it's not absolutely essential."

"Well, it's what I tell myself every day, even if I don't say it aloud."

"I sometimes wonder how much longer these little lunch-time idylls are going to last," she said, when their food had been brought in. "If things go on as they are, there won't be time."

"You're not worried, are you, Elisabeth?"

"No, just thinking my own thoughts." She pushed the dish across to him. Asch never needed to state his preferences on the subject of food because Elisabeth knew them by instinct. "You spent a long time with that reporter this morning, didn't you?"

"I couldn't avoid it."

"And your meeting with the council?"

"Couldn't get out of that either. I am mayor, after all."

"And all those telephone conversations with the army and air force are equally essential, I suppose?"

"One can't ignore the services. They exist, so one has to deal with them."

Elisabeth refrained from looking at her husband. She didn't want him to know what she was thinking, though she was pretty sure he did anyway.

"My trouble is that I've never grown up," Asch went on. "I'm always interested in things which most people would say didn't concern me. But can we really pretend that what goes on in our immediate vicinity doesn't concern us? Look, Elisabeth—when I was in the army, and serving in this very town, in the barracks over there, my pals and I often used to spend off evenings in each other's homes. Our fathers used to ask us how we were—not what we were doing in there or what they were doing to us. They'd done their own service long ago, and if they'd been treated wrongly or unjustly in the past—well, why shouldn't we have a dose of the same medicine? They couldn't have cared less what happened to us, or so we used to think."

"And how do you propose to change that?"

"I'm not quite sure yet," Asch said thoughtfully, "but the main thing is not to be indifferent. We must make it our business to find out whether they're really doing things better these days. We've got to help and encourage the people who are doing better, and rub the others' noses in the results of past experience. To be frank, I've got an urge to stick my mayoral finger in their little pie."

"Isn't that what you've been doing for some time?"

Herbert Asch realized that his wife had seen through him and admired her powers of perception. "Maybe," he said carelessly, "but it's a temptation I can't resist."

SERGEANT MAJOR RAMMLER thought he knew what was wrong with his men: they weren't in a state of absolute combat readiness. A man's fighting spirit could be impaired by the wrong sort of ideas and modern civilization was a softening influence, but, whatever the reason, Rammler told himself conscientiously that things had got to change.

"My platoon will assemble on the parade ground ten minutes earlier than usual," he told the orderly sergeant.

When other platoon commanders made such a request, they were, the orderly sergeant knew, merely making a sug-

gestion designed to cover themselves in case complications arose later on. The others expressed a wish but did not insist on its fulfillment. Rammler, however, was more explicit. "That's an order!"

Prematurely routed out of their rooms, the members of No. 3 Platoon assembled—in Rammler's jaundiced opinion —like a gaggle of tourists gaping at the Brandenburg Gate. He found their chatter intolerable.

"Quiet!" he shouted.

The men fell silent and gazed at him apprehensively as though he were a dangerously overheated boiler with a malfunctioning safety valve.

"I said 'Quiet,' " Rammler announced. "I didn't say 'Shut your traps.' "

"That's just how it sounded," Kamnitzer whispered to Recht.

"Let's see your fingernails," Rammler continued. "You'll notice I didn't say, 'Hold out your grubby paws.' "

This was Rammler's favorite way of demonstrating his observance of modern military etiquette. His men extended their hands while he passed down the ranks, face contorted with displeasure.

"An uncultured man," he said, "would call you a lot of filthy, dirty scum. All I say is, your general standard of cleanliness leaves a great deal to be desired."

The fingernails proffered for his inspection were anything but clean, and the clean body, as Rammler knew, was a prerequisite of the clean mind. "If I had hands like that," he declared, "it'd put me off my food."

"We needed the extra ten minutes, Sergeant Major." The author of this friendly comment was, of course, Kamnitzer. "I didn't manage to clean my boots properly either, if you'd care to have a look."

"On your backs," Rammler commanded. The platoon lay down. "Now let's see your palms."

The palms confronting him were far from clean, thanks partly to dirt acquired when lying down, and Kamnitzer's and Recht's were no exception. Rammler's verdict on the latter sounded comparatively kindly. "Trust you two to catch my eye again! I wish you wouldn't."

"So do I—Sergeant Major." Kamnitzer added the last words almost as an afterthought.

Rammler stationed himself in front of the supine platoon. "Right, on your feet!" he shouted. "The efficient soldier keeps himself and his equipment clean at all times. The same goes for this grass here."

This was not a new subject. Rammler raised it on an average of about twice a week, asserting that he had seen discarded cigarette packets, used matches, or sheets of newspaper in front of the company block. This time, according to his account, there had been scraps of paper—possibly toilet paper.

"Spread out and start looking!" he commanded, not forgetting to add: "I won't say it was one of us who made a pig of himself here, but whoever it was—we won't tolerate a speck of filth on our grass. Anyone care to differ?"

If anyone did disagree he refrained from saying so. When Rammler was bitten by the cleanliness bug, nothing could stand in his way, and if he said the grass was covered with garbage that was all there was to it.

Obediently playing the game, the platoon spread out and combed the area. Anyone who found anything had to hand it over to Rammler, who regarded each piece of treasure trove as a sign of diligence on the part of the finder and had been known to await results patiently for anything up to forty-five minutes.

Today, however, he had a bright idea. When three traverses had been made with deplorably meager results, he shouted: "Right! Success will be rewarded. Anyone who finds any more rubbish can dismiss and push off to the mess hall straight away."

"A lot of good that is," Recht mumbled, expressing the thoughts of all. "There aren't any more foreign bodies to find."

"Then we'll manufacture some," Kamnitzer said airily, groping around in his hip pocket. He pulled out several sheets of toilet paper, tore off a strip about two inches long, dropped it on the grass and stamped on it. Then he picked up his handiwork and took it to Rammler.

"May I hand over what I've found, Sergeant Major?"

Rammler accepted the trophy with extreme reluctance. He examined it for some moments with an air of justifiable suspicion.

"Can I go and get my grub now, Sergeant Major?" Kamnitzer asked brightly. Without waiting for a reply he saluted with commendable precision, turned about and strutted happily away.

Rammler had no time to glower at Kamnitzer's retreating form because his example had now been adopted by the other members of the platoon. Almost to a man, they rummaged in their pockets and produced objects which

103

they trampled on and alleged that they had found. A substantial heap of rubbish grew at the sergeant major's feet.

"All right, pack it in!" he yelled furiously. "Go and get your pig swill!"

No one waited to be told twice. The platoon trotted off, leaving the sergeant major alone with his pile of refuse.

Rammler was not easily discouraged, however. The day was far from over, and he had inexhaustible reserves of energy. He was a man of ideas, too, and his ideas were not limited to the subject of garbage disposal. There were other ways of raising a platoon's morale.

WARRANT OFFICER VOSSLER, inspired by a wish to help his friend—and no trip to Athens or Bordeaux could have dissuaded him from putting his offer into effect at the earliest possible moment—climbed into his pale blue car during the lunch hour and drove off to see Frau Ahlers.

"We've made it," he told her. "Klaus has agreed to accept my help."

"Did he really say he would?" she asked, looking half hopeful, half uneasy. "That's wonderful."

"I used every trick in the book. I don't know whether he wanted to spare me further effort, but he finally agreed."

Frau Ahlers greeted this announcement with evident relief, but she realized what was expected of her. Practical arrangements would have to be made.

First, she went to consult Carolin and asked her whether she would be prepared to undergo another operation.

"Yes," Carolin said promptly, adding, after a moment's hesitation: "But can we afford it?"

"You needn't worry about that, Carolin. All that matters is whether you want the operation."

Carolin's enthusiastic response was conveyed to the waiting Vossler. "That's that, then!" he exclaimed happily. "You wait, I'll be dancing with Carolin before the year's out—if the current girl friend allows it, that is."

Vossler was thereupon dismissed to the kitchen, where Carolin improvised a mushroom omelet for him. While he was eating, Frau Ahlers put a call through to Carolin's surgeon, Professor Martin. He told her that, while such an operation was never devoid of risk, the decisive factor was the patient's general condition and mental preparedness.

When Frau Ahlers told Professor Martin that Carolin

had not only agreed to the operation but seemed bent on having it as soon as possible, he concurred, subject to the usual reservations. Only then did he broach the subject of expense. Rather hesitantly, he told her that his fee and the cost of Carolin's stay in hospital would amount to more than two thousand marks.

"If that's all it is!" said Vossler, when he heard. "Let's call it three thousand. That should cover all eventualities."

He took his leave hurriedly, determined that Klaus Ahlers should get his loan before he had a chance to change his mind. Apart from that, he mustn't be allowed to think that Vossler would lose by lending him the money, or that he was motivated by pure altruism. The only way to ensure this was to draw up a fairly stiff-looking contract which seemed to sail close to the restrictions imposed on money-lenders by law.

Vossler decided to get Gerty Ballhaus to type the contract, but found that she was snowed under with letters for her employer.

"Hasn't Asch got anything better to do than supply this town with reading matter?" Vossler demanded indignantly.

In fact, Asch's letters contained an element of interest. Headed "Relations Between the Bundeswehr and the Civilian Population," they were addressed to Colonel Turner of the air force, Major Bornekamp of the army, members of the town council, and certain specified commercial concerns classified under the heading "Catering and Entertainment."

Every one of these letters expressed a lively desire for the maintenance of cordial and harmonious relations between the garrison and the town. They also invited comments, welcomed suggestions for improvement, and stressed that complaints, if any, could be made in confidence. The one sentence which recurred in each letter read simply: "We are all citizens endowed with equal rights, whether we wear uniform or not."

"Can't you make it clear to Asch that your services are urgently required elsewhere?" Vossler asked.

"In the middle of the day, Viktor?" Gertrud Ballhaus looked positively stern, but her eyes sparkled merrily. "You seem to forget I've got a job to do. It's a job I don't want to lose, either. I'm not a married woman, after all. I'm not even engaged."

Viktor Vossler left the Rathaus hastily. Gerty's hints had been a little too broad for his taste, though not, he reluctantly conceded, wholly unjustified. Banishing the thought

from his mind, he concentrated on the problem of how to draft Ahlers's promissory note as quickly as possible.

On his return to barracks he was lucky enough to find Monika alone in the office—Monika, that happy blend of Europe and the Middle East. It was pleasant to see such a decorative specimen of femininity in such a nest of officialdom, and Monika was an obliging creature.

"Just tell me what you want me to do, Herr Vossler. I'd do anything for you." She giggled. "Well, almost anything."

"A bit of typing will do for the time being. But it's strictly private, so I rely on you to be discreet."

Vossler proceeded to dictate the note. Its terms made him, the lender, look more like a usurer, and gave no hint that he was really an unselfish man who was trying to help a friend.

When this agreeable task was interrupted by a call from Ahlers summoning Monika to his office, Vossler used the opportunity to fetch some cigarettes. The half-completed document remained in the typewriter, and the office remained unattended—unattended, that is, until Captain Treuberg walked in.

As he crossed the empty office, Treuberg's eye caught the letters I.O.U. at the head of the sheet. Somewhat surprised, he read the preamble beneath: *Form of Agreement between Klaus Ahlers and Viktor Vossler* . . . And finally, with an incredulity which gave way to growing excitement: *In respect of a loan in the sum of DM 3000 (three thousand marks)* . . .

"Very interesting," mused Captain Treuberg, "very interesting indeed."

SERGEANT MAJOR RAMMLER used words very sparingly when he was in his natural element, and his natural element was the training area north of the town, which he knew like the back of his hand.

Out in the country he preferred to beckon with his thumb, toot his whistle or clap his hands. One powerful sweep of his arm—not unlike that of a peasant scattering seed—and his platoon adapted itself to the terrain, pressed its collective belly to the ground and tried to crawl into the nearest fold in the ground.

"Looks as though he's got plans for us today," Martin Recht said with foreboding.

106

"Don't worry," scoffed Kamnitzer, "he's all wind and piss."

"For Christ's sake shut up!" Corporal Streicher hissed apprehensively. "There's no need to put his back up."

But Rammler was not so easily provoked today. He was far too sure of himself. He stood there with his legs planted firmly apart, studying the map in his hand. In front of him was the platoon, behind him two three-ton trucks, and around him the open country, which stretched far to the north. It was his idea of heaven: an expanse of tangled undergrowth, dense woods, marshy meadows, and muddy fields.

"Map-reading exercise in individual groups!" he announced.

This came as no surprise to the platoon, since all preparations had pointed to it. Each man was in full marching order and had been issued a map and compass.

"Now get down and crawl to the edge of the wood!"

Rammler regarded crawling, which formed a branch of fieldcraft, as a means of improving his men's physical fitness. The only variable factor was the ground to be covered. This was an average distance, which meant that Rammler's ingenious outdoor game would consume about a quarter of an hour. Satisfied that his schedule allowed ample time for an additional maneuver of this sort, he followed the toiling platoon at a comfortable stroll.

"Grenadier Recht is waggling his bottom in the air," he announced after five minutes. "I hope it's not meant to be an invitation."

Pausing briefly for appreciative laughter, he continued: "Grenadier Recht will go back and start again."

At the edge of the wood Rammler informed the platoon of their rendezvous, a disused watermill about fourteen miles away. "Time allowed, three hours."

"That means a forced march!" muttered Streicher.

"I call it a dirty trick," said Kamnitzer. "What's the point? I've already done that stretch twice in the past three months."

Meanwhile, the sergeant major was handing out prepared slips of paper telling the platoon who was marching with whom and from where. Rammler was a great believer in getting his men to converge on a common destination from widely scattered points. He divided the platoon into about a dozen separate groups and loaded them onto the trucks, which were to deposit them at their individual starting points.

The various groups were to operate under very varied conditions. Some had tracks at their disposal, others had to traverse densely wooded country, and still others had to cope with sand and mud. The members of Group 7 would have to wade through miles of bog unless they were prepared to risk making a long and time-consuming detour.

Group 7, needless to say, comprised Corporal Kamnitzer, Grenadier Recht, and another grenadier named Armke. Armke seldom spoke and scarcely ever registered approval or disapproval. He appeared to remain completely indifferent, whatever the circumstances, a fact which struck his superiors as suspicious in the extreme.

"Every minute under three hours earns you a plus mark," Rammler told them in conclusion. "Every minute over three hours means a minus mark. Lame ducks"—and here he grinned savagely at Recht—"better be prepared to do the whole trip again from scratch."

The trucks lumbered off and deposited the men in their predetermined positions. They jumped out and were soon swallowed up in the surrounding countryside, conscious that every minute counted. Kamnitzer, Recht, and Armke disembarked at the edge of a marshy field, and a few seconds later they were standing alone in a wide tract of deserted country.

"All right, let's go," Martin Recht said resignedly. "We've got no choice."

"What about you, Armke?" asked Kamnitzer. "Are you keen on taking a mud bath too?"

"I don't give a damn," said Grenadier Armke, truthfully.

"You've said a mouthful." Kamnitzer sat down comfortably at the edge of the road. "Let's start with a break for a fag."

"But we can't afford the time!" Recht protested. "We're going to have to pull our fingers out if we want to make the rendezvous inside three hours."

"Calm down," said Kamnitzer. "Get this straight: you'll never get into Rammler's good books, even if you march home on your bleeding stumps. Am I right, Armke?"

"I don't give a damn," said Armke.

Kamnitzer nodded at him appreciatively. "Our pal Armke doesn't say much, but when he does it's always to the point."

"We could have done half a mile while you've been jabbering away here." Martin Recht was consumed with im-

patience. "I've had enough of Rammler's attentions for one day. I don't want to put his back up again."

Kamnitzer winked at Armke. "Did you hear that? The poor lad's peeing in his pants. Never mind, we'll soon cure that." He turned to Recht. "I've got a little brain teaser for you. Question: who can do fourteen miles across a swamp in three hours? Answer: a hippopotamus couldn't and neither can we. We'd be too late whatever we did. So, if we can't use our legs, we better use these." He tapped his head.

Grenadier Armke had no need to utter his favorite maxim —it was obvious what he thought of the idea—but Martin Recht's uneasiness mounted still further. "You're not working out one of your little schemes, are you, Karl? If Rammler catches on, I'll be the one who suffers."

"Just so we understand each other," Kamnitzer said pleasantly. "I'm the senior here, so I hereby appoint myself group leader. You two are under my command, all right?"

"I don't—" began Armke.

"We know, Armke, we know." Kamnitzer got slowly to his feet. "We're supposed to be going north, aren't we? Right, the first thing to do is move south. There's a pub called the Traveler's Rest a mile down the road. We can have a quiet snack there and put away a couple of mid-afternoon noggins."

"You must be out of your mind!" Recht protested furiously.

"March at ease!" ordered Kamnitzer.

Armke set off without hesitation and Recht saw no alternative but to follow suit, maintaining a reproachful silence. Corporal Kamnitzer, who had seen *The Bridge on the River Kwai*, cheerfully whistled a tune which bore a vague resemblance to "Colonel Bogey."

Fifteen minutes' leisurely stroll brought them to the small Gasthaus which Kamnitzer had mentioned, where they relieved themselves of their packs and rifles and sat down. As the only customers, they received a cordial if slightly surprised welcome from the landlord.

"Three large schnapps and three liters of beer for me and my men," Kamnitzer commanded. "They need fortifying. They've got a lot of work ahead of them."

"And a plate of ham and eggs for me," said Armke.

Martin Recht continued to brood in silence. He saw a host of complications looming before him like a dark stormcloud, and above it, thunderbolts poised, a god of

109

vengeance with a face resembling Rammler's. A smell of brimstone assailed his nostrils.

Armke, whose appetite seemed unimpaired, munched in silence but not silently. Kamnitzer asked for a paper and read it from end to end with apparent interest, local stock prices included. Then he demanded to hear some music, and the landlord put on a record. After listening to "O'er Hill and Dale" (*Folksongs in March Tempo*) for a minute, Kamnitzer protested, and it was replaced by some Neapolitan love songs.

After about an hour, Kamnitzer rose to his feet and stretched luxuriously. "I suppose it's about time we made a move," he drawled. Then he went to the telephone and ordered a taxi.

LIEUTENANT DIETER VON STRACKMANN, meanwhile, was neither in barracks nor in the country. Instead, he was spending the afternoon with Frau Elfrieda Bornekamp, esteemed wife of the highly esteemed major, at her personal request.

"I really don't know whether I ought to be here at this hour," he said, vacillating between duty and inclination.

"Why so worried?" She flashed him an encouraging smile. "Didn't you want to come?"

"I can't think of anywhere I'd rather be." Dieter knew how to produce textbook compliments with an air of conviction, and Elfrieda reveled in them.

They still employed the formal mode of address, despite a certain incident that had occurred between them. Even at the crucial moment, Frau Elfrieda had managed to preserve formality—at least in spirit—by whispering: "Go on—Lieutenant!"

As one who considered himself a man of honor, however, von Strackmann was deeply sensible of the tragedy that hung in the air. Where would it end—his love for the wife and veneration of the husband?

"If the C.O. ever questioned me on the subject," he admitted, "I wouldn't know how to answer him."

"He won't question you on the subject," she said firmly. "He's not petty-minded."

"Of course not!" von Strackmann agreed. "Major Bornekamp is the soul of generosity."

"And understanding."

"And understanding too, of course."

"Exactly," said Frau Elfrieda, and leaned against him as though overcome by a fit of weakness.

He scarcely ventured to breathe, but she went on: "You've no need to worry—he knows you're here."

Von Strackmann jumped like a man seared by a red-hot iron and released her hastily.

Elfrieda walked over to a small table in the corner of the room and busied herself with the bottles and glasses that stood there.

"I told my husband I was asking you over, and he agreed. As you so rightly say, he's a generous man."

At first, von Strackmann couldn't take in the vista which these words opened up. The radiant picture which he had so far entertained of his revered C.O. threatened to fade.

Elfrieda looked amused. "Haven't you caught on yet?" she said, handing him a brimming glass. "You're here on duty, so to speak."

"On duty!" yelped the bemused lieutenant. His imagination boggled.

Elfrieda decided that it was high time to enlighten her bewildered admirer. "I suggested organizing a social evening for the officers of the battalion and their ladies, and my husband agreed. You're to help me arrange it."

Von Strackmann experienced a sense of boundless relief. He drained his glass at a gulp, glowing with pride at this fresh token of the C.O.'s confidence. Bornekamp was now entrusting him with his personal administrative problems.

"If the C.O. plans to hold a Ladies' Night," he mused, "the best place would probably be the Hotel Asch."

"Never mind that now," Frau Elfrieda said petulantly. "We can discuss details later. Come here!"

SERGEANT MAJOR RAMMLER stood beside the disused watermill with Corporal Streicher at his side. Streicher had been given the job of checkpoint N.C.O., which he regarded as a special privilege, not to say a definite mark of favor.

Streicher demonstrated his gratitude. "The first groups should be here any time now," he said, looking at his watch. "I'm sure your calculations were absolutely correct, Sergeant Major."

"As usual," Rammler said confidently.

Having spent years familiarizing himself with the district, he now knew every tree and bush, path and bypath.

"Kamnitzer and his bunch are bound to be at least half an hour late." Rammler complacently surveyed the dark, glutinous surface of the nearby marsh, which stretched away into the far distance. "Shall we have a bet on it, Streicher?"

"I'm sure you're right, Sergeant Major."

"I bet you twenty marks."

"I'd be bound to lose, Sergeant Major."

Rammler was gratified by his trusty subordinate's perception, though he would have enjoyed betting on such a foregone conclusion.

Meanwhile the first groups were beginning to straggle in. They reported to Rammler and then handed their slips of paper recording time and point of departure to Streicher.

"Greyhounds, that's what you are!" Rammler said, not without pride. "But that's the way you've got to be in this platoon—fighting fit and ready for anything! We'll smash all the records when it comes to the autumn exercises."

"It can't be!" Streicher broke in suddenly. "My watch must have stopped!"

Turning, Rammler saw what Streicher meant. Kamnitzer's group had apparently emerged from the swamp and was marching jauntily down the road toward them. The sound of cheerful whistling came to the sergeant major's ears, and even at a hundred yards he could detect a broad grin on Kamnitzer's face.

"But there's still seventeen minutes to go," Streicher said helplessly.

Kamnitzer trotted up and reported the arrival of his group. Then he jabbed a finger at his watch. "Seventeen minutes before time means seventeen plus marks—not bad, eh?"

"It's only fifteen minutes now," Streicher said officiously.

"You can blather as much as you like," said Kamnitzer, "but not at my expense. I set my watch by the wireless—isn't that good enough for you?"

"Shut up!" shouted Rammler, momentarily losing self-control.

"Did you hear?" Kamnitzer told Streicher. "Just chalk up seventeen plus marks to us and pipe down."

Sergeant Major Rammler scrutinized Kamnitzer's map-reading group closely. To his experienced eye they looked suspiciously fresh. Neither their boots nor their faces betrayed signs of recent exertion. They were either stouthearted lads or a bunch of crooked double-dealers, and he knew which alternative he favored.

"How did you manage it, Kamnitzer?"

"We just marched," the corporal replied laconically, "and now we're here."

Rammler knew from experience that he would get nowhere with Kamnitzer, so he turned hopefully to the next member of the map-reading group. This happened to be Armke—don't-give-a-damn Armke—and it was easier to get blood out of a stone than to extract a sensible answer from him. In desperation Rammler turned to Recht.

"You there!" he commanded. "Get round the back of the mill—at the double! When you get there, dig in. I've got a special job for you."

Confident that he had put his finger on the weak spot in Kamnitzer's group, Rammler left the platoon in charge of a sergeant and trotted after Recht, scenting trouble and determined to get to the bottom of it.

Reaching the back of the mill he looked about him keenly. Beyond the red brick walls he saw an expanse of lush green meadowland and, in the middle of it, Recht, endeavoring to dig in as ordered. In the background, close to an idyllic-looking birch forest, flowed a stream—waist deep only, to his regret.

"Into the wood, at the double!" called Rammler.

This was a wise move. He didn't want Recht to excavate too deeply because of possible complaints from the local peat cutters, who had quickly learned to enrich themselves at the garrison's expense. Apart from that, the sergeant major wanted no chance passerby to witness his unavoidable tête-à-tête with Recht. The obstinate, pig-headed youth had to be softened up with every means at his disposal. Discipline was in danger!

Rammler proceeded to warm Recht up. He chased him across the meadow, through the stream and into the wood. He made him lie down, crawl through thickets and double on the spot. Having driven him through bog, moor, and water for upward of fifteen minutes, he paused.

"Well, haven't you got anything to tell me?" he asked, when Recht lay panting at his feet.

The fact that he received no reply did not dishearten him. He repeated the whole process from scratch: across the field, through the stream, into the wood and back again. "Just to give you time to think it over, you little bastard!"

Rammler normally selected his epithets with great care, in deference to modern army practice, but this was a special case and there were no witnesses in sight.

"Come here, you shit bag, you blue-assed baboon! I'm go-

113

ing to put you through it until you beg for permission to tell me the truth, you pool of piss!"

Even now, Rammler felt that he was only yielding to force of circumstance. The last thing he wanted to do was violate human dignity as guaranteed by the Federal constitution. On the contrary: anyone who failed to obey an order or indulged in clandestine acts of sabotage was an enemy of the freedom of human dignity which he was pledged to defend, and, as such, had to be dealt with resolutely.

"I'll tear you limb from limb, you little sod, if you don't start cooperating properly with your superiors. Well, what about it? Either you tell me the truth about your map-reading jaunt or I'll have your ass!"

Even this failed to elicit a reply, much to Rammler's righteous indignation. Half an hour later Recht collapsed in an exhausted heap.

"Revolting!" Rammler ejaculated scornfully. "Revolting, the way some people force a man to do things like this."

HERBERT ASCH looked forward to the weekend with an unusual sense of anticipation.

The first person to ring him had been Colonel Turner, commander of the transport wing, area commandant and philosopher. The colonel was something of a phantom. Although Asch had often spoken to him on the phone he had hardly ever seen him in person, just as his own men, though familiar with several hundred of his directives, scarcely knew what he looked like. He reigned from a throne in the clouds, like Zeus.

"I have always attached great importance to our friendly collaboration, Herr Asch," Turner told him. "I read your letter with close attention, and I merely wanted to say at once that we are agreed in principle. My sincerest thanks."

Following on Turner's decidedly friendly call came another from his adjutant, who announced that the colonel would welcome any attempt to widen the social horizons of his officer cadets. "It is proposed to hold a sort of *thé dansant*, inviting specially selected young ladies from the senior form of the local high school. Subject to your agreement, this could take place in your hotel, if you have a suitable room available."

"Aha!" Asch said in some amusement, adding, more audibly, "By all means."

114

Immediately afterward, Asch received a personal visit from an officer to whom he had only spoken on the phone hitherto. Lieutenant von Strackmann withdrew a list from his briefcase and said, in tones of command: "Major Bornekamp has decided to hold a mixed party for about forty people this Saturday. Kindly be good enough to make suitable premises available."

Herbert Asch hesitated before replying. Herr von Strackmann had a jarring effect on his civilian disposition, and for a moment or two he felt tempted to decline the request flatly. The lieutenant seemed to be in urgent need of a little lesson on how to treat people who were not privileged to wear uniform. However, there would be time enough for that when Saturday came, so he said: "I'll arrange it," and left it at that.

"I was sure you would," von Strackmann replied condescendingly.

Determined to have his little bit of fun, Asch at once telephoned Ahlers. "I've already got two mixed parties booked for Saturday," he told him. "All the mixture needs now is a little yeast, if you know what I mean."

"A couple of pike for the goldfish pond?"

Herbert Asch chuckled. "Precisely. Can you supply something of the sort?"

"It's quite possible," said Ahlers. "What about half a dozen young officers who've just finished a stiff training course and are itching to celebrate?"

"Couldn't be better! I can guarantee them reduced prices and preferential treatment. Thanks a lot, then, and don't forget—if I can ever do anything for you . . ."

Asch seldom missed an opportunity to make such an offer because the captain's personal troubles were often on his mind. Officers with a healthy measure of human understanding were a boon—and not only to the men under their command—but how much more effective Ahlers would be, he told himself, if only his financial worries were eliminated.

Asch's next telephone conversation was with Bornekamp. He thanked the major for enlisting his services as a hotelier. "I shall devote my undivided attention to your Ladies' Night," he promised. "And as far as the wines are concerned, I shall take the liberty of sending over a few modest samples."

"You're always on your toes, Asch, I'll give you that."

"Would you allow me to make a small suggestion, Major, just between ourselves?"

Bornekamp gave his assent, and Asch revealed that Colonel Turner had suggested holding a small dance for his officer cadets. In the process, he had not only learned about Bornekamp's plans but—so Asch alleged—evinced a certain amount of interest in them. "Perhaps it might be advisable to invite him, Major."

"Not a bad idea," the C.O. agreed. "I'll do it."

Herbert Asch had now mobilized every influential member of the garrison. Their common destination: his hotel. Estimated time of arrival: Saturday evening. A collision course had been set.

SERGEANT MAJOR RAMMLER surveyed his handiwork with repugnance. By collapsing, Grenadier Martin Recht had once more demonstrated his flabby physical condition and shown himself unworthy to belong to an elite unit.

"Gutless bastard!" Rammler said finally. He left the idyllic meadow behind the watermill and returned to his men, who had all straggled in by this time. The sergeant in charge and Corporal Streicher had supervised their arrival, noting times and awarding plus or minus marks accordingly.

Rammler, however, spared no glance for the results of the map-reading exercise. He strode through the assembled platoon and confronted Karl Kamnitzer.

"I'll give you one last chance," he said threateningly.

"To do what—Sergeant Major?"

"I warn you, Kamnitzer, don't play dumb with me. You know bloody well what I mean."

Corporal Kamnitzer knew very well what he meant, but if Rammler expected to find out from him what he had obviously failed to learn from Recht, he had another think coming.

"What's the matter, Kamnitzer—aren't you talking to me any more?"

"Of course, Sergeant Major. What do you want me to talk about?"

Rammler could endure the corporal's affable grin no longer. He turned on his heel and shouted: "Equipment on! Be ready to move off in ten minutes." Then, to Streicher: "Go and fetch Grenadier Recht. He's behind the mill—he slipped and fell over."

"Right, Sergeant Major!" called Streicher, and trotted off.

Kamnitzer followed him without being asked, much to Rammler's increased fury. However, battalion regulations stated that "initiative" was not to be discouraged.

They found Martin Recht alone in the field. His body drooped like a weeping willow, and his face, where it was visible through its coating of mud, looked white as chalk.

"Pull yourself together." Kamnitzer's tone was deliberately harsh. "In this outfit, anyone who gets himself worked over like that only has himself to blame."

"Come on, Martin," Corporal Streicher said encouragingly. He made a move to help him, but Recht shook off his comradely grasp. "I'll manage," he muttered.

When they rejoined the others they found them drawn up in front of the mill ready to move off. The two trucks stood there, purring gently. Conscious that Sergeant Major Rammler was studying their reactions closely, the men avoided looking at Recht.

"Embus!" shouted Rammler.

The platoon divided itself between the two trucks. The drivers and co-drivers closed the tail flaps and laced up the tarpaulin covers. The engines roared and the convoy moved off in the direction of the baracks, nearly twenty miles away.

"I feel sick," said Martin Recht.

Kamnitzer, who sat next to him in the second truck, wagged his head disapprovingly. "You could have spared yourself that."

"What was I supposed to do?" Recht asked bitterly. "He had me over a barrel, and he knew it—treated me like a piece of dirt."

"If you will put up with that sort of treatment . . ."

"I couldn't have done a thing, Karl."

"Of course you could."

"What do you expect me to do—report him? He'd deny the whole thing. We were alone out there, without witnesses."

"That's just it! There weren't any witnesses—that's precisely why I'm blaming you."

"I don't follow," Recht said dully.

"You say gaily 'there weren't any witnesses'—but what could be better? The fact that there aren't any witnesses works both ways, don't you see? You could have told him to go to hell—among other things. He'd never have been able to prove anything."

Martin Recht closed his eyes. Even if Kamnitzer had put his finger on the truth, he, Recht, wasn't the man to put

117

his theory into practice—certainly not in his present condition. His stomach heaved.

"I feel sick," he repeated.

"Have a good puke, then," said Kamnitzer, opening the tarpaulins.

"Battalion orders," Streicher recited in the background, "expressly state that, in default of instructions to the contrary, opening the flaps while traveling through wooded country or along tree-lined roads is forbidden."

"Belt up!" snapped Kamnitzer. "I don't know of any battalion order that says Recht's got to puke in my lap."

He pulled the flaps apart and helped Recht to crane out. The road danced crazily beneath his eyes as he retched and strained without success.

Suddenly the truck squealed to a halt. Sergeant Major Rammler leaped out of the cab and ran round to the back, where he drew himself up with an expression compounded of undisguised animosity and barely concealed pleasure.

"That," he said, "is all we needed."

He proceeded to quote the battalion order word for word, just as Streicher had done, but added a footnote of his own. "Orders are meant to be obeyed, especially sensible orders like this one. Opening the flaps in wooded areas has often caused accidents, not only to vehicles but to the men inside."

He stood there foursquare, like a breakwater, his face a dull puce and his voice throbbing with satisfaction.

"There has been a direct violation of standing orders," he continued, "not only by the man who leaned out but by the N.C.O. who helped him to do so. Grenadier Recht and Corporal Kamnitzer, you will complete the rest of the trip on foot. You've only got three hours to do it in, so get cracking."

The rest of the trip amounted to eighteen miles. Sergeant Major Rammler ordered Recht and Kamnitzer out of the truck and drove off, leaving them standing beside the deserted road.

"I'm sorry," Martin Recht said glumly.

"Stow it," said Kamnitzer. "You needn't think you're a good-for-nothing just because someone tells you so."

"All the same, it's my fault if we've got to march back to barracks."

"It's a mistake you're going to pay for in hard cash, don't worry." Kamnitzer gave his friend an encouraging wink. "There's no question of marching back. We'll simply take

118

another taxi and you can pay the fare. I'll claim it back from Rammler the first chance I get."

Before Kamnitzer returned to barracks with his resigned and submissive companion, he made a telephone call from the bar parlor of a public house called the Crown, only three miles from the barrack gates.

"Watch out!" Kamnitzer grinned into the receiver, "Careless talk costs lives. I'll give my report in code: special procedure E, six hundred and five."

No one in the bar parlor seemed to appreciate his charade. The few customers within earshot continued to quaff their beer, presumably unwilling to risk being regarded as eavesdropping foes.

"Is that Blockhead?" Kamnitzer inquired of the mouthpiece. "This is Jackass, escorted by Nitwit."

The recipient of this information was Corporal Ramsauer, commonly regarded as C.S.M. Kirschke's right-hand man in the company office. Ramsauer, who had a weakness for Kamnitzer, said: "Rammler blew his stack when he came in. Even Kirschke couldn't calm him down this time. If you two get back to barracks too soon you'll find yourselves on guard duty."

"Forget about that," Kamnitzer told him. "There's no question of our getting back before time."

"They're planning to put you on patrol duty when you do turn up."

"I've got plans of my own," Kamnitzer said. "I'll turn up when it suits me—so you can forget about patrol duty as well. Got it?"

"Got it," said Ramsauer. "I'll pass that on to Kirschke, on the quiet. He couldn't care less, these days."

"Now listen," Kamnitzer went on. "Make out the guard and patrol duty rosters for today and the next couple of days. Get everything down in writing straight away, but make sure my name and Recht's only appear on today's list—not tomorrow or the day after. I like a bit of free time on weekends."

"Fair enough," Ramsauer said. "I'll get Kirschke to sign it at once, then it'll be official. All the same, I wouldn't drift in too late. There'll probably be a celebration tonight. Streicher's just been promoted sergeant."

Kamnitzer laughed. "It's about time that noncommissioned nincompoop was removed from our midst. Still, I certainly won't pass up an opportunity to congratulate him in person."

Kamnitzer's course of action was now clear. He and Recht mustn't return to barracks until the guard had gone on duty and the patrols had been checked for the first time. On the other hand, they mustn't be back too late, or he would miss the free beer in honor of Streicher's promotion, and he was determined not to do that.

Replacing the receiver, he went back to the table, where Martin Recht was still sitting in gloomy silence.

"We've got at least two hours to kill," he announced.

"I've got a date."

"With the lame duck?" Kamnitzer inquired with a grin.

Martin Recht shot his friend a surprised and reproachful glance. "You shouldn't say things like that," he said. "You, of all people."

Kamnitzer decided to give Recht a quick course of mental massage. "You'll have to get used to hearing that expression more often in future."

"It's a mean thing to say."

"Of course, Martin, but people repeat things like that without thinking. They don't mean any harm. You've got to let it roll off your back, don't you see?"

Recht shook his head angrily. "Leave it alone, Karl."

"All right," said Kamnitzer, "we'll leave it for the moment. All I know is, you won't be able to meet the girl in town—now or later."

"I could always phone, I suppose."

"Bravo!" cried Kamnitzer. "You're catching on at last. All the best people fight their wars by telephone these days. Go on, then—jump to it! Get yourself cleaned up and see if you can fix something. I'll be downstairs in the cellar."

Kamnitzer hired the downstairs bowling alley for the next two hours. A ball boy was soon found and Kamnitzer formed two teams, not only acting as the captain and members of each side but refereeing the match as well. According to the slate on the wall, it was a contest between the "Fatherlanders" and the "Internationals." They were so well matched that the issue remained in doubt for some time.

After about half an hour Kamnitzer was joined by two visitors. Martin Recht, hair combed and face and uniform largely innocent of mud, came down the cellar stairs leading a girl. She had a slight limp, not that Kamnitzer noticed it at first.

"How do you do?" the girl said gaily. "I'm the lame duck."

"Glad to meet you," said Kamnitzer, gazing entranced at

120

her gentle smile and wistful face. "You're just in time to bowl the next ball."

Recht looked worried. "Thanks for the invitation, Karl, but I don't think she ought . . ."

"It can't hurt to try," Carolin said.

Kamnitzer gave her an encouraging smile. He handed her a ball, explained briefly how to hold and deliver it, and then shouted: "Watch your front! First ball coming up!"

The girl swung the ball to and fro, took two or three hurried steps and let it go with surprising force. Then she stood back, panting slightly, as the ball rumbled along the gleaming planks.

"Nine!" shouted the ball boy, discreetly manipulating two pins with his foot. Carolin's ball had only knocked down seven, but the ball boy's correction met with Kamnitzer's approval. He decided to give him a bonus.

"Shall we go on?" Carolin asked eagerly.

Kamnitzer nodded. "You look a pretty dangerous customer to me—as a bowler, that is—but I'm always game. We'll play for a bottle—perfume for you, schnapps for me. Martin can act as referee."

They played a thoroughly hilarious match. The ball boy did his stuff so well that after the third game Kamnitzer invested him with the rank of corporal and a five mark piece. Carolin had never felt so happy or so completely oblivious of her disability.

"You're the most athletic lame duck I've come across," remarked Kamnitzer.

Carolin smiled gratefully. "I'm so happy Martin's got you for a friend."

"Not only athletic but cunning," Kamnitzer chuckled, "reminding me of my responsibilities like that. Let's have one more game before I indulge in quite another form of entertainment."

THE FESTIVITIES held to mark Corporal Streicher's promotion took place in the company office. This unusual choice of locale was partly attributable to Kirschke, who had hinted that his room and, consequently, his bed were more easily accessible from there.

Streicher had been notified of his promotion by Lieutenant von Strackmann, who insisted on performing that

pleasant ceremony in person. It took the form of a solemn handshake, an inspiring gaze, and some such words as: "This is a great moment for you, Sergeant Streicher.'"

The freshly minted sergeant shared that sentiment.

"It's usual to stand drinks all round," Kirschke insinuated.

Streicher reacted promptly. "If you would do me the honor of being my guest in the canteen, Sergeant Major . . ."

"No need for all that palaver," said Kirschke. "We can send out for some beer—schnapps, too. It doesn't matter where the party's held as long as there is one."

The party snowballed. Rammler, who was an early arrival, congratulated Streicher with bluff bonhomie, hinting that most of the credit belonged to him. He was followed by other N.C.O.s from No. 3 Company, men who had suddenly ceased to be Streicher's superiors and were now his peers. Ramsauer, the veteran company clerk, started to pour out drinks.

Eventually, Lieutenant von Strackmann himself appeared. He announced his readiness to take part in the impromptu celebration "as a fellow soldier," thus demonstrating his ironclad sense of solidarity. True comradeship knew no rank, provided always that the subordinate was prepared to respect his superior officer. Respect, however, was dependent on personality, and von Strackmann felt himself to be well endowed with that commodity.

Like his comrades of inferior rank, he opened the nearest bottle of beer and, disdaining a glass, conveyed it to his lips. He had some difficulty in draining it at one go, but Kirschke was an expert and the lieutenant was determined not to be outdone, least of all by his *bête noire*.

Von Strackmann drained his beer, panting triumphantly, and followed it with some of Rammler's staple drink— Strong Man's Milk—successfully concealing its explosive effect. Happily noting what he took to be admiring glances on the faces round him, particularly Streicher's, he felt more than ever convinced that he had promoted the right man.

"The solidarity that exists between the commander of a unit and his junior leaders," von Strackmann informed the seemingly attentive circle round him, "is of great and abiding importance. It must be carefully fostered, and it is based on mutual trust."

From there it was only a step to the subject of welfare

representatives, of which the newly promoted Streicher was one.

"He must enjoy the confidence of his superior officers and his fellow soldiers. He is also responsible for the maintenance of comradely trust within his sphere of jurisdiction. His main duty is to serve the community."

Kirschke grinned broadly. He was acquainted with these stilted pharses, all of which appeared in *The Officer's Handbook*.

Before the lieutenant could pursue his enlightening discourse further, Corporal Kamnitzer appeared, accompanied by Grenadier Recht.

Kamnitzer held himself stiff as a ramrod. His bearing would have done credit to a drill sergeant and his salute resembled one of the diagrams in a Prussian drill manual. He asked the lieutenant for permission to speak to Sergeant Major Rammler.

Von Strackmann granted his request with a look of approval, gratified that his unit should contain such a model of soldierly precision. He had obviously misjudged the man hitherto.

Kamnitzer proceeded to make his report to Rammler. "Corporal Kamnitzer and Grenadier Recht reporting back from special duties, Sergeant Major!"

"Carry on!" Rammler called hastily. He was not anxious to discuss the two men's route march in present company, especially as he had omitted to make a full and immediate report on the subject.

"May I request the lieutenant," Kamnitzer ventured, selecting his words with extreme care, "for permission to extend my heartiest congratulations to Sergeant Streicher?"

Address in the third person was not prescribed by any manual of military instruction. Officially, superior officers were supposed to be addressed as "you," followed immediately by their rank, but the third person—sometimes referred to as the "traditional mode of address"—still survived here and there, and Lieutenant von Strackmann was not alone in regarding it as a token of loyalty and obedience.

"Why don't you join us, Corporal?" asked von Strackmann. "Help us to celebrate the occasion."

"Many thanks, sir!" Kamnitzer barked, and sat down.

In between beers, von Strackmann turned to Rammler. "You've obviously got some first-class material in your platoon," he murmured confidentially. "We seem to have

overlooked Kamnitzer till now. You must keep an eye on him."

"I've had my eye on him for a long time," Rammler said grimly. The lieutenant's benevolence toward a charlatan like Kamnitzer caused him a spasm of almost physical discomfort—but, as he told himself, tomorrow was another day.

THE NEW DAY was a long time coming. It was preceded by a long night, not devoted exclusively to sleep.

"A creative night," Colonel Turner murmured to himself.

He formed this conclusion while seated at his desk, having just penned a sentence which struck him as pregnant with significance. It ran: "Just as there is an element of indestructibility in the human being, so there is in the soldier; for the soldier is a basic constituent of the human being."

His thoughts always traveled along these grandiose and exalted lines, and his work would undoubtedly cause a stir if he managed to complete it before the next war broke out. . . .

"A night like a wet sponge," Captain Ahlers remarked to his deputy, Captain Treuberg, as they waited for a transport plane which was on its way from Sicily. The bad-weather front over the Alps might be several hundred miles distant, but it was under an hour's flying time away.

"Nothing can go wrong if we're both on our toes," said Treuberg.

But Ahlers had an exhausting day behind him and was tired. When Treuberg asked if he could "run the shop" himself, Ahlers replied curtly: "Better not."

"The best place for us on a night like this," Warrant Officer Vossler said to Gerty Ballhaus, who was sitting beside him in his car, "is bed."

"Each to his own," she said enigmatically.

Yet another muffled peal of wedding bells, thought Vossler. He was a victim of his own freely chosen profession. If he wanted to fly he had to live in this one-horse hole. He wished he were in Bali or Hawaii—not parked in a narrow side street on the outskirts of a provincial town. At moments like this, Europe shrank to the size of a nutshell and the garrison town to a mere pinhead.

124

"Day and night are all one to me," Major Bornekamp said, buttoning up his trench coat. "I'm never off duty; you ought to know that by this time."

Frau Elfrieda smiled indulgently in his general direction, but made no attempt to prevent his departure. She could very well dispense with his presence at the moment, thanks to von Strackmann's personal attentions.

"You've got some first-class officers," she said. "Lieutenant von Strackmann has made a wonderful job of the arrangements for your Ladies' Night. He's a young man of many parts."

When this sentiment was expressed, Lieutenant Dieter von Strackmann was already lying on his camp bed, half asleep and smiling to himself. The C.O.'s confidence, Frau Elfrieda's favors and his subordinates' adulation—all had filled him with contentment, and alcohol had done the rest.

Elsewhere in the company block, Sergeant Major Rammler endeavored to sleep clad in full uniform and boots. Failing to find sleep but finding his bottle of Strong Man's Milk, which stood ready to hand beside his bed, he placed it to his lips, trumpet fashion, and drank.

A few rooms distant, Streicher was spending the first night of his sergeant's career lying supine with his hands folded on his chest like a knight on a medieval tomb. Suddenly he jumped up, pulled his uniform tunic over his nightshirt and hurried out of the room—not for intimate reasons but in order to admire the splendor of his new chevrons in the corridor mirror.

Martin Recht lay in the bunk next to Streicher's, curled up like a child, his face pillowed on his hands as though he were trying to hide it, and his breathing rapid and shallow. He was dreaming about a duck—not a lame duck, but one which skimmed ahead of him while he, also on the wing, tried desperately to catch up with it.

"Tonight," Frau Ahlers told herself as she watched her sleeping daughter's face, "could be the turning point."

It was true that she felt this almost every night when she peeped in at Carolin, but there really was an air of repose about her slumbering form.

She had come back from her outing full of gay chatter about Martin Recht and his friend, also about the bowling match, which she described in glowing terms. She seemed closer to recovery than she had ever been before.

"If only everything goes well," Frau Ahlers murmured silently.

"I can't stand nights like tonight!" Helen Wieder declared roundly. "Everyone gets so restless. You don't dare go out with men when they're in that state."

"Be that as it may," said Herbert Asch, "there are at least three of them waiting for you out there." He took her order book, checked it briefly, and passed it to his wife.

"You know Karl Kamnitzer, don't you, Herr Asch?" Helen asked. "What do you think of him? Is he as much of a wolf as all the rest?"

"Not being a woman, I couldn't really say, but I know one thing: he's different from the rest. It might be worth bearing that in mind."

"All I know is, he's the only man who's stood me up twice in the same week," Helen said petulantly. "No one treats me like that. I'll line up six dates for tomorrow evening and see how he likes it."

When Helen had gone, Herbert Asch said to his wife: "We've got a pretty complicated day ahead of us tomorrow" —but his smile betrayed that he was far from displeased at the prospect. Some complications appealed to him, especially the sort that showed people in their true colors. It was high time to know which side everyone was on.

"Tiring, a night like this," C.S.M. Kirschke remarked to Corporal Kamnitzer. "Sleep's a great thing. The only thing is, it gets a hold on you."

As the sole survivors of Streicher's promotion party they were still drinking his beer, though not still in his honor.

"You're browned off with this mob, aren't you?" Kamnitzer put the question without a trace of embarrassment. "See no evil, speak no evil, that's your motto these days. That's why you go off for a nap whenever you get the chance, isn't it?"

"You've got a nerve!" Kirschke said ponderously. He drew himself up with an effort, looking rather like a Buddha in a specimen cabinet. "Whatever you may think, I'm a soldier, heart and soul!" he announced suddenly. "I never wanted to be anything else. It's the breath of life to me, man!"

Karl Kamnitzer nodded. "The only trouble is," he said softly, "in this circus they put the horses and tigers in the same stable—and it's not a good arrangement."

"True." Kirschke fortified himself with another bottle of

126

beer—his tenth at least—and went on: "I don't say I'm an idealist—you get over that as time goes by—but I've always done my best. And then along comes a would-be hero complete with blinkers and a built-in loud-speaker—the sort that munches regulations and shits directives . . ."

"You mean Strackmann?"

"I'm not mentioning any names, Kamnitzer. All the same, when an officer's overenthusiastic, whatever his motives— even perverted idealism, if you like—he wears the people round him down, and most of them let themselves be worn down."

"Surely we can do something about it, can't we?"

The C.S.M. shook his head pityingly. "You haven't the first idea how the military machine functions."

"Maybe all one needs to know is how to swap cogs around—or switch the thing off when it's been running too long."

"You're talking balls, my boy."

Kirschke's show of irritation made no impression on Kamnitzer whatsoever. "People can have entirely different motives and still be after the same thing, Sergeant Major. Cooperation has its advantages. Why don't we try it sometime?"

With that question, which remained unanswered, Black Friday, which succeeded Gloomy Thursday, came to an end. If Kamnitzer's prayers had been answered, the next two days might have been christened Sunny Saturday and Splendid Sunday, but they weren't.

THE FOLLOWING DAY's troubles began when Corporal Kamnitzer awoke. The first person his eyes lighted on was comrade Streicher, whom he proceeded to shake vigorously.

"You're the welfare representative here, aren't you?" Kamnitzer inquired. "What's the matter—still pissed?"

"Take your paws off me," groaned Streicher. "I want to stay in bed for a while. It's a sergeant's privilege."

"You mean to say you're a sergeant?" demanded Kamnitzer. "Since when? Have you got it in writing?"

"Do you mind!" Streicher sat up indignantly, his head throbbing with the persistence of a steam hammer. "You were there last night when we celebrated my promotion— you even congratulated me."

"I congratulated you? I can't imagine doing that."

Kamnitzer winked at the other occupants of the room who had gathered round expectantly but were maintaining a cautious distance.

"Do you mind!" Streicher repeated, by now slightly agitated. "You're talking to a sergeant."

"If you're really a sergeant, where are your stripes? I don't see any on that nightshirt of yours. The only thing I'm interested in knowing is this: are you the company welfare representative or not? I'm thinking of lodging a complaint!"

"Another one?" exclaimed Streicher.

"What do you mean—another one? I can put in as many complaints as I like. I know my rights."

"You've got a complaint?" Streicher was wide awake now. He slid hastily out of bed and stood there in his crumpled nightshirt. "Against me, do you mean?"

"Not yet," Kamnitzer said airily. "It's Rammler's turn this time, and as welfare representative you're responsible for seeing my complaint goes through the proper channels."

Having laid his preliminary minefield, Kamnitzer started to get dressed. Streicher squatted on his bed, debating whether to react as a sergeant or a friend in need. Had he automatically ceased to be junior ranks' welfare representative now that he'd been promoted, or did he keep the job until someone else was chosen to replace him? His brain reeled with indecision.

"Why do you always have to stir it up?" Martin Recht demanded, as he accompanied Kamnitzer to the washroom. He felt uneasy. "Wouldn't it be wiser to lie low and say nothing?"

"You're hopeless, Martin. Hasn't anyone ever told you that attack is the best means of defense? That's what the brass hats always say, anyway, so we might as well see if their theory works out in practice."

"All this fuss!" Recht mumbled unhappily. "All I want to do is finish work and go into town. I've got a date with Carolin."

"You'll never make it unless we stir things up a bit."

Reaching the door of the washroom, Kamnitzer handed Recht the roll containing his soap, toothbrush, and shaving kit with a gesture which meant: book my usual place, the basin on the right, next to the window.

"Do we really have to go through with this?" Recht persisted.

"God Almighty!" Kamnitzer said angrily. "Haven't you caught on yet? Look, I'll explain the situation in words of one syllable: Rammler's bound to try and get us on guard duty—or at least patrol duty—let alone any other little treats he's got in store for us, but he won't be able to lift a finger if there's a complaint in the pipeline. Now do you see?"

Recht began to understand at last. Any punitive measure undertaken against the author of a complaint might be interpreted as a form of pressure or coercion. "Shall I lodge a complaint too, then?" he asked.

"No need. Why use two sticks of gelignite when one'll do the trick? You can be my witness this time."

"What do I have to say?"

"Just tell the truth, whatever they ask you. That's the whole point. We'll give them something genuine to chew on. Let's hope it chokes them."

Meanwhile Sergeant Streicher had hurried off to put Sergeant Major Rammler in the picture. Rammler flew into a rage and tried to exert pressure on C.S.M. Kirschke, who endeavored—yawning—to divest himself of his unwelcome visitor.

Rammler, however, was determined not to be shaken off this time. Having come to the conclusion that Kirschke was a sluggard, he did his best to make his opinions plain—which was where he went wrong.

"Do something for your money, Kirschke!" he exhorted. "Don't sit around doing nothing all day. Clobber that fellow Kamnitzer before he opens his trap."

"You haven't got a guilty conscience, surely?"

"What makes you think that?" Rammler glowed with righteous indignation. His conscience was clear, and if his actions ever overstepped the regulation mark—which they seldom did—it was always in the interests of good order and military discipline. "It's just that—well, we're not going to let a pain like Kamnitzer order us about, are we?"

"What do you mean—we?" Kirschke's face beamed rosily as though he had enjoyed an unusually good night's sleep. "I hope you're not trying to talk me into perverting the course of justice? Any soldier—I quote—who believes himself to have been unjustly treated by his superiors or by an official department, or to have been wronged by disloyal conduct on the part of his fellow soldiers, may lodge a complaint to that effect. Army Regulations, para. one."

"I've heard all that cock before! But if I was C.S.M. of

129

this company I'd have shut that bloody malcontent's trap long ago."

"N.B. No soldier shall suffer detriment as a result of lodging a complaint. Ditto, para. two."

Rammler uttered a few quotations of a less printable nature and retired in high dudgeon. He then sent for Streicher and endeavored to make it clear that he had to work on Kamnitzer—in the friendliest way, of course—for the sake of company harmony. Streicher, however, knew that Kamnitzer was too hard a nut to crack. "The most I can do, Sergeant Major, is to show Grenadier Recht where his duty to the company lies."

"If the lad's got a spark of common sense he'll toe the line!" Rammler growled.

But C.S.M. Kirschke, looking for a few brief moments as though he had never yawned in his life, was acting with unaccustomed speed.

The more Lieutenant von Strackmann heard of the distressing news which his C.S.M. was, so to speak, spreading on his morning toast, the more perplexed his expression became. Eventually he aked: "Have we got two men in the company called Kamnitzer?"

Kirschke was obliged to inform the lieutenant that the Kamnitzer in question was the same man who had impressed him so favorably the night before. For a minute or two, von Strackmann felt completely at a loss. His first inclination was to read the riot act to all concerned, but the situation looked tricky. "Do you think it's possible," he asked cautiously, "that Sergeant Major Rammler really has put his foot in it?"

Kirschke savored the moment of weakness—temporary, without a doubt—which had prompted the lieutenant to ask his C.S.M.'s advice for the very first time. "Anything's possible," he replied tersely, "in this outfit."

"I must talk this over with the C.O.," von Strackmann said finally. "In the meantime, kindly ensure that nothing happens to make matters worse. I shall hold you personally responsible if it does."

MAJOR WILHELM BORNEKAMP, Commanding Officer of the local Grenadier battalion, had been looking forward to a pleasant day. After an excellent breakfast came a phone call from Colonel Turner, who expressed thanks for his invitation to the Ladies' Night and promised to

turn up, punctually and with pleasure, accompanied by "a small party—three in all." He concluded by sending his best regards to Bornekamp's wife.

And then Herbert Asch appeared.

At first, he too gave the impression that he had welcome news to impart. "Everything's all set, Major. I've put the Silver Room at your disposal, so the party ought to go with a swing."

"Many thanks," said Bornekamp, with a condescending smile. He always cherished an attitude of superiority toward tradespeople and saw no reason to disguise it. "But you needn't have bothered to call in person—a telephone call to Lieutenant von Strackmann would have done. I've put the entire arrangements for this evening in his hands."

Herbert Asch appeared to ignore this unmistakable hint. He leaned back in his chair and said: "Before coming here this morning I happened to drop in at the newspaper office, and there, quite by chance, I caught sight of some galley proofs of an article about you."

"That's right," said the C.O. "Some local hack came and asked me for an interview. He was mad keen to have one —you know the form, democratic practice and so on. Even asked me for a photograph."

"I saw that as well. They've given you a page to yourself, complete with picture. The headline's already set, too, in inch-high capitals: *We Know What We Want!*"

"I say, that's going a little far, don't you think?" Bornekamp almost bridled, but only for a moment. "Still, it can't do any harm. Why shouldn't the army get a good press for a change?"

"You regard the contents of this article as good?"

The C.O. settled himself comfortably in his chair. "You know, Asch, when I think back—and it's only a few years ago—I remember all the mud that was flung at us. There were plenty of muckrakers about—mostly inspired by the Americans, I regret to say, until they realized that they'd be in the cart without us. Then the wind changed, and the penny-a-line merchants spun like weathercocks. The day before yesterday it was: 'No more war!' and yesterday: 'Look reality in the eye!' or 'Rearmament is a necessary evil!' Today it's: 'Freedom and the defense of the West!' Uniform has become a symbol of national pride once more."

"All the same, Major, things aren't quite to your liking yet, are they?"

"It's a question of time. But you must admit we've made

131

pretty good progress already. Take certain books, for instance—plain unadulterated un-German filth. Booksellers have stopped putting them in the window and readers are becoming ashamed to buy them. Or take these men on television. They've got tired of burning their fingers. One or two of 'em still have a go at us, I grant you, but they're rare exceptions. Even the film industry is doing its level best to cover us with glamour and glory. What more do you want?"

Herbert Asch appeared to be lost in thought. Some of Major Bornekamp's assertions were not incorrect. The last war was almost twenty years old, it was true, and after twenty years even obituary notices have lost their original impact and graves become overgrown with grass. The human memory was a sieve.

"For all that, Major," he said eventually, "a person can't say absolutely anything he wants to, even today."

"Yes, he can at last—if he's got the guts."

"But the Federal constitution still grants a citizen certain rights—and one of them is the right to refuse to do military service."

"In my view," the C.O. reiterated with conviction, "anyone who dares to do that is either a Communist or a coward."

"And all we need do is put them into a striped uniform —i.e., convict's garb—and that'll be the end of them?"

"Precisely!" Bornekamp gave an approving nod. "My view precisely. But how did you know?"

"It says so in your interview with the *Town and Country News*—in bold type." Asch eyed Bornekamp with curiosity. "But what you're saying, in practice, is that you regard the constitution as a shield and buckler for Communists and cowards, and your talk of striped uniforms may awaken memories of concentration camps. Do you really want to create the impression that this is the way the officers of your regiment think?"

The major started. For some moments he registered surprise and incredulity, but gradually he seemed to grasp what he had done. Asch gave him time.

"There must have been some misunderstanding," he said at last, breathing hard.

"But you've been quoted verbatim, Major."

"It's a diabolical liberty!" Bornekamp spluttered, realizing that the interviewer had tricked him into laying a trap for himself. "Besides, that remark wasn't original—it was made by a senior government official."

"Did you quote the source? No? Then you'll have to take responsibility for it yourself. And I can tell you one thing: if the local paper publishes that article on Monday there'll be all hell let loose by Tuesday. *Der Spiegel* will be down on you like a ton of bricks, closely supported by a section of the foreign press. The subject may even be raised in the Bundestag by a member of the opposition."

"Damn it all!" exclaimed the major, by now thoroughly perturbed. "Something must be done about this twaddle. Can't we simply ban it?"

"Twaddle or not, Major, you were responsible for it, I'm afraid." Herbert Asch smiled. "It's impossible to dictate to a free press what it should or should not publish. We haven't reached that stage yet, regrettable as it may seem to some."

"But what about you, Herr Asch? You must have contacts."

"Possibly," said Asch, bland but wary.

"Couldn't you . . ." Bornekamp searched in vain for the right words, and for a second or two he almost stuttered. "I would be uncommonly obliged if you . . . well, I think you know what I mean. . . ."

"It mayn't be too easy, but I can always try—under certain conditions."

Bornekamp did not immediately learn what these conditions were because at that moment the adjutant came in to report that Lieutenant von Strackmann wished to speak to him on an urgent matter.

"Tell him to go to hell!" bellowed the C.O., enraged at this untimely interruption. "Tell him to deal with his own problems. I've got more important things to do."

THE ADJUTANT, who was a man of tact, confined himself to telling von Strackmann that the C.O. could not be disturbed under any circumstances. He was in conference and would be tied up for an indefinite period.

Von Strackmann emerged from the administration block and paused outside, meditating. He came to the conclusion that there was nothing for it but to return to the company office, where Corporal Kamnitzer's complaint awaited him. Reluctantly convinced that he would have to investigate it in person, he stationed himself behind his desk and ordered Kirschke to bring in the parties involved.

Kamnitzer, who was the first to appear, gave the acting company commander a renewed opportunity to admire his

soldierly correctness. Once again, he looked every inch a model grenadier.

Lieutenant von Strackmann cleared his throat. "Have you thoroughly considered this complaint of yours?"

"Yes sir, I have."

"You feel you have received unjust treatment from Sergeant Major Rammler?"

"Yes sir. I might even go so far as to call it chicanery."

This term, though lifted straight out of Army Regulations, von Strackmann declined to accept. He appealed to Kamnitzer's better judgment, but without success. Then he announced his intention of clearing the air by means of an exchange of views and summoned Rammler for this purpose.

"My conduct was entirely proper, sir," stated the sergeant major. "There had been a direct violation of a standing order. Truck flaps are to be kept closed while traveling through wooded areas and along tree-lined roads."

"But this was an emergency," Kamnitzer protested. "Grenadier Recht was sick, that's why the flaps were opened temporarily. And if you'd like to know why Grenadier Recht was sick, sir . . ."

Von Strackmann checked him with upraised hand. It was one of his principles to stick closely to the point. He abhorred digressions into potentially murky details.

"The said grenadier is available to give evidence, sir," Kirschke put in.

"Thank you," the lieutenant said curtly. "I trust that won't be necessary." He got up and began to pace stiffly round the room. "Men," he said, "we're like members of one big family, in a sense, and every family has its share of quarrels and misunderstandings."

"This wasn't a misunderstanding, sir," Kamnitzer interposed. "It was completely intentional."

"It was a direct contravention of orders, sir," Rammler persisted, "and had to be dealt with accordingly."

"Perhaps we ought to call the witness in," Kirschke suggested.

"Nonsense!" snapped von Strackmann. "We'll settle this by ourselves, in the proper way."

He grappled manfully with the situation. On the one hand, contravention of an order, on the other, an alleged emergency—each statement entirely credible and each made by an exemplary soldier. A compromise seemed indicated.

"Men," he said, coming to a halt, "see here. We must try to be realistic. Misunderstandings do occur, and we

134

all make the occasional mistake. Let us assume that Sergeant Major Rammler has made a mistake. He will apologize for it. Let us also assume that Corporal Kamnitzer's suspicions are unfounded. He will apologize, too!"

Lieutenant von Strackmann stared challengingly from one to the other, sensing that he was on the brink of a satisfactory solution. Even Kirschke seemed to be indulging in a smirk of approval.

"Any man worthy of the name," von Strackmann pursued, now confident of victory, "is big enough to admit his own mistakes. He doesn't hesitate to apologize when necessary. Well?"

"All right, sir," said Rammler.

"What about you, Kamnitzer?"

"I'm not vindictive, sir, and I'm not petty-minded either. I'll be glad to accept the sergeant major's apology, but who's going to pay the fare?"

"What fare?" Von Strackmann looked slightly bewildered. "What are you talking about?"

"For the taxi, sir."

"What do you mean—taxi?"

"The taxi, sir."

Von Strackmann gaped at Kamnitzer helplessly.

"I might have known it!" Rammler said in a choking voice. "It's just what I'd have expected from you, Kamnitzer."

"That's rich!" Kirschke was almost groaning with delight. "That's one for the book! He took a taxi. If it gets around, the whole battalion will laugh itself sick."

Lieutenant von Strackmann appeared to be prompted by a similar fear. Laughter, whatever its cause, might prove positively fatal, not only to the reputation of the company he commanded but to him personally.

"Silence!" he yelled. "I won't hear another word on the subject. I shall give all concerned ample time to reconsider the situation carefully. In the meantime, I insist on absolute secrecy. Dismissed!"

"YOU'RE BARKING up the wrong tree, you know," Sergeant Streicher insinuated. "You think you can rely on Kamnitzer, but that's just where you're wrong."

"Kamnitzer's my friend," said Martin Recht.

They were sitting on their beds in Room 13. The rest of the company were out on the barrack square, and Rammler and Kamnitzer were still closeted in the company office. It had fallen to Streicher to work on Recht—in a comradely way—before he could be called as a witness.

"Kamnitzer is a first-rate man up to a point," Streicher said, "but he's too often mistaken in his choice of methods. It's hardly surprising some of his superiors think he's a malcontent, and that's dangerous—for you as well as him."

"He's my friend," Recht repeated stubbornly.

"So am I," Streicher insisted. "That's why I want to help you—and you need help, believe me. You don't want to be on extra duties permanently, do you?"

"Of course not."

"You'd like a free weekend, wouldn't you?"

"Yes. I've got a date, and I want to keep it—if it's humanly possible."

"Why shouldn't it be?" Sergeant Streicher radiated boundless assurance. "Everything's very simple in this mob, really, provided you know the rules. Rammler's not a monster, after all."

"Come off it! He worked me over yesterday until I was all in. I've never been treated like that in my life."

"I grant you, he's a tough nut. He can be quick-tempered too, sometimes, but you and Kamnitzer had provoked him. He means well at heart, take it from me. I can understand your attitude, but what happened yesterday mayn't be as pointless as you tend to think. Rammler's bark is worse than his bite. Once he sees that you realize he means well, everything'll be all right."

"He'll do me again if he gets the chance."

"That's just Kamnitzer talking. You've got the wrong end of the stick, I promise you. Rammler's only human. He's a friendly type, really, but discipline means everything to him. Once you accept that, it's easy to get on with him."

Martin Recht sat motionless on his bed. He was impressed by Streicher's remarks and grateful for the efforts which the newly fledged sergeant was making on his be-

136

half. "All I want," he said, "is to be left in peace. And I want to keep my date in town this afternoon."

"You will, Martin—I'll see to that. Trust me, that's all."

"There's one thing, though: I won't do anything to hurt Kamnitzer."

"No one's asking you to. In any case, Kamnitzer hasn't found out which side his bread's buttered on. He won't be able to hold his own against Rammler indefinitely—the sergeant major's too well in with the lieutenant—so the best thing we can do is stop him doing anything rash. We owe it to him as friends."

"ARE YOU SURE you haven't bitten off more than you can chew this time?" C.S.M. Kirschke asked, with an air of curiosity.

"Quite sure," Kamnitzer said firmly.

They stood facing each other in the company office. Lieutenant von Strackmann had closeted himself in the inner sanctum while Sergeant Major Rammler paced impatiently up and down the corridor outside.

"That taxi business was absolutely brilliant," Kirschke conceded, "but have you thought it out carefully enough? There's a bit of difference between foot slogging and riding in a taxi, after all."

"I know, a taxi costs more. However, if the sergeant major's prepared to refund the fare, I may reconsider my complaint."

"You've got a nerve!" Kirschke said, not without admiration. "Just between us, what makes you so sure of yourself?"

"Lack of clarity when issuing a verbal order." Kamnitzer winked at Kirschke. "When Rammler marooned us, he didn't say clearly and distinctly: 'March back to barracks.' That would have been a straightforward order. Instead, he just told us to hook it. You've got three hours, he told us, so get cracking. He never said anything about marching back."

"That's what he meant, though."

"I'm not disputing that, but I'm not a mind reader."

Kirschke grinned and disappeared into the company commander's office, where he found the lieutenant engaged in leafing through his *Manual of Military Law*, a thick red tome containing collected texts, notes, cross-references, and appendices.

"Must you disturb me now, Sergeant Major?"

"Yes sir," said Kirschke, and repeated—almost word for word—what Kamnitzer had told him. Von Strackmann realized that if the corporal managed to dig up almost any kind of corroborative evidence, which was a fair assumption, Rammler was in the cart and the company's reputation with him.

Lack of clarity when issuing a verbal order was a grave defect. The C.O. himself had repeatedly drawn attention to the fact that if there was one cancerous disease within the Bundeswehr this was it.

"Fetch Rammler," ordered von Strackmann.

The Sergeant Major, who was still lurking in the corridor, appeared, and von Strackmann repeated exactly what his C.S.M. had told him a few minutes earlier. "Well, Sergeant Major," he concluded, "explain yourself."

"The meaning of my order was unmistakable, sir."

"The meaning of an order is important, of course, but the phraseology must match it."

"I can't remember every last detail, sir," Rammler protested, squirming like an eel, "but I meant the men to march back."

"What do you mean—meant? You should have said so." Lieutenant von Strackmann tapped the bulky volume on the desk before him. "Anyone incapable of issuing proper orders," he declaimed, quoting the C.O., "is not fit to command men."

Rammler had turned as pale as the latest consignments of rifle grease, popularly known as "dead man's dripping." He made a final attempt to extricate himself. "There's a certain type of subordinate, like this man Kamnitzer . . ."

"That's enough!" the lieutenant broke in. "I don't want any vague excuses or far-fetched explanations. I'm concerned with the facts alone, and they imply, unfortunately, that a fully grown sergeant major—in my company, what's more—hasn't yet learned how to issue clear and unmistakable orders."

Rammler tottered on his foundations like a weather-beaten war memorial. He found it hard to maintain his martial poise.

"I should never have expected such a thing from you, of all people," the lieutenant said bitterly. "You're obviously not fit to be trusted with a platoon, let alone a whole company."

With that ruthless *coup de grâce*, Rammler was dismissed. He marched out looking pale and rigid.

138

"Shall I call Kamnitzer in now, so that we can settle the matter?" Kirschke asked.

"It needs going into thoroughly first," Lieutenant von Strackmann said, still racking his brains for a satisfactory solution. The taxi presented an almost insurmountable obstacle.

"Right, sir," said Kirschke. He realized that the case had been shelved for the moment, but this state of affairs could not survive indefinitely, especially as Kamnitzer was involved.

The weekend took its course.

Lieutenant von Strackmann continued to pore over the *Manual of Military Law* until his attention was claimed by last-minute arrangements for the Ladies' Night. Sergeant Major Rammler sat brooding on his camp bed for a quarter of an hour and then retired to the canteen, and C.S.M. Kirschke changed his trousers yet again.

Sergeant Streicher had worked on Martin Recht so successfully, meanwhile, that the grenadier now seemed to be suffering from loss of memory.

"You know, Karl," he said to Kamnitzer when the latter returned to Room 13, "I really think we ought to avoid unnecessary fuss, don't you agree?"

Kamnitzer looked thoughtfully, first at his friend and then at Sergeant Streicher, who was standing in the background. He didn't find it hard to guess which way the wind was blowing. "So he's been at you, has he? Three cheers for the voice of conscience!"

"I merely gave him some advice," Streicher said. "He doesn't have to take it, but it was well meant."

"We've thought things out very carefully, Karl," Recht said, eager to convince his friend. "The point is, why make things unnecessarily difficult? Why go out of our way to make an enemy of Rammler?"

"You're talking rot," Kamnitzer said flatly. "You can't turn a lion into a lamb—not with the best will in the world."

Kamnitzer brushed Recht aside and made for his bed. He lay down, unbuttoned his tunic and stretched out comfortably in preparation for a brief morning nap.

Streicher drew closer, looking worried. "Our mutual friend has come to the conclusion that there may have been a misunderstanding—that Sergeant Major Rammler really did give you the order to march, even if indirectly. On the

139

other hand, you may have misheard his order or interpreted it wrongly. I'm trying to be fair to both sides."

"I really think that would be the best solution from everyone's point of view," Recht chimed in.

"The best solution would be for you two to get lost," said Kamnitzer. "You're spoiling my beauty sleep. If Rammler refunds our taxi fare I may reconsider the position—and that's a pretty generous offer. On the other hand, if he doesn't pay up promptly I'll present him with a bill for the other taxi."

"What other taxi?" Streicher asked, perplexed.

"The one we took during the map-reading exercise, of course," said Kamnitzer, and rolled over onto his side.

Streicher glared helplessly at the corporal's back. He had proffered the olive branch, only to see Kamnitzer fling him a hand grenade in exchange. One taxi was bad enough, but two taxis on the same day were catastrophic.

"I don't know what you're talking about," Streicher said, and shot out of the room like greased lightning.

The remainder of the morning passed uneventfully. Kamnitzer snored peacefully to himself while Martin Recht carefully sponged and pressed his dress uniform.

Early in the afternoon, the first inmates of the Grenadier barracks started to stream into town, Corporal Kamnitzer and Grenadier Recht among them. Kamnitzer was contemplating a visit to the air force barracks, whereas Recht intended to have a haircut and then call for Carolin.

"Give anything in uniform a wide berth," Kamnitzer advised his friend. "You're not old enough to play with big boys yet. I'll look forward to seeing you in the Café Asch this evening, preferably in one piece."

Kamnitzer's visit to the air force barracks was a series of surprises. The first came when he presented himself at the barracks gates and asked to speak to Warrant Officer Vossler. All the sentry said was: "If you want to speak to him, you better go look for him."

When Kamnitzer inquired the best place to begin his quest he was referred to Captain Ahlers, who, it seemed, knew everything. Kamnitzer found him in his office, seated behind his desk with his uniform jacket removed and sleeves rolled up. The door stood invitingly ajar.

"Good afternoon," said Kamnitzer, agreeably impressed by such an obvious lack of ceremony in a military establishment. His salute was noticeably casual.

"Good afternoon," replied the captain, eying his visitor with interest. "To what do I owe the pleasure?"

"I'm looking for Warrant Officer Vossler."

"You'll find him in No. 2 Hangar."

"Where do I find No. 2 Hangar?"

"You can't miss it—just make for the control tower and you'll see it immediately next door." The captain smiled. "My name's Ahlers, by the way."

"Mine's Kamnitzer," responded the corporal. "I think I know your daughter—Fräulein Carolin Ahlers, isn't it? I played a brisk game of bowling with her and my friend Martin Recht yesterday afternoon."

"Ah, so it was you!" Ahlers looked pleased. "Sit down for a moment, if you've got time. What about something to drink? We're fairly well stocked at the moment. I can offer you Scotch, Irish, rye, or bourbon."

Kamnitzer sat down with alacrity. Nothing like this had ever happened to him before. After a moment's hesitation he decided to test the resources of the transport wing by asking for raki. Five minutes later a glass was in his hand, brought by a sergeant who served him as if it were the most natural thing in the world.

Ahlers and Kamnitzer continued to chat like members of the same club until a lieutenant strolled in and asked Ahlers if he needed him any longer. If not, he was thinking of going fishing. "No objections," said Ahlers, and the lieutenant strolled off again.

"You mustn't judge our outfit by army standards," Ahlers told Kamnitzer. "We haven't time for them here."

"When do you knock off, usually?"

"Whenever we get the chance," Ahlers said promptly. "It's not unheard-of for us to fly transport missions several nights in a row, weekends included. To make up for it, we occasionally take a midweek break—two or three days, sometimes."

"So there's no set routine?"

"What do you mean, Herr Kamnitzer? We merely fly when we have to fly. You don't imagine wars are fought on a timetable basis do you?"

"Then your men have to be ready for action all the time —without a break? That's even worse than our lot."

"Hold hard," Ahlers said, smiling. "We concentrate on essentials and we make a thorough job of them, but we leave all the superfluous details to other people."

Ahlers' account of air force procedure appealed to Kamnitzer, but further surprises were in store for him when the captain took him to see Warrant Officer Vossler at work.

They found Vossler standing in the middle of No. 2

141

Hangar surrounded by a group of young men, all of them officers.

"Advanced pilots' course," Ahlers murmured.

Vossler had a notebook in his hand and was asking questions. He looked as casual as ever, but his questions were crisp and to the point, and the young officers' replies equally so.

"Well, how are things going?" asked Ahlers.

Vossler nodded cheerfully at the captain without saluting and passed him his notes. "Fair to middling," he said.

While Ahlers was looking through the notes, Vossler caught sight of Corporal Kamnitzer. He walked over and greeted him like an old friend. "Nice of you to drop in. I'll be through in about ten minutes."

Then he devoted himself once more to Captain Ahlers and his young officers. "Well, gentlemen," he said, "if no one's got any more questions, I think we'll call it a day."

Rather naturally, none of the officers had any more questions, but one of them said: "We're having a celebration at the Hotel Asch this evening, and you're cordially invited, Herr Vossler. Will you look in?"

"Thanks," the warrant officer replied. "I'll see if I can manage it."

When the class had dispersed, Vossler turned to Kamnitzer. "Well, what brings you here?" he asked. "Business or pleaure?"

"I always try to combine the two. I could say I was keen to take a look inside this place, just for interest's sake— and it wouldn't be a lie either. There was another reason, though. I wondered if you could lend me a few marks."

Vossler chuckled. "Do I look like an easy touch?"

"Yes," said Kamnitzer with disarming frankness.

"How much do you need?"

"Thirty?" This was only a suggestion, but when Kamnitzer saw Vossler reaching for his wallet he added: "You could make it fifty, of course. I've had a lot of official expenses recently. I had to take a taxi on a map-reading exercise yesterday."

"A taxi? Tell me about it."

"With pleasure," said Kamnitzer, and while they strolled up and down the hangar he gave an account of his privately financed trips. Vossler, who made an attentive audience, eventually burst out laughing, and continued to do so even when a senior officer appeared.

"Excuse me a moment," said Vossler, turning to the officer. All the latter wanted was some technical information,

which Vossler supplied with a total lack of ceremony and formality. By now Kamnitzer would hardly have been surprised if the Inspector General of the Air Force had turned up at Vossler's elbow.

"That's priceless!" said the warrant officer, returning to the subject of Kamnitzer's taxi rides. He looked forward to retailing the story to Ahlers. "And well worth fifty marks," he added.

"Just to complete my pleasure," Kamnitzer suggested, "what about showing me over one of your crates?"

"You want to see one of our planes?" The warrant officer looked dubious. "It's not as simple as all that, I'm afraid. We'll have to get permission."

"Really? I was under the impression you owned the whole establishment. Strikes me you only have to wag your little finger and everyone comes running."

This was not the case, however. Kamnitzer was duly astonished to note yet another reversal of what he regarded as normal procedure. This time, the warrant officer approached a humble corporal in oil-stained overalls. "I'd like to show our Army friend a Noratlas—all right?"

"All these conducted tours!" grumbled the corporal, but he gestured graciously to a big-bellied transport plane in the background. "Don't take any dirt in with you, though," he added warningly. "My mechanics aren't charwomen."

"Is it always like this here," Kamnitzer asked bemusedly, "or is this a special performance for my benefit?"

"Werner's only a corporal," Vossler explained, "but he's acknowledged to be the best mechanic on the station. The same goes for flyers. When a warrant officer flies a plane his co-pilot may be a lieutenant and his navigator a captain—but they both have to obey the orders of the pilot, i.e., the warrant officer. They do, too. It comes naturally."

"But that's terrific!" Kamnitzer exclaimed with genuine enthusiasm. "Performance before rank and ability before authority! I didn't know any outfit operated like that. Why don't we hear more of it?"

Like scores of others in the country, the local town was inhabited by solid and respectable citizens. When the military band played universal harmony reigned. It hadn't always been so, but what resistance there had once been had crumbled. Townsfolk now attended the band con-

certs in droves, and the residents of the market place peered from their windows with evident pleasure at the sight that met their eyes. True, the bandsmen's uniforms were only slate gray, and no weapons, accouterments, or medals glittered in the sun, but the hearts of the crowd involuntarily beat a little higher when the old marches rang out.

"Would you mind if I took Carolin for a stroll?" Martin Recht asked politely.

Frau Ahlers hesitated for a moment—not because she didn't trust Martin Recht, but because she was worried by the thought of Carolin being jostled by the crowds.

"Please, Mother!" pleaded Carolin. "I'd so like to go."

"All right, but be careful."

They heard the strains of the band from a long way off. It was blaring out the Hohenfriedberger March, though any tune would have suited their mood as well. Diffidently, Martin Recht felt for Carolin's hand, which she surrendered without hesitation.

In a sense, the band had helped to break the social ice for the garrison as a whole. It was an army band, and stationed elsewhere, but in response to public demand it now visited the town once every four weeks during the spring and summer months. Major Bornekamp made a point of showing himself at these concerts, accepting the bandmaster's salute with manifest pleasure and standing on the steps of the town hall to greet various notables— tradesmen mostly, but also civil servants, schoolteachers, and junior employees with social aspirations. Mayor Asch seldom attended.

"It beats me why those semi-soldiers have to spoil their program with wishy-washy muck like that," Sergeant Major Rammler averred to his dutiful listener, Sergeant Streicher. "Wishy-washy muck" referred to a Strauss waltz which had been sandwiched between two marches.

"They have to make allowances for the civilians, I expect," Streicher ventured. "They haven't reached the stage of knowing what they really like."

In actual fact, after years of aversion, mistrust, and reserve, a constructively disposed minority of citizens—soon to become a majority—had recognized the signs of the times and come to terms with their community's special position. The town lay off the beaten track. Some might have described it as an idyllic spot, but the surrounding countryside was as bare of industry as it was of thriving agriculture. On the other hand, the town boasted numerous

hostelries and large numbers of marriageable girls without prospects.

What was more, the place had always been a garrison town. In their time, the barracks on the north side had housed imperial troops, men of the Reichswehr, and soldiers of Greater Germany, in that order, and during the Second World War a subsidiary airfield had been built on the south side. Although the postwar garrison had not found it easy to capture the worthy citizens' hearts, the latter were at last beating in time to the bandmaster's baton.

"Look who's here," Rammler said, nudging Streicher, and pointing to the south side of the square. Martin Recht had just emerged from a side street, attentively squiring Carolin Ahlers.

"Her father's a captain, don't forget," Streicher said cautiously.

"Anything he can do," Rammler said, eying Recht malevolently, "we can do better."

He was firmly convinced that, when it came to the pinch, a captain's daughter would know how to differentiate between a sergeant major and a private soldier. Besides, he told himself, a lofty gesture of conciliation on his part might lead to the establishment of contact with the so-called upper crust, and there would be no harm in that.

"Run over and tell 'em we've got a first-class view of the band here," Rammler commanded. "Say we'll be glad to share it with them."

After a moment's hesitation, Streicher obediently trotted off, worming his way through the listening throng until he reached Recht and Carolin.

He greeted Martin like a bosom pal and asked to be presented to his companion, assuring them both how delighted he was to see them.

"Why don't you come over and sit with us?" he asked. "We've got splendid seats."

Martin Recht felt almost honored. Streicher was a good friend who tried, with his best interests at heart, to reach compromises, relax tensions, and establish harmonious relations. Aptly, the band started to blare out the "Old Comrades' March."

"Shall we?" he asked irresolutely.

"No." Carolin sounded friendly but firm. "I wouldn't want anyone to be saddled with a lame duck."

Streicher withdrew hastily and reported the outcome of his mission to Rammler.

"Thinks she's too good for us, does she?" the sergeant

major commented. "It's not surprising, the company these girls keep. Never mind, one day they'll realize what a bunch of miserable deadbeats they're going around with."

The band was now playing "The Glories of Old"—a march studded with fanfares and drum rolls—much to the delight of the assembled citizenry.

FOR THE TIME BEING, the varied festivities in the Hotel Asch were proceeding entirely according to plan.

In the Blue Room, the air force cadets were piloting volunteers from the girls' high school round the dance floor. In the Silver Room, the Grenadier officers and their invited guests were embarking on a decorous social evening. And in the Green Room, also known as the Gun Room, the small but high-spirited party of young air force officers had assembled to celebrate the end of one of their many training courses.

The three parties shared the same cloakroom and lavatories, also a long anteroom which had to be traversed by anyone entering or leaving the three reception rooms. This anteroom was where the organizers of the various gatherings spent most of their time: Captain Ahlers for the air force, Lieutenant von Strackmann for the army, and Herbert Asch for the hotel.

"Everything seems to be going with a swing so far," Asch said contentedly. His own staff was working hard and the mess waiters borrowed for the occasion were also doing their best.

"Let's hope it doesn't go with too much of a swing," said von Strackmann. "Our air force friends in the Green Room are making enough noise already."

"They're young," said Ahlers.

"Of course," von Strackmann agreed cautiously, "but I hope they won't become any noisier."

"It's unlikely for the moment," Asch put in. "The future heroes of the air have already absorbed so much alcohol that they've reached saturation point for the time being. Judging from experience, you won't hear much of them for the next hour."

"In that case I'll stand down until then," said Ahlers, winking at Asch. "Captain Treuberg can deputize for me in the meantime."

"We'll be in my office," Asch told von Strackmann as he followed Ahlers out of the anteroom.

146

The lieutenant stared after them uncomprehendingly, shocked at their casual attitude. Personally he intended to remain at his post.

All was going well in his sector. An atmosphere of tranquillity, cultured decorum, emanated from the Silver Room, which was in his charge. The guests were still dining, their needs assiduously attended to by a team of waiters and orderlies. Von Strackmann reflected that his system was functioning admirably, and the C.O. would be delighted.

The two other reception rooms presented quite another picture. An occasional babble of voices came from the air force cadets, who added insult to injury by bursting into vulgar applause between dances. Their band, which consisted of piano, electric guitar, and drums, was altogether too loud, and the music it produced could only be described as "beat."

What struck von Strackmann as even more grave, however, was that the small party of air force officers was managing to produce considerably more noise than all the cadets, their partners, and the jazz band put together. Alarmed by this, he decided to take precautionary measures.

His first move was to seek out Captain Treuberg, Ahlers' deputy. He found him sitting by himself at a table in the middle of the Blue Room, drinking cider and coolly scanning the enthusiastic throng for potential signs of misbehavior.

Von Strackmann asked Treuberg to follow him outside. "Listen to that," he said when they reached the anteroom. "Quite a din, don't you agree?"

Captain Treuberg considered it important to demonstrate his interservice esprit de corps. "You may be right," he conceded.

"Especially as Colonel Turner is honoring us with his presence this evening." Von Strackmann felt Treuberg to be a kindred spirit—the sort of man one could work with, even if he was wearing the wrong insignia.

The mention of his wing commander's name settled the matter as far as Treuberg was concerned. Determined that Colonel Turner should not be disturbed by his own cadets, he issued the following decrees: subdued music only from now on, e.g., tangos, waltzes, and slow foxtrots, but no more rock 'n' roll, alcoholic drinks subject to authorization only, and lengthy pauses between dances.

Treuberg's directives had a marked effect. In less than half an hour the party spirit was virtually dead and the first cadets drifted off with their high school partners, os-

tensibly to escort them home. Only the best-behaved re-mained behind.

"What about the gentlemen in the Green Room?" von Strackmann inquired, concentrating firmly on his next objective and confident that Treuberg would again lend his support.

The young men in the Green Room seemed determined to extend the scope of their already nerve-racking activities still further. Not only did they grow noisier, but they visited the men's room with increasing frequency, and when, as was inevitable, they encountered young ladies from the high school, they indulged in pleasantries which von Strackmann recognized as barely veiled propositions.

"We must do something about it," he declared stoutly. Captain Treuberg agreed, but added that it wouldn't be easy.

Treuberg was right. The young officers were a sort of closed society which drifted from course to course and station to station. Each garrison town offered a plentiful selection of bars but few unattached girls, so their craving for feminine companionship was intense.

"Do you have to make that frightful row?" Treuberg demanded of one of them, who was steering an unsteady course for the men's room. "Can't you be a bit quieter?"

" 'Fraid not," he said equably.

"But Colonel Turner's next door," Treuberg remonstrated.

"So what? He's not disturbing us."

Unfortunately, this view was not reciprocated. At that moment, Colonel Turner was presiding over the festive board in the Silver Room like a decorative and much-ad-mired centerpiece. The whole brightly lit room seemed to have been built around him, a handsome frame for an imposing picture.

His partner at table was Frau Elfrieda Bornekamp, who sunned herself in reflected glory while he chatted to her with all the gallantry of the old school—though a trifle absently, since he was already pondering his speech. General theme: the constructive values of social intercourse.

Major Bornekamp, meanwhile, sat there stiff-backed and correct, his eyes alert, his commanding voice subdued but clearly audible, his tone jocularly masculine when addressing the ladies, bluff and hearty when conversing with subordinates. Even here, he remained the Ironclad incarnate.

When the dessert—pineapple slices in kirsch—had been served, Major Bornekamp called for silence and handed the floor to Colonel Turner.

"Ladies and gentlemen—dear friends!" the colonel began. "There was a time when real values and true dignity were conspicuous by their absence. That time does not lie very far in the past, but we can now congratulate ourselves on having seen the last of it."

Here the colonel paused for effect so that those present might have time to absorb the significance of his words. The reverent silence that ensued was, however, shattered by the sound of male voices raised in song. The colonel knit his brows, robbed of the power of speech less by the noise itself than by the realization that the words issuing from a dozen lusty throats belonged to a ditty noted for its questionable taste or, to be more precise, its downright indecency.

"She was only a vicar's daughter!" roared the air force officers happily—and distinctly.

Turner preserved his poise with some difficulty. He glared accusingly at Major Bornekamp, who turned to relay the gorgon gaze to von Strackmann. Von Strackmann was not in the room, however, so Bornekamp had no alternative but to rise from the table.

"I'll soon put a stop to that!" he promised grimly.

SERGEANT MAJOR RAMMLER was finding it an unenjoyable evening. "There's nothing to do in this dump," he announced to Sergeant Streicher, who retained the privilege of accompanying him. "They don't mind lining their pockets at our expense, these people, but they won't lift a finger to entertain us."

Sergeant Streicher essayed a nod which might have signified agreement. He knew that it was inadvisable to contradict Rammler unnecessarily.

"Dead as a doornail, that's what it is," the sergeant major pursued, as they strolled aimlessly round the market place. The town guide described it as "bathed in antiquity," but Rammler was blind to its charms.

"Not enough women, and the few there are just want to get married. It's a bloody awful state of affairs."

"Perhaps it's done deliberately," Streicher suggested, "so we won't get distracted from our work. After all, women aren't a standard part of military equipment."

This, however, was a subject on which Rammler felt strongly, especially after duty hours and on weekends. Today was no exception.

"It's lousy organization, that's what it is! What do they think we are, stationing us here without any kind of safety valve? It's a rotten trick, I tell you."

Rammler was a man of wide experience who had, as he put it, "sneaked" his way into the last war at a very tender age. "You can say what you like about the old days, but they knew how to organize things properly. There were brothels in the front line, not to mention servicewomen and nurses, and every unit had a campful of women pioneers or German Girls' Leaguers attached to it. And that's not counting the local grass widows."

Streicher thought he understood. The sergeant major was smarting under all that had happened to him that day. The tough shell of his self-esteem had been punctured, but he had not abandoned hope.

"It's a dog's life," declared Rammler. "The only thing which might make it bearable at this moment would be a bottle of bubbly. One bottle—two at the most. How about it?"

He slapped his companion on the back without conviction and strolled slowly on. Then, outlined against the illuminated windows of a bookshop, he saw a figure which he recognized at once from fifty yards away.

"There's that little sod Recht," he said, slightly cheered by the sight. Raising his voice a degree or two, he summoned the grenadier over.

"Tell me, Recht," said Rammler, when Recht was standing before him, "have you been spreading atrocity stories about me?"

"No, Sergeant Major."

"What about today, at the band concert?"

"Certainly not, Sergeant Major."

"So when that—that young lady brushed us off like a couple of flies, she did it on her own initiative? Do you really think I'm stupid enough to believe that?"

Recht offered no answer to the last question. "Fräulein Ahlers is very shy," he said. "She's been an invalid all her life, so she isn't used to being with a lot of people."

"I can confirm that," put in Streicher, who was worried by Rammler's jaundiced mood and wanted to dispel it. "Fräulein Ahlers really is rather reserved."

Martin Recht rewarded Steicher's remark with a grateful smile. He was a good pal, there was no doubt about that, and Kamnitzer was wrong to underestimate him. For a few moments, Rammler, too, seemed disposed to listen to the voice of reason.

"What the hell!" he exclaimed, brightening suddenly. "Why should we let ourselves be kicked around by a bunch of stupid tarts!" His wrath embraced three women simultaneously—Helen Wieder, Gerty Ballhaus, and Carolin Ahlers—but he seemed prepared to banish them from his memory. "A bird in the hand's worth two in the bush, friends. Let's pay a visit to La Paloma."

"Would you excuse me, Sergeant Major?" said Recht.

Rammler's face stiffened. "What's that? You don't appreciate my company, is that it?"

"I was just on my way back to barracks, Sergeant Major. Besides, I haven't got an overnight pass."

"You don't want to, that's what it is." Rammler was outraged. That a wretched underling should have the effrontery to reject his friendly overtures was the last straw.

"I might have known it," he said bitterly. "When all's said and done, it's only what I'd have expected of you. It's in your blood, after all." His dull rage knew no bounds. Like a bull goaded beyond endurance, he now saw nothing but red. "Once a Jew boy always a Jew boy!"

Martin Recht turned pale and Streicher looked as though he had trodden on a nest of scorpions, but Rammler registered the satisfaction of one who inhabits a country where freedom of speech is an inalienable right.

"Don't look so bloody cretinous!" he cried. "If you haven't got that load of crap out of your system, it's high time you did. Right, you two! Buck your ideas up and try to behave like grown men. To La Paloma, at the double—march!"

A HURRIEDLY ARRANGED CONFERENCE was being held in Herbert Asch's office, those present being Colonel Turner, Major Bornekamp, Captain Ahlers, and, naturally enough, Asch himself. The latter's prime function was to pour oil on troubled waters by dispensing the contents of a bottle of Iphöfer Kalb, vintage 1957.

The sole point under discussion was how to curtail the activities of the group of young pilots whose singing of indecent songs had caused such an unpleasant stir and, as Bornekamp balefully expressed it, "interfered" with the colonel's speech.

"The first thing to do," Herbert Asch suggested, with a covert wink at Ahlers, "is to establish whether the words were really objectionable."

"They were downright crude," said Major Bornekamp.

151

Being well-versed in this field, he was qualified to give an expert opinion.

Lieutenant von Strackmann and Captain Treuberg had already encountered defeat at the hands of the airmen, some of whom were of the same rank and had greeted them like long-lost brothers. Having failed to establish a clear-cut position of authority, they had retired under a barrage of laughter.

"Strictly speaking," Bornekamp told Asch, "this is your problem. You're in charge here."

"You're absolutely right on the last point," Asch replied courteously, "but I'm in charge of a hotel, not a barracks, and there's a subtle difference. Military discipline is not my concern. There's nothing abnormal about people singing on my premises—it's an everyday occurrence in my line of business."

"What do you think, Captain Ahlers?"

Ahlers did not hesitate to say what he thought. "Fighter pilots are a law unto themselves. They travel around from one training course to the next. They're young, so it's not unnatural for them to let off steam occasionally. They're noisy, of course, but fundamentally harmless. The less notice you take, the less row they make. I recommend a little patience. That's all that's needed."

Bornekamp delivered a vigorous lecture on discipline and Colonel Turner advocated diplomacy, but no one seemed prepared to intervene in person. On the contrary, each endeavored to pass the hot potato to the other, a game which might have gone on indefinitely if Lieutenant von Strackmann had not materialized. He looked agitated.

"One of the ladies has been molested!" he announced.

"Physically?" inquired Herbert Asch.

"The lady involved was Frau Bornekamp," reported von Strackmann.

He had been standing with her in the anteroom, engaged in private conversation—he didn't say so, but Frau Elfrieda had hinted that she might allow him to escort her home later—when one of the fighter pilots appeared.

"He addressed her as 'doll,'" von Strackmann concluded.

"He probably meant it as a compliment," said Ahlers.

"Besides," said Asch, "Herr von Strackmann may have omitted to introduce them in time. That's probably how this unfortunate misunderstanding arose."

"It was a direct affront, for all that," Colonel Turner said coolly, satisfied that his well-judged remark would leave Bornekamp holding the hot potato.

The major rose with an air of purpose and left the room. He descended one flight of stairs and strode majestically along the corridor until he came to the Green Room.

On entering, he found the party still in full swing. Some of the fighter pilots were, in his estimation, the worse for wear. Several had shed their jackets and ties and rolled their sleeves up, and two were actually squatting on the carpet like a couple of fakirs. The musician of the party struck three rousing chords on his guitar, and all eyes turned expectantly in Bornekamp's direction.

"I must ask you," he said sternly, "to terminate these proceedings. You're making a nuisance of yourselves."

The young officers regarded him with delight. The evening had been showing signs of flagging, so any distraction merited a hearty welcome.

An angular youth with carrot-colored hair stepped forward, assuming the role of spokesman for the assembled merrymakers. "It remains to be seen who is disturbing whom," he said affably. "We like it here, anyway, and you're not disturbing us—yet."

"I am a major," Bornekamp said, not without dignity.

"I'm happy for you," the fighter pilot said with a cheerful grin. "Most of us are still captains."

"You will oblige me by calling it a day," Bornekamp insisted. "At once, if you don't mind."

"Did you hear what the man said?" demanded the red-haired youth, turning to his companions. "Was it a slip of the tongue—or did I just misunderstand?"

"Do you know who you're talking to?" Major Bornekamp decided to throw the full force of his personality into the scales. "Clear out immediately, do you hear!"

The spokesman surveyed his friends with a twinkle in his eye. Everyone looked highly entertained. The party was proving worthwhile.

"Listen, mate," he said, stationing himself in front of Bornekamp with arms akimbo, "—or Major, if you prefer it. May I point out that we're off duty now? That being so, we left our ranks behind in the cloakroom. Quite apart from that, you're in the army and we're in the air force—which is quite another kettle of fish altogether, in case you didn't know."

"How dare you lecture me! One of you molested my wife."

"There's no question of anyone having molested your wife. One of us may have used a term of endearment or admiration, but that's all. So either have a drink with us or shut the door behind you as you go out."

"You'll be hearing from me!" snapped Bornekamp, turning on his heel.

"A postcard'll do!" a jaunty voice called after him.

Bornekamp squared his shoulders and marched back to Asch's office, purple in the face with frustration.

"What—no luck?" Asch inquired blandly.

Bornekamp concentrated his fire on Colonel Turner. "Disciplinary proceedings must be instituted at once, Colonel. Disobedience is a mild word for the behavior of those young men."

"Gently, Major," said the colonel, bowing his stately head in thought. "We mustn't be precipitate."

"Perhaps it would be best," Herbert Asch suggested, "if you yourself, Colonel . . ."

"I don't think that would be advisable," Ahlers said promptly.

"Why not?" Asch donned an air of surprise. "The colonel is the senior officer present."

"Besides, Colonel, these officers are temporarily under your command," added Bornekamp.

Ahlers maintained a pregnant silence. Looking round, the colonel saw the eyes of those present fixed on him in what he took to be a demonstration of confidence. He had no choice but to act.

"In that case," he said, not without misgiving, "I shall have to take the field myself."

GRENADIER MARTIN RECHT sat hunched in a corner of the Café Asch, staring moodily into space. He pushed his empty beer glass toward the waitress who was serving him.

"Same again," he said. "Better make it two while you're about it."

He didn't notice that the waitress in question was Helen Wieder. He had no wish to see anything, neither the confused blur of tables, chairs, glasses, and bright lights, nor the people that inhabited it.

"Aren't you feeling well?" Helen asked.

Recht gave no sign of having heard. He felt as if he were enclosed by a dense curtain of fog. Then the curtain parted and Karl Kamnitzer appeared.

"What's up with you?" Kamnitzer demanded. "Why do you have to spoil my Saturday night just when it's shaping nicely?"

"I'm sorry," Martin said dully. "I didn't ask you to come. One more glass of beer and then I'll push off."

"What do you mean, one more glass of beer! You've got rid of three already—knocked them back almost before they were on the table, too. I'm well informed, you see. You've not only interrupted my dreams of a rosy future—you've alienated my girl friend's affections. She seems to be far more interested in your welfare than in mine."

Frau Elisabeth had accorded Kamnitzer the special privilege of sitting in the room behind the bar counter, where coffee was brewed and an array of bottles stood ready to hand. This, too, was where Helen Wieder spent her time when she was not actually serving in the restaurant—likewise ready to hand, Kamnitzer reflected, except that she kept eluding his playful advances and had insisted that his friend Recht needed him.

"I'm sorry," Martin said again. "I didn't mean to disturb you."

"Well, you have, and here I am." Kamnitzer sat down and pulled his chair closer. "All right, let's have it. What's the trouble this time?"

Recht shook his head. "Nothing's happened, I tell you."

"Don't give me that," Kamnitzer persisted. "I can read you like a book."

Recht was silent for a moment. Then he gulped down the contents of his glass and said, almost angrily: "Haven't you anything better to do than sit here talking to a Jew?"

"Steady now!" protested Kamnitzer, pricking up his ears. He took a few moments to digest what Recht had just said. "What's that supposed to mean? Besides, you're bragging. You're only half Jewish, aren't you?"

"I'm a Jew, all the same."

"Then be proud of it, man. Actually, it's a shame you're only half Jewish. The Bundeswehr could do with a few genuine Jews. It'd be good for public relations."

Kamnitzer was familiar with Martin Recht's past history, though only vaguely. His father—a Jew—had served as a young but much-decorated officer in the First World War. He later married a non-Jewish woman and founded a successful business with numerous overseas contacts which proved extremely useful to him when he was forced to leave the country. He returned to Germany after the war, and died in his home town. He had never lost his affection for the army, and despite all his subsequent experiences he would probably have approved of Martin's decision to volunteer for the Federal army, had he lived.

"Someone's been bugging you, haven't they?" Kamnitzer demanded. "Who was it? Not Rammler, by any chance?"

Recht nodded mutely.

"When and how? Let's have all the details."

Martin Recht recounted what had happened, and the longer he talked the more relieved he felt. Eventually he even summoned up a faint smile.

Kamnitzer, however, looked more and more grave. "Well, what did you do?" he demanded finally.

"Nothing."

"You didn't knock his teeth down his throat? Didn't you even call him a moronic Nazi swine?"

"No, I just walked off. What else could I do? He's a sergeant major, after all, and Streicher was there too."

"Fair enough," Kamnitzer said slowly. "Maybe you did right, under the circumstances. In any case, there's no reason why you should regard the word 'Jew' as a term of abuse."

"Thanks," said Recht, laying a hand on his friend's arm.

"I see the whole thing in quite another light, of course," Kamnitzer said thoughtfully. "But that's my own affair. Tell me, where did friend Rammler go after his performance?"

"He said he was going to La Paloma."

Kamnitzer's shrewd eyes sparkled. "Not bad," he mused. "In fact, it may be the perfect place. How much cash have you got on you?"

"Just over forty marks."

"It'll have to do," Kamnitzer said firmly. "Hand over the lot. I need some working capital." He snapped his fingers impatiently. "Come on, there's no time to lose."

Recht obediently handed over the money, asking questions but receiving no reply. Kamnitzer added his own money to Recht's and began to count it, nodding happily to himself as he did so.

"I don't know what you're up to," Recht said, "but I don't want you to get into trouble on my account."

"Everything's risky these days," Kamnitzer said grimly. "It's a hard life for everyone—sadists included, even when they hide behind a uniform. The only problem is how to bring it home to them. Never mind, where there's a will there's a way."

COLONEL TURNER stood in the anteroom and surveyed the three doors behind which the social life of the station was pursuing its course. The remaining officer cadets and their high-school girls were still pounding the parquet in subdued fashion in the first room and a hum of lively conversation came from the second, but the occupants of the third were baying like wolves.

"No untoward incidents in my department, sir," Lieutenant von Strackman reported in a courteous, confidential, semi-official manner.

Captain Treuberg also hurried up, conscientious as ever, wanting to know if the colonel needed anything.

All the colonel needed at that moment was a brandy. Having fortified himself, he strode over to the third door, which Treuberg opened for him, and walked in. He was confronted by a jumble of chairs, a battery of empty bottles, and a pile of broken glasses. Through the tobacco smoke and alcohol fumes he could make out a number of perspiring young men in their shirt sleeves.

"Gentlemen!" Turner began.

"Welcome, sir!" called one of the fighter pilots, and his cry was taken up by the whole company. "Welcome!" they bellowed.

"Three cheers for the colonel!" shouted another at the top of his lungs. "Hip-hip-hip!"

"Hurrah!" they roared with fervor.

"Gentlemen!" Turner said again.

He got no further because the guitar-playing officer leaped onto the table with a crash, knocking over several bottles and glasses in the process. "Friends!" he cried in ringing tones. "In the colonel's honor we'll now sing 'The Lodger and the Landlady!' "

This they proceeded to do, in so far as what emerged from their throats could be described as singing.

Colonel Turner stood there transfixed. He opened his mouth to say "Gentlemen!" again, but the din was so terrific that he abandoned the idea. Adopting the only course still open to him, he turned on his heel and left the room.

He re-entered Herbert Asch's office looking slightly distraught and gratefully accepted the glass proffered by Captain Ahlers.

"They welcomed me in unison," he said, with something akin to wonder, "and then they sang a song."

"Something obscene, I'll bet," said Bornekamp.

Turner could only nod. "Ostensibly in my honor, too. I never got a word in."

"It's an old dodge, sir," Ahlers said knowledgeably. "I was caught like that myself once. They're probably laughing themselves sick at this minute."

The last remark was somewhat ill-judged, as Captain Ahlers at once realized when the colonel shot him a reproachful glance, clearly implying that no one laughs himself sick at a colonel.

"Anyway, something definite will have to be done now," Bornekamp said.

"What, for instance?" Asch asked curiously.

"Well," replied Bornekamp, with iron in his tone, "we could simply get together a scratch force, clear the requisite number of cells in the guardroom and lock the fellows up."

Colonel Turner closed his eyes briefly and raised a restraining hand. He was always averse to any idea which might have unforeseen consequences. On the other hand, he could not think of a better one. He stared wearily into space.

"It's a hopeless situation," declared Ahlers.

Bornekamp controlled his rage with difficulty. "My officers would never dream of indulging in a musical performance of that sort," he said harshly.

Colonel Turner stiffened slightly and raised his eyebrows as if to convey that Bornekamp had exceeded the bounds of propriety. "In my command," he said in measured tones, "conditions of service are somewhat different."

"That's what I meant," said Bornekamp.

"In the air force," Turner continued, with a touch of condescension, "we have to master an extremely complex weapons system, and that demands discipline of the highest order. But to maintain it outside the sphere of duty, let alone in the strictly private domain . . ." He paused. "There just isn't time."

"In my view," Bornekamp persisted, "discipline is inconceivable except as a whole. It must be present in any given situation."

"Even when you're on the bottle?" inquired Asch.

"Even when you're on the can, for that matter," averred Bornekamp.

"I don't think we need to go into details of that sort," Colonel Turner said with distaste. "Besides, we're straying

from the matter in hand. The vital question at the moment is how we're going to silence those young savages without causing an unpleasant scene."

"If you'll allow me," Herbert Asch said suddenly, "I'll deal with them for you."

"Don't be ridiculous!" exclaimed Bornekamp. "If the colonel and I failed to stop them, what luck are you likely to have?"

The hotelier looked unabashed. "I can always try."

"Please do," Turner said. "You have my blessing."

Barely ten minutes passed before Asch returned. He resumed his seat with an air of satisfaction, raised his glass to the other three, and drank, "Well, that's that," he said.

"What's what?" Bornekamp asked belligerently.

"The noise. The young gentlemen have promised not to sing or accost the ladies."

"Remarkable!" Colonel Turner said admiringly. "How did you manage it?"

"It was quite simple, really." Asch winked at Ahlers. "I merely told them who I was and pointed out that a hotel owner has certain rights, among them the right to serve whom he likes for as long as he likes and turn unwelcome guests out. What it amounted to was: either they piped down and behaved decently or they'd be ejected without getting another drop to drink."

"And it worked?"

"It always does. You've only got to make it clear that you know the rules of the game. Most of them are based on a bare modicum of common sense, and that, if you don't mind my saying so, gentlemen, is a quality which the services might well display to better advantage."

WHILE KAMNITZER was setting off on his special mission, destination La Paloma, Martin Recht remained sitting in the Café Asch. The thick fog round him had dispersed and Rammler's insult had assumed the reduced proportions of a misunderstanding. He was well looked after, too, first by Helen Wieder and then, after a brief interval, by Vossler and Gerty, who came over to his table. He greeted them delightedly. Vossler was part of Carolin's world, somehow, and anything that reminded him of her was a welcome distraction.

"We won't disturb you," Gerty said.

"We're not staying," Vossler added. "We've got plans for this evening."

"But we're going on a little outing tomorrow," Gerty continued, "and we wondered if you'd join us—you and Carolin, that is."

"I'd love to," Martin said gratefully, "but only on condition that Carolin—Fräulein Ahlers . . ."

"Leave it to me," said Vossler. "I'm one of the family, and a breath of fresh air won't do Carolin any harm. That's settled, then. I'll be outside the barracks in my car at fourteen hundred hours tomorrow, on the dot. Civvies and a cheerful smile to be worn by all."

They said goodbye and waved to him from the door before going out. Recht waved back, smiling. The last few minutes had banished his worries, but they returned with a rush when he caught sight of Sergeant Streicher.

Streicher hurried over to him with an earnest expression on his face. "I've been looking everywhere for you," he said. "I tried half a dozen bars and even rang the barracks to see if you were there. Thank goodness I've found you at last."

Martin Recht looked at his watch. "I'm pushed for time, I'm afraid. I've got to be back in the barracks by midnight."

"Forget about that," Streicher said, sitting down. "What you need is a heart-to-heart talk. It'll do you good."

"Maybe tomorrow," Recht parried. "The last thing I want to do is get put on restrictions."

Streicher laid one hand soothingly on his arm and beckoned for two beers with the other. "You can't get shut of me like that. Don't worry about your pass—I'll see you're all right."

"What do you mean?"

"I've got contacts. After all, I'm a sergeant now, and the guard commander's an old pal of mine. I'll just tell him you left your pass behind—that'll do the trick."

Martin looked dubious, but Streicher reverted from the tone of authority to that of friendship. "You know you can always rely on me, don't you? You need advice, after what happened this evening."

Recht made a noncommittal reply, but he accepted Streicher's offer to sneak him past the barracks gates. "Get this straight, though. Don't ask me to apologize to Rammler for what he said."

Streicher looked shocked. "I wouldn't dream of it," he assured me, ordering two schnapps to go with their beer. "There was no excuse for his behavior. He completely for-

got himself. You just can't say things like that—it's unforgivable."

"He said what he thought."

"I told you I condemned him for it."

"He meant to insult me, He used the word 'Jew' as a term of abuse. You heard him."

Streicher drained his glass hurriedly. He knew that if Recht stirred up any mud—as well he might—he, Streicher, would find himself in it up to his neck, if not deeper.

"You've got to look at it in the proper light, Martin," he said, warming to his subject. "I'm not trying to defend Rammler—not in this instance—but he's not really anti-Semitic. Maybe he just meant it as a sort of joke."

"Oh yes," Recht scoffed, "it was hilarious!"

"I admit it wasn't a proper subject for a joke, but he didn't insult you to your face. He just said: 'Once a Jew always a Jew'—more to himself than anything else. It sounds a bit different put like that, you must admit."

"What exactly do you want, Streicher?"

"I want to stop you from doing anything stupid, that's all. Just think—if this business hits the headlines it could harm the reputation of the whole garrison—of the Bundeswehr itself."

"Rammler should have thought of that first, shouldn't he?"

Streicher lapsed into silence. After a pause, he said: "I take your point, Martin, but why make unnecessary trouble for yourself—and me as well?"

"I'm not making trouble for anyone, Streicher. Other people make it for me. But you haven't told me what you want yet."

"Discernment, understanding, generosity . . . I'm appealing to your common sense, Martin. Sergeant Major Rammler will apologize to you formally, in my presence. How about that? Wouldn't that be the best solution?"

"Perhaps," said Recht, tempted to agree but mindful of Karl Kamnitzer. "Let's hope it's not too late already," he added almost inaudibly.

Streicher, who felt he was in sight of land at last, failed to catch the last remark. If Rammler wasn't completely demented he would apologize, which meant that his own responsibilities would be at an end.

"Leave it to me," he said confidently, and ordered two more beers. He laid his hand on Recht's arm again. "Just one more thing," he said in a low but purposeful undertone. "Could you do me a small favor?"

"What is it?"

"I wouldn't ask if I didn't feel we both trusted each other. I had to celebrate my promotion, see, and it wasn't cheap. One expense after another, and the bills are still coming in. To cut a long story short, I'm completely broke. Could you possibly slip me a fifty-mark note?"

"I'm awfully sorry," Recht said with genuine regret. "I haven't a pfennig left. Someone borrowed my last mark a few minutes back—word of honor."

"Blast!" said Streicher, deeply disillusioned. He went around solving other people's problems, and what thanks did he get? They left him in the lurch in his hour of need.

"Well, I've got to raise some cash somehow," he said, getting up. "I've already left my paybook in one bar as a deposit."

"Don't forget you promised to get me past the guard-room," Recht reminded him.

"First things first," Streicher called over his shoulder. "I shan't get in myself without a paybook. Wait here—I'll be right back."

So saying, he vanished, not to reappear that night.

MEANWHILE, Kamnitzer was launching Operation Reminder, as he had christened it to himself, in La Paloma, or, to be more precise, in the passion parlor.

"Hello there!" he called to the men round the bar. who were all Italians. "How about drinking a toast to international understanding?"

"We shit on it," said one of the Italians, with an admirable command of German idiom.

Kamnitzer was undeterred. "Let's drink to it all the same."

The Italians raised their glasses reluctantly. They were suspicious, and not without reason. The German weather didn't agree with them particularly, nor did German schnapps. They earned fairly good wages, it was true, but their private life was virtually nonexistent, first because of the language difficulty and second because male competition in the small town was positively overwhelming. What with the army, the air force, and an additional kennelful of Americans, there were at least ten men on the trail of every unattached girl.

"And now," said Kamnitzer, when he had ordered the next round, "let's drink to everything in skirts!"

The Italians, who were beginning to warm to Kamnitzer, laughed. The young soldier seemed to be a bit of a wag. What was more, he seemed to enjoy their company. Far from jeering at their clumsy German, he ventured an occasional word of Italian, which they found both endearing and entertaining.

By the time they had demolished a third and fourth round of drinks at Kamnitzer's expense, harmony reigned supreme. It was a harmony which appeared to extend even to their dislikes. To convince themselves of this, all they had to do was glance at the mirror behind the bar. This reflected the furthest recesses of the passion parlor, where, wreathed in tobacco smoke and a haze compounded of alcohol fumes and cheap perfume, sat Sergeant Major Rammler, who had wedged himself between two girls.

The girls were stolidly waiting for him to make his choice in accordance with an unwritten law which stated that, in this garrison town, the military had first call on their professional services. Differences in rank played a role, but civilians and Italians came at the bottom of the scale.

"So you've taken a fancy to me, eh?" Rammler demanded with a grin.

"You could say that," one of the girls drawled wearily. Her eyes flicked over the Italians as she did so, but she knew that a sergeant major had considerably more to offer, financially, than a foreign laborer.

"We're being patient," said the other, "but you'll have to decide on one of us sometime, or the other'll miss the boat."

"I go for you both," declared Rammler, hugging them possessively as if they symbolized womanhood in general. He seemed quite indifferent to what was going on at the bar.

Kamnitzer, who was still sitting there surrounded by his new friends, was telling them about a trip he had made to Italy. He had never been there in his life, but his perusal of the illustrateds and weeklies in the battalion reading room gave him enough material to go on.

"Friends," he said, "what do I do when I go to Italy? Do I take a girl friend along? Certainly not—I behave like an Italian."

"Does it work?"

"Every time," Kamnitzer said firmly. "It all depends on whether you know how to adapt yourself. When I'm in Italy I act like an Italian, so when you're in Germany you must act like Germans."

163

"How do you mean?" asked one of the Italians, intrigued.

"Get used to the way things are done here. Adapt yourselves to local customs. Don't let yourselves be elbowed aside. Charm won't get you anywhere on its own."

As Kamnitzer discoursed in this vein, and round followed round, the Italians began to thirst for action. Their newly awakened pride was stung by thoughts of their defeat of a few days before, and they wagged their heads significantly when Kamnitzer concluded his harangue with the words: "Competition's there to be eliminated."

This way they were determined to follow, though how to put the idea into practice most effectively was less easy to see. However, prompted by Kamnitzer, they all recognized the figure in the corner as a symbol of the competition which had to be eliminated.

Thus, when Sergeant Major Rammler rose in response to a call of nature, the most pugnacious of the Italians started to follow him. Kamnitzer held them back. "Not yet," he said, "not here. Wait for the right moment—I'll see you get your chance."

Ordering his new-found friends another round—this time of invigorating grappa—he slapped them heartily on the back and went over to Rammler's two female companions. He sat down between them uninvited. "I'll pay the normal price," he said without more ado, "plus ten marks special expenses, plus as many free drinks as you like—just so long as you don't work tonight."

"What if we want to?"

"I shall understand," Kamnitzer assured them. "In that case, I'll put my Italian friends at your disposal. All you need do then is take your pick." He eyed the door of the gentlemen's lavatory. "I must get going. We'll discuss details outside in the corridor."

Negotiations were brief but satisfactory. Kamnitzer paid the girls generously in advance and gave them precise instructions. With everything in readiness, Rammler was at liberty to make the next move.

GRENADIER MARTIN RECHT flitted through the streets like an uneasy ghost, looking for Streicher. His pass had expired hours before.

He visited all the hostelries round the market place in turn—The Bunch of Grapes, The Wild Boar, The White Hart—inquiring everywhere for Sergeant Streicher, but without success.

Desperately, he combed the side-street locals patronized by the garrison—The Gay Dog, The Eagle and Child (affectionately known as "The Bustard and Bastard"), and The Black Horse. A sea of faces met his gaze, some stolid and contented, others staring into space like lost souls surveying the depths of their own despair, but the comradely sergeant's was not among them.

Recht was tired now, and far from sober, but still he roamed on. He saw a drunken man propped motionless against a wall, a woman dragging her husband home, a courting couple compressed into the shadow of an archway.

Above him the moon, pale as a corpse and tipsily indifferent, whitewashed such house fronts as it could reach and drew livid chalk marks across the cobbles.

Then Recht found himself standing in front of the block where the Ahlerses lived. How he had got there he had no idea. He stared up at the blank windows, behind one of which Carolin must be sleeping. He had a vivid picture of her lying there with her face buried in the pillow, her long hair flowing free, breathing softly and smiling at some tender dream inspired by memories of him. . . .

In reality, he couldn't see the window of Carolin's room at all. It looked out onto the courtyard where the dustbins were kept. Carolin wasn't smiling, either. She was breathing heavily, her face looked strained, and her hip was hurting. An enjoyable day was taking its toll.

It was not long before Recht's musings were invaded by the harsh realization that he had to find Streicher and get back to barracks, come what may.

But Streicher was nowhere to be found.

"How much longer have we got to sit here?" one of the two girls asked Rammler. "It's time we were going. What about it?"

"I'm champing at the bit," Rammler assured her. "The only thing is, I'm a bit broke at the moment. Could you give me tick—just till next Saturday? I'll pay you interest."

"For you," said the girl, gently removing his hand from her knee, "I'd do anything."

Rammler felt flattered and, for the first time that day, appreciated.

"You carry on," said the girl. "I'll follow you in a minute. Meet me on the corner of Fasanenstrasse and Hobelweg."

"Done," said Rammler. He left the bar enraptured by the notion that no one could resist the power of his personality.

"Well, what about it, sports?" Kamnitzer said encouragingly. "This could be the chance you were looking for."

The Italians conferred quickly among themselves, putting their heads together like pigeons in the Piazza San Marco. Then five of them peeled off and left La Paloma in quick succession. Kamnitzer ordered a glass of champagne. There was nothing to do now but kill the next quarter of an hour.

After about twenty minutes the Italians returned, looking as though they had recently indulged in some mild but exhilarating form of exercise. One of them rubbed his hands.

"That should do it," he said, winking at Kamnitzer.

Kamnitzer bought his energetic friends one more round in token of his appreciation, secretly hoping that they had done their work with a thoroughness worthy of their German hosts. Then, full of expectation, he left La Paloma.

He strolled along the dark length of the Fasanenstrasse toward the intersection with Hobelweg. On the corner of the two streets stood a chestnut tree and a billboard. There was no streetlight, and now that clouds had hidden the moon the outlines of the ruined fence and the scattered houses in the background were blurred and indistinct.

Kamnitzer casually lit a cigarette, threw the match through a gap in the fence and began to whistle, discordantly but with bravura. No particular tune was identifiable.

"Hey, you!" a voice called.

Kamnitzer interrupted his recital. "Who's there?" he asked.

"Me!"

The voice issuing from behind the fence sounded quite

pitiable. Kamnitzer had been expecting it, but its un-sergeant-major-like tone took him by surprise.

"What do you mean—me?" he inquired with relish. "Who's me?"

"Help," pleaded the man behind the fence, "I've been beaten up."

"Are you hurt?"

The man mumbled something inaudible. Then he called: "Hey, don't I know you? Of course! It's Kamnitzer, isn't it?"

"Herr Kamnitzer, if you don't mind."

"Thank God!" the voice cried unsuspectingly. "What a bloody miracle you came along. I need help."

"Who are you?"

"Can't you hear? It's Rammler, Sergeant Major Rammler."

"Anyone could say that," Kamnitzer said in tones of deep suspicion. "Why don't you come out where I can see you?"

"I told you, I was set on. They tore all my clothes off—left me without a stitch."

"Then get dressed."

"Goddamnit!" bellowed Rammler. "They pinched my clothes. Can't you understand, blast you?"

"Kindly moderate your language," Kamnitzer said reprovingly. "You're beginning to annoy me. If you really are stark naked, you're creating a nuisance. It's an affront to public decency. I'll have to report it to the police."

"Kamnitzer!" Rammler called despairingly. "Surely you can recognize my voice, can't you?"

The sergeant major saw no alternative but to show himself. He emerged from the shelter of the fence. White as the belly of a fish in the light of the moon, which had uncharitably reappeared, he trotted toward Kamnitzer with one hand clutching his private parts and the other extended in supplication. Kamnitzer ignored both gestures.

"Do you recognize me now?" he asked.

The corporal shook his head distastefully. "No, why should I?"

"So you refuse, do you?" Rammler's voice resumed its old, menacing tone. "Right, this is an official order. . . ."

"An official order? Don't make me laugh!" Kamnitzer sounded amused. "Since when do people issue orders in the altogether? Sergeant Major Rammler would never dream of doing such a thing. That proves you can't be him!"

"You rotten swine!" Rammler roared. "I see your game! You're mixed up in this business, aren't you, you filthy little sod!"

"Push off, you dirty old man!" said Kamnitzer. "That makes two offenses you've committed—indecent exposure and masquerading as a sergeant major in the German army. I'm going to call the police."

"Kamnitzer!" called Rammler, pleading again. "Be reasonable, for God's sake!"

But Kamnitzer turned on his heel and vanished into the night, whistling.

MARTIN RECHT only meant to pause near the barracks gates just long enough to regain his breath, but ten minutes passed before he screwed up the courage to take the last few inevitable steps.

He leaned back against a tree, worn out by his vain quest for Streicher, but exhaustion could not subdue his mounting anger.

Streicher had obviously broken his word, which meant that he was liable to be put on restrictions. If things really went wrong, he would not be able to see Carolin for some time to come. There was one last chance of retrieving the situation, and he decided to take it.

Drawing a deep breath, he walked up to the barracks gates and wished the sentry a polite good evening.

"What do you mean, good evening?" the sentry asked peevishly. "It's just on four A.M."

"Nice night," Recht remarked.

"Your pass," said the sentry.

Martin Recht donned an air of desperate amiability, but the sentry's bleary face remained sullen. "Sergeant Streicher of No. 3 Company has got my pass," he said, with as much charm as he could muster.

"Let's see your paybook," said the sentry.

"Ask the guard commander," Recht said eagerly. "He knows Sergeant Streicher—they're old pals."

"If it isn't one thing it's another," grumbled the sentry. "It's beginning to get me down." Morosely, he locked the gates and slouched over to the guardroom with Recht.

The guard commander, who was engrossed in a whodunit, did not welcome the interruption. He listened to the sentry's report, eying Recht with some perplexity.

"You say Sergeant Streicher's got your pass? Funny he didn't mention it when he came in. I was speaking to him only an hour ago."

"Perhaps he forgot."

The guard commander stared absently at his detective novel. He wasn't inhuman, but what could he do? Orders were orders.

Even so, he left no stone unturned. First, he rang No. 3 Company and spoke to the duty N.C.O., who tersely informed him that Grenadier Recht's name was not in the leave book. Then he asked to speak to Sergeant Streicher.

No. 3 Company's duty N.C.O. swore under his breath and went to call Streicher. After a considerable lapse of time, Streicher came to the phone. He stated, drowsily but definitely, that he knew nothing about Grenadier Recht's pass.

"There must be some mistake," Recht said agitatedly. "Please ask him once more."

Frowning, the guard commander repeated his question, but Sergeant Streicher's answer was still the same: no, he knew nothing about it.

"That's it, then," the guard commander told Recht with genuine regret. "I'll have to report you. Leave your paybook here."

Recht did so. Then, with shoulders sagging, he trotted along the road leading to No. 3 Company block. His legs felt as if they were made of lead, and he was on the verge of collapse by the time he reached Room 13.

Here he was greeted by Comrade Streicher, who stood there in his nightshirt with arms akimbo. "What do you think you're up to?" he demanded indignantly. "What are you trying to pin on me?"

Recht did not reply. He merely stared steadily at his self-styled friend for several seconds. It was a look conveying extreme contempt, and it annoyed Streicher immeasureably.

"This is the last straw!" Streicher protested. "What are you looking at me like that for? I go out of my way to help you, and what thanks do I get? You try to take advantage of me."

Recht restrained himself with an effort, "What about your promise?" he demanded.

"I promised you nothing—nothing at all! I'll deny anything you say, I warn you."

"Why don't you shut up?" called a sleepy voice.

It being the weekend, some of the beds were empty. Four men were absent, of whom three had weekend passes and the fourth—Kamnitzer, needless to say—was being crafty enough to delay his return to barracks until daylight. Nor-

169

mally speaking, the orderly sergeant did not carry out an early-morning tour of inspection on Sundays.

"So you're running out on me!" exclaimed Recht.

"I've never run out on anyone," Streicher said, with increasing volume. "How dare you make such an accusation! Don't involve me in your troubles, that's all I ask."

"Christ Almighty!" called another inmate, wakened by the noise. "If you want a fight, clobber each other and get it over. I want some sleep—I'm on guard duty tomorrow."

"Mind your own business!" Streicher yelled.

Recht advanced to within a few inches of the sergeant. "So you don't know a thing?" he demanded. "You heard nothing and made no promise?"

"Don't you dare lay hands on me!" screeched Streicher. "I won't be threatened, do you hear?"

"Why don't you go outside?" came a weary voice from yet another bed.

Neither Recht nor Streicher took any notice of these interjections. They stood confronting each other like two fighting cocks.

"Perhaps you'll also deny that Sergeant Major Rammler swore at me for being a Jew?" Recht asked quietly.

"I don't know what you're talking about. It's nothing to do with me."

"You're a dirty, mealy-mouthed bastard," Recht said softly.

"What did you say?"

"I said: you're a dirty, mealy-mouthed bastard."

The occupants of the room sat up in their beds and stared, intrigued by the scene that was unfolding before their bleary eyes. They looked with interest from Streicher's beet-root features to the unexpectedly menacing figure of Recht.

"Clout him, Martin," said someone. "Then perhaps we can get a bit of rest."

"Take that back," Streicher hissed, "or . . ."

But no one ever found what the "or" portended because Recht pushed the sergeant aside. He only meant to clear a path to his bed, but Streicher must have been off balance. He staggered sideways and crashed against a cupboard. Rebounding, he cannoned back into Recht, who seized his nightshirt with both hands, tearing it, and flung him aside with a grimace of disgust.

Streicher crashed into a cupboard once more, lost his balance completely and sat down with a thud. He looked around him in outrage, but his furious protests were drowned by a peal of laughter.

170

THE DAY THAT FOLLOWED came to be known as Mellow Sunday. Although it was not an altogether apt description, the sun dispensed its radiance lavishly and the earth seemed to glow with well-being. Even the barracks-room windows gleamed softly.

Everyone prepared to enjoy the day ahead, local inhabitants and members of the garrison alike. People were up and about early—whether to take the air, drink, or pray—and in the Municipal Gardens the first courting couples disappeared into the willow thickets round the so-called swannery, which only housed ducks.

Colonel Turner sat in his garden, lost in thought. His beloved *Critique of Pure Reason* lay open on his knee, but he was not reading it. He had never read any Kant in his life, but he enjoyed carrying that philosopher's books around. It gave him the sensation of moving in exalted circles, a sensation doubly agreeable after the distasteful events of the previous evening.

After two hours of exacting paper work, Captain Ahlers took a short break. He used it to telephone Professor Martin about Carolin's forthcoming operation.

While they were still talking Captain Treuberg came in, ostensibly in search of a mislaid file. He listened with unabashed attention.

"That was a private call," Ahlers told the switchboard. "Put it down to me, please."

"Pretty expensive, these operations, eh?" Treuberg inquired, when his chief had hung up.

"Extremely. Still, you can't put a price tag on a child's health."

"Anyway, the main thing is, you've got it—the cash, I mean."

"Yes, I've got it," said Ahlers, burying himself in his work again.

Corporal Kamnitzer, who had not got back to barracks until sunrise, was determined to enjoy a few hours' rest. The notice hanging at the foot of his bed—commandeered from a hotel and bearing the legend PLEASE DO NOT DISTURB in four languages—was merely there for decorative purposes.

171

Kamnitzer's roommates were well aware that he seldom rose before lunchtime on Sundays.

When the corporal finally condescended to sit up he saw Martin Recht sitting on a stool beside his bed. One glance was enough to tell him that his protégé had something on his mind.

"What's up now?" asked Kamnitzer.

"I overstayed my leave, Karl."

"Because of Carolin?"

"No, it was Streicher's fault."

"Then you're a stupid clod," declared Kamnitzer. "I can imagine getting into trouble for Carolin's sake, but not on account of that wet fish."

While Kamnitzer made a leisurely toilet, Recht told him the story in detail, He made no immediate comment, but demanded to speak to Streicher. The sergeant had left Room 13 at an early hour, however, and no one knew where he was.

"On lovely Sunday mornings like this," said Kamnitzer, "even the most hardened soldiers suffer from humane impulses. It's worth bearing in mind."

Major Bornekamp had not spent the night at home, which meant that his wife was able to breakfast with Lieutenant von Strackmann.

This meant, in turn, that the battalion and No. 3 Company were both deprived of their commanders, at least until lunchtime, a circumstance which guaranteed everyone else a relatively enjoyable morning.

Company Sergeant Major Kirschke was resolutely applying himself to his favorite pastime. Indeed, he might have continued to enjoy his well-earned Sunday repose indefinitely but for the appearance of Kamnitzer, who drummed on the C.S.M.'s door until he was forced to open it.

"What do you want, little man?" Kirschke asked. He sounded formidable.

"I'll swap you a naked sergeant major for a back-dated pass," Kamnitzer replied nonchalantly.

Kirschke looked suspicious. "Is that supposed to be a joke?"

"Not a joke, Sergeant Major. It's a sad business altogether, but you might be interested to hear about it."

"Come in," said Kirschke, eyeing the corporal curiously. "Anything's possible in this day and age."

Herbert Asch ate with relish. Frau Elisabeth had given him his favorite fish breakfast—salmon, russet-red and fragrant; smoked eel, fat, white, and firm-fleshed; and Norwegian herring, strong-flavored and aromatic—but he found time, as he usually did at Sunday breakfast, to air his current preoccupations.

"You know," he told his wife, "it isn't that my time in the army has made me allergic to everything in uniform. That would be doing a lot of good men an injustice. It isn't that I dispute the army's right to exist, either. I'm prepared to regard it as a necessity, given the present international situation and the vast sums that are being frittered away on the arms race all over the world."

His wife smiled. "If it's such a necessary evil, what are you worried about?"

"I'm worried by the suppression of the individual—I mean the civilian, the democrat, the citizen soldier—that's what he's often called these days, and it's a hopeful sign. But do we worry about him enough? Are we helping him to resist the tendency to turn him into just another digit in an endless column of figures? Politicians have gone back to their old habit of talking in terms of territorial rights, ethnic boundaries and spheres of influence—and the masses copy them like parrots."

"What's the answer, then?"

"Give our two or three hundred thousand soldiers a genuine feeling of security and confidence, that's all."

"You always get so worked up, Herbert, but your fears haven't been confirmed except in a few isolated cases, have they?"

"I know, Elisabeth, but it's the thin end of the wedge. We've got to do everything in our power to ensure that exceptions don't become the rule. It infuriates me to hear that a soldier can be bullied by his superior in a public place without arousing public indignation. It infuriates me when a soldier is ordered to jump off a ledge by a drunken N.C.O. and breaks his neck without inspiring anything more than a passing regret which is quickly allayed by the cheap excuse that such occurrences are a necessary evil. Soldiers are human beings, first and foremost, and they've got to be treated as such. It seems self-evident to me."

C.S.M. Kirschke had his own ideas about what was self-evident and what wasn't.

"I don't care how we arrange this," he told Kamnitzer, "as long as it's not at my expense."

"It's quite simple," the corporal said firmly. "I forget I saw Sergeant Major Rammler wandering about in the nude, and all he has to do is issue Grenadier Recht a postdated pass. I call that a generous offer."

The C.S.M. evinced neither agreement nor disagreement. "Wait here," he said. "I'll go and see which way the wind's blowing."

He found Rammler without difficulty. The sergeant major was sitting in his room, in conclave with Sergeant Streicher. Both men regarded Kirschke expectantly.

Kirschke knew that there was no need to be particularly diplomatic with Rammler. He shooed Streicher into the passage, shut the door, and asked Rammler point-blank how he had got back to barracks that morning.

By the normal route, he was told, though not without difficulty. According to his own account, Rammler had fallen among thieves. They had torn his clothes off his back, but for the sake of the regiment's reputation he had not reported the matter to the police. His main concern had been to avoid attracting attention, and this he had succeeded in doing with the aid of a fellow N.C.O. who had turned up in the nick of time.

"But Kamnitzer saw you wandering around in the buff —bollocky naked, as he puts it."

"That bastard!" Rammler said accusingly. "It's ten to one he organized the whole thing."

"Steady on," said Kirschke. "You might find it hard to prove that."

"I'll hang it on him if I have to turn this place upside down in the process."

"Will you?" Kirschke asked dubiously. "Do you really think you can?"

Rammler knew he couldn't, but he wasn't prepared to admit it. "If that little skunk dares to make anything out of this, I'll dig up enough dirt to bury the lot of us."

This was just what C.S.M. Kirschke was afraid of. He loathed paper work, and von Strackmann was not in the line of fire this time—unfortunately. If for this reason alone, it might be advisable to save some ammunition for later.

Kirschke produced what he described as a suggested compromise: first, Kamnitzer had not seen him in the nude; second, Rammler had forgotten to issue Grenadier Recht an overnight pass; third, Grenadier Recht had been justified in assuming his leave had been granted.

"Agreed," Rammler said at once.

Kirschke found the sergeant major's prompt acquiescence

suspicious, but he could see no grounds for his instinctive mistrust. The main thing was that his responsibilities had once more been shelved and that the reputation of No. 3 Company—still his company, whatever von Strackmann might think—had been safeguarded. Furthermore, Martin Recht need have no fear of being reported. Rammler would vouch for that.

"Everything went like clockwork," Kirschke reported to Kamnitzer. "Rammler agreed at once, without any reservations."

"No reservations at all?" asked Kamnitzer, alarmed.

"What more do you want?" said Kirschke. "Rammler knows he can rely on your word. A promise is a promise. I told you, everything went off smoothly."

"Too smoothly," said Kamnitzer in a worried voice. "If I know Rammler, he's got something up his sleeve. The only thing is, what?"

Herbert Asch received an unexpected visit from Major Bornekamp. Intrigued, he showed the C.O. into his office.

"We're all human," Bornekamp conceded magnanimously, bent on showing himself at his best. "Everyone makes mistakes sometimes."

It would have been unwise to discourage such a realization. "I presume," Asch said politely, "that you've come about that interview you gave to the local paper."

"Is it going to be published?" Bornekamp asked apprehensively. "In full?"

"It's quite possible," said Asch, "but not probable, provided we can come to some acceptable arrangement. I have no direct influence with the press, of course, and everyone in this country has the right to express an opinion. . . ."

"Guttersnipes included, more's the pity!" interjected Bornekamp. "But listen, Herr Asch—even if you can't bring pressure to bear, you can at least pull a few strings. Clear up these unfortunate misunderstandings for me. I know you can."

"I can't guarantee anything, of course," said Asch. "Besides, everything has its price."

"What do you want?" asked Bornekamp.

"I don't know yet," Asch said slowly, "but I'm sure I'll think of something when the time comes. We mustn't rush things, Major. If we can delay publication, that'll be something at least. It won't be in tomorrow's edition, anyway, I can promise you that."

Warrant Officer Vossler tucked Carolin carefully into his car beside Gerty Ballhaus and drove to the Grenadier barracks, where Martin Recht joined them.

They picnicked beside a sparkling blue lake, in a lush meadow encircled by pine forest. The day gleamed like a jewel, and the whole scene resembled an illustration in some glossy magazine: the spotless white cloth spread on the grass, the basket of fruit, the sandwiches, the cool bottles of *vin rosé,* the radiant sunlight and gentle murmur of radio music.

Later, when Viktor Vossler took Gerty off for a stroll, Carolin stretched out on a mossy bank. Martin Recht bent over her to adjust the rug. "Comfortable?" he asked softly.

"Very comfortable," she said, closing her eyes.

There was a long silence. Then Martin Recht said: "I wish it could be like this always."

"So do I," Carolin said happily.

Carolin was still feeling happy when the day departed in a blaze of glory. The setting sun bathed the sky in luminous colors, suffusing it with soft shades of pink and seeming to drown the scattered puffs of cloud in a sea of contentment.

"I love you," Carolin said, gently but distinctly.

Mellow Sunday drew to a close, and Bloody Monday took its place.

KARL KAMNITZER was the first to scent trouble in the Monday-morning air. Climbing out of bed, slightly late as usual, he saw a circle of gray, weary, indifferent faces. This, of course, was a familiar enough sight on Mondays, but one particular face stood out from the others like a sore thumb: Streicher's.

"What's the matter, chum, swallowed a flagpole?" he asked, merely curious at first.

"I'll thank you to remember my rank," Streicher said loftily.

Kamnitzer looked amused. "Bit hoity-toity this morning, aren't we?"

Streicher evidently considered it beneath his new-found dignity to reply. He strode across Room 13 to the door as if he were traversing a municipal rubbish dump.

"I reckon he's got a screw loose somewhere," Kamnitzer remarked, when Streicher had left the room.

"You're dead right," said another inmate. "Promotion

seems to have gone to his head. Yesterday he behaved as though he was semihuman, but this morning he won't talk to us."

"Count your blessings," said Kamnitzer. "Let's hope he keeps it up."

"It's a pity Martin Recht didn't belt him good and proper the other night."

Kamnitzer froze. "What do you mean?"

"Your friend Recht and Streicher—didn't you know? Well, it's hardly worth mentioning. Recht wasn't the sort of chap to make a thorough job of it."

Kamnitzer hurried off to the washroom to find Recht. "What's this I hear?" he asked. "You didn't tell me you'd slugged Streicher."

"I didn't," said Recht. "It's an exaggeration. I just pushed him aside a little—he was in my way. He slipped and fell, that's all. It didn't mean a thing."

"Not to you, maybe," Kamnitzer said, thoroughly alarmed, "but Streicher's the sensitive type, and now he's been promoted he thinks he's a superior form of life. Why the hell didn't you tell me about this?"

"Because I didn't think it was necessary," protested Recht. "I can't understand why you're getting so worked up. It wasn't a fight—it was a bit of a scuffle, that's all—and it's got nothing to do with anyone but Streicher and me."

"What did he say?"

"Didn't say a word—just sat there in his nightshirt looking stupid. It was quite funny, really."

"It's a howl," Kamnitzer said grimly. "Have you spoken to him since?"

"No, I haven't had a chance."

"Did anyone else see this scuffle, or whatever you like to call it? I mean, were there any witnesses?"

"Everyone else in the room—there were five, I think."

"In that case," said Kamnitzer, "I suggest you shave and shine with more than usual care."

"I don't follow," Recht said uneasily. "What do you mean by that?"

"You'll find out soon enough, if I'm not much mistaken. I just hope for your sake that my brain isn't functioning properly—but I've a horrible feeling I'm thinking along the right lines."

177

MONDAY MORNING showed Company Sergeant Major Kirschke in a new light. He was brighter than at any other time in the whole week because the previous day had augmented his reserves of sleep. He might almost have been called energetic, especially as Lieutenant von Strackmann did not put in an immediate appearance. For the moment, Kirschke controlled the company from his office like a captain on the bridge of a destroyer plowing through calm seas without an enemy in sight.

He swapped jokes with the young second lieutenants who commanded two of the company's platoons, telling himself yet again, as he handed them their training schedules for the day, that they were quite nice fellows really. With von Strackmann out of the way, they struck him as thoroughly congenial types.

After they had departed Kirschke turned to Sergeant Streicher, who was waiting, in well-disciplined silence, for permission to speak.

"Well, my lad?" Kirschke asked brightly. "Not out with your platoon this morning?"

"I have a report to make, Sergeant Major."

"That's splendid," said Kirschke, his composure concealing a pang of mistrust, "but reports have to be submitted in writing."

Streicher obediently produced a sheet of paper and tried to hand it over, but Kirschke demurred.

"What's it all about?"

"I have been assaulted, Sergeant Major, physically assaulted."

"By whom?"

"By a subordinate."

Kirschke knit his brows and looked incredulous. He pondered deeply for a moment, and his first reaction was to clear the company office of all superfluous witnesses. His corporal clerk was sent off to the armory and the civilian employee to the administration block, both on unimportant errands.

When he and Streicher were alone, he said: "Do you realize what you're saying? If your report is borne out by the facts, it'll mean a charge under Paragraph 25 of the Military Penal Code."

"I realize that, Sergeant Major."

"Paragraph 25, Streicher, refers to physical assaults on superior officers. The penalty is six months' to five years' imprisonment—in particularly grave cases, twelve months' to ten years' penal servitude."

Sergeant Streicher apparently knew this too, for the revelation produced no visible change in his demeanor. He had solemnly promised his friend Rammler to stand firm as a rock, and that was that. He held out his report once more.

Kirschke skillfully ignored the gesture. Since good advice seemed to be leading nowhere, he promptly went over to the attack.

"Were you injured?"

"No, but I was pushed—several times, too. I fell over."

"You didn't report to the M.O.?"

"No."

"So there's no visible evidence of this alleged attack on your person?"

"No, Sergeant Major." Streicher was not easily shaken. He had obviously briefed himself thoroughly in advance. "But the law states explicitly that a punishable offense can be committed without inflicting injury. If I may take the liberty of quoting: 'It is sufficient for the superior officer to have been tugged by the sleeve or pushed to one side.'"

Kirschke was silent for a moment. It was clear that he was dealing with a tougher nut than usual, and a lesser man than he might have hauled down the flag.

"A thing like this," he said, "needs to be considered carefully. Everything must be just so—not a comma out of place. What about witnesses, anyway? Have you got any?"

"Five of them, Sergeant Major."

Kirschke did not give up, even then. The die was not finally cast. He was still unaware—officially—both of the incident itself and its alleged perpetrator.

The salient feature of the whole affair was that it lay outside a unit commander's jurisdiction. A case of this sort had to be passed on to the competent legal authority, and anyone who violated this rule automatically laid himself open to prosecution.

But things had not yet reached that stage. Everything in Kirschke revolted against the thought of handing one of his men over to justice prematurely. He eventually took the proffered report, but not because he had run out of ideas. He was merely looking for an excuse to shelve the matter temporarily, and he found one straight away.

"All you've put at the head of the report is 'Streicher, Sergeant,'" he said. "That doesn't conform to the rules laid

179

down for military correspondence. You've left out your Christian names and the precise designation of your unit."

Kirschke's practiced eye had meanwhile taken in the essentials of the report. He now knew what had taken place and when, and he also knew the name of the accused, but he behaved as if he were still in the dark.

"You can take your effort back," he told Streicher casually, "and complete it in the proper way. If I were you, I'd write the whole thing out again. That'll give you time to consider the implications."

"Yes, Sergeant Major," Streicher said, looking reluctant but dutifully taking the report.

"One more piece of advice, Streicher—just between ourselves. Don't take all this too lightly. Even if you've got witnesses, do you know for certain what their evidence will be?"

"They'll tell the truth," Streicher said. "It's a question of right and wrong, Sergeant Major."

"Right and wrong?" Kirschke smiled sardonicaly. "Everyone's got his own ideas about that."

Sergeant Major Rammler lent a sympathetic ear to what Streicher had to tell him. His first comment was: "That man Kirschke's anything but an ideal company sergeant major. It's a pity the right people haven't cottoned onto him yet."

He demanded to know every last detail, and Streicher did his best to comply. Rammler had to admit that Kirschke was no fool. His allusion to the unreliability of witnesses carried some weight.

However, Rammler knew the meaning of the word "system." First, he sealed off Room 13 and got rid of Recht and Kamnitzer. Then he ensured the absence of all who had not been present at the time of the alleged assault. This left five men, apart from Recht and Streicher himself.

"Listen, men," Rammler told them. "We've all got responsibilities, and no fellow with any guts tries to shirk them."

He grinned encouragingly at the five blank, expressionless faces.

The fact that they betrayed virtually no reaction did not dishearten him in the least. It only made him more wary. He decided to preface his major assault with a brief lecture.

"We all know," he began, "that it's our duty to tell the truth where military matters are concerned."

This statement of principle could hardly be disputed, since it figured in half a dozen manuals of instruction. The five men reacted to it, predictably, by preserving an acquiescent silence.

"Under conditions of emergency, a lie can cost a fellow soldier his life. Am I right?"

The five prospective witnesses nodded. Rammler scrutinized them closely, seeking out the weakest link, the man whom he could tackle most effectively. He identified him without difficulty, a grenadier who started to perspire at the slightest exertion and was already exuding timid docility. His friends called him Porky.

"What conclusion do we draw from this?" Rammler demanded, staring challengingly at Porky. "Well?"

"Lies must be avoided at all costs, Sergeant Major," said Porky, breaking into a fresh sweat as it dawned on him that he was the sergeant major's chosen victim. It was not the first time such a thing had happened. Some people seemed to find him an irresistible target.

Rammler concentrated on Porky with unwearying persistence. He bombarded him, in the kindliest possible way, with questions. Where was he when Sergeant Streicher was assaulted? What exactly did he see? What else did he see? Why hadn't he seen more? "The truth, kid, stick to the truth!"

After a vain attempt at prevarication, Porky's resistance quickly crumbled. He began by making a partial admission—"There was a bump, and Sergeant Streicher fell down"—but this was the thin end of the wedge. Rammler drove it home with sledge-hammer blows.

He plied Porky with further questions. What caused this bump? Who or what caused Sergeant Streicher to fall down? "What's the matter, lad? Trying to evade your responsibilities? Thinking of telling a lie, are you? They can put you in jail for that, you know."

In the end, Porky could see no alternative but to confirm the contents of Streicher's report in broad outline. His superior officer rewarded him with a beamingly benevolent smile from which Porky derived no immediate satisfaction. For some moments he felt wretched, but a minute later he was already telling himself that the truth was the truth and a man must always do his duty, however hard.

"That's how it was, then!" Rammler said complacently. He turned his attentions to the other four, aware that

now the breakthrough had been effected all that remained was a routine mopping-up operation.

"All of you must have seen at least as much as our friend here"—he indicated Porky—"if not more."

The other four were already looking uneasy. It was more than they could do to stand up to Rammler's barrage. Little by little, like snow beneath the spring sun, they succumbed. All they needed now was a final pep talk.

"If I know you," Rammler said significantly, "you won't be irresponsible enough to accuse an N.C.O. of lying. I'm sure you won't leave one of your mates in the lurch, either, just because he's had the guts to tell the truth. And if that's not reason enough, men—well, we'll be doing some field training later today. All right?"

"Your office," Lieutenant von Strackmann told C.S.M. Kirschke with comparative good humor, "looks like a pigsty."

"I beg to differ, sir."

Von Strackmann allowed himself a superior smile. "You can differ as much as you like, but what I say goes around here, in case you'd forgotten."

"I'll pass your comments on to the appropriate department, sir. I'm not responsible for the cleaning women. Besides, I'd like to point out that this is No. 3 Company office, not my private study."

This conversation, the first of the day, took the place of a normal morning exchange of salutations. Both men remained calm, even cheerful, privately consigning each other to perdition and invigorated by the thought that their wishes might soon become reality.

Lieutenant von Strackmann disappeared into the inner office, leaving the door wide open so that he could hear what was going on outside. All that came to his ears, however, was a creaking noise as Kirschke settled himself more comfortably in his chair.

This provocative sound goaded von Strackmann into activity. Charging into the outer office like a bull into the arena, he saw Kirschke lolling back at his ease, toying pensively with a ruler.

"Haven't you got anything to do?" von Strackmann demanded.

"Of course, sir," replied Kirschke. "There's always something to do. At the moment I'm wrestling with a problem:

whether one ought to take official note of every report that's submitted to one."

"No other worries?"

"Not at present, sir."

Von Strackmann's cheerful mood threatened to desert him. He longed violently for some excuse, some plausible excuse, to get rid of C.S.M. Kirschke. There were other, better, more loyal and trustworthy men—Rammler, for instance, despite his regrettable lapse of the other day.

For the moment, he decided to wear Kirschke down slowly, like water dripping on a rock, unaware that Kirschke favored the same time-honored method.

"I don't like the way the filing cabinets are arranged," he said.

"I like the arrangement," Kirschke retorted. "It's practical."

"They ought to be shifted around against the opposite wall."

"Impossible, sir," Kirschke said tersely.

"Of course it isn't!" snapped von Strackmann. "If you're short of men you can lend a hand yourself."

"Even if you lent a hand too, sir, it would still be impossible. The arrangement of this office was personally supervised by the company commander. It's quite possible he may be discharged from the hospital in the next few days and take over the company again. He'll wonder what's been going on here soon enough, but there's no point in shifting all the furniture around as well, is there?"

Von Strackmann disappeared into his office again. There was no need for Kirschke to rub his nose in the fact that he was only acting company commander. He was well aware of it, but the last word had not been spoken on the subject.

Kirschke continued to toy with his ruler. He glanced at the door through which von Strackmann had vanished. It was still ajar, a potentially dangerous circumstance in view of Sergeant Streicher's imminent return.

Before long, Streicher reappeared. He held out his report. "Error rectified, Sergeant Major," he said. "Christian name inserted."

"You didn't notice any other mistakes?"

"No, Sergeant Major."

"Looked it through carefully, have you? What about your rank? Designation of unit? Name of station? Date? Month in full? Everything in order?"

"Everything, Sergeant Major."

"You haven't forgotten the address? Did you just put in the name of the unit, in accordance with Mil. Regs. para. 33 b?"

At this point, Lieutenant von Strackmann re-emerged from the inner office like a jack-in-the-box, manifestly displeased at Kirschke's petty and uncharacteristic insistence on routine. "Form is important, Sergeant Major," he said didactically, a company commander to his fingertips, "but content is even more so."

Kirschke silently held his breath. Two alternatives presented themselves: either he could allow the lieutenant to plunge headlong into the mire in which he so richly deserved to wallow, or he could make a last attempt to save the company from a scandal of vast dimensions. With some reluctance, he plumped for the latter course.

With abnormal politeness and a deliberate observance of etiquette, he said: "With your permission, sir, I'll deal with this matter. It would be far better."

Von Strackmann, however, was unaware of his predicament. Kirschke had thrown him a life belt and he mistook it for a stone. Resolutely, he held out his hand for the report, and Sergeant Streicher surrendered it.

"You can dismiss," Kirschke said resignedly. "Wait outside."

Lieutenant von Strackmann read the document with mounting agitation, seeming to swell like a rapidly inflated balloon as he did so.

"My God!" he said at length, breathing hard. "Were you trying to keep this from me?"

"Why should I?" inquired Kirschke, grieved by the acting company commander's stupidity. "I don't know what it says in detail, and anyway it's not solely up to you to decide whether it should be taken seriously or not."

"What's that?" von Strackmann demanded furiously. "An N.C.O. is physically assaulted, and you don't know whether to take it seriously or not?"

"Sir," Kirschke said patiently but with a touch of weariness. "Making an allegation is one thing, proving it is another. It's too easy to burn one's own fingers in a case of this sort."

"What are you talking about!" von Strackmann exploded. "This is a most alarming incident."

"Possibly, sir, but not in the way you think."

"I'm not petty-minded," the lieutenant declared, "but if there's one thing I will not condone it's an attempt to undermine the basis of military discipline—and that in-

184

cludes physically assaulting a superior officer. No, I'm absolutely adamant."

"Does that mean prepared to see an otherwise decent soldier go to jail for months or even years, just because of a stupid, drunken scuffle?"

"What do you mean, Kirschke? I don't understand you. What are you trying to hush up? Are you involved in this business in some way?"

Von Strackmann, who had been staring at Streicher's report as though spellbound, looked up in sudden triumph. "So that's it!" he cried exultantly, convinced that he had put his finger on the sergeant major's Achilles' heel. "You're partly to blame for this. The only reason why such a thing could have happened was that you failed to separate a newly promoted sergeant from his subordinates."

"The sergeant's quarters allotted to Streicher won't be free till tomorrow." Kirschke made this statement with almost yawning indifference. "Lack of accommodation and administrative difficulties often make it necessary for sergeants and other ranks to share the same sleeping quarters, but that doesn't mean they have to come to blows. Besides, sir, I've a feeling you don't realize the full implications of this business. The whole thing sticks in my craw. With your permission, I'll go and change my trousers."

C ORPORAL KAMNITZER was one of the few people who could foresee the effects of Streicher's report, especially on Martin Recht, and a private chat with C.S.M. Kirschke confirmed his worst fears.

Accordingly, he decided to mobilize all available reserves. Although he had no very clear idea of how best to go about it, he knew that what had not occurred to him might well occur to someone else, so he made for the air force barracks.

This was comparatively easy to arrange. Kirschke simply ordered the corporal to go into town on an official errand, and he pedaled off on the company bicycle.

The first person he asked for was Warrant Officer Vossler, for whose shrewdness and ingenuity he had a high regard. Vossler knew the ropes, but Vossler had just flown off to Crete and would not be back before nightfall.

Making up his mind swiftly, Kamnitzer went to see Captain Ahlers, who received his unexpected visitor at once and introduced him to Captain Treuberg.

"Playing truant?" Treuberg inquired in jocular tones.

"My presence here is strictly official, sir," Kamnitzer assured him, glancing urgently at Ahlers, who took the hint and asked his deputy to leave the room.

"Grenadier Martin Recht," Kamnitzer began without further preamble, "has been accused of assaulting a superior officer. What's your reaction to that?"

Captain Ahlers thought for a moment. "My first reaction is to tell you that it doesn't concern me. The case lies outside my sphere of jurisdiction. I couldn't exercise the slightest influence on it."

"All right, sir," said Kamnitzer. "Let me put it another way. Do you believe that Martin Recht is capable of assaulting a superior officer?"

"I can't imagine him doing such a thing."

"He didn't." Kamnitzer endeavored to explain what, in his view, had really happened. "But the report has been handed in and officially accepted. You realize what that means, of course."

Captain Ahlers knew only too well. "No unit commander is competent to deal with the sort of case you've described," he said thoughtfully. "Only a court could do that. The report will have to be passed to higher authority. It could lead to criminal proceedings."

"Could?" asked Kamnitzer. "Needn't it?"

"Not necessarily," Ahlers explained. "Not if it appeared subsequently that there had been a misunderstanding. That would show the charge to be groundless, but only if the plaintiff admitted that he had acted prematurely or without due deliberation."

"If I know the plaintiff, he's unlikely to do that."

"Then things look black."

"Can't you do anything, sir?"

"Be reasonable!" Ahlers said with genuine regret. "Your barracks and mine are two different worlds."

"Haven't you any influence—with Major Bornekamp, for instance? Our C.O.'s probably the only person to tackle, under the circumstances. Couldn't you breathe a word in his ear?"

"There wouldn't be much point, I'm afraid."

"Surely you won't abandon a decent lad like Martin Recht just because he wears a different insignia from yours?"

"Of course not," said Ahlers. "I'm prepared to adopt your suggestion and discuss the case with your commanding officer, but I can't promise anything."

"That would be something, anyway," Kamnitzer said

gratefully. "It can't hurt to try." He looked worried. "Don't you know anyone else who could bring pressure to bear?"

"Yes—perhaps I do!" The captain seemed to have been galvanized by a sudden idea. "Come along, we'll pay him a visit."

Ahlers opened the door leading to the outer office and called: "Have my car brought round straight away, would you?" He had just picked up his cap and gloves when Captain Treuberg appeared.

"I gather you're going out. Shall I come with you?"

"No, thanks all the same," said Ahlers.

"Will you be gone long?"

"I don't think so, Treuberg. Probably an hour at the most."

"Where can I reach you?" Treuberg asked with manifest curiosity. "Just in case something urgent comes up."

"I shall be at the Hotel Asch."

When Captain Ahlers entered the hotel, escorted by Corporal Kamnitzer, the first person he met was Frau Elisabeth. She greeted him with restrained but perceptible surprise.

"I'd appreciate a brief word with your husband," Ahlers said, a trifle formally.

"It's something unpleasant, isn't it?"

"What makes you say that?"

"It's written all over your faces. Besides, it's an unusual time of day for you to come visiting."

"You can't call a thing pleasant or unpleasant until it's over," Kamnitzer interjected. "The great thing is to make it go the way you want it to."

Frau Elisabeth showed them into an adjoining room and went off to tell her husband, who materialized as if by magic.

"I'm most intrigued," Asch said brightly, by way of greeting. "My wife says you look as if you're carrying half a hundredweight of dynamite around with you."

"Herr Asch," Ahlers said. "May I begin by asking you a straight question? What's your opinion of Corporal Kamnitzer?"

Kamnitzer looked astonished. "If you gentlemen propose to discuss me, perhaps you'd prefer me to leave the room."

"Anything to avoid hearing tthe truth, eh?" chuckled Asch.

"Not at all," said Kamnitzer. "In the first place I'm thick-

187

skinned, and in the second place I haven't got a particularly high opinion of myself—so what have I got to lose?"

"Corporal Kamnitzer has a story to tell you," Ahlers explained. "I shall be interested to know whether you believe it in every detail."

"Let's hear it first," Asch said with a grin.

Kamnitzer launched into his account, concentrating on essentials. Confident that Asch would be able to read between the lines, he avoided all unnecessary embellishments.

"Well," Asch said, when he had finished, "I'll let you know later whether I believe it or not, but one thing seems certain: it's not beyond the bounds of possibility."

"That's what I thought too," Ahlers said.

"Let's assume," Asch mused, "that everything Kamnitzer has told us is true and that his inferences are correct. What's to be done?"

"Streicher's report is a hot potato," Kamnitzer said. "C.S.M. Kirschke saw that straight away, but Lieutenant von Strackmann was stupid or, if you like, inexperienced enough to pick it up. In my humble opinion, the thing to do now is to prevent the C.O. from making a similar blunder."

Herbert Asch regarded Kamnitzer with growing approval. He was a man after his own heart. Why was he only a corporal? He might even make a successful hotelier.

"I usually feel at home in the bull ring, I grant you," Asch said cautiously, "but before I let you prod me into it I'd like to clear up one important point—starting with you, Captain Ahlers. Why are you taking such an interest in Martin Recht?"

"Personal reasons," replied the captain. "Recht visits my home and my daughter seems to think a lot of him. I'd like to keep him out of jail."

"My reasons are purely personal, too," grinned Kamnitzer. "I like to see the puppets dance. You see—our motives are thoroughly suspect!"

"I beg your pardon," Asch said. "I shouldn't have asked such a question—I deserved that."

"It's quite all right," Ahlers assured him. "I understand your reasons."

Asch took a moment to collect himself. He should have known what had prompted the two men to take such a step—Ahlers, who had always championed a justice founded on generosity and common sense, and Kamnitzer, the gay rebel. He warmed to them both.

"I'll go at once," he said with sudden determination.

"You can rest assured that Martin Recht deserves to be helped," Kamnitzer told him, with a note of affection in his voice. "He always reminds me of a child who's got himself mixed up in something too big for him. If we can't stop children from playing soldiers, the least we can do is keep them out of the clutches of the law."

Herbert Asch jumped into his car and drove, slightly exceeding the speed limit, to the Grenadier barracks. The sentry did not keep him waiting long this time and the C.O. ushered him into his office without wasting a moment.

"I've come to collect," Asch said unceremoniously.

"Is the paper going to abandon that article?" Bornekamp asked.

"Not only that. In order to turn the interview into a token of public esteem and appreciation, the draft will be submitted to you so that you can amend it, add to it, make cuts or round it off—exactly as you want."

"Splendid!" cried Bornekamp. "I feel I owe you a great debt of gratitude."

"That's just what I was banking on," Asch said.

"What can I do for you, my dear chap? Don't hesitate to tell me."

"Right, I'll come straight to point. Have you received a report dealing with an alleged assault on an N.C.O.?"

Major Bornekamp started. "Certainly not."

"All the better." Asch looked pleased. "Then I need only advise you, for your own good, not to accept any such report."

"What are you talking about?" Bornekamp demanded with growing bewilderment. "What report is this? Who's responsible for it? How do you know of its existence, anyway?"

"These things get around," Asch replied coolly.

Bornekamp stared at his desk in dismay as though Asch had deposited a time bomb on it. His eyes became almost glazed when he learned that Asch had—quite fortuitously —heard the story from Captain Ahlers and that the accused man was—no less fortuitously—not only a personal acquaintance of Asch but so well known to him that he had no hesitation in speaking up on his behalf.

"I've come here as much in your own interests as for any other reason, Major," Asch declared. "This accusation could stir up a lot of dust, especially as it's founded on what I judge to be extremely flimsy evidence. I can't imagine that you would embark on such a risky course of action. A badly bungled interview followed by an em-

189

barrassing scandal . . . Altogether too much of a good thing, don't you agree?"

"This . . ." the C.O. spluttered in agitation, "this is pure and unadulterated . . ."

"Blackmail, Major? Don't say the word," Asch remarked kindly. "I know, I know. What I'm asking you to do might be described as—how shall I put it?—beyond the bounds of legality, but I'm sure you won't worry unduly on that account. Besides, it's all between ourselves. You can take it for granted that Captain Ahlers's sole concern is the garrison's good name, so there's no likelihood of his communicating any details to Colonel Turner."

This was more than blackmail, Bornekamp told himself —it was downright impudence. The man was riding over him roughshod, but he could see no immediate prospect of extricating himself unscathed.

"Is there anything you're not clear about?" Asch asked.

Major Bornekamp closed his eyes for a moment. Then he picked up the phone and said: "Company commander No. 3 Company."

Lieutenant von Strackmann announced his presence at the other end of the line, but his tones of loyal devotion were lost on the C.O.

"Listen to me carefully, Strackmann," he barked, "and don't interrupt. I wish to draw your attention to the following: any written report, whatever its content, must be formulated with the utmost precision. It must be checked— thoroughly checked—for accuracy. Every element of doubt must be eliminated. I rely on you not to bother me with efforts of an ambiguous, incomplete, or controvertible nature. I don't care if it's a report on a damaged muzzle cover or a pair of missing socks—or an assault on a superior officer, not that I can conceive of such a thing occurring in my battalion. Quite apart from that, I gauge the efficiency of any company commander by whether or not the men under his command keep their noses clean. Is that clear, Strackmann? Right, carry on."

Bornekamp snorted indignantly and replaced the receiver. "Is that good enough for you?" he growled.

"It ought to do the trick," Asch conceded. He felt that he had won a decisive, if not particularly admirable victory, but not even his acute eyes could penetrate the jungle of red tape, evasions, and unhappy coincidences that lay ahead.

LIEUTENANT VON STRACKMANN stood behind his desk like Napoleon on the outskirts of Moscow—billowing smoke and smoldering ruins met his eye at every turn. Even C.S.M. Kirschke's expression contained a glimmer of sympathy. Major Bornekamp's monologue had been delivered fortissimo.

"Hell and damnation!" von Strackmann said to himself. "What are we going to do now?"

"We, sir?" Kirschke asked ruthlessly. "It wasn't me who accepted that report."

"All right, all right!" the lieutenant snapped. "You've got your ear to the ground. You know which way the wind's blowing—all right, I admit it! What more do you want? It doesn't help me, does it?"

"No." Kirschke uttered the word without triumph. He was still company sergeant major of No. 3 Company, even if von Strackmann was in command, and he felt responsible for it.

"There must be some way out," the lieutenant cried desperately. He had dismounted from his high horse and was staring at Kirschke almost beseechingly. "What if the charge turns out to be unfounded . . . ?"

"As far as I can see," Kirschke said, "that's highly unlikely. Streicher couldn't back-pedal now, even if he wanted to. Rammler would never let him."

"What if I don't pass the report on? What if I simply chuck it into the wastepaper basket?"

"You'd be committing an offense."

"But what about freedom of discretion?"

"You haven't any. According to Paragraph 40 of the Military Penal Code, if I may draw your attention to it, an infringement of military discipline which also constitutes a penal offense may not be dealt with by a unit commander, even when the facts are in doubt. That means you have to refer the case to the public prosecutor. If you don't, you're committing an offense punishable by imprisonment for a period of one month to three years."

Von Strackmann was in a cleft stick, there was no doubt about it. The report was in his possession, the C.O. didn't want it, and he couldn't simply hand it back. An N.C.O. had passed the ball to him, but if he tried to pass it on he would incur the major's Olympian displeasure.

191

"Think, Sergeant Major, think! Perhaps something'll occur to you."

"Plenty of things occur to me," Kirschke said with deliberation, "but you won't want to hear them."

"Speak up," von Strackmann insisted. "The reputation of the company's at stake—our company, Sergeant Major."

"The company's reputation?" queried Kirschke, wagging his head. "What's that? Reputation covers a multitude of sins. You can gain a reputation for efficiency by making them scrub the floor with a toothbrush or polish the nails in their boots . . ."

"All right, all right," von Strackmann interposed. "If the word worries you we'll let it pass. There's no point in arguing about trifles. We're both after the same thing, aren't we?"

"I'd like to think so, sir. But I don't regard a company primarily as a fighting unit which has been trained and equipped to kill. I look on it first and foremost as a hundred or more human beings."

"We're fundamentally in agreement there," declared von Strackmann.

Kirschke looked unimpressed. "With respect, sir, I dispute that, and since you've asked me to be frank . . ."

"I insist on it!"

". . . I shan't hesitate to make myself plain. This seems to be a good opportunity. We're alone, and if you dislike anything I say you can always forget it. In the first place, sir, I won't disguise the fact that in my eyes you're what might be termed a first-rate soldier."

"Please, please! This is no time for flattery," said von Strackmann. He was agreeably surprised to receive commendation from such an unexpected quarter. "But I didn't mean to interrupt you. Please go on being equally frank."

"With pleasure," Kirschke replied. "As I say, I grant that you have a number of valuable professional qualities—for example, endurance, physical energy, initiative, military knowledge, and a smart appearance. These count for a great deal, but are they enough?"

"I really don't know what to say, Sergeant Major."

"But I do, sir. I say that professional qualifications of that sort, however highly developed, are insufficient in themselves. An officer needs human qualities as well, and that seems to be the point at issue here. When you assumed command of this company you quite obviously regarded it as a tool or instrument—though whether of national defense or personal advancement I won't presume to judge."

192

"Steady now, Kirschke! You're going a bit far."

Kirschke leaned against the wall. He did not seem to be particularly involved in what he was saying, and his words matched his negligent stance. "Before you arrived on the scene, this company was a normal unit: the men were a willing lot, the N.C.O.s did their job, and the standard of training was comparatively high. The system functioned and the unit performed its duties—that is, until you introduced your exaggerated notions of efficiency."

"I beg your pardon!" von Strackmann protested. "Do you know what you're saying?"

"I've thought of nothing else for weeks," said Kirschke. "From the moment you assumed command of this company, it became obvious that there had been a sudden reversal of standards. Your first step was to judge everyone by his attitude toward you personally. You mistook yesmen for devoted supporters of your theories. You couldn't tell the difference between discipline and bullying. To you, violent activity became synonymous with devotion to duty."

"That's enough!" von Strackmann bellowed. "We won't achieve anything like this."

"What are we likely to achieve?" Kirschke ventured. "It may seem far-fetched to bring all this up under present circumstances, I admit, but that report on your desk is only the tip of an iceberg. Make a big issue out of it and you'll discover all kinds of things beneath the surface. You'll find, for instance, that a half-Jewish soldier in your company was sworn at for being a Jew boy, that a sergeant major was beaten up one night and wandered round the town in the nude, that one of your sergeants tried to borrow money from a subordinate, that a private soldier has been subjected to systematic persecution. Shall I go on? Believe me, this report of an assault on a superior officer is just a drop in the ocean."

"Stop!" von Strackmann cried in horror. "I won't hear another word!"

"I've finished. There's nothing more to say, anyway."

Von Strackmann sank back in his chair as though exhausted. "What can we do, Sergeant Major?"

"Wait and see, that's all. Perhaps someone'll have second thoughts, though I'm afraid it's improbable, knowing certain N.C.O.s as I do. You've really started something here."

Sᴇʀɢᴇᴀɴᴛ Mᴀᴊᴏʀ Rᴀᴍᴍʟᴇʀ was in full cry. His platoon stampeded through the countryside like a herd of wild buffalo, kicking up the dust behind them.

"There's a good reason for this," Rammler informed his gasping men at intervals. "I don't expect you to understand, but one day you'll thank me for saving your miserable lives."

Rammler knew that explanations to this effect could be found in every reputable infantry manual. Fortunately, the general public had at last developed a broader understanding of the reasons for "rigorous training."

"To a real soldier," Rammler announced cheerfully, "obstacles don't exist. He presses on regardless, with a stiff upper lip—and what else?"

"A tight asshole!" came the dutiful chorus. There was never a dull moment in No. 3 Platoon of No. 3 Company.

"Low-flying aircraft on your left!" yelled Rammler. He might just as well have said "mortar fire dead ahead!" or "enemy M.G. on your right!"—the result would have been identical. The platoon melted into the ground, squirming into hollows, rolling between prominences or cowering behind boulders while Rammler stood erect, lonely, and majestic as a war memorial.

"Now work your way toward the river."

Rammler's men sprang to their feet to acknowledge the order. Then they pressed their bellies to the ground again and wriggled laboriously forward. Rammler could not repress an appreciative nod. They were shaping nicely.

"Disengage!" he announced in magnanimous tones. "But stay under cover."

Sergeant Major Rammler looked upon himself as fair play personified. As long as the men toed the line they earned his approval. He even had a soft spot for them, provided they pulled their fingers out and kept them out. Anyone in his command who fared badly had himself to blame.

"Shin up the nearest tree, Kamnitzer!" he commanded. "Watch out for enemy approaching from the east." He gestured in a southwesterly direction as he spoke, but it was one of his cardinal rules to say "east" whenever there was talk of an enemy.

Corporal Kamnitzer complied with this order willingly and with alacrity. He realized that he was being isolated from the rest of the platoon, but the thought was not unwelcome.

Clambering up a chestnut tree, he squatted between two of the thickest branches, where he had an excellent view of his surroundings but could not be observed from below.

"No. 3 Section, close on me!" ordered Rammler.

No. 3 Section consisted of the inmates of Room 13. Sergeant Streicher, who was commanding them for the first time, glowed with pride at his new status.

In the middle of the section stood Martin Recht, a motionless and seemingly composed figure, even when Rammler's eye lighted on him. Recht, too, was isolated from the rest. He was given the task of crawling to the river and—like Kamnitzer—"observing the enemy."

"I want to see you worm your way forward like a stoat, Recht—like a stoat in the mating season." Here Rammler paused briefly to allow time for an appreciative titter. Three men obliged. "And keep your head down. You're not to stop till you've reached the edge of that water over there, so no faking tiredness—understand?"

Three other members of Streicher's section were told to dig in and the remaining five clustered round Rammler. They were the same five, headed by Porky, who had been selected as principal witnesses in the case of Streicher versus Recht, so Rammler eyed them with appropriate benevolence.

"You're the reserve," he told them. "You can take to the bushes for the next quarter of an hour. It may be half an hour—even longer, if you're lucky. Give your asses a treat, lads, but don't just lie there daydreaming. I'm giving you a chance to think things over. I expect you'll find something to occupy your minds. All right, move!"

The five prospective witnesses dived into the undergrowth like fish into a clump of seaweed. Each knew what was expected of him, and the prospect of an extended rest appealed to one and all.

Sergeant Major Rammler now set out to demonstrate that he was not merely an exacting superior but a comrade in arms, a course on which he embarked all the more wholeheartedly because there was no potentially troublesome superior in sight. Lieutenant von Strackmann was still closeted in the company office with Kirschke, and the two young second lieutenants who commanded the other platoons in the company had their hands full elsewhere. Accordingly, Rammler felt impelled to set an example, to show that nothing could stand in a true Ironclad's path, not even a river.

The river, an innocuous little stream for most of its length, seemed at this point to have bowed to the require-

ments of the military. Its banks abruptly and obligingly converged, transforming it into a natural hazard which made it ideal for training purposes; it might have been used as a course for canoe championships.

At the head of a chosen band, Sergeant Major Rammler plunged into the river. The foaming water almost reached his chest but it failed to dislodge him. His sturdy legs were burdened not only with his own substantial weight but that of a light machine gun and two boxes of ammunition. Nothing could have been more exemplary—or more conducive to stability.

Some twenty feet from the bank he halted with his legs planted firmly apart and stared imperiously at Martin Recht, who crouched in the bushes, looking wan with fatigue.

"Prepare to jump!" he yelled.

Martin Recht rose to his feet. He tensed his muscles and got ready to spring. A bare yard would see him in the water, he knew. He also knew that he couldn't swim, which added to his nervousness. The water was not very deep near the bank but it boiled like a maelstrom, and Rammler was heavier and steadier on his feet than he was.

Rammler was equally aware of all this, and proud of it. It was part of a leader's job to know his subordinates' weaknesses so that he could do everything within his power to combat them.

"Jump!" he called, adding, rather inappropriately: "At the double!"

Recht jumped.

Later, when pressed for "an accurate account," several platoon members said it had been a fine day and that they had welcomed the opportunity to cool off. They had positively enjoyed their cool dip and had splashed around happily. As for the current, the water hardly came up to their chests, so even a nonswimmer should have been in no difficulty.

But the water that hardly reached the others' chests seemed to grip Martin Recht's heart with chill fingers and constrict it. His legs turned to lead and his breathing faltered. He stumbled, lost his balance and went under, striking out desperately as he was swept away.

Still splashing feebly, he floated into the iron embrace of Sergeant Major Rammler, who tried to stand him on his feet—vainly, at first, because his limbs seemed to be made of rubber.

"That's what I like to see!" Rammler muttered grimly. "That'll teach you to lay your grubby paws on a superior of-

ficer. When it comes to the pinch, you youngsters are as soft as liver sausage."

The other members of No. 3 Platoon said later that Recht had folded up like a jacknife—the only one of them to do so. No one could have foreseen this, because although he had never been particularly tough he should have been able to manage the crossing like all the rest. It was a mercy that Rammler had caught hold of him and pulled him ashore. Saved his life? Yes, you could put it like that.

"I should have let you drown, you wet streak," said the sergeant major, bending over Martin Recht's heaving form. "We don't want softies in this outfit, especially the sort that lay hands on their superiors."

Rammler was confident that he had taught Recht a lesson —and the others, too. With luck, it should have beneficial results. Glancing round encouragingly, he saw a circle of submissive faces.

He also saw the approaching figure of Corporal Kamnitzer.

WHAT IS COMMONLY CALLED fate—or chance— can hinge on little things. On this occasion it hinged on a bottle of imported Scotch whisky which bore the name Red Horse and was stocked by Schlachtmann's Delicatessen. Frau Elfrieda, wife of Major Bornekamp, had expressed a desire to try some, which was how Lieutenant von Strackmann came to visit the shop.

With an arduous day behind him and the night still young, von Strackmann was yearning for solace and relaxation. Frau Elfrieda could be relied upon to supply both, and it occurred to him that whisky might be the best possible basis for a congenial evening.

But Schlachtmann's also stocked, among other things, a mixture of beer and German champagne entitled Champi and priced at DM 1.20 per bottle. This beverage was much favored by sundry ladies of the local *beau monde*, among them Captain Treuberg's wife.

Thus it came about that there was a reunion between the air force captain and the army lieutenant—deputies both, both burning with ambition and both equally convinced that their professional ability was not sufficiently appreciated. This accounted for the mutual understanding that had blossomed between them during the supervision of the Ladies' Night and the cadets' dance.

"Glad to see you again," said Captain Treuberg.

"My pleasure," von Strackmann replied cordially.

"In actual fact," Treuberg said, dropping his voice, "I've been wondering whether to give you a ring all day." He piloted the lieutenant into a bay bordered by phalanxes of tinned fruit and fish. "I imagine you've been having a hard time of it."

"These things are sent to try us," said von Strackmann. "But how did you know?"

For a moment, Captain Treuberg forgot all about his wife and her ever-increasing reliance on Champi as a medium of oblivion. As a sensitive person, she was pained by the fact that her husband was still a captain, and doubly pained because he was deputy to Ahlers—Ahlers, of all people!—which meant that she did not enjoy the social status proper to her.

"I know quite a bit," said Treuberg, glancing round.

There was no enemy in sight, but he suggested that it might be advisable to find a place where they could talk undisturbed—the Brace of Pheasants round the corner, for instance.

They installed themselves in the farthest corner of the taproom with two glasses of foaming, golden-yellow beer. The smoke-blackened paneling around them was adorned with painted beer casks enclosed by oak leaves.

"Tell me something, von Strackmann—just between ourselves. Are you aware that you've got enemies? Have you any idea why Captain Ahlers might be prejudiced against you?"

"Is he?" the lieutenant asked, pricking up his ears. "I can't think why he should be."

It began to dawn on von Strackmann that this conversation might be important. He took a deep pull at his beer and asked for further details.

"I ought to tell you," Treuberg said slowly, "that I've always regarded Captain Ahlers as a first-rate officer. Unfortunately, I'm now compelled to admit that his conduct has not been exemplary in every respect—for instance, in the question of divorcing official duties from personal considerations. I imagine you're familiar with the name Martin Recht?"

"Am I!" the lieutenant ejaculated. "What's he got to do with it?"

"Well, this man Recht is always in and out of Ahlers's house. He's keen on his daughter—not that there's anything

198

wrong in that. It may be entirely above board—serious intentions and so on."

"What you're implying," von Strackmann said with scarcely suppressed excitement, "is that Captain Ahlers has intervened on Recht's behalf, behind the scenes."

"I'm not only implying it—I'm stating it as a fact."

"So that's the way the wind blows!" von Strackmann exclaimed. "He went to the C.O. and put a spoke in my wheel —just like that!"

"Things are a little more complicated than that, I'm afraid. Ahlers is much too clever to have intervened personally. He brought up a big gun to do the job for him—Mayor Asch, no less."

"But it's scandalous—trying to pervert the course of justice for the sake of your daughter's boy friend!"

"I wouldn't put it quite like that," Treuberg said cautiously. "Whether the man involved was a future son-in-law or Private X, Ahlers's motives for trying to protect him might be entirely honorable. It wouldn't be easy to prove the opposite."

"But the man's bound to be biased—any fool can see that."

"I wouldn't indulge in speculations of that sort if I were you, von Strackmann. There are other arguments which carry much more weight. I mean, anyone who poses as a champion of justice and morality must have a clean sheet himself."

"And Ahlers hasn't?" Lieutenant von Strackmann snapped at the bait like a ravenous fish. "In what way?"

"As you know, my dear chap, an officer has certain obligations where his private life is concerned. I don't mean affairs with women or anything like that—I mean debts. If an officer runs up debts . . ."

"And has he?" Von Strackmann swallowed the bait whole. "Do they amount to much?"

"Several thousand marks at least." Treuberg sat back contentedly. His work was done. He had lent valuable assistance to a brother officer, and the rest would be plain sailing. "But that's not all. One of the people Ahlers has borrowed from is a warrant officer."

"A subordinate!"

"Vossler by name. He's had to fork out three thousand marks on Ahlers's behalf."

"And a bounder like that dares to stab me in the back! It's almost incredible. I'm very much obliged to you for the information."

199

"It was a pleasure, Herr von Strackmann. I've told you this in the strictest confidence, of course."

"Of course."

"I knew you'd understand. My position makes it impossible for me to act otherwise." Treuberg was Ahlers's deputy, after all. If he stepped into his shoes as a result of the ensuing complications his motives might well be misconstrued. "Besides, what I've told you will do the trick even if you can't name your source. Facts like these speak for themselves."

"Captain Treuberg," von Strackmann said solemnly, "I can't tell you how obliged I am."

"YOU THERE!" Sergeant Major Rammler shouted as Kamnitzer trotted toward him. "You've deserted your post."

Corporal Kamnitzer did not appear to notice the sergeant major. He hurried over to the sodden bundle of clothing that was Grenadier Martin Recht and knelt beside it. Taking his friend's face in his hands he stared into the weary, apprehensive eyes and was rewarded by a gleam of gratitude.

"You had me worried for a moment," he said roughly, trying to disguise his evident relief.

"I'll be all right, Karl," Recht murmured faintly.

"Kamnitzer!" shouted Rammler. "Didn't you hear what I said?"

"What did you say?" asked Kamnitzer, without looking up.

"Kindly stand to attention when you're talking to me!" Rammler bellowed. "And look me in the eye!"

"Certainly, Sergeant Major." Kamnitzer rose to his feet, stationed himself in front of Rammler and regarded him with a cool, appraising, almost imperceptible smile. It was a well-tried expression and guaranteed to have a provocative effect.

Its effect was not lost on Rammler, but he retained his composure—if only because of the numerous soldiers within earshot.

"Corporal Kamnitzer," he said with suppressed fury, "are you aware that you have left your observation post?"

"Yes, Sergeant Major."

"You left it without being ordered to do so by me?"

"Yes, Sergeant Major."

It was clear that Kamnitzer's stereotyped replies were get-

ting on Rammler's nerves. He couldn't fathom why an innately cunning individual like Kamnitzer was behaving so casually, when he, Rammler, had at last got him where he wanted him.

"Good God, man!" Rammler spluttered. "You could be court-martialed for this!"

"For what, Sergeant Major?"

"For leaving your post in the middle of an exercise. Don't you realize what it could mean if this were the real thing?"

To the listening platoon, it looked as though Rammler was safe in the saddle and Kamnitzer up the creek without a paddle. However, Kamnitzer did not keep them waiting long for an answer.

"With respect, Sergeant Major, you've made a mistake— several mistakes, in fact."

"Mistakes?" exclaimed Rammler, squaring his broad shoulders belligerently. "What mistakes?"

"To begin with, Sergeant Major, I was sent up a tree, but no one issued me any clear or comprehensive orders."

"You were supposed to observe the enemy!"

"I know, Sergeant Major, but what enemy? What was I meant to do if I saw them? Where was platoon H.Q.? No one told me anything like that. Anyway, for want of anything better to observe, I observed you, Sergeant Major, and in the process I saw a member of the platoon in danger of drowning."

"Shut your filthy trap!" yelled Rammler.

"Did I hear you say 'filthy trap'?" Kamnitzer inquired politely.

"I said hold your tongue!" The sergeant major was fuming with rage. "I've had enough of your lip for one day."

"There's just one more point, Sergeant Major. When someone looks as though he's in serious danger, I should have thought it was much more important to try and save him than sit back and watch, especially in default of definite orders to the contrary. Isn't that what the C.O. means by initiative?"

"Are you trying to teach me my job?"

"No, Sergeant Major, just trying to save you from making a mistake."

Rammler ground his teeth, but his nutcracker face remained devoid of expression. It was past his comprehension that Kamnitzer should have won yet another round against him, this time in front of the whole platoon.

He decided to banish his audience to the bushes, but be-

201

fore doing so he made an announcement which showed that he realized what a dangerous corner Kamnitzer had maneuvered him into.

"Once and for all," he said emphatically, "I'd like to make it clear that no one was in any danger here. No one has ever drowned in this river, nor ever will, while I'm in charge." He paused. "Corporal Kamnitzer stand fast—the remainder, dig in! Nuclear attack imminent!"

The men dispersed. They drove their shovels into the ground with a will, happy in the knowledge that Rammler was otherwise engaged and would probably remain so for a considerable time to come.

Rammler fixed Kamnitzer with a baleful stare. The bell had gone for the next round.

"We're going to have a little talk," he said significantly. "Just the two of us."

"By all means," said Kamnitzer. On Rammler's instructions, he obediently loaded himself with a machine gun and several pounds of ammunition.

"To the clearing!" Rammler called. "At the double— move!"

The others bent low over their work and delved away with redoubled vigor for a few moments. They knew what Rammler's order portended. The clearing was his favorite place for "individual tuition," as he termed it. Kamnitzer knew this too, but he trotted almost eagerly through the trees to the ill-omened spot.

When they reached it and were alone at last in the idyllic woodland glade, the sergeant major made what he intended to be a brief introductory address.

"Do you know what I think of you?" he demanded, enunciating carefully. "You're a lousy mother-fugging bastard, a stinking little skunk, a shit-faced insubordinate swine. That's what I think of you."

"May I point out," Kamnitzer said mildly, "that expressions of that nature are not in current use these days? They're against regulations."

Rammler laughed scornfully. "You'll be asking me to apologize to you next!"

"Not a bad idea, except that I'm not sure I'd be prepared to accept an apology from you."

"You're a degenerate little swine, Kamnitzer—a malicious little sod, that's what you are."

"Can I make a note of that?" asked Kamnitzer. "It'll look good in my report."

"Get stuffed!" shouted the sergeant major. "We're on our own here, in case you hadn't noticed. Who's listening? Where are your witnesses? You can wipe your ass with your report—that's all it'll be good for."

"Thanks for the advice," remarked Kamnitzer.

The setting sun tinged the surrounding trees with gold and cast long shadows on the verdant grass which carpeted the glade. A belated bird was chirping to itself somewhere near at hand. The forest idyll was complete.

"Lie down!" shouted Rammler.

Kamnitzer did not move. He just stood there blinking at the soft evening sunlight.

"Lie down!" Rammler repeated.

"Why?"

"I'm giving you an order!" Rammler snarled. "If you don't comply with it immediately you'll regret you were ever born."

"Really?" Kamnitzer looked genuinely interested.

"I'll put you on a charge."

"Steady on, Sergeant Major. You seem to have forgotten that we're on our own. Who's to hear? Where are your witnesses? You can take your charge and wipe your ass on it. That's all it's good for."

Although Kamnitzer had used the precise words which Rammler himself had uttered a few moments before, Rammler felt as if he had never heard them before in the whole of his military career. They sounded different when uttered by a subordinate. A whole world—his world—seemed to be tumbling about his ears.

"I could tell you to get stuffed," Kamnitzer continued, "but I won't. I could think of plenty of obscene things to call you, too, but they wouldn't do justice to a man of your caliber. I'll just say this: you're a despicable human being and a rotten soldier. I'm going back to the others now. Are you coming?"

THE STORM CLOUDS continued to gather as the evening wore on.

Carolin Ahlers sat in the kitchen on the bench beside the stove. A book lay open on her lap, but she was not reading it. She was a little uneasy. Martin Recht had promised to call, but there was no sign of him.

"Why doesn't he come?" she asked.

"Perhaps he can't make it," Frau Ahlers said smoothly.

"A barracks isn't like an office, with regular working hours. I've had to wait for your father often enough."

"That's different, though."

"Of course," Frau Ahlers said. "Your father never watches the clock when he's on duty. His private life comes second." Her voice contained no hint of reproach. "But Martin has to do what he's told. He can't dispose of his time as he wants to—you'll have to get used to that. Besides, I expect he dosen't want to disturb you tonight."

"Disturb me? How could he think that!"

"He knows you have to go into the hospital tomorrow, so perhaps he wants to spare you any excitement. That's what it is, I'm sure. You ought to be grateful to him for being so thoughtful."

Carolin was half convinced for a moment, but she went on waiting.

Helen Wieder was not waiting for anyone. At least, she showed no sign of missing Kamnitzer's presence. She went on serving the customers as usual, and the fact that her eyes swiveled repeatedly in the direction of the entrance was, she told herself, purely coincidental.

Kamnitzer, meanwhile, was lying on his bed with a transistor set on the pillow beside him. He glanced across at Martin Recht from time to time with an expression of benevolent appraisal.

Recht was writing a letter to his mother. It was full of the usual assurances: he was well, he got plenty to eat, there was no need to worry about him.

Both Kamnitzer and Recht had been ordered to stay in Room 13 and wait, it was not clear what for. "In case you're needed," they had been told, and their roommates were also on call.

In the meantime, von Strackmann and Kirschke were fighting shoulder to shoulder, to the surprise of the whole company. Both of them were doing their utmost to bury the charge alleging "assault on a superior officer." Kirschke, in particular, had brought his considerable powers of persuasion into play, but Streicher, with Rammler's hot breath fanning the back of his neck, remained adamant.

"Well, we've done all we can," von Strackmann declared at length. "You can confirm that, Sergeant Major."

"I know," said Kirschke, "but we ought to have acted more promptly—more firmly, too. I'm afraid we're going to have to ride out the storm now."

"I don't give up so easily," von Strackmann said. "I'm

going to make the best of the situation, however hopeless it looks."

"At whose expense, sir?"

"Not at the expense of this company, I can tell you that much."

"I hope, sir," Kirschke said, his suspicions suddenly aroused, "that you aren't confusing the interests of the company with your personal welfare."

They were back to where they had been a few hours before. The brief armistice was at an end.

"You don't know what you're talking about!" snapped the lieutenant, and he vanished into his office, slamming the door behind him.

Von Strackmann couldn't bring himself to leave the company block. He felt it imperative to remain at his post, if only to prevent Kirschke from stepping out of line. This meant that Frau Elfrieda Bornekamp had to wait, too, but she did not wait unsolaced. Von Strackmann telephoned his apologies and got an orderly to deliver her bottle of Red Horse.

Elisabeth Asch had no time to wonder where her husband was. Not only was she far too busy, but she had never felt neglected by him. If he kept her waiting he must, she was convinced, have his reasons.

She was right. Herbert Asch was engaged on what he termed "preventive measures." These consisted of conferring with Captain Ahlers and trying to persuade him to contact Colonel Turner.

"I don't know if that would be wise," Ahlers said dubiously. "The colonel's a very punctilious man."

"That's just what we need," said Asch. "We've got to get the ball rolling. If we just sit back and wait, anything may happen. A lot of people could suffer, and in my experience it's always the little people that get hurt in these situations —i.e., Martin Recht. But that's just what we want to avoid, and that's why I'm in favor of clearing the air as soon as possible."

"Perhaps you're right," Ahlers conceded reluctantly. "I only hope we haven't overlooked anything."

The ball started rolling, just as Asch intended, though not in the direction foreseen either by himself or by Ahlers, neither of whom was aware of Captain Treuberg's booby trap.

The explosion was triggered in the following way:

Phase One: Captain Ahlers telephoned Colonel Turner.

"We shall hardly be able to avoid adopting a stand of some kind, sir," he said after a lengthy preamble, "particularly since members of the civilian population are taking an interest in the affair. I would suggest that you consult Herr Asch. He's prepared to make himself available at any time."

"I don't want any fuss, Ahlers."

"Precisely, sir. That's why we ought to take preventive measures as soon as possible."

Phase Two: Colonel Turner telephoned Major Bornekamp. After the customary cordial assurances that he had no wish to give precipitate advice or meddle in the affairs of another arm of the service, he said: "But we shall all be forced to take official note of the affair, in view of the prevailing state of public opinion."

"Which will change again before long, sir, I trust."

"Until then, we must resign ourselves to the fact that it carries a certain weight. In any case, Major, I should be grateful if you would do your best to keep me up to date on developments."

Phase Three: Major Bornekamp telephoned Lieutenant von Strackmann. His introductory remark—"I've got better things to do than lose sleep because of my subordinates' incompetence"—was succeeded by a string of questions, namely: Had von Strackmann dealt with a certain delicate matter? If so, was it settled for good? If not, why not?

The lieutenant took a deep breath.

"Don't beat about the bush, Strackmann! I'll give you precisely ten minutes to produce a final answer."

Phase Four: Lieutenant von Strackmann telephoned Major Bornekamp. "The matter has been investigated with the fullest attention to detail, sir. The charge is corroborated by the evidence of a trustworthy N.C.O. and five men." He paused for a moment. "With respect, sir, there's something fishy going on. I've been reliably informed in confidence that an air force captain named Ahlers has been trying to persuade the mayor to intervene—for personal reasons. Recht is involved with his daughter. Captain Ahlers's private life doesn't seem to be above reproach, either. He's in debt to the tune of several thousand marks."

There was a lengthy pause. Then Major Bornekamp asked: "Is this fact or supposition?"

"Corroborative evidence can be easily produced."

"But you haven't managed to scotch this blasted charge of assault."

"No, sir. I'm very sorry."

Phase Five: Major Bornekamp telephoned Colonel Turner.

He began by assuring the colonel how grateful he was for his advice, how much he appreciated the confidence reposed in him, how receptive he was to suggestions of any kind—but . . . "But I very much fear that personal considerations enter into this. I'm referring to Captain Ahlers."

Apparently, Ahlers looked on the accused man as a future son-in-law. Even that might be all right, but. . . "But I submit that a man whose ostensible purpose is to defend the cause of justice and integrity ought to put his own house in order first. I'm told that he's heavily in debt—ten thousand marks is the sum mentioned. He's even said to have borrowed money from a subordinate."

"That," said Colonel Turner, consternation in his voice, "is news to me."

"I hope you'll treat my remarks as confidential, Colonel."

With that, Bornekamp was confident that he had shaken off the importunate area commandant and equally confident that this distressing affair had been shelved, at least for the time being. However, he had reckoned without the colonel's punctiliousness where official matters were concerned. Turner would not tolerate any loose ends in his command. He summoned Captain Ahlers at once.

"Are you in debt?" he demanded.

"Yes, sir."

"Have you borrowed money from a subordinate?"

"Yes, sir."

"What do your debts amount to?"

Ahlers hesitated. "About twelve thousand marks, sir."

The coloned stiffened. "This is not only serious," he said eventually. "It's quite incredible. I simply can't have that sort of thing—not in my command."

"If I might be permitted to explain how I incurred these debts . . ."

"There's nothing to explain," Turner said sternly. "No explanation, however ingenious, could alter the extent of your indebtedness. That is the only point at issue. Regrettable as it may seem, I must draw my own conclusions. Only one course of action is open to me: you are relieved of your duties until further notice, that is to say, until a court of inquiry has reached a decision on your case."

"May I ask one thing, sir?"

"I'm sorry, no. I must do my duty; I've no other alternative. My decision is final, as much as I regret it personally. You are relieved of your duties as of now, and will hold yourself in readiness to give evidence. Captain Treuberg will take over from you in the meantime."

The die was cast.

Summary proceedings were now to be instituted against two men: against Grenadier Martin Recht for assaulting a superior officer—probable sentence, with luck, several months' imprisonment; and against Captain Klaus Ahlers for excessive indebtedness.

Since the latter case automatically raised the possibility that Ahlers might have been employed as a paid contact by foreign intelligence services (an easy way for an officer to get money to pay off debts), Military Intelligence had to be notified at once. If his debts, at least one of which was incurred by borrowing from a subordinate, proved to be his only misdemeanor, it probably would mean dishonorable discharge, deprivation of rank, and loss of pension.

The disaster seemed complete.

"We must do our duty unflinchingly," Lieutenant Dieter von Strackman declared. "I'm extremely distressed by the whole affair, but it was absolutely unavoidable."

"You can do your duty, sir, if that's what you like to call it," the C.S.M. said wearily. "My duties are over for the day."

"You're not going to leave me in the lurch, Sergeant Major?"

Kirschke avoided looking at his acting company commander. He found the sight embarrassing. He tidied the few things that lay on his desk and closed the drawers, one by one, as though oblivious of von Strackmann's presence.

"Listen, Kirschke," von Strackmann said, almost coaxingly, "I'm in a cleft stick, you must try to understand that. I've got to resolve the situation somehow."

"At whose expense?"

The lieutenant could have tried to explain his motives. He could have said that he meant well, that he was a man of high principles, that it was only natural to defend oneself when everything conspired against one. . . .

But he said none of this, mainly because Kirschke sat there like a rock, motionless, craggy, and unyielding. He looked contemptuous.

"I'll make one last effort," von Strackmann said. "I'll call the Judge Advocate General's office and speak to someone there."

"If you do that, it's as good as reporting the case officially."

"The J.A.G.'s people can dismiss it."

"They won't, though."

"For God's sake, Kirschke!" von Strackmann exclaimed with a mixture of rage and entreaty. "Why do you always have to know better?"

He picked up the phone and asked for the Judge Advocate General's department. Despite the lateness of the hour, he was put through to an official named von Minzlaffe.

"A perfect prima facie case," was von Minzlaffe's terse verdict, when von Strackmann had summarized the situation. "Kindly forward the appropriate particulars as soon as possible."

Von Strackmann registered dismay. "You don't see any possibility, under certain circumstances, after considering all possible interpretations of existing regulations . . ."

"I'm sorry, no," said von Minzlaffe. He knew his trade, as his next words clearly showed. "You many rest assured that I fully appreciate your concern as unit commander, but in this case—believe me—the legal position seems quite clear. A moderate term of imprisonment is inevitable."

Von Strackmann replaced the receiver as though renouncing a crown. His face wore an expression of solemn resignation. "I didn't want to do that," he said.

"But you did," Kirschke retorted.

The lieutenant bowed his crew-cut head in an attempt to convey submission to fate. It was his lot to be misunderstood.

"The inevitable has happened," he announced. "We must take the appropriate steps."

"What sort of steps do you mean?"

"Well," said von Strackmann, squaring his shoulders, "in the first place, full details must be forwarded to the J.A.G.'s office without delay. Then there are certain precautionary measures to be taken, on the basis that Recht must be isolated from Streicher. The safest way of doing that would be to transfer him."

"Out of the question," said Kirschke. Coming to life again, he advanced on the lieutenant. "We must keep the case and the men involved under our jurisdiction, or we won't be able to exert any influence on the outcome."

"But the matter's settled, Sergeant Major."

"Not for me it isn't, sir, nor for you. We shouldn't be under any illusions about that. There's still that chap Kamnitzer to be reckoned with, not to mention a number of other people, including some whose existence we may not even be aware of."

209

"Why do you always have to look on the dark side, Sergeant Major?" Von Strackmann stamped his foot like a boy who has been forbidden to play ball. "I'm prepared to put my faith in the court's judgment, anyway."

"You're welcome, sir," said Kirschke. "I trust you'll still be as happy if their judgment happens to coincide with justice."

"I REGRET THIS SITUATION," Captain Treuberg said with an air of genuine regret, "but there's nothing I can do."

"All right," Ahlers replied curtly. "What do you want?"

Captain Treuberg, yesterday Ahlers's deputy and today his superior, stood unflinchingly behind his desk. It belonged to him, now, as did the maps and plans on the walls. Ahlers was his to command, but he preserved what he hoped was a comradely attitude. "I can't tell you how sorry I am about all this, Ahlers, but I must ask you—at the colonel's request—for an accurate and detailed list of your debts."

"May I draw your attention to one not unimportant point? Any liabilities I may have incurred are of a purely temporary nature."

"However you regard them," Treuberg said courteously, "I'm afraid it doesn't affect my instructions, or yours either."

"You'll get your list. Will you give me an hour?"

Captain Treuberg was magnanimous enough to grant this request. He even placed a pad of paper and his own fountain pen at Ahlers's disposal. "If I can help in any way, please don't hesitate to call on me."

Captain Ahlers retired into the outer office, squatted on a window sill and started to draft the required statement.

While still engaged on this depressing task, he was interrupted by Viktor Vossler. "Just bear one thing in mind, Klaus," he said in a low voice. "A friend is a friend. Nothing can change that."

Ahlers looked up. "Don't overestimate the value of friendship, Viktor. Sober facts are all that matter now."

"I'm your friend, Klaus," Vossler insisted. "Don't ever forget it."

Ahlers gave a wan smile and returned to his calculations. The final figure was DM 11,350—in words: eleven thousand three hundred and fifty marks—nearly all of which had been spent on Carolin's medical expenses. Drawing a double line beneath the figure that symbolized the years he had spent

In trying to prevent his child from becoming a permanent cripple, Ahlers took the completed balance sheet to Treuberg.

Treuberg accepted it with an impassive face, though his eyes glinted involuntarily when he had read it through. "Is that the total?" he asked in mechanical tones. Ahlers responded with a terse affirmative. "In that case, I must convey this to the colonel at once."

Turner laid aside his beloved but unread volume of Kant, stared at the total, impressed, and summoned Captain Ahlers to his office.

"How could this have happened?" he said, shaking his scholarly head in sorrow.

"I know how I can meet these liabilities in full, sir."

Turner looked up expectantly. He was always ready to act on his basic principle, namely, to avoid trouble as long as there was any possibility of doing so. "I'm open to suggestions, Ahlers."

"Well, sir, my late father left me and my sister a piece of land with a house on it. It's nothing very grand, but it must be worth forty thousand marks—perhaps fifty. I'll try to realize my share of it within the next few days."

"You really think there's a chance?" The colonel was not inhuman. His face had assumed an expression of paternal benevolence. "How much time do you think you would need?"

"Ten days or a fortnight ought to do it."

"Right," said Turner. "I'll give you ten days' leave. If you've managed to clear this business up by the end of that time, I'll be the first to welcome it. But don't disappoint me, Ahlers. I should regard that as a sign of ingratitude."

"Certain things have come to my ears," Herbert Asch told Major Bornekamp, "but I can hardly credit them."

Bornekamp emitted an indignant snort. "Can I help it if one of my subordinates rushes in feet foremost and messes everything up? I've got to obey the rules, after all."

The C.O. was visiting Asch at the latter's invitation. They stood facing each other in the mayor's office with seven centuries of local history staring down at them in the shape of parchment scrolls, oil paintings, and a heavy seal in a glass case. In a display cabinet lay a broken dagger, the property, so it was said, of a general of Nordic origin who had allegedly tried to drive it into the mayoral desk during the

Thirty Years' War—without success, because the desk was constructed of stout and well-seasoned oak.

"In that case," Asch said quietly, "you've broken the terms of our agreement."

"What am I supposed to do, with subordinates like that?"

"But they are your subordinates, aren't they, Major?"

Bornekamp writhed, but only briefly. As commander of the Ironclads and a professed fighting soldier, he considered it beneath his dignity to give ground to a mere civilian.

"You've got a nerve, blaming me," he protested, going over to the attack, "after the egg you laid—Ahlers, I mean. The cheek of the man, sticking his nose into our business and stirring thing up when he's got little enough to be proud of himself. Do you expect me to let a chap like that ride rough-shod over me?"

"Kindly note the following, Major," Asch said, retaining his composure with an effort, "I'm not blaming anybody, I'm merely stating facts. And so far as my friend Captain Ahlers is concerned, I'd go bail for him any time."

"For his debts, too?"

"If by that you mean his temporary obligations, yes—to the limit."

"It's probably too late for that." The major looked into a pair of cool, appraising eyes. He was unused to being looked at in this way, and it irritated him. "Anyway, what do you know about our job and its difficulties?" he demanded. "You've no idea what we're up against—thwarted by little pipsqueaks and spat on by bastards who aren't fit to lick our boots! A lot of senior officers are weak-kneed these days, so don't expect any miracles from me!"

"All I expected was that you'd keep your promise."

"What did I promise?" Bornekamp demanded aggressively. "Go on, tell me."

"If you can't remember, there's no point in my reminding you."

"I made no promises."

"Very well, neither did I."

"Are you trying to threaten me?" Bornekamp scented danger in the air. "Come now, surely you're not going to crucify me for the sake of a private soldier? I don't believe it! You wouldn't do a thing like that, after the way we've always worked so well together."

The words started to gush from Bornekamp's lips like water from a fractured pipe. Herbert Asch let him run on, even though he regarded it as a sheer waste of time.

"Would you excuse me?" he said eventually, and walked

out, leaving the Ironclad-in-chief standing there with a face that looked as though it had been daubed with crimson.

In the adjoining room, Asch called Flammer of the *News*. "This is it," he told him. "Go ahead and print."

"In full?" asked Flammer.

"As far as I'm concerned, Herr Flammer. In fact, I suggest you run the article in its original form—preferably tomorrow morning. Major Bornekamp's views deserve the fullest possible coverage and the widest possible public recognition. You follow me?"

"It'll be a pleasure," Flammer assured him. "But I hope you know who's going to carry the can for this in the end."

"Let's get to work, then," said Councilor Mathias von Minzlaffe, peeling off his gloves.

He sat down at the company commander's desk and opened a file containing nothing but virgin white paper. Unscrewing the cap of his fountain pen with long, sensitive fingers, he glanced keenly at von Strackmann through his rimless glasses. "This seems a clear enough case. It shouldn't take long to master the essentials."

"You can count on my support," von Strackmann said.

"I'm banking on it," von Minzlaffe assured him with a smile. The councilor, a civilian judge advocate, was the ideal man for this case, which promised to be a model of its kind. He was, as so often before, in his element.

"First, the plaintiff," he commanded.

Sergeant Streicher made an excellent impression on the councilor. His demeanor was a blend of modesty, determination, humility, and readiness to cooperate. His answers came back pat and without hesitation. In short, he inspired confidence.

"You say you were assaulted by the subordinate in question?"

"Yes, sir."

"No possibility of a mistake?"

"None, sir."

"Will you stand by your evidence, come what may?"

"Come what may, sir."

Von Minzlaffe studied Streicher's earnest features with approval and then glanced at von Strackmann, who experienced a mild sense of pride at having such a subordinate under his command.

"Now the accused," said von Minzlaffe.

213

Grenadier Martin Recht appeared. His manner, the councilor sensed at once, left much to be desired. He did not give a sufficient impression of candor or self-confidence. On the contrary, he betrayed signs of nervousness and diffidence, possibly engendered by a bad conscience. His face looked pale and worried.

"I'm not here to pass judgment on you," the councilor announced. "That's not my function. My job is to handle the preparatory details. I hope—in your own interests—that you'll place the fullest trust in me. You will, won't you?"

Martin Recht hesitated for some seconds before replying. Von Minzlaffe's glasses flashed and he tapped the papers in front of him with his pen, spattering them with ink—not that he appeared to notice. His bland, unwrinkled face had gone as blank as a hurriedly wiped blackboard.

"Are you guilty?" he demanded sternly.

"No," Recht replied. "At least, I'm not aware of having done anything wrong."

Von Minzlaffe screwed the ink-spattered sheet of paper into a ball and tossed it into the wastepaper basket. His lips narrowed and he closed his eyes for a moment. It was always the same—they all denied it. They produced a string of worthless excuses and hoped that people would be stupid enough to believe them. What a world!

"Once upon a time," von Minzlaffe said, "men used to stand by what they said—and did. It was a point of honor, something which accorded with the basic princples of national discipline. People are impressed by a thing like that. It would be taken into account at your trial. Well, Recht?"

"I really didn't do what I'm accused of."

Von Minzlaffe frowned and glanced across at von Strackmann. The implied reproach was not lost on the lieutenant, who felt that he had been failed by one of his subordinates. "Come on, man," he urged. "Don't let us down."

His exhortation was in vain. Recht remained stubbornly silent, and not another word could be extracted from him. Von Strackmann blushed with shame.

"I only hope all of your men aren't like that," the councilor said at length, when Recht had been dismissed.

This was not so, as the succeeding interviews clearly demonstrated. A string of witnesses, directly and indirectly involved, marched smartly in and out, compliant almost to a man. One or two of them expressed cautious reservations or succumbed, as von Minzlaffe put it, to a false confusion of loyalties, but these irregularities were soon ironed out. Von Strackmann's pride in his command revived.

214

He was proud, for instance, of Sergeant Major Rammler, whose replies came back like neatly wrapped bars of chocolate emerging from a vending machine. They tended to be a trifle crude and unpolished, of course, but this did not detract from their cogency. "Recht," he declared, "is a broken reed. Slackers like him always shit their pants when things get tough—everyone knows that." Or again: "Sergeant Streicher's still wet behind the ears, I grant you, but he'd bust a gut rather than let the company down."

Councilor von Minzlaffe smiled indulgently. Men like Rammler were a pleasure to deal with. The sergeant major struck him as a rough diamond, a rude but stout-hearted individual, a martinet, perhaps, but endowed with an unschooled sense of justice.

Company Sergeant Major Kirschke, on the other hand, tried to make trouble. His first words when questioned by von Minzlaffe were: "Why all this fuss? In the normal way, a case of this sort has to be forwarded to the public prosecutor's department—that is, if there's a case at all."

"You don't understand these things," von Minzlaffe said loftily, in a rash attempt to put Kirschke in his place. "We're merely exploring avenues of approach."

"Is that what you call it? It looks more like an encroachment on the functions of the public prosecutor to me. In fact, some people might regard it as official interference."

Councilor von Minzlaffe bridled visibly. Donning an expression of grave concern, he drew von Strackmann into the far corner of the office and addressed him in an agitated whisper. The two men put their heads together and clucked like chickens, leaving Kirschke standing in solitary state like a rooster on a dung heap.

"We needn't detain you further, Sergeant Major," von Minzlaffe said at length, striving to sound firm.

"In that case I'll go," Kirschke replied. "I've got to change my trousers, and my hands could do with a wash."

When the C.S.M. had departed, von Minzlaffe turned to von Strackmann, who had gone pale. "Have you got any more men like that in your company?"

"Unfortunately—yes. A corporal named Kamnitzer."

"Is he directly concerned with this affair?"

"No, not directly."

"Then we can dispense with his evidence. I trust your judgment implicitly on that point. There are some witnesses who only obscure the true issues."

"What if he insists on giving evidence?" Von Strackmann

could not refrain from uttering a word of warning. "He's an unpredictable type."

"Come, come!" said von Minzlaffe, closing his file with an irritable snap. "Take an old hand's word for it, if a man isn't asked anything, he can't answer. Malcontents should be excluded on principle when it's a question of reaching a proper verdict."

Lieutenant von Strackmann was fully convinced of this. Von Minzlaffe was expert at preserving the interests of Justice, he was sure, but had he come across a type like Kamnitzer? It was doubtful.

CAROLIN AHLERS was due for admission to Professor Martin's clinic, and Warrant Officer Viktor Vossler had decided that the occasion must not pass unnoticed. He organized a cortège to escort her there.

"I'm not touting for sympathy," he told Herbert Asch. "I'm merely inviting you to take a drive into town. I'll lead the way in my Mercedes and that big hotel sedan of yours can follow. All right?"

"On one condition. We'll make it a three-car procession, and I'll bring up the rear in my Porsche with Captain Ahlers."

"You're a blackmailer after my own heart," Vossler said gratefully.

He drove to the Grenadiers barracks to see if he could pry out Recht and Kamnitzer, which proved to be easier than he thought. A few words of explanation to Kirschke, and the C.S.M. put the two men on stores detail.

"Don't look so surprised," Vossler said. "You've been assigned to me. You're under my command for the next few hours, and the first thing I want you to do is look cheerful."

"I'm an expert at it," Kamnitzer assured him with a grin, "but I can't vouch for the mental state of this youngster here." He crooked a thumb at his companion.

"Listen to me, boy," Vossler told Recht. "If you're dwelling on your own troubles—forget them. At least keep smiling until Carolin's safely inside the clinic."

"I'd do anything for Carolin," Martin said quietly.

"And remember," Vossler went on, "even if they do jail you for a couple of months, you won't be the first innocent man who's done time. The main thing is not to worry Carolin. Concentrate on the idea that she wants to get well, and that you're one of the reasons why she wants to."

"Fair enough," said Recht. "But we're wasting time. Let's go and fetch her."

They climbed into the enterprising warrant officer's car and drove to Ahlers's house, where they got out and waited patiently until the procession had assembled.

"Right," said Vossler, when Ahlers had greeted him in the hall, "where's the beautiful victim?"

"I'm still wondering if this is the right moment for an operation," Ahlers said cautiously.

Vossler drew his friend into a corner. "What do you mean?" he asked. "You haven't told Carolin anything about your troubles, have you?"

"Of course not, Viktor."

Vossler looked relieved. "Forgive me for asking. I'm sure all you want is to see Carolin cured at last. What's it worth to you? Your uniform? Your pilot's license? Your captaincy? My friendship?"

"You're just delaying things unnecessarily," Ahlers said with a smile.

"Carolin!" Vossler called gaily. His voice rang through the small flat. "Come here, girl! You're not nervous, are you?"

Carolin appeared. She walked over to Vossler, limping only slightly, spread her arms wide, and flung them round his broad shoulders in a gesture of gratitude which made him feel how trivial his financial help was in comparison.

"First, a little refreshment," he announced, extricating himself carefully and with evident reluctance from Carolin's embrace. "No harm in fortifying ourselves before we venture into the lion's den. Are you scared, Carolin?"

"What of? Why should I be scared of being cured?"

Carolin was genuinely unafraid, Vossler realized. She would enter the clinic confidently, unconscious of the difficulties which threatened those nearest and dearest to her.

He walked to the window and opened it. "Come up," he called, "and bring that hamper out of the trunk of my car while you're about it."

Within a minute, Carolin was surrounded by the party which Vossler had mobilized: Vossler himself and Gerty Ballhaus, now officially engaged to him, Herbert and Elisabeth Asch, Kamnitzer and Helen Wieder, her parents, and Martin Recht. Carolin went over to Martin and took his hand.

"I'm a bit worried," Kamnitzer declared. "If Carolin's operation is successful, bang go my chances of ever beating her at bowling."

There was general laughter at this. Vossler produced some glasses and opened two bottles of champagne, assisted —as to the manner born—by Gerty, who contrived to look quite housewifely.

"My dear friends," said Herbert Asch, raising his glass. "I often feel that we take a great deal of what we call life completely for granted. We accept things without sparing them a thought, and we find it only too easy to forget the simplest and most important lessons of everyday existence —things which can be seen on any street corner or read on the faces of our neighbors. . . . .

"Must we go to jail before we know what freedom means? Is personal experience of war essential to a genuine desire for peace? Do we have to be ill before we recognize the blessings of normal good health?

"I raise my glass to Carolin. May she walk, dance and bowl to her heart's content. May she lead a healthy, happy, normal life. I challenge anyone to tell me what could be worth more than that."

T HREE DAYS LATER, while Carolin was preparing for her operation, Ahlers doing his best to liquidate his assets, and Martin Recht awaiting trial, a gray-green Volkswagen purred through the air force married quarters and drew up outside the block in which Captain Ahlers lived.

Two men in civilian clothes got out. Their faces were set in a fixed, chilly smile that looked as if it had been frozen there, and they exchanged few words. In the normal course of events, each knew what the other was thinking.

Trotting noiselessly up the stairs on rubber soles, they rang the bell and waited patiently. When the door opened, one of them inserted his foot in the gap while the other inquired softly: "Are you Frau Ahlers?" Receiving an affirmative reply, he asked: "Where is your husband?"

"Away," Frau Ahlers told him.

"Ah," remarked the man who had his foot in the door. "So he's away. Not in the Eastern Zone, by any chance?"

Frau Ahlers recoiled as she recognized the menace latent in the question. Anyone who read the newspapers knew that, to some people, a suspected concentration camp murderer was a saint compared with someone who was allegedly contaminated with Communism. Absurd though such an insinuation was in her husband's case, she did

not lose her temper. She knew that it would have been pointless. The two men were doing their duty. "My husband is visiting his sister," she said.

"Ah, and does she live in the Eastern Zone?"

"She lives in Bavaria."

"Why?"

"My colleague means, why is he visiting his sister?"

"To deal with some financial matters, I think."

"You think? Don't you know?" The man spoke in the unemotional tones of a gas-meter reader. "You're not trying to cover up for him, are you?"

Frau Ahlers eyed the two expressionless faces nervously. "I don't know what you mean."

"Bavaria," said the other, still with his foot across the threshold, "borders on the Eastern Zone."

Frau Ahlers could restrain her anger no longer. "If you're suggesting what I think you are, I strongly resent it. There's not a scrap of truth in the idea."

"As you wish, Frau Ahlers, but I ought to point out that we've made no insinuations—we've merely explored certain possibilities. From your attitude, you seem determined to withhold further information."

"Under present circumstances—yes, I am."

The two men, small-eyed, greasy-skinned and slightly corpulent—they might have been brothers—glanced at each other and nodded. Almost simultaneously, they turned and padded off down the stairs.

Frau Ahlers hurried to a window and peered out. The men stood motionless on the pavement outside for a few moments. Then, after exchanging a word or two, they separated, one going to the house next door and the other to the house across the road.

Their mode of procedure was identical. Donning an air of courteous inquiry, they requested permission to ask a few questions "in confidence." These questions could have been summarized as follows: Do you know Captain Ahlers and his family? How long have you known them? How well do you know them? What do you know about their financial position? How would you define their political views? Are you aware of any debts incurred by the said Captain Ahlers or a member of his family? If so, what is their nature and extent? Have you noticed any unusual or suspicious callers recently?

Each interview concluded with the parrotlike formula: "I must ask you to treat our conversation as strictly con-

fidential and to refrain from drawing any premature conclusions from it. Thank you for your helpful cooperation."

Within a couple of hours everyone in the officers' married quarters knew—or suspected—that there was "something fishy" about the Ahlerses. As the tide of rumor swelled, vague hints became transformed into concrete allegations and debts into criminal offenses. Some spoke of desertion and others of contacts with Communist agents. The word treason was uttered.

No one knew the exact identity of the men who had asked such fateful questions. True, they had prefaced each interview by flashing a card bearing a photograph and a rubber stamp, but no one had scrutinized or read it with any care. There was talk of detectives and secret police—but no one doubted that they were officials of some sort.

Meanwhile, the men had moved on to the air force barracks, where they separated once more. One, whose long suit was discretion, went in search of Colonel Turner, while the other, a rather tougher type, strode into the offices where Captain Ahlers had worked until a few days before.

"Where's the boss of this outfit?" he demanded, eschewing any form of greeting or introduction and not deigning to produce his warrant card. He evidently felt at home, judging by the way in which he addressed those present—sergeant clerk and female secretary alike—as subordinates. Even Monika's full-blooded charms seemed to be lost on him, which not unreasonably annoyed her. She turned her exquisite back on him, but the sergeant clerk, who scented the presence of authority, cautiously moved closer.

"I asked you a question!" barked the civilian.

Adopting a half-informative, half-respectful tone, the sergeant clerk said: "Captain Treuberg's in the mess and Warrant Officer Vossler's out in the hangars."

"Fetch them," commanded the civilian, adding, as if to reassure himself that he was in the right place, "This is where Captain Ahlers used to work, isn't it?"

"Yes, sir," said the sergeant clerk. "This is it."

He left the room and went in search of Vossler. "Can you come to the office a moment?" he asked. "There's a funny-looking civilian in there."

"If he's so funny why aren't you laughing?" Vossler inquired without interest.

"He asked if Captain Ahlers used to work in our office." Vossler's eyes began to glint. "A snooper, eh?"

"He may be someone from M.I., inquiring about Captain Ahlers. I didn't see his pass, but he smelt rather like it."

220

"That's my boy," Vossler said, setting off in the direction of the office.

The stranger, whose civilian clothes Vossler at once identified as camouflage, was leaning against the doorpost puffing at a cheap cheroot and trying to blow smoke rings.

"Hello, who have we got here?" Vossler inquired brightly.

"Who are you?" the stranger retorted with some asperity.

"I'm on home ground," said Vossler. "Anyone who barges in here has to introduce himself first."

"I'm here on official business."

"So am I—have been for years."

Monika and the sergeant clerk watched, enthralled, as the clash of personalities unfolded. Vossler stood with his legs planted firmly apart like a wrestler waiting for his opponent to spring. The mysterious civilian continued to lean against the doorpost, but he had stopped trying to blow smoke rings and his cheroot appeared to have gone out.

It was Vossler who made the first move. "Either you show me your credentials at once or I'll have you removed."

"What's the matter—got a bad conscience?"

"What makes you think so?"

"That's the impression you give," said the civilian. "In my experience, people who make a lot of noise are scared of something, and anyone who's got a bad conscience needs thorough checking."

Vossler didn't know whether to be annoyed or amused, but his ears had detected at least one revealing phrase: "thorough checking" was one of the principal functions of M.I. or Military Intelligence.

At that moment the civilian condescended to produce his pass, and Vossler read: "Sergeant Major Gross, Internal Security Division, Military Intelligence Service."

"I'm investigating the Ahlers case," the M.I. man declared, "and I must ask you not to be obstructive."

"That's crazy," said Vossler. "There isn't an Ahlers case."

"Kindly allow me to be the judge of that. Anyway, I've got to speak to Captain Treuberg and"—he consulted his notebook—"Warrant Officer Vossler."

"That's me."

The M.I. man looked incredulous. He even tried to step back to get a better view, but the doorpost intervened. "In that case, I must ask you to place any information you may have at my disposal," he said uneasily.

"Come off it!" Vossler protested. "What's this all about?"

"There may have been an attempt to pervert the course

of justice." Sergeant Major Gross seemed to have recovered his self-assurance. "Whether it'll come to an arrest remains to be seen."

THE PROCEEDINGS AGAINST Grenadier Martin Recht in respect of offenses against Paragraph 25 of the Military Penal Code—*Anyone who commits an assault on a superior officer shall be liable to imprisonment or detention for a period of not less than six months*—took their slow and laborious course. As the president of No. 2 Court, Dr. Bohlen repeated several times during the hearing: "We shall take our time. One cannot be too thorough or painstaking in a case of this nature."

The reasons for this cautious approach were fully appreciated by the two military representatives, a sergeant major and a corporal, who quickly recognized the delicacy of the issues involved. Counsel for the prosecution, on the other hand, did his best to hurry things along, confident that he had a clear-cut case and that the evidence at his disposal could not be more conclusive.

"Not even the accused can dispute the salient facts of the case," he asserted.

"But I submit . . ." interposed counsel for the defense. He said this each time he interrupted the prosecutor's argument, glancing keenly but respectfully at the president as he did so.

Dr. Bohlen, a calm and impassive figure, leaned back slightly in his chair. His eyes were friendly, and a suggestion of a smile seemed to play about his lips most of the time. His voice was that of a sorrowing father, and when he raised a restraining hand it was as though Jupiter were temporarily directing the traffic.

"Herr Recht," he said, deliberately eschewing the word "accused," "if I understand you rightly, you were not aware, on the night in question, that the plaintiff was your superior officer."

"That's right, sir," Recht replied, heartened by a brief nod of encouragement from his counsel. "All I saw was a friend who slept in the same room, someone I'd shared my meals with."

"But you knew that the plaintiff had been promoted," prosecuting counsel interposed. "You had seen him wearing sergeant's insignia—you'd even addressed him by that rank."

"Yes, sir."

Recht was the worst conceivable champion of his own cause. He had a conscience, and his conscience persuaded him that he was not entirely guiltless. No one on earth can be that, he told himself. Even a person who does absolutely nothing sins, if only by omission.

Dr. Bohlen made a discreet endeavor to skirt this feature of the proceedings. He tried, as always, to dispense justice in the most humane and conciliatory way possible, though Recht's distressingly uncompromising attempts at objectivity made his task no easier.

"Herr Recht," he said mildly, "you must try not to indulge in speculation. We are not concerned with what would have happened or what might have been if you had or had not done this or that. We cannot assess your thoughts. Facts are the only things that carry weight here."

It was demonstrated by the prosecution that a physical collision had occurred. It was further demonstrated that a roommate who should at least formally have been regarded as a superior officer had fallen to the ground as a result. (Evidence of one witness: "I thought he'd sprained his backside!") Finally, it was a proven fact that Recht made no attempt to deny that the incident itself took place.

"—which argues in my client's favor," asserted defending counsel.

"—which proves that the charge against the accused is well founded," retorted counsel for the prosecution.

The president raised his hand for the fifth time since the start of the hearing, and silence fell immediately. "You are quite at liberty to entertain your own opinions about this incident, gentlemen, but I would ask you to remember that it is the function of the court alone to reach a finding. You can facilitate that function, but you cannot usurp it."

Counsel for the defense bowed. "I request permission to call a witness for the defense: Corporal Karl Kamnitzer."

Prosecuting counsel had been thoroughly briefed as to Kamnitzer's identity and knew what to expect from him. "Irrelevant and immaterial!" he protested. "This man was not present when the incident which forms the sole subject of these proceedings occurred. Consequently, he cannot supply any evidence about it."

"But he can supply evidence as to the circumstances which led up to the incident," argued counsel for the defense. "I submit that Corporal Kamnitzer could make a substantial contribution to the court's understanding of the atmosphere in which all this took place."

223

"On the contrary," prosecuting counsel said resolutely. "From the information in my possession, the calling of this witness would only obscure the real issue."

This virtually clinched the court's decision. Dr. Bohlen, whose curiosity had been whetted by counsels' exchange, said: "I venture to suggest that the court is fully capable of deciding for itself whether or not a witness's evidence is admissible."

Once the green light had been given, Kamnitzer entered the small, bare, shabby courtroom with the same self-assurance which characterized his behavior in barracks or in the Café Asch.

"How's the case going, sir?" he inquired unceremoniously.

Dr. Bohlen, who couldn't remember having been asked such a question in the whole of his career, had some difficulty in keeping a straight face. "Herr Kamnitzer," he said courteously, "if you ask me how the case is going, I must regretfully inform you that I myself have no idea at this stage. I shall only know after the close of the hearing."

"So it's not going too badly?"

"That depends, Herr Kamnitzer, on what you understand by not too badly."

Those present regarded the strange spectacle with astonishment. Elderly judge and unabashed young man were smiling at each other in a positively familiar fashion. Indeed, they appeared to find pleasure in each other's company.

"And now," Dr. Bohlen went on, "may I ask you to abide by our rules? Before we continue our conversation, Fräulein Horn, our stenographer, would be glad to know who she's dealing with. In other words, she has to record your personal particulars."

Kamnitzer readily supplied all the requisite details. "Now do we get down to the case, sir, such as it is?"

Dr. Bohlen concurred. "But I would ask you to remember that we are examining a case of alleged assault upon a superior officer, nothing more."

"You mean you want me to stick to the point?"

"Exactly."

"I get it," said Kamnitzer. He moved a step nearer as though about to embark on a private conversation. "I won't ask you, sir, if you've ever had one too many. I doubt if you'd appreciate the question, and it's none of my business anyway, but you can imagine being in that condition, can't you?"

224

"I can imagine, yes," Dr. Bohlen said with a smile.

"Very well," said Kamnitzer. "The question is: can one regard this incident as a single, isolated occurrence, divorced from everything else? When two people bump into each other in a confined space and one of them falls down on his backside, is that all there is to it? All kinds of thing could have contributed—floor polish, for instance. You can see your face in the floor of our room."

Dr. Bohlen smiled. "That may speak well for the floor-polishing activities of your section, but it doesn't, unfortunately, dispose of the fact that one of the two men who bumped into each other was a subordinate and the other his superior."

"With respect, sir, that's the whole flaw in the argument," declared Kamnitzer. "In reality, they were just two people who'd lived together for months. They got up at the same time, cleaned their teeth side by side, ate together, worked together, and spent some of their leisure time in each other's company."

"For months, you said?" Dr. Bohlen inquired.

"For the best part of half a year, if that sounds better." Kamnitzer felt that he was operating on the right lines. For a pillar of the law, Dr. Bohlen seemed to be an understanding sort. "And throughout that time, Recht, Streicher, and myself have been living in our own little corner of the barracks—tucked up side by side, so to speak."

"Go on."

"I won't pretend I'm a model soldier," Kamnitzer said spiritedly, "but Streicher's no angel either, and Martin Recht isn't just a bone-headed lout who lets fly with his fists every two minutes. They've got their failings, but who hasn't? I've kicked both of them in the pants before now, when occasion demanded. Things like this happen—and if it means someone has to be hauled into court every time, all I can say is, I pity the judges."

"We appreciate your sympathy," commented Dr. Bohlen.

"I haven't said a word against the regiment's reputation. I hope you've noted that, sir."

"It hadn't escaped me, Herr Kamnitzer."

"I've done my best to keep to the point, too, I hope."

"I wouldn't dispute that," said Dr. Bohlen. "Thank you for your remarks. They have been most informative."

This concluded the hearing. Although Lieutenant von Strackmann's name was raised, Dr. Bohlen deemed it unnecessary to call any further witnesses. He listened impassively to the closing addresses by counsel for the prosecu-

tion and defense, and then announced that the court would retire to consider its verdict.

"Well done," defending counsel told Kamnitzer. "You mustn't expect miracles from a court of law. A judge can interpret the law but he can't ignore it altogether. I forecast that young Recht will get away with a comparatively light sentence—six months is my guess. Dr. Bohlen is the sort of judge who thinks human beings are more important than the laws they're subject to."

Dr. Bohlen reappeared, took his seat, and announced: "In the name of the people: the court finds the accused guilty as charged. He is hereby sentenced, subject to confirmation, to three months' imprisonment."

WHEN CAPTAIN AHLERS returned from leave—two days earlier than foreseen—his wife told him what had happened in the interval. He at once reported to Colonel Turner.

"Highly regrettable, this whole business," Turner said, in a tone which dissociated him from it entirely.

"It's not only regrettable, sir—it's disgraceful!"

The colonel shook his head indulgently. He could have avoided this embarrassing interview, but he never shirked responsibilities of any kind—or so he told himself. "This has been a great disappointment to me, Ahlers."

"While I've been away raising the money as agreed, sir . . ."

"Did you manage it?"

"Every last pfennig. I sold the house I told you about—the one jointly owned by myself and my sister. There wasn't time to get a good price, but my share comes to twenty thousand marks, so I shall be able to pay off all my debts."

"I'm very glad, from your point of view."

"But I'm told that I've been investigated in my absence. M.I. has been in action, spreading the most appalling rumors about me. The married quarters are absolutely buzzing with them."

"Most regrettable," repeated Turner, "but the propensity to gossip is a human failing which can never be entirely eliminated. In any case, M.I.'s action was inevitable under the circumstances."

"But I had your approval, sir. I had your promise that the matter would be allowed to rest until I'd managed to raise the necessary funds, and I've kept my side of the bargain."

226

"Is that meant to be a reproach?" Turner inquired icily. "I had your word, sir!"

Turner drew himself up until he resembled an allegorical statue portraying integrity. "You're not, I trust, implying that I have broken my word? I can assure you that the exact opposite is the case."

Ahlers ignored the warning contained in these words. He was conscious only of himself and what had been done to him. "M.I.'s investigations have discredited me, violated my honor, and brought my family into disrepute. Even if I could tolerate that, there's my wife to be considered. She feels like a leper."

"I'm sorry," Turner said coolly, "but you have only yourself to blame for repercussions of this kind—can't you understand that? Captain Ahlers, you drew up an official list of your liabilities which put the total at eleven thousand three hundred and fifty marks."

"It was correct."

"I'm sorry, Captain, it was not." Turner looked stern. "Since then, it has transpired that your statement was inaccurate. To be blunt, it was false, which means that you willfully deceived me, not to say, deliberately lied to me. I learned the full story from a reliable source, and there is ample evidence to corroborate it."

"I don't understand you."

"What about the three thousand marks you borrowed from Vossler—from a warrant officer who was your direct subordinate? You deny it, I suppose?"

"No, of course not, but that sum has nothing to do with my debts as such. Viktor Vossler is a personal friend."

"Possibly, but you are his superior officer."

"Who told you, sir? Or, rather, who denounced me?"

"That is immaterial."

"Captain Treuberg—it couldn't be anyone else!"

"Let's stick to the facts, Captain. They are as follows: You submitted a list of liabilities. I trusted you and gave you a chance to put your affairs in order. It turned out later that your list was bogus. . . ."

"Incomplete, sir, at most."

"It was inaccurate, however you regard it. That compelled me to suspect the worst. . . ."

"Of me, sir? You know me well enough to realize that's absurd!"

"Of course, Ahlers, of course! You are—or were—an officer endowed with very special qualities, nor will I ever hesitate to draw attention to them or speak on your behalf. I

227

know you, yes—but I also know the regulations, and one of them states that cases of excessive indebtedness must be reported to higher authority without delay. Surely you're aware of that?"

Captain Ahlers was not only familiar with the regulation —he approved of it in principle. Any man who incurred liabilities had to discharge them somehow, whether by tapping other sources of credit, by gambling, or by selling himself. And the easiest way for a man in uniform to sell himself was to contact a foreign espionage organization, which would pay up willingly in return for services rendered. Ahlers knew all this, but it had never occurred to him that anyone would suspect him of such conduct.

"I know that I've acted improperly," he conceded frankly, "but I'm unaware of having done anything inconsistent with my honor as an officer."

"Far be it for me to dispute that, Ahlers, but the court will have to decide for itself. Disciplinary proceedings have been instituted against you. Do you know what that means?"

"Yes," Ahlers said bitterly. "Temporary suspension from duty, a ban on wearing uniform, and partial stoppage of pay."

"You're right, I'm afraid." Colonel Turner gave a nod which signified that the interview was at an end. "And I recommend that you consider seriously whether it wouldn't be advisable to submit your resignation from the service."

DARK, TOO, were the days that Major Bornekamp was compelled to live through, thanks to Herbert Asch. The newspaper profile of the Ironclads' C.O. was raising its anticipated cloud of dust.

"Can't a man express his opinions freely any more?" Bornekamp growled furiously. "Why should the malcontents and fellow travelers have it all their own way?"

"All the same, sir," the adjutant ventured, "you are a representative of the state, in a sense. I realize that malcontents and half-witted intellectuals are given free rein these days, but in your position . . ."

"What did I say, then?"

It seemed to him that he had said a lot of highly commendable things, all of them officially sanctioned. Only one thing seriously disturbed him, and that was the misinterpreted analogy between conscientious objectors and convicts,

228

or even concentration camp detainees. How absurd! He had never had the smallest connection with a concentration camp.

"These ridiculous misunderstandings have been deliberately exaggerated. My only regret is that I can't deal with the man responsible as he deserves."

The man responsible was, of course, Herbert Asch, but his attempt to spread the gospel according to Bornekamp had been an extremely laborious business.

"I eagerly await your readers' reaction," Asch had told Flammer, but for a while he waited in vain. The local citizens swallowed Bornekamp's effusions without a murmur, and there had been no immediate comment. This did not necessarily mean that they all agreed with the Iron Major, but even the more rebellious spirits had ceased to wonder at the patriotic, nationalistic, militaristic fare that was set before them. They merely frowned and shrugged their shoulders, while the growing numbers of trusty provincial patriots nodded their approbation: the major had given them something to think about all right!

Accordingly, Asch did his best to ensure that Bornekamp's warlike utterances reached a wider public than the readers of the local paper. A leading illustrated, a radio commentator, and, finally, a member of the parliamentary opposition took the matter up. The result was a cloudburst of publicity which threatened to engulf Bornekamp and wash him away down the plug hole of political controversy.

Being confident of his own innocence, Bornekamp had to find someone whose guilt was demonstrable. Several candidates leaped to his mind. Chief among them was Herbert Asch himself, but Asch was beyond his reach. For want of a better scapegoat, he settled on Lieutenant Dieter von Strackmann, whose appalling incompetence had been ultimately responsible for landing him in his present predicament.

"I never want to set eyes on him again!" the major announced. "He's an utter failure!"

"Dieter's not a failure," retorted his wife.

"What makes you so certain?"

"Have a guess."

Bornekamp ignored the implication. "I'm surrounded by incompetents. It's been one mess-up after another. That's what comes of trusting people."

He was determined to put his house in order, to create the sort of atmosphere in which a man with true iron in his blood could breathe. Consequently, when headquarters asked

229

him to supply a sergeant major, three N.C.O.s, and twelve men for service in a new unit which was to be stationed in a dismal moorland camp, he passed the request to No. 3 Company.

Lieutenant von Strackmann seized the opportunity to rid himself of certain troublesome and undesirable elements.

"Deal with it at once, Kirschke," he commanded. "Make Rammler the sergeant major and Streicher one of the N.C.O.s, and get shut of the whole of Room 13—including Kamnitzer, of course." He added: "They don't need a C.S.M. unfortunately. It would have been a pleasure to say good-bye to you."

"A mutual pleasure," Kirschke murmured, sitting down at his desk to draft the requisite list. ....

He wrote off Rammler and Streicher with pleasure, adding a few more equally pushful types but not including Recht, whose army days were numbered anyway, or Kamnitzer, who merely figured in the top sheet which the lieutenant read but not in the copies which he signed.

Later, when it was too late to rectify the error, Kirschke alleged that he must have misheard. He was sure von Strackmann had said "Room 13—excluding Kamnitzer"—excluding, not including. "With respect, sir, it's essential to speak clearly in the army. Also, it's advisable to run a careful eye over anything one signs."

For a moment, Lieutenant von Strackmann was satisfied. "Good riddance!" he said, pushing the signed papers vigorously aside. "They can rot in hell, for all I care."

Twelve other unit commanders had acted similarly, sloughing off everyone who struck them as troublesome or incompetent. "A fine old shower, that'll be," von Strackmann remarked, smiling complacently to himself.

"Officer commanding the new detachment," Bornekamp's concluding order read, "will be Lieutenant von Strackmann."

THE CASE AGAINST Captain Klaus Ahlers, commanding No. 1 Squadron, Air Transport Wing, charged with conduct prejudicial to good order and military discipline, was heard by Disciplinary Court No. 4. The sessions, which were held *in camera,* took place on July 12-14 and 20-22. Those taking part included the president, Dr. Kruppke, two military observers, a lieutenant colonel, and a captain, an

official from the Attorney General's department, acting as prosecutor, and a stenographer. Counsel for the defense was a Dr. Friedrich Stolle.

The atmosphere was cool, objective, and utterly impersonal. Even the light that streamed in through the tall, slightly dirty windows looked gray and indifferent. The president, Dr. Kruppke, might have been conducting a board meeting.

"Let us stick to the facts, gentlemen," he said. "Kindly remember that we are dealing with a string of figures, nothing more."

No particular attention was lavished on what Colonel Turner felt obliged to say, namely, that Captain Ahlers had always shown himself to be a keen, competent, and enterprising officer who enjoyed the affection and respect of subordinates and superiors alike.

"I'm afraid your remarks have little bearing on the points at issue, Colonel."

"I merely thought it was my duty to draw attention to certain facts. I do not presume to suggest what inferences the court should draw from them."

Captain Treuberg's evidence followed a similar pattern. "I can state that I always respected Captain Ahlers. He was often referred to as the life and soul of the squadron, especially by personnel of junior rank, and I can only describe his working relationship with me, his deputy, as exemplary —all things considered."

"And you never entertained any suspicions about him?"

"How could I have, sir? He enjoyed the colonel's confidence."

"No reservations or suspicions of any kind?"

"Absolutely none. Naturally, I was not in a position to foresee what has happened since."

Everyone extolled Ahlers. The sergeant clerk was so moved by his own evidence on the captain's behalf that he appeared to be on the verge of tears.

"I challenge the prosecution to produce any witness willing or able to say anything detrimental about Captain Ahlers," declared Dr. Stolle.

"Which makes it all the more disturbing," countered the prosecuting attorney, with a burst of rhetorical zeal, "that such a thing could have happened to an officer who inspired universal confidence and trust—sentiments which now prove to have been misplaced."

"No digressions, please, gentlemen," said the president.

"The matter before us is one which can be assesed in terms of straightforward mathematics. We can dispense with emotional coloring, whatever its complexion. Kindly call Warrant Officer Vossler."

CAROLIN AHLERS sat on a chair in the waiting room of Professor Martin's clinic and stared dreamily into space as though the polished parquet flooring were carpeted with flowers.

In the doorway stood Martin Recht, dressed in a dark civilian suit. They were alone in the room, but he seemed reluctant to interrupt her daydream. He watched her solicitously for a few moments, noting how pale and fine-drawn she looked.

"Carolin," he said softly, without moving.

She looked up. Her eyes widened and a gentle flush rose to her cheeks. "Martin!" she cried. "Stay where you are— don't move!"

"I've come to fetch you, Carolin."

"That's wonderful. Don't move, though. I've got something to show you."

She rose to her feet unaided and stood there, erect and relaxed. Then, keeping her eyes fixed on his, she stepped forward with a sure, light, unhesitating tread. When she reached his side she halted, smiling happily.

"You walk like a dream."

"Yes—I can walk properly at last!"

She walked back to her chair, where she paused for a moment. Then she paced this way and that, almost pirouetting as she turned. "I'm not a lame duck any longer, am I?"

"You never were, Carolin."

"Not to you, Martin— I know."

She scampered across the room and threw herself into his arms. Her cheeks felt burning hot against his and her breath came fast. They might have been two disembodied spirits, except that they seemed to hear the blood racing in their veins—though that, as the unromantic Kamnitzer might well have said, was probably due to some quirk of the clinic's plumbing system.

"I'm so glad you came to fetch me," Carolin said, gently freeing herself. "I hope you didn't find it hard to get away."

"Not at all."

"Are you on leave, then?"

"I'm not in the army any more."

Carolin shot him an inquiring glance. Then she said hurriedly: "All the better, Martin. I mean, one serviceman is enough for any family. Father's worth a dozen on his own, isn't he?"

"He's the kindest, most decent person I've ever met."

"Where is he?"

"He's been detained, Carolin."

"On duty?"

"You could say that." Martin avoided looking at her. He went over to the chair and picked up her suitcase. "We mustn't keep your mother waiting. She's outside in Herr Asch's car. Shall we go?"

"Martin," Carolin said, blocking his path, "there's something wrong, I know there is."

"Your mother's waiting."

She gripped his arm. "What's happened? Has Father had an accident?"

"No, Carolin, nothing like that."

"What, then?"

"Just difficulties—trouble at work."

Carolin looked relieved and the pressure of her hands relaxed. "Is that really all?"

"Yes, really—but you mustn't forget how much his work means to him."

Carolin's eyes danced. "I'm sure I mean more. Don't you think so?"

"I not only think, I know. He's proved it."

VIKTOR VOSSLER strode into the courtroom as if it were a canteen and surveyed its occupants as if wondering which of them to invite to a glass of beer.

"I really don't know what I'm doing here," he announced. "This business has got absolutely nothing to do with me."

"Kindly allow us to decide that," said the president, adding, in matter-of-fact tones: "Have you ever lent the accused money?"

"You mean Captain Ahlers? Well, what if I have? That's my business, isn't it? I can do what I like with my own money. I can chuck it out of the window if I choose to."

"That's beside the point," Dr. Kruppke said wearily. "By all means regard yourself as a private citizen when circum-

233

stances permit—but in this case and under present circumstances you are a warrant officer from whom a captain—a direct superior, what is more—is alleged to have borrowed money."

"Who says so—or, rather, who's proposing to prove it?"

Vossler looked challengingly at Ahlers, but Ahlers did not return his glance. He had eyes for no one in the courtroom. The whole performance distressed him immeasurably. He was ready to pay the penalty for his foolishness, if penalty there must be, but he found it humiliating to have his private life subjected to the cool and appraising scrutiny of a roomful of strangers.

"Herr Vossler," the president admonished, "kindly spare us your irrelevant speculations and try to be completely objective."

"Very well," Vossler said indignantly. "If the court is absolutely set on prying into my personal affairs—for instance, into what I choose to do with my private resources—I can tell you, just for your information, that three thousand marks is chicken feed to me." He paused. "And, as I said, who's going to prove that I ever played banker to a superior officer? What happens if I flatly deny it?"

Dr. Kruppke heaved an almost imperceptible sigh. He found the witness's unreasonable attitude slightly irksome. "Why all these evasions?" he asked. "Why these superfluous and time-wasting attempts to rebut straightforward facts and figures with a lot of vague personal observations? The court has heard evidence from Captain Treuberg, among other people."

"That's worthless, for a start!" Vossler exclaimed belligerently. "I venture to dispute Captain Treuberg's ability to give objective testimony in this case."

"Please, please!" defending counsel exclaimed in dismay. "On my own and my client's behalf, I can only deplore such remarks."

"But why?" demanded Vossler. "I'm merely pointing out that Captain Treuberg never felt at home in the role of Captain Ahlers's sidekick. He was hellbent on taking over the squadron himself—everyone knew that. He has never been a friend of Captain Ahlers's and if he's trying to incriminate him now, all I can say is, I smell a rat—and a man-sized one at that!"

For the first time during the proceedings, Ahlers looked up. He glanced at Vossler and shook his head reprovingly. Even if mud was being flung at him, he was not going to fling it back.

"Herr Vossler's personal views may be of psychological interest," the president said, totally unimpressed, "but they are not the decisive factor here. We are concerned with facts alone, one of them being Captain Treuberg's testimony that he actually saw the I.O.U. in question. Do you dispute that?"

"Certainly I do!" said Vossler, still under the impression that he had the upper hand.

"This I.O.U., addressed to you by Captain Ahlers, was typed by one of the civilian employees who work for your unit. Her testimony is already on record. She gave it reluctantly, if that means anything to you, but she gave it all the same."

"But, sir," Vossler protested boldly, "this so-called I.O.U. was meant as a sort of joke. It had no practical significance. People do indulge in jokes sometimes, especially when there's a ready-made butt like Treuberg around."

Dr. Kruppke suppressed a yawn. "The court is in possession of a check which was traced during the course of inquiries into Captain Ahlers's financial position—inquiries which were pursued without any objections being raised by the accused, I must add. This check is made out in the sum of three thousand marks. You, Herr Vossler, drew it, and Herr Ahlers presented it—of that there is absolutely no doubt."

Vossler retained his sang-froid with an effort. "It could have been me that was in debt to Captain Ahlers. Perhaps I was paying him off when I wrote that check."

The president waved a disdainful hand. "How do you propose to prove that? No, Herr Vossler, the facts are beyond dispute."

"Captain Ahlers," defending counsel pointed out, "is fully in a position to pay off all his debts."

"But he incurred them, did he not?"

MARTIN RECHT took Carolin by the hand and led her into the restaurant's private room, with its flower-bedecked table and glittering array of bottles and glasses. Herbert Asch had announced his intention of celebrating his birthday six months early, in honor of Carolin's release from the hospital.

"The others won't be here for a few minutes yet," Martin said. "I've got so much to say, but I don't know how to start."

"It can't be very important, Martin." Carolin slipped her

235

hand beneath his arm and nestled against him. "I know the most important thing already."

He longed to put his arm round her, hold her close, and tell her that she was the whole world to him, but he never got the chance because at the crucial moment Karl Kamnitzer appeared.

"Don't tell me—three's a crowd," he said jauntily. "Never mind, there'll be other times."

Interrupting their idyll in his usual unabashed way, he embraced Martin and seized the opportunity to give Carolin the same treatment. Then he held her at arm's length and looked her up and down. "Well, girl, did the surgeon earn his money?"

"She can walk properly, just like anyone else!" Martin assured him eagerly.

"I can even dance," Carolin chimed in.

"This I must see!" Kamnitzer bowed low. "May I have the pleasure of the next waltz?" he asked with a grin.

Carolin improvised a series of movements which might charitably have been described as a curtsy, and stepped forward. Kamnitzer started to hum a slow, leisurely waltz tune which bore a vague resemblance to something out of *Tales from the Vienna Woods*.

At first they rotated stiffly, like two figures on the lid of a rusty musical box, but before long their movements became lighter, looser, and less constrained. Their bodies began to sway rhythmically. They floated apart, whirling and pirouetting, until Kamnitzer, apparently struggling for breath, came to a halt.

"Good heavens!" he gasped. "Its incredible! Next time we bowl you'll wipe the floor with me. What have I done to deserve this sort of treatment?"

"Thank you," Carolin said happily.

Martin Recht walked over to her, put one arm tenderly round her shoulders and led her to a chair. They gazed at each other as if they were the only people in the room, but Kamnitzer seemed totally unworried by this.

"What's it worth, Carolin?" he asked.

"What, Karl?"

"Everything—the fact that you can walk, dance, run, play tennis, if you like, swim, ride a bicycle, climb mountains. What's it worth to you?"

Carolin looked perplexed. "I don't know what to say. I only know that I feel as if I were starting a new life—my real life, maybe."

"You mean, no price is too high to pay?"

"I suppose you could say that."

"You're thinking along the right lines, then."

"Karl," Martin interposed cautiously, "I don't think this is quite the moment . . ."

"Nonsense!" Kamnitzer retorted. "Of course it is." He turned to Carolin again. "Your father thinks exactly as you do, and the sooner you reconcile yourself to the idea the better."

"What do you mean, Karl?"

"Nothing in life is free, that's what I mean. Everything's got a price tag on it, even happiness. They talk about fate being blind, but I reckon it's more like a debt-collecting agency than anything else."

Dr. Kruppke, presiding judge of Disciplinary Court No. 4, read out the court's findings.

"In the name of the people!" The verdict was delivered with practiced objectivity and a certain measure of dignity. It was obvious that the court had been uninfluenced by emotional considerations of any kind. All that had been evaluated were facts, and facts alone. . . .

"On the basis of the testimony presented . . ." There was a rustle of paper. The observers looked equally impassive, as though earnestly intent on banishing all feeling. Counsel for the prosecution looked round complacently like a winning jockey at the post. Counsel for the defense studied his well-tended hands, conscious that Dr. Kruppke had never arrived at anything other than a strictly proper verdict.

". . . the court finds as follows . . ."

Ahlers did not look up, even then. He sat in the dock like an inanimate figure made of dry, dun-colored clay, seemingly oblivious of what was being said.

He was satisfied of his own guilt, and would have said so in his closing plea to the bench. He and his counsel had worked out the following statement:

"I have always tried to do my duty throughout my twenty years in the service—successfully, as I believe. I can also state that I have always dedicated myself to my work, body and soul. I have never been punished, nor even reprimanded, for any offense. My debts were incurred for purely personal reasons. The fact that my assets were sufficient to cover them is no excuse. I realize that I have acted improperly, but I would ask you to accept that I sincerely believed

myself to be motivated by force of circumstances. I regret what has happened."

These words had been typed out on a sheet of paper but they were never uttered. Meanwhile, the president was announcing verdict and sentence:

"1. The accused is guilty as charged.

"2. The accused is sentenced to be dismissed from the service. In view of his record, however, there will be no deprivation of rank or pension rights."

"There you are!" whispered defending counsel. "Couldn't have been fairer if he'd weighed it out on a pair of scales. It was the best we could hope for."

With his career at an end, Ahlers still clung to what was for him the ultimate military virtue: selfless obedience. "I accept the court's findings," he said simply:

"Now you know everything," Martin told Carolin. "I'm a jailbird and your father has been dismissed from the service."

"He's just bragging, Carolin," Karl Kamnitzer called from the other end of the room. He was inspecting the row of bottles on the sideboard with every appearance of interest.

"You're a fine one to talk," Martin said. "You never come up against any problems. You just sidestep them, or disregard them—or talk people into believing they don't exist."

"It's a method I can recommend to anyone." Kamnitzer studied the label on a bottle of old cognac with relish. "By the way, you needn't expect any interruptions from me for the next few minutes, if you want to make the most of it."

He turned his back on them and poured himself a generous glass of brandy, feeling rather pleased with himself.

"Martin," Carolin said softly. "When I was in the hospital you wrote me and told me you loved me."

"I know."

"Was it just to make things easier for me?"

"No, not just for that."

"Everything's all right, then. Nothing else matters."

"How I envy your sublime innocence!" Kamnitzer chuckled, draining his glass. He inserted himself between them and draped his arms round their shoulders. "I hope you don't look on love as a universal painkiller, my children.

238

Some things exist, and no amount of amorous rapture can banish them for good."

"Stop being such a wet blanket, Karl."

"I'm not—I'm just telling you the facts of life. Strikes me you're badly in need of enlightenment."